Robert
Kaier

PERCEPTION

FOURTH EDITION

Robert Sekuler

Brandeis University

Randolph Blake

Vanderbilt University

Boston   Burr Ridge, IL   Dubuque, IA   Madison, WI   New York   San Francisco   St. Louis
Bangkok   Bogotá   Caracas   Kuala Lumpur   Lisbon   London   Madrid   Mexico City
Milan   Montreal   New Delhi   Santiago   Seoul   Singapore   Sydney   Taipei   Toronto

McGraw-Hill Higher Education

*A Division of The **McGraw-Hill** Companies*

PERCEPTION, FOURTH EDITION

Published by McGraw-Hill, a business unit of The McGraw-Hill Companies, Inc., 1221 Avenue of the Americas, New York, NY 10020. Copyright © 2002, 1994, 1990 by The McGraw-Hill Companies, Inc. All rights reserved. Copyright © 1985 by Alfred A. Knopf, Inc. All right reserved. No part of this publication may be reproduced or distributed in any form or by any means, or stored in a database or retrieval system, without the prior written consent of The McGraw-Hill Companies, Inc., including, but not limited to, in any network or other electronic storage or transmission, or broadcast for distance learning.

Some ancillaries, including electronic and print components, may not be available to customers outside the United States.

This book is printed on acid-free paper.

1 2 3 4 5 6 7 8 9 0 QPF/QPF 0 9 8 7 6 5 4 3 2 1

ISBN 0–07–057943–1
ISBN 0–07–112159–5 (ISE)

Editorial director: *Jane E. Karpacz*
Senior sponsoring editor: *Melissa Mashburn*
Developmental editor: *Mindy De Palma*
Senior marketing manager: *Chris Hall*
Project manager: *Mary Lee Harms*
Production supervisor: *Kara Kudronowicz*
Coordinators of freelance design: *Michelle M. Meerdink/Rick D. Noel*
Cover designer: *Jamie A. O'Neal*
Cover image: The J. Paul Getty Museum, Los Angeles. ©David Hockney, *Pearblossom Hwy., 11-18 April 1986, # 2*. Photomontage, 78 × 111 in.
Senior photo research coordinator: *Carrie K. Burger*
Photo research: *LouAnn K. Wilson*
Supplement producer: *Tammy Juran*
Media technology senior producer: *Sean Crowley*
Compositor: *Carlisle Communications, Ltd.*
Typeface: *10/12 Times Roman*
Printer: *Quebecor World Fairfield, PA*

The credits section for this book begins on page 677 and is considered an extension of the copyright page.

Library of Congress Cataloging-in-Publication Data

Sekuler, Robert.
    Perception / Robert Sekuler, Randolph Blake.—4th ed.
      p. cm.
    Includes bibliographical references and index.
    ISBN 0–07–057943–1
    1. Perception. I. Blake, Randolph. II. Title.

BF311 .S434   2002
152.1—dc21
                                     2001030408
                                     CIP

INTERNATIONAL EDITION ISBN 0–07–112159–5
Copyright © 2002. Exclusive rights by The McGraw-Hill Companies, Inc., for manufacture and export. This book cannot be re-exported from the country to which it is sold by McGraw-Hill. The International Edition is not available in North America.

www.mhhe.com

ABOUT THE AUTHORS

ROBERT SEKULER is the Louis and Frances Salvage Professor of Psychology at Brandeis University, Adjunct Professor of Cognitive & Neural Sciences at Boston University, and Consultant in Neurosurgery at Children's Hospital (Boston). At Brandeis, where he served as the university's chief academic officer, Sekuler is also a member of the Volen Center for Complex Systems, an interdisciplinary center for the study of the brain. After earning his Ph.D. at Brown University in 1964, he held a postdoctoral fellowship at the Massachusetts Institute of Technology. Subsequently, Sekuler was on the faculty at Northwestern University for twenty-four years, where he was John Evans Professor of Neuroscience, and held the rank of professor in the departments of psychology, ophthalmology, and neurobiology & physiology. After chairing Northwestern's department of psychology for six years, he served as Associate Dean in the College of Arts and Sciences. A leader in the fields of motion perception and age-related perceptual changes, Sekuler has published more than 200 scientific papers and has contributed chapters to various books including the *Handbook of Perception,* the *APA Encyclopedia of Psychology,* the *Handbook of Sensory Physiology,* the *Handbook of Experimental Psychology,* and the *Oxford Textbook of Geriatric Medicine.* He chaired the National Academy of Sciences' Committee on Vision, and directed the Academy's study of "Aging Workers and Visual Impairment" as well as its study of "Vision and Aging." Those efforts lead to his co-edited book, *Aging and Visual Function.* During 2000, Sekuler was a visiting scientist at the Rotman Research Institute of Toronto's Baycrest Centre for Geriatric Care, and a visiting professor of psychology at the University of Toronto. He has served on the board of the Hugh Knowles Center on Hearing and its Preservation, and on the Sensory Physiology of Advisory Panel of the National Science Foundation. Sekuler is an elected fellow of the American Psychological Society and the American Association for the Advancement of Science; he is a member of the Psychonomic Society, the Society for Neuroscience and the Association for Research in Vision and Ophthalmology.

RANDOLPH BLAKE is Centennial Professor of Psychology at Vanderbilt University, Nashville, Tennessee; beginning in 1988 he chaired this department for eight years. Prior to this appointment he was on the faculty of Northwestern University for fourteen years. He received his Ph.D. from Vanderbilt in 1972 and then spent two years as a postdoctoral fellow in the Sensory Sciences Center at the University of Texas Graduate School of Biomedical Sciences. Blake has published extensively in major psychology and neuroscience journals and has contributed chapters to edited books including *Models of the Visual Cortex, Frontiers of Visual Science,* and *Early Vision and Beyond.* His research, supported by grants from the National Science Foundation and the National Institutes of Health, focuses on visual perception with particular emphasis on binocular vision, motion perception, and perceptual grouping. In recent years, Blake's research has expanded to include functional brain imaging of visual areas involved in perception of human activity. In recognition of his research contributions, Blake received a Career Development Award from the National Institutes of Health and the American Psychological Association's Early Career Award for Distinguished Scientific Contribution. Blake is an elected Fellow of the American Association for the Advancement of Science, the American Psychological Society and the John Kennedy Center for Research on Human Development. He is a past member of the Committee on Vision of the National Academy of Sciences/National Research Council and the Sensory Sciences Advisory Panel of the National Science Foundation. During 1992, he was a Fellow of the Japan Society for the Promotion of Science, and in 1995, he held the William Evans Professorship in Psychology at Dunedin University, New Zealand. His professional memberships include the Association for Research in Vision and Ophthalmology, Sigma Xi and the American Association for the Advancement of Science.

In addition to this book, Sekuler and Blake are co-authors of the award-winning *Star Trek on the Brain: Alien Minds, Human Minds* (1998; paperback and Japanese editions 1999).

CONTENTS

PREFACE

From the moment you awake in the morning until you nod off at night, you pursue a constantly changing range of diverse mental and physical activities. But one personal activity runs incessantly throughout your daily life: you're constantly dealing with the barrage of environmental information supplied by your senses. All your activities—driving, reading, eating, conversing, typing, exercising—everything you do is guided by what you see, hear, feel, touch, smell and taste. Perception, in other words, is an ability that is at once crucial and fundamental. But unlike the many abilities that you work hard to master, perception comes naturally and effortlessly: everyone is a natural born perceptual genius. In fact, the ease and mindlessness of perception belies its complexity, and that is one reason teaching or writing about perception can be challenging: it is not immediately obvious that there is anything to be explained. If you ask a friend how he or she goes about solving a jig-saw puzzle, they will be able to list the steps involved (turn all the pieces face-side up, arrange the pieces in piles according to color and so on). But if you ask any one to say how he or she goes about reading the words on this page, the person will pause a moment, think, and then say something like, "I just point my eyes at the letters and read." Perception seems easy, but it's not.

Goals of this Textbook   In writing this textbook, one of our goals was to help readers appreciate the complexity and intelligence of all the processes that make perception possible. Our book is an introduction to the exciting behavioral and biological research that illuminates the remarkable achievement we call perceiving. In this respect, our aims have remained the same over four editions: *we have built on the cumulative successes of science to offer readers a new perspective on their own seeing, hearing, touching, smelling, and tasting.* As befits any revision of a textbook, this fourth edition of *Perception* reflects the many developments in the field. In addition, we have listened carefully to feedback from users of previous editions and have tried to accommodate their teaching needs. The result? A new edition that is substantively and significantly different from previous ones. The following sections highlight the ways in which we've tried to improve this fourth edition of *Perception.*

Organization and Coverage   The first chapter summarizes the motivations that inspire people to study perception, as well as the various approaches that such study takes. It also outlines the framework on which the entire text is constructed. Chapters 2 through 8 discuss seeing—the biological bases of vision and the perception of pattern, color, and depth. The treatment of seeing concludes in Chapter 9 with an essay on the perception of visual events, particularly visual motion. Chapters 10 and 11 provide a sweeping introduction to hearing, and its successors explore touch (Chapter 12) and smelling and tasting (Chapter 13). One chapter is new to this edition, and most chapters have been revised substantially in order to capture and communicate the accelerating pace of new discoveries. Just as importantly, material on cognitive influences on perception has been updated and integrated throughout the text, rather than concentrated in a separate chapter as done in the earlier edition. When it comes to methodological details, we continue to believe that this material is best introduced within the context of substantive problems. So readers will be exposed to techniques such as magnitude estimation, signal detection theory and multidimensional scaling within the body of the text. We do, however, offer more concentrated coverage of those techniques in Appendix A.

Special Features of the Fourth Edition   This fourth edition of the book has several noteworthy features. As before, central topics are embedded in historical context, presenting today's perception research as the product of an unfolding intellectual process. At the same time, our source materials are strongly biased toward recently published material. Because we want readers to appreciate developments at the frontiers of perception, we give thorough coverage to "hot," rapidly developing topics, at the same time insuring that such coverage is closely integrated with its intellectual origins. For example, one chapter provides a comprehensive treatment of recent discoveries concerning visual agnosias; another highlights the amazing plasticity of sensory systems; and a third chapter details the latest thinking on genetic determinants of color vision. This special stress on the most recent work testifies that perception is a dynamic and growing field.

Illustration Program

The extensive program of more than 250 illustrations, many brand new or substantially revised for this edition, is another of this book's most important features. And the number of all-important color plates has doubled from the previous edition. Our own years of teaching experience, more than 50 years combined at last count, have taught us that readers don't always see in a diagram or graph exactly what was intended. In fact, the ability to read a graphic is a skill that, like any other skill, requires practice. So instead of merely directing readers to look over the figure, we have crafted and coordinated the text, figures, and figure captions to ensure proper interpretation of the illustrative material. In addition, we have given extra care to the graphic presentation of complex ideas. Such ideas are often conveyed in this book by a short series of illustrations, with each illustration in a series introducing additional concepts. This approach enables every reader to get the point—even those who are novices at interpreting graphs and diagrams. Finally, illustrations that depict previously published experimental results have been adapted and redrawn to maximize clarity and consistency of presentation.

Another special feature that has been introduced in this edition is marginal icons. These icons are designed to highlight thematic links throughout every chapter to emphasize where material deals with a recurrent theme. A brief explanation of each icon is introduced at the end of Chapter One.

Vocabulary and Methods of Perceptual Research

Because the study of perception draws upon a number of disciplines—physics, chemistry, anatomy, psychology, computer science, and several branches of medicine, among others—its technical vocabulary incorporates the terminology of those disciplines. Beginning students of perception can feel bewildered by the flood of new terms they must master. Recognizing this problem, we have introduced only those terms that are absolutely necessary to the discussion. Where it is likely to aid memory or understanding, we explain the term's origin. Also, each term is carefully defined when it is first used, and all these terms appear at the end of each chapter and in a Glossary at the back of the book.

We have kept detailed, abstract descriptions of research methods to a minimum. Where appropriate, we explain particular methods in enough detail that all of our readers can appreciate the methods and whatever constraints they impose on results and conclusions. Various methods for studying perception are discussed within the context of the specific problems that they were designed to solve. By integrating methods and results, we hope to facilitate the reader's genuine appreciation of both.

An Appendix provides much additional information about conventional behavioral methods for studying perception. The Appendix also describes contemporary variants of those methods: forced-choice procedures, sensory decision theory, and adaptive psychophysical methods. The Appendix grounds these methods in their historical context, enabling the student to understand not only the methods but also the reasons for their development.

Links to Everyday Life

In "Talks to Teachers" (1892), William James advised teachers how best to adapt psychology's principles to the classroom. In one chapter, James urged teachers to recognize and exploit the natural interests that students bring to any topic. He suggested that abstract facts and new ideas are most readily assimilated when they have been linked to matters that students find inherently interesting, particularly matters that relate to their own lives. In our own classrooms and while writing this book, we thought of kept James' advice and have kept it in mind. Perception is not just an abstract, scientific discipline, but an integral and fascinating part of everyday life. Recognizing this fact, our book consistently relates scientific research on perception to the reader's own perceptual experiences. To underscore the relationship between science and everyday experience, we present many interesting demonstrations that readers can perform on their own with little or no equipment.

In order to anchor the discussion in the reader's own experience, the text emphasizes the everyday behavioral needs that seeing, hearing, smelling, tasting, and touching are designed to satisfy—the functions of perception. This functional approach to perception is highlighted by the many discussions, throughout the text, of clinical disorders and their intriguing perceptual consequences. Some students will be interested in learning about these disorders for personal reasons; all students should find that the study of perceptual disorders provides insight into the nature of normal perception.

Integration

William James also advised that teachers take care to connect new ideas and facts with what students have already learned. Associate the new with the old in some natural and telling way, so that the interest, being shed along from point to point, finally suffuses the entire system of objects of thought. In his own textbook, "The Principles of Psychology," James followed this counsel, to great success. As we wrote and revised this book, we thought of James' advice and have attempted to make our treatment of perception an integrated one, in part by linking ideas across chapters. These linkages reflect the fact that different areas of perception often utilize similar techniques and related theoretical ideas. Our text is integrated in another way, blending anatomy, physiology, and psychophysics. The information and ideas from each of these three approaches have been carefully selected to ensure a coherent, complete presentation. Structure and function become more comprehensible and memorable when they are integrated. We would like to think that James would approve.

Key Changes in this Edition Instructors who have used an earlier edition of this book will immediately notice that this edition looks and feels different: the page layout is snappier, the section headings are easier to follow and the art program is enhanced. At the same time, previous users will be pleased that this new edition adheres to the same general thematic approach and organization as earlier editions. As previously mentioned, one new feature designed to highlight thematic links throughout the book is the use of "icons" denoting places in the text where material deals with a major, recurrent theme. In addition, this new edition is chock full of updates and changes that provide a fresh, lively portrayal of the field of perception. You will find throughout the chapters, for example, important findings from studies that employ powerful, revealing new techniques of brain imaging. Also running throughout this major revision is more in-depth coverage of the "ecological" approach emphasizing the interrelationship of action and perception.

Chapter Specific Changes
- In **Chapter 1** the main change is a new discussion of computational approaches to various areas of perception. Our aim in reworking Chapter 1 was to establish the principle that, whatever their diversity, all areas of perception draw upon shared principles and face common challenges. In this spirit, some of the philosophical material in Chapter 1 has been revised to give a stronger and clearer treatment of these important foundational issues.
- **Chapters 2 and 3** retain the successful features and organization established in previous editions, however they integrate important new references and figures.
- In its expanded treatment of multiple visual representations, or maps, within the brain, **Chapter 4** gives new emphasis to the advantages and difficulties created by distributed neural representations.
- **Chapter 5** has been substantially revised and updated to incorporate the latest thinking on the role of visual analysis at multiple spatial scales; many of the figures have been completely reworked, and the material on the Gestalt principles of perception has been updated and improved.
- Building on the material presented in Chapter 5, this new edition now includes a completely new **Chapter 6** devoted to object recognition. Here, among other things, students will be exposed to the latest work on perception of environmentally relevant objects including faces and text.
- **Chapter 7,** on color vision, is enhanced by new ideas on the genetics and evolution of color vision, and the number of color plates illustrating principles of color perception has doubled.

- **Chapter 8** goes into more detail on some of the so-called monocular depth cues, particularly those cues that are of great interest to researchers probing machine vision. This chapter also now includes discussion of the perception of visual direction, and it provides a number of stereo pictures along with instructions to students about how to view them.

- The chapter on motion perception, **Chapter 9,** now includes coverage of the latest work on the cortical regions that play special roles in the analysis of global motion. The treatment of eye movements has been sharpened, and discussions of reafference and of structure from motion have been improved by suggestions from instructors and student readers.

- **Chapter 10,** the first of two chapters on hearing, boasts a strengthened treatment of masking and critical bands and coverage of new discoveries on the biophysics of signal transduction in the cochlea.

- Based on reader feedback, we have modified **Chapter 11** by replacing some of the older studies on deafness with new work on cochlear implants. The discussion of loudness in Chapter 11 has also been modified to stress ecologically important roles for loudness perception including judgments of the distance of sound sources. Chapter 11 also takes greater notice of the important role of perceptual organization in hearing. In particular, we have strengthened the discussion of how the auditory system picks out, from the entire acoustic environment, those acoustic features that arise from a single event. Because of the growing body of research and interest in the topic, we have expanded the coverage of speech perception.

- **Chapter 12** on touch perception, which made its debut in the second edition, attracted much favorable comment from readers. For the current edition, we expanded this chapter by adding important new material on haptics, the coordinated interaction between touch and active exploration of the near-environment. Also, the treatment of plasticity in the somatosensory system has been expanded and the chapter includes expanded coverage of pain perception.

- **Chapter 13** on taste and smell integrates new findings on the bases of olfactory transduction and the behavioral consequences of taste disorders. We are confident that readers will find the new material on the genetics of taste and smell as interesting and exciting as we did.

- **The Appendix,** on behavioral methods, now notes the utility of theoretical, "ideal" observers that can provide benchmarks for real, human performance.

We have mentioned just some of the additions and revisions in this fourth edition. Scrutiny of the reference list reveals that some 500 references are new to this edition (nearly 200 references from the last edition have been eliminated as outmoded or superceded). Most of the new references represent contributions that were published in the last three years.

Supplements

Instructor's Manual/Test Bank

This combination Instructor's Manual/Test Bank provides many useful tools to enhance your teaching. For each chapter, a general overview and set of learning objectives, detailed chapter outline, Teaching Tips and Activities, and Summary boxes are provided. This manual also includes Test Bank questions for each chapter that include: 10 matching, 20 multiple choice, 15 True/False, and 5 Essay questions.

Computerized Test Bank

The questions in the *IM/TB* are also available on **MicroTest III,** a powerful but easy-to-use test-generating program by Chariot Software Group. MicroTest is available for both PC and Mac users on a cross-platform CD. With MicroTest, instructors can easily select questions from the Test Bank and print tests and answer keys. Instructors can also customize questions, headings, and instructions; add or import their own questions; and print tests in a choice of printer-supported fonts.

Making the Grade CD-ROM

This *new* CD-ROM to accompany *Perception, 4e,* gives students a variety of opportunities to test their comprehension of the course material. The CD-ROM opens with a Learning Style/Study Skills questionnaire that students can complete to help them identify how they best study. Also included are practice tests that cover topics in the perception course, an internet primer.

Website

The custom crafted website to accompany *Perception, 4e,* includes a number of resources for instructors and students to enhance their teaching and learning experience in Perception. For the instructor, this web site includes an image gallery, web icons, and PowerPoint © presentation. The student portion of the site includes practice quizzes, web links, demonstrations, and other interactive exercises. Visit it at www.mhhe.com\sekuler4.

ACKNOWLEDGMENTS

In preparing various editions of the book, we benefited greatly from many people's comments and suggestions. Special credit, though, should be given to those individuals who either reviewed various chapters and sections or educated us on relevant topics. These individuals include:

Richard Abrams, *Washington University*

Patrick Bennett, *University of Toronto*

Bill Cain, *University of California, San Diego*

Marisa Carrasco, *New York University*

Vivien Casagrande, *Vanderbilt University*

Peter Dallos *Northwestern University*

Madison Dengler, *Luther College*

Francis Fahy *University of Southampton*

John Flowers, *University of Nebraska*

Isabel Gauthier, *Vanderbilt University*

Wilson Geisler, *University of Texas, Austin*

Jim Grau, *Texas A & M University*

Troy Hackett, *Vanderbilt University*

Michael Hall, *University of Las Vegas*

Carol Hayes, *Delta State University*

Jon Kaas, *Vanderbilt University*

Ilona Kovács, *Rutgers University*

Joseph Lappin, *Vanderbilt University*

Willard Larkin, *University of Maryland*

Susan Lederman, *Queen's University*

Mark McCourt, *North Dakota State University*

Dennis McFadden, *University of Texas, Austin*

Claire Murphy, *San Diego State University*

Ken Nakayama, *Harvard University*

Thomas Papathomas, *Rutgers University*

Todd Preuss, *University of Louisiana at Lafayette*

Edward Rinalducci, *University of Central Florida*

Bennett Schwartz, *Florida International University*

Allison Sekuler, *University of Toronto*

Steven Shevell, *University of Chicago*

Therou Stimmel, *Southwest Texas State University*

Matthew Traxler, *University of South Carolina*

Benjamin Wallace, *Cleveland State University*

Fred Wightman, *University of Wisconsin*

Steve Yantis, *John Hopkins University*

While we were writing the first two editions of this book we were lucky to occupy adjoining offices and laboratories. That physical proximity made it easy for us to share materials, ideas, comments and suggestions, and to strengthen our friendship. It also enabled us to do much of the writing while we both sat at a single computer that was specially outfitted with twin keyboards—in the style of pianists playing music for four hands. Because our academic bases are now separated by some 1019 miles, we have exploited other means to support our close, highly-interactive collaboration. We've taken advantage of intense home-to-home visits—Blake to Concord, Massachusetts, and Sekuler to Nashville, Tennessee. For our more usual interaction, though, we depended upon the Internet.

Our electronic virtual closeness gave each of us complete pride of ownership for the entire text. Of course, files, comments and drawings shared over an electronic network are not the same thing as sitting side by side, but they proved to be an acceptable substitute. Both of us have vivid memories of week-end marathons during which we carried on prolonged, high-speed electronic dialogues over some matter or other. During preparation of the previous, third edition, the Internet kept us in touch despite the fact that Blake was working in Japan for several months and despite our separation by fourteen time zones. During preparation of this edition, the Internet helped to smooth over the fact that Sekuler was working in Toronto for half a year. Researchers are adapting computer technology in order to create what is known as virtual reality, computer-mediated experiences that substitute for—and sometimes improve upon—the real thing. In this spirit, we were delighted that the speed and ease of our largely-electronic collaboration enabled us to continue to be close colleagues, if only of the virtual variety.

Thanks are owed to our students, colleagues, and especially our families for their tolerance and good humor during our preoccupation with this project.

CHAPTER 1

INTRODUCTION TO PERCEPTION

The world is filled with objects and events that combine to create a torrent of potential information. Though much of that information is irrelevant to people's daily needs, some is absolutely essential. To exploit this information effectively, human beings are equipped with specialized machinery that captures this information and translates it into the language of the nervous system. The brain refines this translated information into neural "descriptions" of behaviorally-relevant objects and events in the environment. Some of these descriptions reach conscious awareness, allowing us to formulate deliberate plans for further interaction with those objects; other descriptions are used to guide immediate or reflexive reactions to objects and events.

Perception puts us in contact with the world we live in; it shapes our knowledge of that world, and knowledge is power. Our chances of survival improve markedly if we can detect objects and events in our environment and if we can, then, distinguish the safe from the dangerous, sort out the desirable from the undesirable. Knowing about our world allows us to predict the consequences of our actions, a useful skill in an ever-changing world (Barlow, 1998).

Perception doesn't necessarily have to provide us with a perfectly detailed view of the world. What is crucial is that perception provide us with a *useful* view of the world, one that allows us to interact safely and effectively with our environment. As you will learn, perception accentuates the important and diminishes the irrelevant. Perception may even misrepresent an object's true appearance, if that misrepresentation improves our chances of interacting effectively with that object.

The environment generates a powerful stream of sensory information. In fact, there are so many possible objects and events that perception cannot possibly process and respond to each one. Nonetheless—and fortunately for us—perception does work. Our perceptual systems overcome this potential sensory overload in several ways. For one thing, the world we live in is full of regularities dictated by the physical nature of matter and energy. Those regularities make detection and discrimination a whole lot easier. For example, our visual system evolved in a world where light nearly always comes from above and, consequently, we unconsciously use that knowledge to interpret shapes of objects based on shadows. (You will see a compelling example of this constraint in action later in this chapter.) Perception can exploit this and many other environmental regularities to make educated guesses about what in the world gave rise to a particular pattern of sensory stimulation.

There's a second effective way that perception deals with the environment's overwhelming complexity: it simply "ignores" much of what is going on in the world. Much of what the environment has to offer is simply of no interest to us. It is not important, for example, that we sense the minute electrical fields generated by other biological creatures (including other people). Our keen sense of vision makes "electroreception" superfluous. Consequently, our perceptual systems are "tuned" to those sensory events that are biologically relevant (or, more correctly, were biologically relevant to our primate ancestors from whom we've inherited our perceptual systems). As you will learn throughout this text, animal species differ in their behavioral goals, and the goals of some species require sensitivity to sensory stimulation that fall outside our reality.

Perception arises from a complex interplay of mutually interdependent events. To understand perception completely—and we certainly don't yet—requires knowing all the components involved in the process and the ways those components interact. To begin, we must specify the nature of the environment in which we live, for this environment determines what there is to perceive. Aspects of the environment are specified using terms derived from physics, because stimulation comes in various forms of physical energy: thermal, mechanical, acoustic, and electromagnetic. The physical energy that initiates the

chain of events is called a **stimulus** (plural, "stimuli").

Next, it is necessary to understand how the nervous system converts the patterns of physical energy into neural events. Known as **sensory transduction,** this conversion process requires an understanding of the specialized sensory receptors (such as those contained in eyes and ears) that convert physical energy into bioelectrical signals. Once this transduction has been achieved, objects and events are represented solely as patterns of neural impulses within the various sensory nerve fibers. From this point on, all further elaboration and editing of the sensory information must be performed using this neural representation.

As you might expect, the brain plays a central role in perception. So a full understanding of perception also requires knowing how multiple, specialized brain areas process patterns of neural impulses that carry sensory information, including how the activity distributed among those many areas is combined to form our unified sense of the world. How, for example, do the neural signals conveying information about the sounds from an object combine with the signals generating the visual impressions of that object? In addition, we need to discover how neural activity signalling the presence of objects is used to control our behavioral reactions to those objects.

A complete understanding of perception must include a thorough description of the appearances of objects and events: we have to be able to describe systematically the sights, sounds, smells and tastes that populate our conscious experiences. In addition to describing how things appear to us, we must also specify how our abilities to detect, discriminate and recognize objects are governed by the information available to our senses. And, in a similar vein, we must understand the behavioral consequences of sensory stimulation, for our actions will modify those very patterns of sensory stimulation. These represent formidable challenges. Not surprisingly, diverse techniques have been developed for sys-

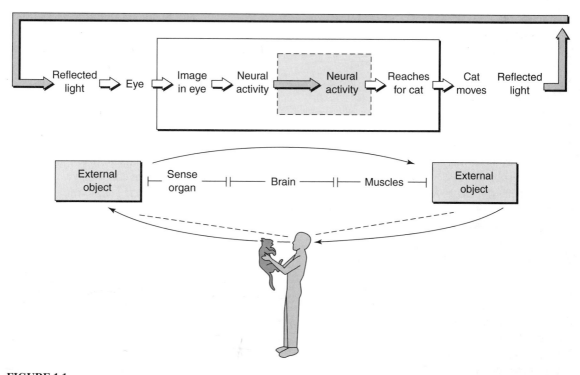

FIGURE 1.1
Perception registers and interprets sensory information from the environment that guides behavior, which, in turn, shapes the nature of input to the senses.

tematically cataloging the performance of our perceptual systems and relating that information to patterns of physical stimulation. The enterprise of relating physical stimulation to perceptual events is known as **psychophysics.** By specifying the relation between physical and perceptual, psychophysics provides important clues to understanding the various steps leading from objects and events to perception.

Perception constitutes a whole sequence of events, beginning with things that happen in the physical world external to the perceiver. From that start, the perceptual process proceeds through the translation of external events into patterns of activity within the perceiver's nervous system, culminating in the perceiver's experiential and behavioral reactions to those events. Those reactions, in turn, can affect the very same sen-

sory events that triggered those reactions. All of this forms a closed loop in which perception alters behavior, and behavior, in turn, alters perception. This dynamic loop is schematized in Figure 1.1. Let's now consider several important implications of this way of thinking about perception.

PERCEPTION IS A BIOLOGICAL PROCESS

In this book, we approach perception as a *biological* process. To be perceived, *any* information about events in the world must be registered by the sensory nervous system. The noted neuroscientist Vernon Mountcastle has vividly described this constraint:

Each of us lives within . . . the prison of his own brain. Projecting from it are millions of fragile sensory nerve fibers, in groups uniquely adapted to sample the energetic states of the world around us: heat, light, force, and chemical composition. That is all we ever know of it directly; all else is logical inference. (1975, p. 131)

Mountcastle is pointing out that sensory nerve fibers provide our only link to the external world; they alone provide our communication channels to reality. If environmental events fall outside the sensitivity range of the sensory channels, those events will not be experienced directly. It may be possible to detect some of these events indirectly, however, using specialized instruments. Such instruments work in one of two ways. Some *amplify* physical energy, making weak signals strong enough to stimulate the senses. For example, a microscope can magnify objects otherwise too small to be seen by the naked eye. This is the only way we're able to know what bacteria actually look like. Other instruments *convert* energy that is outside the normal bounds of the senses into a form that is within those bounds. Geiger counters can warn about the presence of radioactivity, a form of energy that cannot be sensed directly by most creatures. Both types of instrument, though, perform the same function—they extend the reach of our sensory systems into realms of physical reality normally beyond our grasp.

It may be difficult to accept that your rich perceptual world encompasses only a small, restricted portion of the objects and events in the natural environment. Because one's conception of reality is so intimately determined by subjective experience, it seems unnatural to distinguish between one's "perception of the world" and the "world itself." Yet to understand perception fully, you have to make this distinction. Perhaps a few examples will enable you to appreciate what we mean by the limited scope of your perceptual world.

Consider, for instance, how different species of animals probably experience the world. It is well documented that not all animals have the same sensory systems. Consequently, various species have access to different universes of physical events (Hughes, 1999). Dogs can hear sounds in regions of the frequency spectrum where humans are deaf; bees are able to navigate using a quality of light, polarization, that is outside the realm of human visual experience; sharks hunt their prey by following electrical trails given off by their potential meal; bats use self-produced, ultrasonic echoes to navigate in complete darkness; snakes can detect and orient toward infrared radiation; trout have tiny biomagnets in their noses that let them exploit the earth's magnetic field to orient their navigation; zebra finches rely on ultraviolet light to select mates; and some chemical substances odorless to humans elicit powerful olfactory responses in other animals. In general, there is no single "environment" that all animals live in. Members of different species interact with their physical and biological worlds in ways that reflect their own unique requirements and capabilities. As Box 1.1 shows, although all animals inhabit the same *physical* world, their *perceptual* worlds may differ radically.

In fact, not all humans have equivalent sensory systems. For instance, some people have eye defects that prevent them from experiencing the full range of colors that most people see. Many elderly people are unable to hear high frequency sounds that are clearly audible to younger individuals. There are also certain people who cannot taste one of the bitter substances in coffee or grapefruit juice because of abnormalities in their taste receptors. These and similar examples that we will bring up throughout this book underscore the dependence of perception on the function of the sensory nervous system.

Recognition of perception as a biological process underscores another important point: perception entails symbolic representations. A "symbol" is something that stands for something other than itself. Hermann Helmholtz, an influential nineteenth-century contributor to physics, physiology and perception, emphasized this point when he wrote: "Our sensations are for us

BOX 1.1

SEEING THE INVISIBLE

The philosopher Thomas Nagel (1982) challenged people to imagine what it would be like to be a bat. His conclusion? We can never really know without actually becoming a bat because bats rely heavily on a form of sensory information—sonar—that is utterly foreign to us. (We will return to Nagel's bats in chapter 11.)

The logical impasse that Nagel identified also applies to other potential sensory worlds that lie beyond human experience. It's hard to imagine what it must be like to sense forms of energy falling outside our domain of reality. But we can get an inkling of this experience. Normally, humans cannot see electromagnetic radiation in the portion of the spectrum called infrared. This form of radiation is usually associated with heat, including the body heat of living creatures. If infrared is sensed at all, it is experienced as warmth on the skin. Although some animals, notably certain snakes, have specialized sense organs that allow them to detect and respond to objects on the basis of the infrared energy radiated by those objects, humans are fairly insensitive to infrared.

To give you some idea of what it might be like to see infrared radiation, we have prepared the two accompanying photographs. The photograph on the left shows a scene taken with ordinary black and white film; this film is about as *in*sensitive to infrared as the human eye. That is why pictures taken with such film look "normal." The photograph on the right shows the same scene taken with film that is sensitive to infrared; it reveals things in the scene (areas of heat and cold) that humans ordinarily would not see. Thus, for instance, the water in the right-hand photo appears dark because it is cold.

Although the differences between these pictures are interesting, we can't really claim that the photographs provide much insight into the experiences of those infrared-sensitive snakes. In some cases, their infrared-sensitive organs are not even part of their eyes. It's more likely that they *feel* infrared energy rather than *see* it. The photographs do remind us, though, that the human perceptual world is limited to that sample of objects and events with physical energy falling within the range of sensitivity of our sensory systems.

 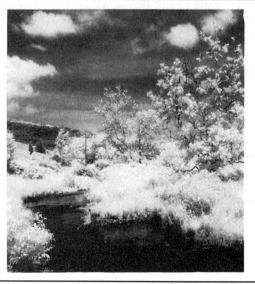

only symbols of the object of the external world, and correspond to them in such way as written characters or articulate words correspond to the thing they denote" (quoted in Park, 1999, p. 8). A road map, for instance, is a symbol of the highways and terrain over which you may wish to travel. Running your finger along some highway on a map is very different from traveling the actual road, but the map symbolizes the reality. The words on this page are symbols, denoting objects, actions and relations among them. When you read the letters Z-E-B-R-A, they symbolize a kind of animal that you're familiar with. The letters don't magically conjure up an actual zebra, but they surely do conjure up in your mind's eye the image of a horse-like animal with black and white stripes. Since words in general have a sufficiently narrow range of referents that are recognized by large groups of human beings we can use them for written communication.

Your perceptual experiences are associated with characteristic patterns of neural activity in your brain (hence we say that perceptual states are produced by brain states). This fact makes perception a symbolic process. Suppose you hear a bird chirping outside your window. Your perceptual experience of that sound is certainly not the same as the actual event that gives rise to the sound, in this case the acoustic energy produced by the bird. However, your perceptual experience does represent important qualities of that acoustic event. In the case of perception, the symbols are not the sort that we usually think of—a screech of brakes, the trill of a cardinal, the crescendo of an orchestra. Instead, the symbols are the various brain states that stand for these sounds. Just like other kinds of symbols, however, the properties of these symbols are not the same as the properties of the things being symbolized: in your brain, the representation of a loud explosion is neither loud nor explosive. What the neural responses *can* retain, however, is important information about the spatial or temporal structure of the objects and events the neural symbols represent. Thus, the beginning and

end of neural patterns in your brain evoked by the bird's chirping will generally coincide with the beginning and end of the bird's call; the temporal structure of the neural activity mirrors the temporal structure of the event. Viewing a single, isolated star in the sky will create a more spatially compact pattern of neural activity in your brain than will viewing a whole cluster of stars; the spatial structure of the neural activity thus mirrors the spatial structure of the objects being viewed.

Evidently, the brain has a constant need for input from the external world. When that input is reduced or eliminated, the sensory systems lapse into a kind of disorderly conduct that yields hallucinations, sometimes quite bizarre. Input to the brain can be shut off by placing a person in an environment that drastically reduces sensory stimulation (Bexton, Heron, and Scott, 1954; Siegel, 1984) or when a particular sensory channel has diminished function. For example, in about 10 to 15 percent of people with eye disease, the impaired vision evokes realistic and complex visual hallucinations (Schultz and Melzack, 1991). In this condition, known as **Charles Bonnet syndrome,** the hallucinations come from impaired sensory systems, not from dementia, as was once assumed. Similarly, following amputation of a body part, many people experience "phantom limbs," compelling and very painful hallucinations that the missing body part is still present (Melzack, 1992). Both the visual hallucinations and the phantom limbs are generated by activity within the brain.

It is truly remarkable how deceptively simple and self-evident our perceptions of the world seem. If you were asked to describe how you solve a jigsaw puzzle, you might give an account of the steps involved: "turn all the pieces right side up, arrange the pieces into little piles according to color," and so on. Likewise, many of you can probably give a reasonable response if requested to describe what you do when brewing fresh coffee ("grind the beans, place a filter in the coffee maker" etc.). But what answer would you give to the following: "How do you read the words on this page?" Most people would probably say, "I open my eyes and look at the page." Of course, this simple description belies the truly complex nature of the process, but it does dramatize the point we wish to make: normal perception occurs immediately and without much effort. But we shouldn't be fooled. Even the simplest perceptual experiences result from a complex series of neural events involving extensive interactions among numerous brain cells. These interactions, which bear a formal resemblance to interactions in an electronic circuit, can be thought of as computations. The computations that shape the symbolic representations in the brain work on environmental information picked up by the eyes, ears, and other sensory organs. Using this information, the brain computes the properties of objects and events (such as their size or their distance from the point of observation).

The philosophy that guides contemporary work in perception is termed **materialism**—it asserts that perceptual experience depends on the operation of the nervous system, with no requirement for the involvement of some noncorporeal force. The materialistic viewpoint has been well expressed by the late Roger Sperry, a Nobel Prize-winning brain scientist. According to Sperry, perceptual experience is a "functional property of brain processing, constituted of neuronal and physicochemical activity, and embodied in, and inseparable from, the active brain" (1980, p. 204).

Although materialism holds that perception is based on neural events in the brain, it does not imply that one could dissect a brain and thereby locate those experiences. Again, Sperry put it quite well:

> Once generated from neural events, the higher order mental patterns and programs have their own subjective qualities and progress, operate and interact by their own causal laws and principles which are different from and cannot be reduced to those of neurophysiology. (1980, p. 201)

To illustrate further what he had in mind, Sperry offered the example of a wheel rolling downhill. The wheel

> carries its atoms and molecules through a course in time and space and to a fate determined by the overall system properties of the wheel as a whole and regardless of the inclination of individual atoms and molecules. The atoms and molecules are caught up and overpowered by the higher properties of the whole. One can compare the rolling wheel to an ongoing brain process or a progressing train of thought in which the overall organizational properties of the brain process, as a coherent organizational entity, determine the timing and spacing of the firing patterns within its neuronal infrastructure. (1980, p. 201)

In other words, though one's experiences have a physical basis, they cannot be entirely reduced to a set of physical components; equally important are their spatial organization, what they communicate to one another, and how both spatial organization and communication change with time. If another analogy would help, consider what would happen if you took a television set completely apart and examined all its components in an effort to understand how it worked. The proper function of the television set demands a particular spatial arrangement of parts as well as a certain sequence of signals in time. The "secret" of the set's operation would have completely eluded you and could not be found in the pile of parts left after the set had been dismantled. And certainly from the parts alone, it would be impossible to deduce the function of a television set.

Not everybody agrees with the materialistic perspective. Some prominent scientists, including the late Sir John Eccles (1979), another Nobel Prize winner, subscribe to an alternative view. This alternative, **dualism,** is often associated with the seventeenth-century French philosopher René Descartes. Dualism holds that perceiving (like any "mental" function) is not solely a phenomenon of the physical brain. Instead, it also entails some special, nonphysical substance—the mind or the soul—that interacts with the brain.

Many people find dualism persuasive because they are unconvinced that perception, a personal, subjective experience, can be fully explained by brain processes, which are certainly not experiences. They object to mechanism's basic claim: a quantity of one sort—neural activity—can cause a quantity of so different a sort—perception.

According to philosopher John Searle, though, no logical barrier prevents cause-and-effect relationships between entities of radically different sorts. In fact, denying that such relationships are possible betrays a misunderstanding of cause and effect itself (1987, p. 223). To drive his point home, Searle draws on the discipline of physics. Physicists commonly distinguish between large-scale macro phenomena and smaller-scale micro elements, postulating causal relationships between the two, even though macro and micro entities are quite different from one another. Take some examples offered by Searle. Heat and lightning are macro-level phenomena; molecular movements and electrical discharges are elements on the micro level. Physics teaches us that a macro phenomenon can be *caused* by the behavior of micro elements: we say that heat is caused by molecule movements or that lightning is caused by electrical discharge. Moreover, either macro phenomenon can be equated to the behavior of its micro elements. Therefore, we can say that heat is the mean kinetic energy of molecule movements or that lightning is an electrical discharge.

Paul Churchland elaborated the main arguments against dualism (1986). Here we'll mention two of them. Against the claim that perception is independent of what happens in the brain, Churchland cites numerous instances in which changes in the brain's condition dramatically alter the content and quality of perception. Throughout the following chapters, we give many examples of perception disordered by brain damage. Against the claim that perception is far too complicated to be the product of things as simple as nerve cells, research on neural networks shows that one can create extraordinarily complex, sophisticated systems out of very simple components, undercutting the need to postulate other, more intelligent agents. As a result, one can account for complex, intelligent aspects of perception without recourse to elements that are themselves complex or intelligent.

Searle expresses the view most investigators in the field of perception have adopted:

> Mental phenomena, whether conscious or unconscious, whether visual or auditory, pains, tickles, itches, thoughts, and all the rest of our mental life, are caused by processes going on in the brain. Mental phenomena are as much a result of electrochemical processes in the brain as digestion is the result of chemical processes going on in the stomach and the rest of the digestive tract. (1987, p. 220)

Within contemporary psychology and neuroscience, perception is an area of scientific research that has made major advances in explaining the relation between brain and mind. Adoption of the materialist position has greatly facilitated those advances.

PERCEPTION INVOLVES ACTION

Perceiving usually requires some action on the perceiver's part. You look around in order to see, searching the visual environment until the desired object of regard is located. Likewise, to make a faint sound audible, you may turn your ear in the direction of the sound. When touching an object, you're better able to identify it if you actively explore it by moving your fingers over it. All these examples remind us that perception is an *active* process, an idea especially championed by James J. Gibson (1966), who expressed this idea succinctly when he wrote, "we must perceive in order to move, but we must also move in order to perceive" (p. 223, 1979).

Active perception accomplishes several goals. First, we sample our environment purposefully, rather than waiting on sensory events to drop into our laps, so to speak. Our sampling behavior—looking, listening, feeling and so on—is usually

moving eyes

moving finger

FIGURE 1.2
While holding your finger in front of your face, shift your gaze from the left to the right of your finger. As you do this, the image of your finger sweeps back and forth over the back of your eye, much the same as it does when you hold your gaze steady and move your finger back and forth.

guided by our needs ("are you hungry, sleepy, afraid, or what?"). Perception, in other words, has purpose. Once active sampling uncovers an object of potential interest, we must decide whether to approach it or avoid it. Here, again, active perception helps us make intelligent decisions. By actively exploring an object we're able to improve the quality of the sensory information we receive. As you investigate an unfamiliar object with your hand, your fingers are directed to the most informative parts of that object, looking for telltale signs of the object's shape, size, texture and, ultimately, its identity. Having identified the object, you may elect to discard it or keep

it. The same kinds of exploratory activities occur with the other senses, including vision and hearing. Your behavior depends on *what* is perceived.

Active perception, useful as it is, introduces a potential confusion that the brain must sort out, namely distinguishing self-produced patterns of stimulation from externally-produced ones. An example should make this point clear. Hold the index finger of one hand in front of your face and look straight at it (Figure 1.2). Now shift your gaze back and forth, looking to the left and the right of your finger. This action causes the image of your finger to sweep back and forth over the light-sensitive surface on the back of your eye.

Now modify the exercise by moving your finger back and forth while staring straight ahead without moving your eyes. This also causes the image of your finger to sweep back and forth over the back of your eye. So here are two distinct situations—a stationary object and a moving object—that can produce comparable patterns of eye stimulation. How does the visual nervous system distinguish one from the other? We'll postpone details of the answer until Chapter 9, but suffice it to say the brain solves the potential dilemma by keeping track of motor commands sent to the eye muscles. A neural copy of those commands can be sent to visual areas of the brain thereby "vetoing" the implication of signals arriving from the eye. This kind of sensorimotor feedback is probably used whenever we distinguish self-produced stimulation from externally produced stimulation.

Perception's links to action orientation produces an interesting distinction among the various senses that has to do with the proximity of the perceiver to the object of perception. Touch and taste require direct contact between the perceiver and the source of stimulation. Because of this restriction, taste and touch can be considered **near senses.** The sense of smell is also effectively a near sense, at least for humans. Volatile chemicals from an odorous substance are diluted with distance, so smell works more effectively for substances in the general vicinity of the nose.* In contrast, for us humans, seeing and hearing, can be thought of as **far senses, or distance senses.** The eyes and ears can pick up information originating from remote sources. In this respect, they function like a ship's radar. They allow one to make perceptual contact with objects located too far away for immediate grasp. They extend one perceptually out into the world beyond the fingertips and nose. These two senses serve as able substitutes for actual locomotor exploration of the environment. They let you explore your surroundings vicariously. They provide advance warning of approaching danger, and they guide the search for friends and desired objects. In general, hearing and seeing open up to you the large world that lies outside your reach. Imagine how vulnerable you would feel if you were denied access to all information picked up by your far senses. Your whole world would shrink to the area within arm's reach. You would be able to sense objects only when you touched them or when they touched you. It is not surprising, therefore, that blindness and deafness, loss of the far senses, are considered so devastating.

Incidentally, this distinction between the near and far senses has an important behavioral consequence. Any crucial reaction called for by taste or touch must be executed swiftly. There is no time to decide whether a bitter substance is toxic—you spit it out reflexively. Nor do you first try to judge what is causing a burning sensation before you remove your hand from a hot object. In these cases, you act first and then consciously think about what it was that triggered your reflex action. However, in the case of the far senses—seeing and hearing—one often deals with objects located some distance away. This distance permits the luxury of evaluating the potential consequences of one's actions.

One final note about active perception. The ability to explore our world actively requires fine motor control over the body parts used for exploration. You could think of your fingers as finely-tuned calipers that adjust their grip force to suit the object you're holding. You're able to do this because the muscles in your fingers contain specialized sensory receptors that gauge the strength of contraction and, hence, the tightness of your grip. Without those internal sensory receptors to monitor grip strength, you'd have trouble squeezing the right amount of toothpaste from a tube, and you could crush a delicate flower before you knew what you were doing. Called **kinesthesia,** this internal sense of muscular contraction is intimately involved in coordinating all sorts of mo-

---

*Actually, this is not true for all species: some animals possess a highly acute sense of smell that allows them to detect odors over great distances, as you'll learn in Chapter 13.

tor activities, including walking, dressing, eating, and typing. We'll not dwell at length on the mechanisms of kinesthesia, but you should keep in mind that the nervous system also includes specialized sensory systems that monitor the internal "perceptual" states of your body's interior parts.*

WHY STUDY PERCEPTION?

Over the years, people have studied perception for a variety of reasons. Some of these reasons, as you will see, stem from practical considerations, such as the need to solve a particular problem. Other reasons do not involve practical concerns, but arise from simple intellectual curiosity about ourselves and the world we live in.

Practical Reasons for Studying Perception

The human senses evolved under environmental conditions in many ways quite different from those we now live in. Many of the challenges confronting the human senses today didn't exist in the more primitive environments for which these senses were designed. It's very important to know just what kind of perceptual demands can reasonably be placed on the human senses without compromising safety and sanity. There is an optimum range of sensory stimulation within which the majority of people work and play most effectively. Intense stimulation—such as excessive noise, glaring light, and harsh smells—can impair immediate performance as well as damage the sensory nervous system. Through the

study of perception, one can identify and correct potentially hazardous environmental conditions that threaten the senses and impair the ability to make decisions.

In a related vein, studying perception enables one to design devices that ensure optimal perceptual performance. Just think how often each day you come in contact with devices designed to communicate some message to you. Traffic lights, alarm clocks, telephones, and video displays are just a few of the myriad inventions that people rely on during work, play, study, even sleep. To be effective, these devices should be tailored to human sensory systems. It would be unwise, for example, to use a high-pitched tone as a fire alarm in a hotel, because most elderly people have difficulty hearing such tones. Similarly, a traffic sign with blue lettering on a green background would be inefficient, since the contrast between these two colors makes letters more difficult to distinguish than, say, red letters on a green background. In general, one wants the signs and signals in the environment to be easy to see and hear, and this requires an understanding of human perceptual capacities and limitations. Understanding perception also makes it possible to design devices to help individuals with impaired sensory function. Take hearing aids as an example. For decades hearing aids amplified not only the sounds the user wanted to hear—such as a person's voice—but also other, unwanted sounds, such as traffic noises. Recognizing this problem, Richard L. Gregory developed a procedure that selectively amplifies just speech sounds (Gregory and Drysdale, 1976). This invention, which is now in wide use, grew out of earlier work on the ear's ability to respond selectively to particular sounds. And recently we've seen the development of devices that boost hearing by direct stimulation of the auditory nerve, using implants driven by speech processors embedded on microchips (Wilson et al., 1991). This device has been a boon to thousands of hearing-impaired children, but the design of such aids requires a solid understanding of mechanisms of normal perception.

---

*One could also construe internal regulatory mechanisms as "sensory" systems, in that they monitor physiological states such as hormone levels and blood oxygen and glucose levels. When those levels drift out of balance, compensatory reactions are triggered (e.g., a change in heart rate). Thus, these internal mechanisms also form sensory/action loops. We'll not include internal monitoring systems in this text, for we're concerned with sensory systems that allow us to interact with our external environment.

Also in a practical vein, companies in the food and beverage industry carefully test the perceptual appeal—the taste, smell, and appearance—of their products before marketing them. Advertising, too, capitalizes on perception research to package and market products in ways that will bring those products to the attention of consumers. There are even claims that subliminal sensory messages—pictures or words presented too briefly or too faintly to be consciously seen or heard—can improves one's memory or enhance self-esteem, although these claims are questionable (Greenwald, et al., 1991).

So far, our practical reasons have focused on human perception. But as the following examples show, there are solid reasons for studying animal perception too. For one thing, animals can be trained to perform jobs that are beyond the sensory limits of humans. Dogs, because of their keen sense of smell, are adept at detecting odors that are too faint for the human nose. This is why dogs are frequently employed to sniff out illegal drugs or to trace the footsteps of a fleeing suspect. In other instances, knowledge of an animal's sensory apparatus allows one to control that animal's behavior. For instance, agricultural scientists control cotton bollworms—moth larvae that damage cotton crops—by spraying crop fields with a chemical that fools adult male moths into mating with moths of a different species. This chemical overwhelms the smell cues that normally guide mating behaviors. As a result, the moths engage in promiscuous and ineffective mating behavior. As a final example, scientists study animals whose sensory capacity is impaired by congenital disorders or by some experimental manipulation such as sensory deprivation (Kaas and Florence, 1996). These studies, in turn, lead to valuable ideas concerning the bases and treatment of comparable sensory disorders in humans.

Perception and Pleasure

Probably in more primitive lifestyles (such as those of our primate ancestors) the lion's share of perceptual processing was devoted to survival—being on the alert to distinguish friends from foes and trying to locate the next meal. As civilization developed, these pressing demands have relaxed. As a result, civilized people enjoy the freedom to develop pastimes—the visual arts, music, cuisine—that engage their perceptual machinery in more amusing and creative ways. All these pastimes involve stimulation of the senses. Besides their immediate aesthetic and sensual qualities, these kinds of sensory experiences play an important role in the cultural heritage of societies. Through various forms of art, people share the joys and pains experienced by others, and to savor vicariously the thrill of discovery that originally inspired the artist. In brief, art embodies much of a culture's wisdom, and transmits that wisdom from one generation to the next by means of shared sensory experience.

Perception and Intellectual Curiosity

Practical and pleasurable concerns aside, learning about perception satisfies an intellectual curiosity about ourselves and the world we live in. Perception can be thought of as each individual's personal theory of reality, the knowledge-gathering process that defines our view of the world. Because this perceptual outlook guides our mental and behavioral activities, we naturally find it fascinating to inquire about the bases of perception.

Natural curiosity leads to a variety of conjectures about perception. When looking at a newborn child, for instance, one cannot help speculating about what that infant sees and hears. Likewise, one is curious to know whether blind people really can hear sounds that escape the ears of sighted people. You may have wondered why colors seem to change depending on the time of day. As dusk approaches, greens take on a deeper richness, while yellows and reds lose some of their brilliance. And why does everyone effectively become colorblind in dim light? One would like to know what sensory cues enable a displaced pet to journey hundreds of miles, eventually returning to its old home. And one grudgingly marvels at how adept mosquitoes are at locating one's bare skin in total darkness.

People are intrigued by their everyday experiences and curious about the bases of those experiences. This curiosity was long ago formalized in philosophy. For centuries, philosophers have argued about how human beings can know the external world. Their arguments reflected a concern about the validity of sense experiences. Though our concept of the world derives from the information of our senses, can those senses be relied on to tell the truth? Might we not be deceived about the world? Perhaps, as Plato suggested in Book VII of *The Republic*, we are like prisoners in a cave, cut off from the world, so that we can see only shadows created by objects and events outside.

In fact, from earliest times, people knew that their senses were fallible. Realizing that sensory information was not totally dependable, philosophers became increasingly skeptical about anyone's ability to know the world as it really is. This skepticism reached full bloom during the late seventeenth and early eighteenth centuries. During that time, the British philosopher John Locke (1690/1924) made a crucial observation: water in a basin can feel either warm or cool to the touch, depending on where your hand has just been. If your hand has been in cold water, the basin's water would feel warm; if your hand has previously been in hot water, the water in the basin would feel cool. The apparent warmth or coolness of the water does not reside in the water itself; it is a quality that depends on the perceiver's own state. Since, to him, some perceived qualities of the external world seemed more subjective than others, Locke distinguished between primary qualities (real qualities, actually present in the object) and secondary qualities (resulting from an object's power to produce various sensations in us). Primary qualities included the bulk, number, motion, and shape of objects. Locke's secondary qualities included objects' color, sound, taste,

and smell. Locke thought we can rely on primary qualities to reflect accurately the nature of objects in the real world, but we must be cautious, or skeptical, about relying on secondary qualities in the same way.

This skepticism about the information of the senses was carried to greater extremes by David Hume in *A Treatise of Human Nature* (1739/1963). Hume rejected the distinction between primary and secondary qualities, banishing all sense experiences to the realm of the subjective and unreliable. Hume's pessimism about the possibility of ever understanding perception is represented quite well by the following comment from his *Treatise:*

> As to those impressions which arise from the senses, their ultimate cause is, in my opinion, perfectly inexplicable by human reason, and it will always be impossible to decide with certainty whether they arise immediately from the object, or are produced by the creative power of the mind, or are derived from the author of our being. (Book I, Part III, Section V, p. 75)

There is good reason, though, to question this Humean skepticism (Schlagel, 1984). As knowledge of our senses has deepened, we have come to understand that lawful processes are responsible for what previously seemed to be mysterious sensory caprice. We know that holding one's hand in a basin of hot water initiates a process called adaptation, an alteration in the skin's temperature receptors. This process produces the thermal paradox that so perplexed Locke. If we understand adaptation—how it grows with time, how long it lasts, and so on—Locke's paradox becomes less of a reason for skepticism. Or suppose you put on some colored sunglasses. If they're strongly tinted, they'll temporarily alter the way the world looks. But that's no reason to dismiss vision as inherently undependable. If you understand how the sunglasses alter the light that reaches your eye, and if you understand enough about vision itself, you should be able to explain changes in how the world looks. In fact, the senses are actually quite dependable—as long as you know enough about how they operate. For instance, you'd be able to take any arbitrary pair of sunglasses and predict quite accurately how the world will look through those glasses, or you'd be able to take any person's hand and any basin of water and predict exactly how warm that water will feel. Perception research can help overcome some of the skeptic's doubts.

Since we are discussing attitudes about the relation between perception and reality, this is a good time to introduce a view that we'll mention from time to time in this book. This view, called **naive realism,** is common among laypersons and beginning students of perception. "Naive realism is the view that what we know about the world is both unadulterated and unexpurgated with respect to even its most subtle details" (Shaw and Bransford, 1977, p. 18). In other words, the world *is* always exactly as it appears.

A simple test can determine whether someone is a naive realist. When asked, "Why does the world look to you the way it does?" the naive realist will answer, "Because it *is* that way." In other words, the properties of experience can always be completely and easily explained by the properties of the world itself. But this simple view of perception is mistaken. For one thing, it cannot explain why different people experience the same environmental event differently. And this does happen, as you'll discover throughout this book. We know, for example, that infants cannot see small objects that adults can see; that young adults can hear some sounds that older adults cannot; and that certain people are completely oblivious to odors that others have no trouble smelling. Such facts challenge naive realism. We all live in the same *physical* world. If naive realism were a valid viewpoint, wouldn't our *perceptual* worlds be identical?

There's another reason to reject naive realism: a single, unchanging physical stimulus can change in appearance from one moment to the next. The classic example of this is the **Necker**

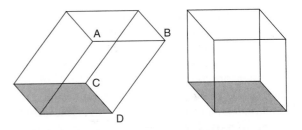

FIGURE 1.3
Below are two transparent figures whose perspectives appear to fluctuate. The darkened surface in each figure seems sometimes to be an inner surface and sometimes an outer surface. The fluctuations of the rhomboid (left) were first noticed by L. A. Necker about 150 years ago while he was examining some crystals. Today these figures are known as Necker's rhomboid and Necker's cube.

cube, named after Swiss naturalist Louis Albert Necker (Figure 1.3). Note how the rhomboid at the left seems to fluctuate in appearance. At one moment line segment AB appears closest to you, while at another moment segment CD appears closest. The appearance of the figure at the right undergoes similar fluctuations. Now if perception were determined solely by the physical properties of the figures, their appearance should be stable. Such examples clearly demonstrate that one's perceptions have qualities not present in the physical attributes of the stimulus.

At the other extreme from naive realism is **subjective idealism,** the view that the physical world is entirely the product of the mind, a compelling mental fiction. This philosophical position is associated with the Irish philosopher George Berkeley, who capsulized the idea in the phrase "to be is to perceive." In other words, the world exists only as a result of perception; no perception, no world. Carried to its extreme, this position leads to **solipsism,** the notion that only your mind exists and all other worldly objects are perceptions of your mind. This position can be entertaining to discuss among friends but is scientifically sterile. If the world in which we exist were not real, there would be no reason to study the relation between perceiving and that (imaginary) world.

Having rejected naive realism and solipsism, what do we propose about the relations between human perceptions and the real world? As stressed earlier, we acknowledge the existence of the real world and assert that its existence does not depend on a perceiver. At the same time, we recognize the perceiver's own contribution to the process of perception. The perceiver's view of the world is not perfectly accurate, of course, because the perceiver's sensory system both *limits* the information that is available and *augments* that information.

To show you more exactly what we mean by the perceiver's contribution, consider a familiar question: "Does a tree falling in the forest make a sound if there is no one around to hear it?" According to a solipsist, no tree, no forest, and no sound would exist in the absence of a perceiver. But according to our view, not only would the falling tree still exist even though no perceiver happened to be around, its fall would create acoustic energy in the form of air pressure waves. But would this constitute sound? If the term "sound" means a perceptual experience, then clearly the falling tree would not produce a sound. For the tree to produce a sound requires the presence of some organism with a sensory system capable of registering the available acoustic energy. But even this does not guarantee that the resulting experience would be what is normally called sound. It's conceivable that the organism that is present might not be able to hear, because it has no ears, but instead could *feel* the energy produced by the falling tree (in the same way that you can literally feel the beat of a bass drum). To qualify as sound, the energy must strike the ears of a human—or some other creature with a nervous system like that of a human. What this boils down to is that the quality of one's sensory experience depends on events within the nervous system, as Box 1.2 underscores.

To sum up: In order to understand perception as fully as possible, one must study not only the properties of the physical world but also those of the perceiver.

PSYCHOLOGICAL, BIOLOGICAL, AND THEORETICAL APPROACHES TO PERCEPTION

At the outset of this chapter we stated that perception entails a sequence of interrelated events that mutually influence one another. Furthermore, we said that to understand perception requires knowing something about each component of the sequence. Understanding these components requires the combined knowledge from several different scientific disciplines, ranging from biophysics to psychology. These disciplines use different levels of analysis, from the microscopic (studying the behavior of molecules) to the macroscopic (studying the behavior of whole organisms). For a complete picture, then, one needs to analyze perception at several different levels, each offering a unique and invaluable perspective. To illustrate metaphorically what we mean by "levels of analysis," look at Figure 1.4. It shows an aerial photograph taken over the Peruvian desert from a very great height. From this altitude, one can see a mammoth sand carving thought to be a thousand years old. The carving, made by people lost to history, is a figure nearly 1,600 meters long. It is so huge that it can be recognized only from a great height. Standing on the ground, you would be unable to take in the entire carving. Thus, to appreciate the carving requires a particular level of analysis, namely, one a great distance above the carving. Suppose, though, that you wished to examine the details of the carving and what it was made of. Such examination would require quite a different level of analysis, one much closer to the ground.

This beautiful and mysterious desert carving dramatizes a point about perception: one must adopt different levels of analysis in order to answer all the significant questions about a subject.

BOX 1.2

HEARING LIGHTNING AND SEEING THUNDER
HEARING AND SEEING WITH THE BRAIN

Seeing and hearing are qualitatively different perceptual experiences. This is shown by the fact that people never confuse sight and sound. The same can be said for touch, taste, and smell. In fact, these qualitative differences form the basis for the classic five-part division of the senses—touch, taste, smell, hearing, and seeing. Our assumption in this book is that these subjectively different experiences are products of neural events within the brain. And yet those events, it is known, all boil down to patterns of nerve impulses within the brain. Since different experiences are represented by the same sort of events, how does the brain manage to distinguish one type of experience from another—sight from sound, and taste from smell? Let's consider this question as it applies to sight and sound.

It is tempting to answer by pointing out that sound waves, the stimulus for hearing, are fundamentally different from light energy, the stimulus for seeing. However, this argument is not adequate because the brain does not directly *receive* either sound waves or light energy. It receives only tiny electrical signals called neural impulses. In other words, from the brain's perspective, all incoming signals are equivalent. But, you might point out, although they resemble one another, those neural impulses *arise* from different sources, namely, the eyes and the ears. And, you might continue, those sources *are* fundamentally different—they are specially designed to respond only to particular kinds of physical stimulation. Because of their specialized receptors, the eyes respond to light but not to sound, while the opposite is true for the ears. So, you might well conclude, the distinctiveness of seeing and hearing depends on the difference between the eyes and the ears.

This explanation, however, is not adequate either because sensations of light and sound can be produced without the participation of eyes and ears. One can bypass them and stimulate the brain directly. During the course of brain surgery on awake, alert humans, neurosurgeons sometimes need to stimulate the brain's surface electrically to determine exactly where they are working. Depending on the area of the brain stimulated, patients report very vivid sensations that seem quite real (Penfield and Perrot, 1963). For instance, stimulation at a point in the back of the brain can elicit sensations of light flashes, whereas stimulation at the proper spot on the side of the brain can cause the patient to hear tones. Here, then, are examples of qualitatively distinct sensations that arise from exactly the same sort of stimulation—a mild electric current. Note, though, that the patients did not *feel* the electric current—they "heard" it or "saw" it, depending on the brain region stimulated.

These observations force a surprising conclusion: the critical difference between hearing and seeing depends not so much on differences between the eyes and the ears but on *where* in the brain the eyes and ears send their messages and how those brain areas are organized. This is actually a very old idea, dating back to Johannes Müller, a nineteenth-century German physiologist. Müller's theory, called the doctrine of **specific nerve energies,** states that the nature of a sensation depends on the particular set of nerve fibers stimulated. According to this doctrine, activity in the nerve from the eye will invariably produce visual sensations, regardless of how that activity was instigated. Nowadays, it is recognized that sensory nerves travel to specific brain areas: the nerve from the eye travels to one place, the nerve from the ear to another. Thus the emphasis has shifted from the nerves themselves to their projection sites in the brain. It is now widely believed that the distinctiveness of sight and sound is related to the unique properties of the neural connections within different regions of the brain, connections that are established during early brain development (von Melchner, Pallas and Sur, 2000).

Müller's doctrine suggested a provocative thought experiment to William James (1892, p.12). To paraphrase his idea, suppose you were able to reroute the nerve from your eye, sending it to the part of your brain that normally receives input from your ear. Suppose that while you were at it, you also rerouted the nerve from your ear, sending it to that part of your brain that normally gets visual information. Now imagine that with this revised nervous system, you are caught in a thunderstorm. A flash of lightning, which stimulates the eyes, should evoke auditory sensations, while the subsequent sound of thunder, which stimulates the ears, should evoke visual sensations. But don't expect the light-evoked auditory sensations to sound like thunder or the sound-evoked visual sensations to resemble lightning—the train of neural impulses carried by the optic nerve and the auditory nerve are unlikely to establish the precise patterns of brain activity associated with thunder and lightning.

FIGURE 1.4
Aerial photograph of sand carving on Peruvian desert. (© George Gerster/Comstock, Inc.)

Consequently, we'll be adopting various levels of analysis in our examination of perception. The three main levels of analysis that we'll explore are the *psychological, biological* and *theoretical.*

Distinguishing among the psychological, biological and theoretical approaches will help organize the discussion that follows. We repeat, though, that these approaches are not mutually exclusive, but are complementary. One simply cannot learn all one wants to know about perception from just one approach.

Psychological Approaches

First, there is no single psychological approach to perception. Instead, there are many, each differing from the others in various ways. Although they all use some behavioral reaction to stimuli as a way of studying perception, they differ in terms of *what* behavioral reaction is used. For instance, one might attempt to train a bird to fly to a red perch but not to a green perch. If the bird succeeds in learning this task, one might infer that the bird can tell red from green. To justify this conclusion, however, requires additional tests to ensure the bird is actually relying on color, not other visual cues such as position or brightness.

Similarly, a human being can be instructed to push one button whenever a red object is presented and to push another button whenever a green object is presented. For birds and humans, behavior is used to infer something about perception. There are actually many specific techniques for studying perception, and we'll describe some of those techniques as the need arises. Now, however, let's not focus on the details of particular behavioral techniques. Instead, let's analyze the methods along more general lines, grouping them according to their degree of *formality.* By "formality" we mean the extent to which stimuli and reactions to them are structured or controlled.

The Phenomenal/Naturalistic Approach   The least formal is the phenomenal/naturalistic method. "Phenomenal" means that the evidence used by the approach consists of one's conscious experiences. "Naturalistic" means that the evidence concerns responses to whatever objects or events occur naturally within the environment; there is no attempt to modify or control those objects or events.

There are certain advantages to this "informal" approach to perception. For one thing, it relies on the most readily obtainable data, which are experiences evoked by naturally occurring events. Such experiences might include the appearance of a sunset, the sound of a police siren, the taste of an artichoke. Everyone has untold numbers of such experiences throughout the waking hours. To study perception, then, you could collect and organize these experiences. Going one step further, you could discuss your perceptual experiences with other people, for purposes of comparison. But what pitfalls would you encounter by following this program?

First, by restricting yourself to phenomenal descriptions, you would not be able to study perception in animals and pre-verbal infants, a serious limitation. Second, even working with humans who *can* verbalize their experiences, you would need to be wary. Verbal reports can be fallible and misleading. For one thing, not all people use words in the same way. For instance, many colorblind people have learned to label colors much as color-normal people do, even though their experiences are surely very different.

Because verbal reports are usually made with such confidence, one may be misled into believing they are a direct pipeline to experience. In fact, that assumption underlies the use of verbal reports as a way to examine perceptual experience. But the assumption is probably unwarranted, for there is reason to doubt that individuals *can* accurately describe their experiences, motives, or thought processes (Nisbett and Wilson, 1977); these often cannot be accessed at a conscious level. In some instances, moreover, people are motivated to avoid telling what they consider to be the truth about their experiences. Here's one example. A malingerer is someone who pretends to have an illness or disability to get some special gain or avoid some responsibility. Feigned deafness is one form of malingering. Ask such a malingerer if he can hear, and you'll get no answer unless the question is communicated in writing, lip reading, or sign language. Then, the malingerer will assure you that he can't hear (a misleading verbal report). But there is a very clever, foolproof way to catch the malingerer: delayed auditory feedback. While the person is reading aloud, record his speech and, following a very short delay, play it back into his ears. If he is genuinely deaf, and not a malingerer, delayed auditory feedback will have no influence on his reading. But if he *can* hear, the delayed feedback of his own voice will invariably disrupt his speech.*

The word "feigns" denotes that someone is purposely lying or pretending. But there are instances where a person's erroneous verbal reports don't really constitute lying. One such instance is **Anton's syndrome,** which was first described by Gabriel Anton more than a hundred years ago (Foerstl, Owen and David, 1993). This syndrome, as rare as it is bizarre, involves complete blindness coupled with denial (the blind person denies that he or she is blind). The condition supposedly arises because two different areas of the brain have been damaged—the one needed for seeing and the one needed for knowing that you're seeing. This damage to the brain occurs quite suddenly—usually as the result of a cerebral vascular accident (a stroke)—and the victim of Anton's syndrome may walk around for quite some time bumping into things and

having other mishaps until he or she becomes convinced that something is wrong. But immediately following damage to the brain, victims of Anton's syndrome confidently insist that they can see. Asked to describe what they see, the victims may give very detailed answers, which are utter fabrications, as evidenced by their lack of correspondence to reality.

Anton's syndrome not only underscores the potential unreliability of verbal reports about perception, but also points up a more general fact: perceptual experiences and knowledge of those experiences are two quite separate things. Many forces that people are not aware of can influence what they perceive. These unconscious influences include expectations, prior experience, and motivations (see Figure 1.5). Although such forces are distinct from the links that form the perceptual chain, the phenomenal approach would foreclose separating these two kinds of influences on perception. As you'll see in Box 1.3, other, more formal approaches *do* allow one to separate the two influences.

Despite its limitations, the phenomenal/naturalistic approach to perception does have an important role to play. For more than a hundred years, careful and thoughtful observers have used this informal approach as a basis upon which to build a more formal study of perception. This

FIGURE 1.5
Look at this drawing for a while. If you cannot discern an animal, look at Figure 1.6 on page 20.

---

*This example raises an interesting issue. What if the person insists that he cannot hear, even though the auditory feedback disrupts his speech? Should one automatically label the person a "malingerer"? Should one put more faith in the delayed feedback's interference than in his verbal report? It's conceivable that delayed feedback impairs speech at a preconscious level—in which case the person might be unaware of any disruption of his speech.

FIGURE 1.6
Outline drawing of the same animal depicted in Figure 1.5. Note how seeing this
figure helps you interpret Figure 1.5. Surprisingly, this effect lasts for months.

book will emphasize these more formal approaches. But it should not be forgotten that many of the ideas for formal study derive from this less formal method.

Experimental Approaches   The phenomenal/naturalistic approach works with stimuli as they exist in nature, without trying to control or manipulate those stimuli. This approach is simple but not entirely satisfactory. For one thing, to study a particular aspect of perception usually requires access to a particular class of stimulus, which may not be available naturally. Moreover, you often need to use a whole series of stimuli—comparing the effect of each to the effects produced by its fellows. And the specific series you wanted might never occur naturally. For example, you might want the members of the series to differ in only one attribute (such as color) with all others (such as intensity) held constant. This would make it easy to ascribe any resulting change in perception to the varied attribute. If several attributes varied simultaneously (as is usually the case with naturally occurring stimuli), you would have trouble knowing how much each attribute contributed to perception.

In addition, naturalistic stimuli do not often repeat themselves precisely. We mentioned ear-

lier that the study of perception should be general: it should involve the perceptions of more than one person, and it should involve perceptions at more than just one moment. To satisfy the need to generalize requires repeated measures of perceptual responses. The same stimuli must be presented again and again, under controlled conditions.

To understand perception fully, one must be able to control and manipulate stimuli. One must often use stimuli that never occur in nature. Such stimuli are sometimes criticized as being "nonecological," because they are not the stimuli for which perceptual systems evolved. Researchers widely agree, however, that simple, artificial (nonecological) stimuli can be valid because they often clarify the effects of more complex, naturally occurring stimuli. This point is well documented throughout this book. There is some merit, though, to studying perception using ecologically representative stimuli. In particular, such stimuli make it easy for one to generalize from studies in the laboratory to situations likely to be encountered every day outside the laboratory.

Control and careful manipulation of the stimulus also allow one to identify exactly *what* aspect of the stimulus underlies some perceptual

BOX 1.3

SHOULD YOU ANSWER THE PHONE?

Everyone has had the following maddening experience. While taking a shower, you faintly hear what sounds like the telephone ringing. Because of the shower's steady noise, though, you're not sure it *is* the phone. So do you decide yes and run, dripping wet, to answer it? Or do you conclude that it's only your imagination?

Your behavior in this situation depends on factors other than the loudness of the ringing sound. For instance, if you are expecting an important call, you will in all likelihood scurry out of the shower to see whether the phone is actually ringing. If, in contrast, you're not expecting a call, you're more likely to attribute the ringing sound to the shower's own noises. Your decision about the reality of the sound, then, is influenced by your expectations. This example illustrates a significant principle, namely, that one's interpretation of sensory data depends significantly on nonsensory factors.

This dependence colors the way in which results from perceptual studies are interpreted. Imagine testing a person's hearing by presenting faint sounds and having the person say whether or not she could hear the sound. Performance on such a test can vary from one person to the next, and not just because some people have better hearing than others. Some people are simply more willing to take a gamble, asserting that they heard something even if they're not 100 percent certain (these people might also want to impress the tester with their keen hearing, say, if the hearing test is part of a job application). There are also more conservative people, who are not gamblers. In the hearing test, such people might require a much louder sound before they are willing to say they heard it. Suppose that two people took a hearing test, one a conservative type, the other a gambler. On the basis of their performance on the hearing test, the tester might mistakenly conclude that the conservative had inferior hearing.

People *do* differ in the sensitivity of their sensory systems. Some individuals, for instance, have a keener sense of smell than do others. But people *also* differ in their motivations, expectations, and willingness to gamble. As an aggregate, these latter differences can be labeled "motivational differences." In studies of perceptual abilities, it is important to distinguish between an individual's sensitivity and motivation. Toward this end, psychologists have developed several strategies for separating the two.

To tell whether a person can *really* hear an extremely faint sound, one needs more to go on than the fact that she is constantly saying that she hears a sound. Logically, one must also ensure that she does not make exactly the same claim when no sound whatever has been presented (Goldman, 1976). Many experiments on hearing, then, randomly intermix two types of test trials. On one type of trial, a weak sound is presented; on the other, no sound is presented. After each trial, the person says whether or not she heard a sound. Someone really interested in impressing the tester might say "Yes, I hear it" after every single trial. Of course, she'd be right regarding every trial in which a sound actually occurred, but she'd be wrong with respect to every trial in which no sound occurred. From this result, the tester should realize that this person could not discriminate the presence of sound from the absence of sound. Omitting the sound and noting the subject's failure to recognize that omission allows the tester to separate the person's sensitivity to sound from other possible factors—such as the motivation to impress.

This general strategy is not limited to the study of hearing; similar methods are used with the other senses as well. To implement the strategy, psychologists have developed a set of sophisticated statistical techniques collectively known as signal detection theory. The Appendix provides additional details of signal detection theory. For a more thorough treatment of this topic, we suggest you consult MacMillan and Creelman (1991), McNicol (1972), or Swets, Tanner, and Birdsall (1961). Meanwhile, before showering the next time, take the phone off the hook.

experience. Here's one illustration: Some rare individuals are able to discriminate among thousands of different wines by taste alone. To determine the basis of this remarkable ability, you could create a series of specially constituted wines that varied in their composition, and using this set of controlled stimuli, you could isolate the cues enabling such individuals to distinguish what most people cannot.

One also needs control over the stimuli in order to conduct two kinds of experiments that are the foundation of the scientific study of perception: matching and detection experiments. Matching experiments ask people to adjust one stimulus until it appears identical to another. This obviously requires stimuli that can be manipulated precisely. Detection experiments measure the weakest stimulus that a person can detect. Again, such experiments require stimuli whose intensities can be controlled.

As we've indicated, the psychological approach to perception uses a variety of methods, ranging from the simple and naturalistic to the highly structured and controlled. Each of these methods makes its own unique contribution. The Appendix describes some of the formal, structured methods. In addition, throughout the book, you'll encounter descriptions of various methods in the context of the research problems for which they were designed.

Although the psychological approach is useful in the study of perception, it leaves unanswered important questions about underlying neural processes. We turn now to a complementary approach that addresses those questions.

Biological Approaches

Throughout the history of scientific research on perception, an enduring theme has been the dependence of perceptual events on brain events. An overriding goal, then, has been to investigate the linkages between perceptual and biological phenomena. Though such investigations can be challenging to carry out, their outcome often

yields information fundamental to understanding perception. Here we'll sketch out some of the strategies used to relate physiology to behavior, without going into the details or the outcomes. In subsequent chapters, you'll learn how these strategies provide answers to specific questions about perception.

Lesion Technique   The oldest method for relating brain events to perception entails destroying some portion of the nervous system and then measuring resulting changes in perceptual function. Called a **lesion,** this delimited area of brain damage can be created by applying strong electrical current to the targeted area, by injecting a chemical that kills nerve cells, or by surgically removing brain tissue. Interpreted with proper caution, these studies can help identify the anatomical locus of neural structures crucially involved in a given perceptual ability.

There are, however, limitations to the conclusions that can be drawn from lesion studies, especially since lesions disrupt more than just the neural operations associated with the lesioned brain region. Destroying the Golden Gate bridge would seriously interfere with the economic activity throughout the San Francisco Bay area, but we wouldn't want to conclude that economic activity is localized *on* the Golden Gate bridge. Likewise, lesioning a particular brain area may destroy an animal's ability to recognize a certain class of visual objects (such as faces), but it would be misleading to state that this brain region was solely responsible for analyzing that class of objects. By the same token, an animal may recover function following the destruction of brain tissue, but this doesn't mean that the lesioned area does not participate in that function normally. Other brain areas may have taken over for the destroyed area. So, in summary, results from lesion studies can be strongly suggestive but seldom definitive.

It is worth noting that this strategy of creating a lesion and then determining its perceptual consequences is merely a systematic, experimental version of what happens when disease or trauma damage the nervous system. Naturally occurring lesions offer insights about the neural basis of human perception and have done so for centuries (Boring, 1942). Since disease or trauma usually create lesions that affect diverse areas of the brain, naturally occurring lesions may offer only limited help in pinpointing the neural basis of perceptual function.

Evoked Potential Technique   Another widely used procedure relates perceptual judgments made in response to a given stimulus with the electrical brain activity evoked by that same stimulus. Measured through small electrodes attached to a person's scalp, this brain activity is termed an **evoked potential (EP)** or, alternatively, an **event-related potential (ERP).** This procedure requires sensitive electronic amplifiers to boost the electrical signals measured from the scalp and skull. These signals, are called massed responses because they reflect the varied activity among several thousand brain cells located near each electrode. In recent years, ERPs have been measured using an array of electrodes distributed over a large region of the scalp. By recording electrical signals from all these electrodes simultaneously, researchers can more accurately localize the source of brain activity associated with a given stimulus. Moreover, using multiple electrodes makes it possible to monitor how brain activity builds and spreads from one location to another.

Over the years, ERPs have been measured in a variety of tasks. In some instances, researchers want to know whether the magnitude of the ERP correlates with a person's subjective impression of the stimulus's intensity. In other cases, researchers measure the ERP in response to unanticipated or novel stimulation. A particularly intriguing application of the ERP technique looks for brain activity in response to visual or auditory events that, in fact, are not perceived. For example, Luck, Vogel and Shapiro (1996) found that unexpected words still elicited a strong "novelty" response in the ERP, even when the presence of those words could not be reported because of the person's attention was temporarily distracted.

The ERP technique is also useful for studying nonverbal individuals—such as human infants or animals—who are unable to report their perceptions. Being able to measure ERPs from such nonverbal individuals indicates that the evoking stimulus generates activity within the brain. Although this does not necessarily mean the individual perceives the stimulus, it confirms that a necessary condition for perception is satisfied. Using ERPs, researchers have harvested important facts about the visual world of infants (e.g., Atkinson and Braddick, 1998) and of animals (e.g., Berkley and Watkins, 1971).

This technique also has its drawbacks. For one, the *failure* to record an ERP doesn't necessarily mean the brain fails to register the evoking stimulus—the neural signals may just be too weak to be picked up or the recording electrodes may be misplaced on the scalp. For another, it is very difficult to pinpoint in exactly what region of the brain ERP activity is arising. So, it is important to realize that the evoked potential provides a rather diffuse measure of brain activity picked up from tiny signals generated by large numbers of brain cells; the evoked potential only reflects omnibus brain activity.

Brain Imaging Techniques   In the past decade, perception research has profited substantially from noninvasive techniques that create detailed pictures of the human brain. When measured under the proper perceptual test conditions, images from brain scanning can reveal regions of the human brain that are uniquely activated during performance of that perceptual task. As you will read, two particularly powerful versions of brain scanning—positron-emission tomography (**PET**) and functional magnetic resonance imaging (**fMRI**)—have produced remarkably revealing "snapshots" of brain regions engaged in various acts of perception.

Both PET and fMRI capitalize on the fact that activated regions of the brain temporarily require additional amounts of glucose and oxygen. PET tracks this increased metabolic demand by applying a radioactive "tag" to a chemical required by this increased metabolism. Sensors can then register the temporary accumulation of this radioactively labelled chemical in particular brain regions. In one procedure, a person first inhales a mixture of air and radioactively labelled carbon dioxide. From the person's lungs, the radioactive material, in trace amounts, enters the bloodstream and then dissipates rapidly. If, immediately after the inhalation, activity in some local region of the brain were to increase that heightened metabolic rate would attract a stronger local flow of blood, bringing along with it additional radioactive material. Knowing the location of this increased blood flow, one can construct an image of the distribution of radioactivity within the brain. Going one step further, the person can now be engaged in a particular perceptual task (e.g., detect changes in the color of a geometric form) while the PET scan is being performed. It thus becomes possible to relate neural activity in specific brain regions with the execution of particular perceptual tasks (Corbetta et al., 1991; McIntosh et al., 1999). Despite its promise, however, PET suffers from a couple of limitations. First, PET has limited spatial resolution: PET cannot distinguish differences in activity between small brain areas that are adjacent to one another. Second, safety and health regulations limit the amount of radioactive exposure an individual may receive, making it impossible to test the same person repeatedly under different conditions. For these reasons, much recent brain imaging work has utilized another technology, fMRI.

fMRI exploits the same principle as PET: increased neural activity triggers a temporary increase in metabolic demand at the site of activation. But unlike PET, fMRI tracks the consequences of this increased demand noninvasively, meaning that there is no need for a radioactive labelling agent. Instead, fMRI capitalizes on the fact that richly oxygenated blood has

different magnetic properties than normally oxygenated blood. Thus, it's possible to detect and localize brief surges in oxygenated blood within the brain, thereby inferring sites of increased neural activity. An fMRI scanner, then, allows researchers to measure fluctuations in the magnetic fields of well-defined areas of the brain. These measurements can be made at the same time that an individual engages in a perceptual task, making it possible to correlate fluctuations in fMRI signal with performance of the task (see Figure 1.7). Depending on the sensitivity of the scanner, fMRI can pinpoint regions of neural activation with very high spatial accuracy (Wandell, 1999). Since fMRI does not involve radioactive material, it can be repeated over and over on the same individual. Throughout the forthcoming chapters, you'll read about the successful application of fMRI for identifying brain regions involved in perception (Heeger, 1998).

Single Cell Techniques The techniques discussed so far all operate on a fairly coarse scale, one whose grain comprises thousands of neurons. Techniques that provide finer-grain analysis are excellent supplements to what we have characterized as coarser techniques. In one fine-grain approach, the physiological responses of individual neurons are recorded while an alert behaving animal, usually a monkey, engages in some perceptual task. While varying the difficulty of the task, the researcher tries to identify single neurons whose responses are strongly correlated with the animal's performance. Correlated activity suggests that those neurons form part of the neural machinery involved in the perceptual task. To be successful, this approach must draw upon prior evidence about the locus of neurons thought to register information utilized in the task. Otherwise, the research would degenerate into an unguided search for a needle in a haystack.

Once an investigator has identified a set of neurons that is believed to undergird a particular perceptual judgment, that hypothesis can be tested more directly. One can artificially stimu-

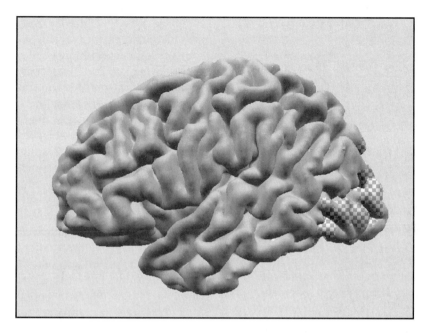

FIGURE 1.7
This is an image of Randolph Blake's left brain hemisphere (Blake is one of the
coauthors of this textbook). The checkered overlay at the back of the brain (the right-
hand portion of image) denotes regions activated when this individual viewed a rotating
checkerboard figure. Other areas within interior regions (not visible in this picture)
were also activated by this visual pattern. Regions of activation were identified by the
brain imaging technique called functional magnetic resonance imaging, or fMRI.
(Image courtesy of Sang-Hun Lee, Vanderbilt University.)

late the neurons by passing weak electrical current into them. If activity in those neurons is crucial, this boost in activity should alter an animal's
performance on an associated perceptual task
(Newsome, Britten and Movshon, 1989). Note,
however, that electrical stimulation activates not
only those neurons in contact with the electrode
but also other neurons nearby. So it would be a
mistake to assume that activity in those neurons
alone is affecting the animal's behavior.

Theoretical Approaches

The previous two sections outlined strategies by
which perception and its underlying neural events
can be studied and ultimately related to one another. Borrowing terminology from computer science, we might say that these sections dealt with
the *input* for perception, the *hardware* of the perceptual process, and its *output*. This metaphor,
however, ignores a crucial element: the *program*.
Here, "program" refers to the set of instructions or
rules that transform input into output.

Sometimes people confuse the program with
the hardware on which it runs. This confusion obscures an important distinction between the two.
To reinforce the distinction between hardware
and program, consider philosopher Daniel Dennett's discussion of an abacus.

Its computational task is to do arithmetic: to yield
a correct output for any arithmetic problem given
to it as input. At this level, then, an abacus and a
hand-held calculator are alike; they are designed to
perform the same "information-processing task."

The algorithmic description of the abacus is what you learn when you learn how to manipulate it— the recipe for moving the beads in the course of adding, subtracting, multiplying, and dividing. Its physical description depends on what it is made of: it might be wooden beads strung on wires in a frame, or it might be poker chips lined up along the cracks in the floor, or something accomplished with a pencil and good eraser on a sheet of lined paper. (1991, p. 276)

In his influential book *Vision,* David Marr (1982) argued the value of studying perception on three complementary levels of abstraction. From most to least abstract, the levels are as follows: one can analyze perception as an information-processing problem; one can examine the set of rules (the program) used to solve the information-processing problem; finally, one can study the neural machinery of perception and how that machinery executes the program. Marr insisted that some effort on the most abstract level ought to precede work on the other two levels.

If, like Marr, one describes perception as a solution to a problem, one needs to appreciate exactly what the problem is. An analogy may help. Suppose a friend tells you that she is thinking of a number between 1 and 20. Your job is to identify that number. You get one clue: the number is odd. Obviously, the clue does not give enough information to identify the number with certainty; it *under specifies* the solution (as opposed to being told, for instance, that the number is the largest prime number in the set). Generally speaking, the information provided to our sense organs under specifies the true nature of objects in the world. Somehow, though, despite significant under specification, the perceptual process manages to yield high-quality, useful representations of those objects.

A researcher may sometimes want to identify not only the processes that make it possible to perform a particular perceptual task, but also how efficiently humans perform that task. The theoretical goal is to identify any aspect of the perceptual process that fails to exploit fully whatever information might be available. One strategy is to compare human performance of a perceptual task against what could be expected from an "ideal perceiver" who was able to utilize all the available information. Often the "ideal perceiver" is a computer-generated model that processes information optimally, with none of the quirks, biases, blindspots or inefficiencies of human perception (Geisler, 1989). Comparisons of human performance against theoretically ideal benchmarks make it possible to identify aspects of perceptual processing that limit actual performance.

Any computation, whether carried out by an ideal observer, by an electronic device, or a biological device, is only as good as its data and its processing rules. The brain's perceptual computations may be accurate or they may be in error, depending on the quality of information supplied by the senses and on the brain's predisposition to process that information in certain ways. But if certain processing rules can lead to errors, why would the brain be predisposed to use those rules?

The information picked up by the senses is not merely a series of unrelated, incoherent data. Instead, sensory information closely conforms to predictable, structured patterns (Snyder and Barlow, 1988). These patterns arise from the very nature of the physical world itself, the world our senses have evolved in. For instance, in our world, objects tend to be compact. The various parts of any object tend to be near one another, not scattered at random all over the landscape (Geisler et al., 2000). In our world, the surface color or texture of most natural objects tends to change gradually rather than abruptly (Kersten, 1987). In our world, light tends to come from above rather than from below (Gregory, 1978). In our world, the hardness of a surface determines how sound energy is reflected from that surface (Handel, 1989).

If the brain's processing rules embodied these regularities, or constraints, that characterize the natural world, the brain's perceptual operation could be more efficient and rapid. Just as processing rules can be embodied within the microchips of an electronic device, rules that assume these regularities of the natural world could be embodied in the hardware of our brains (Ramachandran, 1988). We'll illustrate this with an example.

Look at Figure 1.8, one of many interesting figures devised by Gaetano Kanizsa of the University of Trieste (1976). The figure conveys a strong impression of a white square resting atop four black circles. However, in creating the figure, we had only to make the four sectored disks. Your perceptual system did the rest by creating the white square. It is widely believed that subjective contours, like the ones seen in Figure 1.8, occur because the visual system makes the quite reasonable assumption that nearer objects tend to occlude objects located farther away.

Now, in principle, there's no reason why perception has to include a square in its interpretation of Figure 1.8—a perfectly reasonable alternative would be for you to see four sectored disks, period. In fact, that's exactly what you *do* see when you look at Figure 1.8, a set of four objects seen against a white background. So why does perception fabricate a square in Figure 1.8? Because perception takes into account the likelihood of the layout of objects within a scene when interpreting that scene. For you to see just the four sectored disks in Figure 1.8, and no square, those disks would have to be precisely arranged *in the world* with their missing sectors forming perfect right angles relative to one another. Since such an experience is unlikely, our perceptual apparatus prefers the alternative interpretation of four complete disks partially occluded by a square. Perception, in other words, behaves as if it knew the likelihood of various environmental configurations. In the words of Horace Barlow (1998), "learning the ways of the world consists of learning what does NOT happen as much or more than learning what does."

FIGURE 1.8
Subjective, or illusory, square. (Adapted from Kanizsa, 1976.)

Because vision is designed to deal with partial occlusions within naturally occurring scenes (see Figure 1.9), visual perception automatically treats Kanizsa's figure as though it were one object (a white square) occluding other, more distant objects (four black disks).

Several lines of evidence support the view that **subjective contours** reflect normal, built-in assumptions of the visual system. First, nonhuman creatures also see subjective contours (Bravo, Blake, and Morrison, 1988; Nieder and Wagner, 1999), which is understandable since the visual systems of those creatures evolved in the same environment as ours. Second, brain damage can selectively disrupt the ability to see subjective contours, leaving other aspects of vision unaffected (Stevens, 1983). Third, single neurons in the brains of monkeys respond to illusory contours as if they were real, a point we'll revisit later in this book (von der Heydt, Peterhans, and Baumgartner, 1984). Fabrication or restoration of missing sensory evidence is not limited to vision. Hearing performs a similar feat, when the situation warrants (Dannenbring, 1976).

In the last several paragraphs, we have focused on perception from an information-processing approach, one aimed at specifying the computational problems facing perception. This represents one form of theorizing within the field of perception. In general, the development of theories of perception, whether computational or not, sharpens our thinking, often translating qualitative observations

FIGURE 1.9
Photographs of natural objects occluding on another. (© George Bellerose/Stock Boston.)

into quantitative statements. These kinds of quantitatively explicit theories then serve to guide the design and implementation of experiments in perception. Good theories tell us what to look for and, often, where to look.

SPECIAL CASES

Traditionally, the study of perception has focused on the "typical" perceiver—the normal adult human being. Because large numbers of people fall within this category, that focus is understandable and sensible. This book follows that tradition. But additional important information about perception can be discovered by studying atypical perceivers—individuals who fall outside the category of normal adult human beings. Such studies might involve perceivers who are infants, or nonhuman, or physiologically abnormal. Let's consider each of these special cases in turn. ·

To begin, we can examine perception *developmentally*—studying newborns, infants, children,

and, at life span's other end, elderly people. Systematic changes in perception accompany developmental changes in the sense organs and central nervous system. Thus, studying developmental changes in perception offers one way to understand the relation between sensory systems and perceptual experience.

Animals from nonhuman species represent another type of atypical perceiver. Although special sophisticated techniques are required to study animal perception (Blake, 1998), such work often repays the effort many times over. In this book, some of what you will learn about human perception comes from animal studies. A good deal is known about the anatomy and physiology of the sensory systems of several nonhuman species. This knowledge takes on added significance when it can be related to studies of perception in the same species.

Yet another approach to the study of perception exploits the consequences of certain disorders or diseases. Just as studying pathology illuminates the processes of health, studying the abnormal or deviant perceiver illuminates the normal processes of perception. If the physiological changes produced by some disease are known, as well as how perception is altered by that disease, it becomes possible to relate the physiological changes to the perceptual changes, thereby identifying the physiological basis for that aspect of perception. For example, current understanding of color vision's neural bases has benefited greatly from studying persons with deficient color vision. Even when the basis for some disorder is not fully understood, one can still capitalize on its perceptual effects, especially when those effects are rather specific. In particular, one may determine which aspects of perception are affected by the disorder and which are not. This, by inference, indicates which perceptual abilities depend on shared neural structures. For example, a person with misaligned (crossed) eyes can have diminished depth perception but still be able to see objects and judge whether those objects are moving or stationary. This implies that the disorder of eye alignment has selectively affected portions of the nervous system that are concerned with the analysis of depth information. In general, this kind of selective perceptual loss indicates that the affected perceptual abilities depend on parts of the nervous system different from those mediating the unaffected perceptual abilities (Hebb, 1949; Brindley, 1970).

The previous paragraphs described various categories of atypical perceivers. But atypical perception can also be produced in typical perceivers, by using unusual, provocative stimuli. Such stimuli provoke errors that highlight perception in ways that normal, error-free operation does not. This approach resembles the use of provocative tests in medicine, such as the stress electrocardiogram. In the case of perception, the easiest, most common provocative tests use stimuli that produce errors of perception called **illusions.** These errors can assume many forms, one of

FIGURE 1.10
Zöllner's illusion of orientation.

which was shown in Figure 1.8. To see another illusion, look at Figure 1.10. The long vertical lines are actually parallel, but the central ones appear tilted with respect to one another. This figure was devised by Franz Zöllner in 1860, and it is an example of an orientation illusion. At several places in this book you'll see that illusions are more than just fascinating novelties. It may seem odd, but the special, provocative stimuli that evoke illusions can reveal much about how humans process the ordinary, mundane perceptual information encountered every day. Illusions highlight the processing rules inherent in perception.

GUIDEPOSTS TO RECURRING THEMES

Traditionally, a guidepost is a sign that gives helpful directions to people traveling through unfamiliar territory. We have attempted to facilitate your travel through the territory of perception with specially designed guideposts, icons that appear in the book's margins. These icons, which dot the book's landscape, will call attention to discussions of perception's most general themes.

Throughout this chapter we have introduced a number of issues that are quite central to the study of perception. There are, of course, other common themes that will come up again and again throughout the text. To help you see the connections among these themes and issues, we've summarized the themes and assigned each a special icon.

TABLE 1.1
Perception's Main Themes

Theme	Significance	Icon
Sensory Transduction and Neural Coding	Sense organs transform physical energy into bioelectrical signals; perceptual qualities are coded in patterns of neural activity.	**N** Neural
Differences among Species and among Individuals	Nonhuman animals possess sensory capabilities beyond the realm of human perceptual experience. Perceptual responses may differ from one individual human to another, or from one group of humans to another.	**D** Differences
Clinical Insights and Disordered Perception	Perceptual responses can be disordered by changes in sense organs, by neurological disease or by injury to the brain.	**C** Clinical
Top-down Influences and Attention	A perceiver's intentions and background knowledge can influence perception, as can the context in which objects and events occur.	**T** Top-down
Illusions and Errors	Perception sometimes provides misleading (but useful) descriptions of objects or events in the environment.	**I** Illusion
Research Methods and Demonstrations	Understanding perception requires sophisticated research methods. Demonstrations and exercises provided in the book amplify some of those research findings.	**E** Execute
Plasticity	Experience and practice can modify perception.	**P** Plasticity

These seven themes recur chapter after chapter, but that is not what makes them important. Instead, they recur precisely because they represent general principles of perception. Not limited to just one or two senses, they characterize all or most of perception. You will get the most out of this text if you compare and contrast sections across different chapters that share a common guidepost, for example "sensory transduction/encoding" or "interspecies and individual differences." By taking the time to do that you will forge important mental links that will enhance your overall understanding of perception. You may also gain interesting and exciting insights that would otherwise have escaped notice.

SUMMARY AND PREVIEW

This chapter lays out the framework for our analysis of perception, including the philosophical assumptions we'll be making. We have mentioned some of the practical and theoretical reasons for wanting to know more about perception. And we have outlined three distinct, though complementary, ways of understanding perception: the psychological, biological and theoretical approaches. Now that this general framework is in place, the next chapter will begin to fill in the pieces, starting with some fundamentals about the organ we use for seeing—the eye. Although this book also covers hearing, taste, smell, and touch, it devotes more space to seeing. We know more about vision than the other senses, and we believe vision represents the richest source of environmental information. This preeminence of vision is mirrored in the proportion of the human brain devoted to vision.

KEY TERMS

Anton's syndrome
Charles Bonnet syndrome
dualism
event-related potential (ERP)
evoked potential (EP)
far or distance senses
fMRI (functional magnetic resonance imaging)
illusions
kinesthesia
lesion
materialism
naive realism

near senses
Necker cube
perception
PET (positron-emission tomography) scan
psychophysics
sensory transduction
solipscism
specific nerve energies
stimulus
subjective contours
subjective idealism

CHAPTER 2

THE HUMAN EYE

Differences

During World War II, the United States Navy wanted its sailors to see infrared signal lights that were invisible to the enemy. Normally, we humans find it impossible to see infrared radiation because the receptors in our eyes are insensitive to infrared energy—as far as our eyes are concerned, infrared energy might as well not be there. To make infrared signals visible, Navy scientists had to come up with a way to modify the sailors' night vision. These scientists knew that the eye's receptors contained specialized light-sensitive molecules, and that a portion of each molecule was derived from vitamin A. Knowing that vitamin A comes in different forms, the Navy scientists wondered whether one of the alternative forms might encourage production of photosensitive molecules sensitive to infrared radiation. To find out, they had human volunteers eat diets supplemented by an alternative form of vitamin A (extracted from the livers of walleyed pikes). Over several months, the volunteers' vision changed remarkably, boosting their sensitivity to light extending into the infrared region. The experiment seemed to be working. At the same time, however, other scientists were successfully developing the snooperscope, an electronic device for seeing infrared radiation. This invention made it unnecessary to alter the eye itself, and the experiment was aborted (Rubin and Walls, 1969). Still, the project dramatizes a truth that we'll document throughout this chapter: the structure of the eye governs what we can, and cannot, see. Altering that structure would literally change your vision of the world.

The visual system of any vertebrate, humans included, consists of three major components: *eyes,* which capture light and convert it into neural messages; *visual pathways,* which modify and transmit those messages from the eye to the brain; and *visual centers of the brain,* which interpret the messages in ways useful for guiding behavior. All three components are crucially involved in seeing, so each component's structure and function must be understood in order to comprehend how an organism sees. This chapter and the next one concentrate on the first of these components, the human eye; they discuss its anatomy (structure) and physiology (how it works). These chapters emphasize how the eye is built, how it captures light and how it turns that light into neural messages the brain can interpret. Chapter 4 will discuss the remaining two major sections of the mammalian visual system, the visual pathways to the brain and the brain's visual centers.

Each of these three chapters has features that require special comment. First, we don't spend time talking about anatomy simply because we are fascinated with structure per se. Structure is important because it influences how and what we can see. Second, although mainly interested in the *human* eye, we also consider the eyes of other animals, particularly animals whose environments and lifestyles differ from those of humans. Understanding the diversity of vision—and the uniqueness of human vision—will heighten your appreciation of the processes involved in seeing. Finally, we also consider how various defects impair vision. Besides being fascinating in their own right, visual defects illuminate the intimate connection between structure and function.

In writing these chapters we were very much influenced by Gordon Walls's book *The Vertebrate Eye and Its Adaptive Radiations* (1942). Walls wrote eloquently about the eye, as the following statement demonstrates:

> "Everything in the vertebrate eye means something. Except for the brain, there is no other organ in the body of which that can be said. It does not matter in the least whether a liver has three lobes or four, or whether a hand has five fingers or six, or whether a kidney is long and narrow or short and wide. But if we should make comparable changes in the makeup of a vertebrate eye, we should quite destroy its usefulness. Man can make optical instruments only from such materials as brass and glass. Nature has succeeded with only such things as leather and water and jelly; but the resulting instrument is so delicately balanced that it will tolerate no tampering." (Walls, 1942, pp. iii–iv)

Walls' credo underscores that we cannot understand vision without first understanding the eye's structure. We'll begin our actual discussion of the eye with general questions about the nature of vision—*why* vision took the form that it did.

DESIGNING THE ORGAN OF VISION

The Diversity of Eyes in Nature

Chapter 1 distinguished between near senses and distance senses, putting vision in the latter category. By definition, a distance sense allows you to detect and recognize objects without having to come in immediate proximity to those objects. Both hearing and seeing endow us with this capacity. But vision enjoys a major advantage over hearing: it allows us to sense objects that make no sound. (Hearing offers its own special advantages, including the ability to register the presence of things that cannot be seen—but we'll get to that in Chapters 10 and 11.) Vision also provides important information about objects, information that's simply beyond the reach of hearing. It's sight, not hearing, that can tell us about the color of a piece of fruit, the shape of a cup we're about to grasp, the likelihood of threat posed by an approaching stranger and countless other bits and pieces about objects and events in our environments.

To appreciate vision's power, all we have to do is look at the diversity of creatures that possess eyes. Many species, including varieties of birds and fish, have eyes that follow the same basic design as ours, and are every bit as complicated. Other species, however, possess eyes of a very different structure. Some insects, such as butterflies, have eyes consisting of hundreds of tiny camera-like lenses each focusing light on its own cluster of light-sensitive cells. This array of miniature optical systems is packaged in a single large eye, sometimes mounted on the end of a long stack protruding from the creature's head. These so-called compound eyes work very differently from our eyes, with their single optical system (Figure 2.1). But those species with com-

Differences

FIGURE 2.1
Examples of the variety of eyes in nature.
Cat © PhotoDisc website; Gecko © Gregory G. Dimijian, M.D., 1988/Photo
Researchers, Inc.; Owl © PhotoDisc website; Iguana © Stephen Dalton/Photo
Reserchers, Inc.

pound eyes allow their owners to see what is important to them. In still other species, including some worms, "eyes" consist of nothing more than a patch of photosensitive pigment somewhere on the surface of the skin. By reacting to the presence of light, these light-sensitive spots tell the creature whether it's day or night. It's arguable whether we should refer to this as "vision" but there's no doubt that these creatures are sensing light. In fact, patches of photosensitive pigment in these kinds of primitive creatures probably represent the precursors for the variety of eyes found in other, more advanced animals.

Take a look at the unusual caterpillar pictured in Figure 2.2. If you didn't know better, you'd swear it was staring at you. That's exactly what natural selection—the designer of this caterpillar—wants you to think. This menacing "eye," however, is nothing more than pigmentation on the caterpillar's back. Its real eyes are those tiny pinholes located on the side of its body. This adaptive ornamentation serves as a deterrent to potential predators, alerting them to be wary about trying to sneak up on the caterpillar. This caterpillar with its mesmerizing eye brings to mind the title character in Samuel Taylor Coleridge's "The Rime of the

FIGURE 2.2
Pigmented spots on the back of a caterpillar resemble eyes.
(Edward Wester)

Ancient Mariner," an old seafarer: "He holds him with his glittering eye." These examples from nature and literature remind us that eyes, besides being the organ of sight, also communicate unmistakable messages to others looking at us.

It is estimated that natural selection has independently "reinvented" the sense of vision dozens of times throughout the animal kingdom (Mayr, 1982). Each time vision has evolved, the process has been lengthy and complicated. Indeed, the complex structure of the human eye has led some to conclude that it simply couldn't have arisen by natural selection. Instead, they argue, the grand design of the eye reveals the hand of God in creation. We believe, however, that natural selection alone represents the "designer" of eyes (Dawkins, 1996). But our purpose here isn't to quarrel about the origin of eyes. Rather, we wish to instill in you an appreciation for the quality and service provided by that design. Toward that end, we must start with some basics about light, the messenger

that bridges the distance between you and the objects you see.

Why Have Eyes That Use Light?

Light is just one form of **electromagnetic radiation** (see Figure 2.3). Other familiar varieties include radio waves, infrared and ultraviolet radiation, microwaves, and x-rays. All these forms of energy are produced by the oscillation of electrically charged material. Since virtually all matter consists of oscillating (that is, wavelike) electrical charges, electromagnetic energy exists in abundance. An animal that can sense electromagnetic radiation benefits in two important ways.

First, electromagnetic radiation travels very rapidly (in empty space, at 186,000 miles, or approximately 300,000 kilometers, per second). Any creature able to detect such radiation can pick up information from distant sources with minimal delay. Thus, we receive optical information about objects and events almost instantaneously (except, of course, for extra-terrestrial events transpiring millions of miles away). Second, electromagnetic radiation tends to travel in straight lines. This means that images created by this radiation retain important geometrical characteristics of the objects that reflect that radiation toward the eyes. We'll return to this point in a moment.

The frequency of electromagnetic radiation depends on the emitting material's mode of oscillation. In fact, electromagnetic radiation can be scaled (or arranged) along a spectrum according to the frequency of oscillation. This frequency, or oscillation rate, of light energy can be converted into units termed wavelengths. **Wavelength** is defined by how far the radiation travels between oscillations. High rates of oscillation mean that radiation travels a very short distance between oscillations—hence a short wavelength. Figure 2.3 underscores an important point: light, the form of radiation on which we depend for sight, occupies only a very small portion of the

FIGURE 2.3
The spectrum of electromagnetic energy. The region containing visible light is shown enlarged.

electromagnetic spectrum. Actually, radiation from other portions of this spectrum *could* have been used to bridge the distance between the perceiver and objects of visual perception. So why do the eyes rely solely on this one, very narrow portion of the entire electromagnetic spectrum, the part we call light?

One reason the eyes use light as their medium is that there is a lot of it in the world, courtesy of our solar system's sun. That abundance ensures that terrestrial creatures will have ample opportunity to use their light-sensing apparatus. It wouldn't have made much sense for early vertebrate "eyes" to depend on wavelengths in the ultraviolet range, for example, because most (but not all) of sunlight's energy in this short wavelength region of the spectrum is absorbed by molecules in the earth's atmosphere (mainly nitrogen and oxygen). Consequently, most of the sun's ultraviolet rays energy never reach objects in our immediate environment. Second, light is useful as a medium of information about the world because light interacts with the surface molecules of many objects we're interested in seeing. These interactions, in the form of reflec-

tion and absorption, allow light to convey information not only about the presence and absence of objects, but also about the structure of those objects and their surfaces (Gibson, 1966). Energy from outside the "light" portion of the electromagnetic spectrum—because of the length of the constituent waves—interacts very differently with solid objects that are relevant to behaving organisms. For example, longer wavelengths—including microwave energy—penetrate opaque objects rather than being reflected by them. (By penetrating them, microwaves can more evenly heat objects and therefore are useful in cooking.)

To sum up, eyes are a good idea. And eyes that use light are an even better idea.

The Message and the Messenger: Inverse Optics

As we progress through this discussion of vision, keep in mind that light is the *carrier* of visual information. It delivers messages from environmental objects to your eyes. But light itself is seldom the message of interest. It's the objects we want to see.

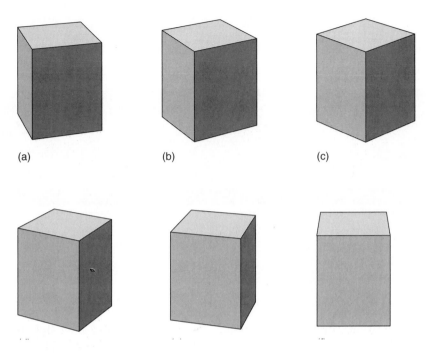

(a)   (b)   (c)

FIGURE 2.4
Images on the back of the eye change when you vary your angle of vision.

In a nutshell, the eye receives patterns of light energy reflected from the surfaces of objects in the environment. Those patterns of energy depend on a host of factors, including the surface properties of objects, the distance from the eye to those objects, and the source of light illuminating the objects. Whenever you change the angle of vision between yourself and an object, for example, you alter the pattern of light energy falling on your eyes (Figure 2.4). Whenever you view an object in natural sunlight and then move indoors to look at it under artificial lighting, you change the wavelength composition of light energy arriving at your eyes (artificial light isn't identical to sunlight). In short, the same object can convey countless different optical messages to your eyes.

So how do the eyes and brain figure out what produced some particular pattern of light energy? That's really what these next three chapters are all about. You will learn how the eye and brain are able to work backward, or inversely, starting with patterns of light and culminating in descriptions of objects in the world. This backward approach, which vision accomplishes automatically and effortlessly, is called **inverse optics.**

As you will learn, solving the inverse optics problem requires that the eye and brain make some assumptions about the objects and events we're likely to encounter in our environments. Fortunately, those assumptions are fairly safe ones because the physical nature of matter imposes certain constraints on the properties of objects. For example, light cannot pass through opaque objects, which means that when one object partially occludes another, we automatically see the partially occluded one at a greater distance than the occluding object (this constraint is discussed in more detail in Chapter 8). In addition, those constraints don't change over time. Nature has exploited this stability to develop

FIGURE 2.5
The placement of the eyes in the head of a cat (frontal eye placement) and in the head of a rabbit (lateral eye placement).

shortcuts for solving the problem of inverse optics. We'll be describing some of these shortcuts throughout this book.

Where Should the Eyes Be Placed?

Recognizing that animals would do very well to have eyes that exploit light, we must now decide *where* those eyes should go. Because embryologically the eyes are an outgrowth of the brain, their most-natural location is in the head, near the brain. But where exactly in the head should the eyes go? Nature has devised several different ways to position the eyes. In vertebrates, there are two popular designs for outfitting the head with a pair of eyes: they can be located in a *frontal* position, as are those of a human being or a cat; or they can be located in a *lateral* position, as are those of a rabbit (see Figure 2.5). Each strategy carries its own advantages: frontal eyes improve depth perception (as discussed in Chapter 8), whereas lateral eyes make it possible to take in more of the visual world at one time. As a rule, predatory animals—those who hunt and eat other animals—have frontally placed eyes. Those who are prey—animals frequently taken as food—

have laterally placed eyes. In other words, those needing excellent depth perception to stalk and capture have considerable binocular overlap of the two visual fields. Those needing a more panoramic view of the environment in order to watch for predators have little binocular overlap.

Why Should the Eyes Be Able to Move?

Because we humans lack panoramic vision, what we see at any given moment is rather limited. (see Figure 2.6). And there is no guarantee that our eyes will always be directed toward things in the environment that we need to see. Fortunately, we can compensate for our relatively narrow field of vision by turning the head and eyes. This is what you do when you look both ways before crossing a street. You also move your eyes because they are not uniformly sensitive. Some parts of the eye provide much better detail vision than other parts. Think for a moment what you do when something suddenly appears out of the corner of your eye. To see exactly what has grabbed your attention, your eyes reflexively move so that you're looking directly at whatever caught your attention.

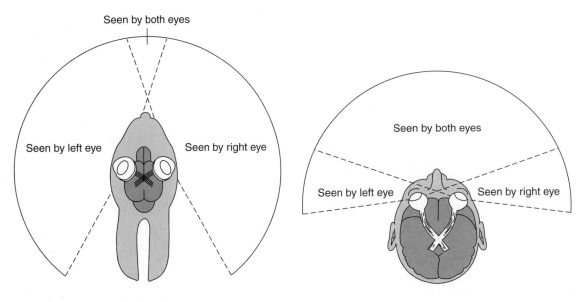

FIGURE 2.6
The extent of visual field of view for a rabbit and for a human. Note that the rabbit has almost completely panoramic vision, whereas the human's field of view encompasses only about 180 degrees.

Differences

Animals use various strategies for changing their field of view: they can move their bodies, turn their heads, or merely move their eyes. Some animals—owls for one—have very limited ability to move their eyes (Steinbach and Money, 1973). This comes about because their eyes are large and fit tightly into their sockets (Walls, 1942, p. 212). Rather than depending on eye movements, the owl moves its entire head. From a human standpoint, the owl's method is slow and inefficient.

Not all birds are our inferiors when it comes to eye movements, however. For example, the European starling, now so numerous as to be a nuisance in most North American and European cities, owes some of its success to its eye movements. Most birds, as they forage on the ground, need to look sideways in order to see what they're about to peck at. But starlings, whose skulls are quite narrow and whose eyes are extremely mobile, can turn their eyes far enough forward so that they can actually see between their opened

beaks. Equally important (and amazing) is the starling's ability to instantly swing its eyes up and back to scan the skies behind its head for possible predators (Martin, 1987). Because it can watch for predators without having to turn its head, the starling remains relatively unobtrusive, another element of protection. With eye movements so well designed both for fruitful foraging and self-protection, it's no wonder that in a mere one hundred years the starling population of North America has gone from approximately 100 European imports to more than 200 million birds.

While we humans can't match the starling's ability to shift its eyes without moving its head, we can shift the position of our eyes with enormous speed. For instance, it takes less than one-fifth of a second for our eyes to turn from their extreme leftward position to their extreme rightward position. When we execute this movement, our eyes are briefly traveling 700 degrees per second! (To make this figure more concrete, think of the moon's rotation. If the moon rotated at this speed, it would complete two revolutions in one second.) Not only do the eyes move rapidly, they move with great accuracy as well. For example, as you read these lines, your eyes skip along from one place of interest to another, alighting with great precision on the desired letter or space. The cooperative interaction among the **extraocular muscles** (six for each eye) makes this rapid and accurate eye movement possible. The extraocular muscles enable movement of the eyes in all directions. Let's consider the mechanical arrangement that makes this possible.

How the Eyes Move Every muscle in your body works by contracting and thereby pulling on the structure or structures to which the muscle is attached. In the case of the extraoculars, each muscle is connected at one end to an immovable structure, the eye socket of the skull, and at the other end to an object that is free to move, the eyeball. So when an extraocular muscle contracts, it pulls on the eyeball and moves it. The *amount* of movement depends on the strength of the muscle's contraction and on the action of the other muscles. The *direction* of movement depends on the place at which the contracting muscle is attached to the eyeball and skull, and on what the other muscles are doing. Because each extraocular muscle is attached to the eyeball at a different position, contraction of any particular muscle turns the eyeball in a characteristic direction. The following is a brief and simplified description of what the extraoculars do.

Each eye's muscles can be divided into two groups, one with four muscles and one with two. The larger group, the **rectus muscles,** run straight back from the eyeball. Muscles in the other, smaller group run obliquely back from the eyeball. We can understand the general principles of the eye's movements by looking just at the muscles in the larger group.

Each rectus muscle is attached to the eyeball at a different location, toward the front of the eyeball (see Figure 2.7). The other end of each rectus muscle is attached to the rear of the bony cav-

FIGURE 2.7

A view of the eye muscles attached to the right eye. The medial rectus, the muscle closest to the eye, is partially obscured by the globe.

ity holding the eyeball; this is the immovable end of the muscle. Whenever a rectus muscle contracts, it pulls the eyeball toward the place at which that muscle connects to the eyeball. When a rectus muscle relaxes, the eye turns back toward its original position.

One muscle, the *medial* rectus, attaches to the side of the eyeball closest to the nose. When it contracts, the medial rectus rotates the eye toward the nose. Another muscle, the *lateral* rectus, has exactly the opposite effect. It is connected to the side of the eyeball farthest from the nose, so its contraction turns the eyeball laterally, away from the nose. The *superior* rectus muscle connects to the top of the eyeball, and its contraction elevates the eyeball, causing you to look upward. The superior's opposing muscle, the *inferior* rectus, is attached to the lower portion of the eyeball and its contraction lowers the eye, causing you to look down.

Now let's consider how these muscles cooperate to move the eyes. Imagine that while looking straight ahead, you decide to glance leftward. Both eyes must move to the same degree and in the same direction. In order for you to look to the left, the medial rectus of the right eye and the lateral rectus of the left eye must both contract, while both the lateral rectus of the right eye and the medial rectus of the left eye relax. You should be able to figure out for yourself what will happen if you now decide to glance rightward.

For the eye movements just described, both eyes have moved in the same direction—upward, leftward, and so on. Eye movements of this type are called **conjunctive** eye movements. But the eyes are capable of other types of movements as well. The eyes can move in opposite directions—both may turn inward or both may turn outward. These are called **vergence** eye movements. For example, the left eye can turn rightward while the right eye turns leftward. As a result, both eyes turn inward, toward the nose. This movement aims the two eyes at a very close object straight ahead of you. This particular type of vergence movement is called a convergent eye movement. To accomplish it, the medial rectus muscles of both eyes contract, while the lateral rectus muscles of both eyes relax. If you look at an object at arm's length and then bring it closer to you, your eyes converge, tracking the object. When the object moves away from you, your eye muscles will engage in the opposite behavior, resulting in a divergent eye movement.

Execute

Much more can be said about eye movements and their role in vision, particularly in reading, and we'll return to these roles in later chapters. But for now, we want to stress that eye movements alone are insufficient to compensate for our limited field of view. To experience this for yourself, try a simple exercise. Hold your head very steady, close one eye and then look around in all directions by moving your open eye. Notice how limited this monocular field of vision really is. Repeat the exercise using your other eye. When the famous Austrian scientist and philosopher Ernst Mach (1838–1916) performed this exercise, he made a sketch of what he saw. Figure 2.8 shows you what Mach drew. Mach firmly believed that scientists should confine themselves to descriptions of phenomena that can be perceived by the senses. In this particular case, Mach's senses revealed a seldom realized truth: Because we're accustomed to moving our eyes

and heads, we seldom realize how limited our actual view of the world is at any given moment. Our grasp on the whole of visual reality comes in bits and pieces assembled over time.

How Should the Eyes Be Protected?

Vertebrate eyes are fragile, complicated devices occupying a very exposed position in the head. Fortunately, various protective measures have evolved to compensate for the eyes' vulnerability. An outline of these protective mechanisms will provide a good introduction to the overall structure of the eye.

The eye is partially protected by virtue of its location within the **orbit,** a bony depression in the skull. Within the orbit, the eye is cushioned by heavy deposits of fat surrounding each eyeball. Without this orbital fat, blows to the head would be transmitted directly to the eye. But by absorbing such shocks, orbital fat cushions the eye against all but the most severe jolts.

The eye is also protected by eyelids, movable folds of tissue. The position of the upper lid relative to the lower one determines the opening through which the front of the eye is visible. The lids move in concert with one another in various modes. For instance, in a fraction of a second, they can open and close (blink). Such blinks usually occur spontaneously, without thought. Blinks clean and moisten the front of the eye to keep it from drying out. The lids can also execute reflexive blinks that protect the eye when it is touched by a foreign object or when an object is on a collision-course with the head. In addition to involuntary and reflexive blinks, we can also voluntarily blink our eyes or, for that matter, close them entirely when we want to go to sleep.

Under normal circumstances, a blink occurs about once every four seconds (Hart, 1992). This figure varies from person to person, depending on emotional state and the environmental conditions. When the air is very dry, we tend to blink our eyes more often, ensuring that the delicate front surface of the eye doesn't dry out.

FIGURE 2.8
Ernst Mach's view of his study.

A blink, measured from the instant the lids begin to close until they reopen, takes roughly one-third of a second. For about half this time, the lids are completely closed, reducing the light by over 90 percent (Crawford and Marc, 1976). If the room lights were momentarily dimmed by this amount, the resulting blackout would be very noticeable. Why is it, then, that we never notice the same blackout when it's caused by a blink?

Volkmann, Riggs, and Moore (1980) offered an intriguing answer to this question. They hypothesized that when the brain signals the lids to close, it also produces an ancillary neural signal that suppresses, or temporarily shuts off, vision for the duration of the blink. Suppression would keep you from noticing that a blink had occurred. This hypothesis, although intriguing, is difficult to test. The appropriate test would be to measure the eye's sensitivity to light during a blink without the lid closure actually affecting the intensity of the eye's exposure to that light. Volkmann and colleagues developed the following ingenious way to stimulate the eye so that the light reaching the retina would not be affected by lid closure.

The eyes lie directly above the roof of the mouth. Thus, a strong light focused on the roof of the mouth under one eye can penetrate this tissue and stimulate the retina—you're actually able to see light delivered through the roof of your mouth whether or not your lids are closed. This procedure makes it possible to measure the ability to see a dimming of the light at various times relative to a blink.

Volkmann and colleagues used a bundle of optical fibers to carry light to the roof of a person's mouth. By abruptly dimming the light, they determined the smallest reduction in light intensity visible to that person. Remember: All the light that could be seen came through the person's mouth, bypassing the lids. At the same time, Volkmann and colleagues used electrodes attached to the skin near the eyelids to monitor when blinks occurred. Since a blink is produced by muscle contractions, it's easy to detect the electrical activity of the lid muscles and know from that activity when a blink begins and ends. These researchers found that dimming was much harder to see *during* a blink than *between* blinks. To be detected during a blink, the light had to be dimmed by an amount 5 times greater than it did between blinks.

These results suggest that the brain suppresses vision just before and during each blink, keeping us from noticing the visual blackouts. Without this suppression, which occurs in tandem with the typical blink rate of 10 to 15 times per minute, we would be bothered by profound blackouts (Riggs, Volkmann and Moore, 1981). To our relief, the visual system uses a temporary, well-timed suppression to protect us from the annoying but necessary behavior of our eyelids.

Our social environment also affects the behavior of our eyelids. We tend to blink more often during casual conversation than when we're alone. And during a heated discussion, our blink rate skyrockets. In addition to our blink rate, the size of the opening between the lids provides a reliable clue as to how interested your listener is. Watch a friend's eyes closely; the opening between the lids will average 8 millimeters (about 1/3 inch). You'll probably notice a change in that opening as your friend's attention varies. When interest is high, the opening between the lids increases to about 10 millimeters. Similarly, drowsiness or boredom reduces the size of the opening. And, of course, we immediately recognize the social message conveyed when someone looks directly at us and gives an exaggerated blink with one eye. A wink speaks volumes.

Tears also convey social messages—sadness, pain, great joy, etc. But tears protect the eyes as well. Although usually associated either with emotional states or with slicing raw onions, tears irrigate the eyes' exposed surfaces. Tears are secreted from a gland situated in the upper, front portion of each orbit (under the upper lid). From there, they pass down over the eye's front surface, moistening it, and then drain through small openings in the lower nasal portion of each orbit. Finally, the tears drain onto the mucous membrane lining the nose's inner surface. This nasal membrane acts as an evaporator for the tears, which explains you have to blow your nose when you've been crying. Tears contain an antimicrobial agent that helps protect the eye from bacteria present in the environment. In addition, the regular flow of tears flushes away debris, such as dust. Tears also lubricate the surface of the eyes so that blinking won't abrade the lids or scratch the front of the eyeball. The constant, very thin film of tears over the front of the eye minimizes the wear and tear produced by constant lid movement. In many older adults, the secretion of tears slows down, producing a condition called "dry eyes." Fortunately, the regular application of opththalmic drops to the eyes provides relief.

Having covered its ancillary features, we are now ready to discuss the structure of the eye itself.

E

Execute

FIGURE 2.9
Cross section of human eye, showing major layers and structures. View is from above the left eye.

THE STRUCTURE OF THE HUMAN EYE

To understand the human eye, let's start with an overview tour of the major features. We'll ignore the details, however, until the second stage of our discussion, by which time you'll have a good idea where those details fit into the eye's grand scheme. In portraying these details, incidentally, people often draw an analogy between the eye and a camera. This analogy is apt, but only to a point. Certainly, both are optical devices designed to record visual images on light-sensitive material (film, in the case of the camera; photoreceptors, in the case of the eye). And the two do have components in common (mechanical, in the case of the camera; biological, in the case of the eye). So where appropriate, we will point out these commonalities. But don't be misled. A camera merely records optical images on film. The eyes do much, much more. Besides recording images, the eyes recode those images, extract biologically meaningful information from the recoded signals, and transmit that information to the brain for interpretation and reaction. In this and the next few chapters, we'll point out other instances where the analogy

fails. For now, let's start with an overview of the eye's major features.

The human eye is very nearly spherical, with a diameter of approximately 24 millimeters (nearly one inch), or slightly smaller than a Ping-Pong ball. It consists of three concentric layers, each with its own characteristic appearance, structure and functions. From outermost to innermost, the three layers are the **fibrous tunic,** which protects the eyeball; the **vascular tunic,** which nourishes the eyeball; and the **retina,** which detects light and initiates neural messages bound for the brain. Figure 2.9 illustrates this three-layered arrangement. In this figure you can see that the eye is partitioned into two chambers, a small anterior chamber and a larger vitreous chamber. Thus the basic layout is three concentric layers and two chambers, plus the iris, pupil and lens.

The Outermost, Fibrous Tunic

When looking directly at someone's eye, you see only about one-sixth of its outer surface. The rest is tucked into the bony orbit, hidden behind the lids and other protective structures. The "white" of the eye is part of the outermost, fibrous coat. Since this white part is made of tough, dense material, it is called the **sclera,** from a Greek root meaning "hard."*

The sclera averages about 1 millimeter in thickness, and microscopic inspection reveals that it's made of tightly packed, interwoven fibers running parallel to the sclera's surface. These densely packed fibers give the sclera its toughness. Actually, the sclera needs to be tough because pressure inside the eyeball is double that of the atmosphere. If the sclera were more elastic, that pressure differential could cause the eyeball to become deformed. As a result, the quality of one's sight would be greatly diminished. We'll return to the importance of the eyeball's shape later, when we discuss the eye as an optical instrument.

At the very front of the eye, this outer coat loses its white coloring and becomes so transparent that its difficult to see it in the mirror. However, if you look at someone else's eye from the side, you will notice a small bulge on the front of the eye. This bulge is called the **cornea,** from a root word meaning "like a horn." (The cornea is composed of tissue comparable to that of an animal's horn.) The cornea's transparency is crucial for vision. It allows light to enter the eyeball unimpeded. The neat and orderly arrangement of the cornea's fibers is the primary reason that the cornea is transparent. In addition, greater transparency is made possible because the cornea has no internal blood supply of its own. Since blood and the requisite vessels could reduce the passage of light, the cornea draws its nourishment from the clear fluid in the anterior chamber.

---

*Most parts of the eye have names related to their character or appearance. Knowing the origin of some of these names can help you appreciate the structure of the eye. Our explanations come from a book, *On Naming the Parts of the Human Body,* written in the first century A.D. by Rufus of Ephesus. Ephesus is an ancient city located in what is modern-day Turkey. We have drawn on an excellent partial translation by Stephen Polyak (1941, p. 96).

The transparent cornea plays a crucial role in the formation of images on the back of the eye. Anything that disturbs the cornea's transparency, therefore, will reduce the quality of these images and, hence, the quality of vision. For self-protection, the cornea has extremely high sensitivity to touch. Foreign bodies, such as dust particles or a misguided finger, contacting the cornea trigger a sequence of protective responses, including lid closure and tear production. There's one reflexive response, however, that should be avoided: as our mothers used to tell us, "Never rub your eye except with your elbow"—these words of wisdom mean leave your eyes alone, for most remedies simply do further damage.

The Middle, Vascular Tunic

For most of its course, the vascular tunic hugs the wall of the eyeball, and only toward the front of the eyeball does it pull away from the wall. We'll begin by considering the rear two-thirds of this middle layer, the part that fits snugly against the wall of the eyeball.

Most of the middle layer consists of a heavily pigmented, spongy structure called the **choroid.** The choroid averages about 0.2 millimeters in thickness and contains a network of blood vessels, including capillaries. Blood from these capillaries nourishes one particular class of cells in the retina, the photoreceptors that turn light into neural signals. Without their nourishing blood supply, these vital photoreceptor cells would starve to death from lack of oxygen.

The choroid's heavy pigmentation also reduces light scatter, the tendency for light to be reflected irregularly around inside the eyeball; light scatter would reduce the sharpness of images formed inside the eye. The choroid's dark pigmentation reduces scatter by harmlessly absorbing light that isn't captured by the photoreceptors. Incidentally, this is the same reason the inside of a camera is painted flat black. The paint absorbs scattered light and protects the sharpness of images on the film.

The Anterior Chamber

Toward the front of the eye, this middle, choroidal layer curls away from wall of the eyeball and runs more or less parallel to the front surface of the eye. Over this part of its course, the middle layer forms a long slender structure called the **ciliary body.** This spongy network of tissue manufactures **aqueous humor,** the watery fluid that fills the smaller, anterior chamber of the eye located behind the cornea and in front of the lens. The aqueous humor serves a number of important maintenance functions. It transports oxygen and nutrients to several of the structures it bathes, and it carries away their waste products. The eye's crucial optical components—the cornea and lens—rely on the aqueous humor as their source of nourishment.

The aqueous fluid also helps maintain the shape of the eyeball. If there were too little fluid in the anterior chamber, the eye would become deformed, like an underinflated soccerball. Constant pressure is maintained, however, because cells in the ciliary body are constantly producing new aqueous to keep the supply of nutrients from becoming exhausted. The creation of new fluid also prevents the buildup of high concentrations of waste products.

Clinical

For pressure to remain constant, of course, a balance must be achieved between the rate at which aqueous fluid is created and the rate at which it is drained from the eye. Sometimes this balance cannot be maintained and too much aqueous accumulates in the eye, which elevates intraocular pressure. Excess aqueous accumulates either because of overproduction or because of improper drainage out of the anterior chamber. Drainage can be blocked or slowed down if the outlets for aqueous (which lie at the junction of ciliary body and cornea) become squeezed shut or clogged. Pressure builds up within the eye, and if the pressure remains high for too long, vision can be impaired permanently. Increased intraocular pressure—the condition called **glaucoma**— is the single most common cause of blinding eye

disease in North America. Fortunately, glaucoma can be treated if the condition is detected early enough. For this reason, eye doctors routinely measure the intraocular pressure in eye examinations these days.

The Iris, Pupil and Lens

The Iris   As it curls inward, away from the wall of the eye, the ciliary body gives rise to the **iris,** that circular section of tissue that gives your eye its characteristic color: brown, blue, green, gray, and so forth. This variety of colors makes the name "iris" very appropriate because iris comes from the Greek word for "rainbow."

The iris actually consists of two layers, an outer layer containing pigment, and an inner layer containing blood vessels. If the outer layer is heavily pigmented, the iris will appear brown. But if this outer layer is lightly pigmented, the inner layer becomes partially visible through the outer one. In this case, the iris will look more lightly colored. Thus, the color of one's eyes results from a combination of the pigmentation of the outer layer and the color of the blood vessels in the inner layer. If the iris's outer layer has no pigment, the inner layer becomes very noticeable, giving the eye a pinkish hue. This condition occurs in albino humans, who, because of a genetic defect, have greatly reduced pigmentation.

The Pupil   Looking in a mirror at the center of your own iris, you'll see a round black region, the **pupil.** The pupil is actually an opening, or gap, within two sets of muscles. The inner set runs circularly around the pupil. When this circular band of muscles contracts, the pupil gets smaller. Another set of muscles runs radially out from the edge of the circular muscles, away from the pupillary opening. When the radial muscles contract, the pupil widens, or dilates. These changes in pupil size regulate the amount of light reaching the back of the eye.

The size of the pupil at any given moment depends on several factors. First, it depends on the

Differences

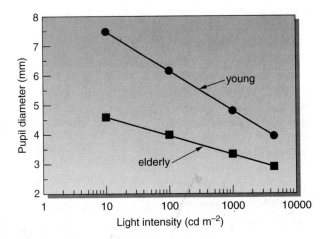

FIGURE 2.10
Pupil size varies according to both light intensity and age. (cd m^{-2} stands for candelas per square meter, a common unit of light intensity.)

light level to which the eye is exposed: the size of the pupil decreases as the level of light increases. In young adults, the pupil diameter varies from about 8 millimeters down to less than 2 millimeters, a fourfold variation in diameter. The amount of light passing through the pupil is proportional to the pupil's *area,* which is itself proportional to the square of pupil's diameter. Thus, as the pupil diameter varies over a range of 4 to 1, the amount of light passing through the pupil varies over a range of 16 to 1. The pupils of older adults change size in response to light in different proportions than their younger counterparts. In dim light, the pupil of an eighty-year-old person is only about half that of a twenty-year-old (see Figure 2.10). As a result, less light reaches the retinas of elderly people. This undoubtedly explains why older people frequently complain about the dim lighting in restaurants.

Besides light level, the size of the pupil also varies in response to events that stimulate the autonomic nervous system. Anything that induces excitement, fear, or sexual interest can change the size of the pupil. Some people, such as seasoned poker players, are quite adept at sensing an opponent's excitement or dismay on the basis of their opponent's pupil size. An opponent's widened pupils are a dead giveaway that he or she has drawn a potentially winning card. Realizing the potential cue involuntarily provided by their eyes, clever poker players will wear dark glasses to hide their telltale pupils.

Although large pupils allow more light into the eye, smaller pupils can sometimes offer an advantage (Cornsweet, 1970). Suppose you are looking at an object located several meters in front of you. While you're looking at that object, other objects—those much closer or much farther away—will tend to appear somewhat blurred. The range of distances over which objects will appear sharply focused varies inversely with the size of the pupil. This range of sharp vision is called the **depth of field.** The easiest way to demonstrate depth of field is to substitute a camera for your eye. In taking the photographs shown in Figure 2.11, the photographer varied the size of the camera's aperture to simulate the effects of changing pupil size. The photograph on the left was taken with a large aperture; the one on the right, with a small aperture. In both instances, the camera was focused on the object centered in the picture. Note that on the left, the picture taken

FIGURE 2.11
The degree of blur in a picture depends on the size of the aperture of the camera. The sharp photo on the right was taken through a smaller aperture than was used in taking the photo on the left, thus increasing the depth of field in the right-hand photograph. (Glyn Cloyd.)

with the large aperture, very few objects appear sharp. The photograph on the right was taken without changing the focus but with a smaller aperture. Now, more objects appear well focused—the range of distances over which objects appear in sharp focus has increased. This range defines depth of field. Whether we're talking about cameras or about eyes, depth of field is determined by pupil (or aperture) diameter.

The Lens One very important optical element of the eye, the **crystalline lens,** lies right behind the iris. The lens takes its name from its resemblance to a lentil, or bean. In adults, the lens is shaped like a very large aspirin tablet, about 9 millimeters in diameter and 4 millimeters in thickness. The lens consists of three distinct parts: an elastic covering, or *capsule;* an *epithelial layer* just inside the capsule; and the *lens* itself. As you might expect, each of these parts has its own job to do.

In fact, the thin, elastic capsule around the lens has two jobs. First, it moderates the flow of aqueous humor into the lens, helping the lens retain its transparency to light. Second, the elastic capsule molds the shape of the lens—varying its flatness and, thereby, the lens's optical power. This variation in optical power is called **accommodation.**

The lens never stops growing. Throughout your life span, the outer, epithelial layer of your lens continues to produce protein fibers that are added to the surface of the lens. Consequently, those protein fibers nearest the center of the lens are the oldest (some were present at birth), whereas the fibers on the outside are the youngest. Between birth and age 90 years, the lens quadruples in thickness and attains a weight of 250 milligrams (Paterson, 1979). In the center of the lens, the old fibers become more densely packed, producing **sclerosis,** or hardening, of the lens. We'll describe the significance of sclerosis later in this chapter.

For good vision, the lens must be transparent—light must be able to pass through it easily, without loss or deviation. Like the cornea, this transparency depends on the material out of which the lens is made. Of all the body's parts, the lens has the highest percentage of protein, and its protein fibers are lined up parallel to one another, maximizing the lens's transparency to light. Anything that disturbs this alignment—such as excess fluid inside the lens—reduces transparency.

Clinical

An opacity (or reduced transparency) of the lens is called a **cataract.** While some cataracts are minor—barely reducing the transmission of light—others undermine vision to the point of blindness. In some cases, cataracts can be traced to cumulative exposure to ultraviolet radiation present in sunlight (Schein et al, 1994), which helps explain why cataracts are more common in elderly people. But not all young people are spared from cataracts. In fact, certain populations (Arabs and Sephardic Jews, for instance) have a very high incidence of congenital cataracts—lens opacities at birth. These opacities severely degrade the stimulation received by the eye, and this can be serious. At birth, the visual nervous system is immature, and its proper development depends on normal stimulation of the eye. Deprived of that proper stimulation, the immature visual nervous system develops abnormally (Hubel, Wiesel, and LeVay, 1977). Realizing this consequence of visual deprivation, physicians now recommend removal of congenital cataracts as early in life as possible.

Surgical removal of a cataractous lens has become more or less routine today. Since the lens contributes to the total optical power of the eye, removal of the lens must be accompanied by some form of optical compensation. Powerful spectacles or contact lenses can be worn, or alternatively, a plastic lens can be surgically inserted into the eye, replacing the missing biological lens (Applegate et al., 1987). None of these alternatives, however, restores the ability to accommodate.

People who have had such surgeries must use different glasses for near versus far vision.

The Vitreous Chamber

The vitreous chamber accounts for nearly two-thirds of the total volume of the eye. This larger of the eye's two chambers is bounded by the lens in front and the retina on the sides and in the rear. This chamber is filled with a transparent fluid called **vitreous,** a substance with the consistency of egg white.

Encased in a thin membrane, the vitreous is anchored to the inner wall of the eyeball. Unlike the aqueous, the vitreous is not continuously renewed, which means that debris can accumulate within it. Sometimes you become aware of this debris, in the form of **floaters,** small opacities that float about in the vitreous (White and Levatin, 1962). If you look at a bright, uniform surface, floaters cast shadows on the back of the eye, producing little dark spots that dart about immediately in front of you. Thanks to gravity, floaters tend to settle to the bottom of the vitreous chamber, out of the line of sight. Although floaters are usually harmless, dense or persistent floaters may be a symptom of retinal detachment, a vision-threatening condition that requires treatment.

The Retina

The innermost of the eye's three layers, the **retina,** resembles a very thin, fragile meshwork, which explains its name—*rete* is Latin for "fisherman's net." Although no thicker than a postage stamp, the retina has a complex, layered organization. Figure 2.12 shows how a section of the retina would look if magnified greatly and viewed from the side. The arrows denote the direction taken by incoming light. From this perspective, you can see that the cells comprising the retina have a peculiar arrangement: light must pass through a complex network of neural elements before reaching the **photoreceptors,**

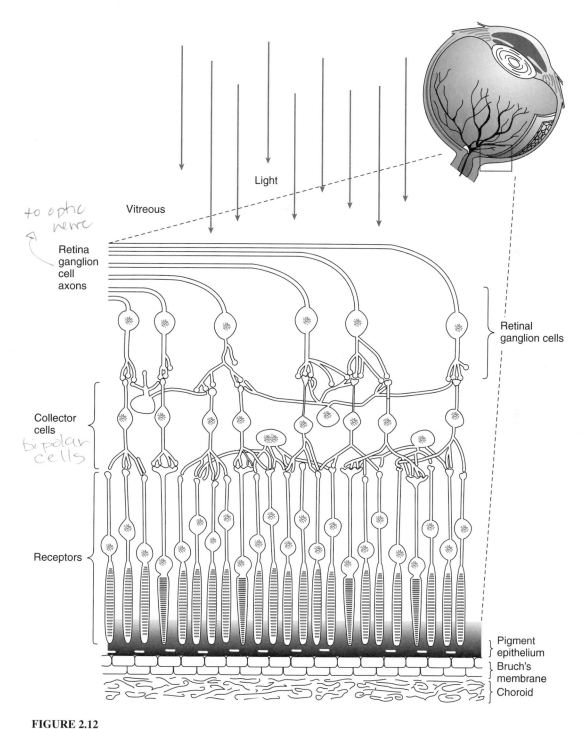

Light

Vitreous

to optic nerve

Retina ganglion cell axons

Retinal ganglion cells

Collector cells

bipolar cells

Receptors

Pigment epithelium

Bruch's membrane

Choroid

FIGURE 2.12
Cross section of the retina. The small box in the inset at the base of the eyeball shows the region of the eye represented in the enlarged drawing.

which are actually responsible for converting light energy into neural signals. Moreover, the light-sensitive part of each photoreceptor, called the **outer segment,** actually faces away from the incoming light and toward the back of the eye. This seemingly "backward" arrangement has one distinct advantage. Photoreceptor outer segments, which have high metabolic demands, end up snuggled into the choroid, which, as we've already learned, contains a rich blood supply.

Neural

The neural signals generated by the photoreceptors, in turn, pass through a network of cells—**bipolar, amacrine** and **horizontal cells** that collect and recombine the photoreceptor signals. These collected, transformed signals are then passed on to the **retinal ganglion cells,** where biologically important information about the distribution of light over space and time is extracted and recoded. The recoded neural messages are then carried by the axons of the ganglion cells out of the eye and into the brain. As you can already begin to appreciate, crucial events underlying visual perception are inaugurated in this complex neural network, the retina.

To a large degree, the retina's complexity reflects its origins. Embryologically, the retina arises from the same tissue that spawns the billions of cells comprising the brain. So the retina is actually a direct extension of the central nervous system. This affinity with the brain has one unfortunate aspect, though: damaged retinal cells, like damaged brain cells, cannot be repaired. The visual consequences of damage are permanent, which is why it's so important to protect the eyes from excessive light exposure (by wearing sunglasses), from trauma (by wearing goggles when playing sports), and from disease (by having a routine, periodic eye examination).

The eye is not just a window out, onto the outside world, it also is a window through which another person can look directly inside your body and view your nervous system. In fact, the eye is the *only* place where the nervous system and blood supply can be viewed directly, without sur-

gery. If you were to look directly into another person's pupil, however, you wouldn't be able to see anything except a dark hole because your head obstructs the light necessary for seeing the back of the eye. Essentially, you're looking through a peephole into a dark chamber. Thanks to the nineteenth-century physicist, physician, mathematician and philosopher, Hermann von Helmholtz, it's possible to illuminate the eye while at the same time looking into it (Figure 2.13). Helmholtz invented a simple, clever device called an **ophthalmoscope,*** which allows us to visualize the interior of the living human eye, including its retina and blood supply. Doctors use this instrument to examine millions of patients every year, usually employing a hand-held, battery-powered model that you've probably encountered during a routine vision exam.

Retinal Landmarks and Blood Supply   Figure 2.14 illustrates what is seen when looking into a normal human eye using an ophthalmoscope. Because the living retina is virtually transparent, the ophthalmoscope mainly reveals structures lying in front of the retina—such as the central retinal artery—and structures lying behind it—such as the choroid. Although not a complete view of the entire retina, this photograph does highlight several of the retina's most significant features. Look first at the nearly circular area in the center. Measuring roughly 1.5 millimeters in diameter, this region is called the **macula.** When you look directly at objects such as the words on this page, the images of those objects are centered within the macula of each eye. Vision is most acute in the center of the macula.

Consider another landmark shown in Figure 2.14, the **optic disk.** This is the region of the eye where optic nerve fibers (the axons of the gan-

---

*Actually, Charles Babbage, who developed a mechanical digital computer in the middle of the eighteenth century, made a working model of an ophthalmoscope some years before Helmholtz but didn't pursue the project (Rucker, 1971).

FIGURE 2.13
German scientist Hermann von Helmholtz who invented the ophthalmoscope, which is illustrated on the right.
Left: © Bettmann/CORBIS
Right: Courtesy of Welch Allyn, Inc.

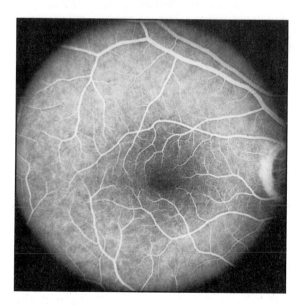

FIGURE 2.14
Photograph showing the inside of the back of the human eye.

glion cells) exit the retina, carrying information to the brain. Normally, the optic disk has a pinkish color because of small blood vessels on its surface; these blood vessels nourish part of the optic nerve. Loss of this pink color can signify the presence of a circulatory problem that could eventually starve the optic nerve and impair vision. Fortunately, such changes in color can be detected quite easily with the ophthalmoscope.

The retina has the highest metabolic rate of any part of the body, so its access to blood—for oxygen and nutrition—is vital. To supply the entire retina with blood is a challenge because metabolically active cells need to be in extremely close contact with the capillaries that nourish them. To meet this challenge, the eye contains two blood supplies: one that primarily nourishes the photoreceptors (the choroidal circulation system), and the other that nourishes the remaining cells of the retina (the retinal circulation system).

BOX 2.1

EYES THAT NEVER STAND STILL

Contractions of the extraocular muscles pull and tug on the eyeballs, guiding their direction so objects of interest can be fixated. But even when you try to keep your eyes absolutely still, small random contractions of the extraocular muscles keep the eyes moving. These involuntary eye movements are usually too minor for you to be aware of, but they are important for seeing. Before learning why they're important, though, try this simple trick that will let you see your own involuntary eye movements.

The trick requires a pattern like the grid in the accompanying figure (Verheijen, 1963). First carefully fixate on the black dot in the center of the pattern for about 30 seconds, keeping your eyes as still as possible. Then quickly move your eyes to the white dot. Again, keep your eyes as still as possible. You'll see an illusory pattern, called an **afterimage,** that jiggles slightly. The jiggling of the afterimage is caused by the movements of your eyes. You can prove this to yourself by now making large, intentional eye movements; the afterimage follows your eyes. The afterimage itself arises from the differential adaptation of neurons in your retina respond-

ing to the light and dark parts of the figure. Of course, the adapted neurons are fixed in place in the eye's retina; it is as if a negative image of the grid is temporarily imprinted on the back of the eye. Thus, whenever you see the afterimage move, you're in fact witnessing your eyes moving—whether you intended them to or not. The slight jiggling of the afterimage even when you try to fixate is the consequence of your own involuntary eye movements.

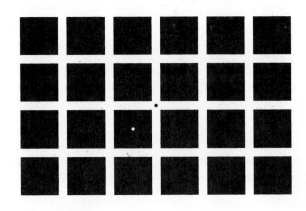

Continued

As you've already learned, the choroid and its blood supply are located behind the photoreceptors and, therefore, out of the path of light that stimulates the photoreceptors. This isn't true, however, for the retinal circulatory system. Notice in Figure 2.14 the large blood vessels that run outward from the optic disk, which are arteries and veins. These vessels make up the retinal circulatory system. They fan out from the optic disk, dispersing into a fine network of capillaries spread throughout the inner part of the retina. Because they're situated in front of the retina, these blood vessels lie directly in the path of incoming

light. This arrangement may strike you as odd, but it's the only way to get the blood vessels in close proximity to the outer portions of the retina that require nourishment.

You may also notice in Figure 2.14, however, the clever rerouting of the arteries and veins around the macula. Within this most important region for seeing, therefore, light is not obstructed on its route to the photoreceptors. But what about the other parts of the retina? Why don't we see the blood vessels and nerve tissue in the other parts through which light must pass? Box 2.1 gives the answer, and also allows you to

BOX 2.1 continued

These small random eye movements are actually very important for vision; when they are eliminated, vision changes dramatically. For example, special optical systems have been developed that move whatever you're looking at in step with the movements of your eyes. This scheme produces a motionless, stabilized image on your retina. Here's one way to produce a stabilized retinal image. A small photographic transparency of some object is mounted on a special high-power contact lens that focuses the image on the retina. Since the contact lens moves along with the eye, the image of the transparency attached to this lens is stabilized on the retina. And the perceptual result is remarkable—within a few seconds, the object begins to fade from view, as if the brightness on a television screen were being reduced. Eventually the object disappears entirely, leaving nothing but a homogeneous gray field. So when the

effects of normal involuntary eye movements are eliminated, vision is eliminated too (Pritchard, Heron and Hebb, 1960; Riggs, Ratliff, Cornsweet and Cornsweet, 1953).

The disappearance of stabilized retinal images is actually quite fortunate. If this didn't happen, you'd constantly be annoyed by the images produced in your eyes by blood vessels. Because they are in the path of light, these blood vessels cast shadows on your retina. Since the vessels move along with your eye, their shadows are stabilized retinal images and, consequently, are invisible to you. However, you can temporarily "destabilize" them by moving a beam of light back and forth across the vessels. This causes their shadow to move back and forth slightly, enough to make them visible. The simplest way to produce this effect is with a small flashlight (a penlight). Looking straight ahead with eyes closed, place the penlight against the corner of your eye—the corner away from your nose, as is shown in the illustration. Gently rock the penlight back and forth. After a second or two you should begin to see what look like the branches of a tree. These are the shadows of blood vessels in your eye. Once you get them into view, stop moving the flashlight and the branches will disappear within a few seconds, as the image returns to its normal, stabilized condition.

see what you've probably never seen before: the blood vessels in your own eye.

Because its metabolic activity is so high, the retina is crucially dependent on normal blood flow. This makes the retina particularly vulnerable to diseases and disorders that interrupt or impede the flow of blood. What sorts of things might interrupt the retina's blood supply? For one thing, feeder arteries can become clogged, blocking the flow of blood to and within the inner retina. This happens in arteriosclerosis ("hardening of the arteries") and sometimes in sickle cell disease, a condition common among Africans and people of African descent.

Impairment of the blood supply to the outer, choroidal system can also have disastrous consequences. The outermost sheath of the retina consists of a single layer of cells, the **pigment epithelium,** which forms a barrier through which choroidal blood must pass in order to nourish the outer segments of the photoreceptors. The pigment epithelium transfers oxygen, nourishment, and vitamin A from the choroidal circulation to the photoreceptors. A steady supply of vitamin A is required for the synthesis of the receptors' light-sensitive pigment, a detail we'll return to later.

Clinical

The pigment epithelium also provides for waste disposal. Molecular garbage shed by the receptors is taken up and recycled within the pigment epithelium. If uncollected debris accumulates, it can eventually impede the transfer of nutrients. So anything that keeps pigment epithelium cells from performing their tasks will cause photoreceptor starvation and, eventually, death.

One natural enemy of the pigment epithelium is aging. Age-related macular degeneration, a condition that causes a progressive loss of vision, is the leading cause of impaired vision in the Western world and accounts for about one-half the cases of blindness among the elderly. Macular degeneration can seriously impair a person's ability to read, to drive an automobile and even to get around on foot (Hazel, et al., 2000). Currently, a minority of cases of age-related macular degeneration can be arrested, but not reversed, if treated early by means of laser surgery.

Diabetes is another common disease that can affect the retina's blood supply. This disease is marked by disordered insulin metabolism that causes too much sugar to accumulate in the diabetic's blood. For reasons not completely understood, the excess sugar can promote the development of a cataract in the eye's crystalline lens. Cataracts, as you've learned, can blur vision to the point of blindness. Besides cataracts, diabetes can have another serious consequence for vision. In some diabetics, the retina's blood supply is severely reduced. Sensing that it is being starved for oxygen (carried in the blood), the retina generates a chemical that stimulates the growth of new, larger blood vessels. Growing new blood vessels may sound like an excellent solution to the problem, but this growth produces devastation of its own. The thick new vessels grow out of control, blocking light and eventually causing blindness. In the last decade, lasers have been used very successfully to stop the growth of these new vessels.

THE EYE AS AN OPTICAL INSTRUMENT

Obviously, to see objects in the environment around you, your eyes must capture light reflected by those objects. But simply capturing the light itself isn't sufficient. The pattern of light reaching the retina must mirror the distribution of light in the scene being viewed. This light distribution, or **retinal image** as it's called, is the raw material on which the retina works. The fidelity of the retinal image depends on the ways that the patterns of light arriving at the eye interact with various ocular structures that influence the passage of that light to the back of the eye where the photoreceptors are located. To appreciate the workings of the eye's retina, then, requires understanding something about the image it receives.

Light conveys to the eyes information about objects in the environment. But how does light acquire that information in the first place? Initially, light originates from a source such as the sun or a light bulb. This is called emitted light, and it's certainly a necessary antecedent for vision: we cannot see in the dark. But emitted light *per se* isn't the stimulus for vision. Rather, we are interested in seeing *objects,* and for that to happen our eyes must pick up and register light reflected off the surfaces of those objects. It is reflected light that conveys biologically important information about the appearance—and hence the identity—of objects. How does this come about?

Surfaces absorb some, but not all, of the light shining on them; the portion of light not absorbed is reflected by the surface. Objects with high reflectance usually appear "light," whereas objects with low reflectance appear "dark." For example, this page has a reflectance of about 80 percent, while the print on this page has a reflectance of about 10 percent. Abrupt changes in reflectance usually signal discontinuities in a surface, such as the letters on this page or the edges and corners that demarcate an object's boundaries (see the top drawing in Figure 2.15). More gradual changes in

FIGURE 2.15
The top drawing illustrates how abrupt changes in reflectance signal the presence of an edge. The middle drawing illustrates how gradual changes in reflectance signal the presence of a smooth surface. The bottom drawing shows how reflected light specifies the texture of a surface.

reflectance usually correspond to curved surfaces (see the middle drawing in Figure 2.15).

Surfaces can "sculpt" the patterns of reflected light in other ways, too. For example, some surfaces reflect light evenly in many different directions. Because such surfaces lack highlights, they appear dull or matte. Other surfaces reflect light strongly in one narrow range of directions, giving those surfaces highlights and making them appear smooth and glossy (Greenberg, 1989). (The differences between dull and glossy surfaces are depicted in the bottom drawings in Figure 2.15.)

So, reflected light is structured by objects in the environment, and this optical structure conveys potential information about those objects and their textured surfaces. But before that potential can be realized, three prerequisites must be satisfied. First, the light must be sufficiently intense to penetrate the eye, reaching the photosensitive material in the retina. In fact, about 50 percent of all light striking the cornea is reflected or absorbed before reaching the retina (Cornsweet, 1970, p. 24).

Second, the distribution of light imaged on the retina must be properly focused. Consider the sharp contours forming this pair of letters: GO. To produce a sharp image of these letters, light reflected from that region of the page must form small, well-defined replicas of those contours on the retina. Blurred replicas would be created if each small, sharp contour were imaged as a larger, spread-out distribution of light on the retina. As a result, different parts of the retinal images of the contours would overlap, blurring one another's boundaries and making it difficult to see separate, individual letters, in which case reading would be impossible. Some effects of blur are illustrated in Figure 2.16.

Third, the pattern of light falling on the retina must preserve the spatial structure of the object from which it is reflected. If that spatial structure is preserved, light arising from two adjacent regions in space—from neighboring parts of an object, for instance—will fall on adjacent parts of the retina. A distribution of light that preserves the spatial ordering of locations in space is called an **image.** If the light distribution on the retina were scrambled or spatially random, it would be useless as a source of information about the structure and layout of objects.

Image Formation in The Human Eye

The sharpness of images formed on the retina depends mainly on two factors. The first is the

FIGURE 2.16
Effect of blur on the legibility of text. (For a legible version, you can find these paragraphs on page 38.)

optical power of the cornea and crystalline lens (where "optical power" means ability to bend, or refract, light). The other factor controlling image sharpness is the size of the eyeball, particularly the eyeball's length from front to back. In a camera, a good picture requires that the film be just the right distance from the lens. In the eye, the same thing holds true: the retina must be the right distance from the crystalline lens. Some eyes are too short, others are too long; either condition impairs vision.

The optical power of the eye is not constant, though. By changing its shape somewhat, the crystalline lens automatically changes its optical power. This automatic change, called accommodation, helps one see objects clearly, regardless of their distance from the eye. To appreciate how these components of the eye contribute to vision, we'll have to consider the behavior of light and its interaction with these components. To simplify our analysis of image formation we'll begin with a very small object: a single point in space that emits light. The same analysis works for other, more complex visual objects, since we can

think of them as consisting of a large set of points. But dealing with just one point will simplify our explanation of the rudiments of image formation.

In the eighteenth century, Thomas Young showed that light seemed to behave as though it consisted of waves. Upon dropping a pebble into a pond, you'll see wavefronts spreading out from the place where the stone hit the water. The stone corresponds to our point of light, and radiating out from that point is a set of spherical wavefronts (see Figure 2.17). Light that spreads out in this way is said to be **divergent.** Divergent light cannot form a well-focused image—a point—unless something is done to reverse its divergence. Let's examine how the eye accomplishes this feat. Certain optical devices can counteract light's tendency to diverge. One such device is a convex lens, which gets its name from its shape. Once a diverging wavefront passes through a strong convex lens, the paths of neighboring points on the wavefront get progressively closer together and eventually converge to a single point. After passing through this point, light di-

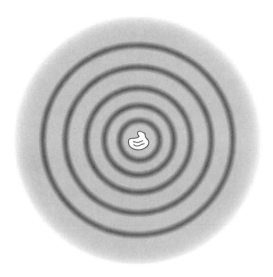

FIGURE 2.17
Light waves radiate out from a source of light in a way that resembles the ripples produced when a pebble is dropped into a pond.

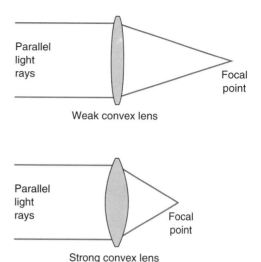

FIGURE 2.19
Convex lenses of different power bring light to focus at different distances. If the light rays striking the lens are parallel, the spot at which the light converges to a point is called the *focal point.*

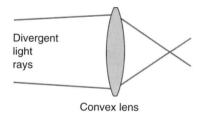

FIGURE 2.18
A convex lens focuses diverging light.

verges once again. Figure 2.18 illustrates this effect of a convex lens.

Lenses differ in their ability, or power, to converge light. A highly convex lens converges light more strongly than does a mildly convex lens. As Figure 2.19 shows, rays that pass through a convex lens of lower power are focused at some distance farther from the lens, whereas rays that pass through a convex lens of high power are focused close to the lens. The distance at which a lens brings light to focus depends on both the power of the lens itself and the degree of light divergence

striking the lens. To converge the light, a convex lens must overcome, or null, the light's divergence. This is demonstrated in Figure 2.20: a lens of constant power is shown converging light of three different degrees of divergence. The most strongly divergent light comes from the source positioned closest to the lens, while the most weakly divergent light comes from the source farthest from the lens. In addition, each object is focused at a different distance from the lens: the most divergent light is focused farthest from the lens, and the least divergent light is focused closest to the lens.

With these optical principles in mind, consider a human eye that is looking at an object sufficiently far away that light coming from that object has essentially zero divergence (in this case we say the object is located at "optical infinity"). To form a useful image, light from the object must be focused on the retina. Since cornea and crystalline lens both contribute to image formation, let's lump them together, calling the combination "the optics of the eye." How

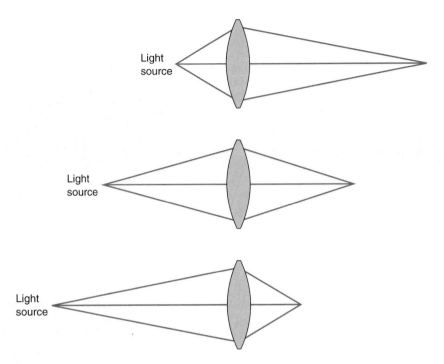

FIGURE 2.20
The spot at which a convex lens brings light to a point depends on the degree of divergence of the light arriving at the lens.

powerful should those optics be in order to produce a sharp retinal image of that distant object? For the retinal image to be sharply focused, the optics' power must match the length of the eyeball—specifically, the distance from the lens to the retina.

This idea is illustrated in Figure 2.21. The top eyeball is just the right length, given the power of its optics. As a result, the distant object is brought to focus exactly on the retina. Such an eye is described as **emmetropic** (meaning "in the right measure or size").

The middle panel shows an eye that is too long, given the strength of its optics. Although an image *is* formed, that image is formed in front of the retina, rather than on it. In fact, the rays have begun to diverge again by the time they reach the retina, so the image on the retina is blurred. Such

an eye is described as **myopic,** or nearsighted, because near objects will be in best focus.

The bottom panel in Figure 2.21 shows an eye that is too short for its optics; an image is formed on the retina, but it, too, is not well focused and hence the image is blurred. Actually, for this eye the best-focused image would lie behind the retina—if light were able to pass through the retina. Such an eye is described as **hyperopic,** or farsighted, because far objects will be in best focus.

What are the perceptual consequences of a mismatch between an eye's length and its optics? You've seen that in myopic or hyperopic eyes, light does reach the retina, but it is not sharply focused. When an eye of the wrong size looks at a distant point, the resulting image on the retina will be a circular patch, not a point. Thus the point in space will appear blurred, or indistinct.

HYPEROPIA

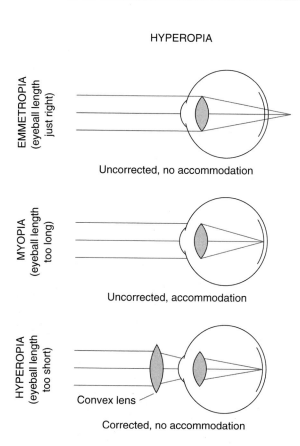

EMMETROPIA (eyeball length just right)

Uncorrected, no accommodation

MYOPIA (eyeball length too long)

Uncorrected, accommodation

HYPEROPIA (eyeball length too short)

Convex lens

Corrected, no accommodation

FIGURE 2.21
Image formation in emmetropic, myopic, and hyperopic eyes.

The degree of blur depends on the extent to which the eye is too short, or too long: the greater the mismatch between the eye's optics and its length, the worse the blur. The photographs in Figure 2.22 illustrate how the world might appear to a properly focused eye (panel A), to an eye that is only one-third of a millimeter too long (panel B), and to an eye that is 2 millimeters too long (panel C). Remember that when we describe an eye as "too long" or "too short," we mean this in relative terms. "Too long" and "too short" are defined relative to the power of the eye's optics.

The blur in panels B and C is so striking that it is hard to imagine that many people actually suffer unwittingly for years with that much blur or

A

B

C

FIGURE 2.22
Focus influences the quality of the image. Panel A simulates the image formed by an emmetropic eye; panel B, by a mildly myopic eye; and panel C, by a more severely myopic eye. (Glyn Cloyd.)

more. They go through their entire childhood and adolescence never realizing that their vision is defective. For reasons that are explained below, if their vision is blurred from myopia, they may have trouble seeing the blackboard clearly. If the blur comes from hyperopia, they may have trouble reading for prolonged periods. Unfortunately, the difficulties they experience in school may be mistakenly attributed to poor learning abilities rather than to poor vision.

Since about half the human race is afflicted with these problems, it's worth our time to consider hyperopia and myopia, and what steps can be taken to correct those problems.

Hyperopia   Imagine an eye whose length and optical power are properly matched. For that eye, a distant object would be in proper focus on the retina. Recall that proper focus demands an object just far enough from the eye so that wavefronts from the object, when they strike the eye, will be diverging at the right rate. If that same eye were shortened—making it hyperopic—by even a fraction of a millimeter, the distant object would no longer be focused as well on the retina. The plane in which the image would be focused best would lie behind the retina, not right on it (see the top panel of Figure 2.23). In its shortened state, this eye's optics would be too weak even for light coming from an object so distant that it is not diverging at all. If it has to deal with light from closer objects (even more strongly diverging), the eye will misfocus the light all the more.

A person with hyperopia—a hyperope—can alleviate this problem by accommodating, increasing the eye's optical power. This enables the hyperope to produce focused images of objects, provided the eye is not too hyperopic and provided the objects are not too close. Accommodation makes the lens more convex, thereby increasing its power and allowing well-focused images to be formed on the retina. The middle panel of Figure 2.23 shows how accommodation helps the hyperope bring an object into better focus on the retina.

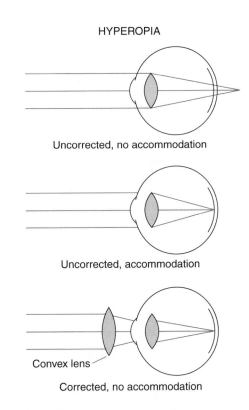

HYPEROPIA

Uncorrected, no accommodation

Uncorrected, accommodation

Convex lens

Corrected, no accommodation

FIGURE 2.23
Mild hyperopia can be overcome either by accommodation or by placing a convex lens in front of the eye.

But the hyperope pays a price for constant accommodation. First, there are limits to the amount of accommodation that the human eye can produce. As a result, if the eye is much too short and the resulting hyperopia substantial, the hyperope may be unable to accommodate enough for close work, such as reading. Second, even if the hyperope *could* accommodate enough to read, accommodation requires maintained muscular effort. The very strong, prolonged accommodation, as might be required in order to read, triggers eyestrain, headaches and nausea (Daum, 1983).

Fortunately, there is an alternative. Since the hyperopic eye cannot make incoming light converge rapidly enough, the light is not focused on the plane of the retina. The problem can be corrected by placing a convex lens in front of the cornea. With such a lens, the total optical power of the eye will be approximately the sum of the eye's own inherent optical power plus the power of the supplementary lens. This increased total optical power allows distant objects to be focused on the retina with little or no accommodation. As a result, the hyperope will need less accommodation when doing close work and will suffer less accommodative strain. The bottom panel of Figure 2.23 illustrates how this added convex lens helps the hyperope see near objects without accommodation.

Myopia Next let's consider an eye that is too long for its optical power. Such an eye is myopic, meaning that an object at optical infinity would be sharply focused somewhere in front of the retina, not at the plane of the retina (top panel, Figure 2.24). This situation could be rectified if we moved the object closer to the myopic person, or conversely, if we moved the myopic person closer to the object. Sometimes, of course, neither of these approaches is practical. Nor is it possible for the blur to be corrected by accommodation. In fact, increasing the power of the crystalline lens increases the overall optical power of the eye, worsening the blur. Fortunately, there is an effective solution to myopia: alter the effective optical power of the eye by placing the proper spectacle lens in front of, or the proper contact lens on, the eye.

What sort of corrective lens would the myopic eye need? We could correct the myopic eye by adding a concave lens (which causes light to *di*verge, combating the myopic eye's tendency to make light *con*verge too much). The bottom panel in Figure 2.24 shows how such a lens helps focus an otherwise misfocused target on a myope's retina.

Clinical

In many countries, myopia is so common that it poses a costly public health problem. For example, in the United States about 25 percent of the adult population is myopic and cannot see distant objects in sharp focus without glasses or

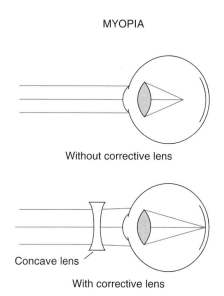
MYOPIA

Without corrective lens

Concave lens

With corrective lens

FIGURE 2.24
A concave lens in front of the eye can correct myopia.

contact lenses (NRC, 1989). It is important to note, however, that this prevalence is not uniform across different populations. For example, in Hawaii nearly 80 percent of people of Chinese descent are myopic (Baldwin, 1981).

Myopia also tends to run in families, suggesting that genetic factors are important (Zadnik, 1997). But genetics doesn't tell the entire story. For example, one recent report implicates the use of night lights during infancy as a possible contributor to myopia.

Plasticity

The prevalence of myopia also varies with environmental factors, including the visual demands of a person's occupation. People who do a great deal of near work, for instance, show an increased incidence of myopia. Submariners are an excellent case in point. They are cooped up for months on end in very small quarters, with little or no opportunity for distance vision (Kinney et al., 1980)—myopia is one consequence of this enforced diet of near vision. Closer to home, a number of studies have documented the slow but steady development of myopia among college students (NRC, 1989). The importance of environmental factors in producing myopia is clinched by a study in which monkeys spent their waking time on the equivalent of near work. In order to simulate near work, newborn monkeys were reared so that there was nothing for them to see more than 50 centimeters from their eyes. Over a 3-year period, these rearing conditions led to severe, permanent myopia (Young, 1981). As Box 2.2 describes, certain conditions produce a temporary, reversible form of myopia.

BOX 2.2

MYOPIA AS A SOMETIME THING

Some conditions have the power to diminish even the best vision, converting emmetropes into myopes, though only temporarily. Because this error in the eye's optical power is temporary, it differs from myopia that we discussed earlier. But as you'll see, the transitory nature of this condition, called **anomalous myopia,** does not reduce its potential seriousness.

It's been known for two hundred years that some people who are blessed with perfectly good eye sight during the daytime become quite nearsighted at night or at twilight. You may have experienced this yourself: nearby objects are seen clearly, but distant ones are not. There exist wide differences among individuals in the severity of anomalous myopia—some people show virtually no myopia at low light levels, while others become extremely nearsighted.

Low light is not the only condition that elicits a temporary myopia. Even in daylight, many individuals become myopic in featureless environments, such as a large open field, or when viewing a clear, cloudless sky. The amount of nearsightedness an individual experiences in such a featureless environment is strongly related to the nearsightedness experienced at twilight. One suspects then that both "open field myopia" and twilight myopia arise from a common cause. Both are subsumed under a single general rubric, anomalous myopia.

What causes this condition? Thanks to the efforts of Herschel Leibowitz and Fred Owens (1975), we know the answer. At low light levels or in open fields, there is no powerful stimulus to control the amount of accommodation. Freed from stimulus control, accommodation returns to a preferred neutral, or resting, level. The eye becomes myopic because that resting level is more suited to seeing near objects rather than very distant ones. In other words, the resting state of accommodation in many people does not produce a perfectly relaxed lens with minimal optical power. Instead, the resting state of accommodation leaves the lens focused for relatively nearby distances. Using laser-based instrumentation, Leibowitz and Owens confirmed that in the dark, most people's eyes tended to focus at some intermediate distance, not optical infinity. The actual distance varied widely among individuals, with an average viewing distance of about 0.67 meters.

The existence of anomalous myopia poses a potentially serious safety threat (Owens, 1984). Imagine you are the pilot of an airplane flying through the nighttime sky or the driver of a car speeding over a dark country road. In both conditions, accommodation will revert to its resting level. This will tend to blur and diminish the visibility of any object that appears within the field of view at a distance other than that associated with the resting level. If you are a pilot, the blurred object might be another aircraft; if you are a driver, it could be a pedestrian.

Like other refractive errors, anomalous myopia can be remedied optically. Leibowitz and Owens (1976) measured the resting level of accommodation for various individuals and then fitted them with concave corrective lenses of the appropriate power. These glasses, although inappropriate for daylight, nonmyopic conditions, produced impressive improvements in drivers' nighttime vision. Perhaps, sometime in the future, drivers and pilots will be routinely outfitted with individually prescribed glasses for nighttime use. The benefits, in lives saved, could be substantial.

Differences

Presbyopia Myopia and hyperopia affect many individuals. But the eye's focus can be disturbed in yet another way that *everyone* who lives long enough will experience sooner or later .

As people get older, their ability to accommodate decreases. As Figure 2.25 shows, the trend begins very early in life and continues until about age 70 (Carter, 1982). For the average 20- or 30-year-old, this loss has no practical consequence; people that age still have sufficient ability to accommodate. But upon reaching the mid-forties, the average person can no longer accommodate sufficiently to bring very close objects into focus. Reduced accommodation arises from various sources, including sclerosis of the lens and reduced elasticity of the lens's capsule (Koretz and Handelman, 1988). Severely diminished ability to accommodate is called **presbyopia,** meaning "old sight." In addition, an old lens is very sluggish in executing even the small shape changes of which it is still capable. This lengthens the time required to change gaze from near to distant objects, and vice versa, causing potential problems in driving and other tasks that entail rapid shifts in focus at different distances.

You have probably seen signs of presbyopia in people who are beyond 40 years of age but have yet to wear glasses or contact lenses. To see clearly, these individuals have to hold their reading material at arm's length, and some eventually complain that their arms need to grow longer. A relatively easy solution is readily available. A convex lens can be placed in front of the eye to substitute for the crystalline lens's own diminished ability to become sufficiently convex.

Benjamin Franklin was about 47 years old when he found that he could no longer read without spectacles. However, his reading glasses made distant objects too blurred. Constantly having to switch from one pair of glasses to another annoyed him, so Franklin invented bifocals—glasses having two separate lenses in front of each eye, with the more strongly convex lens filling the bottom of the frame. Looking down at reading material, Franklin could take advantage

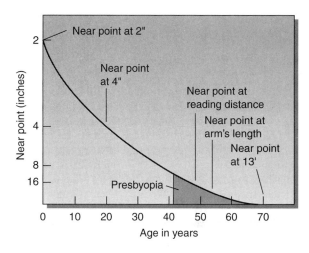

FIGURE 2.25
The *near point*—the closest distance at which an object can be seen without blur—increases with age.

of the extra help given by that lens. Looking slightly upward, he could see the world through a less powerful convex lens, allowing him clear vision of distant objects.

Astigmatism So far, our discussion of image formation in the eye has emphasized the role of the crystalline lens. The cornea, though, contributes more to the formation of sharp images on the retina than the lens does. To be more precise, the cornea contributes about two-thirds of the eye's total optical power, with the crystalline lens contributing the rest (see Box 2.3). As in the case of the lens, the cornea's shape determines its power—the more spherical the cornea, the more strongly it will converge incoming light. When the cornea is misshapen, the retinal image will be distorted. The most common distortion of shape produces a visual problem called **astigmatism.**

You can test yourself for astigmatism by using the spoke pattern in Figure 2.26. Look at the center of the spoke pattern. Without shifting your gaze, note whether some lines look fainter or have fuzzier edges than others. If they do, you may have astigmatism. This condition is not uncommon. It's

BOX 2.3

SEEING UNDER WATER

The next time you go swimming, try this experiment. Hold your hand under water and, with your head out of the water, look at your hand. Now, keeping your hand where it was, put your face into the water with your eyes open. When you look at your hand, you'll notice it doesn't look as sharp and clear as it did when your eyes were out of the water. The reason is that the cornea has effectively been eliminated as part of the eyes' optical system.

When light moves from air into the cornea, the path it travels is altered. This alteration, or bending, of light is called **refraction.** The amount of refraction depends on the difference between air and the material out of which the cornea is made. Under water, light enters the eye not from air but from the water itself. Because of the strong similarity between water and the material out of which the cornea is constructed—a large percentage of the cornea is water—light from the water is bent very little as it enters the cornea. Thus, when under water, the eye has effectively no cornea. Putting your face under water has reduced the optical power of your eye by about two-thirds, so it's no wonder you can't see so well. Of the eye's usual optical system, only the crystalline lens remains functional. But steps can be taken to restore the effectiveness of your cornea under water. A transparent diving mask keeps water away from direct contact with your corneas, allowing them to work just as they did with your face out of water.

Other creatures also need to use their eyes under water but don't have access to face masks. How do they do it? If an animal spends all of its time under water there's no problem; its eye is designed so that the cornea contributes little optical power anyway. The lens is strong enough to do all the necessary light bending. Most fish eyes have extremely powerful convex crystalline lenses—a perfect adaptation to their aquatic world.

But what about animals who spend some time above water and some below? They face the same problem that humans do. We'll consider two particularly interesting creatures who solve this challenge in different ways. Think about the problem that a diving bird faces. Flying along, it looks for fish swimming near the surface of the water below. When it spots a fish, the bird dives into the water and tries to snatch the fish. But as soon as it enters the water, the bird's cornea will lose its optical power, handicapping the bird visually. Some diving birds avoid this effect by using the equivalent of an adjustable face mask. The cormorant, for instance, has thick but partially transparent eyelids that close when the bird enters the water. Keeping water from coming into contact with the bird's corneas, the lids preserve much of the cornea's optical power.

But some animals face a situation that is even more optically demanding. Instead of going into and out of the water, these creatures are simultaneously both in and out of the water. The most famous of these creatures is *Anableps anableps,* a freshwater fish found in South and Central America. Because some of its food supply consists of insects above the water, anableps swims along the surface of the river, its eyes half under water and half above water. Anableps has a rather interesting adaptation to this peculiar environmental niche. The upper portion of anableps's eye (the part that is exposed to air) is distinct from the lower portion (the part that is exposed to water). Anableps has two pupils in each eye (one below and the other above the water), but relies more on aerial vision than on aquatic (Albensi and Powell, 1998). In addition, the lower half of its lens is more powerful than the upper half (Sivak, 1976). Anableps is commonly referred to as *cuatro ojos* (Spanish for "four eyes"), but having four eyes rather than two suits Anableps's lifestyle very well indeed.

Differences

FIGURE 2.26
Chart for testing astigmatism.

caused when the cornea is more sharply curved along one axis than it is along another. These differences in curvature mean that the cornea cannot sharply focus two different line orientations simultaneously on the retina. You may be wearing glasses that correct an astigmatism. To find out, remove your glasses, look through just one lens and slowly rotate the glasses through a 90-degree angle. If the lines on the test chart change in appearance, your glasses contain a correction for astigmatism. People with astigmatism who wear contact lens automatically have their vision corrected. The contact lens itself is perfectly spherical, and it is cushioned snuggly against the eye by a thin film of tears. The contact lens thus compensates for any irregularity in the cornea's shape and, thereby, nullfies any astigmatism.

Almost all eyes have some degree of astigmatism because the cornea is almost never perfectly shaped. But for some people the astigmatism may be severe enough to interfere with perception. Figure 2.27 illustrates how severe astigmatism can distort the appearance of a common, everyday scene. Astigmatism can be corrected by providing a lens that compensates for the cornea's distortion by an equal and opposite distortion of its own.

The previous section detailed the optical components responsible for forming images on the back of the eye. Now we're ready to resume looking at the back portion of the eye—the

FIGURE 2.27
The photograph at the right was taken using a lens that simulates astigmatism. (Glyn Cloyd.)

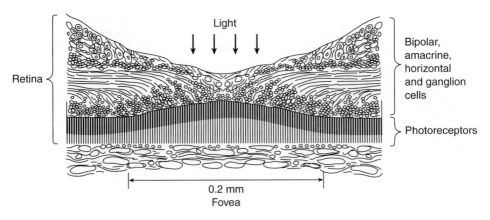

FIGURE 2.28
A sideways view of the central portion of the human retina. (Redrawn from Polyak, 1941.)

retina—which serves as the screen on which the image is cast. As mentioned earlier, this screen is actually located *behind* a complex network of nerve cells. The carefully formed image must pass through this network before the image can be registered by the photoreceptors. Let's take a look at this odd but obviously successful arrangement.

A SIDEWAYS LOOK AT THE RETINA

Figure 2.28 shows a thin slice of the retina viewed from its side. To create this slice, the retina was carefully removed from the eye, stretched out on a flat surface, and cut downward, through the thickness of the retina. (Special chemical dyes applied to this tissue make different types of retinal cells visually conspicuous under a microscope.)

The cross section in Figure 2.28 was taken from the center of the retina, the region known as the macula. This cross section is arranged so that if it were actually in an animal's eye, incoming light would first pass through the *top* part of the cross section. Notice that the photoreceptors are situated toward the *bottom* of the drawing. This drawing again reminds us that before light can reach the photoreceptors and initiate the re-

sponses that eventuate in vision, light must traverse the entire thickness of the retina.

Not all regions of the retina have the same thickness. Note in Figure 2.28 that the retina thins out in the center of the macula, forming a pit called the **fovea** (in Latin, *fovea* means "pit"). The retina in the foveal neighborhood is thin because some overlying structures have been pushed to the margins of the foveal pit. There's a good reason for this small clearing around the fovea. As light passes through the retina, some of it is absorbed or scattered before it can reach the photoreceptors. The thinness of the retina's fovea minimizes absorption and scatter, thus eliminating the obstacles to the passage of light to this particularly important region of the retina (Hughes, 1977).

With this overview of image formation and the retina firmly in mind, let's now consider how the photoreceptor cells in the retina sense the presence of light and initiate the process of seeing.

THE PHOTORECEPTORS

The human eye contains two major classes of photoreceptors: **rods** and **cones.** In humans, each eye contains about 100 million rods and approximately 5 million cones (Curcio and Hendrickson,

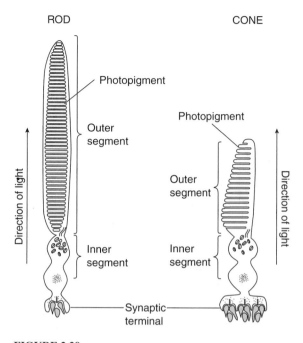

FIGURE 2.29

A single rod photoreceptor and a single cone photoreceptor, magnified approximately 1,500 times.

Think back to the analogy between the eye and a camera. The eyes' photoreceptors would be analogous to the camera's film. Because human eyes contain two types of photoreceptors, they resemble a camera that holds two different kinds of film at once. The type of film in a camera—color versus black and white—determines what kind of pictures are produced. Our eyes are simultaneously loaded with two different kinds of "film" (rods and cones). The duplex nature of the human eye produces some interesting idiosyncrasies in the way that we see. These idiosyncrasies will become apparent as we survey the differences between the rods and cones.

The Distribution of Rods and Cones

Rods and cones are not uniformly distributed throughout the retina: cones predominate in central vision, and rods predominate in peripheral vision. This differential distribution is shown in Figure 2.30, which plots the density of rods and cones in samples taken from different parts of the retina. In the very center of the macula, only cones are found. There, the cone's tips are thinner than elsewhere and they're very tightly packed. About 150,000 cones occupy an area 1 millimeter square (about the size of this letter: o). As we move away from the macula, the number of cones decreases while, at the same time, the number of rods increases. In fact, about 7 millimeters away from the fovea—moving along the retina in a direction toward the nose—rods reach a density approximately the same as that found for cones in the center of the macula. This difference in geographical distribution of rods and cones means that central and peripheral parts of the retina are useful for different aspects of vision. We'll get to those differences in a moment, but first let's consider a small, inconspicuous island of complete blindness found within each and every eye.

Notice the interruption in the plots shown in Figure 2.30. This gap denotes the complete absence of photoreceptors at the optic disk.

1991; Wandell, 1995). Figure 2.29 shows an example of rod and cone photoreceptors. The two types derive their names from their appearance. The tip of a cone is tapered, resembling a teepee or an upside down ice cream cone. In contrast, the tip of a rod has straighter sides and a blunt end—it looks like rod. But their differences go well beyond shape. In fact, functional differences between the two types of photoreceptors determine the lifestyles of their owners. Creatures who have a preponderance of rods in their retinas, such as the owl, tend to be most active at night. (We call such creatures "nocturnal" animals.) Creatures who have a preponderance of cones, such as the squirrel, tend to be active only during daylight hours. (We call them "diurnal.") We humans have duplex retinas, containing both rods and cones; we're called "arhythmic" since our activities are not limited to just one part of the day/night cycle.

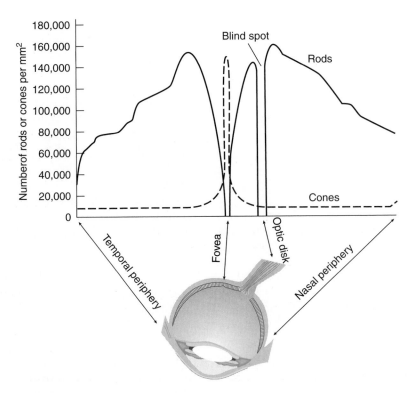

FIGURE 2.30
Distribution of rods and cones over the extent of the retina of the right eye, as seen from above. In the left eye, the nasal and temporal areas of the retina would appear reversed, but the relative distributions of rods and cones would be the same. Note the complete absence of rods within the fovea, where cones abound.

Because you cannot see without photoreceptors, you're actually "blind" to any image falling within this area of the retina devoid of receptors. We referred earlier to an analogy between the photoreceptors and photographic film. Following this analogy, the optic disk would correspond to a defective area of the film, on which the factory neglected to put any light-sensitive chemical. If that defective film were used in a camera and developed, the resulting picture would have a noticeable blank region. Surprisingly though, we almost never notice the large gap that the optic disks create in our retinas. Box 2.4 will help you see what you've been missing all these years.

Let's now return our attention to those parts of the retina that contain photoreceptors. The array

of approximately 100 million photoreceptors in each eye converts the optical image on the retina into a neural image that will be transmitted to the brain. But as Figure 2.31 shows, the density of photoreceptors varies regionally throughout the retina. This means, therefore, that the optical image is not being uniformly sampled by the photoreceptors. Again using our film analogy, it is as if our camera were loaded with film in which the light-sensitive chemical emulsion were unevenly spread over the film's surface. As a result, parts of our photograph would contain sharp detail (where the emulsion was dense) while other parts would appear grainy and blurred (where the emulsion was sparse). Photographic film isn't made this way, of course, but the retina is: it does

BOX 2.4

A GAP IN YOUR VISUAL FIELD

The optic disk—that place where the axons of the retinal ganglion cells come together to form the optic nerve—contains no photoreceptors. Consequently, it cannot support vision—it is literally a blind spot. Note that we're distinguishing between a region defined anatomically, the optic disk, and a region defined perceptually, the blind spot. Before we go on about the blind spot, you may want some proof that it actually exists.

Of course you cannot *see* a blind spot (though you can see an optic disk, using an ophthalmoscope). What you can see are the consequences of your blind spot—an object imaged within this blind region of your retina will be invisible. The figure below will help you see the consequences of this blind spot. Making sure that the book is propped up at right angles to the tabletop, view the figure from a distance of about 60 centimeters (about 2 feet). Close your left eye and, using only your right eye, stare at the fixation cross in the figure. At this viewing distance, the black disk to the right of the cross should fall on your optic disk, and will therefore disappear. Since the location of the optic disk varies from one person to the next, you may have to stare at a point slightly different from the fixation cross.

The demonstration of the existence of a blind spot represented a milestone in understanding the eye. Edmé Mariotte, the French scientist who discovered the blind spot in 1668, did not simply stumble upon it by accident (Mariotte, 1668/1948). Instead, his dissection of human eyes suggested to him that vision might be impaired in the region of the optic disk. This was the first time that anyone had predicted a previously unknown perceptual phenomenon simply from an anatomical observation. From the geometry of the eyeball, including the location of the optic disk, Mariotte correctly predicted where stimuli would have to be placed relative to a fixation point in order for the image to fall on the optic disk. Mariotte also confirmed that there were individual variations in the precise location of the blind spot, corresponding to individual variations in the optic disk itself.

It's been claimed that England's "merry monarch," Charles II, exploited the retina's blind spot to "behead" symbolically members of his court who were in disfavor (Rushton, 1979). After placing them at the right distance from his throne, Charles would adjust his gaze so that the head of his "victim" was imaged on the optic disk. Although this is an intriguing story, the more so because Charles I, the father of Charles II, had been beheaded, Adam Reeves (1982) describes the story as "a baseless canard" against Charles II. Frankly, we're not sure who's correct.

While you were looking for your own blind spot, you may have noticed something else strange. When the black disk disappeared, you weren't left with a "hole" in your visual field. Instead, the background appeared uniformly white. This phenomenon is called *completion* or "filling in." Blind spot completion has been cleverly exploited by Ramachandran (1992) to study the filling-in phenomenon in more detail. His article, which contains some delightful demonstrations, concludes that completion of vision across the blindspot is just one instance of a more general process called interpolation, an aspect of perception we shall take up in Chapter 7.

X

Fixation cross

●

FIGURE 2.31
Highly magnified photograph of an outer segment of a rod
photoreceptor from a monkey's eye. The array of thin
vertical stripes are stacks of tightly packed disks that house
the photosensitive molecules responsible for generating
electrical signals when stimulated by light. (John Dowling.)

unevenly register the spatial detail in the image
formed on it. In the fovea where cones alone exist, the image is very finely sampled, while out in
the periphery, sampling is coarse. You can easily
preview the consequence of these sampling differences by trying to read small text out of the
corner of your eye—the image of that text is not
registered with sufficient detail to convey the identities of individual letters.

If one knows how densely the photoreceptors
are packed, it's possible to calculate the finest
pattern that any particular array of receptors
could reproduce (Yellott, 1982). In the foveas of
most young adults, the photoreceptors are packed
very densely, in an orderly arrangement that produces a near-constant distance between neighbors. As one progresses away from the center of
the retina, the distances increase between neighboring receptors and the orderliness of the packing diminishes (Hirsch and Miller, 1987). When
the photoreceptors are photographed end-on,
they suggest a carefully laid mosaic, such as one
would make out of small, hexagonal tiles. In the
center of the retina, this remarkably orderly and

tightly packed mosaic allows the photoreceptor
array to reproduce the finest details that the eye's
optics can transmit to the retina.

We've commented admiringly on the exquisite packing of photoreceptors in the central
retina of the human adult and on the contribution
of that packing to the excellence of vision. The
situation is quite different, though, for young infants. It takes about four years for an infant's
retina to reach its final, adult state. During that
time, photoreceptors migrate toward the center of
the retina from the periphery, a migration that
creates the pit known as the fovea. Even as late as
15 months of age, the distance between neighboring photoreceptors of the central retina is
twice the comparable value in the adult eye
(Yuodelis and Hendrickson, 1986). Although
some of the infants' poor visual acuity arises
from the immature state of their brains, the lion's
share results from immaturity at the retinal level
(Banks and Bennett, 1988; Teller and Movshon,
1986).

An analogous, though far less dramatic,
change occurs at the other end of the life span. In
old age, the packing of receptors in the central
retina changes because of cell death and other
factors (Weale, 1986). Undoubtedly, this contributes to the drop in acuity that accompanies
aging (Owsley, Sekuler and Siemsen, 1983).

Although retinal anatomy and retinal function
follow parallel courses, in some humans, retinal
anatomy and retinal function are permanently arrested at the infant stage. These humans, whose
skin, hair and eyes lack pigmentation, have a genetic disorder known as albinism (Abadi and Pascal, 1989). Melanin, the pigment that gives color
to skin, hair and eyes, is particularly abundant in
the macular region of the normal retina. The
melanin promotes the inward migration of photoreceptors and the formation of the foveal pit.
The albino eye, lacking melanin, does not have
much receptor migration and never develops a
foveal pit. As a result, the number of photoreceptors per unit area in the central retina of the albino
eye is far below that of pigmented adults. Hugh
Wilson and colleagues have studied the vision of

human albinos and liken their central retinal anatomy and function to that of a normal 10-month-old (Wilson et al., 1988). All these unusual cases—infants, the aged, and albinos—reinforce the idea that the retina's photoreceptor mosaic sets important limits on the information that can be extracted from the retinal image.

THE FIRST STEP TOWARD SEEING

Neural

Light registers its presence on the retina by interacting with special light-sensitive molecules contained within the photoreceptors. These molecules, called **photopigments,** are contained in the membrane portions of an array of discs that are tightly packed within the outer segment of each and every photoreceptor (see Figure 2.31). Light passing through these discs triggers a cascade of biochemical events that culminate in the generation of electrical signals within the photoreceptor. We'll start by considering the chemical basis of the photopigment molecules.

Each photopigment molecule consists of two components: a very large protein, *opsin;* and another component, *retinal,* derived from vitamin A. Normally, the two components are tightly connected, producing a stable molecule that won't break up spontaneously. But when light strikes one of these molecules, some of the light's energy is imparted to the molecule, causing it to change shape, or *isomerize.* Once this shape change occurs, the photopigment molecule is no longer stable and its two components undergo a series of changes, eventually splitting apart.

This change in shape alters the flow of electric current in and around the photoreceptor. In the absence of light, electrical current flows into the stack of discs within the photoreceptor's outer segment. This inward current flow, then, signifies that the eye is in darkness. Photopigment isomerization, triggered by the presence of light, briefly reduces this flow of current. That change in current flow signifies the presence of light. The greater the amount of light, the larger the number of molecules isomerized and the greater the resulting change in electrical potential.

This change in current moves down the length of the photoreceptor to its terminal end, where specialized chemical messengers, called **transmitter substances,** are housed. In the photoreceptors, these messengers are glutamate molecules. In the absence of light, glutamate is continuously released by the photoreceptor into the very small gap that separates the photoreceptor from the cells with which they are in chemical communication. This gap is called the **synapse.** The presence of light—through its effect on the photopigments and the electrical current flow—reduces the rate of glutamate released into the synapse. Light, in other words, turns *down* the release of chemical messages by the photoreceptors. Like the photoreceptors pointing backward into the eye, this is another one of those counterintuitive ways that nature constructs biological mechanisms. But obviously it works, and very efficiently. The entire chain of events—from absorption to isomerization to current flow is called **phototransduction.** It occurs in less than a thousandth of a second. In the next chapter, we'll learn how the cells in communication with the photoreceptors make sense of these odd messages.

Not all light wavelengths are equally effective in triggering phototransduction. While retinal is the same for all human photopigments, opsin comes in four different molecular forms, each having its own unique sensitivity to lights of different wavelengths. These different molecular forms are genetically determined, and genetic mutation can and does alter the form of the opsins in some individuals. The various sensitivities of opsins to light wavelengths is fundamentally important for vision, but we'll postpone discussing that until the next chapter. For now, let's survey the different types of photoreceptors as defined by their wavelength sensitivity.

Exposing a photoreceptor to light from various regions of the wavelength spectrum makes it possible to measure how much of that light is actually absorbed and, therefore, how much that wavelength stimulates the photoreceptor. When this is done, one finds that for any given receptor there is one wavelength of light that most

FIGURE 2.32
This graph shows how the amount of light absorbed by rod photoreceptors varies with the wavelength of the light.

FIGURE 2.33
This graph shows how the amount of light absorbed by each of three types of cone photoreceptors varies with wavelength.

strongly stimulates the receptor. There is, in other words, one wavelength to which the receptor is most sensitive. Rods give their biggest response when stimulated with approximately 500 nanometers (the wavelength of light is measured in **nanometers,** billionths of a meter); shorter or longer wavelengths give a diminished response. A summary of the rod's spectral sensitivity is graphically illustrated in Figure 2.32. To appreciate the stimulus to which rods are most sensitive, you should know that under daylight conditions, light of 500 nanometers looks bluish-green.

The corresponding story for cones is more complicated, since the wavelength at which sensitivity is optimum depends on *which* type of cone is being studied. There are three distinct classes of cones. One is maximally responsive to light of about 440 nanometers, a second class responds best to light of 530 nanometers, and a third class has its peak response at 560 nanometers. The responses of these three classes of cones are shown in Figure 2.33 as functions of the wavelength of stimulating light. Again, to give you some reference points, under daylight conditions, light of 440 nanometers looks violet, light of 530 nanometers looks green, and light of 560 nanometers looks yellow.

The curves shown in Figures 2.32 and 2.33 underscore an important feature of human vision. The curves separate electromagnetic radiation that one *can* see ("light") from electromagnetic radiation that one *cannot* see. For example, one cannot see infrared radiation (wavelengths longer than 700 nanometers) because human photopigments do not respond to wavelengths that long. (Recall the story about the World War II sailors whose vision was altered by extending the range of wavelengths to which their photopigments were responsive.)

To actually see, though, requires more than just a change in a photoreceptor's own electrical state. Messages about the presence of light must be transmitted from the receptors to the intermediate network of bipolar, amacrine and horizontal cells and then to the retinal ganglion cells, which communicate the outcome of all this neural analysis to the brain. The first three boxes in Figure 2.34 summarize the events that we've been describing. The remaining boxes represent the concerns of the next two chapters.

Box 2.5 provides tantalizing clues for the existence of a third type of photoreceptor in the eye, one whose job is entirely different from that of the rods and cones.

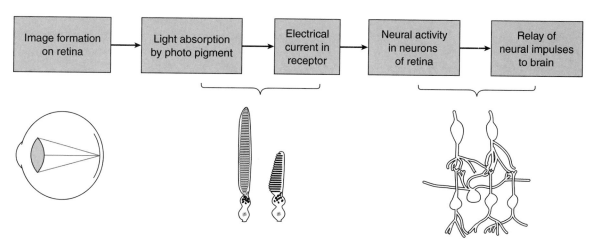

FIGURE 2.34
The three boxes at the left of this figure summarize the events discussed in this chapter. The remaining boxes represent the topics of the next two chapters.

YOUR DAILY DOSE OF LIGHT

The text stresses that vision isn't concerned with seeing light but, instead, with seeing objects and events. Thus, light is simply the messenger that carries optical information from the environment to our eyes. There is one aspect of vision, however, where light itself *is* the message. We don't normally stop to think about this aspect of vision. Light calibrates the internal, neural clock that our brains use to regulate our sleep/wake cycles, our appetites and our hormone levels. It's this clock that temporarily gets out of whack when we travel overseas.

Called **circadian rhythms,** these periodic activities and bodily functions are normally coupled to our 24-hour light/dark cycle. In the absence of light, however, the clock that regulates circadian rhythms can drift out of synch. Thus, rats placed in complete darkness for weeks at a time, or humans who voluntarily live in dark caves for several months slip into sleep/wake cycles that deviate significantly from the normal solar cycle. Once these light-deprived individuals return to environments with normal light exposure, their clocks quickly resynchronize. The eyes are critical for this resetting of the clock.

One would naturally expect either rod or cone photoreceptors to be responsible for setting the daily clock, but recent evidence suggests this is not the case. Mice lack both rod and cone photoreceptors, and yet they maintain normal activity cycles and their light-dependent hormone levels remain normal (Freedman et al., 1999). Evidently, the eye contains a third class of light-sensitive neural elements especially designed for internal clock control. Speculation currently centers around a protein found in the eye called cryptochrome (Barinaga, 1999). But the cells housing this time-keeper protein remain unidentified, as do the ganglion cells that communicate the photoreceptive signals to those regions of the brain responsible for regulating circadian behaviors.

SUMMARY AND PREVIEW

This chapter has laid out the basic design of the human eyeball, emphasizing the good fit between its structure and the job it must do. Because vision depends on an interaction between light and the eye, we also considered how light itself manages to capture information about the environment, information that is conveyed by light. This led us to a discussion of the eyeball's optical characteristics and various common imperfections in those characteristics. The chapter ended with the capture of light by photopigment molecules and the first step toward seeing—photoreceptor responses that are communicated to other neurons in the retina and eventually to the brain. The next chapter follows these messages as they pass from one retinal neuron to the next. You already know that your vision mirrors the properties of your photoreceptors; the next chapter will show you how other elements in the retina also control what you see.

KEY TERMS

accommodation
afterimage
amacrine cells
anomalous myopia
aqueous humor
astigmatism
bipolar cells
cataract
choroid
ciliary body
circadian rhythms
collector cells
cones
conjunctive
cornea
crystalline lens
depth of field
divergent
electromagnetic radiation

emmetropic
extraocular muscles
fibrous tunic
floaters
fovea
glaucoma
horizontal cells
hyperopic
image
inverse optics
iris
macula
myopic
nanometers
ophthalmoscope
optic disk
orbit
outer segment
photopigments

photoreceptors
phototransduction
pigment epithelium
presbyopia
pupil
rectus muscles
refraction
retina
retinal ganglion cells
retinal image
rods
sclera
sclerosis
synapse
transmitter substances
vascular tunic
vergence
vitreous
wavelength

CHAPTER 3

THE EYE AND SEEING

To appreciate how complex the eye is, just talk to an engineer who has tried to build one out of electronic components. The first stage in the visual process—registering the presence of light within an image—is not so difficult. It can be simulated with an array of special transistors called photodiodes. These tiny devices produce voltages that accurately represent the amount of light impinging on them, just like the photoreceptors in your eye. But then what? How do you make any sense out of an array of voltage values? How does the artificial eye figure out what objects in the world produced particular patterns of voltage values in its array of photodiodes?

To accomplish this feat engineers have turned to nature, which holds all the copyrights on the most successful eye designs on earth. Using ideas borrowed from biological eyes, engineers working together with physicians have created wafer-thin silicon microchips whose circuitry mimics some of the neural processing accomplished by the retina

(Humayun, de Juan and Dagnelie, 1996). Still, the performance of those artificial retinae pale in comparison to the real thing. At best, the bionic eyes can provide vision capable of supporting limited mobility. In this chapter, we're going to try to think like design engineers, examining the circuitry and neural computations performed by the retina.

By way of preview, here's a partial list of components for the retina of a single human eye: approximately 100 million photoreceptors (rods and cones); 10 million horizontal, amacrine and bipolar cells; and 1.25 million ganglion cells. All these millions of parts are segregated into different layers of the retina, which is no thicker than a postage stamp (recall Figure 2.28). Our goal here is to see how the retina's parts function together to generate biologically useful descriptions of the retinal image for the brain to interpret. To start, let's briefly review what photoreceptors do, since they kick off the series of neural events that culminate in visual perception.

Millions of Points of Light

Each and every photoreceptor performs one simple job: it gauges the amount of light it is receiving. Photoreceptors perform these measurements by generating electrical currents proportional to the amount of light absorbed by the photopigment contained in their outer segments. Over the entire retina, this operation results in millions of separate measurements, each one specifying the light level falling on the tiny region of the eye occupied by a photoreceptor. Viewed this way, we can characterize the photoreceptor matrix as a two-dimensional array consisting of millions of cells. At any given moment, each cell is generating its own unique response to light that expresses the degree to which the electrical current in that photoreceptor cell has been altered. That alteration in current is directly related to the amount of light absorbed by the photoreceptor pigment (Figure 3.1).

But vision doesn't consist of tiny points of light signalled by our photoreceptors. The objects we see in nature aren't like the pictures printed in newspapers, where images are synthesized from clusters of tiny light and dark dots. The array of light measurements registered by the photoreceptors get passed on to a network of neurons that reorganize those millions of raw measurements into more efficient, biologically-relevant messages about the distribution of light in the retinal image. Individual light measurements are transformed into visually important information about the contrast, color, edges and textures, as well as the ingredients, or features, that comprise objects. To understand those transformations, we need to define exactly what is meant by "information about objects."

Think back to our discussion of image formation in the preceding chapter. There we noted that objects absorb some of the light hitting their surfaces and reflect the rest. In effect, objects in our environment "sculpt" the light that eventually arrives at our eyes. The optics of the eye maintain that sculpted spatial structure, forming an image of the sculpted light on the retina. Thus, when it reaches the retina, the amount of light reflected from some object usually differs from the amount of light reflected from the object's surroundings. The key word is *differs*. If there were some way of registering when neighboring retinal regions were being illuminated by *different* amounts of light, one would be on the way to identifying an object's edges or borders—places where the amount of reflected light changes. If one is interested in objects and edges, one is *not* interested in regions of the retina over which the light level remains constant. Homogeneous, uniformly illuminated regions of the retina probably do *not* represent the image of an edge. To identify an edge, the retina needs to note where there are *differences* between the light levels at adjacent locations. As you'll see, many retinal cells are designed to do precisely that: respond to differences between adjacent levels of light.

Our immediate goal, then, is to understand how the retina condenses and reorganizes the multitude of messages supplied by the photoreceptors. Then we will consider how the condensation and reorganization actually affect the appearance of objects and their surfaces.

Eventually, we need to examine the neurons forming the middle layers of the retina: the bipolar, amacrine and horizontal cells. They are the circuit elements that radically transform the photoreceptors' signals into something much different from light measurements. But for the moment, let's skip to the **retinal ganglion cells,** the neurons responsible for the last stage of processing within the eye itself. Once you understand what the ganglion cells do, you'll find it easier to see how those middle layer cells make the visual process possible.

During our discussion, keep in mind two important facts about the ganglion cells. First, although they do respond to visual stimulation, they do not themselves absorb light; they are *not* photoreceptors. Ganglion cells process neural information that the other retinal cells have received from the photoreceptors. Without input from

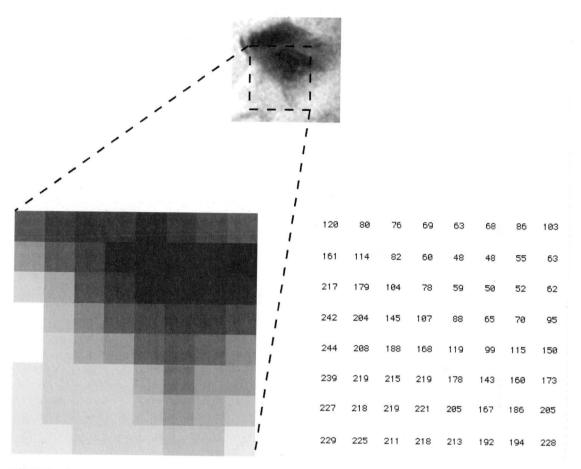

120	80	76	69	63	68	86	103
161	114	82	60	48	48	55	63
217	179	104	78	59	50	52	62
242	204	145	107	88	65	70	95
244	208	188	168	119	99	115	150
239	219	215	219	178	143	160	173
227	218	219	221	205	167	186	205
229	225	211	218	213	192	194	228

FIGURE 3.1

Photoreceptors generate electrical signals proportional to the amount of light impinging on them. The array of spots on the left depicts a portion of the image of a human face as "seen" by an array of photoreceptors. The matrix on the right contains numerical values representing electrical signals. The value of each "signal" is proportional to the intensity of light striking a given photoreceptor. Notice the spatial correspondence between intensity levels and matrix signal values.

those other cells, the ganglion cells would be blind to everything happening in the visual world.

Second, ganglion cells can only signal the outcome of their processing by generating **action potentials,** brief electrical discharges carried by the nerve fibers of the ganglion cells to the central visual stages within the brain. So whatever a ganglion cell has to "say" about a visual stimulus must be expressed using this one-"word" vocabulary. This restriction actually applies to *all* fur-

ther stages of visual processing—neurons talk to one another in a language composed entirely of action potentials, or neural impulses, as they are sometimes called. Particular neurons speak with a burst of impulses only when certain types of visual stimuli appear. By virtue of their early position in this chain of visual processing, retinal ganglion cells set this neural dialogue in motion. Let's examine now what the ganglion cells have to say.

THE RETINAL GANGLION CELLS

Neural

The human eye contains an estimated 1.25 million retinal ganglion cells. Comparing this figure to the roughly 100 million receptors in the eye, you know from the outset that ganglion cells must be condensing the raw messages from the receptors. Imagine you are handed a 1,000-word essay (about 4 double-spaced, typed pages) and told to edit it down to 12 or 13 words (1 or 2 sentences)—without losing the essentials of its message. To meet this challenge, you must identify the essay's major points and then rephrase them, condensing in a way that preserves the essence of the original. Retinal ganglion cells face the same kind of problem: they must collate messages from the more numerous photoreceptors and—with help from the horizontal, amacrine and bipolar cells—summarize those messages in a biologically relevant way. How do the ganglion cells accomplish this?

The most direct way to tackle this question is to determine what kinds of visual stimuli are best able to activate ganglion cells. Figure 3.2 illustrates the experimental procedure for determining a visual cell's preferred stimulus. An experimental animal, a monkey in this case, is shown facing a screen. A tiny, fine-tipped wire called a **microelectrode** is surgically and painlessly inserted into the part of the visual system under study, in this case, the optic nerve (which com-

Execute

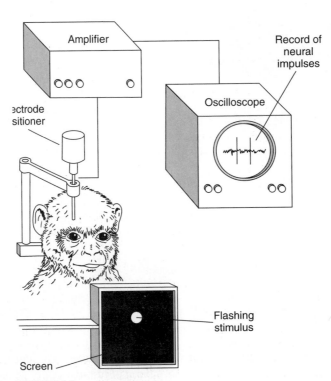

FIGURE 3.2
Laboratory setup for recording action potentials from single neurons. The placement of the recording electrode governs which stage of the visual nervous system will be examined. In the case shown, the electrode would pick up action potentials generated in the axons of the retinal ganglion cells.

prises the axons of the ganglion cells). The probe can be positioned close enough to an individual ganglion cell **axon** (the portion of the cell that carries its impulses out of the retina) so that the electrode picks up the action potentials (neural impulses) arising from just that cell. One can then monitor the number of action potentials generated by this single cell, and try to influence the cell's activity level by presenting various sorts of visual stimuli on the screen. This technique, called **single cell recording,** has been successfully employed to determine what kinds of visual stimuli activate cells at different stages within the visual system. Here we are interested in the retina. In effect, we wish to ask the ganglion cells "What sort of visual stimulus do you reliably respond to?"

Before presenting *anything* on the screen, you discover that the ganglion cell is already active. The electrode is picking up an irregular but persistent chatter of action potentials from the cell. This spontaneous activity continues even when the monkey is in complete darkness. The occurrence of individual action potentials over time is plotted in Figure 3.3. In each of the three panels, small vertical lines represent single action potentials from one retinal ganglion cell. Time is traced out along the horizontal axis. Looking at panel A, you see the impulses occurring in the absence of visual stimulation—this is the cell's spontaneous activity.

Since it is spontaneously active when no light is present, the cell must signal the presence of light by a change in its *level* of activity. Suppose your job is to discover what it takes to produce that *change* from spontaneous activity. Knowing that photoreceptors (from which the ganglion cells receive input via those middle layer cells) are small, you start by moving a small spot of light around over the screen in front of the monkey. By doing this, you are moving the light over the monkey's retina, stimulating photoreceptors wherever you move the spot. So, in effect, your job is to search for an area of the retina where the image of the spot of light will influence the ganglion cell's level of activity.

FIGURE 3.3
Neural activity (shown as vertical lines) of retinal ganglion cells. See the text for a full discussion.

As we proceed with our example, it is very important to keep the following in mind: different regions on the screen in front of the monkey correspond to different areas on the monkey's retina. To maintain this correspondence, the monkey's eye must remain perfectly still. If the monkey moved its eye around during the experiment, you could never be certain when your spot of light fell on its retina. Monkeys can be trained to hold their fixation very steady, but sometimes investigators use a drug that temporarily stabilizes the eye during the experiment. Once the monkey's eye is immobilized, positioning the spot in the center of the screen places the image of the spot on the center of the monkey's eye, in the macula. With this in mind, let's start our experiment.

By moving the spot of light around on the screen, you discover a region of the retina where the spot causes an increase in the recording cell's activity. Concentrating on this region, you find that the cell generates a burst of impulses when you turn the light on this area. When you turn the light off, the cell's activity quickly settles back to its background (spontaneous) level. This outcome is shown in panel B of Figure 3.3. Next, you test a neighboring area of the retina in the same way. Now you find just the opposite result—turning the light on causes the activity level to drop *below* the background level. But when you turn the light off, the cell emits a short, vigorous burst of impulses. This second outcome is illustrated in panel C. So, this cell responds in two antagonistic ways, depending on where you place the light on the screen and, hence, on the retina. In one region it responds to an *increase* in light, whereas in the other it responds to a *decrease* in light. To distinguish these two kinds of responses, let's call the first an "ON response" and the second an "OFF response."

While still recording from this same cell, suppose you now test at other, nearby locations on the retina. You find that ON responses can be elicited from anywhere within a restricted, circular region. In fact, enlarging your spot so it just fills this circular region produces a very vigorous response. The regions giving an OFF response, however, form a ring that completely surrounds the circular ON region. So the same spot of light has opposite, or antagonistic, effects in the center versus the surrounding area, usually shortened to the surround. If you label these two regions using plus signs (for ON) and minus signs (for OFF), the composite looks like a small circle of plus signs surrounded by a ring of minus signs, as shown in panel A of Figure 3.4.

Light placed anywhere *outside* this donut-shaped composite has no influence whatsoever on this cell's activity. In other words, only light falling within this restricted, concentrically shaped area of the retina is registered by this ganglion cell. This area constitutes that cell's **receptive field**—the patch of retina within which a cell's activity may be influenced. (The term "re-

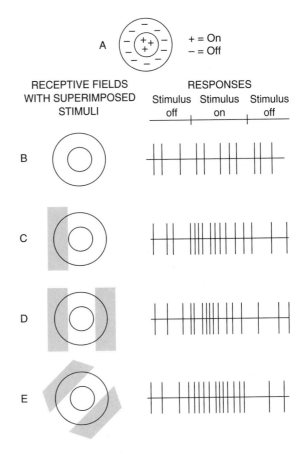

FIGURE 3.4
A single ON-center retinal ganglion cell (A) responding to uniform illumination (B), to a dark/light edge (C), to a vertical bar of light (D), and to an oblique bar of light (E).

ceptive field" was coined by H. K. Hartline [1938] in his classic work on retinal ganglion cells in frogs.) The concept of a receptive field is extremely important for understanding visual processing. As you will come to appreciate in this chapter and the next one, the receptive field serves as a kind of template with which a cell gauges the pattern of light falling within a restricted area of the retina. That pattern of light must fit into the receptive field in order to activate a cell.

Neural

To illustrate what we mean, consider the receptive field mapped out in panel A of Figure 3.4. Can you picture an optimal visual stimulus for this cell, one that would produce the most vigorous increase in neural activity? First, imagine illuminating the entire retina, in effect filling the cell's receptive field with light. As shown in panel B of Figure 3.4, the cell gives only a weak response to uniform illumination. This is because such a stimulus produces opposite effects in the center and the surrounding area. The two antagonistic regions compete with one another, resulting in a near stand-off. This interaction between antagonistic regions is called **lateral inhibition.**

Now imagine what happens when an edge is positioned in the manner shown in panel C. The ON-center portion of the receptive field receives an increase in light, its preferred stimulus, while a good portion of the surround receives a reduced level of light, its preferred stimulus. The net result is a vigorous response from the cell. As panels D and E show, the cell would also respond well to bars of light positioned appropriately within the receptive field. Incidentally, because these center/surround areas are nearly always concentrically arranged, ganglion cells will respond well regardless of whether the edge is oriented vertically, horizontally, or diagonally. The orientation of an edge or bar is irrelevant so long as the edge or bar is positioned appropriately within the receptive field.

This antagonistic arrangement of center and surround within the receptive field enables the retinal ganglion cell to perform its filtering work. Lateral inhibition has enabled the cell to condense the messages from a patch of photoreceptors into a single statement: "I detect a light/dark boundary." By accenting the *difference* in light levels on adjacent areas of the retina, the cell has begun the process of extracting perceptually relevant information.

Nearly all ganglion cells have concentrically arranged receptive fields, composed of a center and a surround that respond in an antagonistic

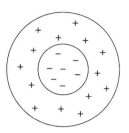

FIGURE 3.5
A receptive field of an ON-center retinal ganglion cell.

fashion. Some of those cells have ON centers and OFF surrounds, like the receptive field illustrated in Figure 3.4. (Box 3.1 discusses one interesting perceptual phenomenon thought to result from these cells.) Other cells have just the opposite layout, with an OFF center and an ON surround. An example of this latter type of cell is shown in Figure 3.5.

There are about as many ON-center cells as there are OFF-center cells. Both types respond best to light/dark boundaries. Together, the 1.25 million receptive fields of the ON-center cells and OFF-center cells are interwoven to comprise a mosaic covering the entire retina. As a result, whenever light falls on a limited patch of the retina, that light is bound to affect a number of retinal ganglion cells of both types, producing opposite effects in the two. Don't imagine, though, that these opposite effects cancel one another. At higher stages of the visual system, information from ON-center and OFF-center cells remains segregated, allowing information from both types to be used (Wässle, Peichl, and Boycott, 1981). Moreover, behavioral studies of animals in which activity within the ON cells has been chemically disrupted reveal that the ON and OFF cells support different aspects of vision (Schiller, Sandell and Maunsell, 1986). With the ON cells inactivated, animals have difficulty detecting increments in light, whereas light decrements are readily perceived. Low-contrast objects are also more difficult to see without a functioning ON system.

BOX 3.1

BLACKER THAN BLACK

Because of its spontaneous activity, an ON-center cell sends the brain a stronger message when no light falls in its receptive field than it does when its surround alone is illuminated. This curious state of affairs suggests the possibility that some light may actually appear darker than no light at all. In fact, surrounding a dim area with a sufficiently intense light makes that dim area appear darker than an area that contains no light whatever. Probably the intense surround drives the activity of ON-center ganglion cells *below* their spontaneous levels, signaling the brain that something blacker than black is present (Brown and Mueller, 1965).

The consequences of this spontaneous activity show up in everyday life. Think about what it's like to wake up in the middle of the night in an absolutely dark room. Usually the room doesn't appear totally black. In fact, many people experience dim, illusory, swirling lights, the result of spontaneous activity in the visual system (Hurvich and Jameson, 1966).

Some artists exaggerate discontinuities in intensity in order to highlight the outline of figures in their work. If an artist wants to create the deepest possible black region in some painting, he or she must do more than simply use black paint. Even if that black paint reflected no light at all (which isn't really possible with paint), receptive fields in which the black paint was imaged would still be sending spontaneous messages to the brain. To reduce those messages to a minimum, the artist surrounds the black paint with an area of white or other light-colored paint. The contrast between the two areas intensifies the blackness produced by the dark paint. Ratliff (1972) contains a good introduction to the uses of lightness illusions in art.

The same effect is exploited by your television set and your computer monitor. The screen cannot get any darker than it is when the power is off. Yet the screen doesn't look black when the video monitor is off—it looks dark grey. So how is it that black objects are produced when the monitor is on? Gray regions appear black when surrounded by other, light-colored regions.

Some parents and children also take advantage of light's ability to create darkness, often unwittingly. Many children have a hard time falling asleep unless conditions are just right. Not only must it be past their appointed bedtime, but conditions outside must also confirm that it is bedtime—it must *look* sufficiently dark outside. Some wise parents take advantage of a lightness illusion to hasten bedtime—as some children realize. The Finnish-American poet Anselm Hollo captured this idea by putting the following words into the mouth of a 4-year-old:

switch on the light
so it gets dark outside
and we can go
to bed.
(1977, p. 30)

The Neural Architecture of
ON and OFF Regions

We have more to learn about ganglion cells and their center/surround properties. But now is a good time to look more closely at the cells in the intermediate layers of the retina, for it is those cells that are responsible for the spatial layout of ON and OFF regions. Look at Figure 3.6, a highly magnified schematic of the arrangement of the retina's parts at one small location. Let's concentrate on the three types of cells that lay between the photoreceptors and the ganglion cells.

First, notice that the photoreceptors (shown pointing upward in this drawing) are interconnected by laterally spreading cells, aptly named "horizontal cells." Any horizontal cell may be in contact with dozens of neighboring photoreceptors, and each photoreceptor makes contact with several horizontal cells. Each and every horizon-

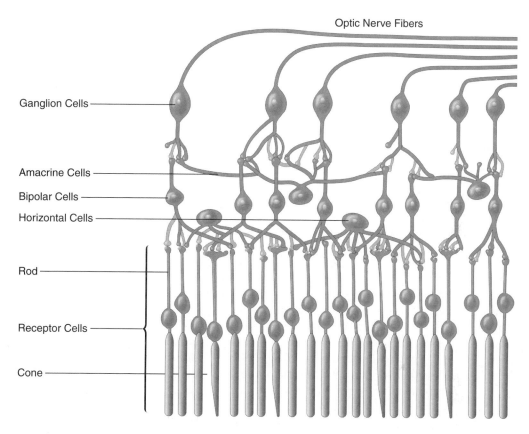

FIGURE 3.6
A magnified view of retinal cells.

tal cell does only one thing: it modifies the strength of the signals generated by its neighboring photoreceptors.

It's an ingenious arrangement. Any one horizontal cell receives input from a cluster of photoreceptors and, in turn, provides input back to those very photoreceptors. Horizontal cells turn down (attenuate) the strength of the signals generated by those individual photoreceptors. This attenuation most strongly affects those photoreceptors whose signals are the weakest to begin with. The more active photoreceptors are less affected and, hence, their signals become *relatively* larger. Thus, when one small cluster of photoreceptors within the neighborhood is more active

than the rest, the horizontal cell accentuates the strength of their signals relative to the signals in the other, less active photoreceptors. This feedback arrangement accentuates differences in photoreceptor signals, differences that can be traced to locations in the retinal image where there are transitions in the spatial distribution of light. Horizontal cells, in other words, amplify photoreceptor signals associated with edges—they are a fundamental part of the lateral inhibition described above.

But how are these modified photoreceptor signals conveyed to the ganglion cells? Here's where the bipolar cells enter the picture. As you can see in Figure 3.6, they, too, make synaptic

Neural

contact with the photoreceptors. Their receiving ends are tucked into the spaces at the terminal ends of the photoreceptors where the transmitter substance glutamate is released. The bipolar cells generate electrical signals, and the strength of those signals is proportional to the amount of glutamate they receive. Of course, the amount of glutamate they receive is determined by the amount of light energy captured by the photoreceptors. Interestingly, the bipolar cells come in two varieties: one type responds positively to *decreases* in glutamate concentration, while the other responds positively to *increases* in glutamate concentration. Remember that photoreceptors release glutamate in inverse proportion to the amount of light they receive. The more light, the less glutamate, and vice versa. So bipolar cells that respond positively to a *drop* in glutamate levels are signalling an *increase* in light level, while bipolar cells that respond to an *increase* in glutamate levels are signalling a *decrease* in light level. Now we can begin to understand how photoreceptor signals are transformed into ON and the OFF components within the receptive fields of ganglion cells—the bipolar cells provide the circuitry for the two types of ganglion cells.

Actually, there are at least a dozen different kinds of bipolar cells in the human retina. They differ in both size and the patterns of connections they make with rod and cone photoreceptors and with ganglion cells. But they all do essentially the same thing: recombine photoreceptor signals (which have been modified by horizontal cell connections) and pass those recombined signals to the ganglion cells.

What about the amacrine cells? Relatively little is known about their role in retinal processing. We do know that amacrine cells receive inputs from bipolar cells and, in turn, modify the responses of those bipolar cells. (In this respect, amacrine cells behave like feedback cells, comparable to the horizontal cells.) It is thought that amacrine cells may influence the temporal dynamics of ganglion cells, meaning how vigorously they respond over time.

In summary, the network of cells in the retina's intermediate layer form the circuitry underlying the center/surround layout of ganglion cell receptive fields. Figure 3.7 shows how these elements are thought to be interconnected within the circuitry for one, ON-center ganglion cell. The central portion of the cell's receptive field is "constructed" from signals collected from a relatively small, circular patch of neighboring photoreceptors. For an ON-center cell like the one we're considering, those photoreceptors' signals are registered by inverting-type bipolar cells, which become more electrically positive when their contributing photoreceptors become more electrically negative (as they do when light levels increase). These positive electrical responses are passed on to the ganglion cell, giving that cell its ON-center response. The surround portion of this ON-cell's receptive field arises from signals collected from a larger, concentrically arranged circular patch of photoreceptors. The signals from this larger collection of photoreceptors are registered by noninverting-type bipolar cells that become electrically more negative when the photoreceptors decrease their responses. These negative electrical responses are passed on to the ganglion cell, giving the cell its OFF-surround response. Note, by the way, that the central interior of this surrounding region includes the same photoreceptors that contribute to the center.

To show the net outcome of this center/surround arrangement, we can plot the sensitivity of the ON-center and OFF-surrounding regions in the manner shown in Figure 3.8. It is conventional to use a pair of bell-shaped curves (called Gaussian curves) to depict the responsiveness of the center and surrounding portions. The center and surrounding Gaussian curves subtract from one another, yielding a resultant called the difference of Gaussians (or **DoG curve,** for short). A DoG curve provides a good approximation of the spatial layout of most retinal ganglion cells. It is simple to apply the same scheme to the construction of an OFF-center receptive field, just by inverting

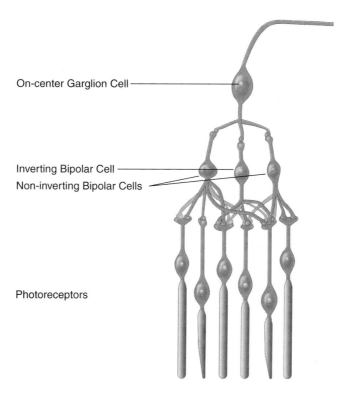

On-center Garglion Cell

Inverting Bipolar Cell
Non-inverting Bipolar Cells

Photoreceptors

FIGURE 3.7
Schematic showing how a center/surrounding area receptive field is "constructed" through interconnecting retinal cells.

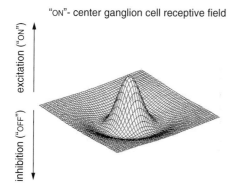

"ON"- center ganglion cell receptive field

excitation ("ON")

inhibition ("OFF")

FIGURE 3.8
Sensitivity profile of a retinal ganglion cell with center/ surrounding area organization.

the signs of the two Gaussians contributing to the center and surround.

This completes our overview of the intermediate circuitry within the retina, and we'll be referring back to this stage of processing in subsequent discussions. But armed with this expanded view, we're now ready to return to the ganglion cells, to learn more about the neural messages they encode and transmit to the brain. To do this, let's imagine that we've moved our microelectrode from ganglion cell to ganglion cell, determining what visual pattern of light produces the most vigorous responses in each cell. In the course of this exercise, we would discover several important receptive field properties.

Receptive Field Size

The sizes of receptive fields vary systematically with retinal location (Wiesel and Hubel, 1960; de Monasterio and Gouras, 1975). Receptive fields in the center of the retina, within the macula, are quite small, with some on the order of 0.01 millimeters. Cells with these centrally placed receptive fields monitor tiny areas of the visual world wherever the monkey is looking. As you move away from the macula into the periphery of the retina, you find that the receptive fields grow increasingly larger. In fact, 10 millimeters away from the fovea, receptive field centers may be as large as 0.5 millimeters, 50 times larger than their foveal counterparts. Cells with these peripherally placed receptive fields collect information from larger areas of the retina. Figure 3.9 graphs the relation between receptive field size and retinal location. The horizontal axis represents the reti-

nal location around which the receptive field was centered; "fovea" stands for the center of the macula. The vertical axis is the diameter of the center portion of the receptive field. Note that with increasing **eccentricity**—deviation from the center of the retina—the size of receptive fields tends to increase.

In and around the fovea, receptive fields are quite small, so it naturally takes more ganglion cells to cover a given area of retina in the fovea compared to more peripheral parts of the retina. In fact, the fovea accounts for only about 2 percent of the total retinal area, whereas about 33 percent of all ganglion cells are devoted to the neural analysis of image features within this small, but critically important, retinal territory.

The graph in Figure 3.9 also reveals another important fact. At each of the various eccentricities, we have data for more than just a single re-

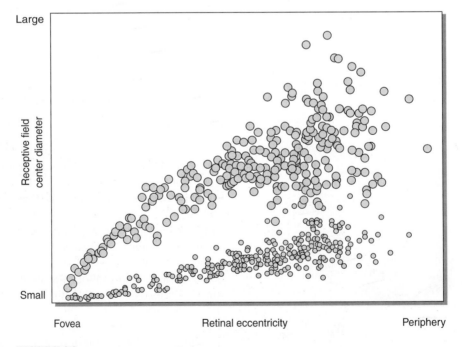

FIGURE 3.9
Graph showing how the sizes of receptive field centers increase with distance from the fovea. The size of the entire receptive field is larger than just the center diameter, since the entire receptive field consists of a center *and* a surround.

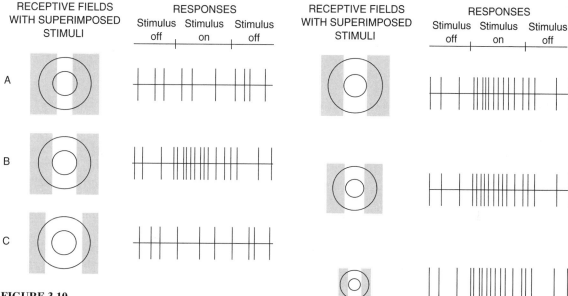

FIGURE 3.10
A single ON-center receptive field responding to bars of
light of varying width.

FIGURE 3.11
Three ON-center receptive fields with different-sized
receptive fields responding to bars of light of matching
width.

ceptive field. Comparing data collected at the
same eccentricity, we see that not all receptive
fields at that eccentricity have exactly the same
size. Because these size differences occur at a
single locality on the retina, the phenomenon is
known as *local variation.* So the sizes of receptive fields differ in two ways: first, they vary with
retinal eccentricity; second, they vary locally. In
fact, we see two clusters of receptive field sizes at
different eccentricities, a point we shall return to
in a moment.

Think what this variation in receptive field size
means for the sort of stimulus that would be best
suited to activate a particular cell. As shown in
Figure 3.10, there is one bar width size (panel B)
that elicits the best response from that cell. Bars
smaller (panel A) or larger (panel C) than this produce a less than optimum response. As you can
see in Figure 3.11, cells with small receptive
fields will respond best to small objects, while
those with large receptive fields will prefer larger
objects. This principle suggests that analysis of
object size may be inaugurated in the retina.

Three Types of Retinal Ganglion Cells

So far we've distinguished retinal ganglion cells
on the basis of receptive field size and center type
(ON versus OFF). But retinal ganglion cells differ
in other ways, some of which are particularly relevant for understanding vision. These differences
form the bases for classifying ganglion cells into
one of three groups, the **M cells,** the **P cells** and
the **K cells** (Hendry and Calkins, 1998). *M* stands
for magnocellular, *P* for parvocellular* and *K* for
koniocellular. These three terms refer to the three
classes of brain cells to which the M, P and K
cells relay their neural impulses. Let's survey
some major differences among these three cell

---

*Some researchers refer to the P and M ganglion cells as
"parasol" and "midget" cells, respectively. These terms are
derived from the anatomical shapes of the two classes of ganglion cells.

types. We'll start by contrasting the M and P cells, which have been studied in much more detail than the K cells.

Seen under a microscope, M cells are larger than P cells, and the M's axon is thicker. This means that neural impulses travel more rapidly to the brain over M cell axons, since the conduction velocity of neural impulses increases with axon thickness. Second, these two types of cells differ greatly in number, with approximately 80 percent of all primate ganglion cells belonging to the P class. Third, at any given retinal eccentricity, the receptive fields of P cells are several times smaller than the receptive fields of M cells. (This difference is responsible for much of the vertical scatter in receptive field size seen in Figure 3.9.) The difference in field size between P and M cells means that P cells will respond better to small objects than will M cells (recall Figure 3.9). Fourth, M cells respond well to very small differences in light levels in center and surround. P cells require greater contrasting difference in light between center and surround portions of the receptive field before they will respond strongly (Kaplan, Shapley, and Purpura, 1988). This distinction between cell types suggests that M cells may be especially important for the perception of objects of low contrast, such as dark gray letters on a medium gray background. P cells may be more important for seeing high-contrast objects, such as black letters on a white background. Fifth, M cells respond well even when a visual stimulus is turned on and off very quickly, whereas P cells respond poorly if at all to such a temporally modulated stimulus. This difference in temporal sensitivity means that M cells are better able to register transient visual events, such as the presence of a rapidly moving object.

The sixth difference between M and P cells is especially intriguing, since it probably relates to color vision. For P cells, an excitatory response is evoked only when the receptive field is stimulated with light of a particular color (for example, red). P cells are inhibited by the presence of another, quite different color (for example, green). For M cells, in comparison, color makes no difference.

They respond to light regardless of color. To illustrate this important difference between P and M cells, imagine looking for a ripe, red apple lying on a lawn of green grass. If the apple and grass reflect the same amount of light (that is, if they are equal in lightness), the M ganglion cells would fail to signal the presence of the apple. Everywhere you look, the responses of the M cells would be the same. The P cells, however, would solve the problem: as your gaze roams over the grass, a P cell sensitive to red would be silent until your gaze brought the image of the apple into the P cell's receptive field, thus evoking a robust response.

Not as much is known about the third class of cells, the ones comprising the koniocellular pathway. Cells in this pathway get their name from the neurons that they innervate in the lateral geniculate nucleus, which we will learn about in Chapter 4. Those geniculate neurons are extremely small (*konis* is Greek for "dust") and, therefore, very difficult to isolate for physiological study. In terms of their response properties, K cells more closely resemble P cells, in that their responses depend on the color of light within their receptive fields. In particular, most K cells are excited by blue light and inhibited by yellow light (Dobkins, 2000). K cells may also play a role in shutting down vision temporarily whenever we move or blink our eyes. Detailed reviews of the K cells are provided by Casagrande (1994) and by Hendry and Reid (2000). Table 1 summarizes these three classes of cells.

TABLE 1
Physiological Properties of P, M and K Cells

Characteristic	P cells	M cells	K cells
Cell size	Small	Large	Very small
Conduction velocity	Slow	Fast	Slow/variable
Cell population percentage	80%	10%	>10%
Spatial resolution	High	Low	Moderate
Temporal resolution	Low	High	High
Contrast sensitivity	Low	Good	Modest

Although P, M and K cells constitute the lion's share of neurons in the retina (over 90 percent of the total), there are other, less researched cell types. These other cell types send their axons to phylogenetically older regions of the brain that are probably involved in the control of eye and head movements. These other cell types are also thought to provide the visual information that drives circadian rhythms and influences your sleep-wake cycle. In contrast, the P, M and K cells, project to higher, phylogenetically newer brain centers mediating visual perception. As you will learn, nature has gone to great lengths to keep separate the information carried to these higher centers by these three classes of cells. In the next chapter, we will learn more about the separate visual pathways that originate from the retina's P, M and K cells, and will discuss further their possible roles in visual perception.

This completes, then, our abbreviated survey of retinal ganglion cells. By examining the workings of the retinal ganglion cells, you have learned several important things about the eye's processing of visual information. You now know that this processing begins with the photoreceptors, which act like an array of tiny photocells, each specifying the level of light falling within the purview of the photoreceptor. These 100 million messages about light intensity are then passed on to a complex network of intermediary cells that integrate information from groups of neighboring photoreceptors. The results of this integration are conveyed to the retinal ganglion cells. Because of the center/surround organization of their receptive fields, the vast majority of ganglion cells are designed to detect differences in light level, or *contrast,* as it is called. These cells are much less concerned with the overall level of light.

In some of these cells, this center/surround organization is designed to extract information about color contrast. This kind of local receptive field analysis is performed over the entire retina by the 1.25 million or so ganglion cells in the eye. Hence, everything you see must have registered its presence within this retinal machinery. The particulars of this machinery necessarily influence the *way* you see. There is no other route to visual perception but through the retinal ganglion cells.

The remainder of this chapter relates certain properties of vision to events occurring in the retina. A few of these events transpire in the photoreceptors, while others occur at the level of the retinal ganglion cells. It's important that you understand what we mean when we claim that some property of vision is caused by the idiosyncrasies of some retinal cell. We are *not* saying that conscious visual perception occurs in the retina. Most visual scientists think that the processes underlying what we call "vision" actually take place in the brain not in the eye.

Instead, we're saying that events in the retina *shape* vision by emphasizing some information (such as differences in light level) and by de-emphasizing other information (such as uniformities). For example, retinal ganglion cells respond very strongly to discontinuities in illumination, and this operating principle reveals itself, sometimes vividly, in visual experience. Potentially important information, in other words, gets accentuated. In contrast, retinal cells fail to respond to images composed of wavelengths longer than 700 nanometers, meaning that the brain receives no information about such images. So some information gets ignored. Thus, even though sight occurs in the brain, the retina preordains much of what we can and cannot see. Brindley (1970) and Teller (1989) discuss the logical bases for attributing perceptual events to the behavior of certain physiological processes.

PERCEPTUAL CONSEQUENCES OF CENTER/SURROUND ANTAGONISM

The preceding section emphasized the antagonism between the center and the surround of a retinal ganglion cell's receptive field. The net response of such a cell is the sum of these two opposing influences. This antagonistic arrangement reorganizes the receptors' raw information into neural signals associated with light/dark boundaries (such as with edges and contours). In the process, center/surround antagonism accentuates those boundaries and, at the same time, de-emphasizes regions where light intensity is uniform. This differential boost given to edge information has led to the popular but controversial idea that the perceived lightness over regions of a surface is related to activity in retinal ganglion cells. In the following sections, we consider a couple of intriguing perceptual illusions that explore the operation of center/surround antagonism in human vision.

From the outset of this discussion, we need to clarify the distinction between the terms "brightness" and "lightness." They're often used interchangeably, but they should be differentiated. Among vision experts, the term "brightness" refers to the amount of light that appears to be arising from a given spatial location. For instance, we may speak of the brightness of the light reflected from, say, a piece of white paper. Brightness also refers to the perceived level of illumination produced by an emitting source. For instance, we may speak of the brightness of a room light or a star. "Lightness" is a property of object surfaces illuminated by light; it depends on the amount of light reflected from the surface of an object (which itself depends on both the amount of light illuminating the object and the amount of that illumination reflected by the surface). Lightness ranges from black, through shades of gray to white. A sheet of white paper is always lighter than a sheet of gray paper, but the gray sheet may look brighter when it is in direct sunlight compared to being in the shade. To reiterate, brightness is a property of light (reflected or emitted), while lightness is a property of surfaces. In most instances, it is the lightness of a surface that we are concerned with. Our everyday activities entail recognizing objects, not light, and surface lightness is one property that aids recognition.

With this distinction in mind, let's take a look at some intriguing visual illusions that have been devised to test retinal mechanisms involving local spatial interactions.

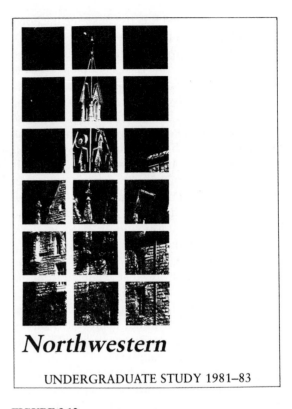

FIGURE 3.12
The cover of a catalog from one of America's outstanding institutions of higher education.

The Hermann Grid

Two decades ago, one of America's well-known private universities published what turned out to be a beguiling cover on the catalog of its course offerings (Figure 3.12). When the catalog was distributed, it generated a stir: viewers experienced what seemed to be spots that disappeared whenever they tried to look directly at them. By inspecting Figure 3.12, you can experience these illusory spots in most of the intersections between the horizontal and vertical white stripes. Note, too, that when you move your eyes to look *directly* at one of these phantom spots, it disappears.

Illusion

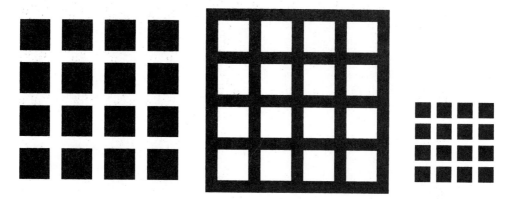

FIGURE 3.13
Three conventional versions of Hermann grids.

Actually, these illusory spots were first described more than a century ago. The pattern inadvertently used by the university resembled what is known as a **Hermann grid,** first described in the nineteenth century by Ludimar Hermann, a German physiologist. More traditional versions of Hermann's grid are shown in Figure 3.13. Looking at the left-hand grid, you'll notice dark spots located in most of the intersections of white horizontal and vertical stripes. Looking at the middle grid (a photographic negative of the other), you'll notice light spots in most of the intersections of black horizontal and vertical stripes. Looking at the right-hand grid (a smaller version of the one on the left), you'll see dark spots at *all* the intersections. Although they are vivid, every one of these spots is illusory. Where, then, do they come from? And why do they appear where they do? It is generally accepted that these illusory spots are the product of center/surround antagonism within receptive fields of retinal ganglion cells.

We'll make use of ON-center receptive fields to explain why spots are seen in the left-hand grid. Two questions must be answered. First, why are the spots that you see located only at intersections between horizontal and vertical stripes, not elsewhere? Second, why do you *not* see a spot located in an intersection when you look directly

at it? To answer the first question, we've drawn receptive fields on Hermann's grid (Figure 3.14). This allows you to compare how the retinal image of the grid would affect the two receptive fields shown, one being stimulated by an intersection and the other stimulated by part of a white stripe that is not at an intersection.

To determine the response of either retinal ganglion cell, we must analyze how each of its components—the center and the surrounding area—would be affected by the grid pattern. Assume that a viewer gazes steadily on the spot labeled "fixation point." Now, note that the centers of both receptive fields receive the same amount of light, but the surrounds receive different amounts. Remember that light falling in an OFF portion of a receptive field reduces that cell's activity. This means that the cell whose receptive field is centered *on* the intersection will respond less than the cell whose receptive field is centered *between* intersections. Consequently, between intersections, the white stripes will look comparatively lighter. Since the reduced response is confined to cells with receptive fields centered on the intersections, one experiences dimming at such locales—gray spots.

Why, though, don't you see a spot in the intersection when you look directly at it? Recall that receptive fields vary in size according to their

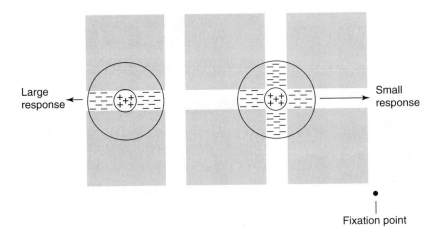

FIGURE 3.14
A possible neural explanation of Hermann grids.

eccentricity, the smallest receptive fields coinciding with the fovea. When you look directly at an intersection, you are using receptive fields whose centers and surrounds are so small that *both* fit completely within the width of a stripe. We've illustrated this in Figure 3.15.

Assume that a person fixates on the right-hand intersection of the grid. As you can see, these small receptive fields all receive the same amount of stimulation within their centers and surround. Consequently, all the cells around the region of fixation will give the same response, whether on the intersection or not. As a result, there will not be any local dimming at that intersection.

To test your understanding of these ideas, see if you can apply this same line of reasoning to the middle grid in Figure 3.13, where light illusory spots are seen. Finally, see if you can explain why spots are seen at *every* intersection, including the one you are fixating on, in the right-hand grid in Figure 3.13.

You might also try looking at Figure 3.13 under very dimly lit conditions. (Be patient; you must let your eyes adapt to the darkness.) You'll be amazed to see that the phantom spots, unlike most apparitions, actually disappear when the lights are low (Wist, 1976). Why should this happen? To give

you a clue, remember that the illusory spots arise because of the surround portions of the receptive fields, which are differentially stimulated depending on what part of the grid they are analyzing. If we were to eliminate the surround's contribution to each cell's response, the spots should disappear. Evidently that's exactly what happens: the surround portions of ganglion cell receptive fields become ineffective at low-light levels, leaving only the center region to generate responses (Barlow, Fitzhugh and Kuffler, 1957).

Some features of the Hermann grid illusion aren't readily explained by the responses of ganglion cells (Wolfe, 1984). For one thing, the number of intersections present in the figure influences the strength of the illusory spots at those intersections. Increasing the number of intersections strengthens the illusion. The regularity of the intersection's spacing also modulates the strength of the illusion. These observations imply that far-reaching influences, not just local center/surround interactions, also play a role in creating these phantom spots.

Let's turn from illusory spots to another peculiarity of human vision that suggests the involvement of center/surround antagonism, Mach bands.

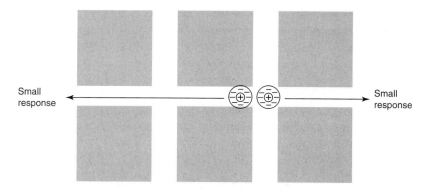

FIGURE 3.15
A possible neural explanation for the absence of local dimming of Hermann grids at the point of fixation.

Mach Bands

Illusion

In Chapter 2 you were introduced to Ernst Mach, the Austrian physicist and philosopher who made important contributions to a number of scientific disciplines during the last part of the nineteenth century and the early part of the twentieth. We're concerned here with one small part of his work. The interested student will find an excellent, highly readable account of Mach's life and work in Ratliff (1965).

Mach became interested in the connection between the intensity of reflected light and the sensation it engendered. To explore this interest, Mach created various patterns out of paper that portrayed gradients of light, ranging from white through gray to black. Mach carefully studied whether perception of the gradients conformed to the actual distribution of light reflected from those patches of paper. In some instances, the two did not correspond. Mach had the great insight that these idiosyncrasies of perception were caused by antagonistic influences within the retina. Because we have much more information about retinal physiology and anatomy than was available to Mach, we are able to infer that these idiosyncrasies could be caused by the center/surround antagonism evidenced in the receptive fields of retinal ganglion cells.

The upper portion of Figure 3.16 shows one of the kinds of patterns Mach developed. The graph below the pattern plots the actual distribution of light intensity in the pattern. The horizontal axis of the graph represents position in the pattern. The vertical axis shows how much light the pattern reflects at that position. From left to right, the graph shows the level of intensity in the pattern increasing in a stepwise fashion. Thus, the pattern really consists of a number of bars, each of uniform intensity and each giving way abruptly to another level.

When you look at the pattern itself, though, you'll notice some things that don't seem to correspond with the graph. In particular, the lightness of each bar does not appear uniform. Take, for example, one of the bars in the middle. One edge—near the bar's left-hand, darker neighbor—seems extra light, whereas the other edge—near the bar's right-hand, lighter neighbor—seems extra dark. In other words, the *lightness* within the bar's interior varies even though the *intensity* of light reflected from the page does not. Most people describe the edges of each bar as having bands, extra dark and extra light regions. These bands are called **Mach bands** in honor of the first person to study them systematically.

These bands, no matter how vivid they may seem, are illusory. They don't exist on the paper,

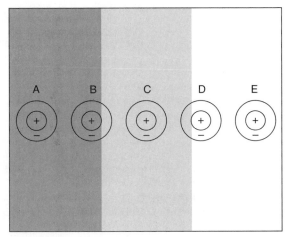

FIGURE 3.17
Possible neural explanation of Mach bands.

FIGURE 3.16
The lightness of each stripe in the pattern (upper portion of the figure) varies even though the intensity of each stripe is constant (lower portion of the figure).

only in your head. To understand the classic explanation of where they come from, consider how the retinal ganglion cells respond to such a pattern of bars. When one looks at the pattern in the upper portion of Figure 3.16, a distribution of light is produced on the retina similar to the distribution shown by the graph in the lower part of Figure 3.16. This distribution of light is broad enough so that it extends across the receptive fields of many retinal ganglion cells. To simplify the discussion, let's consider only three adjacent bars from the pattern (see Figure 3.17). Suppose that the image of the three bars falls on some small number, say five, of ON-center receptive fields (though this assumption is not crucial to our point). These ganglion cells are each responsible for signalling the brain about the intensity of light falling within their individual receptive fields. What sorts of messages would the brain

get if these cells were stimulated by the pattern shown in the upper part of Figure 3.16?

To see what response any cell would give, we must weigh how much light falls in each of its two regions. (Remember the convention: "plus" indicates an ON region, "minus" indicates an OFF region.) Let's take the three easiest ones first. Receptive field *A* (leftmost ganglion cell in Figure 3.17) receives the least light, field *E* the most, and field *C* an intermediate amount of light. Each cell's response will be proportional to the amount of light falling within its receptive field. So the bar *A* "sees" will seem the dimmest; the one *E* "sees," the brightest; and the one *C* "sees," appearing intermediate to the two. That leaves *B* and *D* as the interesting cases.

Receptive field *B*'s center is stimulated by the same level of light as *A*'s. Their respective surrounds, however, are *differentially* stimulated. All of *A*'s surround is dimly illuminated, thereby producing little antagonism to combat the response produced by the center. Although the left part of *B*'s surround is similarly illuminated, the right part is stimulated by the higher light level of the middle bar. As a result, the surround of *B* generates *more* antagonism than does the surround of

A, diminishing the overall response of *B* to a level below that of *A*. Consequently, the region *B* "sees" appears darker than *A* "sees." *B* creates a dark Mach band.

Now consider *D* and *E*. The net response from *D* will be larger than that from *E* because *D*'s surround is partially stimulated by the reduced light from the center bar, rather than by the higher level from the right-hand bar. As a result, *D*'s surround generates *less* antagonism to its center's response, yielding a net response that is *greater* than that from *E*. So the region *D* "sees" will appear lighter than that *E* "sees." *D* creates a light Mach band.

Mach bands emphasize the important distinction between intensity and lightness. **Intensity** is an objective, physical variable, something that a light meter can measure. **Lightness** is a subjective, perceptual variable, whose measurement requires a biological visual system. Often, intensity and lightness covary, with surfaces reflecting more intense light appearing lighter. But Mach bands show that the correlation is not perfect. Although intensity changes in a stepwise fashion, lightness does not.

Mach thought that these illusory bands arose from neural processing within a system that had center/surround antagonism. Numerous investigators since Mach have endorsed this idea and, going one step further, have identified that system as the retinal ganglion cells (for example, Cornsweet, 1970; Ratliff, 1984; Hubel, 1988; Dowling, 1998). Despite the plausibility of this simple, elegant theory, recent work has challenged the idea that center/surround antagonism in the retina provides an adequate account of lightness illusions such as Mach bands. Even when the pattern of retinal stimulation remains constant, the vividness of illusory Mach bands varies depending on how you interpret the surface upon which the intensity gradient appears (Lotto et al., 1999). If the gradient is construed to be a shadow on a flat surface, Mach bands are not nearly as salient as when that same gradient is associated with a curved surface (Figure 3.18). The same light intensity profile, in other words, is

perceived differently simply by changing what it is you think you're looking at. There is no obvious reason why the responses of retinal ganglion cells in the eye should be susceptible to this kind of "cognitive" influence. Consequently, vision

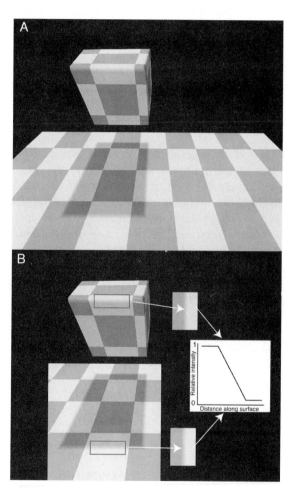

FIGURE 3.18
The vividness of Mach bands depends on the figure's interpretation. Looking at panel A, compare the lightness of the curved edge of the box (the upper outlined region in panel B) with the shadow cast on the textured floor (the lower outlined region in panel B). The two parts of the image are physically identical (as denoted by the graph in panel B), but the Mach band seems more pronounced in the region associated with the surface of the object than in the region of the shadow. (Lotto, Williams and Purves, 1999)

scientists now believe that while the center/surround antagonism in retinal ganglion cells does contribute to Mach bands, such antagonism cannot be the complete explanation.

Next let's consider another illusion of surface lightness, this one known as simultaneous lightness contrast. To set the stage for this illusion, let's perform a few more experiments on the retinal ganglion cells we've been talking about.

Two More Center/Surround Experiments

In the first experiment, we'll compare how a retinal ganglion cell responds when its center is stimulated by light of different intensities while its surround is subjected, in turn, to no illumination, some illumination, and finally, intense illumination. Suppose that we are recording from a retinal ganglion cell of the ON-center variety. Finding the cell's receptive field center, we focus a small spot of light within just that area, avoiding the surround altogether. The test spot is turned on for a second and the resulting number of impulses is recorded. After repeating this procedure with test spots of varying intensities, we plot the results as the curve labeled *A* in Figure 3.19. The graph's vertical axis represents the number of impulses. The horizontal axis represents the light intensity that evoked each response.

The spontaneous activity of the cell (the activity when no light is present at all) is plotted at the extreme left of the horizontal axis. The graph reveals that very weak intensities of light fail to change the cell's spontaneous activity. Notice the arrow extending from curve *A* to the horizontal axis of the figure. It indicates the weakest intensity of light that will evoke a response appreciably different from that occurring with no light at all. In a sense, this is the minimum amount of light that this cell can "distinguish" from complete darkness.

As the spot's intensity increases, the cell's response grows larger. Finally, at some high intensity, the response of the cell *saturates,* meaning that further increases in intensity fail to produce

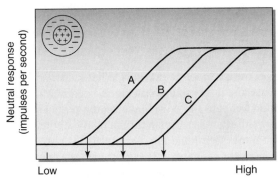

FIGURE 3.19
Graph showing the response of an ON-center ganglion cell to light of varying intensity falling on the center of the cell's receptive field. The three curves represent the effects of different intensities of surrounding stimulation.

corresponding increases in response. As far as this cell is concerned, all spots more intense than the point of saturation are indistinguishable from one another. From the cell's viewpoint, all such spots are equally intense.

Now suppose we repeat this experiment with one notable modification. The small spot again falls in the receptive field center, but now the surround is also illuminated. Again, we vary the intensity of the spot in the receptive field center, holding the surround illumination constant. The cell's response under this condition is shown by curve *B* in Figure 3.19. What are the differences between curves *A* and *B?* For both, arrows extending to the horizontal axis indicate the dimmest intensities that will produce an appreciable change in the cell's spontaneous response rate. As you can see, when the surround is illuminated, the center must be more strongly stimulated in order to change the cell's response. More generally, adding light in the surround reduces the response produced by any given intensity of light in the center. This is another demonstration of antagonistic forces at work: light has opposite effects on the ganglion cell's activity, depending on where the light strikes within the cell's receptive field.

Before considering how these antagonistic forces might influence vision, let's repeat the same basic experiment one more time. Again, the surround is illuminated constantly, but now with a more intense light than was used before. The results of the cell's response to various intensities of light in the center are shown by curve *C* in Figure 3.19. With this strongest light in its surround, the cell requires an even more intense light in its *center* before its response can noticeably increase.

Lightness Contrast and Constancy

How would our vision be affected by ganglion cells that behave in the manner shown in Figure 3.19? Suppose the magnitude of a ganglion cell's response is signalling the brain about the light intensity within its receptive field, with large responses signalling high light levels.* With this assumption in mind, consider Figure 3.20. The two graphs in this figure add several features to what you saw in Figure 3.19. The left-hand graph indicates the three different intensities of light that produce the same response—a *constant response*—from the ganglion cell with various surrounds. This line of constant response is represented by a broken line parallel to the horizontal axis. The vertical arrows extending from each of the three curves to the horizontal axis point out the three different spot intensities that produce the same response from the ganglion cell.

The right-hand graph of Figure 3.20 analyzes the cell's response in a different way. Here we are interested in the response magnitude produced by a central spot of *fixed intensity*. This line of fixed intensity is represented by a broken line parallel to the vertical axis. The horizontal arrows extending from each of the three curves to the vertical axis point out the cell's response to this intensity with various surrounds.

In the left panel, the line of constant response indicates that with various lights in the receptive field's surround, different intensities of *center* stimulation are required to produce the same response. Alternatively, in the right panel, the line of fixed intensity indicates that with various lights in the surround, the same intensity of center stimulation will produce different responses. Both panels highlight the same idea: the cell's response to a stimulus falling in its receptive field center is affected by the level of stimulation in the receptive field surround. Thus, the messages that the brain will get about exactly the same stimulus will vary depending on how much light is falling in the receptive field of the surround.

From the behavior illustrated in these two panels, one might conclude that ganglion cell responses provide unreliable information about lightness. Does this seeming unreliability disqualify ganglion cells as carriers of lightness information? The answer is, "No." Although the cell's behavior (as represented in Figure 3.20) would certainly produce errors of perception, the errors would have two sorts of consequences, one good and one not so good. Let's consider the not-so-good one first.

The right-hand panel of Figure 3.20 shows that a retinal ganglion cell could send the brain rather different messages about a spot of fixed intensity, depending on what other light happens to fall in the cell's surround. Translating this into perceptual terms, objects identical in intensity could appear different in lightness. In fact, such an outcome is experienced. Figure 3.21 demonstrates this effect, called **lightness contrast.** The two center regions are equal in *physical* intensity, but they appear different in lightness. To verify that both center regions are identical in intensity, you must eliminate the influence of their surrounds. In a piece of paper, cut a hole just slightly smaller than either spot. Position the hole over each spot in turn, occluding the surround in each case. By looking only at the spots, without contamination by their surrounds, you will see that both are identical in lightness. This proves that the different

---

*The following analysis holds for ON-center cells. A corresponding, separate analysis could be made for OFF-center cells whose increased activity signals increasing darkness.

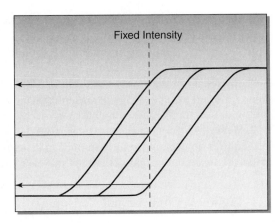

Intensity of light falling on receptive field's center

FIGURE 3.20

Two graphs showing the response of an ON-center ganglion cell to light of varying intensity falling on the center of the cell's receptive field. The left graph shows that a single, constant response (broken horizontal line) can be produced by several different intensities, depending on the amount of light falling on the cell's surround. The right graph shows that a fixed intensity of light (broken vertical line) can produce several different levels of neural response.

FIGURE 3.21

Demonstration of simultaneous lightness contrast. Both central disks are physically the same.

surrounds are responsible for the differences in perceived lightness. This perceptual outcome means that one's judgments about lightness can be in error by a substantial amount—a seemingly disadvantageous consequence.

Lightness contrast represents a case where the *same* physical intensity can yield differences in perceived lightness. The converse also occurs—*different* physical intensities can yield the *same* lightness. This routinely happens when you view an object under different levels of light. Under such conditions, your perception of lightness

tends to remain constant despite variations in the amount of light falling on the retina. This phenomenon is called **lightness constancy.** You can demonstrate lightness constancy for yourself. Hold an object, such as an aspirin tablet, under strong light, and notice how light the object looks. Then dim the lights. As the amount of light falling on the aspirin falls, so does the amount of light reflected from the aspirin to your eye. Nonetheless, its lightness remains unchanged over a fairly wide range of light levels. This constancy of perceived lightness is the good perceptual error alluded to above.

Why do we characterize constancy as "good"? You might argue that lightness constancy means the human visual system is flawed—perception of light intensity fails to keep pace with the actual changes in light reflected from the aspirin tablet. But in fact, it's lucky that perception fails in this manner, for it allows recognition of an object even when the level of illumination change drastically. Because of this "flaw," the surface appearance of an object remains constant despite changes in the surface's level of illumination. After all, we are more concerned with seeing objects than with judging the level of illumination of those objects.

To understand how lightness constancy works, return once more to retinal ganglion cells. Let's measure the response of the retinal ganglion cell when a light of intensity x is flashed inside a surround several times more intense than the spot. For example, let the surround be three times the intensity of the spot, or $3x$. We now vary *both* the spot and the surround intensities, being careful to keep them in a ratio of 3 to 1. So long as this ratio remains constant, the ganglion cell will give the same neural response when the spot appears within the center. Assuming the retinal ganglion cell's response signals lightness, this invariant response means that lightness of the spot will remain constant even though the actual light from the spot is changing. The same result holds for most other ratios between the spot and its surround. This ratio explanation of lightness constancy was suggested by Hans Wallach (1963), a pioneer in the field of human perception.

Now let's apply this ratio principle to the illumination of real objects, not just circular spots of light. Lay a dark-colored pen down on a piece of white paper. Because the paper reflects more light, it looks lighter than the pen. No surprise here. Using a light meter, we could actually measure the amount of light reflected by these objects. Typically, a clean piece of white paper reflects about 80 percent of the light falling on it; depending on its color, the pen might reflect about 10 percent, giving us a ratio of 8 to 1.

Now take a strong desk lamp and shine its light on both pen and paper. More light is falling on the pen than before you turned the lamp on. Consequently, more light is being reflected from the pen into your eyes. But the pen looks no lighter than before (lightness constancy). The reason is that with the lamp on, more light is also being reflected from the paper. Since the ratio of light from the paper to light from the pen (8:1) is unchanged, with more light coming from *both*,

perceived lightness remains unchanged. Recent research shows just how robust the ratio explanation can be. Under the proper conditions, observers exhibit lightness constancy, even though the overall level of illumination varies by more than 1 million to 1 (Jacobsen and Gilchrist, 1988). Of course, if you did something to alter that ratio (such as illuminating *just* the pen), lightness constancy would fail: the lightness of the pen would change as you varied the amount of light falling on it alone. As Box 3.2 shows, under certain conditions, lightness constancy does indeed fail.

Although the ratio between the amounts of light reflected from two adjacent retinal areas can explain many aspects of lightness constancy (and its failures), these ratios don't tell the whole story. Alan Gilchrist of Rutgers University (1977, 1988) has identified several conditions where lightness constancy and lightness contrast are influenced by factors that have nothing to do with retinal mechanisms. In one study, for instance, Gilchrist showed that the perceived lightness of a piece of gray paper varied dramatically, depending on whether it was perceived to lie in front of or behind the background against which it was viewed. When the paper rested directly on a dark background, it appeared light. But when it was positioned some distance in front of the background, the gray paper appeared darker. These changes in perceived lightness occurred even though the amount of light reflected to the eye from the paper and from the background remained unchanged. Here, then, lightness perception varied even though adjacent retinal areas were receiving unchanging amounts of light. This finding is reminiscent of Mach bands, where the illusion's strength depended on what you thought you were seeing.

Top-down

M.I.T. psychologist Edward Adelson (1993) published an equally dramatic demonstration of knowledge's effect on perceived lightness. A version of his illusion is shown in Figure 3.22. Look first at the array of patches in the left-hand part of the figure and compare the appearance of the

BOX 3.2

WHEN LIGHTNESS CONSTANCY FAILS

Usually lightness constancy works, keeping you from erroneous interpretations of what you are seeing. But when constancy fails, it fails dramatically, as the following incident suggests. Some years ago, one of us (R. S.) woke up, looked at his sleeping wife lying next to him, and was shocked. Overnight, a large patch of her hair had turned silvery white (it had been brown the night before). He could not imagine what terrible nightmare could possibly have made a patch of her hair go white in just a few hours.

Reaching over to touch the strange patch, he discovered the silvery appearance was illusory. In fact, when he touched her hair, his hand also turned silvery. Despite this temporary disfigurement of his hand, he was relieved that he wouldn't have to break the news about her hair to his wife.

But why did this illusion occur? The partially open shutters passed a narrow beam of light into the room, illuminating part of his sleeping wife's hair without illuminating anything else in the room. In 1929, the psychologist Adhemar Gelb showed that this sort of arrangement—illumination confined to one object with no illumination of its surrounding area—tends to defeat lightness constancy. Perhaps you've had a more common version of this experience while walking in a forest dappled with sunlight. Suddenly, you come upon a large, shiny coin on the ground. Bending down to pick it up, you discover it is a leaf that had been illuminated by a narrow beam

of light coming through the branches of a tree. Here, again, constancy failed. The lightness of the leaf was so much inflated relative to its background that the leaf appeared to shine like silver.

Some researchers have tried to relate this breakdown of lightness constancy to the viewer's lack of knowledge, a cognitive explanation. Usually, these researchers follow the line of Hermann Helmholtz, who said that lightness constancy depends on an "unconscious inference" about the true conditions of stimulation. According to this theory, constancy breaks down when the viewer is confused about the actual level of illumination (Williams, McCoy and Purves, 1998). It would seem to follow, then, that lightness judgments should be corrected if the confusion is eliminated. Yet this doesn't necessarily happen. For instance, even after R. S. recognized the illusory nature of his nighttime experience, the silvery appearance of his wife's hair persisted. Knowledge of the correct stimulus conditions did not override the illusory perception of lightness (see also Hurvich and Jameson, 1966).

These failures of lightness constancy, and the inability of mental effort to remedy them, reinforce the idea that lightness constancy depends, at least in part, on lateral interactions within the visual system, interactions that are initiated by the registration of different amounts of light from adjacent areas of the field.

---

patches labelled a_1 and a_2. Patch a_1 appears much darker than a_2 but, in fact, they're identical. (If you find this hard to believe, punch two small holes in a piece of paper and view the two patches in isolation from their surroundings.) Next, look at the right-hand part of the figure, this time comparing patches b_1 and b_2. This pair looks much more similar, yet they're physically identical to patches a_1 and a_2. Your perception of these patches is being strongly influenced by the three-dimensional appearance of the image. In the con-

figuration on the left, patch a_1 appears to be a dark gray patch that is brightly illuminated, whereas patch a_2 is a light gray patch that is dimly illuminated. In the configuration on the right, however, both patches appear to receive the same level of illumination and, therefore, appear about equal in lightness. Retinal ganglion cells know nothing about the 3D layout of objects. Thus, these cells should be insensitive to the global context in which the patches appear. Evidently, then, retinal mechanisms cannot fully ac-

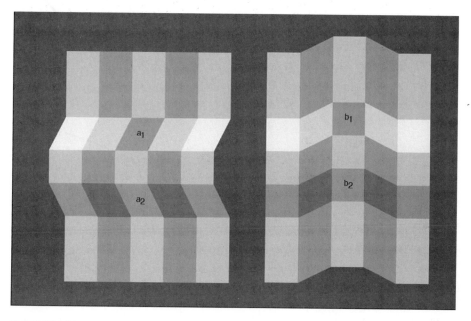

FIGURE 3.22
The vividness of simultaneous lightness contrast depends on how you interpret the 3D layout of the scene; see text for details. (Edward Adelson.)

count for illusions of surface lightness. We must look beyond the eye to the brain for a complete account of these illusions (for clues about brain areas that might be involved in perception of surface lightness, see Rossi, Rittenhouse and Paradiso, 1996).

Despite what these demonstrations may seem to indicate, the retina does play a role in signalling lightness levels within local regions of the image. Even with his compelling demonstrations, Adelson (1993) acknowledges that retinal processes contribute to illusions of lightness and brightness. No one would deny that retinal signals are crucially involved in registering information about surface perception. To the contrary, retinal ganglion cells are the *only* vehicles for communicating visual information from the eye to the brain. Everything that we see—whether veridical or illusory—must be represented in the neural activity among the 1.25 million ganglion cells of each eye. Without a doubt, their receptive field properties help shape the world that we see.

SENSITIVITY VERSUS RESOLUTION

Aspects of Convergence

Earlier we noted that over the entire retina, information from 100 million photoreceptors converges on about 1.25 million retinal ganglion cells. This suggests an average convergence, over the entire retina, of about 80 photoreceptors to 1 ganglion cell. But this summary statistic is actually a little misleading.

Suppose we examine the number of receptors and the corresponding number of ganglion cells locally in different small patches throughout the retina, ranging from the macula to the periphery. For each patch of retina, we can calculate the degree of convergence by taking the ratio of receptors

Photoreceptors

Amacrine and
bipolar cells

ON ganglion cells

FIGURE 3.23
A ganglion cell receiving input from just a few receptors (left-hand example)
has a smaller receptive field and, thus, responds best to small stimuli. A cell
receiving input from more receptors (right-hand example) has a larger
receptive field and responds poorly to small stimuli.

to retinal ganglion cells. This calculation reveals two important facts. First, the convergence ratio varies widely and systematically from one part of the retina to another. Second, near the center of the macula, the convergence ratio approaches unity—about one photoreceptor per ganglion cell—whereas in the periphery of the retina, the ratio is several hundred to one. In other words, there is a strong connection between retinal eccentricity and the amount of convergence. The connection is so strong that it suggests the operation of some grand plan. What might that plan be? To answer this question, we need to explain what is gained and what is lost by this neural convergence. As we proceed, keep in mind that the extent of receptor to ganglion

cell convergence is directly related to the ganglion cell's receptive field size. The greater the number of receptors contributing to the receptive field of a given ganglion cell, the larger that cell's receptive field. This principle is illustrated schematically in Figure 3.23. Two ganglion cell receptive fields are shown schematically in the top panel, one small (left) and one large (right). Note that fewer photoreceptors contribute input to the small receptive field compared to the larger receptive field. We'll get to the bottom part of the drawing in a moment.

To picture the consequences of convergence, consider an extreme form of convergence. Suppose your eye had only a single retinal ganglion cell—a convergence ratio of 100 million to 1. In effect, your entire retina would be the receptive field for this solitary cell. How would your vision differ from its present form? It's certain that your vision would be changed in two ways, one for the good, one for the bad.

We'll start with the bad. With only one retinal ganglion cell to tell your brain what the eye saw, you would not be able to read or watch television. In fact, you would be virtually blind. Imagine the problem the brain faces with this solitary retinal ganglion cell as its only link to the visual world. The brain would be unable to distinguish different distributions of light falling on the back of the eye; all distributions would have the same effect on the cell. You would confuse letters of the alphabet and be unable to recognize your friends by sight. In brief, your resolution would be awful—not a good situation.

Resolution refers to the ability to distinguish differences in the spatial distribution of light in an image. The best-known measure of resolution is **visual acuity,** which we will discuss in a moment. With only one retinal ganglion cell to "describe" the image on the retina, your resolution would be nil. So long as the total light falling on the retina remained constant, you wouldn't be able to distinguish one letter of the alphabet from another—even with extremely large, headline type. You don't need to go to the extremes of our single-ganglion-cell example to discover that convergence is incompatible with good resolution. Generally, greater degrees of convergence lead to poorer resolution. That's because when visual information from a large region of space converges onto a single ganglion cell, the visual system inevitably loses track of exactly where within that region of space the information originated. That is why *convergence is the enemy of resolution.*

To see this enemy in action, look at the distribution of light within the ON and OFF regions of the two receptive fields shown in the bottom panel of Figure 3.23. Although the cell with the larger receptive field receives input from a larger number of receptors, responses to the dark and light contours would cancel one another. As a result, this cell would fail to respond to the pattern that is superimposed on the receptive field. In contrast, the cell with the smaller receptive field, receiving input from fewer receptors, would give a vigorous response to the pattern, since the light and dark portions of the pattern "fit" within this cell's receptive field profile. The smaller receptive field has superior visual acuity because convergence—the enemy of resolution—is more limited for this cell.

Now for the good news about convergence. Let's begin with two hypothetical ganglion cells, A and B. Suppose A receives input from a large array of neighboring receptors while B receives input from just a small cluster of neighboring receptors. How well are these two different ganglion cells able to signal the presence of dim light? In other words, how sensitive to light are the two cells? You've learned that for a ganglion cell's activity to change, it must receive a sufficient amount of transmitter substance from the bipolar cells. In effect, a retinal ganglion cell weighs all the neurochemical "evidence" it receives and "decides" whether the cumulative evidence exceeds some minimum threshold. If that threshold is exceeded, the ganglion cell's activity level is altered, signalling the brain that a visual event is occurring. In weighing the cumulative evidence, the ganglion cell disregards which particular bipolar cells (and, hence, which photoreceptors) provides the individual pieces of evidence. From the ganglion cell's perspective, only the total is important. With this in mind, let's compare the abilities of ganglion cells A and B to inform the brain about the presence of dim light imaged on the retina.

For this comparison, we'll use a large but dim spotlight that can be centered on either ganglion cell's receptive field. Let's start with ganglion cell B, the one receiving input from a small cluster of photoreceptors. Even though the image of the dim spot fills this cell's receptive field, the receptors would give a weak response to the light. Some of these weak photoreceptor messages get passed along to cells in the intermediate layers of the retina, but those cells, too, will generate weak messages at best. As a result, ganglion cell *B* may well receive too little transmitter substance to disturb its spontaneous activity. So this ganglion cell will fail to inform the brain that a dim spot of light is present.

What about ganglion cell *A,* the one receiving input from a much larger array of photoreceptors? These photoreceptors will also give a weak response because the light is dim. But there will be substantially more photoreceptors contributing weak signals to the ganglion cell via the bipolars. The ganglion cell, therefore, will receive more transmitter substance ("evidence"), thereby increasing its chances of being activated. Consequently, the brain is much more likely to receive messages about the dim spotlight.

The principle is simple: increasing the number of receptors contributing input to a retinal ganglion cell allows weak signals to be summed, yielding a total input strong enough to change the activity of that ganglion cell. A retinal ganglion cell sums weak signals originating from an array of retinal locations, an ability known as **spatial summation.** Spatial summation enables you to see very dim light. In other words, it enhances the sensitivity of your eyes. Because summation depends on convergence, one can say that *convergence is the ally of sensitivity.*

Note the conflict. On the one hand, convergence is a prerequisite for high sensitivity; on the other, convergence interferes with good resolution. To design an eye that detects very dim lights *and* possesses good spatial resolution represents a real challenge.

The Duplex Solution   How do your eyes manage to resolve these two conflicting demands—resolution and sensitivity? To answer this question, let's return to an analogy we've already used, the analogy between the eye and a camera.

Photographers face the same kinds of problems we've been discussing. Some types of film, such as those used for night-time surveillance, have extremely *large* grains of photosensitive

material and, thereby, a high sensitivity to light. This makes such film usable at very low light levels. (As you may know, a film's light sensitivity is indexed by its ISO or ASA rating.) Highly sensitive films usually have relatively poor resolution. They don't produce very sharp photographs.

Other types of film, such as the microfilm used by librarians, have exceedingly *small* grains of photosensitive material and therefore produce very sharp photographs (even in huge enlargements). However, these types of film work properly only at relatively high light levels. With film, then, as with the eye, there is a trade-off between resolution and sensitivity. The photographer can solve this dilemma by simply changing the film in the camera, matching the film to the available light. The eye, however, doesn't allow the capability of loading and unloading different types of film as needed. In fact, this is unnecessary because the "film" in the eye is **duplex,** meaning that the eye contains two types of photosensitive elements (or "films"). One—associated with the rod photoreceptors—provides high sensitivity to light; the other—associated with the cone photoreceptors—provides high resolution. In the human eye, the two types of "film" occupy somewhat different locations along the back of the eye.

To see how this duplex arrangement works, think back to the convergence of receptors onto ganglion cells. Recall that the central region of the eye (where cones predominate) has very little convergence. Hence, it has excellent resolution but only average sensitivity to light. Peripheral regions of the retina (where rods predominate) have high degrees of convergence, hence poor resolution but good light sensitivity. (For further discussion of high sensitivity, see Box 3.3.)

The preceding chapter pointed out that the center of the primate retina contains mainly cones and very few rods. As a result, activity of retinal ganglion cells with receptive fields near the center of the retina reflects mainly the responses of cones. Because of the predominance of rods in the retinal periphery, activity of ganglion cells with receptive fields in that region re-

BOX 3.3

ADDING PHOTONS OVER TIME AND SPACE

Multiple factors govern the eye's sensitivity. Some have already been discussed—the wavelength of light, its intensity and spatial pattern, and where on the retina the stimulus falls. But there are two other, very important variables: its duration and its size.

To understand the importance of duration and size, we must consider exactly what events need to occur before one can detect a very weak stimulus. Suppose that seeing the stimulus requires that the photoreceptors absorb some small number of photons—a **photon** being the smallest unit of light energy. (The actual number of photons doesn't matter so long as it is greater than 1.) Imagine that we split the stimulus into two installments, each intense enough to cause the receptors to absorb exactly one-half the total number of photons needed for seeing. Now let's introduce one condition: allow 1 hour to elapse between delivery of the first and second installments of photons. Will you see the stimulus? No, because by the time the second installment of photons arrives, the effects of the first installment will have long since disappeared.

Granting that an hour's delay is unreasonable, how much time can elapse between installments of photons before the effects of the first installment completely dissipate? Photoreceptors have a limited memory—called **temporal summation**—with the rods' "memory" being somewhat longer than that of the cones. But whichever system is stimulated, the shorter the interval between the two installments, the greater the chances that the residue of the first installment will be available to add to the effects of the second. Delivering all the photons within a very short time period guarantees that effects produced by the earliest photons will add to those of the later ones. If the stimulus is stretched out in time, a greater *total* number of photons must be delivered to the eye, since losing the advantage of temporal summation makes each photon less efficient.

This fact has been formalized as **Bloch's Law,** which states that a constant product of light intensity and time will be equally detectable. Sometimes Bloch's Law is expressed as

$$I \times T = C$$

where I stands for intensity, T for time, and C for constant visual effect. Bloch's Law says that time can be traded for intensity. Lengthening the presentation of some relatively weak light makes it just as visible as another, more intense light that is presented only briefly. So long as each has the same product (of intensity and time), the two stimuli contain the same total energy and will be equally detectable. These relationships are depicted in the figure at the end of this box. There, the vertical axis represents the stimulus intensity that is just barely detectable (I), and the horizontal axis represents the stimulus's duration (T). Two lines are shown on the graph, one representing the behavior of the scotopic system, the other representing the behavior of the photopic system. Bloch's Law predicts that data should fall on an oblique line, of 45 degrees slope. Note that in both lines this prediction holds when the durations are relatively short.

For the rods, Bloch's Law breaks down at about one-tenth of a second. For cones, it breaks down much earlier, at about one-twentieth of a second or less (Hood and Finkelstein, 1986). These values reflect the temporal memories—temporal summation—of the two systems.

There is a *spatial* analog to the *temporal* law just discussed. We mentioned before that many photoreceptors will share a single collector cell. In other words, the

BOX 3.3 continued

collector cell adds together signals from spatially separate sources—two or more photoreceptors—a capacity referred to in the text as spatial summation.

Suppose we take a very small stimulus and by trial and error determine how intense it must be in order to be just detectable. This stimulus causes the absorption of a minimum, or threshold, number of photons. If we distribute that same number of photons widely over the retina, seeing will not result. The spatially dispersed photons stimulate photoreceptors that do not contribute to the same collector cells. As a result, the opportunity for cooperative effect is reduced.

Within certain limits, all stimuli having the same product of intensity *and* area will be equally detectable. This is not completely surprising since any two stimuli having the same product of area and intensity contain identical amounts of total light. This trade-off between intensity and area is known as

Ricco's Law. Ricco's Law holds only in the fovea; and even there, it holds only for very small stimuli.

We don't want to leave you with the idea that the visual system responds *solely* to the number of photons gathered over time and space. If it did respond that way, you'd confuse long, weak flashes with brief, intense ones. This confusion would be particularly strong when flashes of different durations contained the same total number of photons, since according to Bloch's Law, they would be equally detectable. However, even when two flashes contain the same total number of photons (and hence, are equally detectable), people can still discriminate between a long, weak flash and a brief, intense one (Zacks, 1970). In other words, the visual system registers more than just the total number of photons. It also discriminates how those photons are distributed over time. At present, though, it is not known how the visual system manages this discrimination.

flects mainly the influence of rods. As you are about to learn, rods and cones differ in numerous ways important to vision. This means that ganglion cells in the rod-dominated periphery make different contributions to vision than do ganglion cells in the cone-dominated central region of the retina. While some ganglion cells receive input from both rods and cones (Enroth-Cugell, Hertz, and Lennie, 1977), thereby sharing communication pathways to the brain, they tend to operate under different light conditions.

In particular, the rod-dominated ganglion cells support vision even when light levels are several hundred times less than that required by their cone-dominated counterparts. This results partly from the rods' own greater sensitivity (Detwiler, Hodgkin and McNaughton, 1980), as well as greater convergence on rod-dominated retinal ganglion cells. Vision under dimly lit conditions is termed **scotopic** (from the Greek words *skotos,* meaning "darkness," and *opsis,* meaning "sight"). We'll use the term "scotopic vision" to signify vision that depends on rod photoreceptors. You

must keep in mind that these rod signals are still passed through the intermediate retinal layers to ganglion cells, which send those rod-mediated messages to the brain.

The cones—and hence, the ganglion cells innervated indirectly by them—require higher light levels in order to function properly. Thus, vision using this class of photoreceptors is described as **photopic** (from the Greek word *photos,* meaning "light"). Figure 3.24 indicates the light levels considered photopic, and those considered scotopic. This is an important distinction because, as you'll see later, photopic and scotopic vision differ in a number of significant ways. There is a narrow, intermediate range of light levels where both rods and cones operate, and vision in this very limited range is termed **mesopic** (from the Greek word *mesos,* meaning "middle"). In this chapter, we shall concentrate on vision in the much larger photopic and scotopic ranges.

As noted earlier, the eye must satisfy two competing goals, good resolution and good sensitivity. We now discuss each of these goals in turn.

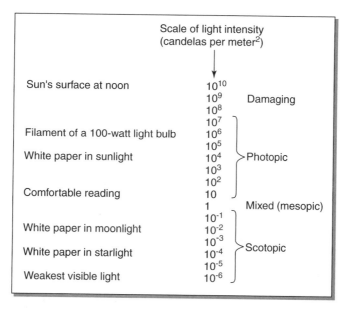

FIGURE 3.24
Scale of light intensity expressed in units called "candelas per square meter," a measure of light energy.

Resolution

Since convergence is the enemy of resolution, the photopic system, having less convergence, should have better resolution. It is estimated that 33 percent of all the retina's ganglion cells receive input from cones occupying the fovea, which itself accounts for only 2 percent of the retina's total area. Thus, we expect resolution to be best in the center of the macula, where the ratio of cones to ganglion cells is about 1 to 1. We do not yet know precisely how the convergence of the cone system changes across the retina (the extensive physiological measurements required to answer that question have yet to be performed). Instead, we must infer the answer using related information: the density of cones at various places on the retina. The solid line in Figure 3.25, labeled "Cones (number)," shows how the number of cones per square millimeter decreases with distance from the fovea (eccentricity). The dotted curve in the same graph shows visual resolution measured for various regions of the

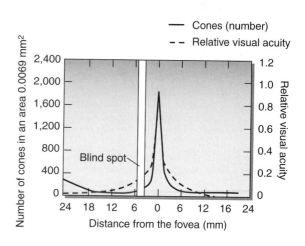

FIGURE 3.25
Graph showing how visual acuity and the number of cone photoreceptors covary with retinal eccentricity. In this graph, a visual acuity of 1.0 corresponds to an image of about 0.005 millimeters in diameter on the retina. Values less than 1.0 correspond to larger images on the retina and, hence, poorer acuity.

retina. This second curve, showing "Relative visual acuity," comes from measurements taken from humans who tried to read a well-lit eye chart while directing their gaze at various distances away from the center of the chart. Fixating in this way causes the letters on the chart to be imaged at different, known places on the retina. Note the fairly good correspondence between the perceptual measurements of resolution (visual acuity) and the anatomical measurements (the number, or density, of cones).

You can see one consequence of the variation in acuity with eccentricity by gazing steadily at any letter on this page. You'll have little trouble recognizing that letter. However, if you're careful not to move your eyes, you'll notice that letters in the periphery appear less distinct. Only the bigger letters, such as those used for the section headings, can be read without looking directly at them. Figure 3.26 (created using a technique described by Anstis, 1998) shows a pair of pictures, one in clear focus and the other progressively blurred from the center outward. The blurred picture simulates the fall-off in visual acuity with eccentricity. Stare directly at the center of the focused picture, maintaining your fixation on the word *stare* in bold. Then stare at the center of the blurred picture, at the word *stare* in bold. If you're careful to maintain strict fixation in each time, the text in the two pictures should look in-

You can see one consequence of the variation in acuity with eccentricity by gazing steadily at any letter on this page. You'll have little trouble recognizing that letter. However, if you're careful not to move your eyes, you'll notice that letters in the periphery appear less distinct; only the bigger letters used for the titles for the section heads can be read without looking directly at them. Figure 3.27 (adapted from Anstis, 1998) shows a pair of pictures, one in clear focus and the other progressively blurred from the center outward. The blurred picture simulates the fall-off in your acuity with eccentricity. **Stare** directly at the center of the focused picture and then stare at the center of the blurred picture -- if you're careful to maintain strict fixation each time, the two pictures should look indistinguishable. That's because your visual system is effectively blurring the details in the top picture everywhere except in the central region where you're looking. The bottom picture, in other words, simulates what you're actually seeing when you look at the top picture. It's remarkable how unaware we are of our relatively poor spatial resolution in the visual periphery.

You can see one consequence of the variation in acuity with eccentricity by gazing steadily at any letter on this page. You'll have little trouble recognizing that letter. However, if you're careful not to move your eyes, you'll notice that letters in the periphery appear less distinct; only the bigger letters used for the titles for the section heads can be read without looking directly at them. Figure 3.27 (adapted from Anstis, 1998) shows a pair of pictures, one in clear focus and the other progressively blurred from the center outward. The blurred picture simulates the fall-off in your acuity with eccentricity. **Stare** directly at the center of the focused picture and then stare at the center of the blurred picture -- if you're careful to maintain strict fixation each time, the two pictures should look indistinguishable. That's because your visual system is effectively blurring the details in the top picture everywhere except in the central region where you're looking. The bottom picture, in other words, simulates what you're actually seeing when you look at the top picture. It's remarkable how unaware we are of our relatively poor spatial resolution in the visual periphery.

FIGURE 3.26
Pair of pictures demonstrating the fall-off in visual resolution in the periphery. Follow the instructions given in the text.

FIGURE 3.27
The photographs on the left and the right simulate the degraded spatial detail present when you fixate on the middle picture. (Wilson Geisler.)

distinguishable. That's because your visual system is effectively blurring the details in the top picture everywhere except in the central region where you're looking. The bottom picture, in other words, simulates what you're actually seeing when you stare at the top picture.

Another excellent example of our blurred peripheral vision can be seen in Figure 3.27 (this one created by Wilson Geisler at the University of Texas). The middle photo is the original, which is sharply focused. Take a moment to look at the eagle's eye and talons in this middle photo. The picture on the left simulates what you're actually seeing when you gaze directly at the eagle's eye in that middle picture. The version on the right simulates what you're actually seeing when you shift your gaze to the eagle's talons in the middle picture. Again, the spatial detail is significantly obscured for portions of the scene falling outside your fovea. It's remarkable how unaware we are of our relatively poor spatial resolution in the visual periphery.

Stuart Anstis was interested in how the ability to recognize letters varies depending on how far from the fovea the letters are imaged. With a person seated 57 centimeters (about 22 inches) from

a bright, white screen, Anstis moved a letter inward from the edge of the screen. Starting far enough away from fixation point so the person could not identify the letter, Anstis brought the letter in, toward the fovea, until the person could recognize the letter. After he did this with letters of various sizes, Anstis found that small letters had to be brought much nearer to the fixation point than did larger letters (Anstis, 1974).

Figure 3.28 demonstrates Anstis's results. Hold the chart a little less than arm's length away from your eyes and stare steadily at the dot in the center. All the letters should be equally legible because the size of the letters increases at the same rate that your visual acuity decreases.

Although the data in Figure 3.25 demonstrate a close connection between visual acuity and the density of cones, cone density is not the entire explanation of visual acuity. Ganglion cell density also falls off with eccentricity, while the receptive fields of the 1 million ganglion cells of the eye enlarge as we move from the fovea to the periphery. These two factors—decreased cell density and increased receptive field sizes—also guarantee that acuity will be poorer in the periphery. It is estimated that the eye would have to

FIGURE 3.28
All letters in this chart should be equally legible when you
fixate on the small dot in the center of the chart.

contain 35 million ganglion cells in order to support uniform, high acuity throughout the retina. To accommodate this many ganglion cells, each of your eyes would have to be as large as your whole head!

Acuity also decreases appreciably as the level of illumination drops (you probably already know this from your own difficulty reading a menu in a dimly lit restaurant). Yet it's obviously not the number of cones or the density of ganglion cells that changes with light level. The reduction in acuity with decreasing illumination is probably caused by changes in the spatial layout of receptive fields of the ganglion cells. As the overall level of illumination drops, the surrounding portions of ganglion cell receptive fields becomes less effective and, consequently, the center regions become larger (Barlow, Fitzhugh, and Kuffler, 1957; Maffei and Fiorentini, 1972). Box 3.4 completes the story by describing additional influences on visual acuity.

BOX 3.4

VISUAL ACUITY: THE MEANING OF 20/20 VISION

Clinical

Visual acuity can be defined in several different ways. One common definition relates acuity to the smallest target, such as a letter, that can be correctly recognized. A person able to recognize smaller letters is said to have better acuity. You may have heard someone comment with pride about having 20/20 visual acuity. What exactly do these numbers mean?

When optometrists and ophthalmologists began quantifying acuity more than a century ago, they created eye charts containing letters of various sizes. Patients tried to read ever smaller letters, until they came to letters so small that reading was impossible. One Dutch doctor, Hermann Snellen, tested hundreds of people who had no eye diseases (so-called "normals") and found that half these people were un-

able to see details smaller than a certain size. He designated this size—details whose images on the retina were about 0.005 millimeters high—as "normal." For any given detail, the viewing distance is crucial. If you move far enough away, even headlines become impossible to read. So visual acuity is expressed in relation to the distance at which the eye chart is read, usually 20 feet. Someone is said to have "normal" visual acuity if, while standing 20 feet from the chart, that individual can read the same letters that the average healthy person can read at 20 feet. Hence, the notation "20/20." The metric equivalent of 20/20 is 6/6, since testing is carried out at a viewing distance of 6 meters.

BOX 3.4 continued

Acuity can be either better or worse than 20/20. If you cannot see small print, your acuity may be only 20/60. This means that you must get as close as 20 feet in order to read what the average person can read from 60 feet. Likewise, if you have really sharp eyes, your vision may be 20/15 or even 20/10. This means that you can read letters at a distance of 20 feet that the average person cannot. He or she has to move closer to the letters in order to read them: within 15 feet in the first case, 10 feet in the second.

But 20/20 is not good enough. A normal, healthy young person should be *better* than 20/20. The graph below shows that for young people, visual acuity is on average better than 20/20. Acuity declines as we get older. Part of this decline is due to the reduced size of an older person's pupils, which allows less light to reach the retina (Owsley, Sekuler and Siemsen, 1983). Older people also have particular difficulty with eye charts whose letters are of low contrast. On such charts the test letters are printed in various shades of gray rather than in black (Robson, 1993). Tony Adams of the University of California's School of Optometry used a low-contrast eye chart to measure the acuities of young and old people, all of whom had 20/20 acuity when tested with the normal, high-contrast eye charts. Adams and his colleagues (1988) found that the older observers showed a far greater decline in acuity at low contrast. This result bears on the design of work and home environments in which older persons have to function.

Visual acuity varies with things other than age and light level. Some people have particular trouble reading eye charts composed of letters bunched together. They'll be able to read smaller letters on a less crowded line of the eye chart, even though they fail with a line of larger letters that are crowded together. You can see this **crowding effect** in an eye chart prepared by Stuart Anstis, shown to the right. Compare the legibility of this crowded chart to the legibility of the chart in Figure 3.28. They are almost the same, except that Anstis has added many extra letters to the chart in this box.

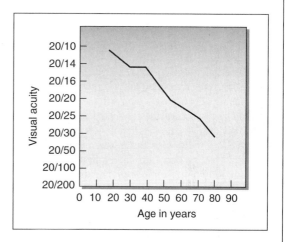

Visual acuity scores may also be affected by cognitive factors, including memorization of the eye chart (by someone who is particularly anxious to "pass" an eye test). Sometimes these cognitive factors play a role even though neither patient nor doctor intend them to. Erica, the youngest daughter of

BOX 3.4 continued

one of the authors (R.S.), was having her eyes examined by a well-meaning though inexperienced ophthalmologist who, to make matters worse, was in a hurry. Wanting to measure acuity separately for each eye, the ophthalmologist asked Erica to close her left eye and read the five small letters at the bottom of the chart, using only her right eye. After she had finished a perfect rendition of the requested letters, she was told to switch eyes, now using her left eye to read the letters. Since the doctor had not bothered to change the chart, she asked him incredulously, "Do you want me to read the *same* letters again?" Of course,

most people would have no difficulty remembering the five letters they'd read aloud only a few seconds before. But the doctor urged her on. No surprise: her second rendition of the letters was every bit as good as her first. When the testing procedure was complete, she almost—her good manners alone stood in the way—offered to read the bottom line with *both* eyes closed. The moral? Although tests of acuity are supposed to assess only one's vision, they can be influenced by other factors as well if the tester is not careful.

Sensitivity

Scotopic Vision   A rod photoreceptor is at the theoretical limit of its sensitivity when it can generate a measurable electrical signal even though only a single photon is absorbed by its photopigment (Lewis and Del Priore, 1988; Hecht, Shlaer, and Pirenne, 1942). But the capture of a single photon does not constitute seeing. In order for you to see—experience light—more than one rod, though not many more, must catch at least one photon each. To efficiently activate the small number of rods needed for seeing, conditions must be exactly right. Examining some of these conditions gives a very good, quick introduction to scotopic vision in general. Let's consider the conditions, one at a time.

The first requirement is that the eye have a full supply of photopigment molecules. Exposure to light uses up these molecules, much as exposure to light consumes the light sensitivity of film. Since we're exposed to light just about every waking moment, our eyes rarely maintain a full supply of unused molecules (except when we sleep). To restore the full supply of photopigments (without going to sleep) requires keeping the person you're going to test in complete darkness for about 35 minutes. This period of adapting to the dark suffices to build the rod photopigments to maximum levels.

Second, the photons need to be imaged on an area of the retina where rods are plentiful. Thus it makes no sense to present the stimulus to the fovea, where there are no rods. Rods are most plentiful in a region slightly more than 3 millimeters away from the fovea. To stimulate this retinal region requires knowing where the person is actually looking. So the person is asked to fixate on a small, continuously visible spot. As illustrated in Figure 3.29, knowing the position of fixation makes it possible to situate the test stimulus at the appropriate distance from that fixation spot. The test stimulus must be fairly small so that it stimulates only the desired retinal region.

Remember that the goal is to determine the dimmest light necessary for detection. The fewer photons needed for vision, the higher one's visual sensitivity is said to be. Not all wavelengths of light are equally effective in stimulating rods. Therefore, to find the wavelength to which the scotopic system is most sensitive, we must stimulate the eye with various wavelengths of light, noting how many photons are needed to detect each wavelength.

The left-hand panel of Figure 3.30 displays the results of such testing. The horizontal axis shows the wavelength of light used to stimulate the eye. The vertical axis shows sensitivity (the reciprocal of the number of photons needed to

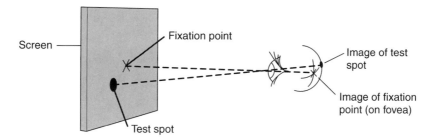

FIGURE 3.29
When fixating on the X, the test spot falls in the periphery of the retina.

elicit a visual sensation). The curve represents the sensitivity of the rod-based system and is usually called the scotopic sensitivity function. The scotopic sensitivity function peaks at 500 nanometers, with the eye being less sensitive when stimulated by either shorter or longer wavelengths of light. In daylight and at sufficient intensity, light of 500 nanometers appears blue-green. To the person whose scoptopic vision is being tested, however, the faint test target will appear colorless (the explanation for this failure of color vision is given in Chapter 7).

Photopic Vision Though sensitivity is not the speciality of photopic vision, it's worth considering photopic sensitivity so that we can compare it to scotopic sensitivity. To measure *photopic* sensitivity requires imaging the target on a retinal area containing only cones; rods should play no role. Again, for stimuli of different wavelengths, we want to determine the minimum number of photons required for photopic vision.

The right-hand panel in Figure 3.30 is the photopic sensitivity curve, with sensitivity plotted as a function of stimulus wavelength. (Box 3.5 discusses one very practical implication of this curve's shape.) Comparing the two curves, note that scotopic sensitivity is greater than photopic sensitivity at all except the longest wavelengths, the "red" end of the spectrum. Note also that the

peaks of the two curves occur at different wavelengths. Maximum scotopic sensitivity occurs at 500 nanometers, whereas photopic sensitivity peaks at 550 nanometers.

The Purkinje Shift The difference between the wavelengths at which the photopic and scotopic curves peak has an important perceptual consequence, one that you may have experienced. This effect was first described by Johannes Evangelista von Purkinje, a Bohemian physiologist of the early nineteenth century (Kuthan, 1987). During the day, when vision is photopic, objects close to 550 nanometers wavelength will tend to appear lighter than objects of 500 nanometers. As night falls and vision becomes scotopic, the situation will be reversed; objects reflecting 500 nanometers will become lighter than those reflecting 550 nanometers. This variation in relative lightness with time of day is known as the **Purkinje shift.**

Fortunately, the Purkinje shift can be easily seen under rather pleasant conditions. Get a comfortable chair and a good book, and sit in a flower garden on a nice, warm day. Compare the lightness of yellow daisies to the lightness of the green foliage. During the day, the daises will look lighter because their reflected wavelengths fall closer to the peak of the photopic sensitivity curve. But as twilight falls, the foliage will

BOX 3.5

DOES THE ELECTRIC COMPANY GIVE YOU YOUR MONEY'S WORTH?

The bill from your electric company has just arrived. Shocked by the numbers, you want to know if you're getting your money's worth. A dollar value cannot be placed on the pleasure you may have gotten from playing your stereo and the like, so let's ignore those uses of electricity, sticking to one we can say something about—the use of electricity to produce light for reading.

Because it is the photopic system that affords reasonable resolution, we use that system when reading. So we can begin the analysis by looking at the photopic sensitivity curve (the right-hand panel of Figure 3.30). Since the photopic system is most sensitive to light whose wavelength is 550 nanometers, your electricity dollars would be most efficiently spent if they were used to produce radiation of only that wavelength. Electricity devoted to producing ultraviolet or infrared radiation is, of course, wasted because you can't see either one. Moreover, any electricity spent to produce visible radiation but at wavelengths other than 550 nanometers is not being used as efficiently as it could be.

Execute

Suppose you use only ordinary, tungsten light bulbs for reading. How could you determine the effectiveness of each dollar spent to power one of these bulbs? The answer depends on the spectral distribution of the light emitted by these bulbs. If they emitted only at 550 nanometers, they'd be highly efficient—putting out light precisely at the wavelength that has the greatest impact on the human visual system. The left graph in the accompanying figure shows the spectral distribution of the radiation emitted by a typical tungsten bulb. Note that most of the radiation that you pay for consists of wavelengths that you can't see, let alone use, for reading. For quantification, we must turn to **Abney's Law** (named for a British physicist of the early twentieth century).

Abney's Law describes the effectiveness of a stimulus that simultaneously contains many different wavelengths, which is certainly the case for light from a tungsten bulb. For each wavelength present in such a stimulus, Abney's Law instructs one to take the product of two quantities: the amount of light present at that wavelength and how sensitive the photopic system is to that wavelength. The first of these quantities can be obtained from measuring devices (spectrum analyzers of various sorts); the second can be obtained from a table of the photopic sensitivity function's numerical value at various wavelengths. After these products are obtained for each wavelength in the stimulus, Abney's Law requires that one sum up all the products. The resulting sum is a numerical statement of the visual effectiveness of the spectrally complex stimulus. Stated simply, Abney's Law says that one can predict the impact of a complex stimulus composed of many wavelengths by evaluating the effectiveness of each of its component wavelengths and then adding together their separate effects.

To make quantitative sense of the outcome, though, we need some reference point, such as a stimulus that represents 100 percent efficiency, the maximum obtainable. Since that's the best you could achieve, let's say that such a stimulus gave you a full dollar's worth of light for each dollar spent on electricity. Compared to that standard, you get only 3 cents worth of light for each dollar put into electricity for a tungsten bulb. Some tungsten bulbs do a little better—5 cents return per dollar spent—but these lamps tend to burn out quickly.

We can apply the same analysis to another common type of light used for reading—fluorescent lamps. The spectrum of a typical fluorescent lamp is shown in the right-hand graph in the accompanying figure. Compared to the tungsten bulb, the fluorescent lamp emits far more of its radiation within the visually effective band (400 to 700 nanometers) and far less in the infrared (which is experienced as heat, not light). Applying Abney's Law to the spectrum of a fluorescent lamp, we find that you get 10 cents worth of reading light for each dollar's worth of electricity, a much better buy.

Oddly enough, the most efficient light source for reading is one that doesn't require any electricity at all. The distinguished French vision scientist Yves

BOX 3.5 continued

LeGrand pointed out that fireflies and glowworms emit light very near the peak wavelength of the photopic sensitivity curve (1968, p. 82). Because fireflies achieve very high photopic efficiencies, a lamp full of fireflies would certainly give you your money's worth of reading light.

We don't usually tell you things that we don't want you to remember. But for your own peace of mind, the next time you have to pay an electric bill, maybe you should forget how few of your dollars are going for something you actually used.

FIGURE 3.30
Visual sensitivity of the rod-based scotopic system (left-hand panel) and the cone-based photopic system (right-hand panel) varies with the wavelength of the light source.

appear lighter, since it reflects wavelengths closer to the peak of the scotopic sensitivity curve. This is the Purkinje shift.

Dark Adaptation The retina's duplex nature produces the differences between photopic and scotopic vision. We've already explored some of these differences. The duplex retina also affects vision by controlling the recovery from exposure to light, a process called **dark adaptation.**

Anyone who goes to the movies is already familiar with dark adaptation. Upon first entering the darkened theater from the bright lobby, you have difficulty finding a seat or seeing the faces of people around you. After a while, though, you "get used to" the dark and can see better. A small part of your improved vision can be traced to changes in your pupil. In darkness, the pupil dilates, allowing more light into the eye. But dark adaptation cannot be explained solely by pupillary dilation. For one thing, as you adapt to the dark, your sensitivity to light may improve by a factor of 100,000 or more, whereas the change in pupil area is relatively small, a factor of 16 at most. Moreover, your sensitivity may continue to improve for 30 to 40 minutes, whereas the pupil reaches its maximum size within a matter of seconds.

When dark adaptation is studied in the laboratory, it is possible to measure the recovery time of vision. Such experiments are numerous and have revealed a lot about vision's duplex nature. We'll present some of the highlights here; for a more extensive treatment, see Hood and Finkelstein (1986).

Execute

Studies of dark adaptation typically begin by exposing a person to a strong light, called the *adaptation stimulus.* The idea is to determine how quickly a person's visual sensitivity recovers from exposure to that strong light. After the adaptation stimulus has been extinguished, the person sits in complete darkness and tries to detect a very dim, briefly flashing light (the *test stimulus*), which is presented about once per second. The test light's intensity slowly increases until the light becomes visible to the person. At that point,

the intensity of the light is immediately dropped so it becomes invisible again. This cycle is repeated over and over, for up to 30 minutes. Each time the test stimulus becomes visible, two values are recorded: the *intensity* of that just visible stimulus and the *time* at which it was seen (that is, the time elapsed since the person entered into darkness). The general outcome can be described simply: the longer the person stays in the dark, the less intense the test stimulus needs to be in order to be seen. To put it another way, the person's sensitivity steadily increases the longer he or she spends in the dark.

Now suppose that we wanted to measure the recovery of rod sensitivity separately from the recovery of cone sensitivity. How might that be done? You could capitalize on the uneven distribution of these two types of photoreceptors to isolate their separate behaviors. To measure dark adaptation using cones only, the test stimulus could be presented to the fovea. To do the same for rods, the test stimulus could be presented in the periphery, where the rods predominate.

The left-hand panel of Figure 3.31 shows how dark adaptation measurements turn out when the test stimulus is presented to the fovea. The drop in the curve over time shows an improvement in photopic sensitivity the longer one remains in darkness. The middle panel shows the results of a comparable experiment in which the test stimulus is imaged away from the fovea. Because the stimulus primarily affects rods, the curve reflects the changing sensitivity over time of the scotopic system.

Compare the two curves. Note that at "0" time, the scotopic curve (middle panel) is higher than the photopic curve (left-hand panel). Immediately after entering darkness, in other words, the scotopic system is less sensitive (it needs more light to see) than the photopic system. Now compare the curves later in time, say at 20 minutes. Here the scotopic system is more sensitive than the photopic system, the opposite of what we just saw. The greater scotopic sensitivity after prolonged darkness is consistent with the large difference between the peak sensitivities of pho-

FIGURE 3.31
Graphs showing changes in sensitivity relative to the length of time in darkness.

topic (cone) and scotopic (rod) spectral sensitivity curves (Figure 3.30).

Returning to the dark adaptation curves in Figure 3.31, note that the scotopic system starts out less sensitive than the photopic system but ends up more sensitive. After an interval of about 8 to 10 minutes, their *relative* sensitivities reverse. One other point emerges from these curves. The photopic system completes its recovery from the adaptation stimulus rather quickly (since the curve stops declining after 5 to 6 minutes). The scotopic system takes a lot longer to recover completely (the curve doesn't stop declining until at least 15 minutes have elapsed).

Next, suppose we modify the previous study by imaging the test stimulus on a retinal region that contains both rods and cones. Measuring recovery from the same adaptation stimulus as before, the outcome will resemble the curve shown in the right-hand panel of Figure 3.31.

Compare the curve in this panel to the others, noting the kink in this new curve. Things seem to go along smoothly until about 8 minutes. In fact, recovery seems to have leveled off. Then all of a sudden, at the 8-minute mark, recovery starts over again, eventually subsiding once more at about the 15-minute mark. What is going on here? Notice that the left-hand part of the kinked curve bears a striking resemblance to the early part of the photopic dark adaptation curve (left

panel in Figure 3.31), whereas the rest of the kinked curve resembles the late part of the scotopic curve (middle panel in Figure 3.31). The explanation of the kinked curve, then, is simple. Because in this third case the test stimulus affects both cones and rods, we have measured both types of adaptation simultaneously. Early in dark adaptation, the photopic system is more sensitive, so it alone determines the threshold. Later in dark adaptation, the scotopic system is more sensitive, so it alone determines the threshold.

The exact outcome of these studies depends on a number of experimental details, notably the strength of the initial adaptation stimulus, the size of the test stimulus, and the wavelength of light used in the test stimulus. All these variables as well as many others (including an individual's diet, as Box 3.6 indicates) change the curve of dark adaptation in ways that are predictable from understanding the retina's duplex nature.

You don't need special equipment to verify some of these observations. Pick a clear night, and just before going outside, stand for a few moments in a brightly lit room. Then quickly go outside and look at the sky. At this point you probably won't be able to see any stars. Keep looking, though, and after a while some will become visible. The first ones you'll be able to see will probably be right around the location you're fixating on because early in dark adaptation the

BOX 3.6

RECOVERING FROM LIGHT

When people compare the human eye to a camera, they liken the retina to the camera's film. But in one sense, the retina is more like videotape than film—both the retina and videotapes are reusable. Even this analogy is inadequate, though, because unlike videotape, the retina can be used and reused millions of times. Wilhelm Kühne, a German physiologist and one of the first to study the retina's recovery, commented that,

> bound together with the pigment epithelium, the retina behaves not merely like a photographic plate, but like an entire photographic workshop in which the workman continually renews the plate by laying on new light-sensitive material, while simultaneously erasing the old image. (Translation by Wald, 1950, p. 33)

How does the retina renew itself, recovering sensitivity after being exposed to light? When a photopigment molecule breaks up, it is said to have become "bleached," an apt term. When Franz Boll first studied this process, he noticed that the retina of the frog was usually intensely red. But when the frog's eye was exposed to light, the color of the retina disappeared; that is, it was bleached. Now we know that this loss of color is associated with the splitting apart of the retina's photopigment molecules.

In the 1880s, Kühne was struck by the analogy between the retina and the photographic plate, then still a novelty. Kühne exploited this resemblance scientifically, using retinas to make "retinal photographs" or, as he called them, "optograms." An optogram treats the retina as though it were a photographic plate or piece of film, actually developing and fixing the image on the retina using special chemicals (Kühne, 1879/1977). Kühne used this approach to examine the image that various objects cast on the retina.

To make one particularly imaginative but gruesome optogram, Kühne got the cooperation of a man sentenced to die on the guillotine. The man's eyes were shielded from light for several hours before the execution, allowing light-sensitive material to accumulate in the retina. Then, just before the beheading, his eyes were uncovered. Immediately after the execution, Kühne removed the eyes and chemically treated the retinas to preserve the image of the last thing the man had seen (Wald, 1950). Unfortunately, the optogram was ambiguous, perhaps because instead of staring fixedly at just one object, the condemned man understandably moved his eyes around, taking his "last look" at one thing after another.

How does the retina manage to process millions of images over a lifetime? The secret lies in the retina's ability to restore its own sensitivity to light through a complex biochemical process (Stabell, Stabell and Fugelli, 1992). Remember Boll's observation on bleaching in the frog's eye? He also noticed that the retina regained its normal, reddish color if the frog stayed in the dark for a short time (Boll, 1877/1977). We know now that the reddish color returns because new photopigment molecules have been created. This restoration is just as important for the visual process as the bleaching. If photopigment could not be restored, an animal would quickly become blind because when all the available photopigment molecules became bleached, they would be unable to signal the presence of light.

To produce new photopigment after light has bleached part of the retina requires that a derivative of vitamin A diffuse through the retinal pigment ephithelium and combine with protein available within the retina. Since all the body's vitamin A comes from the food one eats, a serious deficiency of vitamin A in the diet slows down the restoration of photopigments. In vitamin A deficiency, once a photopigment molecule is bleached, its return to the unbleached state is slowed. A person with a vitamin A deficiency is described as "night blind" because he or she typically experiences difficulty seeing at night or in other dim light (Dowling, 1966). Such people might have extreme difficulty seeing after entering a darkened theater, be unable to recognize friends on the street in a dim light, or be unable to see clearly while driving at night.

Vitamin A deficiency is common in developing countries, where diet is often inadequate and vitamin supplements rare. Even people in developed countries are not immune to poor diet and night vision problems. For example, many years ago, one-third of a test sample of medical students showed diminished night vision that was attributable to their diet (Jeghers, 1937). These medical students were simply too busy to eat proper quantities of carrots and leafy vegetables.

photopic system is more sensitive than the scotopic. After a few minutes, your scotopic system will catch up and then exceed the photopic system's sensitivity. At that point you'll be able to see very dim stars using the rod-dominated periphery of your retina.

After you've adapted to the dark for a few minutes, you can verify that the rod-dominated periphery of your retina is more sensitive than the cone-dominated central region. Glance slowly around the sky, stopping when you can just barely see some very dim star that lies away from the spot you're looking directly at. If the star is just barely visible using the most sensitive part of your retina (where rods are most numerous and convergence is greatest), that star will become invisible when you look directly at it (imaging it on a less sensitive part of the retina).

SUMMARY AND PREVIEW

This chapter outlined how various aspects of visual perception are shaped by the properties of the retina, notably the center/surround antagonism of retinal ganglion cells and the differences between the photoreceptors that feed the ganglion cells. Clearly, though, not all vision is determined by the retina. We encountered several visual phenomena that defy explanation at the retinal level, and there are lots more where those came from. To broaden our understanding of vision, we have to push farther into the nervous system, following the messages generated by the retina, back into the brain itself. There you'll see that these messages originating in the retina are further refined and reorganized in ways that account for still other properties of the way you see the world.

KEY TERMS

Abney's Law
action potentials
axon
Bloch's Law
crowding effect
dark adaptation
DoG curve
duplex
eccentricity
Hermann grid
intensity
K cells
lateral inhibition
lightness
lightness constancy
lightness contrast
M cells

Mach bands
mesopic
microelectrode
P cells
photon
photopic
Purkinje shift
receptive field
resolution
retinal ganglion cells
Ricco's Law
scotopic
single cell recording
spatial summation
temporal summation
visual acuity

CHAPTER 4

CENTRAL VISUAL PATHWAYS

In this chapter we'll forge ahead into the brain as we continue our examination of vision's neural machinery. But before proceeding, let's pause to consider some of the visual products of that neural machinery. Take a look at the series of drawings in Figure 4.1. Each reveals an essential characteristic of visual perception. Because these characteristics operate in the background of our visual awareness, they ordinarily escape our attention. Here's a chance to see what is normally hidden.

What do you see in panel A of Figure 4.1? Most people readily perceive a white square resting on top of four black disks. But if you take away the disks you discover that the white square disappears too. This square is a figment of the visual processing machinery in your brain—the visual portions of your brain have literally created the square from the bits and pieces of contour information contained in the drawing. This so-called illusory figure underscores the constructive nature of visual perception: the brain goes beyond

the optical information provided to the eye to generate plausible interpretations of the visual layout giving rise to that optical information. That's the first characteristic to keep in mind: perception is constructive.

Next look at panel B of Figure 4.1. The serpentine, segmented curves at the top of each panel have been duplicated and embedded in the tangle of random lines below them (the left-hand snake within the tangle at the left, and the right-hand snake within the tangle at the right). Take a moment to search for each hidden snake. Although both embedded curves are exactly the same length and composed of the same number of segments, one is quite conspicuous but the other is hard to see. Why? Adjacent segments making up the conspicuous snake differ in orientation by only 30 degrees from one another, while those comprising the inconspicuous snake differ by 60 degrees. The similarly-oriented segments are more strongly unified and, hence, form a more salient figure. Evidently, the brain

A

B

C

D

FIGURE 4.1
Vision depends on more than the patterns of light striking the eye, as these four figures illustrate. See text for instructions.

does not concentrate on individual features in isolation but, instead, exploits relationships among features as contextual clues about how those features ought to be knitted together. That's the second characteristic to remember: perception is context dependent.

Next, look at the drawing in panel C of Figure 4.1. Here you'll probably have trouble deciding what you're looking at because the figure's appearance keeps changing. At one moment the figure appears to be a white vase seen against a dark background but then, without warning, it turns into a pair of dark faces looking at each other against a white background. This so-called ambiguous figure illustrates that the same optical information can generate multiple perceptual interpretations. So, perception involves interpretation, the third characteristic.

Finally, look at the seemingly random collection of black splotches in panel D of Figure 4.1. While initially indecipherable, the splotches will eventually become organized into a meaningful scene. Take a moment to study the figure before reading on. Can you tell what the scene depicts? Don't be discouraged if the answer escapes you—we'll provide a more recognizable version of this figure at the end of this chapter. To make sense of this picture, your visual system must synthesize contour information gathered from a large portion of the picture. This illustrates a fourth characteristic of vision: there is a strong tendency to group bits and pieces of information into meaningful forms, even when those forms are only vaguely suggested by the bits and pieces.

These entertaining figures all point to the same general principle: visual perception depends on more than just the pattern of light striking the retina. Vision, rather than being a mindless process of measuring how much light enters the eye, is an intelligent activity of a finely tuned brain. To paraphrase Donald Hoffman (1998), we are all visual virtuosos, unaware of our talent for constructing what we see. Some of those "talents" are embodied in the neural elements within the eye itself, as we discovered in the two previous chapters. But the eyes are just launching stages for our marvelous visual talents. In this chapter we continue tracing the flow of information within the visual nervous system. You'll learn how visual information about objects and events in the world is carried to the brain and distributed to different sets of neurons in the visual cortex. You'll also see how patterns of activity within these brain cells can be related to various aspects of visual perception.

Let's begin by examining the **optic nerve,** the bundle of fibers carrying information from the eyes to various processing stages in the central nervous system.

THE OPTIC NERVE

Each eye's optic nerve comprises axons from all its retinal ganglion cells. Thus, the optic nerve from each eye resembles a cable that contains approximately 1.25 million individual wires. Multiplied by two eyes, this means that the brain receives visual input from 2.5 million separate channels, each carrying information about a small region of the visual world. That may seem like a huge number of communication lines, but it is really quite modest compared to the hundreds of millions of neurons populating the visual areas of the brain. Keep in mind that all neural processing of visual information within the brain depends on the optic nerves for input data. The optic nerves provide the brain with the raw material for visual perception. Interruptions in the flow of that information to the brain destroy vision.

Within the eye itself, the axons of ganglion cells are not covered by **myelin.** As you may know, myelin is a membrane that both insulates the axon from activity in neighboring axons and speeds the conduction of nerve impulses. Presumably, axons within the eye remain unmyelinated in order to reduce the clutter through which light must pass to reach the receptors (a coating of myelin could double the diameter of an axon). Once outside the eye, though, this restriction is removed, and individual axons acquire a coating of myelin.

Within each optic nerve, fibers from different regions of the retina congregate in an orderly fashion, with fibers carrying information from neighboring regions of the retina running adjacent to one another within the nerve (Torrealba et al., 1982). From the point it leaves the eye, the optic nerve travels approximately 5 centimeters (2 inches) before rendezvousing with the optic nerve from the other eye.

The optic nerves from the two eyes converge at the **optic chiasm.** The term "chiasm" comes from the Greek word meaning "cross," and a glance at Figure 4.2 shows why this term is appropriate. At the chiasm, there is a wholesale rearrangement of the constituent fibers. Using Figure 4.2, carefully trace the fibers from different regions of either eye as those fibers enter and leave the optic chiasm. Notice that some fibers always remain on the same side of the brain—

these are called uncrossed or **ipsilateral fibers** ("ipsi" means "same"; "lateral" refers to side). Regardless of which eye they come from, these ipsilateral fibers originate from that eye's temporal retina ("temporal" refers to that half of the retina nearest the temples). Other fibers cross to the opposite side of the brain at the optic chiasm. These are the crossed or **contralateral fibers,** and they come from the nasal retina of each eye ("contra" means "opposite"; "nasal" refers to the half of the retina closest to the nose). Thus, the optic nerve from each eye branches into two segments—one crossed, the other uncrossed. Within the chiasm, crossed fibers from one eye join with uncrossed fibers from the other eye, producing two new combinations of retinal axons. These new combinations, which run from the chiasm to structures deeper in the brain, are known as **optic tracts.** Don't be fooled by the terminology—an

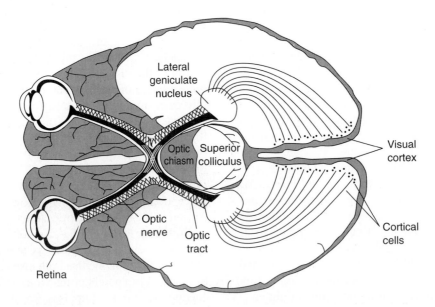

FIGURE 4.2
The projections of the optic fibers from the two eyes to the two hemispheres of the brain. The fibers represented by the solid black lines originate from the nasal retina of both eyes; they cross at the optic chiasm to the opposite hemisphere and are called contralateral fibers. The fibers represented by the hatch marks originate from the temporal retina of both eyes; they remain on the same side of the brain and are called ipsilateral fibers.

optic tract is still composed of axons from gan-glion cells; the change in name from "nerve" to "tract" is simply a convention used by anatomists. The important thing to understand is that each optic tract contains fibers from *both* eyes, the temporal retina of one eye and the nasal retina of the other.

The proportion of crossed and uncrossed fibers in the optic tract varies among species. The percentages are not related to the species' position on the evolutionary scale. Instead, they relate to the position of the animal's eyes within its head. In animals with laterally placed eyes, such as the rabbit, nearly all of the axons cross to the opposite side of the brain. In humans, about 50 percent of the axons from each eye cross at the chiasm, while the other 50 percent remain un-crossed. This division between crossed and un-crossed occurs along an imaginary vertical seam bisecting the fovea.

But why should eye position in the head be related to the percentage of crossing fibers? To figure out the answer, think about the relation between the position of an object in space and the position of that object's image on the retina. The following exercise will help (see Figure 4.3). While looking at the center of this page, place your thumb on the right-hand edge of the page. The image of your thumb will now fall on the temporal retina of your left eye and nasal retina of your right eye. Looking at Figures 4.2 and 4.3, you will see that fibers from these regions of the

Execute

FIGURE 4.3
Objects to the right of the point of fixation cast images on the nasal retina of the right eye and the temporal retina of the left eye. Fibers from these two retinal areas project to the left side of the brain (left drawing). Objects to the left of the point of fixation cast images on the nasal retina of the left eye and the temporal retina of the right eye. Fibers from these two retinal areas project to the right side of the brain (right drawing).

two retinas wind up together in the optic tract on the left side of the brain. Keeping your gaze on the center of the page, place your thumb on the page's left-hand edge. Now your thumb is imaged on the nasal retina of your left eye and the temporal retina of your right eye. Figures 4.2 and 4.3 show that these two regions end up sending fibers to the right side of the brain.

As this exercise demonstrates, there is a general rule to describe how inputs from the two halves of the visual field are distributed to the hemispheres of the brain: the right hemisphere processes information from the left visual field, while the left hemisphere processes information from the right visual field. Those portions of the left and right eyes that look at the *same* area of visual space send their nerve fibers to the *same* region of the brain. The partial crossing of axons at the chiasm makes this possible. Rerouting the axons sets the stage for combining information from the two eyes, a process we'll learn more about shortly.

In animals with eyes on the side of their heads, the two eyes look at *different* areas of visual space. For these animals, it would be extremely maladaptive to mix information from the two eyes because such information specifies different objects located in different regions of the visual field. Mixing information from the two eyes could lead to serious confusion about the location of those objects. To avoid this potential for confusion, the optic fibers from the two eyes remain strictly segregated, crossing in their entirety at the optic chiasm. This serves to route information from the two laterally placed eyes to different halves of the brain.

Let's resume tracing the destination of the fibers of the optic tract. Remember we're still talking about the axons of the ganglion cells located back in the retina. About 80 percent of the fibers project to a cluster of cell bodies known as the **lateral geniculate nucleus.** The remaining 20 percent of the optic tract projects to several neighboring structures in the midbrain, the most prominent being the **superior colliculus.** Since

the superior colliculus and the lateral geniculate nucleus are both regions of the brain to which retinal axons project, these places are referred to as *projection sites.*

To make it easier to follow the flow of visual information from the optic tract, we'll discuss the two major branches of the optic tract separately. We'll first briefly describe the branch to the superior colliculus and then cover in more detail the other branch, to the lateral geniculate nucleus and its projection site, the visual cortex. But don't let our separate treatment of these areas of the brain mislead you. These visual centers are richly interconnected, and their functions can be carried out only when all the components work in harmony. Moreover, there are several other midbrain structures—thought to be involved in control of pupil size, registration of self-motion, and postural adjustments—omitted from our discussion.

THE SUPERIOR COLLICULUS

Tucked away at the top of the brain stem (see Figure 4.4), the superior colliculus is a phylogenetically older, more primitive visual area than the visual cortex. In many lower animals, such as frogs and fish, the superior colliculus represents *the* major brain center for visual processing. In human beings and other higher animals, however, the phylogenetically newer visual cortex has supplanted the superior colliculus as the more important visual area. Nonetheless, even in these higher animals, the superior colliculus plays a prominent role in visual orienting reflexes, including the initiation and guidance of eye movements (Schall 1991; Horwitz and Newsome, 1999). The evidence pointing to this conclusion comes from several sources.

For one thing, cells in the superior colliculus have receptive fields with rather ill-defined ON and OFF regions. These cells will respond to just about any visual stimulus—edges, bars of any orientation, light flashes—falling within their receptive fields, regardless of the shape or orientation of that stimulus (Goldberg and Wurtz, 1972).

Neural

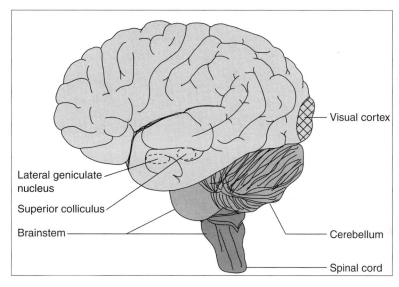

FIGURE 4.4
View of the left side of the brain showing the relative locations of several visual
structures. The lateral geniculate nucleus and superior colliculus (drawn with dotted
lines) are actually located within the brain and are not visible from its surface.

These properties suggest that the colliculus is not concerned with precisely *what* the stimulus is but rather with *where* it is.

For another thing, cells in the superior colliculus clearly are involved in controlling eye movements. Many cells in the superior colliculus emit a vigorous burst of activity just before the eyes begin to move. This burst of activity occurs, however, only if the eyes move in order to fixate on a light flashed in the visual periphery. Eye movements made in darkness evoke no activity in these cells. So the *intention* to move the eyes toward some object seems to be critical for the cells' responsiveness. Besides initiating eye movements, the superior colliculus also plays some role in guiding the direction and extent of those eye movements (Carpenter, 1992). Thus damage to the superior colliculus impairs the accuracy of visually guided eye movements in monkeys (Kurtz and Butter, 1980; Albano et al., 1982) and in humans (Heywood and Ratcliff, 1975). However, the superior colliculus is just one of several brain areas playing a role in the

guidance of eye movements; other prominent areas include the visual cortex (Seagraves et al., 1987) and the frontal eye-field situated in the frontal lobe (see Schall, 1991, for an excellent review of this literature on neural control of eye movements). Eye movements themselves will be discussed in more detail in Chapter 8.

Besides receiving visual input, cells in the superior colliculus also receive auditory input from the ears, as evidenced by their responsiveness to sound stimulation (Gordon, 1972). Because they receive sensory input from the eyes *and* ears, these are called *multisensory cells*. For these multisensory cells to respond, the auditory and visual stimulation must originate from the same region of space. For example, if a particular multisensory cell responds to a spot of light appearing in the upper right portion of the visual field, that cell will respond to a sound only if it, too, comes from the same vicinity. Additionally, when visual and auditory inputs occur simultaneously, a multisensory cell responds more strongly than when either input occurs alone. Because of this property, a weak auditory input can amplify the effects of a weak visual input, producing a strong combined response. As a result, sight and sound can reinforce one another in these multisensory cells, enabling an animal to detect the location of feeble environmental events (Stein, Wallace and Meredith, 1995).

In summary, the superior colliculus seems designed to detect objects located away from the point of fixation and to guide orienting movements of the eyes and head toward those objects (Sparks, 1988). The colliculus does not, however, contain the machinery necessary for a detailed visual analysis of such objects. That job, instead, belongs to the other branch of the optic tract, the one projecting to the lateral geniculate nucleus and then on to the visual cortex. It is to those sites that we turn next.

THE LATERAL GENICULATE NUCLEUS

In this section we shall first consider the interesting structure of the lateral geniculate nucleus (LGN) and the way in which retinal input is distributed throughout the structure. Then we'll describe the receptive field properties of geniculate neurons and speculate about the role of these neurons in vision. Figure 4.4 indicates the area of the brain where the LGN is located.

Structure of the LGN

The LGN has a very distinct, layered appearance, as you can see in the left panel (A) of Figure 4.5. The layers consist of cell bodies, and the number of layers in the LGN varies from one species to another. In humans, the LGN on each side of the brain contains six layers stacked on top of one another and bent in the middle. This bend gives the LGN its name: "geniculate" comes from a Latin word meaning "with bent knee," as in "genuflect." For purposes of discussion, let's number the successive layers 1, 2, 3, 4, 5, and 6, going from the bottom to the top of the structure. Cells in layers 1 and 2 are larger than those in layers 3 through 6. These two large-cell layers are termed

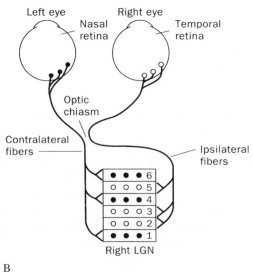

A   B

FIGURE 4.5
Cross section through the LGN showing its distinct layers (A). Diagram showing projections from both eyes to the right LGN (B); a corresponding diagram could be drawn for the projections to the left LGN.

the **magnocellular layers,** and the four small-cell layers are called the **parvocellular layers** (the prefixes of these two terms come from the Latin words *magnus,* meaning "large," and *parvus,* meaning "small"). You will recall the P and M retinal ganglion cells from the previous chapter. The P ganglion cells provide the input to the parvocellular layers of the LGN while the M cells feed into the magnocellular layers of the LGN. Recall also that the P and M cells differed in the kinds of visual stimuli to which they respond best; those response differences are maintained at the level of the LGN, as we shall discuss in a moment. Also shown in this diagram are the K cells mentioned in Chapter 3. In the LGN, these very small K cells are sandwiched between the successive layers of M and P cells.

Let's take a closer look at the LGN, beginning with the pattern of connections between fibers of the optic tract and cells in the different layers of the lateral geniculate nucleus. Remember that each optic tract contains a mixture of fibers from both eyes, the temporal retina of the ipsilateral eye and the nasal retina of the contralateral eye. These fibers become very strictly segregated when they arrive at the lateral geniculate nucleus: the contralateral fibers contact only the cells in layers 1, 4 and 6, whereas the ipsilateral fibers contact only the cells in layers 2, 3 and 5. Take a moment to study Figure 4.5 to be sure you understand this pattern of input to the various layers. In sorting out these projections, keep in mind that the brain contains a pair of lateral geniculate nuclei, one located in the left hemisphere and the other in the right hemisphere. This paired arrangement means that a single eye provides contralateral input to one lateral geniculate nucleus and ipsilateral input to the other. Now let's look at how retinal input is registered within these layers.

Retinal Maps in the LGN

Each layer of the LGN contains an orderly representation, or map, of the retina. This point is illustrated in Figure 4.6. As you can see, axons that carry information from neighboring regions of the retina connect with geniculate cells that are themselves neighbors. This way of distributing retinal information within any layer of the LGN creates a map of the retina within that layer. Since such a map preserves the topography of the retina, it is known as a **retinotopic map.** Each of the six layers contains its own complete retinotopic map, and these layers are stacked in such a way that comparable regions of the separate maps are aligned with each other. For instance, the foveal parts of adjacent layers are situated on top of one another.

Receptive Field Properties of P and M LGN Cells

Just like their retinal counterparts, LGN cells have approximately circular receptive fields, subdivided into concentric center and surround components. As in the retina, these two components interact antagonistically. Some cells have ON centers paired with OFF surrounds, whereas others have exactly the opposite configuration. There is an important difference, though, between the LGN and retina: the surround of an LGN receptive field exerts a stronger inhibitory effect on its center than does the surround of a retinal ganglion cell (Maffei and Fiorentini, 1972). This means the LGN cells amplify, or accentuate, differences in illumination between neighboring retinal regions even more than do retinal ganglion cells. Incidentally, because their fields are circular in shape, LGN cells, like their retinal counterparts, will respond to borders or contours of any orientation.

This center/surround layout of LGN receptive fields is characteristic of essentially all LGN cells, regardless whether they are located in a parvocellular layer or a magnocellular layer. There are, however, several major differences between cells in the magnocellular layers and cells in the parvocellular layers (Livingstone and Hubel, 1988; Schiller and Logothetis, 1990), differences that relate to the P versus M ganglion

Neural

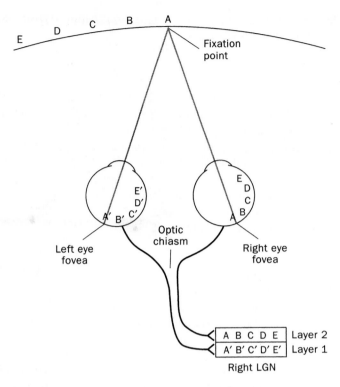

FIGURE 4.6
Drawing showing how different areas of the visual field are mapped
onto the two retinas and then onto various layers of the right LGN.
For simplicity, only two layers are shown.

cell inputs to these layers. These differences
strongly imply that the two subdivisions—magnocellular and parvocellular—make unique contributions to visual perception.

Color   Nearly all parvocellular cells (that is, the
cells in layers 3 through 6) are differentially sensitive to the *color* of light imaged within their receptive fields (DeValois et al., 1958; Wiesel and
Hubel, 1966; Dreher, Fukada, and Rodieck,
1976). A vigorous response can be evoked from
these cells only if the center of the field is illuminated by one particular color (for example, red).
When the center is illuminated by a different
color (for example, green), the cell's activity is
inhibited. When the surround is illuminated by

the same color as the center (for example, red),
the cell's response is reduced. But when the surround is illuminated with a different color (for
example, green), the cell's response is aug-
mented. Because of their unique response to the
pairing of "opposite" colors, these cells are called
color opponent cells. Some opponent cells exhibit red/green organization, while others exhibit
blue/yellow organization. We'll consider these
opponent cells in greater detail in Chapter 7. Just
to reiterate, the opponent color cells in the parvocellular layers are thought to receive their inputs
from the P cells in the retina.

Cells in the magnocellular layers (and a small
fraction of cells in the parvocellular layers) respond to all colors. Their response depends

solely on the relative intensity of light falling in the center and surround portions of their receptive fields. To reiterate, cells in the magnocellular layers are thought to receive their inputs from the M cells in the retina.

Acuity   Within each of the six layers of the LGN, receptive fields vary systematically in size, with the smallest fields devoted to representation of the fovea. For a given region of the retina, cells in the magnocellular layers have receptive fields that are 2 or 3 times larger than receptive fields for cells in the parvocellular layers. Hence, parvocellular cells analyze spatial information at a finer level of detail than do magnocellular cells.

Temporal Variations   Magnocellular cells respond vigorously to fast, abrupt fluctuations of light intensity within their receptive fields, whereas parvocellular cells respond sluggishly— if at all—to such fluctuations. Rapid motion of an object generates these intensity fluctuations within a cell's receptive field, implying that magnocellular cells, but not parvocellular cells, are able to signal the presence of rapid movement.

But what about the K cells occupying the interlayer regions of the LGN? It's not so easy to speculate about what they contribute to vision, for relatively few studies have measured their receptive field properties. K cells in the LGN do have relatively large receptive fields compared to M and P cells, and some K cells respond to sound as well as visual stimulation. One clue to their possible role in vision is provided by the regions of the cortex to which they project. (We'll discuss K cell projections shortly.)

These three distinct populations of LGN neurons—M, P and K cells—all send their axons to the visual cortex. As we will discover shortly, however, those axons terminate in different parts of the visual cortex, thus maintaining the functional segregation of information found within these different layer types. Before moving up to the cortex, though, let's spend a moment speculating about the importance of the LGN for vision.

Possible Functions of the LGN

You now have a thumbnail sketch of the chief characteristics of the LGN, the relay station between the retina and higher visual areas in the brain. What do the various anatomical and physiological properties we've discussed suggest about the LGN's role in vision? As just described, cells in the LGN are primarily concerned with differences in intensity between neighboring regions of the retina, and in some instances with the color of light. These cells are unconcerned with the overall level of light. In other words, LGN cells are designed to register the presence of edges in the visual environment. This alone, however, does not represent a unique contribution to vision. Retinal cells have already accomplished the job of signaling the presence of edges. So we are led to ask: Does the LGN seem uniquely suited for some other role? Or does it merely relay messages broadcast from the retina straight to higher brain sites with no editing or censorship? There are several reasons for thinking the LGN is considerably more than just a relay station.

For one thing, the LGN receives input not only from the retina, but from the **reticular activating system** as well (Burke and Cole, 1978). Buried in the brain stem, the reticular activating system governs an animal's general level of arousal. Hence, the flow of visual information from the LGN to higher visual centers could be modified by the animal's state of arousal. The LGN may well operate like the volume control on a radio, modulating the intensity of retinal inputs according to the animal's current state of arousal. In support of this idea, Livingstone and Hubel (1981) found that when an animal was in a drowsy state (as evidenced behaviorally and by brain-wave recordings), the overall level of activity in the LGN was low. The reduced level of LGN activity meant that the higher visual centers of the drowsy animal were receiving signals that were attenuated compared to those they would have received had the animal been more alert. This interplay between arousal level and the strength of signals going to the higher visual centers could promote attentiveness to visual information.

A subset of cells in the LGN—the K cells—may also play a modulatory role in vision. (Hendry and Reid, 2000). K cells receive strong inputs from the superior colliculus, the subcortical structure thought to be involved in the generation and control of eye movements. Vivien Casagrande (1994), a neuroanatomist who has argued for the importance of this overlooked category of cells, believes that K cells may serve to shut down vision temporarily whenever gaze is shifted rapidly from one part of the visual scene to another. According to her scheme, at the time the superior colliculus begins generating signals to move the eyes it also activates K cells in the LGN. They, in turn, briefly turn down the activity of cortical cells to which they project, thereby muting the neural consequences of the abrupt shift in the retinal image accompanying a rapid eye movement.

In addition to input from the reticular activating system and the superior colliculus, the LGN also receives a large input from the visual cortex. You may find this intriguing, since the visual cortex itself *receives* a substantial amount of its input from the LGN. In effect, the LGN formulates a message and transmits it to the cortex. The cortex, in turn, sends back a reply to the LGN, thereby allowing that message to be altered. This kind of arrangement is known as a *feedback loop,* and it is widely used in electronics to regulate electrical current within a circuit. At present, the biological purpose of the visual feedback between the cortex and the LGN is not known, although intriguing speculations have been advanced (Martin, 1988).

The highly organized arrangement of this structure and the distinct physiological differences between magnocellular and parvocellular layers strongly suggest that the LGN plays another crucial role in vision. Recall that information about color is processed exclusively in the parvocellular layers, while information about large, rapidly moving intensity contours falls

within the domain of the magnocellular layers. This orderly sorting of visual information sets the stage for the next level of processing occurring in the visual cortex. An analogy may help clarify what we mean.

Think for a moment about the most efficient way to assemble a complex jigsaw puzzle. You usually begin by sorting the jumble of pieces into groups, according to some shared property. You might locate and place all the pieces that make up the border into one pile, the pieces of comparable color into another pile, and so on. In general, before assembling the puzzle pieces into a picture, you will organize them so that the solution emerges with minimal trial-and-error effort. The lateral geniculate nucleus may perform an analogous sorting operation. The orderly arrangement of information within the LGN could help the next stage of visual processing begin piecing the puzzle together. This stage of processing takes place in the primary visual cortex, our next destination.

THE VISUAL CORTEX

The visual cortex is located at the very back of the cerebral hemispheres (see Figure 4.4), in a region called the **occipital lobe.** If you place your cupped hand on the back of your head just above the base of your skull, your hand will be resting over the occipital region. Actually, the occipital lobe consists of a cluster of neighboring brain regions each devoted to neural analyses of some aspects of the visual scene. Together, these areas comprise the visual cortex. One portion of the visual cortex—the primary visual cortex—receives input from the LGN, and it is anatomically more complex than the LGN. This anatomical complexity is paralleled by an increase in physiological complexity, particularly in the variety of receptive fields exhibited by cortical cells. But before tackling the anatomical and physiological details of this fascinating region of the brain, let's consider some important findings from clinical neurology that first pointed to the cortex as a major visual center.

Cortical Blindness

By the middle of the last century, neurologists had developed a keen interest in how the brain was subdivided. To examine its subdivisions, they removed localized regions of tissue from animals' brains and noted the behavioral consequences (this is the lesion technique described in Chapter 1). Using this technique, neurologists observed that an animal seemed to be blind after destruction of the posterior area of its cerebral hemispheres.

Clinical

At about the same time, case records began appearing in the medical literature describing permanent loss of vision in humans who had suffered brain damage in this area (Glickstein, 1988). This evidence also pointed to the occipital lobe as the visual center in humans. The most thorough set of case studies was published by the Irish neurologist Sir Gordon Holmes. Most of his patients were veterans of World War I with localized brain damage from gunshot wounds. Holmes (1918) measured areas of blindness within the visual field of each patient by moving a small spot of light throughout the field of view while the patient stared at a stationary point. The patient reported when the light was visible and when it was not. Holmes was thus able to locate patches of blindness, or **scotomas,** within the patient's visual field. (Recall from Chapter 2 the simple demonstration of the small scotoma in *your* visual field, associated with the optic disk; also, see Box 4.1.) Holmes compared the size and location of the scotoma with the extent and position of the damage within the occipital cortex.

His results showed that the visual field (and, by extension, the retina) is represented within the cortex in a very orderly, topographic fashion. The center of the visual field maps onto the posterior region of the occipital lobe, and the periphery of the field maps onto the anterior portion. The upper portion of the visual field is represented in the lower portion of the occipital lobe, and vice versa.

Holmes found that visual disturbances always appeared in the visual field contralateral to the damaged hemisphere of the brain. Thus, a wound to the left occipital lobe would be accompanied by blindness somewhere within the right visual field. Holmes also observed that the cortical map of the visual field appeared greatly distorted. The amount of cortical tissue devoted to the central portion of the field far exceeded the amount devoted to the periphery. This distortion, in which representation of the center of the field is highly exaggerated, has come to be known as **cortical magnification.** From a retinal perspective, cortical magnification means that a large portion of the cortex is devoted to a very small area of the retina (Azzopardi and Cowey, 1993). That area of the retina is the *fovea,* on which the central portion of the visual field is imaged (see Figure 4.7). Thus, the lion's share of the cortex is devoted to that region of the retina responsible for highly acute vision.

Holmes's clinical work provided the earliest description of the retinotopic map on the visual cortex. Since these pioneering studies, many other neuroscientists (such as, Teuber, Battersby and Bender, 1960) have cataloged the visual deficits that result from damage to various brain centers. We will describe some of these unusual and informative syndromes later in this and other chapters. In general, the unfortunate victims of accidents have greatly advanced scientific understanding of the anatomy of vision. As Box 4.2 indicates, even the study of persons who are totally blind can shed light on the neural basis of visual perception. Now let's look in more detail at the structures that are implicated in Holmes's clinical work.

Structure of the Visual Cortex

The primary visual cortex is that portion of the occipital lobe receiving input from the lateral geniculate nucleus. It is sometimes referred to as area V1, in recognition of its being the first in a hierarchy of cortical visual areas. Other names for this area include Area 17 (based on a postal-codelike labeling scheme, whereby neighboring, anatomically defined areas of the brain are sequentially numbered) and striate cortex

BOX 4.1

LOOK BOTH WAYS BEFORE CROSSING

Damage to different parts of the visual system produces predictable losses of vision within regions of the **visual field.** A visual field is easy to envision: while staring at some point straight ahead of you, your visual field is the entire region of space that is visible to you. Your attention is naturally focused on the center of the visual field, but you are aware of events occurring on the periphery as well.

Physicians and vision researchers use a routine procedure to measure a visual field; it is called **perimetry** (from the roots *peri,* meaning "around," and *metron,* meaning "measure"). While an individual has one eye covered and the open eye staring at a fixed point, a small, dim exploring spot is moved around slowly in front of that person's open eye, and the individual reports when the spot disappears. The positions where the spot disappears are traced out on a map of visual space. The map shows areas of sight (unshaded regions) and areas of blindness (shaded regions). Keep in mind that a visual field map describes visual space, not the retina. (To draw the map based on retinal geography requires inverting and reversing the map of visual space.)

A normal visual field map for each eye looks like the pair numbered 1 in the accompanying figure (for simplicity, the blind spot has been omitted). Note that the nose obscures the right portion of the left eye's view and the left portions of the right eye's view. Now suppose that because of some accident the left optic nerve were completely severed. This would totally eliminate the left eye's field, leaving the right eye's field intact. This situation is shown by the pair of maps numbered 2.

Let's consider a more complicated visual field loss. In humans, the pituitary gland lies immediately behind the middle of the optic chiasm. A tumor in the pituitary gland can press this structure against the chiasm, damaging the fibers that cross through the chiasm. These fibers, you will recall from Figure 4.2, originate from the nasal portion of each retina. The

resulting visual field loss will resemble that shown in the pair of maps numbered 3. The lost regions of visual space are those that are normally represented within the fibers originating from the nasal retinas.

Consider a case that is virtually the opposite of the one just described. The internal carotid arteries, branches of the prominent arteries in the neck, pass very near to the sides of the chiasm. These arteries can develop an **aneurysm,** a balloon-like bulge of the arterial wall. This bulge can push against the fibers that form the outer margin of the chiasm (recall that these are *un*crossed fibers). Thus, for example, an aneurysm of the left internal carotid artery would affect uncrossed fibers coming from the left eye; that is, fibers carrying information about the right half of the left eye's field. In this case, the visual field map would resemble the fourth pair of maps. See whether you can determine the visual field loss produced when *both* left and right internal carotid arteries have developed aneurysms, a condition that does occur at times.

This close connection between visual field loss and disease makes perimetry a very useful diagnostic tool. But there's one surprising aspect to visual field loss, even for severe cases such as those noted here: the person exhibiting the loss is often unaware of it! Apparently, by moving the eyes around, a person's residual visual field can provide coverage that's adequate for most situations. But sometimes the coverage proves inadequate, and the outcome may be fatal, as the following study documents.

Freytag and Sachs (1968) examined the records for a specific category of traffic accidents in Baltimore: pedestrians killed under circumstances suggesting that the victims should have seen the vehicle that struck and killed them. Autopsies revealed that the visual systems of some accident victims had been damaged *before* the accident. In these cases, the location and extent of that damage implied a visual field loss that explained the accident. In one case, for instance, a man was struck and killed by a car ap-

Execute

Clinical

BOX 4.1 continued

proaching from his right. Autopsy showed that his right optic nerve was completely atrophied. Consequently, if this man were looking straight ahead, a car approaching from his right would fall within the blind portion of his visual field. Thus, while this man's vision was probably good enough for his activities at home, his unsuspected visual deficit proved lethal when he had to cross the street.

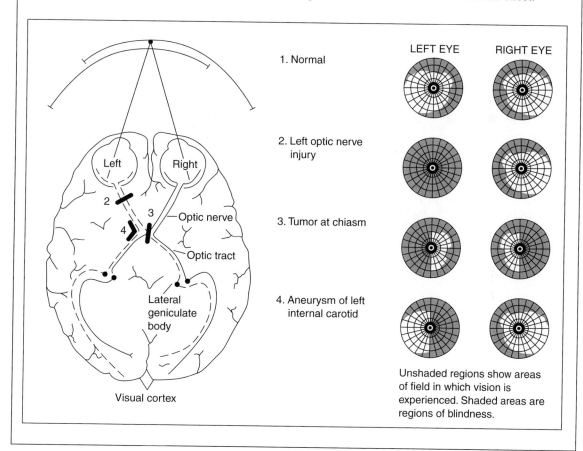

1. Normal

2. Left optic nerve injury

3. Tumor at chiasm

4. Aneurysm of left internal carotid

LEFT EYE   RIGHT EYE

Left   Right

2

3

4   Optic nerve

Optic tract

Lateral geniculate body

Visual cortex

Unshaded regions show areas of field in which vision is experienced. Shaded areas are regions of blindness.

(owing to the region's faintly striped appearance when seen under a low-power microscope). But the terms "V1," "Area 17," "striate cortex," and "primary visual cortex" all refer to the same portion of the brain.

Like the rest of the cerebral cortex, the visual area consists of a layered array of cells about 1.5–2.0 millimeters thick. In all, there are approximately 100 million cells in area V1 of each hemisphere, although this figure varies widely among normal people* (Andrews, Halpern and Purves, 1997).

Figure 4.8 is a magnified image of human brain tissue from V1. The tiny black dots denote the cell bodies of neurons located throughout the

---

*People in whom area V1 is exceptionally large also tend to have unusually large LGNs and large optic tracts. It is not known whether these people have superior visual abilities.

A

B

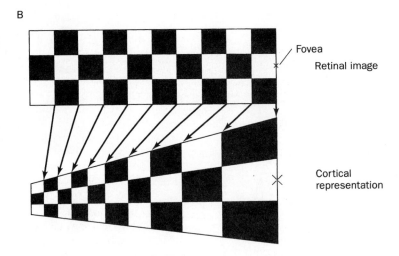

FIGURE 4.7
Imagine looking at the right-hand edge of a checkerboard pattern (A). The
resulting retinal image will look something like the upper portion of panel B.
Notice the position of the fovea in this image. By means of the processes
described in chapters 2 and 3, this retinal image is converted into neural signals
and is conveyed to the visual cortex via the LGN (represented by arrows in B).
The bottom portion of drawing B depicts how this retinal image is transcribed into
neural activity within the visual cortex. The size of each square in the cortical
representation is proportional to the *number* of cortical cells activated by any given
square on the checkered surface being viewed. (This is not to imply, however, that
a checkered pattern appears in the cortex.) Notice that the squares near the point of
fixation are expanded in the cortical representation. This expansion reflects the
disproportionately large number of cortical cells devoted to neural representation
of information falling on and near the fovea. Conversely, squares located far from
the point of fixation appear small in the cortical representation, reflecting the
relatively small number of cortical cells devoted to the peripheral retina.

2 mm thickness of the cortex. Here you can see
that the different layers vary in thickness and that
the concentration of cells varies from layer to
layer. The million or so axons arriving from the
six layers of the LGN connect with cortical cells
within layer 4 of the visual cortex. The axons of
cells from the magnocellular layers of the LGN
make their contacts within an upper subdivision
of cortical layer 4, while LGN axons from the
parvocellular LGN layers contact the lower sub-

Clinical

BOX 4.2

SOME ILLUMINATING FINDINGS ON BLINDNESS

Everyone knows what the word "blindness" means—an inability to see. However, two recent developments in neurology (the branch of medicine concerned with the nervous system) and ophthalmology (the branch of medicine concerned with disorders of vision and the eye) are forcing a reconsideration of the conception of blindness. One of these developments comes from an attempt to design an artificial eye that would permit the blind to see. The second development concerns the ability of people, who, despite blindness due to visual cortical damage, can still "see" in one sense. Let's consider each of these intriguing developments in more detail.

First, keep in mind that loss of sight can result from disease or injury affecting the photoreceptors in the retina, the fibers of the optic nerves, or various areas of the brain. If damaged photoreceptors are the cause of blindness, then in principle one could install a tiny electronic microcircuit that stimulated the ganglion cells directly, at least crudely mimicking the inputs from photoreceptors. Efforts to create such a device are underway (Rizzo and Wyatt, 1997). But if it's the ganglion cells themselves that are damaged, visual information cannot be relayed to higher brain centers that, in fact, may still be functional. In such cases, it is the absence of input that prevents sight.

For several decades researchers have been exploring the possibility of directly stimulating the visual cortex in blind patients with non-functioning eyes, thus bypassing the defective route to the cortex (Schmidt et al., 1996). The scheme would work something like this. The blind person would be outfitted with a small video camera that converted optical images of the environment into a pattern of electrical signals. This pattern of signals would then be applied directly to the person's visual cortex, through an array of electrodes placed directly on the surface of the brain (see accompanying illustration). It has long been known that direct stimulation of the visual cortex generates conscious visual sensations (Dobelle and Mladejovsky, 1974; Brindley and Lewin, 1968). Called *phosphenes,* these sensations are said to resemble small, glowing spots or grains of rice. Increasing the duration of the stimulating pulse makes the phosphenes brighter; occasionally, even colored phosphenes are reported, but most appear white. When several phosphenes are evoked simultaneously, patients describe seeing crude but recognizable shapes. Conceivably, this could provide the patient with useful information about the identity and location of objects in the environment. Before this procedure can be perfected, however, more work must be done to determine the number and placement of electrodes necessary to convey useful pattern information. In the meantime, this research very clearly demonstrates that the visual cortex *can* generate conscious visual sensations in the absence of input from the eyes.

Perhaps even more intriguing are the residual visual abilities of some cortically blind people. In these individuals, the eyes and optic nerves remain intact. Their permanent loss of sight results from damage to the visual cortex caused by an accident or stroke. The extent of the region of blindness (the *scotoma*) depends on the size of the damaged area of cortex. By definition, light flashed anywhere within this scotoma elicits no sensation of vision. Yet when asked to guess *where* a light is flashed within this blind region by *pointing* to it, these individuals can do so with reasonable accuracy. At the same time, they deny seeing any hint of the flash and describe the exercise as rather silly. Some patients can even direct their gaze toward an unseen light, can report the color or orientation of a visual stimulus, and can adjust their hands and fingers to grasp an object they cannot see! These puzzling abilities, summarized by Weiskrantz (1995), are all instances of what is termed **blindsight.**

The common denominator in all these studies is the use of **forced-choice testing** (see Appendix). With this procedure, an individual doesn't describe what is seen but rather judges where a stimulus is presented or when it is presented, guessing if necessary.

By what means can a blind person accurately "guess" the location of a flash he or she never saw? Think back to the superior colliculus, that subcortical

Execute

BOX 4.2 continued

area of the brain thought to be involved in visual orienting reflexes. Because it lies below the cerebral
hemispheres, the superior colliculus could be unaffected by injury to the visual cortex and hence remain
available to provide visual information for the guidance of hand or eye movements (Rafal et al., 1990).
Because in blindsight, behavior is divorced from
awareness, we might even conclude that subcortical
brain regions process visual information at an unconscious level. Some scientists are skeptical about this
hypothesis, however, arguing instead that small is-
lands of cortical tissue are still intact, and provide
crude but usable visual information for guidance of
the eyes or hand (Fendrich, Wessinger and Gazzaniga, 1992).

division of layer 4. From here, connections
within the cortex carry information to neurons in
other layers above and below layer 4 and, eventually, to other areas within the brain.

Recall that the regions between layers of the
LGN are populated with the small K cells. Their
axons, too, project to area V1 where they make
contact with cortical cells in layers 1, 2 and 3.
There's actually some disagreement among neu-
roanatomists about the exact boundary between
layers 3 and 4. Figure 4.8 shows the version
(Hässler, 1967) endorsed by Casagrande and Kaas
(1994). For our purposes, this controversy is beside
the point: everyone acknowledges that layer 4 is the
area that receives input from the P and M portions
of the LGN, with K cells projecting to upper layers.

What this picture cannot convey is the remarkable transformations of visual information
occurring within this cortical area. To appreciate
these transformations you must know something
about the visual stimuli necessary to activate
these cortical cells. This brings us to the research
of David Hubel and Torsten Wiesel, neurobiolo-
gists whose pioneering studies of the visual cortex earned them a Nobel Prize in 1981. Their discoveries and the subsequent work stimulated by

those discoveries have very greatly expanded our
understanding of the neural machinery of visual
perception. The following paragraphs highlight
some of those major findings.

Retinal Maps in the Cortex

The first notable property of cortical cells is that
each cell responds to stimulation of a restricted
area of the retina—this area constitutes that cell's
receptive field. You will recognize this property
as a continuation of the processing scheme inaugurated in the retina and carried forward in the
lateral geniculate nucleus: at each of these processing stages, individual cells analyze information from a limited area on the retina.

Considered as a group, the receptive fields of
cells in each hemisphere of V1 form a topographic
map of the contralateral visual field. This cortical
map, like its counterpart in the LGN, is said to be
topographic because adjacent regions of visual
space are mapped onto adjacent groups of cells in
the visual cortex. The map in each hemisphere is
said to represent the *contralateral* visual field because the left half of the visual field is represented
in the right hemisphere, and vice versa.

1
2
3
4A
4B
4Cα
4Cβ
5
6
wm

0.5 mm

FIGURE 4.8
Magnified picture of a section of brain tissue from the human visual cortex, with the various layers labeled. The top of the brain is situated just above layer 1. Below layer 6 lies the "white matter" of the brain, tissue consisting of the incoming axons from the LGN. Those LGN axons make connections with cortical neurons in layer 4. (Todd Preuss and Jon Kaas.)

Now let's consider *how* this map of the visual field is distributed over the cortex. Recall that Holmes's studies of brain-damaged people implied that a great deal of cortical area is devoted to representation of the fovea. This implication has since been confirmed by actually plotting the locations of receptive fields of cells sampled from

throughout the primate visual cortex (Hubel and Wiesel, 1974a). It is estimated that about 80 percent of the cells in the visual cortex are devoted to representing the central 10 degrees or so of the visual field (Drasdo, 1977). Earlier we pointed out that this exaggerated cortical mapping of central vision is referred to as cortical magnification.

Much of this bias toward the central portion of the visual field is inherited from the retina and the LGN. Remember from our discussion of the retina, that the number of ganglion cells subserving the fovea is considerably larger than the number devoted to the rest of the retina, even though in terms of area the periphery dwarfs the fovea. This foveal bias appears in the LGN's retinotopic map, too, where it is even further exaggerated (Malpelli and Baker, 1975). Moving on up to the cortex, the foveal representation swells to even greater proportions.

This magnified foveal representation makes sense when we consider the sizes of receptive fields of cortical cells representing different retinal eccentricities. Cells concerned with the fovea may be "looking at" a retinal area covered by no more than a few photoreceptors, whereas cells devoted to the periphery "look at" areas hundreds of times larger. Because foveal receptive fields are so small, it stands to reason that many cells may be required to cover a given patch of retina. In the representation of the periphery, a comparably sized patch of retina may be monitored by relatively few cells (recall Figure 4.7). This principle explains why local damage to visual cortex (from a bullet wound, for example) may produce scotomas of different size. Damage within the foveal representation will destroy cells with small receptive fields, yielding a small scotoma in the center of vision. Damage within the peripheral representation may destroy the same number of cells, but the scotoma will be considerably larger because those cells have bigger receptive fields. This large scotoma will also, of course, be located away from the center of gaze.

So, in effect, the bulk of the machinery in the visual cortex processes information about objects that are viewed directly. This is why head and eye movements play such a prominent role in seeing: such movements turn the eyes toward objects of current interest. These newly fixated objects then cast their images on the fovea, ensuring that those objects will receive the most detailed visual analysis possible by the visual cortex.

So far we've considered the orderly layout of cortical receptive fields and the resulting topographic map. Our discussion focused on *where* in the visual field different cortical cells are "looking." Now let's ask *what* each cell is "looking for." Exactly what kind of visual stimulus must be present within a cell's receptive field in order to evoke activity in that cell? On the basis of your knowledge of the retina and the geniculate, you can probably anticipate one fact: cortical cells are unconcerned about overall levels of illumination. Simply increasing or decreasing the ambient illumination has no appreciable impact on a cortical

cell's activity. Instead, cortical cells respond best to gradients in light intensity, such as those produced by borders, edges and lines. In this respect, cortical cells behave like their retinal and geniculate relatives from whom they inherit input. But cortical cells exhibit several notable characteristics not present in their precortical relatives, characteristics described in the following section.

Functional Properties of Cortical Cells

Orientation Selectivity   One of the most striking characteristics of cortical cells is their **orientation selectivity.** Recall that retinal and geniculate cells, because of their circular-shaped receptive fields, respond indiscriminately to all orientations. In marked contrast, most cortical cells are very fussy about the orientation of a stimulus. As shown in Figure 4.9, any particular cell will respond only if the orientation of an

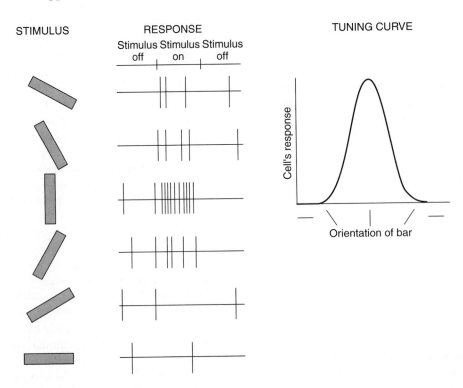

FIGURE 4.9
Response of a single cortical cell to bars presented at various orientations.

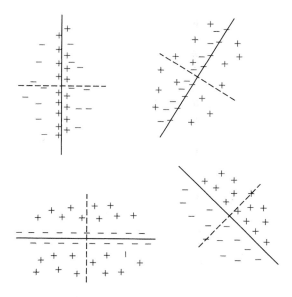

FIGURE 4.10
Layout of ON regions (+) and OFF regions (−) of several representative cortical receptive fields. The ON regions are sometimes called "excitatory zones" and the OFF regions, "inhibitory zones."

edge or line falls somewhere within a rather narrow range. Each cortical cell has a "preferred" orientation, one to which it is maximally responsive. If a line tilts a little away from this optimum, the cell's response is markedly decreased; if the line tilts even more, the cell no longer responds at all. This behavior can be summarized by graphing a cell's response strength as a function of orientation. The resulting "tuning curve" resembles a teepee with its peak defining the cell's preferred orientation (see the right-hand portion of Figure 4.9).

The preferred orientation of a V1 cell can typically be sharply defined. In many cells, a tilt of no more than 15 degrees away from the optimum orientation is sufficient to abolish that cell's response completely. An angular deviation this small corresponds to about the difference in position of a clock's hand at 12:00 and at 12:03! Just about all V1 cells are selective for orientation, although those in cortical layer 4 are not

nearly so finely tuned for orientation as those outside of layer 4 (Leventhal et al., 1995). Likewise, regularly spaced patches of cells near the cortical surface show only coarse orientation selectivity. In all other regions of V1 outside these restricted areas, orientation matters greatly.

Let's take a look at the layout of ON regions and OFF regions comprising the receptive fields of some cortical cells. From these layouts you should be able to see why these cells are selective for orientation. Some representative cortical receptive fields are shown in Figure 4.10. There, you can see that receptive fields are elongated, not circular, as in retinal and geniculate cells. Notice, too, that the discrete zones of ON and OFF activity are arranged differently depending on the particular cell. Simply by inspecting these various arrangements, you should be able to picture what kind of oriented stimulus would evoke the best response from a given cell. For this reason, cortical cells with these well-delineated zones are called **simple cells:** there is a simple relation between their receptive field layout and their preferred stimulus. For cells of this type, a properly oriented bar or edge must be positioned exactly within the receptive field to yield a large neural response—changing either the orientation or position of the stimulus will reduce the cell's response. This specificity of response means that simple cells are able to signal the orientation of a stimulus falling within a particular region of the visual field.

Other cortical cells do not have such well-defined ON and OFF zones, yet they also exhibit a preference for a particular orientation. These are called **complex cells** because it is more complicated to predict just what stimulus will optimally activate them. Just looking at their responses to spots or bars of light does not give us a map of the best shaped target. Unlike simple cells, complex ones will respond to an appropriately oriented stimulus falling anywhere within the boundaries of the receptive field—precise location is not nearly so important for a complex cell, so long as the stimulus falls somewhere within its receptive field and remains properly oriented.

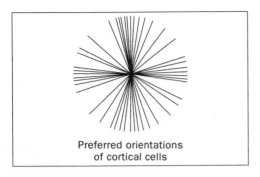

FIGURE 4.11
The distribution of orientation selectivity from a sample of
neurons in the primary visual cortex (V1) of a monkey.
Each line designates a given neuron's preferred orientation.
(Redrawn from Mansfield, 1974).

FIGURE 4.12
Test figures for experiencing the oblique effect. Follow the
instructions given in the text.

There is a third category of cortical cells, called
hypercomplex cells, whose responses depend not
only on contour orientation but contour length as
well. These cells will give their maximum response
to an appropriately oriented bar whose length and
width "fits" their receptive field. Extending the
bar's length beyond this optimum value dramatically reduces the cell's response.

Within area V1, preferred orientation varies
from cell to cell; and within an ensemble of cells,
all orientations are represented. However, the distribution of preferred orientations is not uniform.
Recordings made from many cells in the visual
cortex of the monkey reveal a distinct bias in favor
of the principal axes, vertical and horizontal. Figure 4.11 (adapted from Mansfield, 1974) illustrates this finding. In this polar plot, each line represents the preferred orientation of a single cortical
cell. As you can see, while all orientations are represented, there is a clustering of cells that prefer
vertical and another clustering of cells that prefer
horizontal. The unevenness of this anisotropic distribution is most pronounced among cells with receptive fields close to and within the fovea. This
raises two intriguing questions: What are the perceptual consequences of this bias in favor of vertical and horizontal? And what factors produce this
bias in the first place? The following section addresses these two questions.

The Oblique Effect   Long before the discovery
of orientation-selective cortical cells, vision scientists had noted that horizontal and vertical lines
can be detected more easily and identified more
rapidly than can lines oriented obliquely. For instance, visual acuity is highest for vertical and
horizontal lines, and lowest for lines oriented 45
degrees in either direction from vertical. Compared to horizontal or vertical lines, oblique lines
are also more difficult to see when the contrast of
the lines is faint. (**Contrast** refers to the difference in intensity between the dark lines and their
light background.)

You can experience the oblique effect by looking at the two bar patterns in Figure 4.12. Prop the
book up so that you can view the pair of patterns
from a distance. Backing away from the book,
you should discover that at some distance the thin
vertical bars remain visible while the diagonal
ones blend together and are, thus, unresolvable.
By turning the book sideways, you can repeat this
exercise, now comparing horizontal to diagonal.

This general superiority in the visibility of horizontal and vertical is called the **oblique effect**
(Appelle, 1972). Most people experience the
oblique effect, but there are some individuals who
do not. In fact, others show the opposite tendency:
they see oblique lines of a particular orientation
more clearly. Usually, those who fail to experience the oblique effect or who show a reverse
oblique effect have some degree of astigmatism.
Recall from Chapter 2 that astigmatism (an irreg-

Execute

Clinical

ularly curved cornea) causes contours of certain orientations to appear blurred while other orientations appear sharply focused. Depending on the direction of the astigmatism, this condition can nullify the normal oblique effect, and it can also lead to a superiority in vision for oblique lines, a sort of reverse oblique effect. Interestingly, in cases where oblique is favored, the bias endures even when the astigmatism is optically corrected, thereby making all orientations equally sharp on the retina (Mitchell et al., 1973). This condition is called **meridional amblyopia** ("amblyopia" literally means "dull vision," and refers to a visual loss that cannot be corrected optically). Apparently the astigmatism, prior to optical correction, altered the brain in a direction favoring oblique over horizontal and vertical. In fact, animals made artificially astigmatic exhibit just such alterations— cortical cells in these animals prefer orientations centered around the one most clearly focused, with very few cells responding preferentially to the blurred, astigmatic orientation (Freeman and Pettigrew, 1973). The ability of biased visual experience to alter the orientation preferences of cortical cells provides a ready explanation for meridional amblyopia. Presumably, people with this condition have a paucity of cortical cells tuned to the previously blurred orientation. This finding may also help us understand the neural basis of the oblique effect in people who are *not* astigmatic but who *do* see horizontal and vertical more clearly. Why would the visual cortex in nonastigmatic individuals exhibit a preference for horizontal and vertical over oblique?

Plasticity At present, there are two general theories. One attributes the bias to the carpentered environment in which most people grow up (Annis and Frost, 1973). According to this idea, people receive more exposure to vertical and to horizontal contours than to oblique contours, because horizontal and vertical exist in abundance within an urban landscape of houses and buildings. Indeed, measurements have confirmed an overabundance of horizontal- and vertical-oriented contours in both our indoor and outdoor environments (Coppola et al., 1998). This biased visual exposure,

the theory continues, influences the development of orientation preferences among the cortical cells. This theory is supported by animal studies demonstrating that the brain *is* susceptible to biased visual experience early in life (Blakemore and Cooper, 1970; Hirsch and Spinelli, 1970). The carpentered environment theory also receives support from studies testing the vision of people who grew up in agrarian environments where no particular orientation predominates. These individuals *fail* to exhibit an oblique effect (Annis and Frost, 1973), presumably because their brains did not receive a heavy dose of vertical and horizontal contours.

As an alternative to this environmental theory of the oblique effect, another view attributes the neural bias for horizontal and vertical to unspecified genetic factors that operate to favor the development of cortical cells tuned to horizontal and vertical (Timney and Muir, 1976). Those who favor this genetic theory point to the fact that infants only a few months old exhibit an oblique effect (Leehey et al., 1975). It is hard to imagine, this theory argues, how visual experience could already have shaped the brains of infants so young.

The debate about origins of the oblique effect is really part of a larger concern with the genesis of orientation selectivity of neurons in the visual cortex. Is experience necessary for the development of oriented cortical cells, or is orientation selectivity an intrinsic property of the visual cortex present from birth? As we so often see in science, the emerging consensus appears to be a compromise of both views: some degree of orientation selectivity is specified by genetically controlled, intrinsic connections, but these connections are modifiable by environmentally determined experience (Sengpiel, Stawinski and Bonhoeffer, 1999). For another interesting twist on the link between visual-orientation perception and cortical physiology, see Box 4.3.

Selectivity for Direction of Motion Besides preferring contours of a particular orientation, a large subset of cortical cells also respond best

Neural

BOX 4.3

WHAT'S UP?

If asked to point your index finger in the *upward* direction, you'd readily point to the ceiling. You'd do the same thing if you were lying on your side or on your back or, for that matter, if you were standing on your head. We automatically interpret *up* in terms of gravitational coordinates. The fixed reference frame for *up* is possible because our brain keeps track of gravity's pull, using information from the vestibular system housed in the inner ear. (The vestibular system registers the body's movements and its position in space.)

Now, what about the orientation of the contours on the left- and right-hand sides of this box? You'd immediately label them "vertical" and you'd be correct. But tilt your head sideways (keeping the book stationary), and look at the contours. What is the orientation of the contours now? If you're like most people, you'd stick with "vertical" because you reference their orientation with respect to gravity. This tendency to judge orientation based on gravity is called **orientation constancy** because an object's perceived orientation remains constant even when we turn our heads.

Are the orientation-selective cells in area V1 of your brain smart enough to keep track of which way your head is tilted? Does a cell that prefers "vertical" when your head is upright continue to prefer "vertical" when your head is tilted? To find out, suppose we perform the following experiment.

Execute

We train an alert monkey to remain seated in a chair with its eyes fixated on the center of a video monitor. From an electrode implanted in area V1 of the monkey's brain, we record responses from orientation-selective cells. With the monkey sitting upright, suppose we locate a cell whose preferred orientation is "vertical" (see Figure 4.9). This cell's response dwindles considerably when the contour within its receptive field deviates from vertical by as little as 25 degrees in either direction. Now suppose we tilt the chair in which the monkey is sitting, rotating the monkey's body and head 25 degrees clockwise from upright. Unlike the monkey, the video monitor isn't rotated, so now the "vertical" contour on the monitor is oriented 25 degrees counterclockwise on the monkey's retina. What happens to the V1 cell's response? Does the cell continue to respond vigorously, taking into account the head's tilted position? Or does the cell fall silent because the image of the contour no longer matches the retinal coordinates of its receptive field? For nearly all V1 cells studied, the preferred orientation is tied to retinal coordinates. Turning the head silences the cells. To resurrect their responses, the orientation of the contour must be tilted by an amount sufficient to match the body's tilt. This means, then, that V1 cells don't know whether the orientation of a contour has changed or whether the tilt of the head has changed. Evidently, V1 cells don't have access to the vestibular information necessary to specify orientation in gravitational coordinates.

Fortunately, visually activated cells in other regions of the brain are not so uninformed. Cells in a higher visual area, called V3, do respond to orientations specified in gravitational coordinates (Sauvan and Peterhans, 1999). Tilting the monkey tilts the preferred orientation of those cells. Evidently, these cells do receive information about gravity necessary to compensate for bodily rotation.

Think back to the oblique effect described in the text. Our perceptual bias for horizontal and vertical contours, like the responses of V1 neurons, is tied to retinal coordinates. When you tilt your head sideways 45 degrees, oblique contours are more visible than vertical ones (where oblique and vertical refer to gravitationally defined orientations). This is strong evidence that the oblique effect originates within the V1 area. On other, more complex, tasks that involve vertical, horizontal and oblique contours, however, human performance *is* governed by gravitationally defined orientation (Marendaz et al., 1993). So, what's *up* depends on what you're up to.

BAR MOVING THROUGH
RECEIVE FIELD

RESPONSE

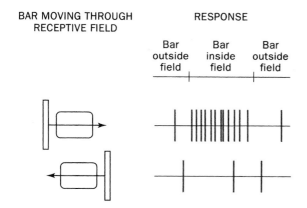

FIGURE 4.13
Response of a complex cell to a bar moving through the cell's receptive field (shown in outline) either from left to right or from right to left.

when those contours *move* through their receptive fields. Among these movement-sensitive cells, simple cells tend to prefer relatively slow moving contours, while complex cells can respond even when contours travel rapidly across the receptive field. Movement-sensitive cells typically respond to one *direction* of motion only. For instance, a cortical cell (like the complex cell illustrated in Figure 4.13) might give a burst of activity when a vertical contour moved from left to right, but would remain unresponsive when that same contour moved in the opposite direction, right to left. A different cell might respond only to a contour moving from right to left. This property—known as **direction selectivity**—suggests that this class of cells plays an important role in motion perception. We'll return to this idea when we discuss motion perception in Chapter 9.

In area V1, direction-selective cells respond vigorously when an appropriately oriented contour sweeps through their receptive fields. These cells also respond when an eye movement sweeps the receptive field across a stationary contour. In both cases, the image of the contour moves through the cells' receptive fields and the cells respond to this movement. Their responses,

in other words, are ambiguous with respect to the source of image motion (Ilg and Thier, 1996). Yet when we look about the world, we don't usually confuse image motion caused by eye movement with image motion caused by a moving object. Evidently, the motion signals generated in V1 cells are made unambiguous in later stages of processing.

Size Selectivity   We've already mentioned that receptive fields of cortical cells vary in size, with those in the fovea being smallest, and those in the periphery, the largest. This is true for both simple and complex cells. Moreover, in any given region of the visual field there is also some variation in field size. Thus, some cells have receptive fields favoring, say, a narrow vertical bar, while others prefer a wider bar. This is reminiscent of the situation in the retina (recall Figure 3.9) and the lateral geniculate nucleus. But in the cortex, orientation selectivity is combined with size selectivity.

There are other, more subtle, distinctions between simple and complex cells (see, for example, Lehky, Sejnowski and Desimone, 1992), as well as other cell types with even more complicated receptive fields. But for the present, let's refocus our attention on a property that all these cell types seem to have in common, binocularity.

Binocularity   Recall that information from the two eyes is distributed in separate layers of each lateral geniculate nucleus, with individual cells receiving input from either one eye or the other. This ocular segregation is retained in layer 4, the cortical layer receiving input from the LGN. Only now the left and right eye cells are segregated into snake-like stripes, which can easily be visualized by injecting specially labeled dye into area V1 (Horton and Hocking, 1996; Menon et al., 1997). Figure 4.14 shows a magnified view of ocular dominance stripes in postmortem tissue from human area V1. The interdigitated stripes of cells innervated by the right and left eyes appear as alternating light and dark gray

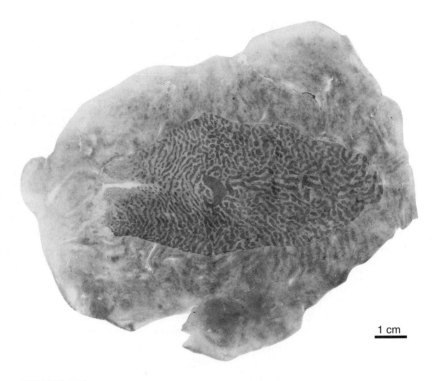

1 cm

FIGURE 4.14
Magnified photograph showing the ocular dominance stripes of a piece of postmortem
tissue from layer 4 of human area V1. The alternating light and dark bands correspond
to the array of cells receiving input from the right and left eyes, respectively. Each stripe
is approximately 1 millimeter in width. (Jonathan Horton.)

bands. This approximately 1-millimeter-wide
banded slice of tissue cuts across layer 4.

Cells in layer 4, in turn, send signals to other
cortical layers immediately above them, and at
this stage, **monocular** (meaning "one eye") *segregation* gives way to **binocular** (meaning "two
eyes") *integration*. Within area V1, and outside
layer 4, individual cells, with few exceptions, are
innervated from both eyes.

Figure 4.15 shows how a typical cortical cell
responds to stimulation of the two eyes. This particular cell responds moderately well to a line
presented to either eye alone, but its response is
even stronger when both eyes are stimulated simultaneously. Some cells respond more vigorously to stimulation of the left eye, whereas other

cells favor right-eye stimulation. This variation in
the relative strength of the connection between
the two eyes is called **ocular dominance.** Any
cell that can be excited through both eyes, regardless of its ocular dominance, is called a
binocular cell.

Because they can be excited by either eye, all
binocular cells actually have two receptive fields:
one for the left eye and one for the right eye. The
two fields of a binocular cell are nearly always
matched in type (simple or complex), preferred
orientation, and preferred direction of motion. If,
for instance, the cell responds best to a horizontal
line moving upward in front of the left eye, then
upward movement of a horizontal line will evoke
the largest response via the right eye as well.

RECEPTIVE FIELD LAYOUT
WITH STIMULUS
SUPERIMPOSED

RESPONSE

FIGURE 4.15
Response of a single cortical cell to stimulation of the left eye, right eye, and both eyes. The plus and minus signs show the receptive field layout for this cell.

The two receptive fields for any particular binocular cell also fall on approximately equivalent regions of the two eyes. Thus, if one field is located to the right of the fovea in one eye, the other field will fall to the right of the fovea in the other eye. In general, binocular cortical cells respond most strongly when corresponding regions of each eye are stimulated by forms of corresponding size and orientation.

With this correspondence in mind, think for a moment about where a single object must be situated in the world in order to maximally activate the cell we've just described. To begin, suppose the two eyes fixate a point in the center of a viewing screen, as shown in Figure 4.16. In order for stimulation of the right eye to activate the binocular cell described above, an object has to be located within the area of the screen labeled "right eye" (see panel A). Note, though, that at this position the image of that object does not fall within the cell's receptive field in the left eye. So at this position, stimulation of the left eye would not activate the binocular cell. To be imaged within the left

eye's receptive field, and therefore activate this cell, the object must be displaced laterally on the screen, closer to the point of fixation (see panel B). Note, however, that in this location the image of the object no longer falls within the right eye's receptive field. In fact, there is no single position *on* the viewing screen where one object could simultaneously stimulate both the left and right eyes' receptive fields. But there is a position *in front of* the screen that could accomplish this, as shown in panel C. When the object is at a particular location in front of the screen (and hence closer to the eyes), both receptive fields are stimulated.

Similarly, for each binocular cell there will be one position in three-dimensional space where the two receptive fields can be simultaneously stimulated. This position will vary, of course, from cell to cell, depending on the retinal placement of the pair of receptive fields for a given cell.

Take a minute to be sure you understand why this is so. A little extra effort at this point will pay nice dividends when we talk about binocular depth perception in Chapter 8. As you will learn then, the layout of binocular receptive fields plays an important role in one's ability to judge the distance from one object to another. For now, though, you should appreciate two properties of binocular cells: they respond preferentially to the same type of stimulus in both eyes, and the relative positions of the two receptive fields of a cell specify the location of the stimulus that will optimally excite the cell.

Color   Besides orientation, direction of motion and binocularity, some cortical cells in area V1 also register information about color. Some of these color-sensitive cells are concentrated in bloblike regions regularly spaced throughout the upper layers of visual cortex (Livingstone and Hubel, 1984), while others are found outside these regions (Lennie, Krauskopf and Sclar, 1990). Each of these so-called **blobs** contains neurons that receive their inputs from the lower subdivision of layer 4, the one innervated by color-selective cells of the parvocellular pathway.

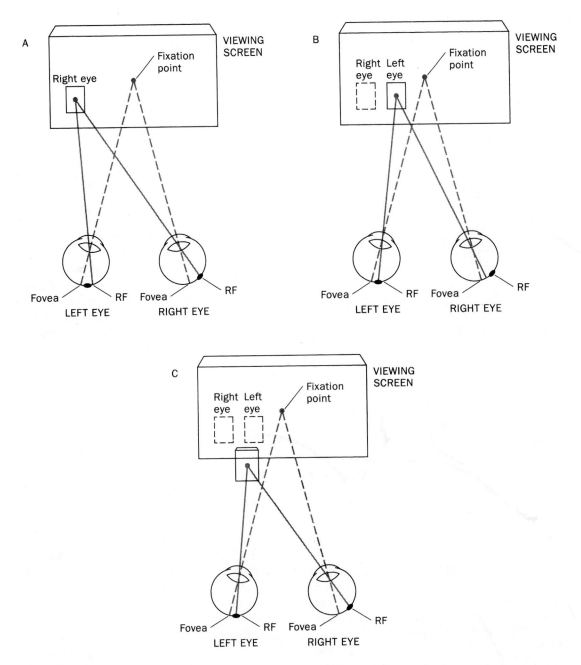

FIGURE 4.16
This series of drawings illustrates why a single object must be situated in a particular location in visual space to optimally stimulate both receptive fields (RFs) of a single binocular cell. For details, see the text.

Cells in the blobs constitute one of the unusual cortical groups that show no strong preference for contour orientation. Blob cells do, however, exhibit a complex form of color opponency, wherein the effect of a color (excitatory versus inhibitory) depends on whether that color falls within the center or the surround of the cell's receptive field.

Having summarized the major response properties of V1 cells, let's look at how two of these properties—orientation and binocularity—are arranged within the cortex.

Columns and Hypercolumns   Earlier we mentioned that cortical cells vary in their preferred orientations, some responding best to vertical, others to horizontal, and still others to orientations in between. These orientation-selective cells are not haphazardly arranged; they are grouped in a very orderly fashion within the cortex. To envision this grouping, imagine we are able to unfold the visual cortex so that this thin, layered sheet of tissue is lying flat. Now suppose we randomly se-

lect a position somewhere on the surface of this unfolded cortex. Starting here, we gradually move straight downward through the various layers in a direction perpendicular to the surface of the cortex. Throughout our short, 2-millimeter journey we carefully catalog the preferred orientation of each cell encountered. After penetrating all six cortical layers, we will discover that all cells along the path of this penetration have identical preferred orientations (except for cells in layer 4, which respond to *all* orientations). Along the way, there may be variation in the size of these cells' receptive fields, and some are likely to prefer edges while others prefer bars. But *all* cells will exhibit the same orientation preference.

Suppose we now repeat this sampling procedure, this time beginning at a position just a fraction of a millimeter away from our initial penetration. Now we will find that all cells prefer an orientation slightly different from the one encountered in the first sample. This is illustrated in Figure 4.17.

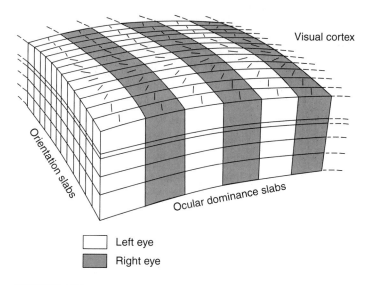

FIGURE 4.17
Orientation and ocular dominance columns in the visual cortex. All cells in a column have the same orientation preference and the same ocular dominance. An aggregate of columns representing a complete range of preferences is known as a hypercolumn.

Note that the preferred orientation has changed by about 10 degrees from the first sample to the second one. If we repeat this sampling procedure over and over, always being careful to make the penetrations perpendicular to the cortical surface, we will uncover a regular sequence of preferred orientations. Each time we make a new penetration, spacing it about 0.05 millimeter from the last one, the preferred orientation will change by about 10 to 15 degrees. By the time we have sampled a strip of cortex less than a millimeter in width, the sequence of preferred orientations will have progressed through one complete rotation. This regular progression through a complete set of orientations is comparable to the range of positions assumed by the second hand of a clock as it advances from vertical (at 12:00 o'clock) to horizontal (at 3:00 o'clock) and back to vertical (at 6:00 o'clock). This tidy packaging of orientation-selective cells recurs throughout the visual cortex (Hubel and Wiesel, 1974b).

As we make these repeated samplings, another intriguing regularity emerges: within a given penetration perpendicular to the cortical surface, all cells have the same ocular dominance. If the first cell encountered responds strongest to stimulation of the right eye, all cells in that sequence will be right-eye dominant (with the exception of the monocular cells in layer 4). Moreover, if we now make another sampling penetration right next to the first one, the cells encountered will exhibit a different pattern of ocular dominance, perhaps responding equally well to stimulation of either eye. So ocular dominance—like preferred orientation—varies systematically as we move laterally over the cortex. This, too, is illustrated in Figure 4.17.

At first, all these facts may seem bewildering. But taken together, they produce an interesting and coherent picture. The visual cortex appears to be composed of columns of cells, with each column consisting of a stack of cells all preferring the same orientation and exhibiting the same ocular dominance.* Altogether, it takes roughly eighteen to twenty neighboring columns to cover

a complete range of stimulus orientations and ocular dominance. This aggregation of adjacent columns is collectively known as a **hypercolumn.** Each hypercolumn contains tens of thousands of cells whose receptive fields all overlap on the same retinal territory. The hypercolumns themselves are all uniform in size throughout the cortex, but the hypercolumns devoted to the central retina deal with a much smaller area of retina than do the hypercolumns concerned with the peripheral retina. This emphasis on central vision, you will recognize, is the principle of cortical magnification described earlier in this chapter.

Hence each hypercolumn contains neural machinery for analyzing visual information within a local region of the retina. Throughout the entire visual cortex there are many such hypercolumns, each receiving input from different portions of the retina. Working simultaneously, the hypercolumns analyze multiple aspects of the retinal image—orientation, direction of motion, binocularity, size—in a local, piecemeal fashion. Each hypercolumn provides a "description" of that portion of the image falling within its own, restricted field of view. This description is embodied within the activity of cells in the constituent columns of the hypercolumn.

At the end of this chapter we shall consider how these cells might be involved in aspects of visual perception. For the moment, though, let's consider what might transpire within the visual cortex as a person stares with both eyes open at a very large picture composed exclusively of, say, vertical lines. This visual stimulus should maximally activate those cells in the cortex which prefer a vertical orientation, and since both eyes are

---

*Besides containing columns for orientation and ocular dominance, area V1 also contains an orderly map of preferred directions of motion (Weliky, Bosking and Fitzpatrick, 1996). Thus, neighboring cells respond best to similar but not identical directions of motion. The systematic map of direction selectivity is interdigitated with the orientation map in a manner that divides a given orientation column into cells preferring opposite directions of motion.

open, ocular dominance preference should not matter. Cells signalling all other orientations would respond much less vigorously or not at all. Now suppose we could look directly at the person's cortex and visualize those cells activated by the vertical lines. On the basis of what you have just learned about the organization of the cortex, can you imagine what we would see?

Because the orientation and ocular dominance columns are more or less evenly spaced throughout the entire cortex, we should see regular patches of active cells interspersed among patches of inactive ones. And, in fact, this is exactly what is seen. Vivien Casagrande and her colleagues actually measured orientation columns in a small primate called a galago. Its brain is organized much like that of the macaque monkey and of humans. The galago viewed an array of oriented lines while, at the same time, the investigators used an optical imaging procedure to measure local blood flow in the animal's visual cortex. (Optical imaging resembles functional magnetic resonance imaging, except that its spatial resolution is much better because the measurements are being taken directly from the surface of the brain.) The display was large, and the bars moved back and forth to ensure that the visual cortex received a healthy dose of visual stimulation at a given orientation.

Figure 4.18 shows what those investigators saw when the grating's bars were vertically oriented. In this photograph, we're looking down onto the cortical surface, so the columns are parallel to your line of sight. The black patches denote highly active regions of cortex; the white regions, are areas of no activity. The regularly spaced dark patches correspond to the columns of cortical cells activated by the vertical bars. The lighter patches in between denote regions of cortex containing cells unresponsive during the stimulation period.

Casagrande and colleagues repeated these measurements, using horizontal gratings. As you would expect, the previously white regions now appeared dark (denoting activation) and the re-

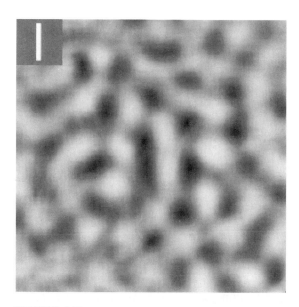

FIGURE 4.18
Magnified picture of a flattened slice of visual cortex from a galago (a small primate species), viewed from above. The dark regions show activated columns of neurons associated with viewing a set of vertical bars. (Vivien Casagrande.)

gions darkened by "vertical" now appeared white in response to horizontal. Measuring the distance between the centers of the dark patches (where maximum activity was concentrated) yields a value close to half a millimeter. This corresponds nicely to the dimension of an individual hypercolumn estimated from physiological recordings of cortical cells.

These elegant imaging experiments substantiate that orientation-selective neurons are packed in columns. To test your understanding of the material on hypercolumns, suppose these animals had been exposed to a set of lines that slowly rotated through all orientations. What would the distribution of local blood flow have looked like then? And what if, while viewing all orientations, the galago's vision had been confined to just one eye?

This completes our overview of the receptive field properties of cells and the architecture of hypercolumns in the visual receiving stage of the brain, area V1. As mentioned at the outset of this section, our survey just hits the highlights of this stage in visual processing. Neurophysiologists have studied cortical cells in considerably greater detail than we've gone into here. They have also begun to unravel the neural circuitry (that is, the connections between cortical cells) underlying such receptive field properties as orientation selectivity. Although fascinating, that research is not immediately germane to the questions about visual perception that will occupy our attention in the next several chapters.

VISUAL PROCESSING BEYOND AREA V1

So far in this chapter, we have been focusing on cells in area V1, where a relatively early stage in visual processing occurs. From this stage, neural information is distributed over a number of pathways to higher visual areas of the brain. Figure 4.19 represents one attempt to summarize the connections among the multitude of brain areas that can be visually activated (Felleman and Van Essen, 1991). Each labeled box represents a different visual area, starting with the retina (RGC), LGN and V1 at the bottom. These visual areas are distributed widely throughout the cerebral cortex.

Most of the details of this wiring diagram are not so important for our purposes; they simply underscore the large number and hierarchical arrangement of these brain areas associated with vision. However, the pathways denoted by thick lines are of interest, for they represent the neural pathways formed by the P and M systems. From our earlier discussion of inputs to V1 from LGN, you will recall that the P and M cells remain segregated within area V1. This segregation remains in effect through the first several stages of processing following V1. Thus, the M pathway projects through V1 via certain parts of V2 to area MT. The P pathway, in contrast, projects to an anatomically distinct area of V2 and then on to V4. There are also direct M projections from V1 to MT and direct P projections from V1 to V4. Within each of these areas—V1, V2, V4 and MT—there exists an orderly retinotopic map.

The flow of information within this complex network is not unidirectional. Every cortical region receiving input from another region also sends feedback connections back to that other region. Thus, for example, portions of area V1 provide input to area V4, which, in turn, sends neural messages back to V1. Then portions of V2 send signals to area MT, which broadcasts its own signals back to V2. In addition, those visual areas activated by the P and M pathways are richly interlinked, with the neural operations carried out in one set of areas influencing the operations carried out within the others (see the review by Gegenfurtner, Kiper, and Fenstemaker, 1996).

Judging from the receptive field properties of cells in these various areas (Maunsell and Newsome, 1987; Merigan and Maunsell, 1993), some areas appear specialized for analyzing information about color (for instance, area V4) and about object shape (areas forming the IT complex in the upper right portion of Figure 4.19), whereas other areas are more concerned with motion (areas MT and MST). There is even a brain region (the two areas labelled STP in Figure 4.19) containing neurons responsive only to human faces viewed from particular angles (Perrett et al., 1991; Desimone, 1991).

Neural

The Duality of Visual Processing

The idea that vision consists of multiple, distinct pathways is deeply ingrained in contemporary thinking. The roots for this idea can be traced back to the 1960s, when vision scientists spoke about an "ambient" system that registered where objects in space were located and a "focal" system that registered the identities of those objects (Schneider, 1969). The focal system was often identified with cortical structures and the ambient system with subcortical structures. In the 1980s "focal" and "ambient" vision gave way to another version of this "dual systems" hypothesis, a version positing the existence of two separate cortical pathways, or streams, as they were sometimes called (Mishkin, Ungerleider and

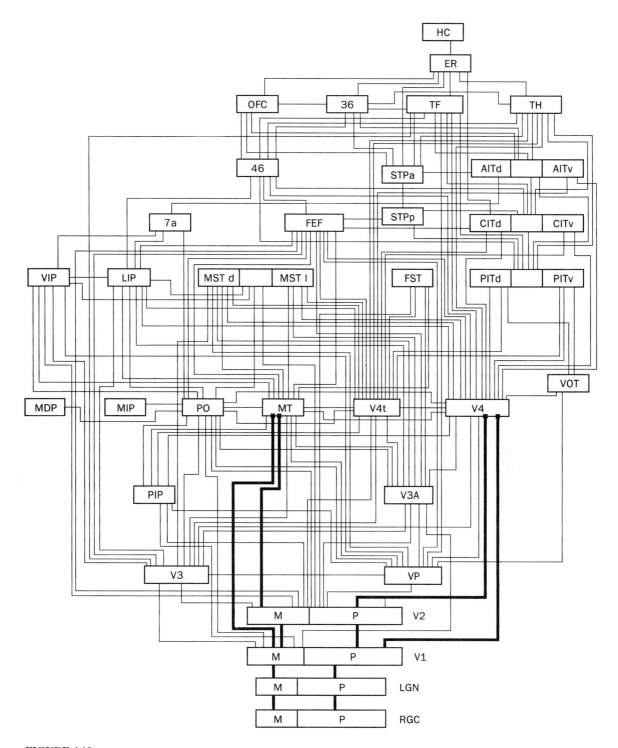

FIGURE 4.19

Diagram showing the hierarchical arrangement of visual processing stages, starting with the retina (bottom of diagram) and moving up through the multiple visual areas of the brain. The bold lines show the P and M pathways discussed in the text. (Adapted from Felleman and Van Essen, 1996.)

Macko, 1983). One pathway, the so-called **parietal** stream, consisted of visual areas laid out along a trajectory leading from occipital to parietal brain regions (recall Figure 4.4). This stream, it was thought, is concerned with the locations of objects in space. Some researchers termed it the "where" pathway. The second pathway, the **temporal** stream, comprised a network of visual areas spanning the occipital and temporal lobes. This stream was thought to be involved in object identification and, therefore, was often referred to as the "what" pathway. You will sometimes see the parietal pathway referred to as the **dorsal** stream since it projects into more dorsal parts of the brain (dorsal refers to the upper parts of the brain). The "temporal" pathway, in this nomenclature, is dubbed the **ventral** stream because it projects into more ventral (lower) parts of the brain.

You can probably see the similarity between the "what/where" model and the earlier "focal/ambient" model—the two differ primarily in terms of the anatomical structures embodying the separate pathways. Looking again at Figure 4.19 you may also deduce that the "what" and "where" pathways are more or less synonymous with the P and M pathways. As originally proposed by Livingstone and Hubel (1988), the P and M pathways were thought to carry information about color and form (P pathway) and about depth and motion (M pathway). As we shall discuss in a moment, behavioral experiments have provided qualified support for some parts of the P/M model.

More recent, detailed anatomical studies reveal, however, that the P and M systems do not remain strictly segregated throughout the visual cortex (Sawatari and Callaway, 1996); contributions from both P and M cells can be traced into both the parietal and temporal pathways.

The latest incarnation of the dual systems hypothesis provides a somewhat different interpretation of the functions of the parietal and temporal pathways (Goodale and Milner, 1992). According to this version of the hypothesis, our visual awareness of objects and events arises from activity in structures comprising the temporal pathway. This pathway would constitute the machinery responsible for the "seeing" aspect of vision that we ordinarily associate with "perception." Activity in the parietal pathways, in contrast, is responsible for directing and guiding our activities within the visual environment, activities such as orienting toward and reaching for objects of interest. This constitutes the "action" part of vision.

In our everyday lives, we don't stop to think that these two aspects of vision—seeing and acting—might be dissociated. Yet brain damage to certain regions within the parietal system can throw the two aspects into sharp relief. Goodale and Milner (1992) describe a tragic case where a young woman suffered localized brain damage caused by anoxia from inadvertent carbon monoxide poisoning. Fortunately, the patient retained her intellectual and social skills, but her vision was permanently impaired in a bizarre and revealing way. When shown objects and asked to describe them, she gave no sign that she could even see them. She utterly failed to distinguish shapes as simple as cylinders and blocks. Yet when asked to pick up an object, she deftly moved her hand toward it, and her fingers began conforming to the shape of the object before she ever made contact with it. Notice what *your* hand and fingers do when you reach for a cup or a pencil—that's exactly what this "blind" patient did. The parts of her brain controlling her motor actions seemed to "know" what she was reaching for, even though she was visually unaware of what she was doing. This intriguing case, in turn, has led to other studies documenting that our visually guided actions seem to be mediated by neural processes that are distinct from those providing us with visual awareness of the objects of those actions (see Goodale and Humphrey, 1998, for an excellent review of this literature).

So the "seeing versus acting" model continues the legacy that vision consists of multiple pathways specialized for different visual tasks. The different versions of this dual systems hypothesis all seem to acknowledge that the temporal stream is doing something rather different from the parietal stream. There is also agreement that, at least in its early stages, vision can be subdivided into P and M cell systems that are inaugurated in the retina. Let's take a moment to examine evidence showing the specializations of these two systems.

P and M Cell Contributions to Vision

Direct evidence for the role of P and M pathways in vision comes from studies in which one pathway—either the P or the M—is rendered inoperative by lesioning it, leaving only the other to mediate vision. This section summarizes the consequences of those selective lesions

Execute

To examine the visual contributions of P and M pathways, Schiller and Logothetis (1990) created localized lesions in either parvocellular or magnocellular layers of the LGN of monkeys and

then measured the perceptual consequences. (A lesion at this level of the LGN interrupts processing within this and subsequent stages of the pathways subserved by that cell type.)

Schiller and Logothetis adapted a behavioral technique that was both sensitive and highly versatile, enabling them to study many different aspects of vision. Monkeys were trained to stare at a central spot on a television monitor. In discrimination tests, stimuli were presented in a circular array, centered about the fixation spot. The monkeys had to move their eyes from the fixation spot toward the one target in the array that differed from the others. In the detection tests, just one target appeared, in a randomly chosen location. On these trials, the monkeys simply shifted the eyes from the central fixation spot to the location of that target. Some of the stimulus arrangements employed by Schiller and Logothetis are illustrated in Figure 4.20.

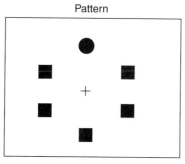

FIGURE 4.20
Illustration of some of the displays used by Schiller and Logothetis (1990) to test visual capacities of monkeys in which the P or the M pathway was inactivated.

Function Tested	Result of Lesion in P-pathway	Result of Lesion in M-pathway
Color vision	**Deficit**	Normal
Texture perception	**Deficit**	Normal
Pattern perception	**Deficit**	Normal
Acuity	**Deficit**	Normal
Contrast perception	**Deficit**	Normal
Flicker perception	Normal	**Deficit**

FIGURE 4.21
Visual consequences of lesioning the P or the M cells in the LGN.

Results of LGN lesions suggest that P and M pathways do tend to be associated with particular functions. For example, texture discrimination and color discrimination are severely impaired with parvocellular lesions; these same functions are unaffected by lesions of the magnocellular layers. Conversely, discrimination of high rates of flicker is greatly impaired by lesions in magnocellular layers, but not at all affected by parvocellular lesions. Schiller and Logothetis' principal results are given in Figure 4.21.

Although the figure does captures the broad outlines of P and M pathway specialization, it misses some important nuances. Consider the case of color. The parvocellular lesions (and only parvocellular lesions) destroyed ability to make subtle color discriminations (for example, one color patch versus another color patch when the patches have the same brightness), but those same lesions did not diminish ability to locate a single, large target whose color differed from that of its background even when the target and background were equal in brightness. Presumably, this detection task is also accomplished by using color information, but apparently the M pathway is able to support such tasks even when the parvocellular layers have been damaged.

Or consider the case of a patch that flickers on and off repetitively. As Figure 4.21 shows, only magnocellular lesions impact the discrimination of flicker. But, if the flicker rate is low, the same lesion has no effect. Evidently, the P pathway does have some capacity to process temporal modulation, so long as the modulation rate is not high.

These exceptions should not obscure the importance of the generalizations that can be made. First, under many conditions, the P pathway is primarily responsible for perception of color, spatial detail, and texture. Second, under many conditions, the M pathway is primarily responsible for motion and flicker. Third, when the tests are made increasingly more subtle, by employing smaller details or lower contrast between the test object and its background, the division of specialization becomes sharper.

The anatomical diagram in Figure 4.19, the physiological measures of receptive field properties, and the lesion experiments described in the last few paragraphs all involved the study of non-human primates, principally the monkey. But several lines of evidence point to the existence of similarly organized, multiple visual areas in the human brain, too.* We'll summarize just some of that evidence in the next section.

Differences

Specialized Visual Areas in Human Vision?

One line of evidence is provided by some hitherto perplexing visual disorders described by people with lesions confined to specific areas of the brain. You've already been introduced to Goodale and Milner's female patient with damage within her temporal pathways. While unable to recognize objects, she could readily reach and grasp for them. There are other, equally fascinating

Clinical

---

*While comparable in general organization, monkey visual cortex and human visual cortex differ in terms of the fine structure of the layers of the cortex (Preuss, Qi and Kaas, 1999). At present, we do not know whether these anatomical differences have perceptual consequences.

cases. For example, damage to portions of the brain located on the interior part of the occipital lobe near its junction with the temporal lobe can produce **achromatopsia**—permanent loss of color vision (Cowey and Heywood, 1995). Damage to specific portions of the temporal lobe (which includes the visual areas in the upper right-hand portion of Figure 4.19) can produce **prosopagnosia**—the inability to recognize previously familiar faces even though visual acuity and general intellect remain intact (Damasio, Tranel and Damasio, 1990). And brain damage confined to the vicinity of area MT can interfere just with motion perception, a condition termed **akinetopsia** (Vaina, 1998). The selective nature of these visual disorders suggests, of course, that the damaged area was responsible for processing information relevant for the impaired ability. We will return to each of these interesting disorders in subsequent chapters.

Execute

The tentative conclusions derived from studying people with brain damage are buttressed by investigations using the modern neuroimaging techniques described in Chapter 1. These studies reveal that distinct brain regions are metabolically active during performance of different sorts of visual tasks. Color Plate 1 (color plates appear on pages in the middle of the book) gives one interpretation of the layout of these brain regions (Tootell et al., 1998). Shown in this diagram are two views of the right hemisphere of the human brain, the top view showing the medial surface (visible only by lifting away the left hemisphere) and the bottom view showing the lateral surface of the right hemisphere. The colored regions with labels denote visual areas identifiable by their unique activation to some aspect of the visual scene.* Thus, for example, area V8 in the lower part of the occipital lobe is highly active when a person views multicolored displays (Hadjikhani et al., 1998). In the lateral view of the occipital lobe, we see area MT. It's activated when a person watches objects such as dots or lines moving around within the visual field (Tootell et al., 1995). Area V3A, toward the top of the occipital

lobe, is also activated by motion, especially if the moving elements are arranged to form a shape (Tootell et al., 1997). Turning to more complex visual objects, pictures of human faces will activate specific regions within the folds of the temporal lobe (Kanwisher, McDermott and Chun, 1997), located (but not labelled) just in front of area V8. Viewing scenes depicting rooms, landscapes and buildings activates a different set of structures within the temporal lobe, situated forward in the brain closer to the hippocampus (Epstein and Kanwisher, 1998). Area V1, in comparison, is activated by all sorts of visual displays—faces, moving dots, colored patches, complex scenes—with the distribution of activation highly dependent on the region of the visual field stimulated (Engel, Glover and Wandell, 1997). The ubiquitous activation of V1 merely confirms that it serves as the distribution center to these other, more specialized visual areas. In subsequent chapters, we shall return to the idea of cortical specialization.

So we have seen converging lines of evidence for the existence of separate visual areas, each specialized for processing a particular aspect of the visual scene. But what is nature's motive for distributing visual processing among multiple areas of the brain? Research in computer science suggests one possible advantage:

> Any large computation should be split up and implemented as a collection of small sub-parts that are as nearly independent of one another as the overall task allows. If a process is not designed in this way, a small change in one place will have consequences in many other places. This means that the process as a whole becomes extremely difficult to debug or to improve, whether by a human designer or in the course of natural evolution, because

---

*There are fewer labelled areas in Color Plate 1 than in Figure 4.19 simply because neuroimaging studies have yet to explore many of the cortical territories identified by single cell recordings and anatomical tracing techniques used to construct Figure 4.19. More and more areas in Color Plate 1 will get filled in as neuroimaging expands its horizons.

a small change to improve one part has to be accompanied by many simultaneous compensating changes elsewhere. (Marr, 1976, p. 485)

Just how many of these distinct visual areas exist remains a guess, and much remains to be learned about how activity in these separate areas is orchestrated to guide our actions in the world. An even more perplexing question remains unanswered: How does activity in visually activated neurons produce visual perception. In the next section, we shall consider this question in more detail.

RELATING VISUAL PERCEPTION TO NEUROPHYSIOLOGY

Neural

The previous sections outlined the receptive field properties of neurons at various stages along the visual pathways, with particular emphasis on V1. What can be said about the role these neurons play in visual perception? That is a question we take up in this section.

No one seriously doubts V1's crucial involvement in visual perception. This involvement is sadly evidenced by the blindness accompanying damage to this area of the brain. It is further underscored by the fact that visual sensations can be evoked by brief pulses of electric current applied directly to cortical cells (Schmidt et al., 1996). In these cases of direct brain stimulation, people see flashing spots and lines, sometimes colored and sometimes moving, at various locations in their visual fields. The specifics of the visual sensation depend on where brain stimulation is directed (Lee et al., 2000). Because they occur even with the eyes closed or in total darkness, these **phosphenes,** as the sensations are called, must arise entirely from within the person's visual system. Visual hallucinations experienced under the influence of psychoactive drugs (Gregory, 1979) and visual auras experienced during migraine headaches (Richards, 1971) may also reflect the abnormal discharge of cells in the visual cortex.

Execute

Another piece of evidence underscoring the tight link between vision and the visual cortex comes from a novel technique called **transcra-**

nial magnetic stimulation (TMS). With this technique, a strong but brief pulse of magnetic energy is directed to a small region on the scalp. If the pulse is strong enough—about 20,000 times greater than the Earth's normal magnetic field—and if it is narrowly focused, TMS can selectively disrupt neural activity within a highly restricted region of the brain (Walsh, 1998; Walsh and Cowey, 1998). Using this technique, investigators have created temporary scotomas by applying TMS to the region of the scalp overlying the occipital lobe (Kamitani and Shimojo 1999; Kammer, 1999) and have interfered with visual motion perception by applying TMS to the scalp region over area V5 (Hotson et al., 1995).

Although these observations are intriguing, they merely demonstrate that certain areas of the brain are active during visual perception. They don't prove that these cells actually cause perception. What more can we say about the cellular events that actually mediate vision? How much of what you see can be explained by the activity of brain cells that "prefer" various kinds of visual stimuli? To answer these questions intelligently requires that you be familiar with the various aspects of visual perception—movement, color, form, and so on. Since you will read about these topics in the following chapters, it is premature for us to consider the above questions in specific detail now. However, it *is* worthwhile to consider what sort of activity in visual neurons would most likely explain visual perception.

WHAT INFORMATION DO CORTICAL CELLS REGISTER?

It is tempting to conclude that the activity of a cortical cell asserts something very specific about the nature of an object located at a particular region of visual space. This idea was most well developed by Horace Barlow (1972; 1995), who coined the term "feature detector" to characterize visual neurons with very specific stimulus requirements. According to this idea, feature-detecting neurons at higher and higher levels of
Neural

visual processing become increasingly refined, to the point where they respond only to one very specific object or event (such as a red Miata sports car).

But this line of reasoning runs headlong into a stumbling block: it requires there to be as many feature detectors as there are unique, recognizable objects. These feature detectors would even have to be prepared to construe novel objects that had never before been seen by anyone. Even the enormously large number of brain cells available for this task would hardly seem adequate to cover the repertoire of visual experiences that most people will enjoy in their lifetimes.

We run into another problem when talking about cortical cells as feature detectors. Ideally, such a detector would respond only when the requisite feature was present in the visual image, and in the presence of any other feature it would remain completely silent. To behave otherwise would introduce ambiguity into the detector's message, for one could never be sure which feature had activated the cell. Yet real neurons suffer from exactly this **ambiguity problem.** Here is what we mean. As you learned earlier in this chapter, the responses of cortical cells may vary depending on such stimulus features as orientation and direction of motion. A change in any one of those features would be sufficient to reduce the level of activity in such a cell. But purely on the basis of such a reduction in the level of activity of that cell, we could never be sure *which* stimulus feature, or features, had actually changed.

Let's illustrate this problem of ambiguity with an example. Suppose a single vertical line moves slowly from left to right in front of you. Presumably this event will produce a burst of activity in those cortical cells maximally responsive both to slow rates of movement and to vertically oriented contours. Panel A of Figure 4.22 illustrates how one such cell might respond to this stimulus. We can go so far as to presume that activity in cells such as the one illustrated *causes* you to see the moving line. But now suppose the same vertical line moves more rapidly from left to right. This

FIGURE 4.22

The response of one cortical cell to different combinations of speed and orientation of a moving bar.

increased speed will reduce the neural activity within your set of cortical cells, for they prefer slower motion. Such a reduction is illustrated in panel B of Figure 4.22. But an equivalent reduction in neural activity could be produced another way as well. We could present the line at the preferred, slow rate of movement but change the orientation of the line slightly, so that it was no longer exactly vertical. As panel C of Figure 4.22 shows, this change in orientation also reduces the cell's response. Thus, changing *either* orientation *or* speed of movement would diminish the level of activity in cells such as the one illustrated. Just looking at the activity level of a small set of cells, then, we cannot tell which stimulus event actually occurred. The activity level of a cell provides an ambiguous message.

Neurons in the visual cortex cannot really be called feature detectors, then, because individual cells cannot signal the presence of a particular visual feature with certainty. The ambiguity inherent in the response of a single cell can be overcome, however, by *collaboration* among an ensemble of neurons. To illustrate, let's reconsider the example involving a moving line. When the line is tilted slightly away from vertical, neurons preferring vertical will show a drop in activity, just as we pointed out above. But at the same time, neurons preferring the new orientation will show an increase in their level of firing. By comparing the levels of neural activity in these two sets of cells, each tuned to slightly different orientations, we could infer that the line had changed in orientation, not in speed. In other words, ambiguity within single neurons can be overcome by considering the pattern of activity within an ensemble of neurons tuned to different values along a stimulus dimension such as orientation. To amplify on this idea of ensemble coding, let's apply it to a visual illusion of orientation that you can experience.

Illusion

We start with the observation that cells in the visual system, like those in other sensory systems, undergo a process called **adaptation.** When stimulated intensely for a period of time, they become temporarily adapted and are, therefore, less responsive (Movshon and Lennie, 1979). What might be the perceptual consequences of temporarily reducing the responsiveness of the orientation-selective cells of the visual cortex? One consequence may be the **tilt aftereffect,** a temporary change in the perceived orientation of lines. First you should experience this intriguing illusion, and then we can consider how it might be explained in terms of neural fatigue, or adaptation, within an ensemble of cortical neurons.

Execute

To begin, look at the three sets of bar patterns shown in Figure 4.23. Note that the bars in the middle set (the "test" pattern) are oriented straight up and down. Now stare for a minute or so at the left-hand pattern, the one where the central patch of bars tilt counter-clockwise. Let your gaze wander around the circle within the pattern while you are "adapting" to it. At the end of this period of adaptation, quickly look back at the test pattern in the middle. You will see that the vertical bars within the interior now appear tilted slightly clockwise. This compelling illusion wears off rather quickly, so you can repeat this adaptation procedure as soon as the entire test pattern looks perfectly vertical again. This time, adapt for a minute to the tilted bars in the right-hand pattern, again being careful to move your eyes around the circle. After you have adapted to this clockwise orientation, the bars within the interior of the test pattern will appear rotated in a counterclockwise direction.

So you have learned that the apparent orientation of the test bars deviates *away* from the orientation of the adapting bars. Now let's consider how this tilt aftereffect may be explained. Recall our discussion of the ambiguity inherent in the response of any single cell. We concluded that this problem could be circumvented if stimulus properties such as orientation were represented by the relative activity within an ensemble of orientation-selective cells. In the case of vertical

Adapt   Test   Adapt

FIGURE 4.23
Displays for generating the tilt aftereffect. Follow the instructions in the text.

lines, this activity profile might look like that shown in the left-hand portion of Figure 4.24. In the upper part of the diagram, below the test pattern each teepee-shaped curve represents the orientation tuning curve for a cortical cell with a particular preferred orientation (recall Figure 4.9). The preferred orientation for each of the cells shown is represented just above the peak of the cells' tuning curve. For example, the middle

tuning curve corresponds to a cell maximally responsive to vertical. When this ensemble of cells is stimulated by vertical test bars, the cells within the ensemble respond unequally. Cells with preferred orientations at vertical respond most vigorously, and those with preferred orientations slightly removed from vertical respond less vigorously. This distribution of responses is depicted in the left-hand bar graph, just below the tuning

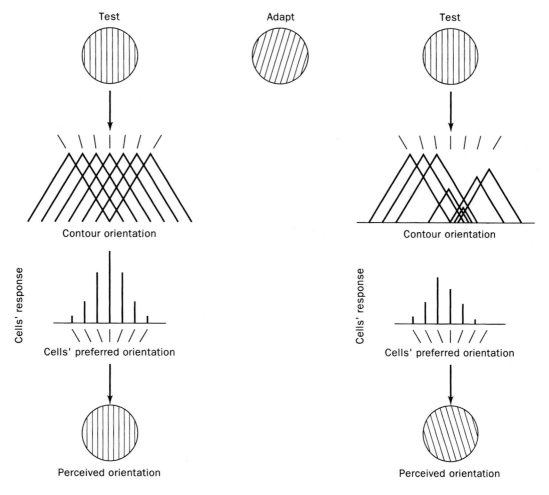

FIGURE 4.24
Possible explanation for the tilt aftereffect, based on the concept of ensemble coding of orientation information. The left-hand portion of the drawing shows neural activity evoked by vertical bars prior to adaptation. The right-hand portion shows activity evoked by vertical bars after adaptation to bars tilted slightly clockwise.

curves. Because this distribution of activity peaks at vertical, this is the perceived orientation of the test pattern.

Suppose we now adapt this array of cells to bars tilted clockwise from vertical (the pattern labeled "Adapt"). With prolonged exposure, the cells activated by this orientation will be fatigued. The cells maximally responsive to the adapting orientation will be maximally fatigued and hence least responsive following adaptation. The upper right-hand portion of the diagram shows what will result when the partially adapted array of cells is again confronted with vertical. Notice that cells maximally stimulated by the tilted adaptation pattern are now fatigued and hence less able to respond to the vertical test. These fatigued cells include ones whose preferred orientation is vertical. Thus, the distribution of responses produced by the vertical test pattern (which is shown in the right-hand bar graph) is no longer centered around vertical. Instead, the peak of this distribution is centered on those cells whose preferred orientation is slightly counterclockwise to vertical. For this reason, the test bars, though physically vertical, seem tilted counterclockwise to vertical. Evidently, the fatigued cells recover quickly, since the tilt aftereffect lasts for a very short time.

See whether you can apply the same reasoning to explain why adapting to an orientation counterclockwise to vertical generates a clockwise tilt aftereffect. Using this theory, predict what will happen if you alternately adapt to both orientations by looking at one for 5 seconds and then the other for 5 seconds and so on, until a minute has elapsed. Presumably, this should fatigue cells on both sides of vertical. After you have derived your prediction, you can test it by actually adapting in that alternating fashion.

According to this activity profile scheme of information coding, then, stimulus features are specified by patterns of activity within an ensemble of cells. The ensemble, in effect, would inspect the contour information within a local region of the retinal image and "vote" on the most

likely feature producing the activity profile within that ensemble. These local "elections" would be occurring among a large number of ensembles devoted to different regions of the retinal image. In fact, these ensembles could consist of the hypercolumns we described earlier. At the moment, however, we have no idea how "votes" would be tabulated within an ensemble, or hypercolumn; physiologists have not yet uncovered a cellular mechanism for reading the output of hypercolumns.

For the sake of argument, let's assume that the ambiguity inherent in the responses of individual cells can be solved by some local collaboration process such as that described above. This would mean that the visual cortex *does* contain a neural representation of biologically relevant features, such as oriented lines and edges. This brings us back to the entertaining figures introduced in the very beginning of this chapter. Let's reconsider those figures in light of what we now know about cortical processing.

CORTICAL NEURONS AND VISUAL PERCEPTION

Vision is Constructive

Look again at the illusory square resting on top of the four black disks (Panel A, Figure 4.1). The contours defining the outlines of this square seem visually distinct, even within the white regions of the figure. Yet those contours are fabrications, not real ones—their existence underscores the constructive nature of visual perception. It appears, however, that the construction process is undertaken by neurons in V1. Approximately half of the orientation selective cells in this area respond to illusory contours defined by discontinuities in a series of abutting lines like those shown in the left-hand potion of Figure 4.25 (Grosof, Shapley and Hawken, 1993). The cells are not responding to the horizontal lines themselves but, instead, to the illusory vertical "edge" defined by the offset between the two sets of lines. In visual area V2,

FIGURE 4.25
Two versions of illusory contours that activate cortical cells in visual areas V1 and V2.

which receives input from V1, cells have been found that respond to an illusory contour created by sectored disks like that shown in the right-hand part of Figure 4.25 (von der Heydt and Peterhans, 1984). And, in humans, illusory contours like these produce enhanced fMRI signals in visual cortical areas immediately adjacent to V1, areas likely to include V2 (Hirsch et al., 1995).

These observations imply that cortical cells in V1 and V2 aren't just replicating features present in the retinal image but, instead, are deducing the locations and orientations of object boundaries. These are crucial first steps in describing the identity and layout of objects within the visual scene.

Vision is Context Dependent

Next, look back at Panel B in Figure 4.1, the one illustrating context's impact on visual perception. In one context, the snake is conspicuous, but in the other, the snake is hard to ferret out. Evidently, when linking together the segments making up the snake, the brain is influenced by the contextual relationships among those segments (Field, Hayes and Hess, 1992). But how does this context effect come about?

Top-down

As you've learned, a V1 neuron responds best to an appropriately oriented contour located within its receptive field. Thus, for example, a cell preferring vertical responds vigorously when an upright bar is imaged within its receptive field. By definition, that cell does not respond when that vertical bar (or one of any other orientation)

is positioned *outside* the cell's receptive field. However, for many cells in area V1 of the monkey's brain, the cell's response to an oriented bar appearing *within* its receptive field is strongly influenced by the simultaneous presence of other contours just *outside* its receptive field (Das and Gilbert, 1995). Although these interactions can take several different forms, one form of context effect is especially relevant for understanding the visibility of the snakes in Figure 4.1 Panel B.

A cell's response to an optimally oriented line within its receptive field is amplified when a neighboring line outside the receptive field has approximately the same orientation and is roughly collinear with the optimally oriented line. Once the line orientation outside the receptive field differs by 60 degrees from the line within the receptive field, this neural facilitation disappears (Kapadia et al., 1999). This enhanced response is even stronger if the bar activating the cell is the central figure within an array of oriented contours. If the bar is simply one of the background elements, its response is more muted (Lamme, 1995). Attention to a given figure, in other words, can amplify cortical responses to that figure (Ito and Gilbert, 1999).

These observations demonstrate that V1 cells are performing pretty sophisticated neural operations. Instead of merely registering the locations of simple features, these cells can highlight particular features and segregate them from background elements. And, in addition to its dependence on context, this highlighting operation is guided by the organism's intentions. Thus, individual neurons respond even more vigorously to features imaged within their receptive fields when those features are the object of the organism's attention (for example, Luck et al., 1997). As John Maunsell (1995, p. 768) put it, "[T]he cortex creates an edited representation of the visual world that is dynamically modified to suit the immediate goals of the viewer." By the way, the consequences of this dynamic modification can also be seen in neuroimaging experiments with humans. An unchanging visual figure can evoke extra large metabolic activity in visual brain areas when that figure is the focus of a person's attention (Tootell et al., 1998).

Let's continue with the visual objects introduced in Figure 4.1, considering a couple of phenomena that present more formidable challenges for V1 neurons.

Vision and the Ambiguity of Perception

The vase/face figure in panel C in Figure 4.1 documents that a single figure, although physically invariant, may be seen in two strikingly different ways. Figure 4.26 shows another well-known ambiguous figure introduced into the scientific literature by E. G. Boring (1930).* If you look at the picture for a few moments, you may appreciate why it's known as the "Wife and Mother-in-Law" figure. Sometimes the figure looks like a shy young woman and other times it appears to be an unattractive old woman. These fluctuations in the figure's appearance occur even though the stimulus information reaching your eyes remains unchanged. Recall that in the vase/face illusion, the ambiguity concerned which part of the drawing constitutes the "figure" and which part, the "background." With the young/old woman drawing, however, it's not figure and ground that swap places in perception, it's the interpretation of the figure itself that fluctuates.

From what we know about the response properties of V1 cells, their activity should not be changing over time as you stare at these ambiguous pictures—the contour information comprising the figures remains invariant. It is generally assumed that the neural events responsible for the spontaneous changes in the appearance of the figures arise at higher level of processing, far beyond the visual cortex (Logothetis, 1998;

FIGURE 4.26
An ambiguous figure that can be seen in either of two ways.

Leopold and Logothetis 1999). This idea is bolstered by the effect of prior knowledge on the perception of ambiguous figures. Perceptual reversals are far more frequent when people are told ahead of time that a figure can be seen in either of two ways and when they are given some idea of what those alternatives look like (Rock and Mitchener, 1992).

So where in the hierarchy of visual areas (Figures 4.19 and Color Plate 1) does knowledge exert its influence on visual interpretation? Studies of brain damaged patients suggest that the kind of knowledge promoting perceptual reversals is embodied neurally in frontal regions of the brain, well beyond the occipital lobe at the back of the brain where V1 resides. Frontal lobe damage limits an individual's ability to switch between alternative visual interpretations of an ambiguous figure (Ricci and Blundo, 1990; Cohen, 1959; Meenan and Miller, 1994). And in alert, behaving monkeys trained to "report" fluctuations in visual perception, cells whose activity waxes and wanes in synchrony with perception are readily found in visually activated regions located more toward the front of the brain, but not in area V1 of the occipital cortex (Logothetis, 1998; Leopold and Logothetis, 1999).

Clinical

---

*For many years, the creator of the figure was thought to be British cartoonish W. E. Hill, who published it in 1915. Recently, though, it was revealed that Hill almost certainly plagiarized from a French original published fifteen years earlier (Wright, 1992).

Integration of Local Features

Still stumped by the last drawing in Panel D of Figure 4.1? It's an overexposed black-and-white photo of a scene containing, among other things, an animal. Gert van Tonder and Yoshimichi Ejima (2000) showed this very image to a dozen people who had never seen it before, asking them to describe what they saw. Most said that the upper left portion of the figure showed a dark circular ring, with a tree sticking up from its center. Ten of the twelve people described seeing a bulging object in the middle of the image, which they took to be an animal. They described this animal variously, as a lion cub, an iguana, a dog with a tiny head, a human runner doing stretches, and an elephant. Although people disagreed on *what* they saw, curiously, all ten agreed on the mystery animal's general location: below and to the right of the dark ring.

Incidentally, the animal actually caught by the camera for this image was neither a lion, an iguana, nor a human being; it was a Dalmatian dog with head pointed toward the tree, nose sniffing the ground. It's easy to understand the image feature that causes people to see the dark ring, but what in the image triggers the perception of an animal? And why do people see so many different animals? Van Tonder and Ejima hypothesized that the answer lay with the dark blobs in the region where the dog is located. In particular, they suspected, that the blobs' orientations gave away the existence of a convex object.

To test their idea, van Tonder and Ejima (2000) randomized the orientation of each individual blob on the animal's body in the image. They showed this randomized image to a new group of people and asked them to describe what they saw. Now, fewer than half the people saw a bulging object. Now, the randomly oriented blobs on the animal's body tended to blend into the randomly oriented blobs in the background, which effectively camouflaged the animal. This brings us to why individuals in van Tonder and Ejimi's original experiment saw so many different animals, rather than the Dalmatian dog that was the photograph's actual subject. Because the dog's spots are relatively sparse, there are large areas of its body (such as its left hind leg) within which orientation information is weak. The shape and orientation of such areas are therefore ambiguous, and are consistent with varying interpretation. Also, some parts of the dog's body occlude other parts, which further undermines the quality of information available in the image. Finally, the dappled, blotchy background in the image blends smoothly into the dappling on some parts of the dog, such as the dog's dorsal surface and butt. As a result, there is even more uncertainty about the animal's precise outline and species.

Incidentally, if you still can't see the Dalmatian in Figure 4.1 Panel D, turn the page and look at Figure 4.27, which shows the dog in outline. Be forewarned, however, once you find the dog, it'll never go away! If you come back to Figure 4.1 weeks, months or even years from now you'll spot the Dalmatian immediately.

Plasticity

Looking at only local regions of the picture, as V1 cells do, would never lead one to recognize the scene and the central object within that scene. Rather, we see the scene and the object because of some more widespread, or global, comparison of local contour information. Moreover, knowledge of what to look *for* dramatically simplifies the job of realizing what you are looking *at*. It is doubtful whether V1 neurons possess the "knowledge" and "memory" necessary to assemble these pieces into a dog. For that accomplishment, we must look to higher visual areas.

To sum up, it would be a mistake to make the visual cortex bear the entire burden of visual perception. The cortex is elegantly designed to derive information concerning the shapes and locations of boundaries in the retinal image—an important early step in the process of seeing (Marr, 1982). But seeing involves more than this. Rather than experiencing a conglomeration of unconnected contours scattered throughout the field of view, we see these contours organized into whole objects whose sizes and shapes remain constant.

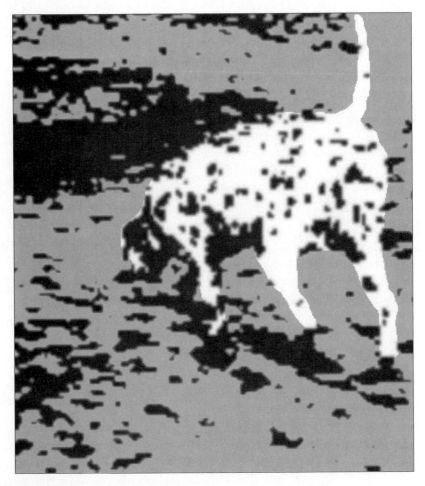

FIGURE 4.27
The figure from panel D in Figure 1, now with the mystery animal highlighted for you.

This organization in perception mirrors the organization of real objects as they actually exist. The correspondence between perceptual experience and the objects represented in that experience is not accidental (Campbell, 1974; Shepard, 1981). After all, the visual system did evolve for a purpose, namely to inform one about the objects with which one needs to interact. Presumably, natural selection has sponsored this correspondence between perception and the physical world. William James (1892) put this idea succinctly: "Mind and world . . . have evolved together, and in consequence are something of a mutual fit" (p. 4).

SUMMARY AND PREVIEW

These last two chapters have provided an overview of some of the neural machinery of visual perception, including the multiple visual areas scattered throughout the brain. We are now ready to shift the focus to perception itself. In the next several chapters, we are going to examine different aspects, or qualities, of vision. These qualities of vision—shape, color, movement and depth—serve to differentiate objects from one another. In discussing each of these qualities of vision, we will treat them as the final product of the visual system's processing. We will also consider what sort of mechanism would be needed to yield this product. However, the major emphasis will be on *what* you see, rather than on *how* you see.

KEY TERMS

achromatopsia
adaptation
akinetopsia
ambiguity problem
aneurysm
binocular
binocular cell
blindsight
blobs
complex cells
contralateral fibers
contrast
cortical magnification
direction selectivity
dorsal stream
forced-choice testing
hypercolumn
hypercomplex cells
ipsilateral fibers
lateral geniculate nucleus
magnocellular layers
meridional amblyopia
monocular
myelin

oblique effect
occipital lobe
ocular dominance
optic chiasm
optic nerve
optic tracts
orientation constancy
orientation selectivity
parietal pathway
parvocellular layers
perimetry
phosphenes
prosopagnosia
reticular activating system
retinotopic map
scotomas
simple cells
superior colliculus
temporal pathway
tilt aftereffect
transcranial magnetic stimulation
ventral stream
visual field

CHAPTER 5

SPATIAL VISION AND FORM PERCEPTION

Execute

Sight serves many different purposes: reading a menu, watching for vehicles when crossing a busy street, catching a baseball, using a mirror to put on makeup, selecting ripe apples at a roadside stand, spotting a friend in a crowded airport, and countless other activities. As these examples suggest, vision-based tasks nearly always revolve around objects. Some tasks require picking out an object from its surroundings, such as spotting the evening's first star in the twilight sky. We can call this process **detection.** Other tasks require the additional step of distinguishing one object from another, such as selecting a quarter from a mixture of coins on your desk. We can call this second, more refined, process **discrimination.** Or you may need to identify with precision a particular object or a specific person. Finding your picture in the college yearbook requires this level of specificity. This third process we can call **identification.** To deal with the environment successfully, people must be able to accomplish all

three tasks rapidly and accurately: detect, discriminate and identify.

Detection discloses the presence of an object or objects; discrimination and identification serve more complicated purposes. For example, visual discrimination allows an organism to sort important objects from unimportant ones. Of course, importance varies with one's current needs.

Overwhelming hunger means you'd better be able to distinguish the edible from the inedible; in preparing a research paper, you must be able to distinguish potentially relevant books from irrelevant ones. For some animals, it is imperative to discriminate potential mates who are in heat from those who are not. Identification demands one more step—not only must one object be distinguished (discriminated) from others, the precise identity of that object must be specified. To find *your* red Miata in a crowded parking lot, you must discriminate the red cars from all the rest *and* then identify yours based on other familiar, more specific cues such as the small dent in the hood.

These examples suggest a hierarchy of processes in which discrimination builds on detection, and identification, in turn, builds on discrimination. Of course, you do not consciously step through this sequence. The perceptual act of identifying some object in a complex scene often occurs effortlessly, in the blink of an eye, and mostly without your being aware. Nonetheless, the stimulus information required for the three processes differs, with each successive process requiring more refined information.

Even the seemingly simple act of detection has prerequisites. To be detected, an object must differ from its surroundings in at least one of several possible ways. The differences can involve color (a ripe, red berry against the green leaves of its bush), movement (an ant crawling on your ice cream), shape (a chocolate-covered cherry in a box of mixed chocolates), or depth (an aspirin that's fallen on a white tile floor). Usually, several of these sources of information are available at the same time, which facilitates detection. For example, a breeze causes some red berries to *move* relative to the green leaves, making the berries even more conspicuous. But once the berries are detected, ripe ones must be discriminated from the unripe, which can require judging subtle color differences. And, of course, to guard against poisoning, it is a good idea to identify the type of berry you're about to eat. Identification entails comparing the current environmental stimulus with stored knowledge about categories of berries.

This chapter and the four that follow deal with visual information that makes detection and discrimination possible. These chapters also go into the details of how the nervous system registers and processes that information. The present chapter examines how an object's spatial properties influence detection and discrimination. We use the term "spatial properties" to refer to those attributes of an object that determine the perceived size and shape of the object. Defined in this way, the term "spatial properties" is more or less syn-onymous with the often used terms "form" and "visual pattern." In this chapter, we'll be focusing on what some experts would characterize as "early vision," meaning that the underlying processes represent the initial stages of what will become a more refined description of a visual scene. In the following chapter, we'll move to the rules governing that more refined description. Of course, objects have color and three dimensionality, and some characteristically move about in the environment—these are aspects of vision that are discussed in chapters 7, 8 and 9, respectively.

We should start by defining what is meant by an "object." To do that, let's start with a real-world problem.

WHAT DEFINES AN OBJECT?

Sojourner is as tall as a Border Terrier, and weighs only slightly more. But unlike any self-respecting terrier, Sojourner has neither ears nor a tail, but it does have six wheels, sophisticated, built-in cameras, and its very own onboard alpha proton X-ray spectrometer. In July of 1997, Sojourner finished a six-month journey through space to become the first human-made vehicle to move across Mars' surface. Working hand in hand with its companion, the Martian lander, Sojourner explored Mars' surface. Its cameras registered images as electronic signals, which were passed along to the Martian lander for retransmission to earth.

Information from Sojourner's "eyes" arrived on earth as a torrent of numbers: numerical snapshots of what Sojourner encountered from moment to moment. In any snapshot, one number represents how much light fell on a particular place on the rover's camera during that snapshot. A big number signifies a lot of light, a small number means very little light. The numbers hold the secrets to Martian topography—the hills, valleys, rocks and boulders of the red planet. But how can those secrets be unlocked so that scientists, back here on earth, can reconstruct the objects that Sojourner encountered?

Figure 5.1 shows the collection of numbers produced when Sojourner had its camera-eyes fixed on the distinctive rock formation that NASA scientists fancifully named "Yogi Bear."* To transform the numbers into meaningful descriptions of

*Yogi Bear was a large, friendly cartoon character in an American television series of that name. The character's name is a play on "Yogi" Berra, a large, friendly baseball player and manager. "Yogi" Berra gained fame from athletic prowess and philosophical observations such as "The future ain't what it used to be."

FIGURE 5.1

At the upper left is an image of the Martian surface taken by one of Sojourner's onboard cameras. Light levels of the pixels in a small rectangular section of the image were measured and digitized (converted into numerical values). The results of digitization are shown in the large rectangle at the bottom of the figure. High numerical values represent brighter pixels; low values dimmer pixels. Contours drawn around groups of numbers enclose regions of similar lightness (regions that are likely to correspond to given objects in the scene). At the same times, a contour separate groups of numbers of different lightness (regions that probably correspond to different surfaces). (Sang-Hun Lee.)

Martian objects, researchers perform operations much like ones the human visual system performs when our eyes gather information from some complex scene here on earth. Of course, operations on data from Mars are carried out numerically, by high-power computers, but our visual system performs these operations neurally, using even higher powered biological brains.

Sojourner's numerical snapshots convey to us something about Martian objects. But how can we sift through the numbers to find signs that an object was present? For the answer to this question, we must exploit physical properties of matter. As described in Chapter 2, the patterns of light reflected from objects depends on the surface properties of those objects. Suppose that an object, let's say a rock, is composed of different material from its surroundings, say the dust-covered surface of Mars. Because different materials usually reflect different amounts and different wavelengths of light, there are visual consequences to the fact that an object and its surroundings are made of different stuff. Differences in light reflection can distinguish an object from its surroundings based on color, texture, lightness, and shape. A properly programmed computer can find regions in Sojourner's Martian snapshots where clusters of numbers differ systematically from surrounding numbers. The computer, in other words, has "detected" an object (or parts of an object).

So, one of vision's basic aims is to identify regions where clusters of numbers (if done by computer image processing) or neural signals (if done by biological hardware) differ appreciably from surrounding numbers or neural signals. There are several ways that light reflected from an object can differ from the light reflected by the object's immediate surroundings. For example, the two might differ in intensity (bright versus dim light), spectral content (long wavelengths versus shorter wavelengths), or in the way that the reflected light is patterned (uniform versus uneven). These three kinds of differences produce perceptual qualities that are called brightness, color, and

glossiness. Success in detecting an object or a part of an object depends on the *difference* between the light reflected by the object and the light reflected from its surroundings.* As Chapters 3 and 4 noted, neurons at multiple stages of the visual system are well suited to register such differences. In Figure 5.1 the connected lines denote regions where the light levels change abruptly, suggesting the presence of different surfaces. Identifying the retinal image's distinctive areas is a necessary step in biological vision, but it is by no means the final step. After all, distinctive areas do not by themselves tell us what we're looking at. Sojourner's clusters of numbers are meaningless without further analysis. The next step is to translate information about distinctive regions into information about form.

WHAT DEFINES "FORM"?

You probably have some intuition about what is meant by an object's "form." The term typically refers to the attributes of size and shape. All objects have form. For nebulous ones such as clouds, the form may be changeable. For most biological objects, such as a person or an orange, however, stable form is more long-lasting. And for many nonbiological objects, such as the Martian boulder, Yogi Bear, form is really long-lasting. Are there universal laws governing the perception of form? Is it useful to consider a given visual form as some composite of more elementary features? And if so, what are those features? How does the visual system extract form information from the retinal image? These questions are explored in the next several sections.

From the outset, keep in mind an important caveat about the study of form perception. Like

---

*As the intensity of an object's background increases, light reflected from that object must be more intense in order for the object to be seen. This is why you cannot see the stars in the daytime sky even though they are present and giving off no less light than they do at night. This is an example of a more general principle known as Weber's Law, which is discussed in the Appendix.

other aspects of visual perception, form is the culmination of many processing steps, most of which transpire without your approval or awareness. Just looking at an object tells you nothing about the steps involved in deriving your impression of that object's form (Snyder and Barlow, 1988). To make this point concrete, consider an analogy. The end product of cooking can be a sophisticated dish, but just tasting the dish does not disclose the steps involved in preparing the dish. Complete understanding of the cooking process requires knowing the ingredients as well as the recipe by which those ingredients were prepared and combined. The same requirement applies to our attempts to understand form perception.

As we move through this and the next chapter, it is useful to distinguish between processing carried out within local spatial neighborhoods and processing carried out on a more widespread, global basis. This local/global distinction will become clearer as we move through this and the following chapter, but for now an analogy may help. The text on this page consists of words composed of letters constructed from simple lines and curves. Obviously to read the text requires that vision register the simple features comprising individual letters. We can construe that registration process as local since it deals with simple features in local regions of the retinal image of the page. But reading also involves clustering of letters into larger, coherent groups: words and then sentences. These grouping processes assemble local features into more global patterns that are meaningful to our task.

So, our exploration of spatial vision and form perception begins with short-range, local analysis of the retinal image, and then proceeds to longer-range, global analysis. For starters, we'll consider the question of form and its components from an historic perspective.

What Are the Components of Form?

Execute

The structuralist tradition, which germinated in Europe during the late nineteenth century and flowered after being transplanted to the United States, had a simple guiding notion, namely, that ideas and perceptions are created by combining fundamental components. According to this view, simple sensations constitute the building blocks of perceived form. OK, so far, but how do we identify these simple sensations? Edward Bradford Titchener, a leader of the structuralist movement, championed a very simple method, called **analytic introspection.** He trained people to ignore all aspects of an object except its immediate, primary qualities. By attending only to an object's appearance and nothing else, people tried to enumerate the various sensations evoked by that object. For example, a person looking at an apple might report seeing 4 different colors and 73 different levels of lightness, with both color and lightness distributed over the apple's surface. According to the structuralists, these ingredients constituted the sensations from which perception of the apple was built. After analytic introspection had been in use for a while, the number of approved "elementary" sensations ballooned out of control, to more than 40,000 (Boring, 1942). Compared to the number of chemical elements in the periodic table (currently 119), 40,000 perceptual elements seemed excessive. To make matters worse, one person's reported elementary sensations often differed from those of another person. These disagreements were particularly striking because they involved people working in different laboratories. This suggests that the technique of introspection is susceptible to such nonperceptual influences as motivation and instruction. As you might imagine, what people *say* they see depends partly on what they *expect* to see ("Aren't apples typically red?").

In addition to these drawbacks, introspection suffers from a logical flaw as well. Even if someone can learn to recognize a particular sensation when it occurs all by itself, there's no guarantee that the person will be able to recognize it when that sensation occurs in combination with other sensations. Is an apple's particular shade of red really independent of the glossiness of its skin?

These difficulties undermined the usefulness of analytic introspection. Nonetheless, one can embrace the structuralists' idea that perceptions are built from elementary sensations without subscribing to introspection as the method for isolating those sensations. But how can we identify the units of sensation with minimal contribution from our prejudices and expectations about what those units *ought* to be (Harris 1998) and thus be confident we've got the right answer? One approach is to use physiological and psychophysical experiments to let the visual system itself tell us the answer, even if those experiments produce answers that go against our intuitions.

A Local Analysis: Differences Between Neighbors

Figure 5.2A is a photograph of Nashville, Tennessee, a city in the southeastern United States. Like other environments, natural or human-made, this scene comprises a range of different levels of spatial information, from coarse to very fine (Field, 1987; Tolhurst and Tadmor, 1997). Each level of spatial information defines a **scale.** To illustrate this idea, we have used a computer to break down the scene into three different sets of spatial scales, extracting and then displaying each scale separately.* The photograph in Panel B captures the content of the scene on the broadest scale, the proverbial "big picture." Panel D contains the smallest scale of structural information from the scene—the scene's details. Panel C shows the scene's information on a scale intermediate to the other two. In Panel E, you can see what happens when the three isolated scales, in Panels B, C and D, are put back together. The result is identical to the original. The differences in scale of the three images emphasize different aspects of the scene: the top image (B) emphasizes the skyline, the middle (C) highlights individual

buildings, and the bottom (D) image spotlights architectural details.

The objects we encounter every day contain spatial information on multiple spatial scales. Normally, when the scales are put together, they harmonize with one another. But to highlight the concept of spatial scale, hybrid images can be created in which the various scales are in conflict with one another. An example of such an image is shown in Figure 5.3. Upon looking at this photograph, most people see the unsmiling face of a man. But this indicates that they're actually only seeing half the picture. To create this photograph, Philippe Schyns and Aude Oliva blended two different faces—one an unsmiling male, the other a smiling female. Although the image contains both faces, the unsmiling male is what we see because his face has been computer-processed to make it dominate the blend. Want to see the other member of the composite? Try squinting or defocusing your eyes as you look at the figure—you should see the other face, smiling female. If you wear glasses, simply removing them should do the trick. If none of these work for you, try dimming the lights or moving farther away from the picture until the male face appears. All of these maneuvers—squinting, dimming the lights, and so forth—alter the balance of information in the two composites, reducing the effectiveness of the small scale (detailed) information and allowing the form carried by the lower scale information to emerge. Ordinarily, of course, information registered at low and at high spatial scales are concordant, so you'd never see this kind of perceptual competition.

As we noted before, objects and scenes in the natural environment typically contain information at many different spatial scales, from very fine to very coarse. A viewer's goals determine what components of this blend are paramount. Sometimes it's important to see the forest, while at other times it's the trees or even the leaves that interest us. Ideally, then, your brain's neural representation of a scene would contain information from all scales simultaneously.

---

*The scene actually contains a continuum of scales, not just three. We worked with three for ease of illustration.

FIGURE 5.2

Photograph of the skyline of Nashville, Tennessee, (a) that has been decomposed, or filtered, into component parts (b–d) depicting different spatial scales present in the original. Recombination of those filtered images recreates the original (e). (Susan Adcock.)

Top-down

To probe vision's flexibility in using information on different scales, Schyns and Oliva (1997) employed hybrid images like the one in Figure 5.3. After each hybrid was briefly presented, observers reported what they saw. From these reports Schyns and Oliva inferred which spatial scale observers were relying on. For example, if you look at Figure 5.3 and report seeing smiling woman, you must be accessing the figure's coarse scale of spatial information.

In the first phase of Schyns and Oliva's experiment, observers were sensitized to one scale of information—for some people this was the coarse scale, for the others, it was the fine scale. During this sensitization phase, observers saw

hybrids that contained meaningful information on only one scale; the other scale constituted a meaningless pattern. The aim of this sensitization phase was to "tune" or "prime" each observer's visual system to one scale or the other. Then, without warning to the observer, the nature of the hybrids changed. In this phase of the experiment, each hybrid contained meaningful images on both scales, coarse and fine. Nonetheless, observers continued relying on the scale they had been sensitized to ("coarse" for those sensitized to "coarse," and "fine" for those sensitized to "fine"). So the sensitization experience dramatically influenced how observers saw the ambiguous test hybrids. Moreover, after the experiment,

FIGURE 5.4
The puzzle piece on the right fits somewhere in the complete puzzle on the left. Can you find the piece's location?

FIGURE 5.3
Two superimposed faces, one portrayed at a coarse spatial scale (smiling woman) and the other at a fine spatial scale (unsmiling man). Under normal viewing conditions, you will probably see that the male's face dominates the percept. The text explains how you can tip the balance in the direction of the other, female face. (Philippe Schyns and Aude Oliva.)

virtually all observers were surprised to learn that the test hybrids actually contained two different meaningful images since they had seen just one.

Access to representations of scenes and objects at different spatial scales allows the visual system to solve problems that would be intractable using just a single representation (Hildreth, 1986). You will learn about some of those potentially intractable problems in later chapters. For now, a simple analogy may illustrate the utility of creating neural representations of a visual scene on several different scales simultaneously. Think about the optimum strategy for assembling a complex jigsaw puzzle (a thought experiment we introduced in Chapter 4, when speculating about the lateral geniculate nucleus's function). Before attempting to fit together small, individual pieces, most people sort them into larger clusters based on common features. For example, we gather all the light blue pieces in a pile, knowing that they probably all go together to represent the sky; the dark brown pieces are placed in a sepa-

rate pile because they'll make up the large tree trunk in the foreground. The large dark regions (foreground) and the large light regions (background) define the image's coarse spatial information. In effect, you're exploiting spatial scale information to get a head start on the assembly process. If you started by trying to assemble the pieces based on the picture's fine detail, the task would be overwhelming.

To illustrate spatial scale's utility, we've created a special jig-saw puzzle that's unusually hard to assemble. Shown in the left-hand part of Figure 5.4, the puzzle consists of an irregular array of black and white checks, with little meaningful structure in their layout. Shown on the right of Figure 5.4 is one small piece that appears somewhere within the puzzle. Can you figure out where the piece originated? Taking a hint from the visual system, we've recreated the puzzle and the piece as they would be represented at a coarse spatial scale—these modified images are shown in Figure 5.5. Note that operating on coarse-scale information, the task becomes a lot easier—you probably have less trouble locating where this piece came from.

But this analogy is a little misleading. Assembling a puzzle involves figuring out which pieces interlink with one another. You begin by randomly shuffling the pieces to scramble their spatial arrangement. In vision, however, the 2D spa-

FIGURE 5.5
Same puzzle and piece as in Figure 5.4, only now portrayed at a coarse spacial scale.

tial layout of the image is preserved; there's no scrambling involved. But here's a key: there are neural operations in vision where the brain must compare the spatial arrangement of "pieces" from one image and match them to the spatial arrangement of "pieces" in another image. This is true for binocular vision (where the separate images are formed in the two eyes), and it's true for motion perception (where the successive images are formed over time); you'll learn about both in Chapters 8 and 9, respectively. For now, you should have a clearer understanding of the concept of spatial scale and its potential utility when it comes to image analysis.

But how is this multiscale analysis actually implemented in human vision? In 1968, two vision researchers, Fergus Campbell and John Robson, hypothesized that the visual system uses neurons with different sized receptive fields to create a series of neural representations on different scales. Their theory was inspired by physiological studies of neurons in the visual system. At different levels of the visual system, responses of various neurons form a neural representation of the light that is falling on the retina. As discussed in Chapters 3 and 4, because receptive fields vary in size among neurons, the responses of different subsets of neurons constitute a neural representation at different spatial scales. Each subset of neurons conveys a characteristic kind of information defined by the spatial scale, so each set comprises an information *channel*. Because

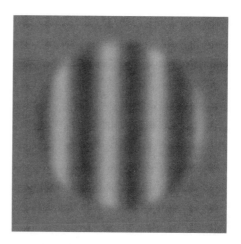

FIGURE 5.6
A sinusoidal grating pattern.

Campbell and Robson's theory relates vision of spatial form to activity within many such channels, it is known as the **multichannel model.**

To test their hypothesis, Campbell and Robson needed visual patterns whose properties could be varied systematically in ways that would have a varying, but predictable, impact on neurons in the visual cortex. Because cortical neurons are tuned to stimulus orientation and scale, the researchers needed patterns whose orientation and scale could be varied systematically. In addition, knowing that neurons' responses vary with image contrast (the difference between adjacent regions' light levels), they needed to specify and vary contrast as well. The visual pattern shown in Figure 5.6 satisfies these requirements. Such patterns, called **gratings,** can be generated on a computer monitor or television display. The one in Figure 5.6 is called a **sinusoidal grating** because the intensity of its light and dark bars changes gradually across the grating's width, in a sinusoidal fashion.

Gratings as Tools for Exploring Form Perception

What Are Gratings? Gratings have four defining characteristics: **spatial frequency, contrast,**

Execute

orientation and **spatial phase.** These characteristics can vary independently of one another, which means that one can be changed without affecting the others. Let's work through these characteristics one by one.

Spatial frequency refers to the number of bar pairs imaged within a given distance on the retina. One third of a millimeter is a convenient unit of retinal distance because an image that size subtends one degree of visual angle. To give you an idea of this angular unit of size, your index fingernail forms an image one degree in width when your finger is viewed at arm's length; a typical human thumb, not just the nail, but the entire width, forms an image about twice as big, two degrees of visual angle (O'Shea, 1991). The size (or visual angle) of the retinal image cast by some object depends on the distance of that object from the eye. As the distance between the eye and the object decreases, the object's image subtends a greater visual angle.

The unit employed to express spatial frequency is the number of cycles that fall within one degree of visual angle (one cycle consists of one dark and one light bar). A grating of high spatial frequency—many cycles within each degree of visual angle—contains narrow bars. A grating of low spatial frequency—fewer cycles within each degree of visual angle—contains wide bars. Because spatial frequency is defined in terms of visual angle, a grating's spatial frequency changes with viewing distance. As this distance decreases, each bar casts a larger image. As a result, the grating's spatial frequency decreases as the distance decreases. To give you an example, when held at arm's length, the grating in Figure 5.6 has a spatial frequency of about 1.0 cycle per degree of visual angle. Doubling the viewing distance doubles the grating's spatial frequency to 2.0 cycles per degree.

Contrast is related to the intensity difference between the light and dark bars of the grating. If this difference is great, the grating's contrast is high; a small difference means the contrast is low. If the contrast is low enough, the bars of the grat-

ing may not even be visible. At sufficiently low contrast, the computer monitor or television screen would appear uniform and unpatterned; the grating contrast would be "below the threshold for visibility." At higher contrasts, the pattern would be visible. In Figure 5.3, the unsmiling male face tends to predominate because its contrast exceeds that of its companion female face.

Quantitatively, contrast runs from 0 percent (when there is no difference at all between the intensity of the light and dark bars) to 100 percent (when the difference between light and dark bars is at its maximum).* The contrast of the print you are reading is about 90 percent; the contrast in the grating shown in Figure 5.6 is about 40 percent.

Orientation refers to the axis of the grating's bars. The grating in Figure 5.6 is a vertical grating. If it were rotated through 90 degrees, it would become a horizontal grating.

Spatial phase refers to a grating's position relative to some landmark (such as the edge of the television display). A convenient landmark is the left edge of the display. Looking at that edge, we can say that a grating "begins" with a dark bar, a light bar, or something in between. The gratings at the top and bottom of Figure 5.7 are in opposite phase; one begins with a light bar, the other with a dark one. The phase of the middle grating is midway between those at the top and bottom.

Phase specifies how components of an image relate to one another, which is a crucial aspect of form perception. In fact, when we create hybrid gratings composed of two components, the appearance of the hybrid depends on the relative spatial phase of the two. Figure 5.8 shows a pair of hybrid gratings consisting of a 1 cycle/degree grating added to a 3 cycle/degree grating (these spatial frequencies assume viewing at arm's length). In the

---

*There are several formulae for computing contrast. For gratings, though, contrast is equal to the difference between the light intensity of the lightest part of the grating and the light intensity of the dimmest part, divided by the sum of these two quantities.

FIGURE 5.8
The same components added in different phases yield distinctly different compound gratings.

right hand hybrid, the two components were added so that their bright bars in the middle of the figure were superimposed. In the left hand hybrid, the middle bright bar of one coincides with a dark bar of the other. Notice that these two hybrids are noticeably different even though they are composed of identical components; phase affects the appearance of the combination.

Manipulating these four properties of gratings—spatial frequency, contrast, orientation and phase—we can construct any visual pattern, including a human face. To start, let's see how far we can get using just two orientations. Our plan is to start with a pair of gratings, one with bars oriented diagonally clockwise (CW) and the other with bars oriented diagonally counterclockwise (CCW), and add pairs of higher-frequency gratings, each additional pair consisting of a CW and a CCW component. Looking at Figure 5.9, in *A* you see the first two gratings superimposed. Adding in the next two components (*1*) results in *B*. Adding to this the next two components (*2*) produces the pattern shown in *C*. In each case, the added components are nothing more than a pair of obliquely oriented gratings of a particular frequency. Note two things about *C*'s evolution. First, from *A* through *C*, the combination begins to resemble a plaid. Here, interactions between components are creating visual structures (diamonds) that are not associated with the individual components themselves (Kelly, 1976).

FIGURE 5.7
These three gratings differ in phase only.

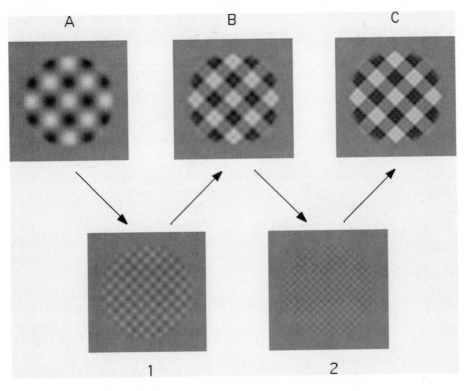

FIGURE 5.9
Steps involved in generating a plaid.

Second, from *A* through *C,* the diamonds become more sharply defined, even though only unsharp, sinusoidal components were used. Repeating a point made earlier, you cannot always tell what elementary components make up a pattern.

Now let's try to synthesize an even more complex figure, a photograph of a natural scene. This synthesis requires that we use more than just two orientations. Because it would take a great many frequency components to synthesize the natural scene, it would be tedious to show each individual step of the process. Instead, at each stage we'll add whole clusters of frequencies. Looking at Figure 5.10, *A* shows the frequency and orientation cluster with which we start. From this point, we follow the same procedure used in Fig-

ure 5.9, successively adding the clusters shown in *1* and *2* to create *B* and *C.* Note how each cluster makes its own unique contribution to the final product, *C.* Bear in mind that this complex scene results from adding various simple components that differ in frequency, contrast, orientation and phase. Notice, incidentally, that *A, 1* and *2* represent the low, medium and high spatial frequency information of the final product.

As just shown, spatial frequency components can be used to create a visual scene. Because they provide a vocabulary rich enough to express important aspects of visual form, gratings became a popular tool for studying form perception. However, just because a scene can be synthesized from spatial frequency components does not

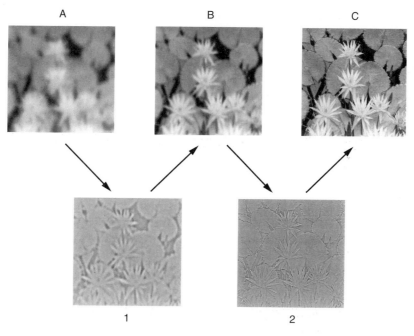

FIGURE 5.10
Steps involved in generating a natural scene, in this instance a photograph of flowers.

mean that the visual system analyzes that scene into such components. We will consider evidence for scale-dependent analysis later.

Eventually, we'll show you how gratings are used to explore human pattern perception. However, since *human* vision is rather complicated, we begin with a much simpler system. As you already know from chapters 2 and 3, there are many parallels between the eye and a camera. As an entrée to human pattern perception, then, let's see how the performance of a camera's lens might be measured. A lens, as you know, is the optical component responsible for producing a focused image on the plane of the film. The quality of that image is only as good as the optical quality of the lens. The following section explains how we can express the optical quality of a lens.

Execute

Using Gratings to Measure Performance
Measuring a lens's performance requires two steps. First, we use the lens to create an image of an object, preferably one like a grating whose spatial content can be quantified. Then we compare the image produced by the lens with the actual object. For example, using a lens, we would create an image of a grating of specified spatial frequency and contrast. We could then determine how good an image the lens had created. But "good" is an extremely vague term. How can we quantify it?

One approach is simply to judge the appearance of the image. But subjective impressions can be misleading. To illustrate, look at the three gratings in Figure 5.11 and rank them in terms of their apparent contrast. Most people would rank them in the order shown, with the leftmost grating deemed lowest in contrast. But this is wrong, for all three gratings have precisely the same physical contrast. In a moment, we'll consider why this error in subjective judgment occurs. But

FIGURE 5.11
Which of these three gratings appears highest in contrast and which appears lowest in contrast?

first, let's explore in greater detail this problem of evaluating image quality. A better, more objective way to assess the quality of images such as the one in Figure 5.11 is by means of a photometer, an instrument that measures light levels. The following example shows how this can be accomplished.

Suppose we use an expensive, high-quality lens to cast an image of a grating on a clean white paper. We can use the photometer to determine the intensity of the light and dark portions in the image and, hence, the contrast of the image of the grating produced by the lens. We'll repeat these measurements for different spatial frequencies, always using gratings of the same contrast. We can graph the results in the following way. The horizontal axis of the graph will show spatial frequency; the vertical axis will show the image's contrast (as a percentage of the target's contrast). The resulting plot is termed a **transfer function,** because it specifies how contrast is transferred through the lens. A typical graph of this kind is shown in Figure 5.12.

Look first at the heavy line in the graph. Note that up to a certain spatial frequency the contrast in the image is identical to that of the target. For these frequencies, the lens faithfully reproduces the target. However, for still higher spatial frequencies, the contrast in the image is reduced even though the contrast in the target is constant. For these spatial frequencies, the lens reproduces the target less faithfully. The frequency at which

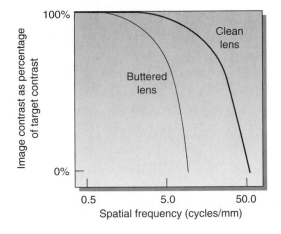

FIGURE 5.12
Two transfer functions for a lens. The curves specify how contrast in the image formed by the lens is related to contrast in the object.

the image contrast falls to zero is called the **cutoff frequency.** Once the frequency in an actual target exceeds this value, the image will no longer contain any contrast whatsoever—the target itself might as well have zero contrast.

Notice the second curve in Figure 5.12 (the thin line). This curve connects the points we would observe if we repeated the experiment after having made one messy modification: smearing the lens by running a buttery finger over its surface. At very low spatial frequencies, the smear makes little difference in the performance of the lens. However, at intermediate and high spatial frequencies, the contrast in the image is degraded by the butter on the lens. This is shown by the difference between the curves for the lens in its buttered and unbuttered states. Note also that the cutoff frequency for the buttered lens is lower than that for the clean lens. This difference between the curves makes intuitive sense: a high-quality lens excels at imaging fine spatial detail *and* coarse spatial detail, while a low-quality lens images only the latter.

But few people dedicate their cameras exclusively to taking photographs of gratings. To see how transfer functions such as those of Figure 5.12 can be applied to photographs of more natural scenes, the information in the scene must be related to gratings.

One method for doing this comes from the work of Jean Baptiste Fourier, a nineteenth-century French mathematician who, happened also to be a friend and an associate of Napoleon. As part of a prestigious mathematics contest, Fourier had to develop equations expressing how heat is transferred from one body to another. He recognized that extremely complex equations would be needed and that those equations would have to be general enough to apply to a wide variety of different bodies. To satisfy these requirements, Fourier developed a powerful simplification. He showed that if some quantity (such as heat) changed in a complex manner over time, that complex function of time could be approximated by a series of simple sinusoidal functions. This simplification was an enormous breakthrough because it allowed Fourier to simplify a mathematically difficult function down into less complex, more tractable components. From here the problem could be solved by working with the simple components (incidentally, he won the contest). In recognition of his accomplishment, his technique is known as **Fourier analysis** (Bracewell, 1989).

But how does Fourier's solution enable us to relate simple sinusoidal functions to a photograph of some scene taken through a lens? First, we treat the scene as the sum of a series of simple sinu-

soidal components. Then, using the transfer function of the lens, we evaluate how the lens would image each of those components individually.

Consider the lens whose transfer function is given by the lighter line in Figure 5.12 (the lens smeared with butter). If we used that lens to photograph a scene containing many *very* fine details, the resulting image would be low in contrast and would appear *very* washed out. This is because fine detail is equivalent to high spatial frequency. As the transfer function shows, the buttered lens does a poor job of transferring high spatial frequencies. It reduces the contrast of any high spatial frequencies contained in a scene. Although this lens could faithfully represent the general shape of a large target (such as a tree that is near the camera), it would not be adequate for fine details (such as the wrinkles in the tree's bark). This illustrates that sinusoidal targets can predict the quality of a photograph produced by a lens.

To reiterate: Several steps are involved. First, we determine the transfer function of the lens. Second, we analyze the visual scene into its spatial frequency components. With these pieces of information in hand, we determine which spatial frequency components will be preserved in the image of that scene and which will not. The first step, measuring the transfer function, is straightforward in the camera. But how easy is it to measure a transfer function for a visual system such as your own? If we did know your transfer function, we could predict the visibility of scenes you might look at. As we'll describe later, these predictions confer some practical benefits. Our next goal, then, is to derive a transfer function for human vision comparable to the one we derived for a lens.

The Contrast Sensitivity Function as a Window of Visibility

The Human Contrast Sensitivity Function
There's one major stumbling block to measuring a transfer function for human vision: we cannot duplicate with humans the procedure employed with a lens. While we can produce sinusoidal gratings

of known contrast, it's difficult to measure the image such gratings produce because that image is inside the eye. Besides, measuring this image would give only part of the visual system's complete transfer function. While describing the eye's *optical* components, this transfer function would not reflect the *neural* components of the visual system. And since we are interested in visual perception, not just the image formed in the eye, we must be concerned with the *perceptual* transfer function, which depends both on the optical transfer function and on the neural transfer function.

How, then, can we measure the *perceptual* transfer function? If your visual system (both its optical and its neural components) did a good job of transferring some spatial frequency, it stands to reason that you'd need little contrast to see a grating of that frequency. In other words, you'd be relatively sensitive to that frequency. However, if your visual system did a poor job of transferring that spatial frequency, you'd need more contrast to see it. You'd be relatively *in*sensitive to that frequency. In general, the sensitivity of the visual system determines the threshold contrast needed to detect a given spatial frequency. By measuring **contrast thresholds** for different spatial frequencies, we can derive a curve that describes the entire visual system's sensitivity to contrast. We call this curve the **contrast sensitivity function (CSF),** to distinguish it from the transfer function of a lens. The term *sensitivity* is a reminder that we are dealing with a property of the visual system, not just a property of the stimulus. As you'd expect from everyday usage of the term *sensitivity,* someone is said to have high sensitivity if that person requires little contrast to see a pattern. By the same token, someone is said to have low sensitivity if that person requires considerable contrast to see a pattern. Defined in this way, sensitivity is inversely related to threshold contrast.

Figure 5.13 shows a CSF for a human adult. This curve defines the adult's **window of visibility.** Before explaining the importance and usefulness of the CSF, let's describe how it was meas-

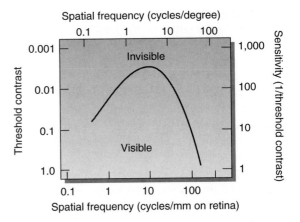

FIGURE 5.13

A contrast sensitivity function for an adult human. The upper horizontal axis is scaled in units specifying the number of pairs of light and dark bars of the grating falling within 1 degree of visual angle on the retina.

ured. A test grating was created electronically on a specially designed and calibrated television screen. The screen displayed a grating of fixed spatial frequency. Using a knob (like the contrast control on a television set), the contrast was adjusted until the grating was just barely visible. This threshold contrast was recorded by an experimenter. Typically, several estimates of the contrast threshold were measured for that spatial frequency and these estimates were averaged. This procedure was then repeated for other spatial frequencies, and the results were displayed in the graphical format shown in Figure 5.13. This curve defines a window of visibility: the region underneath the curve represents combinations of contrast and spatial frequency that can be seen, while the region above the curve represents combinations that cannot be seen. To clarify this idea, pick any point on the CSF curve. Because this point is the threshold contrast for seeing that pattern, decreasing the pattern's contrast (moving upward from the curve) renders the pattern invisible. Conversely, increasing the pattern's contrast (moving downward from the curve) makes the pattern more visible.

Note that in one respect the *shape* of the human CSF resembles the shape of the transfer function of a lens (Figure 5.12): each displays a high-frequency cutoff. However, in another respect the two are different. In particular, the CSF drops at low frequencies, whereas the lens's function does not. The visual system, in other words, is less sensitive to very low spatial frequencies than it is to intermediate ones. As a result, there is a range of spatial frequencies, toward the center of the horizontal axis in Figure 5.13, where humans are maximally sensitive. Gratings are less visible if they lie on either side of this optimum spatial frequency; a person requires higher contrast in order to see them. The same line of reasoning can be applied to a visual scene or photograph of that scene. If the objects in a scene have most of their spatial frequency information around the optimum point on the CSF, those objects will be clearly visible even when they are of low contrast. If those objects contain only very low spatial frequencies (very large objects) or only very high spatial frequencies (very small objects or fine details), they will be less visible and their contrast will have to be high in order for those objects to be seen. This also explains why the gratings in Figure 5.11 *appear* different in contrast: their apparent contrast varies with your sensitivity to different spatial frequencies.

You know from experience that you are able to see better under some conditions than others. If the CSF and your ability to see are importantly related, conditions that change one should also change the other. In fact, this is precisely what happens. Let's consider one such condition.

As discussed in Chapter 3, resolution is poor under scotopic conditions. That is why it's hard to read in dim light. Since resolution involves seeing fine detail, we'd expect decreased light to affect particularly that portion of the CSF corresponding to fine detail. Indeed this happens, as the curves in Figure 5.14 illustrate. The upper curve shows a photopic (daytime) CSF; the middle curve shows a mesopic (twilight) CSF; the

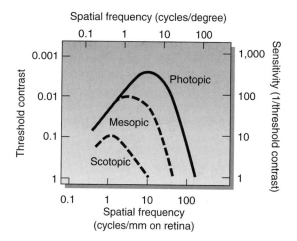

FIGURE 5.14
Contrast sensitivity functions measured at three light levels.

lowest curve represents a scotopic (nighttime) CSF. As the level of light decreases from daylight to twilight, visual sensitivity drops primarily at high spatial frequencies; lower frequencies are little affected. But when the light falls to extremely low levels (nighttime), sensitivity decreases even at low frequencies.

Think about what these curves imply for your vision under changing conditions of illumination. Driving at night, you may be unable to see the fine details (high frequencies) of the shrubs alongside the road. At the same time, you probably will be able to see larger objects (low frequencies), such as another car, just about as well as you do under daylight conditions. If you park your car in an unlit place and turn off your headlights, you will be operating under light conditions like those producing the scotopic curve. Under such conditions, even large objects will be difficult to see. Box 5.1 gives several examples of practical and medical uses of the CSF.

In summary, the CSF characterizes the ease with which people are able to detect objects of various sizes and perceive the structural detail, such as texture, of those objects. Conditions that alter the CSF, such as light level, change the visibility

BOX 5.1

PUTTING THE CSF TO WORK

Differences

The contrast sensitivity function captures aspects of human vision that escapes measures such as visual acuity. Visual acuity, as described in Chapter 3, is a measure of the finest spatial detail that the visual system can resolve. Visual acuity measures only the spatial (size) factors that limit vision, so other factors are optimized. For instance, when an eye chart is printed with very light gray ink on a gray card stock rather than with very black ink on a white card stock, the letters are harder to see (Regan, 1988). In this case, the letters' reduced contrast limits visual acuity, preventing one from assessing performance on the basis of size alone. When measuring visual acuity, then, one tries to optimize contrast and illumination so they do not limit performance.

When measuring visual acuity, one is interested in how size *alone* limits vision. When measuring the CSF, one is interested in how *both* contrast and size limit vision. In fact, two people can have exactly the same visual acuity but have different contrast sensitivities, as the following demonstrates.

Arthur Ginsburg and his associates used the CSF to predict how well pilots would be able to see objects in the air and on the ground. At least under conditions of reduced visibility (twilight or fog, for example), visual acuity gives a poor account of a pilot's visually guided performance. In fact, very fine details that might normally be seen are invisible at twilight or in fog. Ginsburg found that a pilot's CSF was a good predictor of ability to see targets on the ground from the air.

Ginsburg tested pilots in a sophisticated aircraft simulator that provided a panoramic view through the plane's windscreen. Pilots flew simulated missions and then landed. On half their landings, an ob-

stacle (another plane) blocked the runway, requiring the landing to be aborted. Ginsburg determined how close each pilot came to the obstacle before aborting the landing. Even though all were experienced jet pilots, they varied in the distance at which they could spot the obstacle. The best pilots saw the obstacle three times farther away than did the worst. Significantly, pilots with the highest contrast sensitivities were able to see the obstacle from the greatest distances. Pilots with the lowest contrast sensitivities had to get closer to the obstacle before it became visible. Visual acuity was unrelated to the performance of the pilots on this test (Ginsburg et al., 1982).

In another application of contrast sensitivity, Mary Jo Nissen measured the CSFs of some patients with Alzheimer's disease, AD (Nissen et al., 1985). Although this progressive disease of the brain is best known as a destroyer of memory, in many patients, AD brings other symptoms, including diminished vision. Nissen's patients showed substantial but varying degrees of contrast sensitivity loss, affecting both coarse (low frequency) and fine (high frequency) patterns. These findings raise the possibility that some portion of the cognitive losses shown by AD patients results from diminished vision (Sekuler and Sekuler, 2000).

Clinical

These are just two examples of CSF's usefulness in predicting visual performance in everyday settings. Other uses include predicting how well various visually impaired people can get around in their environments (Marron and Bailey, 1982), gauging the disabling effects of glare from various types of lighting sources (Carlsson et al., 1984), and enhancing printed materials for use by the visually impaired (Peli and Peli, 1984).

and appearance of objects. In a sense, these conditions thrust one into a different visual world. From this it follows that creatures with different CSFs must actually perceive different visual worlds. The next two sections develop this intriguing possibility.

CSFs of Other Species   Cat owners sometimes notice that their pets seem to watch things their owners can't see, as if there were ghosts present. Such inexplicable behavior enhances the cat's reputation for spookiness. While we don't deny that cats can be spooky, it may well be that under
Differences

FIGURE 5.15
Apparatus for testing the cat's contrast sensitivity. (Drawing adapted by courtesy of Karin Boothroyd.)

certain conditions they actually do see things that are real, though invisible to their owners (Blake, 1988a). We'll explain this, and in so doing, show how the CSF allows you to compare your vision to that of other animals.

Just as it does for humans, the CSF defines a window of visibility for other species. Provided they have sufficient contrast, objects producing retinal images composed of spatial frequencies falling within the range of a creature's CSF will be visible to that creature. Objects producing images composed of frequencies outside that CSF will be invisible, regardless of their contrast. Thus, by knowing an animal's CSF, one can predict what that animal will be able to see and what it won't be able to see. But how does one measure the CSF in a nonverbal animal such as the cat? The basic problem is to determine how little contrast a cat needs to distinguish a grating from

a uniform field of the same brightness. One setup for doing this is illustrated in Figure 5.15.

The cat faces two adjacent television screens, one displaying a grating, the second a uniformly bright field. The cat is rewarded with a morsel of food if it pushes against a small plastic switch located just in front of the television displaying the grating. The experimenter randomly presents the grating on the left or right television screen. When the contrast of the grating is above the cat's threshold, a hungry cat will respond correctly on virtually every trial. When the contrast falls below the cat's threshold, the animal will simply guess and will be correct only half the time. The cat's threshold, then, is defined as the contrast that allows it to respond correctly on 75 percent of the trials, a level of performance midway between chance and perfection. This threshold contrast can be measured for different spatial frequencies, and

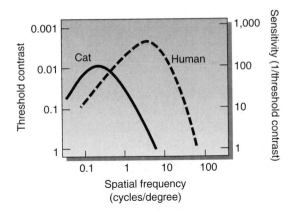

FIGURE 5.16
Contrast sensitivity functions for cats and human beings.

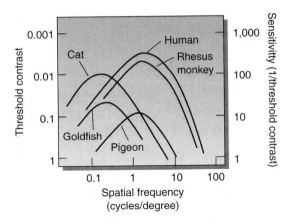

FIGURE 5.17
Contrast sensitivity functions for five species. (Adapted from Uhlrich, Essock, & Lehmkuhle, 1981.)

the cat's CSF can then be plotted in the same way as it is for humans. (This procedure, incidentally, constitutes a forced-choice threshold test, and the details of this method are covered in the Appendix.)

Figure 5.16 shows a typical CSF for a cat (solid line) and for a human (dashed line) tested under comparable conditions. Note first the area common to the two CSFs. This overlapping region defines combinations of spatial frequencies and contrasts that both you and a cat can see. Next, note the regions where the two CSFs do not overlap. Within these two regions one creature—you or the cat, depending on which one has the higher sensitivity—can see patterns that are invisible to the other. At high spatial frequencies, your sensitivity is better than the cat's; at low spatial frequencies, the reverse is true. Now suppose that a cat is sitting on your lap. If you are watching television, you will be able to see fine details in the picture that your cat cannot see. This is because those fine details are composed of high spatial frequencies that fall outside the cat's window of visibility. At the same time, if something large and very low-contrast appears in the room—say, an indistinct shadow on a wall—the cat may see it even though you cannot. In this instance, the shadow falls outside your window of

visibility. These large, low-contrast objects could be the invisible "ghosts" that enhance the cat's reputation for spookiness.

To date, CSFs have been measured for over a dozen different species, and it's instructive to compare them (Uhlrich, Essock, and Lehmkuhle, 1981). Figure 5.17 shows several representative curves. Look first at the curve labeled "Human"; this is the human adult CSF that you've seen in several previous figures. Next note the curve labeled "Rhesus monkey." Like several other nonhuman primates that have been studied, the rhesus monkey's CSF is highly similar to that of a human—suggesting that the world would probably appear very similar to you and to a monkey sitting on your lap. It is certainly unlikely that you'd see things that the monkey could not, or vice versa. Next note that the goldfish's CSF is displaced toward lower spatial frequencies, a fact that makes sense considering where the goldfish lives. Its aquatic environment prevents high spatial frequencies from ever reaching the fish's eye (Lythgoe, 1979). Like the cat, the goldfish is equipped for seeing either very large objects or smaller ones that are quite nearby. In general, there seems to be a good fit between what an animal uses its eyes for and where its CSF lies along the spatial frequency scale.

FIGURE 5.18
An infant's preference for looking at a pattern can be used to measure the infant's contrast sensitivity.

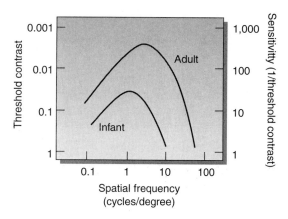

FIGURE 5.19
Contrast sensitivity functions for an infant and for an adult. (Infant data redrawn from Banks, 1982.)

Differences

Age and the CSF On the basis of differences between the CSFs of various species, we've pictured what the world might look like to the owners of these CSFs. In the same way, let's consider how the world might appear to human individuals at various points in their lifetimes. To begin, suppose while you are reading this book, someone puts a human infant on your lap (where previously you've held a cat and a monkey). How does your visual world compare to that of the infant? This question, incidentally, has intrigued philosophers and parents for centuries.

It is hard to know what very young, preverbal infants see. Obviously, you can't use the same methods to study infant vision that you use with cooperative, attentive adults. To get around this limitation, researchers have exploited a naturally occurring tendency exhibited by infants: they prefer to look at complex rather than dull scenes (Fantz, 1961). Preferential looking can be exploited to measure the infant's ability to see gratings (Atkinson and Braddick, 1998).

Confronted with a patch of grating and a patch of uniform brightness, an infant will prefer to look at the grating (see Figure 5.18). If the infant shows no preference for the grating over the uniform field, it is inferred that the infant cannot see the grating. This could happen for one of two reasons: either the contrast of the grating is too low

or the spatial frequency of the grating falls outside the range visible to the infant.

The basic findings are summarized in Figure 5.19, which shows CSFs for an infant somewhere between 3 to 6 months old and for a typical adult. Note that the infant's window of visibility is very different from the adult's. An infant held on your lap will not be able to see fine spatial details visible to you. In this respect, the infant more closely resembles a cat. But unlike a cat, the infant does not have an advantage over you at low frequencies: you should be able to see everything that the infant can see. Also, even for spatial frequencies visible to both of you, the infant will require more contrast than you do.

The CSF in Figure 5.19 delimits the range of visible spatial frequencies visible to the infant, but it doesn't portray what the infant sees when looking about the natural environment. To get some idea of what the world looks like through an infant's eyes, We have simulated infants' quality of vision at several different ages. The simulations, shown in Figure 5.20, are grounded in measurements of contrast sensitivity (Teller, 1997).

In a sense, these simulations confirm what some parents have noticed: their very young infants seem oblivious to everything except very

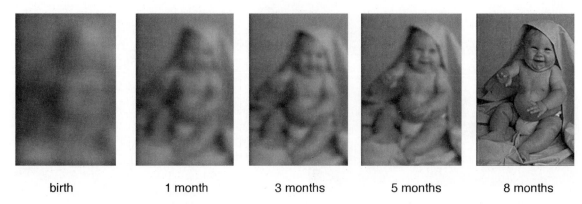

| birth | 1 month | 3 months | 5 months | 8 months |

FIGURE 5.20
This series of photographs shows what the world would look like through the eyes of infants at different
stages of development. As acuity improves with age, the infant is able to see finer and finer spatial detail.

large, high-contrast objects (Banks, 1982). Incidentally, the lack of sensitivity to high frequencies does not stem from optical causes but from the fact that the infant's immature visual nervous system fails to encode high frequencies. In effect, infants are best suited for seeing objects located close to them (recall that spatial frequency is distance dependent), which makes sense from a behavioral standpoint.

The infant's CSF improves gradually over the first year or so of its life. The improvement stalls at an immature level if the infant does not receive normal visual experiences. There are several visual disorders that can alter the quality of visual experiences received by an infant and hence keep spatial vision from its normal course of development. First of all, any condition that chronically blurs the images reaching the infant's retina will limit the information available to the visual system. Optical blur of this sort can result from myopia or hyperopia, and from congenital cataracts or corneal scars (see Chapter 2). Misalignment of an infant's two eyes can also retard the development of good spatial vision. When its eyes are not properly aligned, an infant must suppress or ignore visual input from one eye in order to avoid seeing double (a condition we will discuss in Chapter 8). For reasons still to be learned, con-

tinuous suppression of one eye can lead to a loss in spatial vision, a condition called *amblyopia* (a visual disorder introduced in Chapter 4).

Fortunately, infants afflicted with any of these disorders can recover normal spatial vision, providing the disorder is corrected sometime during the first few years of life (von Noorden, 1981; Maurer et al., 1999). But if correction is postponed until the child reaches school age, the prognosis for full recovery is much poorer.

Apparently there is a critical period early in life when the visual nervous system requires normal input to mature properly. During this period, neural connections are still being formed. This critical period of neural development ends by the time a child reaches 3 or 4 years of age. If the visual nervous system arrives at this stage incompletely developed because of inadequate visual experience, any neural abnormalities are irrevocably preserved throughout the remainder of life.

Plasticity

Because early visual experience is crucial to the brain's normal development, visual disorders in infants must be detected and then corrected as early as possible. The realization that early detection and intervention are vital has revolutionized the way that pediatric ophthalmology and pediatric optometry treat human infants. For example, if congenital cataracts are left untreated

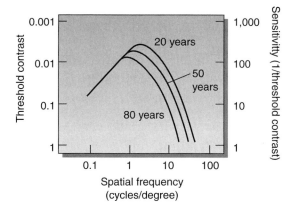

FIGURE 5.21
Contrast sensitivity functions for three age groups.

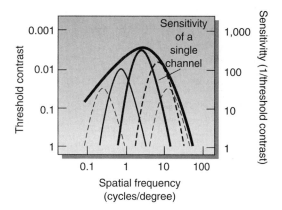

FIGURE 5.22
The overall contrast sensitivity function is determined by the individual sensitivities of neurons responsive to limited ranges of spatial frequency.

Differences

for several years, the development of normal connections in a child's brain is retarded, and even if surgery is done, later in life, the quality of vision is unlikely to be optimal.

So far our discussion has focused on spatial vision in infants and young children. Consider now what happens to the CSF during the remainder of the life span. The CSF remains more or less stable through young adulthood, but after age 30, systematic changes in the CSF begin reappearing. Figure 5.21 shows how the CSF changes from age 20 to age 80 (Owsley, Sekuler, and Siemsen, 1983). By now you should have no trouble interpreting what a CSF implies about a person's ability to see. Suppose an elderly aunt takes the place of that infant on your lap; you should be able to predict from Figure 5.21 how her visual world might differ from yours.

At least some of your aunt's diminished sensitivity to high frequencies results from optical changes in her eyes. For example, as she has grown older, her pupil has become smaller, which means that her retina receives considerably less light than yours (Weale, 1982). This reduced illumination of her retina mimics changes that would be seen in your CSF as you went from photopic to mesopic conditions (see Figure 5.14). Still, there remains some degree of loss in con-

trast sensitivity that cannot be accounted for by optical factors, implicating age-related neural changes (Bennett, Sekuler and Ozin, 1999). Whatever its origins, changes in the CSF and other measures of vision (Haegerstrom-Portnoy, Schneck and Brabyn, 1999) from birth to old age document that people experience very different visual worlds at different stages of their lives.

The Structural Basis of the CSF   As we mentioned earlier in this chapter, Campbell and Robson (1968) proposed that the human visual system contains sets of neurons, each capable of responding to targets over only a restricted range of spatial frequencies. This range of "preferred" frequencies varies from one set of neurons to another. According to this hypothesis, the sensitivities of these frequency-tuned neurons, or channels, together determine the overall CSF (see Figure 5.22).

One reason for believing that the CSF depends on several different channels is the fact that certain conditions can alter one portion of the CSF without affecting others. As Box 5.2 explains, diseases attacking the visual system can produce this frequency-selective change in the CSF. (Evidently, only subsets of neurons are affected differentially

BOX 5.2

WHEN THINGS GO WRONG WITH PATTERN VISION

Clinical

The way in which diseases affect vision can provide clues about the structural basis of the CSF. Some neurological cases can produce a notch in the CSF—a loss of contrast sensitivity limited to a certain range of target sizes. Moreover, the location and severity of sensitivity loss can vary from one patient to the next.

In a study by Ivan Bodis-Wollner (1972), patients' notch losses resulted from stroke damage to the visual cortex. (A stroke, sometimes called a "brain attack," is caused by an interruption of the blood supply to a portion of the brain.) Other diseases can produce similar losses. The most common of these diseases is *multiple sclerosis,* a disease that attacks the insulation on nerve fibers, including fibers that make up the optic nerve. Even though their visual acuity is good, some multiple sclerosis patients complain that the world appears "washed out." Presumably, this washed-out appearance is related to the nervous system's diminished capacity to code contrast.

In addition, about 30 percent of all people who have multiple sclerosis experience *Uhthoff's symptom,* a condition first described by Wilhelm Uhthoff, an eminent turn-of-the-century ophthalmologist. For individuals with Uhthoff's symptom, exercise or emotional strain heightens their visual problems for several minutes. No one yet understands how emotional or physical strain or exercise causes these effects. But these conditions offer a unique opportunity to study the visual system under conditions of transient impairment. In one study (Sekuler, Owsley, and Berenberg, 1986), a 30-year-old accountant with Uhthoff's symptom reported that when he was emotionally upset his vision grew hazy and objects lost much of their apparent contrast. For example, during a confrontation at work, his boss's face appeared totally washed out and featureless. Surprisingly, during these episodes the patient retained his ability to read columns of small numbers, an important part of his job. Thus, he seemed to suffer a size-selective loss, retaining the ability to see fine details while losing the ability to see larger objects.

This strange set of symptoms was confirmed by comparing the patient's contrast sensitivity before and immediately after he exercised. Contrast sensitivity for high spatial frequencies was unchanged by exercise, but sensitivity for intermediate frequencies dropped. Longer periods of exercise produced an even greater loss of vision: not only was contrast sensitivity drastically reduced at all frequencies, but visual acuity was seriously impaired as well.

We do not yet understand the specific physiological basis for these restricted losses in the CSF. But such losses do imply that the CSF—and the ability to see patterns of different sizes—depends on the coordinated responses of different sets of visual cells, any one of which may be attacked and damaged by disease.

by disease.) But we don't have to wait for disease to change the CSF. We can change it intentionally, using a technique called **selective adaptation.** This procedure, mentioned in Chapter 4, produces a temporary loss of sensitivity to particular spatial frequencies.

Illusion

Measurement of selective adaptation requires several steps. First, you assess the person's CSF. Then, the person views a high-contrast grating for a minute or so, thereby adapting to one spatial frequency. Steady viewing of this adaptation grating decreases responses from visual neurons that respond to the grating (Movshon and Lennie, 1979; Albrecht, Farrar, and Hamilton, 1984). After the person has adapted to this grating for a minute or two, you redetermine the CSF (interspersing threshold measurements with additional adaptation to keep the level of adaptation high). The typical outcome of such experiments (for example, Blakemore and Campbell, 1969) is shown in Figure 5.23. In each panel, the arrow on the horizontal axis indicates the frequency to which the person adapted. Note that the notch carved in each CSF is centered about the adaptation fre-

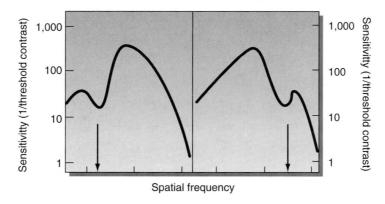

FIGURE 5.23
Adapting to a particular spatial frequency produces a temporary depression in
the contrast sensitivity function at and near the adapting spatial frequency.

quency. So adapting to one spatial frequency diminishes sensitivity to that frequency and neighboring ones, leaving more remote frequencies unaffected. This process of selective adaptation works even when the adaptation frequency is contained in a complex pattern.

To understand how selective adaptation works, look again at Figure 5.22. If just one of the channels is fatigued by adaptation, that channel will respond more weakly when its preferred spatial frequency is presented. This means that a grating of that preferred spatial frequency will look somewhat washed out compared to its normal appearance (Blakemore, Muncey, and Ridley, 1973). A low-contrast grating that is normally visible will stimulate the adapted channel so weakly that the grating will be below threshold. In order to attain visibility, this grating's contrast will have to be boosted, resulting in a dip in the CSF. The width of this dip depends on the selectivity of the fatigued channel. Presumably, unaffected regions of the CSF depend on channels that were not fatigued by the adaptation grating.

You can demonstrate selective adaptation for yourself. Figure 5.24 shows several different low-contrast test gratings and one high-contrast adaptation grating. Before looking at the adaptation grating (in the center of the figure), note the

apparent contrast of the test gratings surrounding it. Now inspect the high-contrast grating for about a minute. Don't stare fixedly, but allow your eyes to roam around the circle in the grating's center. Then, without delay, look at one test grating and note its apparent contrast. After looking back at the adaptation grating for another minute, note the apparent contrast of another test grating. By adapting and then examining each test grating in turn, you'll find adapting alters the appearance of only some test gratings. Now you've seen for yourself that spatial frequency adaptation is selective.

Selective adaptation probably occurs in visual cortical cells (Albrecht, Farrar, and Hamilton, 1984). Such cells are selective for spatial frequency (size), but as Chapter 4 showed, they are also selective for orientation. As a result, you might expect grating adaptation to be selective for both orientation *and* spatial frequency. The logic behind this assertion resembles that used to explain spatial frequency selective adaptation.

You can demonstrate for yourself that this adaptation effect really is selective for orientation. Rotate this book by 90 degrees (turn it sideways) and then adapt to the high-contrast grating in Figure 5.24. This maneuver will orient the contours in that grating horizontally. After adapting

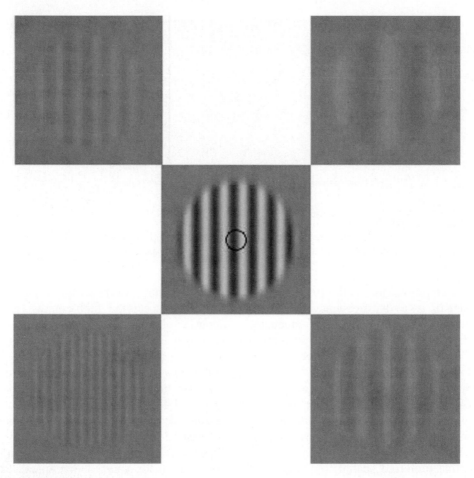

FIGURE 5.24
By following the instructions in the text, you can experience the consequences of selective adaptation.

for a minute, quickly return the book to its upright position and look at the vertically oriented test gratings. Unlike before, *all* of the test gratings should be as visible as they were prior to adaptation. In other words, adapting to horizontal has no effect whatsoever on vertical, regardless of similarities in spatial frequency. This implies that the cells adapted by the horizontal grating are not at all involved in seeing vertical contours.

This demonstration is a reminder of one of the properties exhibited by visual cortical cells: orientation selectivity. Recall that another character-

istic of cortical cells is their binocularity: most of them receive input from *both* eyes. This implies that if you adapt just one eye to a grating, you will be able to observe the consequences of adaptation while looking through either the adapted eye or the unadapted eye (Blake and Fox, 1972). You can use Figure 5.24 to verify this fact also.

These adaptation effects imply that different neural channels are used to detect different spatial frequencies, since it is possible to affect the sensitivity of one without altering the others. However, these distinct channels do interact with

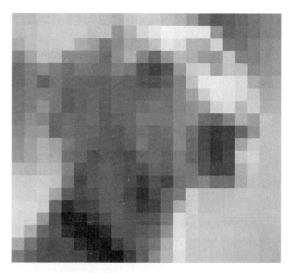

FIGURE 5.26
Can you tell what is pictured here?

FIGURE 5.25
Checkered pattern containing a few squares incorrectly
shaded. (Courtesy of Richard Kirkham.)

one another, as is evidenced by the checkerboard
in Figure 5.25. In manufacturing this check-
board, Richard Kirkham purposely made some
squares the wrong shade, which creates some
clusters of dark squares. To find these clusters,
try squinting your eyes. This should make the
clusters stand out. Squinting blurs your vision,
reducing the high-frequency details in the retinal
image of the checkerboard. Once those details
are removed, the clusters, which constitute a
lower spatial frequency, become conspicuous. In
effect, the high frequencies were camouflaging
the lower-frequency clusters. Another example
of this principle is shown in Figure 5.26. Again,
squinting your eyes will reveal the lower-
frequency pattern that otherwise is masked by the
higher frequencies of the edges of the blocks. To
understand how this block portrait was created,
see Figure 5.27. In this instance, strong high-
frequency information camouflages and weakens

FIGURE 5.27
The picture in the previous figure was constructed by
setting the light level of each block so that it was the
average intensity of the region covered by the block.
Squinting (thus blurring the high frequencies) should make
the detail in the two photographs equivalent.

low-frequency information. But when all frequencies are more nearly equal in strength they
can interact more cooperatively (see Box 5.3).

BOX 5.3

NOT SEEING THE FOREST FOR THE TREES

Top-down

This chapter has developed the idea that certain channels process information about fine spatial detail while others process information about coarse structure. Let's think what this idea means in terms of an everyday situation where form information is simultaneously present at several different scales (recall Figure 5.10). If you were standing near a forest, one set of visual mechanisms would be responsible for allowing you to see the overall forest while another set would be responsible for your seeing individual trees. How might this neural specialization of function be helpful? According to one view (Broadbent, 1977), after the low-frequency mechanisms have defined the global structure of some object, it becomes easier to make sense of the detailed information provided by the high-frequency mechanisms. In the example at hand, once you see that you're standing in front of a forest it's easier to see its individual components. (This is reminiscent of the jigsaw puzzle example earlier in this chapter.)

This view is attractive for several reasons. First, it is consistent with the idea that people respond more quickly to low-frequency information than to high-frequency information (Breitmeyer, 1975; Calis and Leeuwenberg, 1981; Navon and Norman, 1983). Second, when stimuli are presented very briefly, only low-frequency components find their way into perceptual experience—the stimuli appear like "blobs" or "blotches" (Petersik, 1978).

Normally, then, perception depends on cooperative interaction between the processing of global (low-frequency) and local (high-frequency) information. To study these interactions requires stimuli that contain both kinds of information. Ronald Kinchla and Jeremy Wolfe (1979) used stimuli in which the relation between high and low spatial frequencies could be easily varied. Their stimuli, devised by Kinchla (1974), were large letters made up of small letters. The small letters were always different from the large letter that they defined. An example is shown in the accompanying figure, where the global structure creates the letter *H* (large letter),

while the local structure consists of the letter *E* (small letters).

In each trial, the observer first heard the name of a letter. Then, several seconds later, one of the stimuli was briefly presented. The observer had to judge whether the stimulus contained the letter whose name had been spoken. If *either* the global or the local structure matched that spoken name, the observer was to respond yes; otherwise, no. Kinchla and Wolfe compared how long people took to say yes when the spoken letter matched the *global* structure, and how long people took to say yes when the spoken letter matched the *local* structure. They made these comparisons for stimuli of various overall size.

When the overall stimulus was very large (about the size of the retinal image cast by this book seen at arm's length), observers were quicker at detecting a match between the spoken letter and the local structure. However, when the overall stimulus was five times smaller, observers were quicker at detecting a match between the spoken letter and the global structure. To Kinchla and Wolfe, this result demonstrates that neither the lowest spatial frequencies nor the highest spatial frequencies enjoy guaranteed priority in processing.

Returning to the example at hand, we could say that when you're standing close to a very large forest, it's easier to see the trees than the entire forest, but when the forest is small, it's easier to see the forest than the trees.

```
E       E
E       E
E       E
E       E
EEEEEE
E       E
E       E
E       E
E       E
```

To sum up, recent studies of detection and pattern visibility converge on a common view of the human visual system. In this view, detection of any spatial target depends on responses generated in a set of visual cells tuned to contours of a particular size and orientation. Each set of cells is responsible for signalling the presence of targets on a particular scale and orientation. In the next sections, we'll see how this view may account for other aspects of form perception as well.

Form Discrimination

So far we've described how the CSF defines a window of visibility within which objects can be seen. Our emphasis was on form detection as determined by an observer's sensitivity to contrast and spatial frequency. Now we are ready to extend our analysis of spatial vision to form discrimination, the ability to tell one object from another. Before getting into details, though, it will be useful to specify what must go on within the visual system to make discrimination possible.

The perception of pattern, or spatial structure, depends on the responses of cells in the visual system. This dependence sets limits on what stimuli will appear different and what stimuli will look alike. Logically, all stimuli that produce *identical* effects within the visual system will be indistinguishable from one another. But if stimuli produce different effects, potentially you have some basis for telling them apart. Whether you actually can tell them apart depends on how different the neural responses are (Brindley, 1970). In Chapter 4 you read that the response of any one cell, say a simple cell in the visual cortex, provides ambiguous messages about the characteristics of visual features of objects in the visual world. As a result, the visual appearance of objects probably depends on the pattern of activity within an *ensemble* of cells, not just one cell alone.

Metamers   If you look at two exact duplicates of the same object, each will produce precisely the same effects on your visual system and they will look identical. But two objects that are physically different can also have identical neural effects and, therefore, appear identical. In other words, things need not *be* identical to *look* identical. Two objects that are perceptually indistinguishable from one another, despite their physical differences, are called **metamers.**

We can learn about neural processing in human vision by determining which visual patterns are metamers and which are not. Metamers exist because of a "blindness" to certain stimulus characteristics—characteristics that the visual nervous system fails to register. If the human visual system generates identical responses to two objects, the objects will appear identical, even if they are physically different. This might happen when two objects are identical except for one physical attribute too small or too dim to be detected.

But the fact that two stimuli are metameric for your visual system does not mean that they will be metameric for all visual systems. In Figure 5.28, the two photographs are identical except for the presence of high spatial frequency information in the left-hand photograph. You are probably able to tell the two photos apart because from this reading distance, these high spatial frequencies are visible to you—in other words, the two photographs are not metameric for you. However, if a cat were to view this same pair of photographs from your viewing distance, the high frequencies in the left-hand photograph would be outside of its window of visibility. Thus the two photographs would be indistinguishable to a cat, meaning the pair would be metamers for the cat.

Moreover, two stimuli that are not metameric for you under one condition (say, intense light or close viewing) might become metameric under another condition (say, dim light or distant viewing). For example, if you move away from Figure 5.28, the high frequencies in the left-hand photograph will fall beyond the limits of your acuity, rendering the two photographs metameric.

But it's not only light level or distance that determines whether two stimuli are metameric. Any

FIGURE 5.28
The two photographs are identical except that frequencies falling above the cat's high-frequency cutoff have been eliminated from the right-hand photograph.

condition that alters the response of the nervous system influences whether stimuli are metameric. One good example derives from the work of Campbell and Robson, discussed earlier. We've already seen that the appearance of a compound grating depends on the responses it evokes in visual channels tuned to different spatial frequencies. If these responses could be temporarily altered, the grating's appearance should change.

Illusion

A good way to appreciate this point is to have your own vision temporarily altered, so you can experience such a change yourself. The **size aftereffect** is a particularly easy and robust change, so let's do that one. To understand how the effect works, imagine that the visual system represents size by the patterns of neural activity among channels tuned to spatial frequencies (Blakemore, Nachmias, and Sutton, 1970). This theory is depicted in Figure 5.29. In the two upper panels, the horizontal axes represent spatial frequency and the vertical axes represent sensitivity. To make the argument easier to follow, only three channels are shown. As the upper left panel indicates, channel *A* prefers the lowest frequency of the three, *B* prefers an intermediate frequency, and *C* prefers the highest frequency.

Suppose we present a test grating whose frequency was halfway between the preferred frequencies of *A* and *B*. (This condition is not crucial for the argument; it merely simplifies the description.) Note that the test grating produces equal responses within channels *A* and *B* (bottom left panel). According to the theory, this neural code—equal activity in *A* and *B*—determines the way the grating looks.

But if we did something to change the distribution of activity produced by that same grating, the grating's appearance would be altered. This idea was tested using an adaptation procedure much like that described in the text. First, a person looked at a grating and judged its spatial frequency. We'll refer to this as the "test grating." Next, the person adapted to a high-contrast grating whose spatial frequency was lower than that of the test grating. We'll call this the "adaptation grating." Finally, after one minute of adaptation, the person looked back at the test grating and again judged its spatial frequency. Did the test grating still look the same? To answer this question, consider how adaptation would have affected the neural code previously described.

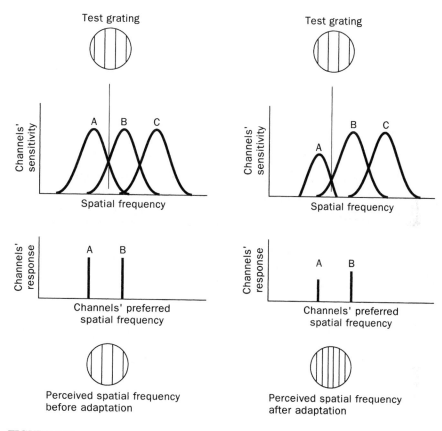

FIGURE 5.29
A neural account of how contour size is encoded in the visual system. (See text for details.)

Suppose that prior to adaptation, the test grating produced equal responses in channels *A* and *B*. Suppose also that the adaptation grating is one to which *A* is highly sensitive and to which *B* is relatively less sensitive. Prolonged adaptation will thus fatigue *A* considerably but *B* very little (upper right panel). When presented again, the test grating will evoke a nearly normal response from *B* but a weakened response from *A* (lower right panel). This pattern of responses—a greater response in *B* than in *A*—is not usually produced by the test grating. Instead, this pattern of responses is usually evoked by a spatial frequency *higher* than that of the test grating. As a result, after adaptation, the spatial frequency of the test

grating should *appear* higher than usual. This was the effect that Blakemore, Nachmias, and Sutton (1970) found. On the basis of this theory, can you predict what will happen if the person has adapted to a spatial frequency *higher* than that of the test grating?

You can experience this so-called size aftereffect for yourself using the test displays shown in Figure 5.30. To prove that this aftereffect is not peculiar to gratings, we've borrowed from Stuart Anstis a demonstration using more familiar patterns: alphabetic text. Still, the outcome is the same—a temporary change in apparent size. To make the effect easier to see, this demonstration simultaneously produces two size aftereffects in

mountains to the perate business of ssenia. It was not ansion but land-gr I brought its neme ne a garrison in the omitted to the rigid gus," their legenda ame the most form	ry camp, artistically and in ren. The part Spartans pla airs became, oftener than those who were internation nded to be treacherous, stup home, the ownership of l e qualification for being a concentrated in fewer t so that from the fourth c s the effective population ations supervened, and Spa the miserable inheritor

●   ▬▬▬

mountains to the perate business of ssenia. It was not ansion but land-gr I brought its neme ne a garrison in the omitted to the rigid gus," their legenda ame the most form	which was the citizen, was fewer hands, tury onwards clined, revolu became only treat name ar

FIGURE 5.30
These samples cause the viewer to experience the size-shift aftereffect. (Follow the instructions given in the text.)

Execute

opposite directions. Here's how to use Figure 5.30. Look at the black dot between the upper and lower panels of the left side of the figure. With your eyes fixed on the black dot, verify that the letters in the text above the line look the same size as the letters below.

We'll now explain what you must do to alter the apparent size of these letters. Because timing is important, finish reading the instructions *before* you begin to execute them. First, adapt, using the right side of the figure. The patch of small, tightly packed letters corresponds to high spatial frequencies, while the patch of larger, more spread out letters corresponds to low spatial frequencies. To adapt, slowly move your eyes back and forth along the bar between the two patches of letters. Keep this up for about 90 seconds. *Caution:* Do not look directly at either patch; keep your gaze on the horizontal bar between the two. Otherwise, you'll intermix the two types of adaptation. Finally, at the end of adaptation, look back at the dot between the

patches in the left side of the figure. Keeping your eyes on the dot, note the sizes of the letters above and below. You will see that letters in the upper patch look smaller than those in the lower patch. Here, then, is a situation where altering your visual system's sensitivity converts stimuli from metamers to nonmetamers.

Form Defined by Texture Differences

So far we have focused on detection and discrimination of forms defined by intensity differences that create spatial contrast at different spatial scales. Thinking back to Sojourner as it explored the Martian surface, its camera would register the presence of a rock if that rock reflected a different amount of light than did the background upon which it was resting. But what if the rock and its background were the same color and reflected equivalent amounts of light? Would Sojourner miss it altogether? Not necessarily. Rocks, after all, typically have surface markings—scratches, streaks and other irregularities—that differ from the more regular, grainy texture of the dusty Martian ground upon which the rock rests. If NASA scientists had programmed Sojourner and its image processing computers to register spatial discontinuities in texture (**texture contrast,** we could call it), the rock could be detected even though its lightness was no different from the ground. Texture contrast provides another, complementary, means for detecting and discriminating form. Let's spend a few moments considering texture.

To begin, think about some familiar objects whose textures are distinctive—for example, a pebbled path, the skin of an alligator, the bark of a tree, or a brick wall. Think about what makes each of these surfaces distinctive, putting color aside. As a first approximation to a definition, these examples suggest that texture depends upon the sizes and shapes of the surface's markings as well as the distribution of those markings over the surface. In Figure 5.31 equal numbers of black and white squares appear in each section of the figure. As a result, a photometer would confirm

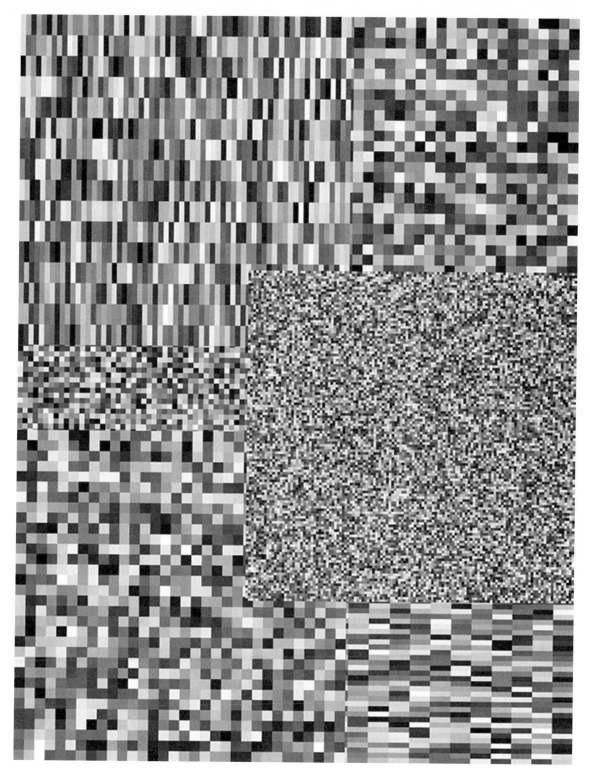

FIGURE 5.31
Texture discontinuities create visually conspicuous borders.

that the same average amount of light was re-flected from each section. So perceptual differ-ence among sections is not a matter of light level alone, but depends upon how the sections' ele-ments are distributed. Rao and Lohse (1996) sought to identify the key stimulus variables that control perception of texture in natural and man-made surfaces. Their test materials were photo-graphs of 56 different surfaces taken at various magnifications and conditions of illumination. Based on similarity judgments made by people who viewed these images, Rao and Lohse identi-fied three main physical dimensions that gov-erned texture properties. One of the dimensions captures the repetitiveness, or regularity, of tex-ture elements. Figure 5.32A shows examples of textures at opposing extremes of this dimension. The second dimension reflects the granularity of the texture. An extremely granular texture is com-prised of randomly distributed, large elements of roughly uniform size. Examples are shown in Fig-ure 5.32B. The last main dimension reflects the presence of a strong local orientation within the surfaces' various regions. Examples of the various categories identified by Rao and Lohse are shown in Figure 5.32C. To make sure you understand their scheme, look around you, note three or four different textured surfaces and try to place them into Rao and Lohse's framework.

Rao and Lohse's work provided a way to de-scribe textures. Work by other investigators (for example, Nothdurft, 1985; Wolfson and Landy, 1998) shows that human observers are quite good at judging shapes that are defined solely by texture differences (the skill we'd like to embody in Sojourner's circuitry). An example of shape defined by texture appears in Figure 5.33. Notice how the cluster of plus signs stands right out from the surrounding L-shaped elements. The cluster can been seen immediately and with no effort—the shape appears to "pop out" from the background. Anne Treisman (1986) and others have exploited this pop-out effect as a way to distinguish features that can be quickly and ef-fortlessly registered from those that require time-consuming scrutiny. Some typical displays

FIGURE 5.32
Examples of textures representing ends of the perceptual dimensions identified by Rao and Lohse (1996). Row A: repetitive versus random; Row B: granular versus agranular; Row C: oriented versus disoriented. (From Brodartz, A Photographic Album for Artists, and Designers, 1996. Copyright © Dover Publishing.)

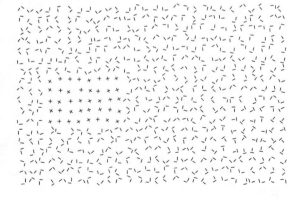

FIGURE 5.33
Shape can be defined by texture differences.

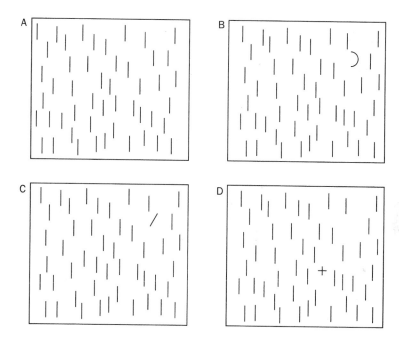

FIGURE 5.34
Four displays typical of those in Treisman's work on target pop-out.

are shown in Figure 5.34. Presenting a "target" at randomly chosen locations among a field of "distractors," Treisman measured how long observers took to locate the target. To distinguish targets that pop out from those that do not, judgment times were measured with varying numbers of nontarget, distractor elements. If a target popped-out, the time needed to spot that target would be relatively unaffected by the number of embedded distractor elements. Pop-out, in other words, would imply that visual mechanisms are carrying out their searches for the target simultaneously, in parallel, throughout the entire visual field.

Many experiments show that pop-out may be produced by differences in stimulus attributes including color, line curvature, line tilt, and familiarity. And, of relevance to our present discussion, pop-out can be produced by texture differences between "target" and "background" (Bravo and Blake, 1990). There are, however, limits to pop-out from texture defined shapes. To see this, look back at Figure 5.33. If you look very, very hard

you may see a region of texture difference that you didn't see originally, in the figure's right half. See the cluster of *Ts* embedded in the *Ls*? Only by scrutinizing the elements individually, and comparing them against one another, do you discover the existence of a group of *Ts*.

Ellsworth Kelly, a noted contemporary American artist, has used texture differences in paintings to create interesting illusory edges. A black and white reproduction of one of Kelly's paintings appears in Figure 5.35. You'll probably see a set of sharp vertical edges that divide the painting into nine equal sections. As Robert Shapley's commentary on this painting noted, the artist was attempting to capture the essence of a pattern of shadows he had seen on a staircase (Shapley, 1996). The artist stripped away brightness differences, leaving only shadow textures to define the nine steps. To get really good insight into what actually produces the illusory steps, take a card or sheet of paper and move it slowly up and down over Kelly's painting. By

FIGURE 5.35
"La Combe I" by Ellsworth Kelly (painted in 1950). Note the strong illusory vertical contours along the endpoints of the thick diagonal bars. The figure shown here is a black and white reproduction of the original, which is red paint on white canvas. The original is 38 inches by 63.5 inches. (Ellsworth Kelly La Combe 1, 1950, Oil on canvas, 38 × 63½ inches. Courtesy Matthew Marks Gallery, New York, NY.)

occluding or revealing various sections of the painting you should be able to identify minimal texture information that is needed to produce Kelly's illusory steps.

This is a good time to take stock of what you've learned so far in this chapter. We have focused on visual processes that extract information about spatial scale and contour orientation. These same processes locate the edges and boundaries of objects by signalling the presence of discontinuities in light level or texture. These processes, which represent an early stage of vision, generate a map of whatever local features happen to be present throughout the visual field. Roughly speaking, these local features comprise parts of objects (often quite small). Although visual perception may begin by creating a neural inventory of parts and their locations, it certainly doesn't end there. To appreciate this point, let's go back to Sojourner, the Martian explorer trying to identify objects using its onboard camera.

Putting it All Together: A Global Analysis

When we last looked, Sojourner had helped to create an inventory of Martian object parts and their locations. These were represented in the snapshots taken by Sojourner's camera (Figure 5.1B). The many clusters and strings of similar numbers provide some clues about locations in the image where object parts seem to be located. But how do we put these clues together to reproduce the objects in the scene that Sojourner's camera caught? This next step is challenging, for it requires assembling the parts into meaningful wholes. To appreciate this challenge, look at Figure 5.36. We have no trouble recognizing this as a young girl gazing out a window. Simple, it seems, until we stop to realize what vision has to accomplish to arrive at this conclusion. At early stages, vision must identify regions in the image that are most likely to be neighboring parts of a single surface and, hence, neighboring parts of a single object. This must be done even when parts of the image (such

Top-down

FIGURE 5.36
Seeing an object entails segregating contours into a meaningful whole. (R. Sekuler.)

as the girl's cheek) are partially obscured by other objects in the scene (like the crosspieces of the window). In effect, vision must assign different image parts to various objects even when those parts overlap. If you still think the task is easy, look back at Figure 4.1D, the seemingly random array of black and white splotches. Remember how difficult it was initially to identify this as a Dalmatian? This demonstration reminds us that assembling image parts into meaningful wholes is not always as easy as it seems.

So, how does Sojourner's electronic visual system compute which feature parts should be grouped together to comprise a shared object? What rules must be embodied in its circuitry to accomplish this feat? For clues to the answers, we again should consider how our own, biologi-

cal visual systems do it. To do that, we need to go back in time to the early part of the twentieth century, long before Sojourner was even imaginable.

Putting the Parts Together: The Gestalt Principles

Earlier in this chapter, we mentioned the structuralists' idea that perceptions could be decomposed into primary sensations. In Germany, shortly after the turn of the twentieth century, a school of thought emerged in reaction to the structuralist idea that composites could be decomposed into their parts. Called the **Gestalt** movement, this school of thought argued that objects appear as they do in virtue of the parts' *relations* to one another. It follows, therefore, that the process of decomposition—the structuralists' manifesto—destroys the essence of the object. Listen to the words of Wolfgang Köhler, one of the founders of the Gestalt movement:

> We do not see individual fractions of a thing; instead, the mode of appearance of each part depends not only upon the stimulation arising at *that* point but upon the conditions prevailing at other points as well. (1920/1938, p. 20)

A compelling, contemporary confirmation of this statement is provided by James Pomerantz (1981). Pomerantz had people view arrays of elements like the ones shown in Figure 5.37. For each array, observers had to identify as quickly as possible the single item that was perceptually distinct from the others. For each presentation, Pomerantz measured how long it took to make this judgment. On average, observers took 1.9 seconds to spot an odd element among a cluster of four (in Panel A of Figure 5.37, the odd element is the reverse diagonal at the lower right). Pomerantz also created a second array of figures, by adding to each diagonal an L-shaped figure (see panel B), producing the more complex figures shown in panel C. When required to spot the odd item in this new set, observers took

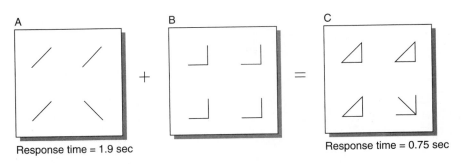

Response time = 1.9 sec   Response time = 0.75 sec

FIGURE 5.37
Displays producing the configural superiority effect.

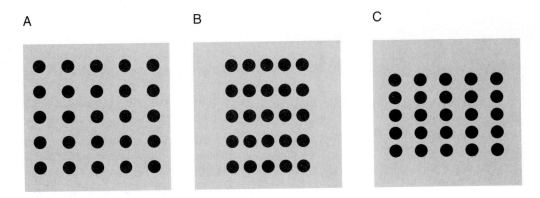

FIGURE 5.38
Objects close together tend to unite perceptually into groups.

only 0.75 second—65 percent faster than with the "simpler" figures. The more complex figure, in other words, acquired an emergent property not available in its individual, component features, a property that made it easier to discriminate from its neighbors. This so-called **configural superiority effect** dramatizes what became the credo for the Gestalt psychogists: "The whole is different from the sum of its individual parts." (In more contemporary parlance, one could say that a given feature is known by the company it keeps.)

For the Gestalt psychologists, then, the key was identifying principles of organization that

specified how parts relate to one another. In the following paragraphs we'll examine those principles and see examples of them in action (for a more extensive discussion, see Palmer, 1999).

Gestalt principles of organization   The principle of **proximity** describes the tendency of nearby objects to group together as a single perceptual unit. As you can see in panel A of Figure 5.38, no strong, stable organization seems to predominate when the circles are equally spaced. Instead, they can be seen sometimes to cluster into rows and other times, into columns. (You may occasionally even see the circles grouping into diagonal strings.) None of these weak organizations persists, however, and none seems compelling. But notice what happens when the vertical distances among neighboring dots are made larger than the horizontal distances, as in panel B of the figure. With this simple modification, the dots form horizontal strings, or rows. Panel C illustrates what happens when the horizontal distances are made larger than the vertical: dots group into vertical strings, or columns. So, simply varying the proximity of circles biases the perception in favor of one organization or the other. Proximity, then, is one of the relational principles used to organize a visual scene into distinct objects.

Wertheimer called attention to another major organizational tendency, known as the principle of **similarity.** "Other things being equal, if several stimuli are presented together, there is a tendency to see the form in such a way that the similar items are grouped together" (1923/1958, p. 119). The dimensions of similarity that control grouping include lightness, orientation, and size. Examples of these effects are illustrated in Figure 5.39. Notice in the left-hand panel how the circles form a perceptual group in the midst of the squares. Apparently the differences between circles and squares in both lightness and shape contribute to this grouping. In the right-hand panel, the disks form two diagonals criss-crossing the squares. Here, shape alone promotes grouping.

A third, related grouping principle called **closure,** is illustrated in Figure 5.40. At first the figure may look like a meaningless row of heartlike forms. But actually the pattern contains a handwritten version of a simple and common word—"men." In fact, the pattern contains two copies of that word, one a mirror image of the other. Closure causes the two mirror images to cohere into a single, closed pattern, which obscures the characteristics of the two separate components.

Another of the Gestalt principles is **good continuation,** or more simply, continuation. This refers to the tendency to perceive clusters or strings of individual elements as forming a single contour, or path (Polat, 1999). In the preceding chapter, Figure 4.1B showed you one example of contour integration based on the alignment of individual features. A "snake" in the left-hand panel of the figure was easy to spot in a field of randomly oriented lines. But the "snake" in the other panel was hard to find. The random figures in the background were the same in both panels, but the snakes differed from one another in the amount by which their successive segments changed. The individual segments of the more visible snake differed from one another by angles of 30 degrees, whereas the less conspicuous snake's segments differed by 60 degrees. By the way, the snake would have been even more conspicuous if successive angular differences were even smaller or if the snake's "head" had grabbed onto its "tail"

FIGURE 5.39
Objects similar in shape and size tend to group together.

FIGURE 5.40
A demonstration of closure. (Adapted from Köhler, 1969.)

to form a closed figure (Pettet, McKee and Grzywacz, 1998).

Chapter 4 also described a scheme for implementing the principle of good continuation in the case of oriented line segments like those comprising the snakes. Neural responses to nearby contour segments of similar orientation could be enhanced if neurons with neighboring receptive fields and similar preferred orientations were interconnected in a way that allowed them to reinforce one another's activity. These highly selective linkages could arise out of long-range horizontal connections that selectively associate neurons with adjacent receptive fields. These associations would selectively favor continuities between neurons whose preferred orientations were similar, and discriminate against continuities between neurons with dissimilar preferred orientations (Gilbert, 1992). The presence of an appropriate stimulus would be signalled by simultaneous activation of a set of neurons whose receptive fields had the appropriate orientation tuning and spatial locations.

Neural mechanisms that contribute to visual grouping would be most useful if their preferred visual features were ones that occurred often in natural images—images generated as one views the natural, everyday world. After all, there would be little value to having mechanisms that boosted sensitivity to contour shapes that were rarely encountered. But how well do the contour integration preferences of human vision actually mirror the characteristics of natural images? To answer this question, one must first ascertain the characteristics of natural images. To that end, Bill Geisler and colleagues (Geisler et al., 2001) at the University of Texas measured the geometrical properties of various representative natural images, including images of flowers, trees, a mountain, a lake and a river, and some woods (see Figure 5.41). To characterize the contours in such images, the researchers displayed each image on a computer monitor and had people move a cursor to select all the oriented elements that belonged together in a single, shared contour. For example, if there were a riverbank in an image, people selected each of the oriented segments that outlined that bank. This operation was repeated for all the contours in every image.

From this vast collection of measurements, the researchers extracted the essential statistical properties of natural contours. Recognizing that the geometrical relationships among segments were particularly important, Geisler and colleagues computed the orientation and position differences among all pairs of segments that people had attributed to each shared contour. Their quantitative findings can be summarized broadly and qualitatively: adjacent segments of any single natural contour tend to have very similar orientations (take one small stretch of riverbank and an immediately adjacent stretch), but segments of the same contour that are further apart (one stretch of riverbank versus another, more distant

FIGURE 5.41
Examples of natural scenes used by Geisler, Perry, Super and Gallogly.

stretch of that same bank), tend to have orientations that are more disparate from one another.*

Geisler and colleagues used this information about natural images to create 216 different families of synthetic test figures—serpentine, broken contours made up of varying numbers of line segments. Within each family, all members shared the same quantitative relationship to the statistical properties of natural contours. But the families varied in how well each conformed to those natural statistics.

These carefully designed figures were then used in a forced-choice psychophysical experiment. In each trial, participants saw two patterns: one was a collection of many, small, randomly-oriented line segments; the other pattern was a similar collection, but with a test figure embedded in it. The participants had to identify which pattern contained the serpentine contour. Geisler reasoned that if the contour integration properties of the human visual system mirrored the statistics of the natural world, the detectability of any particular test contour should depend upon how closely *its* statistics matched the average co-occurrence statistics of contours in the natural world.

Detailed predictions of contour detectability were derived from a simple, but elegant computer model whose few rules mimic the way the human visual system might perform the same task. The model linked individual line segments into a shared, larger contour, but did so in accordance with the statistics of natural images. In particular, the probability that any two segments would be linked together grew as their orientations became more similar, but declined as the distance between segments increased. Finally, linkages were transitive, that is, if the computer model linked line segment A to line segment B, and it also linked segment B to segment C, then the model would link A and C, creating, in this example, an extended contour three segments long.

Figure 5.42 gives you some idea of how the model behaved. The panel at the left shows a typical visual array that Geisler used to test observers. At first glance, the short segments in the array may appear to be random in orientation. If you scrutinize the array, though, you will find a number of places where nearby segments have similar orientations. The computer model would tend to link these together into a contour. In the right-hand panel, lines are drawn through individual segments that Geisler's model would connect. As you can see, the model's rules for connecting segments generates a number of small contours, and one long one. Note in particular, that the model discriminates against linkages between adjacent segments whose orientations differ widely from one another.

For each of their 216 families of synthetic figures, Geisler and colleagues compared the model's predictions to the actual performance of human subjects. To illustrate the power of this simple model, Figure 5.43 shows, for each condition, the model's prediction plotted against observers' actual performance. If the model were perfect, and if performance had no inherent variability whatsoever, all the data points in the figure would lie along the diagonal line. Given how elementary the model was, Figure 5.43 shows excellent agreement between the predictions of this very simple model, on one hand, and human performance, on the other. This agreement strongly supports the hypothesis that development of contour integration mechanisms, either during evolution or during the first years of any individual's life, is driven by the occurrence statistics of images encountered in the natural world.

This speculation makes it important to know at what stage in visual development the Gestalt principles of perceptual organization actually begin operating. Elizabeth Spelke and her colleagues used the preferential looking technique (described earlier) to assess infants' sensitivity to objects whose boundaries were defined by

---

*Obviously, there are exceptions to these tendencies, such as instances of relatively sharp changes in orientation, as with the pointy leaves of maple trees, but overall these tendencies do capture the main statistical characteristics of natural images.

FIGURE 5.42
Contours extracted by Geisler's model. At the left is a set of contour segments used to test both human observers and the computer model. At the right are the contours extracted by the model.

Gestalt principles such as figural similarity and good continuation (Spelke et al., 1993). Although adults described the objects as compelling, three-month-old infants seemed oblivious to the objects, implying that the individual features defining the objects were not being grouped. During the next half-year, infants slowly but surely show signs of increasing use of grouping rules.

But perceptual integration of oriented contours, which underlies some Gestalt principles, takes several more years to reach a fully-adult level. Ilona Kovács and colleagues (1999) measured contour integration ability in more than 500 people, ranging in age from 5 to 30 years. Their test stimuli, samples of which are shown in Figure 5.44, comprised (a) circular contours made up of about a dozen oriented segments, which were embedded in (b) backgrounds of randomly oriented, "noise" elements. By varying the spatial density of noise elements, Kovács and her colleagues generated stimuli whose embedded contours were easier or harder to see. For example, it is relatively easy to see the circular contour in Figure 5.44A, but considerably more difficult in Figure 5.44C, with Figure 5.44B being intermediate.

FIGURE 5.43
Agreement between predictions of Geisler's computer model and performance of human observers. The diagonal line represents perfect agreement between the computer model and people's performance.

With figures of carefully graded difficulty, like those in Figures 5.44A–C, the researchers were able to define for each person a "threshold" figure, which was the most difficult figure that still allowed the person to see the contour. Their results showed that older people could spot contours in figures that were beyond the ability of

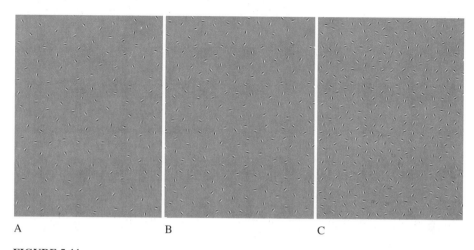

A   B   C

FIGURE 5.44
Circular figures made of small contours are difficult to see when embedded in a background of
"noise" elements. (Kovács et al., 1999.)

younger individuals. Surprisingly, contour integration continues to improve all the way up to least 10 or 11 years of age. Kovács and her colleagues speculate that such delayed maturation may mirror the slow maturation of the human cerebral cortex.

Gestalt principles of organization are sometimes called *laws*. If they're truly laws, however, they're obeyed only when reinforced by other rules and regulations. When two or more Gestalt laws of organization are placed in conflict, one can modify or even nullify another (Quinlan and Wilton, 1998). In Figure 5.36, for instance, the proximity of the window frame to the girl's face would tend erroneously to foster perception grouping of the two, but differences in lightness and texture seem to oppose this tendency.

Top-down There are even circumstances where grouping tendencies are stymied, and need lots of help, effort and extra time. Take the twisted and tangled pairs of curves in Figure 5.45. Start with the left panel, by fixating on the black circle. Now decide whether the x lies on the same curve as the fixation mark. Do the same for each of the other panels.

Although you certainly can perform the task, it's not easy. In fact, the time it takes to determine whether the x and the fixation point share a line depends upon how far apart the two are on that line (Jolicoeur, Ullman and MacKay, 1986; Pringle and Egeth, 1988). The visual system seems to require time to trace the curve from the fixation point, by moving the focus of attention along the curve.

As you know, proximity *promotes* perceptual grouping, but here, grouping by proximity *retards* perception: the tracing time lengthens as the two curves are brought closer together. After all, performance in this task requires keeping the two curves separate, not grouping them into a single entity. This is further demonstrated by the fact that curve tracing slows dramatically if the two curves touch or cross one another (Roelfsema, Scholte and Spekreijse, 1999). Apparently, the task requires not only differentiation of one contour from its background, but also differentiation of one contour from another contour.

So, the Gestalt "laws" operate more like suggestions than reliable, ironclad laws. But laws that operate this way are common in science. Take

FIGURE 5.45
Figures used to study visual assessment of contour relationships ("curve tracing"). Each figure consists of a pair of intermingled curves. For each figure, fixate the black circle and judge whether the x lies on the same curve as the disc or not. Note how the ease of judgment varies from figure to figure. (Adapted from Jolicoeur, Ullman, and Mackay, 1986.)

Boyle's law. It tells us that the volume occupied by a gas is inversely related to the gas's pressure. But pressure is not the only factor that comes into the equation. To predict what volume will be occupied, you also need to take into account the temperature, as the combined gas law does. No Gestalt principle operates in isolation, unless a stimulus has been specially designed to allow it to do so (as we did in Figure 5.39). In the natural world, potentially conflicting Gestalt principles are reconciled in accord with rules that are not yet fully understood.

Why do the Gestalt principles work at all?
Brunswik and Kamiya (1953) pointed out that the Gestalt grouping processes capitalize on certain regularities that characterize our physical world.

They described the grouping processes as having "ecological validity," which mean that the presence of any particular grouping process gave fairly dependable information about the objects in the environment. For example, if elements in the retinal image are close to one another, it is a good bet—though not a sure bet—that the corresponding elements in the world are near each other.

The Gestalt principles of organization also embody other regularities that typify the natural world. For example, in the natural world, objects tend to be compact; their parts, if there are identifiable parts, are connected rather than scattered hither and yon. As a result, perception of natural objects is well served by a tendency to group adjacent elements (the principle of proximity) and

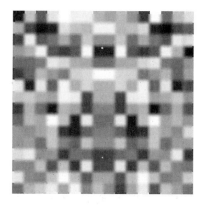

FIGURE 5.46

Demonstration of symmetry detection. Both squares comprise elements of varying lightness. In the square at the left, those elements are distributed randomly; in the other square, the random elements in the left-hand side of the square have been duplicated in mirror-image fashion on the right-hand side. This gives rise to bilateral symmetry that is easily seen.

to treat extended contours as a single form (good continuation). Also, the parts of natural objects tend to be made of a single material, which reflects light in a uniform and characteristic way. Changes in material (and hence, light reflected from the material) usually mark the boundaries between parts or the boundaries between one object and its surroundings. So object perception is helped by grouping elements that are similar and segregating elements that are dissimilar (similarity and closure). The net result is our ability to segregate objects from one another and from the background against which they appear.

Global Structure and Symmetry

Some objects, including most biological ones, have an unusually conspicuous structural property that deserves special comment: that property is **symmetry,** the tendency for those parts of an object centered about a given axis to be highly similar in shape, texture and color. Symmetry influences many of our perceptual judgments, including the quality of fruit (round apples are preferred to irregularly shaped apples), the structural integrity of a bridge, and the aesthetics of art (Ra-

machandran and Hirstein, 1999). The human body is approximately bilaterally symmetric, and some evolutionary biologists even believe that bilateral symmetry of the human face significantly contributes to perceived attractiveness (Mealey, Bridgstock and Townsend, 1999). Given the ubiquitous importance of symmetry, how does the visual system recognize this important characteristic of objects?

For an answer, consider Figure 5.46. Perceptually, the figure's two panels are quite distinct from one another: the one on the left looks like a collection of random black, gray and white squares. The panel on the right is also a collection of black, gray and white squares, but these squares are bilaterally symmetric; the two halves are mirror images of one another. To make this panel, we duplicated one half of the righthand panel, flipped it around a vertical axis, and then put the two halves together, side by side. But you could detect the bilateral symmetry even before you heard how the figure was made. Detecting individual squares—regions that differ from their immediate surroundings—is an early step in the process for detecting symmetry about a vertical axis. But it's not enough. The visual system also has to register similarities in the spatial arrangement of the squares, and this requires recognizing comparable structures—such as the figure's horizontally-elongated and aligned patterns (Dakin and Herbert 1998).

Symmetry is undoubtedly a powerful contributor to aesthetic responses, including human beings' responses to representational and nonrepresentational works of art (Ramachandran and Hirstein, 1999). What's the origin of this aesthetic impact? And can experience override that preference? To explore these questions, Ingo Rentschler of the University of München turned to some very simple figures: compound gratings comprising two different spatial frequencies in varying phase relationships to another (Rentschler et al., 1999). You can see some of these compound gratings in Figure 5.47. Compound gratings may not be as beautiful as your own favorite painting, but using them rather than paintings makes it possible to connect known physical properties to any aesthetic responses they may evoke.

Rentschler and colleagues presented all possible pairs of 16 different compound gratings. For each pair, people chose the compound they liked best. The entire set of preference judgments was converted into a quantitative measure preference for each grating. Overall, people had strongest dislike for compounds 2 and 4 shown in Figure 5.47, and they had the strongest preference for compounds 1 and 3. Apparently, two factors underlie these ratings (and the ratings for the other 12 gratings, which are not shown here). One factor is symmetry—compounds 1 and 3 have greater bilateral symmetry than do 2 and 4. The other factor is simplicity, as reflected in the number of easily visible bars—the preferred compounds have fewer visible bars. In a follow-up experiment, Rentschler found that experience with these compounds altered people's preferences. Bilateral symmetry remained as potent as ever, but preference for complexity was increased or decreased depending upon a person's prior training.

Preference for symmetry, then, depends on a relatively invariant processing of visual information, but the aesthetic pleasure derived from simplicity/complexity depends upon experience. At any moment, your preferences reflect both the enduring properties of your nervous system as well as taste acquired through experience.

This completes our survey of the spatial properties that define objects and their parts, and hence, determine our ability to detect and discriminate those objects. As we close, think back once more to Sojourner slowly traversing the Martian landscape as it surveys whatever its camera encounters. If Sojourner's circuitry can mimic the perceptual operations described in this chapter—multi-scale analysis and shape-from-texture grouping—then our little robot has taken one giant step in humankind's attempt to discover the Martian environment. But Sojourner's electronic messages still must be transformed into identifiable objects. Clues about how that can be accomplished are the focus of Chapter 6.

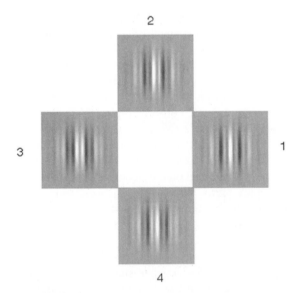

FIGURE 5.47
Compound gratings representing the two preference dimensions Rentschler extracted from people's judgments of liking. Compounds 1 and 3 exemplify bilateral symmetry; compounds 2 and 4 exemplify visual complexity. (Based on images provided by Ingo Rentschler.)

SUMMARY AND PREVIEW

This chapter emphasized that visual information is used to distinguish objects from their backgrounds and to discriminate objects from one another. We presented various views of form perception, including structuralism, Gestalt psychology, and the multichannel model derived from measurements of the CSF. The multichannel model is an attempt to relate human form perception to what is known about the visual cortex. It can account for many aspects of human and animal vision, including detection, discrimination, and certain visual illusions, but it, too, has its limitations. In the next chapter, you'll learn how the visual system puts together the information it acquires to generate useful representations of objects.

KEY TERMS

analytic introspection	good continuation	size aftereffect
closure	gratings	spatial contrast
contrast	identification	spatial frequency
configural superiority effect	metamers	spatial orientation
contrast sensitivity function (CSF)	multichannel model	spatial phase
	orientation	symmetry
contrast threshold	proximity	texture
cutoff frequency	scale	texture contrast
detection	selective adaptation	transfer function
discrimination	shape constancy	window of visibility
Fourier analysis	similarity	
Gestalt	sinusoidal grating	

CHAPTER 6

OBJECT PERCEPTION: RECOGNIZING THE THINGS WE SEE

As the planetary rover Sojourner slogged across the surface of Mars so far from home, its goal was to gather information that would help identify objects on the Martian landscape. In the preceding chapter, we explained how the torrent of numbers Sojourner sent home could be divided into snapshots, and then each snapshot could be broken down into different regions. Breaking a scene into distinct regions is a good start, but is still far from Sojourner's ultimate goal. To begin to accomplish that, Sojourner needs to understand *what* it's looking at—to *recognize* objects in its field of view.

What do we mean by *recognize?* Consider the Latin roots of its constituent parts: the prefix *re* means "again," and the verb *cogito* means "to think" (recall Descartes' famous musing "*Cogito ergo sum,*" which means, "I think therefore I am"). Putting the two roots together, re-cognition means, "recalling to mind." In terms of perception, it means that what we are seeing now puts us in mind of something we already know or are familiar with.

You may, for instance, recognize an object on your table as a coffee mug. You may further recognize that it's your favorite mug, the one covered with pictures of spotted cows. That recognition, in turn, governs how you interact with the mug (or whatever it is you're looking at). Categorizing the object as a "mug" supports your actions of filling it with coffee, reaching for it, grasping its handle and lifting it to your lips. Of course, this all occurs without much, if any, conscious mental effort. As a result, it's easy to take recognition for granted, underestimating the complexity of the process.

To begin understanding just how complex the process of recognition is, look at Figure 6.1, a photograph of the Martian terrain taken by Sojourner. By the standards of earth's urban environments, this is a pretty barren landscape, but it poses real challenges for a robotic vehicle outfitted with a computer-based visual system. Of course, if we were only interested in obtaining photographs of the Martian surface, Sojourner

FIGURE 6.1
Photograph of the Martian landscape (NASA).

would have been unnecessary; a camera mounted on a rotating turret could have done the job. But NASA's scientists wanted more than photographs. They wanted Sojourner to maneuver around the surface, picking up rocks and collecting soil samples. To accomplish these tasks, Sojourner needed to know where to go, and to do that, it had to know what it was looking at.

As Figure 6.1 confirms, the Martian surface is full of hills and valleys, and it's littered with rocks and boulders of various sizes and shapes. "Vision" is the only means by which Sojourner can navigate this challenging terrain. A crater must not be confused with a shadow on the ground; small rocks must be distinguished from larger ones; and even Sojourner's visible tire marks in the dust might be needed to backtrack after a soil-hunting expedition. And there's always the outside possibility that Sojourner might encounter something completely unanticipated, such as an empty soda bottle left behind by an earlier extraterrestrial visitor. Sojourner has to be

able to examine potentially interesting objects that it spots on the Martian surface. To accomplish that, it must be able not only to detect the presence of something but also to recognize *what* that object is.

Humans engage in object recognition all the time, and we're remarkably good at it. Think about lounging in front of the television set surfing the channels for something interesting to watch. Holding your finger down on the remote control button, you're bombarded with a rapid sequence of unrelated images—two chefs cooking and laughing; a race car flipping end over end; a woman doing aerobic exercises; a close-up of a pianist's hands flying over the piano keyboard; Sammy Sosa completing a home-run swing; a weather map full of graphic symbols of sunshine, clouds, low and high pressure systems. Each image is visible for only a fraction of a second, but you have little trouble sorting through this rushing visual stream to identify not only what you are looking at, but whether you have found what you want to watch. Confirming your experience with the video remote control, laboratory studies show that people can identify scenes that are displayed for as little as a tenth of a second (see the review by Henderson and Hollingworth, 1999).

Execute

Most of the time, of course, we aren't forced to recognize objects that appear and then disappear in a flash. Nonetheless, we're constantly shifting our gaze from one location to another, looking at different objects. We do this, you will recall, because the area of keenest vision—the

fovea—is quite small and must be reoriented all the time to take in all there is to see.

As we look about the environment, our eyes first seek out the visually complex regions in the scene, ignoring large expanses of uniform color or luminance. But once we've gotten a quick lay of the land, our eyes tend to revisit objects of potential significance.

This unfolding fixation behavior is illustrated in Figure 6.2. While people looked at this photograph, the successive positions of their eyes were

FIGURE 6.2
A pattern of successive eye fixations (bottom panel) as a person looked at this kitchen scene (top panel). (John Henderson and Andrew Hollingworth.)

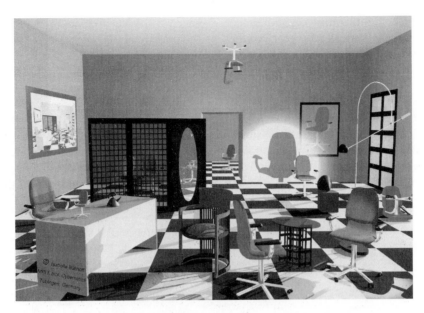

FIGURE 6.3
Computer generated depiction of a room full of chairs (Isabelle Bülthoff.)

recorded. The dots and lines denote the changing pattern of eye movements during a 10-second inspection period. Notice that people tended to look at specific objects in the kitchen scene, ignoring the floor and blank walls. In general, individual durations of fixation last about a quarter of a second (Henderson and Hollingworth, 1998), and the features attracting the greatest number of fixations are precisely those regions that independent judges rate as most informative (Mackworth and Morandi, 1967). This suggests that the eye movement control system of the brain draws on stored information about the characteristics of various scenes and scenarios (Land and Furneaux, 1997). We will reconsider the role of eye movements in object recognition later in this chapter, when we take up reading.

But there's much more to object recognition than merely selecting something to look at. To appreciate some of the additional obstacles that recognition has to overcome, take a look at Figure 6.3. Isabelle Bülthoff, of Germany's Max

Planck Institute, used a computer to design this unusual scene. The obstacles illustrated in this scene revolve around the recognition of chairs, but the same points could be made with other types of objects.

Let's start with an obstacle to recognition that you've already been introduced to. Look carefully at the mesh screen near the figure's left side, where you'll see a couple of objects partially obscured by the mesh. You have no trouble recognizing these as chairs even though some portions are hidden from view. The entire bottom half of the chair behind the desk is invisible, yet you have no trouble recognizing it because you understand that the base is there but occluded. Look up at the ceiling where a chair is suspended precariously. You may never before have seen a chair hanging upside down from the ceiling, unless you've seen the 1951 Fred Astaire movie, "Royal Wedding." Despite the novel perspective, you recognize the dangling object as a chair. However, at first glance you might not pick up on the

Top-down

presence of this odd chair, for unexpected or inconsistent objects in a scene tend to produce more perceptual errors and take longer to recognize (Palmer, 1975; Biederman, 1972).

Look at the painting on the rear wall. It creates a retinal image equivalent to that created by the real chair in the right foreground, but you easily recognize that one is a chair and one is a picture of a chair. Note, too, that the chair visible through the archway into the next room casts the same retinal image as the miniature chair on the desk. But, again, you recognize one as the real thing, and the other as a model—one that you could sit on, the other that you could put in the palm of your hand. Finally, you immediately recognize that the slatted arm chair, although it looks different from the rest, belongs to the same family of objects—chairs—as the rest in this scene. All are in a shared category of objects, chairs.

So how is it that we can recognize objects even when we cannot see all the parts? And how is it that we can distinguish among objects that share many features in common, or recognize the common membership of objects that look rather different from one another? The next several sections describe some of the sources of information that human vision exploits to achieve object recognition.

A MATTER OF PERSPECTIVE: RECOGNIZING 3-DIMENSIONAL OBJECTS

Look again at that room full of chairs in Figure 6.3. Notice how they're scattered about in varying orientations relative to your line of sight: right side up, upside down, turned frontally, turned away, and so on. These variations in orientation produce corresponding variations in the chairs' images on your retinas. Somehow, despite variation in the retinal image your recognition remains unchanged. You may notice the viewpoint has changed, but as far as rough categorization goes, that change is irrelevant. A chair is a chair, regardless of the perspective from which you view it. Recognition can be slowed down by unusual viewpoints, but rarely is it completely stymied.

Several competing theories have been developed to explain recognition's robustness in the face of varying viewpoints (summarized in Wallis and Bülthoff, 1998). Of these, we'll consider two theories that represent contrasting approaches to object recognition. One of these theories, championed by Irving Biederman, is called **recognition by components;** the other theory, developed by Heinrich Bülthoff, Michael Tarr and others, is described as **view-based recognition.**

Recognition By Components

Neural

According to Biederman's theory, when people try to recognize a visible object, they first create a rough classification of the object, on the basis of its three-dimensional (3D) shape. This rough classification sorts objects into broad, entry-level categories such as "chair" or "mushroom" or "mug." Note that this classification does not put objects into finer categories, such as "a Queen Anne chair" or "a Stickley chair." Because the initial classification is rough, the details needed for more subtle discriminations (for example, to distinguish one type of chair from another) are not used. Biederman argues that any view of an object can be represented as an arrangement of just a few, simple, three-dimensional forms called **geons** (for **geo**metrical ic**ons**). The left-hand panel of Figure 6.4 shows some of the geons postulated by the theory. The right-hand panel illustrates how several different common objects could be represented by a combination of two or three geons. The ability to represent a very large number of possible objects by means of just a few components makes Biederman's approach simple and efficient (meaning that relatively few "parts" can be used to represent an indefinitely large number of objects).

Biederman's geons share two essential properties. First, they can potentially be distinguished

FIGURE 6.4
Biederman's geons and simple objects created by them. (From Biederman, 1990.)

from one another from almost any viewing perspective. So, with just one singular exception, from all viewpoints a sphere will always look different from a cylinder.* Second, even when some randomly chosen parts of any geon are obscured or erased, the rest will almost always remain recognizable. So, if the midsection of a cylinder is occluded, what's left will continue to look more like a cylinder than, say, a cone. As a result, neither changes in perspective nor partial occlusion disrupts registration of the geons and, hence, recognition of the object. Once the appropriate geons have been extracted from the visual image, the object is recognized from matches against internal representations of previously seen objects (visual memory). These representations are aggregations of the geons needed to construct particular objects.

The theory's virtues include its ability to explain why it is hard to recognize an object from a highly unusual perspective. Take the various views of the horse shown in Figure 6.5. The horse depicted in the lower righthand photograph in that figure would be difficult to recognize because the image hides several geons that are crucial for defining the category "horse." At the same time, we would have little trouble recognizing the horse in the upper right-hand photo because the image makes it easy to extract the crucial geons despite the odd perspective.

Among the theory's weaknesses is the absence of physiological evidence that the brain actually generates representations like the ones Biederman envisions. Also troublesome for the theory is the fact that in many situations, recognition accuracy and recognition speed *are* dependent on viewpoint. Finally, the theory does not attempt to explain how people recognize specific objects—

*This one exception arises when a cylinder is viewed end on, either from its bottom or top. Then the shape of the cylinder's retinal image is circular, like that of the sphere.

FIGURE 6.5
A single object seen from twelve different perspectives. (From Palmer, Rosch, & Chase, 1981.)

such as a specific species of bird—that share the same geons with many other species.

View-Based Recognition

Bülthoff, Tarr and their colleagues believe that recognition of a 3D object depends upon multiple, stored views of objects. Suppose you get a momentary glimpse of an object you're attempting to recognize. The pattern of neural activity evoked by that brief view of the object can be matched against stored representations of activity patterns that have been previously elicited by views of different objects. If the current activity pattern matches a stored pattern, it's a reasonable bet that the same object is responsible for both. If no match is really close, then your visual system settles for second best, finding the best approximation for a match. While this account sounds

plausible, a number of objections have been raised against this view-based scheme for recognition. Here are just a few.

The first objection concerns novelty. As you read about this account of view-based recognition, you may have wondered what happens when someone is faced with an object never before encountered. The theory proposes that a novel object is recognized by neural interpolation to the object whose neural representation most closely matches the representation produced by the novel object. So a particular coffee mug that you'd never before seen can be recognized as a mug because the neural activity evoked by the novel mug is similar to the neural activity evoked by other, familiar mugs. Similarly, you might wonder about the case where you're viewing a familiar object from a novel viewpoint. Provided the view is not extremely

Neural

FIGURE 6.6
Computer-generated objects, both familiar and novel. (From Blanz, Tarr and Bülthoff, 1999.)

unusual—like the view of the upside-down chair on the ceiling—the object can be recognized by interpolation to the nearest known view.

Most objects tend to have their own, most natural viewpoint from which they are most easily recognized (Palmer, Rosch and Chase, 1981). These natural viewpoints could provide clues about the stored representation used for recognition of that object. For example, if the stored representation strongly resembled the object's natural viewpoint, that resemblance could explain the relative ease of recognition. But what constitutes a natural viewpoint for an object? That depends upon what information the visual system needs to perform a particular task, as Blanz, Tarr and Bülthoff (1999) showed. Blanz et al. created computer-generated, 3D objects on a video screen. Using a trackball, a person could rotate the objects on the screen to simulate viewing from different angles. People rotated each object until they found the best perspective for placing each object in a brochure. The 3D test objects, which appear in Figure 6.6, included familiar objects—faces, motor vehicles, and chairs—as well as a few novel objects. The novel objects are the three shown at the lower right of the array. Two of them were created out of simple basic volumes, like Biederman's geons, and the remaining one, a kind of artificial paper clip, was created by stringing together four similar components.

On each trial, people rotated the image of the object until they were satisfied that the viewpoint was best for the brochure. Blanz then tallied up the preferred viewpoints, and for most objects found a consensus on what constituted each object's best, or canonical, viewpoint. Typically, people chose an oblique viewpoint rather than a viewpoint from above, below, straight on, or entirely sideways to the object. However, the three novel objects did not follow this pattern. For them, there was no consensus on the canonical viewpoint. People's notions about the best viewpoints were all over the place. The absence of a consensus suggests that any object's canonical or best view develops as people have experiences with that or similar objects.

Many experiments have produced results consistent with a view-based recognition scheme. To give one example, Palmer, Rosch and Chase (1981) reported that object recognition slows as the viewpoint departs from that judged most typical for an object. For view-based theorists, such results make perfect sense. If the typical view is an excellent match for a stored representation, no interpolation is needed—hence, short recognition time. If a view is atypical, however, the required interpolation will be lengthy, and recognition time will be longer.

Such an explanation may strike you as *post hoc* (after the fact). Is there some way to put the account to a real test? Suppose we create some novel object and train people to recognize it from just one viewpoint. When we test recognition of that object in a variety of views, it's no surprise that recognition is fastest at the trained viewpoint. If recognition speed really depends on viewpoint interpolation, then sufficient exposure to that object from a wide variety of viewpoints should eliminate the need for interpolation, and hence, speed up recognition. And this is exactly what happens: practice does eliminate viewpoint dependence over the range of trained viewpoints. Of course, viewpoint dependence reasserts itself when people again confront novel perspectives (for example, Edelman and Bülthoff, 1992).

But this discussion of recognition has left out one important source of recognition information. In everyday life, we are not usually restricted to a single view of an object. We can move around an object or, if it's small enough, we can pick it up and examine it from various angles. This movement—of the viewer or of the object—generates information that changes over time in a highly predictable way. Might such dynamic sequences facilitate recognition?

To examine this possibility, James Stone (1998) created a collection of different ameboid 3D structures. People were trained to recognize four of the ameboid shapes, discriminating these target objects from other "distractor" ameboids. Ameboids in the training set or in the distractor set were always presented as a short movie in which an ameboid appeared to rotate in 3D space. Each movie's starting image was chosen randomly for each trial, but regardless of the starting image, the movie always played in the same order.

Throughout the trials, participants' recognition performance improved—they were able to decide more quickly whether the animated amoeba was from the target set or a distractor set. Learning was taking place, but *what* was being learned? To answer that question, Stone tested people using movies in which the direction of 3D rotation was reversed. Now instead of seeing a target ameboid tumble through a series of positions in one order, people saw the same images but in reverse order. The result? Recognition times slowed and accuracy of recognition dropped; only with practice on the new versions did performance recover.

Plasticity

Playing a movie backwards means that a movie's individual "snapshots" remain unchanged; only their order of presentation is altered. This makes the ameboid appear to tumble through a novel sequence of positions. The impact of this change on recognition suggests that recognition incorporates spatio-temporal information when it's available. As Stone notes, spatio-temporal continuity is a fundamental property of the physical world. If an object rotates around a particular axis, that rotation generates a characteristic set of changes in the retinal image over time. Quite sensibly, then, vision can associate objects with characteristic spatio-temporal sequences, and use those sequences in object recognition.

There are plenty of real-world examples of this skill at work. Expert bird-watchers learn to rely heavily on patterns of wing and body movements to distinguish species of birds that are highly similar in size and shape. And all of us are adept at identifying friends based on their characteristic gait, even when other cues to identity are absent. We'll discuss perception of spatio-temporal events in greater detail in Chapter 9.

Vision's reliance on spatio-temporal sequences rests on an assumption about the physical world: Matter tends to maintain its spatial coherence over time. This is just a fancy way of saying that objects don't tend to abruptly change into other objects—with the exception of explosions and special effects in movies. As a result of the world's spatio-temporal coherence, an object we see today is likely to appear the same tomorrow, next week or next year.

But does object recognition actually take advantage of the world's tendency toward spatio-temporal continuity? To test this idea, Guy Wallis (1998) subverted objects' usual spatio-temporal continuity, and then measured how this subversion altered recognition. Wallis's subversion required several short, five-frame sequences that depicted faces in changing perspective, rotating from left profile through a frontal view to right profile. When the frames were shown in succession, vision knitted them together, creating the impression of one person whose head rotated smoothly from left to right. But, in fact, people were not seeing the same face. Instead, Wallis' film sequence contained a series of five different faces at each of the five perspectives. Because the five faces resembled one another, people tended to see the sequence as the movement of a single face—not five different faces in different views. This means, of course, that the "face" people saw never actually existed. It was a chimera* pieced together by their visual systems, aided and abetted by Wallis.

———————————
*In Greek mythology, Chimera was a creature who was, from front to rear, part lion, part goat and part snake.

Illusion

After people saw these shifting chimeras several times, Wallis measured their ability to recognize various faces. In the test, people saw two faces, one after the other, but in different, randomly chosen perspectives. They had to judge whether the two images portrayed a single person or two different people. When the two test faces had never been shown together in the same chimera, people correctly recognized that they were different faces about three-quarters of the time. However, when the two faces had appeared in the same chimera, recognition fell to near chance levels. Seeing the two different faces as a single chimera undermined discrimination. And the more chimeric sequences people saw, the poorer discrimination became. So practice does not always make perfect, particularly when you're practicing with misleading material.

LEARNING TO SEE

Plasticity

So we now know that object recognition can be educated. When you encounter the same object again and again, the way you perceive that object can change, sometimes dramatically. This experience-driven "tuning" of the visual system is an important, but often neglected, aspect of seeing. James Elkins, an art historian at the Art Institute of Chicago, has a keen sense of what educating vision is all about. Elkins recalls his own experiences with visual plasticity:

> The world is filled with things we do not see, even though they are right in front of us. When I was younger I kept a collection of insects, and for several years I was especially entranced by moths. . . . Some kinds of moths don't care about light at all, and they stay in the woods and fly only at night. . . . To catch them you mix a pail of beer, mashed rotten bananas, and molasses and walk through the woods painting it on tree trunks with a house-painting brush. . . . The moths we were after also have excellent camouflage, and their wings are perfect facsimiles of bark. . . . After several summers sugaring trees, I developed a special eye for the subtle outlines of those moths: I learned to see the little rounded triangle of their bodies, the very slight

FIGURE 6.7
Series of drawings with two alternative interpretations.

Illusion

shadow they cast when they pressed against the wood, and the minute differences between their patterned wings and the texture of bark. . . . And now, over twenty years later, I still have the ability to spot those moths. It seems to be built into my neurons. (1996, pp. 54–55)

Figure 6.7 doesn't show any of these hard-to-spot moths, but it does illustrate what Elkins had in mind. The figure shows an ambiguous image, much like one in Chapter 4 (Figure 4.26). Looking at the middle version first, you can see it either as the face of a man or a nude woman with her head coyly turned away from you. And if you look at the figure for a minute or so, you'll see one person and then the other, each one's perceptual dominance lasting several seconds. On the left is a version of the drawing that more clearly depicts the man; on the right you see a version that favors the nude woman.

When people are shown only the ambiguous drawing (middle panel), some initially see the man, others initially see the woman. However, this tendency can be altered by having a person look first at one of the less ambiguous versions of the drawing. When people are first shown the left panel of Figure 6.7 and then the middle panel, virtually all initially see the ambiguous, middle figure as depicting a man. Conversely, when peo-

ple are first shown the right panel and then the middle panel, virtually all of them see the ambiguous drawing as depicting a nude woman. Exposure to either unambiguous drawing "primes" the subsequent perception of the ambiguous drawing, biasing it in one direction or the other. Priming's influence on perception can be quite enduring. A single exposure to a "priming" object can influence perceptual judgments made several days or even weeks later (Cave, 1997).

Priming, then, involves experience at one moment influencing subsequent experiences, which is a sign of visual plasticity. Chapter Four described another form of visual plasticity, in which neurons' receptive fields change in response to environmental stimulation experienced early in life. These results during early infancy led researchers to wonder whether adult vision might also be plastic (Buonomano and Merzenich, 1998). Figure 6.8 shows the test stimuli for four experiments on adults that demonstrate the powerful effects of practice in a variety of visual tasks.

Plasticity

Panel A tests the ability to discriminate between lines in slightly different orientations from one another (Schoups, Vogels and Orban, 1995). With practice, the smallest orientation difference that can be discriminated decreases by

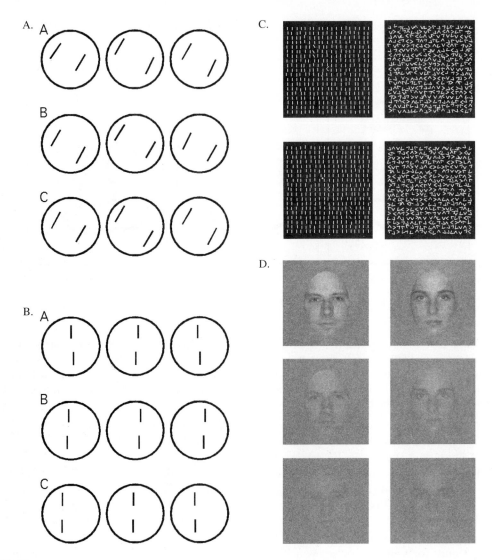

FIGURE 6.8

Perceptual learning improves performance on the four tasks illustrated in these panels. Panel A: Stimuli used to assess orientation/discrimination. In each circle, judge which of the two short lines is the more clockwise in orientation. Difficulty in discrimination increases as you move from top to bottom because the orientation differences decrease. With practice, discrimination improves, eventually rendering even the most difficult patterns relatively easy. Panel B: Stimuli used to assess vernier acuity. In each circle, judge which of the two lines is shifted more leftward. Discrimination difficulty increases from row to row. Practice enhances the ability to discriminate even the most challenging line pairs here. Panel C: Sample figures used by Karni and Sagi (1993) to study perceptual learning. Observers identified the orientation—horizontal vs vertical—of a tiny "bar" composed of three diagonally oriented lines seen against a background of lines all of the same orientation (left column). This array of lines was presented for a brief duration, immediately followed by an array of irregularly oriented lines that foreclosed further processing of the test array. With practice, observers were able to identify the orientation of the test "bar" at ever briefer durations, indicating that the display was being processed more effeciently. Panel D: Sample stimuli that illustrate the improvement in effective stimulus strength that comes with practice. The stimuli, devised by Gold, A.B. Sekuler and Bennett (1999), are images briefly presented in the midst of random "noise." At appropriate levels, the "noise" makes the faces difficult to recognize. With practice, a given level of "noise" becomes less effective in interfering with recognition. By scanning the photos in this panel from top to bottom, an observer is able to correctly perceive the continuity of faces despite the increasing visual "noise." (Jason Gold.)

more than five-fold. The orientation difference between lines in each pair grows smaller from the top row to the bottom, which makes the discrimination more difficult. This is meant to simulate the observation that orientation discriminations that at first were impossibly hard became easier with practice.

Panel B measures the ability to perceive tiny offsets between collinear lines, an ability called *vernier acuity* (Fahle, Edelman and Poggio, 1995). Even before practice, people can make very fine discriminations between offsets. But with practice, that skill improves dramatically, making it possible to discriminate between even the slightest offsets. In each pair of lines the offset of one line relative to the other grows smaller from the top row to the bottom. This makes the judgment of the lines' offset more difficult. This is meant to simulate the observation that offset (vernier) judgments that at first were very difficult, like the ones at the bottom, with practice became easier, like the ones at the top.

Panel C tests the ability to spot a small, briefly-presented "target" item embedded in a field of "background" texture elements (Karni and Sagi, 1993). Throughout the trials, the orientation of the target's three items varied randomly between horizontal and vertical; its precise location in the field also varied. Participants had to identify the orientation. At first, correct performance required that the target be visible for more than 130 msec. After several days' practice, people only required a 30 msec exposure for the same level of performance.

Panel D examines the ability to identify a low-contrast, human face that is partially camouflaged by random visual noise (Gold, Sekuler and Bennett, 1999). The relatively clear face at the top of the panel illustrates the initial level of contrast people needed to identify a face. Over time, performance sharpened so that after several days, people became highly proficient at identifying faces like the barely visible one at the bottom. The middle face represents an intermediate level of proficiency, which participants displayed partway through the experiment.

These substantial improvements in visual performance also seem to endure, lasting as much as two years after practice ceases (Karni and Sagi, 1993). Moreover, improvement tends to be highly specific to the visual figures encountered during training. When people are trained with figures that, say, always appear in the left half of the visual field, practice induced improvement may not generalize to test figures imaged in the right half of the visual field (Shiu and Pashler, 1992; Karni and Sagi, 1991; Fahle, Edelman and Poggio, 1995). Likewise, when people get better at distinguishing a vertical line from a line slightly tilted from vertical, improvement does not transfer to other orientations, such as ones near horizontal (Schoups, Vogels and Orban, 1995).

Improvements in vision are not limited to the laboratory. People who devote lots of time to particular visual discriminations develop proficiency that leaves the rest of us awestruck (Sowden, Davies and Roling, 2000). Sometimes these visual skills develop as part of a hobby, such as bird watching or moth hunting; others develop in connection with one's job. Consider the case of professional chick sexers. Chickens are big business in many parts of the world. Farmers who raise chickens for egg-laying are not eager to feed more male mouths than absolutely necessary. As a result, within hours of hatching, chicks are sorted according to sex, so that males can be discarded. On large farms, specialists, called "chick sexers," do this job with blazing speed and unerring accuracy. Over the course of a career, a sexer might sort 50 million chicks, taking just a half second per chick. Looking over the shoulder of a sexer at work, it's hard to figure out what visual information is being used. But, with a little help from expert chick sexers, Biederman and Shiffrar (1988) cracked the code, allowing them to educate people who had never sexed a chick before. People got a simple diagram explaining exactly what part of a chick to look at and some rules for interpreting what they saw there. With only modest practice, the novices were transformed into highly-skilled chick sexers.

Differences

FIGURE 6.9
Examples of black-and-white images that are difficult to recognize. (From Dolan et al., 1997).

Plasticity

In Chapter 4 you encountered other forms of visual learning. Remember that Dalmatian dog whose spots blended so well with its background? Unless you'd seen it before, the dog was initially hard to see. But eventually, with effort and prompting, the dog emerged. What happens in the brain to transform unrecognizable or misrecognized objects into recognizable ones? Recently, researchers have begun to understand how the brain deals with things that are initially hard to recognize.

Using positron emission tomography to image the brain in action, Dolan and colleagues (1997) presented people with two-tone, black-and-white photographs of objects, including faces. Such im-

ages are difficult to recognize because all the normal shades of gray have been removed, leaving the image with just two extreme intensity levels— black and white. Examples of their images are shown in the left column of Figure 6.9. As expected, people performed poorly, correctly recognizing only 55% of the faces and 13% of the rest of the objects. Then Dolan and colleagues showed people normal, easy to recognize grayscale versions of the two-tone images. As expected, exposure to the normal versions boosted subsequent recognition rates of the original black-and-white images to 87% for objects and 93% for faces.

To identify the brain changes accompanying this improvement, Dolan and colleagues com-

Execute

pared regions of brain activated during the first, "uneducated," exposure to the images to those areas activated during the second, "educated," exposure to the same images. Two different, widely separated parts of the brain, the temporal lobe and the parietal lobe, showed the changes with education. Specifically, improved recognition of faces and improved recognition of objects were linked to increased activation in two small regions in the inferior portion of the temporal lobe. Prior studies had shown that neurons in these regions respond preferentially to easily recognized faces or to objects presented in their normal colors. In addition, improved recognition activated regions in the parietal lobe. Earlier work had revealed that these activated regions participate in directing attention and in generating visual imagery.

The pattern of activation led Dolan and colleagues to hypothesize that improved recognition resulted from feedback from the parietal lobe's stored representation of the easily recognized, full-grayscale stimulus. This feedback, they argued, amplifies the responses of face- or object-sensitive neurons in the temporal lobe. This result reminds us that recognizing objects under impoverished viewing conditions benefits from visual imagery stored in memory. This kind of influence is often described as "top-down," in order to distinguish it from sensory influences, which are described as "bottom-up" (you may recall these terms from Chapter One). We shall return to such influences later in the chapter. For now, though, let's consider object recognition from the brain's perspective, focusing on those hierarchically arranged visual areas that are involved in identifying objects.

The Temporal Pathway and Object Recognition

Chapter Four introduced you to two streams of visual processing, the parietal stream and the temporal stream. Recall that the temporal stream is sometimes described as vision's "what" specialist because its major responsibility seems to

be in object recognition, telling us *what* we're looking at. (Analogously, the parietal stream is the "where" specialist, putting visual information into a spatial context, telling us *where* things are located, and therefore where our actions should be directed.) Remember, the brain's temporal stream originates in V1, the occipital lobe's rearmost region. It progresses through V2 and V4, and then crosses the occipital lobe's border with the temporal lobe. There, it makes synaptic connections in several areas of the temporal lobe's lower, or inferior, half, which is known as the inferotemporal (IT) cortex.

The vast terrain of IT cortex* is home to several functionally different regions, each with cells preferring a somewhat different assortment of complex stimuli. In some areas, many neurons respond vigorously when the image of a face falls within a neuron's receptive field. We can describe these regions as "face-selective," without implying that when we recognize a face *only* cells in such areas participate in that recognition (Tovee, 1998).

Converging lines of evidence show that the IT cortex plays a vital role in object recognition. For more than three decades, it's been known that damage to this region in monkeys produces a large deficit in visual object recognition. In humans, inferotemporal damage has similar effects on object recognition.* The effects of inferotemporal damage are especially dramatic when people must recognize complex visual patterns that cannot be easily coded in words (Milner, 1968). Because of its unique contributions, IT cortex has been described as the brain region where visual perception interfaces with memory and imagery (Miyashita, 1993).

Clinical

---

*The cortex covering IT constitutes almost one-tenth of the brain's entire cortical surface.

*Portions of the temporal lobe may be surgically excised from the human brain in order to arrest epilepsy that does not respond to medical (drug) treatment. In many forms of epilepsy, seizures tend to start in the temporal lobe. Removal of the offending brain tissue stops or reduces seizures in most of these otherwise untreatable cases.

Recall that neurons in area V1 respond to simple patterns such as bars and oriented edges. Within IT cortex, however, few neurons prefer oriented bars and edges (Tanaka, 1997). Instead, the vast majority of IT neurons exhibit much more complex selectivity, with some neurons responding only when a specific object such as a brush, a plant or a person's face is imaged within the receptive field. This extraordinary selectivity has been known since records of single cell activity in IT cortex were first made by Charles Gross and his colleagues (see Gross, 1998). IT neurons have huge receptive fields (in contrast to V1 neurons), meaning that they will respond to an object appearing anywhere within a large region of their visual field.

Look back to Figure 6.3, with the room full of chairs. As we pointed out, that figure illustrates some challenges that visual recognition effectively overcomes. Guy Orban's research group in Leuven (Belgium) has shown that some neurons in IT overcome some of the same challenges. Take occlusion, for example. As Figure 6.3 illustrated, occlusion does not foreclose accurate recognition of objects. In our three-dimensional world, this ability is vital—in real-world scenes, objects commonly occlude one another. Kovacs, Vogels and Orban (1995) showed that many neurons in a monkey's IT cortex are unaffected by occlusion of part of their optimum stimulus.

Figure 6.3 also reminds us that we're able to recognize an object despite large variations in the size of the retinal image of that object (variations produced as we view it from different distances). The same sort of size invariance is seen at the level of individual cells in IT cortex (Sary, Vogels and Orban, 1993).

In general, recognition allows us to categorize objects to varying degrees of specificity, ranging from general class membership to a specific instance of a subclass of objects. So, with some effort you could pick out every chair in the room, treating them all as members of a general class. But you could also make various finer discriminations, picking out chairs that had slotted backs, for example (members of a particular subclass).

Individual neurons in the inferotemporal cortex are likewise able to convey different levels of information about objects. Sugase and colleagues (1999) recorded the sequence of neural impulses elicited in monkey brains when faces were presented in the receptive fields of "face" neurons. The test displays included human faces, monkey faces, and simple geometrical objects such as circles and squares. Moreover, within the collections of human and monkey faces were sets of faces defined by their emotional expression: neutral, surprised, angry and so on. When Sugase and his colleagues examined the time course of neural activity evoked by various figures, they found that, for at least some neurons, the early and later portions of a neuron's activity conveyed information about different aspects of the stimulus. Neural activity triggered 50 msec following stimulus onset conveyed information about the general class of object in the neuron's receptive field. This portion of the neuron's response, in other words, could discriminate whether the stimulus was a monkey face, a human face, or a geometric object. However, this early activity gave no clue about the particulars of the stimulus. In contrast, activity occurring several hundred milliseconds later was selective for the details of the image, such as the expression conveyed by a face. Sugase and his colleagues believe there might be a functional significance to this time delay between neural activity related to an image's global identity and its fine detail. You might liken the early, global information to the subject heading of an e-mail message, which provides a general, nondetailed preview of what is to follow, leaving it to later neural activity to fill in the details.

Teaching Old IT Neurons New Tricks You've
already learned that human vision is educable. Among other signs of educability, practice improves (or at least alters) visual recognition. Here we'll consider just two forms of plasticity that IT neurons exhibit (another form will be described later in the chapter).

Recall Dolan's demonstration (Figure 6.9) that a brief glimpse of a grayscale image can confer instant recognizability on a previously unrecognizable, black-and-white only version of that image. The technique used in that demonstration, functional neuroimaging, assesses activation in millions of neurons, but doesn't pinpoint what is happening in individual neurons. To take this more microscopic view, Tovee, Rolls and Ramachandran (1996) demonstrated what may be a neural analogue to Dolan's behavioral observation. Tovee and his colleagues measured responses in monkey IT cortical neurons evoked by figures whose stark, black-and-white only rendition made them hard for humans to recognize. Then, following Dolan's procedure, they presented a full, easy to recognize, grayscale version of the figures. When the black-and-white only versions were presented again they elicited considerably more activity from the same neurons studied before training. Confirming Dolan's account, the result is one-shot learning at a the level of individual neurons.

In another demonstration of plasticity in IT cortical neurons, Kobatake, Wang and Tanaka (1998) assessed neurons' responses while a monkey tried to recognize stimuli from a set of complex geometric figures. On each trial, one of 28 figures was presented, and then, after a delay, the same figure appeared again, but this time along with three of the other figures. The monkey's task was to identify the stimulus that had been repeated, a standard recognition task. To make the task harder, Kobatake steadily lengthened the delay, from 1 to 16 seconds. With practice, the monkeys' recognition improved even at the longest delays. This behavioral change in practiced monkeys was accompanied by changes in the responses of IT cortical neurons. Compared to neurons in nontrained monkeys, practice caused neurons' responses to become more differentiated from one another. In other words, practice made responses to various stimuli more distinctively different from one another than they'd been prior to practice. Presumably, differentiation of responses at the level of single cells contributes to increased ability to discriminate at the behavioral level.

But the ventral stream and area IT are not the entire story on object recognition; objects also imply actions, and to guide actions, we rely heavily on the dorsal stream (Colby and Goldberg, 1999). Box 6.1 offers one perspective on the relation between objects and the actions they afford.

Now that we've explored some basic facts about object recognition and some of its underlying neural machinery, we can apply what we've learned to two categories of objects that we encounter every day—faces and printed words—as well as to an unusual category of objects you've never seen before, computer-generated creatures called "greebles."

Faces

Of the countless objects we encounter during our everyday activities, one category of objects stands out: the human face. It's not surprising, therefore, that face perception is a major focus of research on object recognition.

We'll begin our discussion of face recognition with a brief overview, summarizing just how good we are at this task (and how bad we can be when faces are presented in odd perspectives). Then we'll consider one of the most bizarre syndromes in neurology, one in which brain damage destroys the ability to recognize familiar faces.

Perceiving Faces/Perceiving Minds Shakespeare's King Macbeth wisely noted that, "There's no art to find the mind's construction in the face" (I. iv). With these words Macbeth anticipated what researchers have confirmed centuries later: 1) a person's facial appearance provides reliable clues about that individual's mood, character and intentions, and 2) we're all experts at reading faces.

The human face speaks volumes about a person. It reliably tells us whether the person is male or female (Bruce et al., 1993); whether the person is happy, sad, angry, frightened or surprised (Ekman, 1984; de Gelder, Teunisse and Benson, 1997); whether the person is young or old (George and Hole, 1995); and whether the person

BOX 6.1

OBJECT AFFORDANCES

Objects manifest what James Gibson (1979) termed "affordances," which can be construed as perceptual invitations from the objects to do things with them. The specific activities "afforded" by an object are governed by the object's structural characteristics. Some objects are designed to provide a particular affordance, but others offer affordances just because of their natural shape and size. A chair affords sitting, but so does a fallen log or a porch step. Moreover, a given object can have multiple affordance. A cup, for example, is designed to convey liquid to your mouth, but you can also use it to scoop dirt, to hold pencils or to trap a small insect.

Some psychologists concentrate on identifying object affordances and relating them to the physical characteristics of those objects. For example, when it comes to judging the sizes of containers—such as boxes, jars and cans—adults tend to focus heavily on the container's height when judging its volume. Thus, a typical spice jar 10.2 cm tall is judged larger than a common jar of baby food 7.7 cm tall, even though the baby food jar holds more (Raghubir and Krishna, 1999). As you can imagine, marketing analysts and product designers are keenly interested in these kinds of affordance judgments, which undoubtedly influence purchasing decisions.

The concept of affordance reminds us that object recognition serves behavioral purposes. We don't just recognize the object on the desk as a compact disk (CD); we reach out, pick it up, insert it into the CD drive and listen to it. Our behavioral reactions to objects, then, need to be tailored to the perceived structural qualities of those objects. Thus, when you reach for that CD disk, you hand begins conforming to its circular shape before you even make contact with it. At the moment you grasp it, vision has already estimate the object's dimensions. As a result the distance between your grasping fingers is just a little bit greater than the CD's diameter. And it's not just shape that vision estimates. You perceive whether an object is solid and sturdy (for example, billiard ball) and, therefore, can be grasped firmly, or whether it's thin and fragile (for example, a fresh egg) and must be handled with care. Vision tells us whether an object is sticky or slippery, rough or smooth, light or heavy, dangerous or safe. When you climb a set of stairs you've never been on before, vision tells you when and how high to lift your feet (Warren, 1984).

Given this intimate link between object recognition and object affordance, it's natural to assume that our perceptions of an object will coincide with our motor reactions to those objects. If one coin looks bigger than another, you're going to spread your fingers farther apart to grasp the larger looking coin by its edges. That's true if the two coins are genuinely different in size. but suppose the coins are actually equal in size but only look different. What would happen then? Before venturing a guess, you'd probably like to know how it's possible to make two round objects that are equal in size look different. We'll tell you how this is done, then tell you what your hand does when you go to grasp the coins.

The accompanying figure shows one of the most famous illusions in psychology, the Ebbinghaus illusion. If you're like most people, you'll judge the disk surrounded by small circles to be larger in diameter than the disk surrounded by larger circles. In fact, they're equal in diameter (as you can confirm using a ruler). Rather than worry about why this illusion occurs, suppose you're simply asked to reach out and pick up one disk, lay it aside and then pick up the other disk. How far apart will you adjust your fingers just before grasping each disk?

Imagine further that you've not been told anything about the actual sizes of the two disks. All your hand knows is what your visual system tells it, so it stands to reason that your grasp width should differ for the two disks. In this case, however, reason is misleading.

Illusion

BOX 6.1 continued

In fact, people employ identical grasp widths when reaching for one disk or the other, even though they reliably report the one disk being larger than the other. The hands, in other words, aren't fooled by the illusion. These and comparable findings have led Goodale and Humphrey (1998) to conclude that visually guided actions such as reaching are controlled by "mechanisms that are functionally and neurally separate from those mediating our [conscious] perception of that object" (p. 183). According to this way of thinking, Gibson's affordances, with their emphasis on opportunities for action, may speak more to the dorsal stream than to the ventral stream.

FIGURE 6.10
The contrast has been reversed in this photograph of a familiar face, making it more difficult to identify.
©Reuters NewMedia Inc./CORBIS

FIGURE 6.11
Notice anything strange about this upside down face? Invert the book to see what you're looking at. (Victoria Ahlström.) (By the way, if you didn't recognize the person in the reverse contrast photo in Figure 6.10, it was Tiger Woods.)

is healthy and reproductively fit (Perrett et al., 1998). Without even knowing it, we use facial cues during conversation to help interpret what someone is saying (Massaro and Stork, 1998). Most importantly, we're able to identify the significant people in our lives—family members, loved ones, friends and enemies—from a glance at the face, and we're able to do this despite variations in viewing angle, lighting and size (Moses, Ullman and Edelman, 1996).

Expert though we are at recognizing faces, it doesn't take much to foil that expertise. Reversing the contrast in photographs of faces makes it more difficult to recognize people, even well-known people (see Figure 6.10), probably because this procedure reverses the color of skin pigmentation and distorts shading cues that define facial features such as the nose and eyes (Bruce, 1994). Our face recognition abilities are disrupted even more dramatically when faces are shown upside down (Valentine, 1988). Suddenly, we're lousy at recognizing faces, and we're downright pitiful at judging expressions on faces. To discover your own ineptitude at perceiving upside down faces, take a look at Figure 6.11, a

FIGURE 6.12
A hybrid face whose top and bottom parts come from two
well-known actors
(Photograph courtesy of Isabel Gauthier.)

photograph created using an image editing technique devised by Peter Thompson (1980). Notice anything odd? Turn the book upside down, and you'll discover what you missed when the face was upside down.

This so-called **face-inversion effect** has been taken to mean that faces, unlike other objects, are processed in a *holistic* fashion, meaning that a face is more than the sum of its individual parts. In this respect, holistic processing is reminiscent of the Gestalt notion of relationships among components discussed in Chapter 5. In addition to the face inversion effect, other results also point to holistic processing of faces (Tanaka and Farah, 1993). For example, consider the "hybrid" face shown in Figure 6.12. With scrutiny you may be able to tell that the top half and the bottom half belong to different people. When asked to name the person pictured in, say, the top half of such hybrids, people are slower and less accurate than when only the top half is shown by itself. Evidently, we can automatically process faces as global configurations, which interferes with the ability to attend just to one part of a face (Hole, 1994; for related findings, see Tanaka and Farah, 1993).

When it comes to facial expressions, people of all ages and cultures seem to recognize the same six basic emotions: sadness, happiness, anger, fear, surprise and disgust (Ekman, 1984). Figure 6.13 shows prototypes of these six, and you can probably identify the facial characteristics that uniquely signify each of the emotions. When it comes to salience, however, not all six are equal. A single angry face stands out conspicuously within a crowd of otherwise neutral or happy faces. In contrast, a neutral or happy face does not stand out in a crowd of angry faces (Hansen and Hansen, 1988). This probably makes sense from an evolutionary perspective, since anger forewarns the threat of aggression. From the standpoint of mobilizing for action, it's much more important to detect a potential enemy among friends than it is to detect a friend among a crowd of enemies.

In view of the importance of face perception in our everyday lives, it's almost impossible to imagine being unable to recognize faces. Yet some individuals suffer this exact problem. Their tragic misfortune provides us another opportunity to learn about the neural responses to face perception.

Prosopagnosia: Failure of Face Recognition
Chapter 4 introduced you to several types of **agnosia** (from the Greek, meaning "without knowledge"), visual disorders produced by lesions (tissue destruction) of specific areas of the brain (Kolb and Whishaw, 1996). Among the most fascinating of the agnosias is **prosopagnosia,** the condition where a patient can see and describe another person's face but cannot recognize *whose* face it is, even if the person is a close relative (Sacks, 1985). We'll discuss this relatively rare condition in some detail because this dramatic failure of object recognition illuminates key theoretical and methodological ideas about object recognition in general. Let's start with a case description that typifies this fascinating, bewildering condition:

> When her husband or mother visited her, she failed to recognize them immediately, and only when a conversation was begun did she identify her visitors. When she was shown photographs of her two

FIGURE 6.13
Face displaying the six basic emotions. (From Robert Sekuler and Randolph Blake's,
Star Trek on the Brain: Alien Minds, Human Minds [1999], New York: W. H. Freeman.)

older children of preschool age, she failed to iden-tify them; when she was told that these were indeed her children, she remarked that 'they don't look like they should.' Her failure in facial recognition extended to public personalities such as television stars. When watching television, she was unable to identify performers who were well-known to her until they spoke or sang. (Benton, 1980, p. 178)

It's important to understand that the patient's problem is not blindness—her sight remains in-tact. Thus, when prosopagnosic patients look at photographs of different faces, they can judge whether one photograph is different from the other, even when the poses in the photographs show the faces from different perspectives (Ser-gent and Poncet, 1990). And these patients can readily tell whether a face is male or female (Tranel, Damasio and Damasio, 1988). Despite all that, they cannot tell you *whose* face it is, even when they're looking at photographs or mirror images of their own face.

Now, we've all experienced difficulty remem-bering the name of an acquaintance, but name re-trieval is not the problem in prosopagnosia—these patients can readily identify a friend, a loved one or a famous individual based on the person's voice. Nor is the problem a general im-pairment of cognitive function. As Antonio Damasio explains:

(People) who have never seen a prosopagnosic pa-tient may be tempted to dismiss the phenomenon as the result of psychiatric illness or dementia. These interpretations are not credible considering that these patients show no evidence of language impairment, have intact cognitive skills and do not have psychiatric symptomatology before or after the onset of prosopagnosia. (1985, p. 133)

The problem, in other words, is genuinely visual, and it centers around recognition: faces no longer have meaning for these patients.

Prosopagnosia is almost always accompanied by brain damage to regions in the lower, inferior part of the temporal lobe, particularly in the right hemisphere of the brain. Earlier in this chapter you learned that the homologous region in the monkey brain is where neurons responsive to faces are found. And in Chapter 4 we mentioned that brain imaging studies in humans pinpointed the inferior temporal lobe as a region uniquely activated when human faces are seen (Kanwisher, McDermott and Chun, 1997). These converging lines of evidence make it tempting to identify the inferior temporal lobe as the location of the face processing area. But that conclusion oversimplifies the way the brain does its work, and underestimates the versatility of the so-called "face" areas.

For one thing, in some prosopagnosic individuals recognition deficits extend beyond faces. These deficits, however, tend to get downplayed because the distress of not being able to recognize faces is so paramount. Damasio, Damasio, and van Hoesen describe patients who are unable to recognize other previously familiar objects besides faces. One such patient was an avid bird watcher who knew a bird when he saw one but had lost the ability to identify the species of bird he was seeing. Another was a cattle farmer who had lost his once proud ability to recognize individual members of his own herd by sight. More recent work on prosopagnosic patients reveals that, in addition to faces, they can have trouble recognizing synthetic snowflakes or three-dimensional artificial, computer-generated creatures (Gauthier, Behrmann and Tarr, 1999). In general, these patients experience little difficulty recognizing objects as belonging to some broad class ("It's the face of a male"); the problem in-

volves identifying the specific object under scrutiny ("It's my son Geoff").

There's another reason why we should be skeptical that prosopagnosia results from damage to a single "face" area of the brain: prosopagnosia can take different forms. To demonstrate this point, Sergent and Poncet (1990) showed prosopagnosic patients photographs of eight different faces, two photographs at a time. For each pair, the patient rated how similar the faces were to one another. Sergent and Poncet then used a data analysis technique called multidimensional scaling (see Appendix A) to deduce what facial features the patients were relying on to make those judgments. From this analysis there emerged two distinct modes of face processing. Scaling results from one type of patient resembled the results from normals: patients based their judgments on the overall similarity of the faces' configurations, integrating various facial features into a comprehensive, global configuration (Sergent and Poncet, 1990). We can call this **configural processing.** The other type of patient, in contrast, performed very differently when making similarity judgments about the pairs of face photographs. This patient's judgments indicate that he singled out individual facial components (such as the hairline) without really integrating those components into an overall impression (Sergent and Villemure, 1989). We can call this **featural processing.** When either mode of information processing—configural or featural—is damaged, face recognition suffers.

Why though do some prosopagnosics, whose vision is normal, still experience problems recognizing faces? According to Damasio (1985), face recognition in these types of patients suffers because of an inability to access pertinent stored information about the face's owner. According to this view, brain damage has somehow uncoupled normal perceptual representation of a face from stored memories that make it possible to identify the face. In support of this "uncoupling" hypothesis, tests that bypass conscious recognition reveal the existence of intact knowledge of faces. In

Execute

one study, the skin's electrical resistance was monitored while prosopagnosic patients viewed photos of familiar and unfamiliar faces. (Skin resistance reflects activation of the body's autonomic nervous system, which is activated when a person becomes aroused.) Despite their lack of conscious recognition, the patients showed signs of heightened arousal upon viewing the faces of relatives and friends, compared to faces of unfamiliar people (Bauer, 1984; Tranel and Damasio, 1985). These and other results that probe unconscious memory (Sergent and Poncet, 1990) imply that in some forms of prosopagnosia faces receive normal visual processing, with the problem resulting from connections between face perception and explicit memory.

P
Plasticity

Faces, chairs, birds and vegetables have something in common. Like all objects, they can be characterized at a very general level of description, yielding a list of generic qualities (a bird is a two-legged, feathered creature with wings). But when necessary, we also can focus on characteristics of specific members of an object category (a wren is a small, brown perching bird with a curved bill and stubby tail). These more subtle distinctions are known as *subordinate-level* distinctions because they require more detailed information than is needed to make global category distinctions.

For many objects, we get by perfectly well with global descriptions—"chair" works perfectly fine when you're looking for something to sit on; then the kind of chair is irrelevant. But with faces, it's different. With faces we almost always need to identify specific instances within the category (Gauthier et al., 1998). In that respect, faces are not like other objects, a point stressed by Isabel Gauthier (Vanderbilt University) and Michael Tarr (Brown University). Because faces are of paramount importance in our lives, we are highly experienced at face recognition, and we're very good at it—indeed, we all qualify as face experts. Is it possible, then, that the specialized "face" region in the temporal lobe is, in fact, a more general purpose brain area designed to sup-

port object expertise? If you were to devote a lifetime to distinguishing among, say, different species of birds, would the "face" area be transformed into a "bird" area? Gauthier and Tarr were interested in testing this idea, but they wanted to start with a set of entirely unfamiliar objects, so that all people would begin as novice recognizers. To accomplish this, they turned to greebles.

Getting Acquainted with Greebles

E
Execute

Look at the objects shown in Figure 6.14. These strange-looking "creatures" are examples drawn from a set of 3D, computer-generated objects dubbed "greebles." To make it easy to describe these exotic creatures, greeble parts have been given fanciful names. For example, the horns on each side of greeble's head are called "boges." The upper protrusion on the front is the greeble's "quiff," and the protrusion below that is called a "dunth."

A greeble may not look like someone you know, but its geometrical structure has something

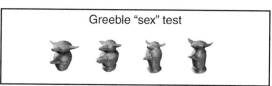

FIGURE 6.14
Computer-generated "creatures" dubbed greebles. (Isabel Gauthier.)

in common with faces and with other objects, too. Just as a human face has a mouth, eyes and a nose in a fixed spatial relationship to one another, a greeble has characteristic parts in fixed relationships to one another. For example, the "dunth" always appears below the "quiff." And like humans, "related" greebles also bear a family resemblance to one another. In the population they created, Gauthier and Tarr defined different greeble families. Greebles also come in two sexes, and you can tell whether a greeble is plok or glip from the tilt of its boges, quiff and dunth. As Figure 6.14 suggests, you can recognize greebles at different levels: according to sex, family membership, or individual identities.

Gauthier and Tarr used training to turn utter "greeble" novices into bona fide "greeble" experts. Then Gauthier and Tarr used neuroimaging to examine activity levels in the "face" area of the "greeble" experts' brains.

But this raises a question: how do we tell when someone qualifies as a greeble expert? Recognition experts for other categories of objects exhibit a hallmark characteristic—they can recognize objects at a subordinate level as quickly as they can at the most general level. For example, a longtime bird-watcher can correctly categorize a creature as a black-capped chickadee (a narrow category) just as quickly as she can categorize that same creature as a bird (a broad category). To apply this criterion to greebles, Gauthier and Tarr capitalized on the fact that even novice greeble-watchers can instantly tell the sex of a greeble—all you have to do is notice the angle of its protrusions, and you've got the answer. This can be done in less than half a second (check it out for yourself using Figure 6.14). You can easily learn what to attend to and the rule relating that detail to the greeble's sex. Very quickly you'll be sexing greebles as quickly and efficiently as the best expert in the chick sexing study described earlier.

Plasticity

Because all greebles are either ploks or glips, the sex of a greeble constitutes a broad category. Family membership (five possibilities) and individual identity (dozens of possibilities), however,

are both narrower categories. Not surprisingly, it takes a novice much longer to identify a greeble's family than it does to recognize its sex; and it takes even longer to identify a particular greeble. But novices become experts after training on greeble recognition for several thousand trials (recognition times are identical for broad and for narrow categories).

Having shown that it's possible to produce greeble experts, Gauthier, Tarr and colleagues (1999) were ready to examine neural activation in the "face" area of the brain. At several points during the greeble training regimes, these investigators made fMRI measurements of responses to greebles and to faces. During this portion of the study, trainees were shown pairs of faces or pairs of greebles. Following each presentation, the trainees judged whether the two figures were the same or different. Not surprisingly, the "face" area was activated from the outset of training when people viewed faces. The more interesting result was the brain activation measured when people viewed greebles: as people gained expertise at discriminating greebles, the "face" area of the brain exhibited greater and greater activation.

The brain's growing activation to greebles did not occur simply because people had learned to recognize particular greebles. In fact, the greebles used during fMRI testing were novel ones that had never been seen before. Evidently, the "face" regions in the adult brain have more versatility than previously suspected. These brain areas can support subordinate-level recognition for categories of objects other than faces, provided that the brain's owner gets enough practice to become expert with those objects. Note, however, this finding does *not* mean that areas in the inferior portions of the temporal lobe are irrelevant for face perception. On the contrary, these areas are intimately involved because they deploy visual coding schemes ideally suited for faces. The unresolved issue, which is hotly debated by object recognition experts, is the extent to which other categories of objects benefit from the same coding schemes that are optimal for face perception (for example, Moscovitch, Winocur and Behrmann, 1997; Tong and Nakayama, 1999).

We have described and illustrated some of the challenges confronting perception when it comes to recognizing objects. Those challenges arise whether we're dealing with chairs, faces, greebles or Martian rocks. Fortunately, as you've learned, experience helps perception overcome some of those challenges. There are other aids to recognition, too, and the following section summarizes several of these. These aids are sometimes characterized as "top-down" influences, meaning that "higher" mental processes sway the products of perception. As we move through this discussion of aids to recognition, keep in mind that those aids provide ancillary information about what in the world it is that you're looking at. They make weak signals stronger, render ambiguous signals more unequivocal, and help distinguish objects from one another.

Attention and Object Recognition

Top-down

At any given moment, visual perception usually has a goal, and that goal actively shapes our visual behavior. When you're at a busy airport terminal to pick up an arriving friend, you concentrate on people whose appearance matches your friend's, ignoring the visual "clutter" that has nothing to do with your mission. In addition to goals or intentions, expectations can also shape visual perception. The friend whose arrival you're awaiting said she'd be wearing a large, floppy red hat, so you don't notice her when she deplanes wearing a snug-fitting blue stocking cap. These interrelated factors—intentions and expectations—create a context within which perception operates (Chun, 2000). This context engages a selective process called "attention" that can modulate object recognition.

Execute

Stop reading for a moment and look around you. You're probably seeing lots of different objects scattered throughout your visual environment. No doubt, some of those objects are "competing" for your attention. In most visual environments, one or two objects immediately grab our attention. These are the ones that stand out among the crowd because of their unusual color, size or shape (picture a single red apple in a basket of bananas). In perception, this initial orientation to unusual objects that pop out at you is dubbed "preattentive vision." It's driven by physical characteristics of conspicuous objects, without particular regard to the identity of those objects.

As you survey your visual environment, you're engaging in a form of attention that's not reflexive but purposeful and selective. You select from among the crowd of objects just those that you wish to scrutinize in more detail. Why? Because attention behaves like a limited resource that must be deployed selectively; there's not enough attention to be evenly distributed throughout a crowded visual world. And *what* you select for attention often depends on your intentions. If you need to correct a misspelled word penciled on a page, your attention sweeps your desk until you locate an eraser. If the pages of your term paper must be kept together, attention's spotlight searches for a paper clip. Sometimes, attention remains riveted on one thing for a period of time, allowing you to scrutinize it in detail (look at the intricate pattern of creases in the palm of your hand).

What, if any, are the perceptual consequences of focused attention? When the metaphorical spotlight of attention falls on some object does it make the object look sharper, brighter or more colorful? According to some authors, the answer is "no"—objects' appearance is unaffected by attention. Instead, they claim, attention reduces variability in perception. For example, Prinzmetal and colleagues presented a series of colored objects to people and measured the variability in perceived color when some objects were repeated (Prinzmetal et al. 1998). When participants were distracted by other objects in their field of view, they showed more trial-to-trial variability in color judgments than they did when they were able to attend fully to the test object. However, other researchers argue convincingly that attention to an object actually alters the object's appearance. According to Marisa Carrasco of New York University, attention boosts the quality of the neural signals associated with some object, which effectively provides a more fine-grained sample of the object's features. In this way, attention enhances spatial resolution (Yeshurun and Carrasco, 1998). Similarly, attention can increase contrast sensitivity for stimuli (Carrasco, Penpeci-Talgar and Eckstein, 2000).

When you focus your attention on an object, what actually benefits from attention's spotlight, the entire object or just those parts you're interested in? To reframe the question, at what level of detail does attention operate? Common experience alone does not provide an answer. Instead, researchers must create special conditions that allow

them to infer the subject of attention's focus. Consider one particularly clever technique for making such inferences.

Egly, Driver and Rafal (1994) presented people with a pair of vertically oriented rectangles side by side on a video monitor (see Figure 6.15). At unpredictable times, the inside of one end of a rectangle was suddenly filled in. The participants in the experiment were asked to press a button as quickly as possible to indicate which rectangle—left or right—had changed. This filling-in comprised the "target" event, and it occurred with equal probability in the two rectangles. Participants were given a cue just prior to the presentation of the target. Most of the time, the target was where the cue had indicated it would be, but sometimes, elsewhere.

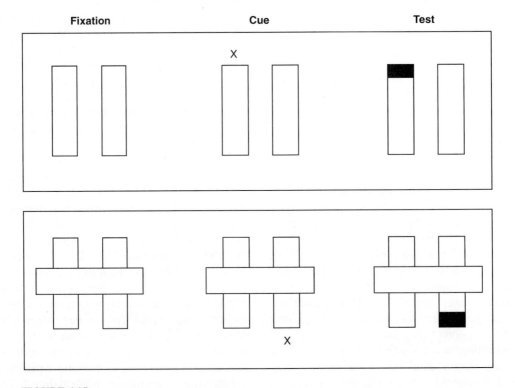

FIGURE 6.15
Figures used for testing the spread of attention over occluded portions of an object. (Adapted from Egly, Driver and Rafal, [1994].)

As you might expect, reaction times were shortest when cue and target position coincided, which occurred the vast majority of the time. Evidently, people were correctly playing the odds, attending to the spot where the target was most likely to appear.

The most interesting results came from trials when the cue *did not* validly predict the upcoming target's location. In these trials, reaction times were still fast when the uncued target was a component of the object containing the (invalidly) cued target. When the uncued target belonged to the other object, however, reaction times were slow. This was true even though the distance between cue and target was the same distance for both conditions. It seems, then, that cueing one end of an object causes the entire object to be affected. Attention operates on the *entire* object, not just an isolated component of an object at a given spatial location.

Top-down

Egly, Driver and Rafal's finding makes perfect sense if you stop to realize that objects in the real world are often partly occluded by other objects. Just look around your immediate environment and notice how few objects appear completely unoccluded. Because of occlusion, optical input to the visual system is missing information about occluded parts. Yet the brain usually manages to generate a complete representation (recall the illusory object in Figure 4.1A). In fact, attention directed to one part of a partially occluded object spreads to other parts, even those disconnected from the attended part. This we know from a study by Moore, Yantis and Vaughan (1998) who modified the stimuli shown in Figure 6.15 by placing a horizontal rectangle across both vertical objects, cutting their bottom halves off from their top halves. Strictly on a physical basis, top and bottom halves are separate and distinct from one another, but perceptually, they are seen as part of a single object whose midsection happens to be occluded. Which characterization—physical or perceptual—would govern selection by object-based attention? Moore, Yantis and Vaughan found that the occluding object barely affected

peoples' responses. Reaction times were faster when cue and target occupied the same vertical rectangle, even though the rectangle had been physically divided by the horizontal rectangle.

These are just a few samples of **object-based attention** experiments that confirm attention's ability to operate on objects. Others are nicely summarized by Egeth and Yantis (1997).

Attention Can Induce Blindness   Repeat the exercise you tried a moment ago: look around your visual environment and notice the objects in your field of view. Once you've completed your visual survey, concentrate your attention on one particular object, such as this book. Do the other, nonattended objects dissolve from visual reality? Of course not. They remain part of your visual awareness, even though you're not actively attending to them. If one of those unattended objects were to disappear at the same time that you were directing attention elsewhere, surely you'd notice such a bizarre event, wouldn't you?

In fact, you probably wouldn't. Studies show that when your attention is diverted elsewhere within the immediate visual environment, you're unlikely to notice otherwise conspicuous changes in unattended objects in the visual scene (Simons, 2000). Compare, for example, the two snapshots shown in Figure 6.16. It won't take you long to realize that the glass of wine on the table in the left-hand photograph is missing in the right-hand photograph. But instead of being presented side-by-side, suppose these two photographs had been shown successively, one after the other, starting with the one containing the wine glass. As these two photographs cycle on and off, that "conspicuous" change—the disappearing wine glass—might go completely undetected for some time. In fact, this is highly likely, if your attention were diverted to another part of the photograph by, say, the presence of an interesting person (Simons and Levin, 1998).

This failure to notice an otherwise conspicuous change because of the diversion of attention is known as **change blindness.** It's just one of sev-

FIGURE 6.16
Compare the two photographs, and find what's missing in the one on the right. If shown successively—
not simultaneously—spotting the missing object is much more difficult. (Photographs courtesy of Ron
Rensink.)

eral perceptual phenomena showing **inattentional blindness:** an impairment in perceiving the appearance of, or changes to, unattended objects (Mack and Rock, 1998). Inattentional blindness, including change blindness, not only underscores the limited capacity of attention but also discloses a very interesting property of perception. Contrary to subjective impression, we do not continuously maintain a high-fidelity representation of the entire visual scene. We evidently lack the processing capacity to do so. Consequently, what we "see" outside the focus of attention is a rather sparse representation based in part on our visual memory of what was there when we last looked.

Most of the time inattentional blindness isn't a problem. All we have to do is shift our attention. The world is right there for our scrutiny any time we wish. And we take advantage of that ready availability when we perform tasks like straightening up a desk (Hayhoe, Bensinger and Ballard, 1998). There's no need to commit the desk's contents to memory, because those contents remain visible as we work on them. As British psychologist Robert Snowden (1999) comments, "[W]hy should I go to the trouble of constructing a complex detailed visual scene inside my head? There is, after all, a perfectly good one right in front of my eyes!"

But there is a downside to inattentional blindness. Unexpected events that reflexively draw attention may obscure our ability to perceive important changes in other objects within the visual field. O'Regan, Rensink and Clark (1999) suggest that change blindness could be triggered by splashes of mud on a car windshield. In the immediate wake of a splash the car's driver would be unable to detect changes in roadway conditions.

Inattentional blindness implies that the clarity and completeness of the appearance of objects within our visual environment are, in fact, illusory. Odd as it may sound, we seem to confuse visual reality with visual imagination. This "confusion" is adaptive, though, for the world itself and the objects in it usually remain stable and, therefore, available for attention's scrutiny. We can draw on resources stored in visual memory to decide how to allocate attention (Chun and Nakayama, 2000). One bridge between memory and visual attention is imagery, another effective aid to object recognition. It is to that aid that we now turn.

Imagery: Vision's Helper

Think back to the bedroom you had when you were 10 years old. Visualize the room in your mind's eye. How many windows did it have?

Were any of the windows directly opposite the doorway? With coaxing, most people can answer such questions, and those answers usually bear some relation to reality (Chambers and Reisberg, 1992). To begin answering questions like these, people draw on memory to construct a mental image of the room. Then, with that image firmly in place, they survey its contents. Mental images have fascinated and mystified people through the ages. And for years they have eluded efforts to understand what they were. Researchers have devised improved experimental methods to study mental images (for example, Shepard and Cooper, 1982; Kosslyn, 1994; Kosslyn, Sukel and Bly, 1999). These efforts have significantly improved our understanding of images' properties, limitations, neural bases and their relation to perception.

From one perspective, visual imagery and visual perception can be seen as two sides of the same coin. As you saw when you tried to answer questions about your childhood room, your visual image of that room contained some of the same visual information that your eyes picked up, years ago. In fact, the two processes resemble one another sufficiently that they can be mistaken for one another.

One of the most original demonstrations of confusion between imagery and perception is found in work by the pioneer female experimental psychologist, Cheves Perky (1910). While seated in a completely dark room, Perky's observers stared steadily at a screen some distance away. On a signal from Perky, an observer conjured up a mental image of some particular object, such as a banana. While the observer was generating the requested image, Perky surreptitiously cast a dim image on the screen. This image matched the object that the observer was trying to imagine. For instance, when an observer was told to imagine a banana, a banana-shaped, yellow image was cast on the screen. Prior testing showed that this real image would be just barely visible. To further mimic a mental image, the real image on the screen was jiggled slightly, producing a shimmering quality. (If all this

sounds complicated, it was; three researchers were needed to run Perky's apparatus.)

Top-down

Twenty-seven different observers were asked to describe various "imagined" shapes. Twenty-four of the twenty-seven never realized that they were seeing things, not just imagining them. (Experimenter's error allowed the other three observers to catch on to Perky's deception.) When the experiment was finished, "the observer was asked if he was 'quite sure that he had imagined all these things.' The question almost always aroused surprise, and other times indignation" (Perky, 1910, p. 431).

The observers' descriptions of their "imaginings" are remarkable. One person volunteered, "I can get [the image] steadily so long as I keep my mind absolutely on it." Another commented, "The banana is up on end; I must have been thinking of it growing." Many observers unwittingly combined what they saw with what they imagined: one reported seeing a lemon (the real image) lying on a table (from the mental image); another reported seeing a leaf (the real image) covered with red veins (from the mental image). Even after they were shown the entire setup and told about having been fooled, many observers still refused to believe that they had actually seen something real and argued steadfastly that everything they "saw" was from their imagination. Using more sophisticated methods, Segal and Fusella (1970), Reeves (1981), and Craver-Lemley and Reeves (1992) have confirmed Perky's main findings. They showed that when real stimuli and images conflict, the images can interfere with seeing the stimuli. After ruling out various alternative explanations such as factors related to optics, attention, and response bias, Craver-Lemley and Reeves concluded that images produce a kind of sensory interference, resembling the effect of a reduction in target energy.

Where Does Visual Imagery Come From?
Execute

These and other findings show strong parallels between the phenomenology of imagery and the phenomenology of vision (Finke, 1985). Further, imagery and vision seem to share a common

FIGURE 6.17
Example of test figures used by Kosslyn and colleagues
(1999) to measure brain activity associated with imagery.

neural basis. Functional neuroimaging has identified a number of brain regions that participate in
both vision and imagery. Included among these
regions is the primary visual cortex, area V1. In
one study of imagery's neural basis, Stephen
Kosslyn and his colleagues (1999) used fMRI to
identify regions that were activated during visual
imagery. To ensure that imagery was actually engaged, Kosslyn asked people look at a complex
stimulus and then, some seconds after the stimulus had disappeared, people closed their eyes and
made a judgment about what they had seen. More
specifically, on each trial people saw a square divided into four quadrants, each containing a set
of stripes. The stripes' attributes—thickness,
length, orientation and the space separating adjacent bars—varied randomly. A sample stimulus
is shown in Figure 6.17.

After the stimulus had been removed from
view, Kosslyn randomly selected two of the
square's quadrants and one of the stripes' attributes. People used their image of what they'd
seen to compare the stripes in those two quadrants with respect to the chosen attribute. For example, they might be told to compare the thickness of stripes in quadrant 1 versus those in quadrant 3, or the number of stripes in quadrant 1 versus quadrant 4. Compared to a control condition,
Kosslyn found that the imagery task strongly activated V1, among other visual areas of the brain.
(As you know, V1 is the cortex's primary receiving area for visual information.)

To nail down V1's role in imagery, the researchers had people repeat the task while bursts
of transcranial magnetic stimulation (TMS) induced fluctuating magnetic fields in V1. The fluctuating magnetic field induced a localized, alternating current in the brain, temporarily disrupting
whatever functions depended on V1. As a result,
response times were lengthened by about
200 msec. In the same people, TMS applied to V1
had a comparable effect on judgments based on
vision rather than imagery (judgments made with
squares and stripes that were actually visible).

This result suggests that visual perception and
the generation of visual imagery share some of
the same areas of the brain, including the area
that is the brain's initial processing center for incoming visual information. Presumably, this
sharing of neural structures could facilitate interactions between vision and imagery. The possibility that imagery and perception engage common neural processes should not be entirely
surprising. After all, imagery—like vision—can
serve to guide our actions within the world. Imagery makes it possible for us to envision the consequences of some behavior without actually going through the motions.

What Does Visual Imagery Look Like?
Perky's study suggested a striking equivalence
between vision and imagery, which Kosslyn's
work has now confirmed at the neural level.
Clearly, imagery does look something like the
thing being imaged, but how close is that resemblance? This is a question that people have been
trying to answer ever since Perky's own experiments. For example, one of Perky's contemporaries, Lillien J. Martin, studied imagery by asking people to form a mental image of a real
object, project the image alongside the real object

FIGURE 6.18
Upper panels: Photos of a male and female. Lower panels: The photos transformed
so that they would match a subject's mental image of the originals. (Photographs and
computer image processing courtesy of Lewis Harvey.)

and then describe the differences between image and object (Martin [1912], cited in Harvey, 1986). One impediment to this direct approach is the difficulty of finding descriptor words perfectly suited to the unusual task. In a modern study of imagery, Lewis Harvey (1986) extended Martin's basic procedure, but avoided the problem of reliance on observers' word pictures.

Harvey investigated observers' mental images of a face, using two techniques: spatial frequency analysis and multidimensional scaling. Observers used a rating scale of 1 through 7 to express perceived similarity. From his own previous research, as well as that of Martin, Harvey believed that a mental image of a face would have reduced detail (that is, less high-spatial fre-

quency content) compared to the original. To test this idea and to quantify the image's appearance, Harvey created a set of photographs. Each showed the face with a different set of spatial frequencies removed.

Observers studied the original, unfiltered photograph of the face to form a clear visual image. They then made two kinds of similarity judgments. In one, they saw pairs of filtered photographs and rated how similar one was to the other. For the second kind of judgment, just one filtered photograph was shown at a time and the observer rated how similar it was to their mental image of the original. The similarity judgments, analyzed by multidimensional scaling, confirmed that the visual image most closely resembled a face from which a certain set of high spatial frequencies had been removed, reducing the sharpness of edges and borders. The top panels of Figure 6.18 show photographs of two faces; the bottom panels show the photographs after they've been transformed to match the mental images that a person might have of the originals.

Harvey offered some intriguing speculation about the character of mental images. He suggests that we don't need to store much detail in the image because detail can be encoded by means of words. According to Harvey, relying on words as a medium for storing visual detail may also reflect a developmental coincidence: human infants develop full capacity to see visual detail just about the same time that they learn to speak.

Having surveyed some of the aids that counter the challenges to object recognition, let's now turn to a form of object recognition that we engage in all the time. In fact, you're doing it right now.

PERCEPTUAL ASPECTS OF READING

Reading printed text is one of the most complicated tasks that vision does. Among other things, reading requires rapid, parallel identification of complex symbols which must be translated into phonological and semantic codes. Given the complexity of this task, is it any wonder that many people have difficulty mastering it?

Because reading depends upon cooperation among so many brain systems, it is especially vulnerable to the effects of developmental abnormalities. Moreover, damage to the brain later in life can also produce severe reading disabilities, known collectively as *alexia* (meaning, "without reading"). One form of alexia, called "letter by letter reading," highlights reading's connection to visual object recognition. As the name of the condition suggests, people with this form of alexia can read only one letter at a time (their writing skills, by the way, may be perfectly normal). As a result, their reading speed varies with the length of words that they encounter. For example, a word ten letters long will take about twice as long

to decode as a word that is just five letters long. In addition, many letter-by-letter readers make errors recognizing letters, confusing visually similar letters for one another. Letter-by-letter readers may also experience problems with a host of other visual tasks (Behrmann, Nelson and E. B. Sekuler, 1998), such as interpreting musical notation, recognizing faces, and reading numbers (Patterson and Ralph, 1999).

For people with normal reading ability, the task doesn't seem complicated. We've forgotten though how difficult it was to *learn* to read. What perceptual skills had to be mastered on the way to becoming an accomplished reader? And how are those skills supplemented by "top-down" influences?

While reading, your eye movements and fixations control the rate at which you extract information from the printed page. Ordinarily, the movements of your eyes vary with your comprehension of what you're reading. Thus, it's possible to learn a lot about reading by studying readers' eye movements and fixations. Exactly what do your eyes do when you read? They jump, or saccade, as your gaze shifts from one object to another. But they're relatively still between saccades. In this respect, reading words is much like reading a map or reading someone's face. Each of these activities requires a mix of saccades and fixations. The number of saccades and the duration of fixations depend on a reader's skill and on the difficulty of the text (Rayner, 1978). We'll confine the discussion to the behavior of a skilled reader (such as yourself) who is reading moderately difficult material (such as this text).

As you read individual lines in this paragraph, your eyes make about five saccades, which fixate on selected words in the line. On average, a fixation lasts one-quarter of a second, although fixations can range from as little as one-tenth of a second to more than half a second, depending on the familiarity of the word being fixated on. In addition, the distance traveled by a saccade can vary from just two letters to as many as eighteen letters. Finally, the direction of saccades also varies. About 90 percent of the time, a saccade moves your gaze rightward, to a word you have yet to look at. Occasionally, though, you make a leftward, regressive, saccade to recheck a word you've already read and perhaps misinterpreted. Of course, with English and other Western language texts, you make a large leftward saccade at the end of each line.

To understand how you acquire information while reading, we need to consider two questions. First, how fast is the textual information taken in while you're reading? And second, what accounts for the variability among saccades while you're reading? The eyes move very fast during a saccade, so most processing of visual information must occur during the fixations between saccades. But the entire duration of any fixation cannot be devoted exclusively to text processing, since the visual system has more to do than this. Decisions have to be made about where next to move the eyes, and those decisions must be relayed to those portions of the brain responsible for controlling the direction and speed of saccades. What part of a fixation, then, is devoted to analyzing the fixated word and what part to programming the next saccade?

To examine this question, Keith Rayner used a computer to monitor a person's eye movements while that individual read text presented on a video monitor (Rayner, 1998). The computer used information about eye movement to modify the video display: every time the reader's eyes fixated a portion of the text, a masking stimulus covered the letters being fixated. This scheme is depicted in Figure 6.19. When the mask came on immediately after the eyes began fixating (a condition that resembles trying to read without a fovea), reading was difficult. But when the mask was delayed by as little as one-twentieth of a second, people had little trouble reading the text. This shows that only a small fraction of the entire fixation duration is required to encode the text. Incidentally, if this seems like a very short time to do so much, recall the finding that people can extract a complex scene's gist very quickly. Rayner's results suggest that the bulk of a fixation period is spent programming the next saccade, planning how far the eyes should move.

According to Rayner's idea, reading would be more efficient if the visual system could be relieved of this programming chore. This can be accomplished by presenting words one after another, all in the same spatial position on a computer display (Sperling et al., 1971). With this mode of presentation, an observer needs to fixate on just one position, which eliminates time and effort spent on saccadic programming. After some practice, eye-movement free reading averaged 3 to 4 times faster than conventional reading (Rubin and Turano, 1992). But of course, saccade-free reading requires special hardware that old-fashioned, slower modes of reading do not.

FIGURE 6.19
Setup used by Rayner and colleagues (1998) for studying the ability to read without central vision.

Top-down

It's obvious that words are important units for reading and that various characteristics of words strongly influence reading accuracy and speed. Imagine this situation. It's dark and you're driving to visit someone whose house you've never been to before. She lives on Thoreau Street, which you know is a right turn off the road you're presently driving on. Street lights are few and far between in this town, so a street sign is impossible to read until you are close to it; even then it's not easy. But from a distance you're able to gauge the length of the street's name—"THOREAU" is not likely to be confused with "OLD ROAD TO NINE ACRES CORNER." And this rough information is valuable in making a decision about whether this turn might be the correct one. If the length of the name is about right, you slow down and look harder; if it's not, you pass it by. Street names on signs are usually in upper case letters, which obscures another source of information:

word shape. But that source is helpful in reading ordinary text.

Words have other characteristics that can facilitate reading. For example, in written English, the letter *u* is redundant after a *q*. Once you have seen the q, you know what follows. But information may be redundant even if it is not as perfectly predictable as the *u* after a *q*. In fact, there are varying degrees of redundancy, and methods have been developed to quantify them and their effects on perception (Garner, 1962).

More than one hundred years ago, James McKeen Cattell described a puzzling phenomenon that relates to redundancy in reading. Cattell was interested in how long it took to perceive letters, words, colors, and pictures of objects. In one study, he pasted letters on a revolving drum (see Figure 6.20) and determined the rate at which the letters could be read aloud as they passed by a slit in a screen. Cattell found that it took about twice

FIGURE 6.20
Cattell's apparatus for testing the word superiority effect.

as long to read unrelated words as it did to read words that formed a sentence. He also found a similar disadvantage for reading unrelated letters compared to letters that formed a word (1886, p. 64). The relative ease with which letters can be read if they are embedded in a word rather than presented with unrelated letters is known as the **word superiority effect.** (This may remind you of the configural superiority effect described in the previous chapter.)

Since Cattell's original report, dozens of follow-ups have confirmed his original finding. But what causes word superiority? One possibility is that the surrounding letters of a word make it easier to derive the remaining letters. For example, once you've seen the letters *LABE,* the chances are good that the next letter will be *L.* In this case, the letter recognition might be expedited because the prior letters reduced the need to spend much time on the last letter.

More recent studies have used methods more sophisticated than Cattell's to demonstrate that the word superiority effect cannot be chalked up entirely to logical deduction (Reicher, 1969; Wheeler, 1970). These studies suggest that familiarity directly affects the process of extracting visual information. In one study (Johnston and McClelland, 1973), either a word or a single letter was briefly shown to people. In either case, this test stimulus was followed by a patterned masker that obliterated any afterimage (see Figure 6.21). After this sequence of events, people saw two alternatives and had to pick the one that corresponded to the test stimulus. For example, if the word *COIN* had been the test stimulus, the observer might have to choose between the alternatives *COIN* and *JOIN.* Since either *C* or *J* could form a word with the remaining three letters (*OIN*), the observer could not use the other letters to deduce the correct answer. Instead, a correct answer required actually being able to see the first letter clearly enough to decipher whether it was a *C* or a *J.* The letter that distinguished the two alternatives could occupy any position in those words (for example, *BENT* or *BUNT*). Thus, the observer could not just attend to one particular position in a test word. When the test stimulus consisted of a single letter, such as *J,* the observer again had to choose from two alternatives, such as *C* and *J.* Again, the observer could not do better than chance unless he or she had seen the letter.

FIGURE 6.21
The sequence of events seen by observers in the study by Johnston and McClelland (1973).

FIGURE 6.22
Setup used by Rayner and colleagues (1981) for studying the ability to read with only central vision.

The results were typical of many word superiority studies. Observers were more accurate in choosing between *COIN* and *JOIN* than they were in choosing between *C* and *J*. Although trials with single letters presumably required less processing, observers were nonetheless more accurate on trials in which they had to process all four letters (Johnston and McClelland, 1973). So, when normal readers see a word, they do not process each letter separately, in isolation from the rest. In fact, people who try to restrict their attention to just one letter of a word are less accurate in perceiving that letter than when they attend to the word within which the letter was embedded (Johnston and McClelland, 1974). A large unit (such as a word) may be perceived more accurately than any of its isolated component parts (such as a letter).*

By exploiting the redundancies and structural features of texts, good readers process printed or electronic text very rapidly. But exactly what are they processing? While reading this page, you probably have a sense that each line (or perhaps even the entire paragraph) is focused sharply. But this uniform sharpness is illusory, because only

the very center of your retina allows good acuity (recall Figure 3.27). For example, one participant in Rayner's studies (McConkie and Rayner, 1975; Rayner and Bertera, 1979) who was kept from using the fovea, misread the sentence "THE PRETTY BRACELET ATTRACTED MUCH ATTENTION" as "THE PRIEST BROUGHT MUCH AMMUNITION." Such errors are not surprising, because with foveal information excluded these people were reading with retinal regions that could specify only the general length and shape of words but could not clearly identify each letter (recall the street sign example above).

When the fovea is available for use, though, how many letters does a person see clearly at any one moment? To find out, one could determine how reading is affected when the number of letters displayed at any moment is reduced. So long as the number of letters exceeds the number that the reader actually uses, reading speed should be unaffected. To produce this situation, Rayner programmed the computer to reveal only that portion of the text on which the person fixated, masking all other portions with small "x"s. Thus, as the person's eyes moved, new letters were constantly being revealed. This procedure, illustrated in Figure 6.22, gave people the impression that they were reading through a "window" that moved along in synchrony with their eyes.

When the window was extremely narrow (so that people saw just one letter at a time), they

---

*McClelland and Rumelhart (1981) presented a model of processes that could produce word superiority effect. Their model was a network of interacting elements arranged in layers. The elements represent the features of various letters, the letters themselves, and four-letter words.

could read correctly about 90 percent of the words. Needless to say, though, reading under these conditions was slowed. As the window widened to include seven or nine letters, entire words could be read at once, enabling error-free performance. However, reading was still slower than normal. Reading did not even reach normal speed until the window was wide enough to reveal about four words. Presumably, readers use words to the right of fixation to guide decisions about the next saccade. Though only dimly perceived, these words furnish a preview of what will be encountered on the next fixation (Rayner and Pollatsek, 1987).

You can prove to yourself how valuable peripheral vision is in reading. Take a 5 × 8 file card, and cut a rectangular "window" in it one-half inch wide and one-quarter inch high. Orient the card so that the window's larger dimension is vertical. Then place the card over some page in this book. When the window is properly aligned on the page, you will be able to see about one word at a time through the window. Move the card along the line of text as you try to read. After you've practiced a while, have a friend measure how long it takes you to read a passage of text 100 words long. Now, using new text, repeat this test with a window large enough to expose four words at a time. Comparing your reading speeds with the two windows, you'll discover that peripheral vision does indeed play an important part in reading.

Just and Carpenter (1980) identified the major processes involved in reading. This effort is summarized in the flow chart shown in Figure 6.23. Note that a number of the processes represented

E Execute

 Top-down

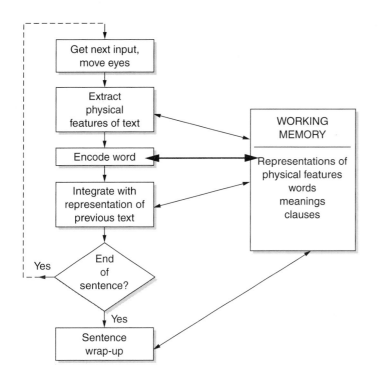

FIGURE 6.23
Schematic diagram of the major processes involved in reading comprehension. (Adapted from Just and Carpenter, 1980.)

are top-down ones of the kind mentioned earlier in this chapter. For example, the right-hand box, "Long-Term Memory," includes rules about letter shape (orthography), the normal structures used in writing (discourse structure), and background information for what is being read (episodic knowledge). As each new word or short phrase is encountered, these top-down processes guide the reader.

If you are reading an ordinary novel, these top-down influences can be enormously helpful in processing the text. To give a simple example, after reading "John hit the nail with a," there is little uncertainty about the next word, making it easier for you to process "hammer." However, certain books minimize the usefulness of top-down influences, forcing you to deal with each word, one at a time. The following brief passage from James Joyce's *Finnegans Wake* illustrates what we have in mind. First read it silently. Then read it aloud, listening carefully to yourself.

> [S]he thawght a knogg came to the dowanstairs dour at that howr to peirce the yare and dowandshe went, schritt be schratt, to see was it Schweep's mingerals or Shuhorn the posth with a tillycramp for Hemself and Co, Esquara, or them four hoarse-men on their apolkaloops, Norreys, Soothbys, Yates and Welks (1939/1967, p. 480)

Reading this passage was difficult because your expectations were of little help. Sometimes expectations actually get in the way. Suppose you've just read the words, "There were tears in her brown . . ." Usually, you'd interpret the word *tears* as referring to liquid produced by the lacrimal gland, rather than as referring to a rip in something. This interpretation leads you to expect the next word to be *eyes*. So on encountering the word *dress* you fixate on that word longer than you normally would. This kind of sentence has been called a "garden path" sentence (Carpenter and Daneman, 1981) because its early part leads the reader astray—down the proverbial garden path. If a word (such as *tears*) has several meanings, the reader selects among them according to rules, or expectations, that maximize the chances of being right. For example, a common meaning is usually selected over a less common one. Or if only one likely meaning has the grammatical form required by the phrase (say, a noun), that meaning is selected. Presumably the errors revealed by garden path sentences reflect these normally helpful selection factors.

If you look at any line of text in a book, you'll find successive words separated by a space. This feature of texts is so ubiquitous that you might assume that you couldn't really read without the help of spaces, but that view is mistaken. In fact, texts in Western languages did not originally use spaces to separate words (or punctuation marks, for that matter). These ubiquitous and seemingly crucial word separators weren't introduced until the time of Charlemagne. People were reading long before then, spaces or no (Boorstin, 1983, p. 497). In fact, Julie Epelboim and her colleagues have shown convincingly that we don't much need spaces. Reading without spaces is not that different, in speed or in comprehension, from reading with spaces (Epelboim, Booth and Steinman, 1994; Epelboim et al., 1997). In most of their experiments, subjects were asked to read aloud normal passages of text (with spaces between words) and doctored passages (from which spaces had been excised). At the same time, Epelboim and her colleagues used a high-fidelity fixation-monitoring system to determine where in the texts readers fixated. The results were surprising: subjects read space-free texts almost as fast they read texts with normal interword spaces. Decrements in reading speed ranged from 0 to 30%. In addition, subjects' fixations—an important clue to how texts are being processed—were essentially unchanged by the removal of spaces. If you doubt, as we originally did, that you can read without the crutch of spaces, read the following space-free text aloud. Read on, no matter how difficult the task seems at first. Just do it.

Inexpensiveredwineslackamajoradvantageof inexpensivewhitewines,theyshouldn'tbeservedcold.

Execute

Unlikewhites,theycan'thidebehindapalatenumbing
chill.Whentheyareflawed,itshows.Iftheyaresimple,
itcan'tbedisguised.Inshort,redsriseandfallontheir
ownmerits.Thatmakesfindinggoodinexpensive
examplesdevilishlydifficult.Butitalsomakestastinga
winnerthatmuchmorerewarding.Fortunately,with
resoluteshopping,it'squitepossibletoputtogether
alistofqualitybargainreds.

If you were able to set aside your doubts about
doing it, the task was probably much easier than
you thought it would be. Booth, Epelboim and
Steinman (1996) pointed out that some modern
languages, such as Thai and Japanese, have no
spaces between words, and that other modern
languages, like Dutch and German, have relatively sparse spacing. Spaces are relatively few
and far between, because such languages frequently use very long compound nouns, like the
Dutch noun "fietsenstallingbewakers," which
translates roughly as "people who oversee the
bike storage shack." If spaces are not all that important in guiding our fixations and text processing as we read, what is?

Keeping words intact was more important than
separating words, as Epelboim and colleagues
(1994) showed by inserting spaces into a passage,
but at incorrect places. Spa cesinthew ro ngpla
cesm aderea dingex trem elyhard. This suggests a
possible explanation for the small but real slow-
down in reading speed when spaces are removed.
It may be that space removal makes some letter
groupings ambiguous, which slows down word
recognition. In other words, reading rate may be
governed less by the physical features of text, such
as the presence or absence of spaces, than by the
time needed to extract meaning. To test whether
reading rate was limited by word recognition
rather than by limits on the speed with which saccadic eye movements can be programmed, Booth,
Epelboim and Steinman (1996) devised new paragraphs in which the availability of interword
spaces was pitted against the paragraph's meaningfulness. Subjects read aloud four different
types of passages; all the material was drawn from

a.

FIGURE 6.24
A series of five photographs with decreasing amounts of
blur. Starting with this one, take a guess about the
photograph's content. Continue through the next four
versions, guessing each time.

the work of the English novelist, G. K. Chesterton.
Half the passages had normal, interword spacing;
half had none. In addition, in half the passages the
order of words was just as Chesterton had intended, which made those passages meaningful; in
other passages, each word was replaced with a
word of equal length drawn randomly from elsewhere in the same piece. This randomized order of
words rendered such passages meaningless.

As in earlier experiments, removing spaces
from meaningful passages did slow reading down

b.

somewhat. With meaningless passages, though, the impact of space removal was considerably greater. A similar pattern showed up when errors in reading, rather than speed, were evaluated, which suggests that semantics—meaning—rather than spaces per se are more important for determining reading speed and accuracy. This result is ironic because in the past decade or so, many researchers tried to put meaning on reading's back burner, thinking that meaning arose only after information had been extracted from the page, rather than guiding the extraction process. Booth's results remind us that when it comes to reading, meaning means something very important.

Temporary Failures of Recognition

Imagine that you are walking along a deserted country road. It's very foggy and the light has begun to fail. Suddenly, you spot a blurry shape moving about down the road, but you can't tell exactly what it is. Another person? A bear? A cluster of fallen leaves blown about by the wind? You're uncertain about what you're seeing because the impoverished visual information you've received cannot be unambiguously categorized. You entertain the possibility of several alternative objects. You're in a paradoxical situation: You can *see,* but you can't tell *what* you're seeing.

Top-down

If it's imperative for you to decide *what* you're seeing, your best bet is to consult visual memory to identify the stored representation best matching the visual impressions you've gathered. It would also be wise if you took account of the situation in which you find yourself, weighing the *a priori* probabilities that various objects would be present at twilight on a country road (Eckstein, Whiting and Thomas, 1996). But no matter how rational you are in reaching a decision, the degraded quality of the image means that the best matching representation will be no more than an educated guess, the best bet among a number of alternatives. You may be correct, but you may be wrong. And your educated guesses will be guided by your expectations, your emotional

c.

state and your past experiences in that environment (see Box 6.2).

Degraded or ambiguous images force vision to work overtime. Instead of being its usual speedy self, recognition takes a while. But what goes on during the prolonged processing? To examine this question, Jerome Bruner and Mary Potter (1964) intentionally put roadblocks in the way of recognition, hoping to slow it down enough to catch it in action. Bruner and Potter created a series of slides depicting various scenes and objects, such as a dog standing on a lawn, a traffic intersection seen in aerial view, and a fire hydrant. Bruner and Potter started each trial by showing a person one of the slides with the projector highly defocused. They then slowly reduced the blur, gradually bringing the slide into sharper focus. Starting when the slide was extremely blurred, people repeatedly wrote down what they thought they were viewing. When the slide was badly out of focus, people's descriptions were usually inaccurate; for example, similarities in their overall shape might cause a pile of earth to be mistaken for a scoop of chocolate ice cream. Not surprisingly, as the slide's focus improved and details became visible, people became more accurate.

You can experience this phenomenon yourself by successively viewing the series of pictures appearing in the right-hand corner of the next five pages of this chapter (Figure 6.24, panels A through E). Start with the blurred picture at the top of this page and work your way through the

BOX 6.2

RECOGNITION IN THE FACE OF EXTREME AMBIGUITY

It's commonly thought that a person's interpretation of ambiguous sensory messages reveals something about that person's motivation and interests. The Viennese psychiatrist Sigmund Freud discussed this idea in his book *The Psychopathology of Everyday Life* (1910/1938). Although most of the errors Freud dealt with involved mistakes of speech or memory, so-called "Freudian slips," he also considered some visual errors.

Take two examples. Freud described one woman who was so anxious about having children that she often mistook the word *stock* for the word *stork,* presumably reflecting her preoccupation with the arrival of a child. The second example pertained to Freud himself. An avid collector of antiques, Freud confessed that he saw the word *antiquities* on every shop sign that bore any resemblance to that word. So despite his sophisticated knowledge of unconscious influences on the mind, even Sigmund Freud was not immune to top-down influences.

Some people who treat mental disorders exploit ambiguous stimuli to aid them in personality assessment. So-called projective tests are types of psychological tests that use ambiguous pictures and designs that presumably provide an outlet for the person's private fantasies and perceptions. The best-known projective test is the one developed in the 1920s by Hermann Rorschach, a Swiss psychiatrist. As you may know, the **Rorschach test** uses a set of inkblots, which the person is asked to describe. Some psychiatrists believe that they can draw inferences about a person's mental state if that person describes seeing something bizarre, such as a bloody axe buried in a man's head. For our purposes, these bizarre responses are less important than the fact that people can give detailed descriptions of what they see—proof that even very ambiguous stimuli can provide enough structure to fuel perception (Wertheimer, 1957).

A stimulus even more ambiguous than an inkblot—namely, a single point of light in a dark room—can also be used as a projective test. Imagine sitting in a dark room looking at a small, stationary spot of light, such as the glow from a cigarette. Un-

der these conditions, the spot of light will appear to drift about (Matin and MacKinnon, 1964). This illusory motion is called the **autokinetic effect** (*autokinetic* means "self-moving"). Some people believe that it results from the eye's involuntary drifting movements. Certain drugs, such as marijuana and alcohol, increase the autokinetic effect (Sharma and Moskowitz, 1972), perhaps because these drugs increase the eye's tendency to drift.

Rechtschaffen and Mednick (1955) treated the autokinetic effect as a kind of projective test, like the Rorschach test. Observers sat in a totally dark room, about 2.5 meters from a very small, dim, stationary light. They were told that the experiment would test their ability to see the words that would be written by the movements of the small light. Though the light never actually moved, the autokinetic effect did produce considerable illusory movement. Every one of the nine observers reported that the light had written at least two words, and one observer reported 43 words. Some of the words were innocuous (such as *the* or *and*), others were highly personal. In fact, after "reading" the words, one observer became very upset and demanded to know where Rechtschaffen and Mednick had gotten all that information about him. We don't mean to encourage prying into other people's business, but you may wish to try this fascinating projective test on your friends. They may find it hard to believe that the light didn't really "write" all that stuff about them.

Autokinetic "writing" demonstrates how important suggestions can be when perceiving impoverished stimuli. Seeing words is not an inevitable consequence of autokinetic motion. In fact, most people simply see random motions, not words. Rechtschaffen and Mednick's viewers were different, though, because they had been told to expect the light to write something. When they experienced illusory motion, the viewers naturally tried to decipher what the light was writing. Under the same circumstances, suggestion could just as well have caused viewers to interpret what they were seeing as outline drawings or the messages on traffic signs.

series. Look at each one a few moments and then make your best guess about what actually appears in the photograph. Don't peak at the pictures out of order. Study each one, make a guess then move to the next one. Before reading on, stop right here and try it.

If you're like most people, it wasn't until the fourth or even the fifth photograph that you realized what you were looking at. Now, if you had skipped the first two blurred photographs and started with photograph number 3 (panel C)—the moderately blurred one—you would have had a much better chance of recognizing the content of the photograph. That's what Bruner and Potter found: the accuracy at identifying a given photograph depended upon the initial degree of blur. When an image was first presented far out of focus, observers often failed to recognize what they were looking at until the image was pretty well focused. However, when the initial blur was only moderate, observers tended to recognize what they were looking at rather quickly.

Why should early exposure to a high degree of blur retard later recognition of a moderately blurred but otherwise recognizable image? A clue came from the comments by people who were looking at Bruner and Potter's pictures. No matter how blurred the picture, people generated a plausible interpretation of what they were looking at, and this interpretation influenced what they saw in subsequent pictures. Thus, an individual who initially sees a highly blurred image gets locked into a plausible but incorrect interpretation, and this error is self-perpetuating. Researchers argue whether this involves a genuine change in perception or, instead, a bias in responding. Does a blurred picture really *look* different to you than it does to a friend, just because you interpret it as a rabbit, while your friend judges it to be a television set? In a sense, it doesn't matter, for you and your friend are going to react differently to that object when the two of you hold different views about that object's identity. And don't forget, perception is designed to guide action.

This tendency to get locked into one interpretation varies with age. Potter (1966) demon-

d.

strated this by repeating the original experiment, but testing observers ranging in age from 4 to 19 years old. For any given age, some observers tended to be rapid recognizers whereas others tended to be slow. As shown in Figure 6.25, however, younger observers took about 50 percent longer to recognize the picture than did older observers. Besides differing in speed of recognition, young and old observers seemed to arrive at solutions in different ways. The older observers' descriptions formed a coherent series, with a guess at one moment evolving into another, related guess the next moment. In contrast, younger observers' descriptions consisted of a parade of unconnected guesses, often focusing on a single, small detail, rather than on the entire scene. This difference between older and younger individuals suggests that experience may be necessary before top-down information becomes maximally effective.

Potter's study underscored the differences in speed and accuracy with which individuals extract information from images. When it comes to medical images, such as X-rays and CAT scans, speed and accuracy can be a matter of life and death. These images are among medicine's most important diagnostic tools, making it possible to visualize tumors, detect bone breaks, and identify regions of brain atrophy. Interpreting a medical image requires good vision and considerable practice (see Figure 6.26). Radiologists skilled at interpreting medical images can achieve high

Differences

e.

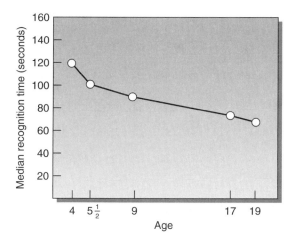

FIGURE 6.25
Median time for recognition of pictures as blur was reduced. (Adapted from Potter, 1966.)

FIGURE 6.26
Reading x-rays, such as this image from a female breast, requires good vision and lots of practice.

Plasticity

levels of accuracy, though a number of abnormalities do get overlooked. To explain these oversights, Harold Kundel, a radiologist, and Calvin Nodine, a psychologist, recorded the eye movements of interpreters who were reading x-rays (Kundel and Nodine, 1983). Because the eye's visual acuity is not uniform over the entire retina, the interpreter must successively fixate on different regions of the x-ray.

To guide fixation, an interpreter draws upon several forms of knowledge (Carmody, Nodine and Kundel, 1980). From the outset, that person usually knows what anatomical structure (for ex-

ample, the chest) is depicted in the x-ray. This initial knowledge establishes expectations about that structure's normal appearance, drawing on memory of previous x-rays. An experienced x-ray interpreter is guided by knowledge of what particular parts of that structure are most likely to be abnormal. These parts should be scrutinized first and most carefully. Kundel and Nodine found that when interpreters were instructed where to look, a glance as brief as one-third of a second was enough to spot the abnormality. (This may remind you of the blazing speed of expert chick sexers.)

Still, on occasion, the interpreter fixated on the correct spot but failed to detect the abnormality. You might say that the interpreter was looking at the right place but not attending to the right thing. To perform optimally, the interpreter needs to know *where* to look and *what* to look for.

SUMMARY AND PREVIEW

This chapter was a journey through the realm of object recognition, the all-important ability to categorize what we see. This ability is the basis for using, and/or reacting appropriately to, what we see. As you learned, recognition has to overcome a number of challenges, including occlusion and variation in viewpoint. Among the ways that vision deals with these challenges is neural plasticity: with practice and experience, the nervous system adjusts its sensitivity to conform to the demands of visual inputs. You also learned that the temporal pathway, and particularly its inferotemporal (IT) cortex, is a major contributor to object recognition. Along the way, you were introduced to imagery and memory, which play important supporting roles in object recognition. You learned that imagery and vision seem to depend upon some common regions in the brain. Theories of recognition were tested for their abil-

ity to account for important aspects of face and "greeble" recognition. As we noted, much of our understanding of recognition comes from studying failures in recognition that are specifically linked to brain damage (as in prosopagnosia) or from diminished visual input. You learned also that memory for what you've just seen is far more fallible than you might imagine. Finally, we applied some basic information about vision and visual recognition to the challenges of reading printed text.

This chapter and the previous ones intentionally ignored several important aspects of vision—color, motion and depth perception. Now that you're familiar with the fundamentals of vision and object recognition, you will learn how we deal with a world of color, movement and objects arranged at varying distances in the next three chapters.

KEY TERMS

affordances
agnosia
autokinetic effect
change blindness
configural processing
face-inversion effect
featural processing
geons (geometrical icons)

inattentional blindness
object-based attention
prosopagnosia
recognition by components
Rorschach test
view-based recognition
word superiority effect

CHAPTER 7

COLOR PERCEPTION

Staying up all night studying for an examination is not much fun. There is one small consolation, though—a chance to see the beauty of sunrise. As you stare at the horizon through half-open eyes, you realize that all through the dark night the world outdoors has been a drab, colorless collection of blacks and shades of grays. Then just before the sun itself becomes visible, you see a marvelous transformation. That drab world springs to life as objects don their daytime colors. When the world puts on its colors, you realize how bland it would appear without them.

But color gives you more than unending wonder and beauty. In fact, it influences many facets of your life. For example, color can alter the "taste" of the food and drink you consume (Duncker, 1939). Prove this to yourself by using food coloring to create red milk or green orange juice. The color of prescription pills can influence how you expect the medicine to affect you and, for that matter, how it actually does affect you (de Craen et al., 1996). Some people believe

that the world's colors ebb and flow with mood—that envy can make you "green," infuriation makes you "see red," and all too many circumstances make you "blue." These, of course, are merely figures of speech, but some people believe that the connection between emotions and color is more than just figurative (Kuller and Mikellides, 1993). Some tavern owners decorate their walls with colors that they expect will stimulate greater consumption of alcoholic beverages. Certain shades of pink reputedly calm prisoners in jail and quiet irate football fans. It has been said that Knute Rockne, the legendary Notre Dame football coach, painted his own team's locker room red to excite his players, and the opponent's locker room blue to induce calm and relaxation.

According to one study, people also use color to mark their territory. When selecting a color to paint their home, families are much more likely to select a color different from their immediate neighbors (Barber, 1990). People are even more selective about the colors they wear. In fact, it's been claimed that you can tell a lot about people—perhaps even about an entire nation— just from the colors of their clothing. One person who made such a claim was Johann Wolfgang von Goethe, the nineteenth century German poet-philosopher. Goethe wrote:

> *Lively nations, the French for instance, love intense colours . . . ; sedate nations, like the English and Germans, wear straw-coloured or leather-coloured yellow accompanied with dark blue. Nations aiming at dignity of appearance, the Spaniards and Italians, for instance, suffer the red colour of their mantles to incline to the passive side.* (1840/1970, p. 328)

But all these effects, whether real or fanciful, are simply byproducts of color's real purposes, which we now turn to in the next section.

WHY IS IT IMPORTANT TO SEE COLORS?

Color vision must be enormously advantageous, for the ability to see color has evolved in numerous orders within the animal kingdom, including mammals, fish, birds and insects. Color vision offers many advantages, including the ability to detect and discriminate various objects, including foods whose edibility depends on their ripeness. Let's consider these two, related aspects of vision that are enhanced by color.

Color provides a unique source of information for picking out an object from its background (**detection**). Manufacturers of sporting equipment exploit this fact by producing yellow tennis balls that are easier to see on the court and orange golf balls that are hard to lose on the fairway. In some instances, the presence of an object would go completely undetected were it not for the color differences between that object and its background. Take a look at the two pictures in Color Plate 2. Besides appreciating the enriching quality color brings to the picture on the left, notice the green patch on the red sleeve of the girl's sweater.

That patch literally disappears in the achromatic version of the picture. That's because the intensity of light reflected from the patch on the shoulder is essentially identical to the intensity reflected from elsewhere on the sleeve (the patch is said to be **isoluminant** with its background). Without color vision, the patch goes undetected; with color vision, the patch is conspicuous.

Nature too exploits the conspicuity of color. Many animals call attention to themselves by means of color, especially for purposes of mating. Plants announce their presence with color, inviting butterflies and bees to assist unwittingly with pollination. At the same time, however, nature can use color to make creatures and plants inconspicuous (Owen, 1980). For example, the color of a praying mantis blends in so well with the color of the leaves it frequents that unless the insect moves, it is virtually invisible. Similarly, the arctic fox's white pelt provides excellent camouflage when it hunts on snow-packed land, giving the fox a considerable advantage over its prey. To see how one familiar animal exploits color for camouflage, take a look at Color Plate 3. Can you find this creature among the branches and leaves? If not, the answer appears at the end of this chapter, just before the Summary and Preview.

So, one of color's important contributions is to promote figure/ground segmentation, causing an object to stand out from its background. In some instances, color is the only source of information available for detection, but in many other instances color reinforces other cues. For example, in a cluttered environment, it's easier to determine the direction in which a cluster of objects is moving when those objects are all the same color (Croner and Albright, 1997). Their common color promotes grouping of the objects, segregating them from other, differently colored objects moving within the visual scene. Low contrast figures are also easier to detect and localize in space when those figures differ in color from their background (Rivest and Cavanagh, 1996; Gur and Akri, 1992).

Besides aiding our ability to detect the presence of objects, color also helps us recognize **(identification)** and distinguish **(discrimination)** them from among various objects in the environment. Subtle differences in the shade of red can tell you whether an apple or tomato is ripe and ready to eat. One shade of yellow tells you that a vehicle is a taxi rather than a police car; another shade of yellow ensures that Kodak's photographic products will be recognized worldwide merely from the color of the box. Farmers use color to identify fertile soil and to determine when their crops are ready for harvest. Doctors routinely rely on color to make diagnoses: blood that is pale red indicates anemia, and a yellowish skin pallor suggests a possible liver disorder. Meat inspectors pay attention to the color of animal tissue when they judge the meat's fitness for human consumption (Collins and Worthey, 1984). Even a perceptual judgment as simple as distinguishing circles from ellipses becomes easier when highly visible geometric figures differ in color from their backgrounds (Syrkin and Gur, 1997). Evidently, color provides a patent landmark that allows us to direct our attention to objects within a cluttered environment, thereby improving our ability to notice changes in those objects or to judge their shapes (Brawn and Snowden, 1999).

So, while color has emotional and aesthetic impact, the main purpose of color perception is to help creatures detect and discriminate objects. To explain how color serves these goals, this chapter describes important characteristics of color perception. The chapter also explains how the colors we experience depend on several factors: the ambient light illuminating the objects, the surface properties of those illuminated objects, the colors of other objects in the visual scene and, most importantly, the properties of the viewer's eyes and nervous system.

WHAT IS COLOR?

Let's start with the most basic of questions: What is color? Simple questions usually call for simple

answers, but no simple answer is available in this case. As the following sections disclose, describing what is meant by the quality called "color" is anything but simple. To illustrate the elusive nature of color, consider the following thought experiment.

Suppose a blind friend implores you to describe what it's like to see. It's a challenging question, but you manage to convey some sense of the meaning of visual form and shape by appealing to the blind person's tactile experiences with objects. And because your friend can travel and walk about, you'll be able to get across the notion of visual distance and visual motion. But when it comes to color, you'll be stumped. Color has no referent outside the quality itself. None of the other senses convey qualities that are remotely analogous to color. We don't have words to describe the quality of color, aside from color terms themselves (for example, *red*).

So what is this visual quality called color? Let's consider several alternative approaches to the question.

A Multitude of Color Names

People typically tie their experiences of color to the names used to describe those colors. So we might expect to get some idea of the nature of color perception by asking a seemingly simple question: How many color names are there? Some dictionaries list hundreds of color names, and advertisers invent new names all the time. However, in almost all cultures studied, everyday language manages to get by with about a dozen color terms (Berlin and Kay, 1969). When people in our own culture are asked to assign names to various color samples, there is good agreement on the names for just a handful of basic colors (Boynton and Olson, 1987); beyond those basic few, color names assigned to color samples are idiosyncratic.

Differences

Do adults and children in cultures remotely different from ours categorize colors into the same four hue groups that we do? At least some evidence says no, they do not. The Berinmo, a primitive hunter/gatherer tribe inhabiting a remote region in Papua New Guinea, use five basic color terms. Interestingly, the boundaries that define these basic Berinmo color categories differ markedly from ours. For example, the Berinmo do not distinguish between green and blue, but they subdivide our single category called "green" into two: "nol" and "wor" (Davidoff, Davies and Roberson, 1999). Moreover, color memory tests reinforce the conclusion that the Berinmo color categories differ from ours. Berinmos are much more likely to remember "blue" as being "green" than we are because those two colors fall within the same color category for them but not for us. Evidently, then, cultural influences do play a role in shaping color categories; this is not a surprising conclusion given all the other evidence that experience plays a crucial role in constructing our perceptual world.

At least within western cultures, it appears that the categories implied by color names are present in very young, preverbal infants. Bornstein, Kessen, and Weiskopf (1976) used a special technique that capitalizes on the fact that infants, like adults, get tired of looking at the same thing. When first shown some color, an infant looks at it intently. But when the same color is repeatedly presented, **habituation** occurs—the infant loses interest and looks away.

Bornstein and colleagues assumed that infants would habituate to not only the particular color they had been looking at but to other, similar colors as well. Given this assumption, Bornstein and colleagues used habituation to test whether infants categorize colors in the same way adults do. These researchers set up experiments using three different wavelengths, for example, 480, 450 and 510 nanometers. An infant would first see a 480-nanometer light. After an initial period of fascination with that light, the infant would lose interest. Once the infant had habituated to this 480-nanometer light, Bornstein determined whether the infant's interest could be rekindled by either the 450- or the 510-nanometer wave-

length. Note that in terms of wavelength, these two lights are each 30 nanometers from the 480-nanometer habituation light—an equivalent numerical difference in wavelength. In *perceptual* terms, however, they are not equally different. When viewed by adults, the 450-nanometer light falls in the same color category as the 480-nanometer habituation light (blue), whereas the 510-nanometer light (green) does not. Evidently, infants have the same blue-green categories as adults: the infants showed renewed interest in the 510-nanometer light but ignored the 450-nanometer light. In other words, the infants reacted as if the 450- and 480-nanometer lights fell in the same category, and the 480- and 510-nanometer lights fell in different categories. Similar tests were made for other color categories. In all cases, these preverbal infants categorized colors in the same way adults do, separating colors into blue, green, yellow and red.

But color names and their implied categories certainly don't capture the richness of our color experiences. In attempting to define color, perhaps it would be more useful to concentrate on color discrimination. One could ask: How many different colors can people see? Unfortunately, this simple question yields more than one answer. If color samples are placed side by side, most people can distinguish a huge number of different colors, with one recent estimate (Pointer and Atridge, 1998) placing that number at 2.3 million! Next time you're in a paint store, thumb through the hundreds of different color samples. You'll see that our color vocabulary is quite large. If those paint samples are presented one at a time, however, our color categories shrink to fewer than a dozen (Halsey and Chapanis, 1951). So how many colors *can* people see—millions or just a dozen? The difficulty in answering this question suggests that we need to rely on something other than naming to get at the essence of color. Let's consider the nature of light itself, starting with the landmark observations of one of history's greatest geniuses.

The Insights of Isaac Newton

Any discussion of color perception must include the contributions of Isaac Newton, who revolutionized the way we think about color vision. During a brief retreat to his mother's farm while a plague was raging at home in Cambridge, England, Newton discovered the binomial theorem, invented calculus, and devised a theory of gravitation. He also bought a prism that he later used to study the nature of light and color (Westfall, 1980). These studies led Newton to make a distinction that remains fundamental to this day—the distinction between *physical* phenomena and *perceptual* phenomena. In particular, Newton observed that

> *the rays, to speak properly, are not coloured. In them there is nothing else than a certain Power and Disposition to stir up a Sensation of this or that Colour.* (1704/1952, pp. 124–125)

These two sentences imply that even the most compelling intuitions can be wrong. Objects themselves have no color, and the light reflected from them is also colorless. Color is a *psychological* phenomenon, entirely *subjective* in nature. Objects *appear* colored because they reflect light from particular regions of the visible spectrum. But even that is not enough. For an object to appear colored, light reflected from that object must be picked up by an eye outfitted with the right kind of photoreceptors and visual neurons. Because some people have abnormal eyes or abnormal nervous systems, their experiences of color differ radically from those most people enjoy.

Actually, waves in that portion of the electromagnetic spectrum called "light" are no more colored than waves in any other portion of the spectrum, such as radio waves. Color arises from the capacity of particular light rays to evoke certain responses in the nervous system. To illustrate this, imagine seeing someone wearing a red sweater. According to Newton, there is nothing inherently red about the light reflected from that sweater. No matter how firmly rooted in the sweater it may *seem,* the redness ultimately depends on your eyes and brain.

Strictly speaking, then, it is incorrect to refer to a "red sweater." To be technically correct, you should describe it as a "sweater, which when seen in daylight, evokes a sensation most humans call 'red.'" However, we don't advise going into a clothing store and using such language to inquire about the availability of red sweaters.

While on the subject of terminology, we should further clarify the term *color.* Our dictionary offers nineteen different meanings for *color* in its noun form alone. If you've ever sorted objects such as crayons or "orphan" socks, you know that colors differ from one another in various ways. Blue and green socks differ from one another but not in the same way that two green socks do—say, one brand new and another that's been washed many times. In the study of perception, the single word *color* covers three different qualities. To distinguish one quality from another, each quality is given a particular name, *hue, brightness* and *saturation.*

Hue refers to the quality that distinguishes red from yellow or green, or blue from orange, and so on. Incidentally, the word *color* is not an acceptable synonym for *hue.* In fact, technically, you should refer to the "hues of the rainbow" and to Joseph's "coat of many hues" (Genesis 37:3). The second quality of color, **brightness,** is related to the perceived amount, or intensity, of light. This quality enables you to describe an object (like a star in the sky) as "bright" or "dim." Or suppose you're dining by candlelight and it's hard to see with just one candle. If you increase the illumination by lighting additional candles, you'll increase the brightness of your surroundings. The third quality, **saturation,** characterizes a color as "pale," "vivid," or something in between. After your jeans have been washed numerous times, their blueness will be less saturated than when you first got them. Color Plate 4 will help you to visualize more easily what is meant by *hue, brightness* and *saturation.*

Since your color experiences vary along these three dimensions, describing a color completely requires specification of all three: hue, brightness, and saturation. Moreover, an adequate theory of color perception must explain the origin of these dimensions of color experience. Having clarified what we mean by *color*, we're now ready to consider the observations that led Newton to propose that color resides within the perceiver, not within the light rays themselves.

Execute

What a Prism Reveals About Color   In a simple but elegant experiment, Newton allowed a beam of sunlight to pass through a small circular hole in a shutter and then through a glass prism (see Figure 7.1). After passing through the prism, the light fanned out into a rainbow of **spectral colors.** Newton believed that this spectrum was divisible into seven different regions—red, orange, yellow, green, blue, indigo and violet. These seven colors are indicated in the spectrum shown in Color Plate 5. In this plate, the upper scale defines the spectrum in terms of color experiences, a psychological dimension. The lower scale defines the spectrum in terms of wavelength of light, a physical dimension. The latter dimension, wavelength, was not known to Newton, which is why he had to describe color solely in psychological terms (color names).

Long before Newton, it was known that a prism could decompose sunlight into a spectrum of colors (Ronchi, 1970). For centuries, people had seen spectra created by glass chandeliers, soap bubbles and diamond jewelry. Newton's lasting contribution stemmed from his unique exploitation of the prism to divide light into spectral components and to recombine those components to produce colors.

To accomplish his experiments, Newton first developed a simple scheme for selectively blocking out portions of the color spectrum, thereby producing a modified spectrum containing only certain wavelengths of light. Newton then used a convex lens to collect this modified spectrum and pass it through another prism (see Figure 7.2). The combination of these two techniques allowed him to distinguish between **pure light** and light that is made up of several different components—**composite light.** For instance, if he blocked out all the colors of the spectrum except for green, and then passed the green through a second prism, the resulting light continued to be green. Because the second prism could not further break green into other components, Newton deemed the green to be pure light.

To Newton these observations suggested that light from the sun was *not* pure but consisted of seven different colors that could not be decom-

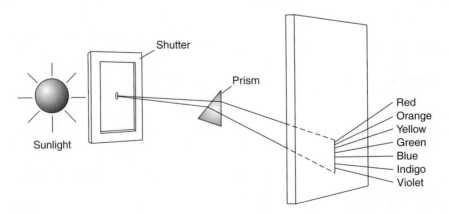

FIGURE 7.1
Setup for Newton's basic experiment.

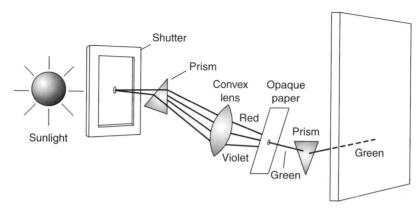

FIGURE 7.2
Setup for modification of Newton's basic experiment.

posed. Though the first conclusion (that sunlight is not pure) is correct, the second (that sunlight contains only seven pure components) is not. Since the mistakes of geniuses can be as enlightening as their successes, let's see why Newton went wrong.

Like anyone else, scientists must be alert to the possibility that their observations can be influenced by expectation. Newton's conclusion that there were seven colors in the spectrum was influenced by just such an expectation, one based on his belief that seeing and hearing were closely related (Gouk, 1988). In particular, he thought that since the musical scale included seven tones and semitones within each octave, the light spectrum had to contain seven colors (Boring, 1942).*

But this error should not diminish the fact that Newton's main idea was right—light from the sun, sometimes called *white light,* can be decomposed into many different colors. In modern par-

lance, light from the sun is said to contain various amounts of energy in different regions of the electromagnetic spectrum (recall the discussion in Chapter 2). The distribution of sunlight's energy over the visible portion of the electromagnetic spectrum is shown by the heavy line in Figure 7.3. Note particularly that light from the sun consists of relatively equal amounts of energy at

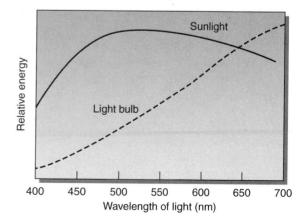

*There is reason to believe that Newton originally noticed only five different colors in the spectrum. Some claim that he later added two—orange and indigo—to bolster the analogy between spectral colors and intervals in the musical scale (Houston, 1917).

FIGURE 7.3
Energy distribution of sunlight (heavy line) and of light from an ordinary light bulb (dashed line).

all the visible wavelengths. Contrast this with the distribution of energy from an ordinary incandescent light bulb. As shown by the dotted line, a typical light bulb emits more energy at longer wavelengths than it does at shorter ones. This is why photographs taken with indoor lighting can have a slightly more yellowish tint than those taken in natural light.

The idea that white light is decomposable into elementary components is universally accepted today. However, when Newton first suggested the idea, it aroused passionate disagreement that continued well after Newton's own lifetime (see Box 7.1). At the time people were upset that their eyes couldn't be trusted. Surely what appears to be innocent white light cannot actually consist of a congregation of invisible components. In reality, the situation is even worse than people imagined: using far fewer than seven components you can fool the eye into seeing white. We now know that what humans experience as *white* can be light that consists of a mixture of just two, properly chosen spectral components. Because this does not work with all pairs of components, we give a special name to those pairs for which it does work. Any two spectral components which when added together appear white are said to be **complementary.** For example, a mixture of appropriate amounts of blue and yellow produces what looks white. Moreover, this same blue/yellow mixture would be indistinguishable from another mixture that included orange light and greenish-blue light. That mixture, too, would appear white. In each of the mixtures, complementary components cancel one another, yielding a colorless or achromatic sensation (white).

We should stress that components of a light mixture don't cease to exist when they're combined. An instrument that measures the amount of light throughout the spectrum will still register the presence of energy at the component wavelengths—the instrument never confuses a mixture of blue and yellow for white. It's the human eye that gets confused. These mixtures of complementary colors appear achromatic be-

cause of the way the visual nervous system registers and processes spectral information.

What Can Metamers Reveal About Color?

Neural

What lessons can we draw from the observation that physically different combinations of energy can produce identical color experiences? By studying the conditions under which color mixtures of different components appear equivalent, vision scientists gained important insights about the neural processes underlying color vision. And they did this long before those neural processes were actually isolated and measured. As you saw in Chapter Five, the term *metamers* is used to describe stimuli that are physically different but perceptually equivalent. Newton's experiments identified many examples of metamers in color vision. He found, for example, that a light appearing orange was metameric to a mixture of lights: one that appears red and one that appears yellow. In addition, pairs of complementary colors (that yield white) are also metameric to one another. And those two pairs of mixtures are metameric to a mixture of Newton's seven spectral colors, which as you know, also yields the perception of white.

The existence of metamers implies that the visual system is generating equivalent neural responses to physically different stimuli. Thus, for example, orange is indistinguishable from a mixture of lights that appear red and yellow, presumably because orange is generated by the same pattern of neural activity within your eye and brain as that generated by the mixture of lights that appear red and yellow. If you can't tell two different stimuli apart by looking at them, your visual system most likely is ignoring whatever it is that makes those stimuli physically different (Teller, 1989). Conversely, if you *can* visually discriminate two objects from one another, your visual system must be generating reliably different responses to the two stimuli. Orange *looks* different from red because orange is generated by different neural responses than red. As you're about to learn, much of our understanding of color perception comes

BOX 7.1

NEWTON STIRS UP A HORNETS' NEST

Newton first presented his work on light and color in 1672, when he was 29 years old. His ideas were greeted with such fury and disdain that Newton had to wait more than 30 years before publishing his complete work on these topics in *Opticks*. By that time, 1704, Newton's genius was nearly universally acknowledged. Despite his eminence, his ideas about light and color continued to provoke angry attacks for more than a century. None of these attacks was more impassioned than one launched by the German poet Goethe.

Goethe believed that he would be remembered not so much for his poetry as for his refutation of Newton (Pirenne, 1967, p. 153). Being a strong believer in the power of intuition and common sense, Goethe was shocked at the patent absurdity of Newton's prism demonstration. Goethe considered Newton a "Cossack" for denying the purity of white light (Southall, in Helmholtz, 1909/1962, vol. 2, p. 115). Since the time of Aristotle, white light had been regarded as the very essence of purity. According to this view, color represented the contamination of white by less exalted, worldly substances. Newton's decomposition of white into colors implied that white was no more special than any other color.

In addition to these aesthetic considerations, Goethe also objected to Newton's ideas on philosophical grounds. He believed that to accept Newton's claim about white light was tantamount to treating *all* sense perception as subjective and unreliable, an idea he detested. Feeling absolutely certain that white light could *not* be a mixture of other colors, Goethe urged people to disregard the experiments performed by Newton in a darkened room in Cambridge:

Friends, escape the dark enclosure,
where they tear the light apart
and in wretched bleak exposure
twist and cripple Nature's heart.
Superstitions and confusions
are with us since ancient times—
leave the specters and delusions
in the heads of narrow minds.
(Weisskopf, 1976)

To combat Newton further, Goethe got a prism and attempted to disprove some of Newton's scientific observations. Although he did use the prism for many different experiments, Goethe never correctly repeated what Newton had done. For example, Goethe looked directly through the prism and failed to see a spectrum of colors, which convinced him that Newton, in addition to being a Cossack, was a charlatan. Goethe went further. He enlisted the services of a young man, Arthur Schopenhauer, who would later become a distinguished philosopher in his own right. Goethe interested Schopenhauer in his ideas about light and color, and persuaded him to continue the assault on Newton. Using Goethe's own optical equipment, the younger man began to do experiments with light (Birren, 1941, p. 214). Unfortunately for Goethe, these experiments convinced Schopenhauer that his employer was wrong and Newton was right: sunlight *does* consist of many different colors.

from studying stimuli that are confused with one another (metamers) and stimuli that are discriminable from one another.

Newton's Color Circle   Newton did not have the degree of control over light that scientists enjoy today. Still, he managed to explore the per-

ceptual results of various mixtures of light with great effectiveness. To see what happens when two pure lights are combined, he blocked out all the other spectral components and used a convex lens to combine the remaining two. Examining the appearance of various mixtures of light, Newton developed the basic ideas of color mixture

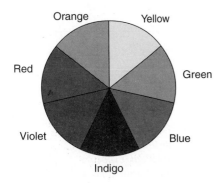

FIGURE 7.4
Newton's color circle.

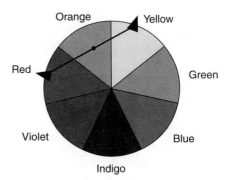

FIGURE 7.5
Newton's color circle can be used to predict the color
produced by mixing equal amounts of yellow and red light.

and expressed those ideas in a graphic model of color perception. Known as **Newton's color circle,** the model is depicted in Figure 7.4. Although modest in appearance, this circle represents an incredible insight on Newton's part, namely that a simple geometric form could represent the properties of something as complex as color vision (Wasserman, 1978). Each of the seven wedge-shaped sectors represents one of the spectral colors. As Newton put it, "the Circumference representing the whole series of colours from one end of the Sun's colour'd image to the other" (1704/1952, p. 154). The circle, though, is only part of the model. Newton also devised several rules that relate colors and mixtures of colors to locations on and within the circle. Let's see how the appearance of various mixtures might be predicted by this geometric model.

Suppose we were to combine two lights of equal intensity, one that appears red and the other, yellow. These two equal-intensity lights are represented by two equal-sized triangles in Figure 7.5. One triangle is located on the circle, in the middle of the arc for yellow; the other triangle is also located on the circle, but in the middle of the arc for red. To find the color that results from the mixture of these two, connect the two triangles with a straight line. The color of the mixture corresponds to the line's center of grav-

ity. (You might imagine this line as a seesaw, and the triangles as people on either end; the sizes of the triangles signify how much the people weigh.) The location of the line's center of gravity gives the predicted color of the mixture. In this case, the center of gravity lies in the middle of the orange sector. In fact, orange is what you see when equal amounts of red and yellow light are mixed. Moreover, the orange produced by that mixture is metameric with the orange produced by just a single wavelength of light, or with the orange isolated with Newton's prism and slit apparatus.

Consider what happens when unequal amounts of light are mixed, say, a large quantity of red and a smaller quantity of yellow. This case is shown in Figure 7.6. The center of gravity of the line connecting the two unequal-sized triangles swings closer to the border between the red and orange sectors, signifying that the mixture will look reddish-orange. And it does. Adding two colors near one another on the color circle yields a mixture whose color is a compromise between the components, with the exact appearance depending on the proportions of the colors in the mixture.

Combining the appropriate components of light, Newton also discovered he could produce a color whose appearance was not like any of his

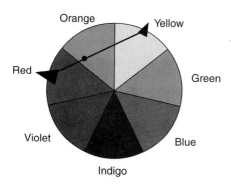

FIGURE 7.6
Newton's color circle can be used to predict the color produced by mixing unequal amounts of yellow and red light.

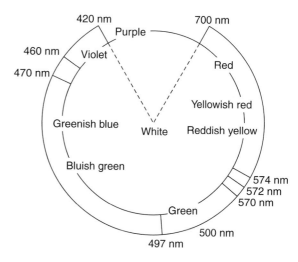

FIGURE 7.7
A revised color circle. (Adapted from Southall, 1937/1961.)

Execute

seven pure lights. For example, if you add long-wavelength light (from the red end of the spectrum) and short-wavelength light (from the blue end of the spectrum) the result is purple. Today we call such colors **nonspectral colors.** The existence of nonspectral colors reinforces the distinction between light's physical properties and its perceptual consequences. From the perceptual point of view, the physical spectrum has a gap—it does not contain all the colors that can be perceived by the human eye. To put this in other words, the eye can combine wavelengths from the light spectrum to create some colors not available from any single region of the spectrum.

When Newton examined the seven colors in his spectrum, he noticed that they were very vivid (today we would describe them as saturated). But when he added these vivid components together, the resulting mixtures invariably appeared less vivid (today we would say they appear "washed out," or desaturated). This perceptual fact, that mixtures appear desaturated, is also represented in Newton's color circle. The most vivid colors fall along the circle's circumference; less vivid colors fall within the interior of the circle. At the extreme, a completely desaturated color (white) is represented at the center of the circle.

As mentioned earlier, the seven pie-shaped wedges in Newton's color circle reflect his belief

that there should be seven discrete pure colors. A color circle based on that erroneous assumption makes incorrect predictions about some mixtures involving colors widely separated on the color circle. To make correct predictions, Newton's color circle must be adjusted in two ways. First, the boundaries that divide the circle into discrete sectors must be erased, because those sectors imply the existence of discrete pure colors. A circle without sectors correctly reflects the fact that color varies continuously. Second, some rational scheme for spacing the color names (or wavelengths) around the circle's circumference must be used. Complementary colors should be placed opposite each other on the circle, so that when they are connected, their balance point falls at the circle's center (white, or achromatic). A circle satisfying both of these requirements is shown in Figure 7.7, with associated color names and light wavelengths shown around its circumference.

The circumference of the larger interrupted circle indicates the position of various spectral lights from 420 nanometers to 700 nanometers. Note that the wavelengths are not spaced uniformly; the wavelengths from 500 to 700 nanometers occupy less of the circumference than do those from 420 to 500 nanometers. In fact, the wavelengths have been positioned on the circle so that along any diameter, complementary colors stand directly opposite each other. Note also that some wavelengths, such as 497 nanometers, have no partner wavelength that is complementary.

Though this revised color circle is an improvement over Newton's original, it still fails to capture some elementary facts about color. For example, Newton noted that "some colours affect the senses more strongly" (1704/1952, p. 97). He meant that with lights of equal energy, yellows and greens are brighter (that is, more visually conspicuous) than reds or blues. We now know that the visibility of various wavelengths of light defines the photopic sensitivity function (see Chapter 3), with maximum brightness at 550 nanometers.

There's another important fact that neither Newton's original circle nor the revised version can account for: bright colors tend to look washed out or desaturated. You can see this for yourself in Color Plate 5 by comparing the colors in the "yellow" region of the spectrum (which appear relatively bright but less saturated) to those at either end (which appear less bright but more saturated).

It's possible to quantify how strongly saturated a color appears. While looking at a light of a particular color, you can add white light to it, thereby desaturating that color. In this way, you could determine how much white light would be needed to eliminate the color completely. The amount of white light needed would depend on the color you start with. Certain colors, in other words, are more strongly saturated to begin with—they stand up better to the diluting effect of white light. Other, less saturated colors are easily washed out by the addition of small amounts of white light. Typical results of this procedure are shown in Figure 7.8. The horizontal axis specifies the wavelength of light used to produce the color; the vertical axis shows the intensity of white light needed to desaturate that

FIGURE 7.8
Intensity of white light needed to desaturate colors of various wavelengths.

color completely. This V-shaped curve shows that light near the middle of the spectrum (yellow) appears less saturated than do lights toward the end of the spectrum (blue or red). Adding white light to light of a given wavelength can also alter the hue produced by that wavelength. For instance, adding white to long-wavelength light (red) shifts its hue slightly toward yellow (Kurtenbach, Sternheim and Spillmann, 1984). For more on mixing colors, see Box 7.2.

The Constancy of Color

In developing the concepts of color perception, our examples have utilized simple spectral lights and their mixtures. These kinds of light consist of a narrow band of wavelengths artificially isolated from the rest of the visible spectrum. However, narrowband light of this sort is rarely encountered outside the laboratory. Ordinarily, vision depends on broadband, "white" light (sunlight or artificial light) that illuminates the objects we see.

Although the illuminating light in our environment is white, we see most objects as colored, not white. That's because those objects absorb certain wavelengths contained in the white light and reflect the rest. The wavelengths absorbed by an object depend on the surface pigments of that object. For instance, "green" grass reflects a band

BOX 7.2

MIXING COLORS

Every schoolchild knows it is possible to create colors of various shades using just a few so-called primary colors. Various shades of green, for example, are readily achieved simply by mixing blue and yellow paints or inks. This is called **subtractive color mixture,** since the component primaries each subtract a portion of the incident light, keeping that portion from reaching your eye.

To illustrate this point consider the curve in panel A of the accompanying figure (adapted from Pirenne, 1967), which shows the reflectance spectrum of a typical light blue ink. The curve indicates that the ink reflects lots of light from the short-wavelength portion of the spectrum but less from the longer-wavelength portion. This happens because the ink contains a pigment that selectively absorbs light of particular wavelengths. Now look at panel B, which shows the reflectance spectrum for a typical yellow ink. Note that it reflects mainly wavelengths longer than 500 nanometers—hence its yellow appearance. Again, this is because the ink contains a pigment that absorbs light in a characteristic way. The curve in panel C shows the distribution of wavelengths reflected by a mixture of equal amounts of the two inks. How does this distribution come about, and why does it appear green?

When you mix the yellow and blue inks together, the mixture contains pigments from both components. Now suppose you view a surface that is coated with the mixture and illuminated by sunlight. The yellow pigment in the mixture will *absorb* part of the light that otherwise would have been *reflected* by the blue pigment. In other words, the yellow pigment removes much of the short wavelengths from the reflected light. Similarly, at longer wavelengths, the blue pigment will *absorb* some of the light that otherwise would have been *reflected* by the yellow pigment. Although the actual calculations are complicated, panel C reveals that the mixture of the two inks reflects light mainly around the middle of the spectrum, the only region of the spectrum at which *both* pigments reflect appreciable amounts of light. As a result, the mixture will look neither yellow nor blue but instead, greenish.

The principles of subtractive color mixture were employed 25,000 years ago by the prehistoric artists who worked in the caves around Lascaux (in what is today western France). Ever since then, people have used the same principles to color objects in their environment. But it was nature that devised the technique: plants and animals contain pigments that selectively absorb or subtract certain wavelengths. This selective absorption gives rise to the characteristic colors one associates with those plants and animals.

Color can also be produced by a process of **additive color mixture.** This additive process is almost never used by nature and has been used by people only very recently, mainly for purposes of entertainment or research. We'll illustrate additive mixture using a familiar example, color television.

The tube in a color television set contains hundreds of thousands of small spots packed very

BOX 7.2 continued

closely together. These spots light up when they are struck by an electron beam inside the set. A spot will appear red, blue or green, depending on the material out of which the spot is made. Each small section of the television tube contains many closely packed spots of each type. You can verify this by looking very closely at the screen of a color television set. (At normal viewing distances, the spots are too small to be seen separately. Instead, they are blended, or added together, by your eye.) The color from your television set is produced by an *additive* process.

Because the strength of the blue, red or green glow varies with the intensity of the electron beam at any spot, the relative proportions of the three colors in the mixture also vary. As a result, although the tube itself produces only the three colors, the properties of your own nervous system generate perceptions of a wide range of different colors according to the laws of additive color mixture.

Color Plate 6 allows you to experience additive mixture. The painting on the left, "Susan," by the contemporary American artist Chuck Close, consists of many small spots of different colored paints. From a normal viewing distance, your eye does not separate the individual spots, resulting in an additive mixture

of the individual colors. (Incidentally, when Newton superimposed lights of different wavelengths, he, too, was employing a form of additive mixture.)

To the right of "Susan" is a magnified view of one small part of Close's painting. Here, you can see the individual spots. Note that colors are less vivid in this magnified image because the white from the background desaturates the color of the spots. The size of the spots used in Close's painting affects not only the saturation of the colors, but also the visibility of forms that are depicted in the painting. Pelli (1999) has documented how spot size affects viewers' ability to perceive the face: when the scale of the spots is too big, the face becomes unrecognizable.

We've seen, then, that there are two different techniques for color mixture. In one technique, the color is produced by the addition of wavelengths; in the other, by the subtraction (absorption) of wavelengths. The difference between these techniques of color mixture has nothing to do with the nature of color vision. It shows only that light is absorbed or reflected differently under different circumstances. For both types of mixtures, the color of a surface depends on the distribution of wavelengths reaching your eye.

---

of wavelengths more than 100 nanometers wide, nearly one-third the width of the entire visible spectrum. This distribution of reflected wavelengths reaches the eyes and initiates the perception of color. Surfaces containing different pigments will reflect different distributions of wavelengths and will therefore appear different in color (compare the three distributions shown in Figure 7.9).

The color names we give to objects generally depend on the light they reflect, not the light they absorb. Thus, the pigments in the skin of a ripe "red" tomato predominantly absorb wavelengths outside the "red" region of the spectrum (see the middle panel in Figure 7.9). In a sense, a ripe tomato is everything but red. This play on words

merely underscores a theme we've stressed over and over: vision is designed to provide us with information about objects, not about light. And that brings us to a remarkable "computation" that the human visual system performs automatically when it specifies the colors of objects.

You now know that the color of an object is specified by the pattern of light reflected from its surface (its so-called "spectral reflectance"), and it's an object's surface color that we're interested in knowing. Yet the light reflected from a surface also depends on the wavelengths contained in the light that's illuminating that surface (the "illuminant," as it's called). When the spectral composition of the illuminant varies, the spectral distribution of the reflected light will also vary. For

FIGURE 7.9
Distributions of light reflected from the surfaces of three common objects.

example, the composition of sunlight varies with the time of day—late afternoon sunlight contains more long-wavelength light than does the noon-day sun. As a result, the light reflected outdoors by any object will vary from one time of day to another. Moreover, the spectral composition of ordinary indoor lights (tungsten light bulbs) differs from the spectral composition of sunlight—the indoor light contains less short-wavelength light (recall Figure 7.3). Thus, the light reflected from an object changes when you view the object indoors versus outdoors. Even though the light reaching your eye varies, the perceived colors of objects remain the same: green grass nearly always looks green, and yellow roses stay yellow. **Color constancy** is the name given to this propensity for an object's color to remain constant even though the spectrum of light falling on that object, and thus the light reflected toward the

viewer from the object, changes (Jameson and Hurvich, 1989).

To achieve color constancy, the visual system must disentangle a surface's spectral reflectance from the spectral distribution of light that is illuminating that surface. Since the light received by the eye is determined by both factors—the surface's spectral reflectance and the spectral quality of illumination—how can the visual system differentiate the two?

To start to answer this question, imagine that you're sitting outdoors reading this book. After a while, it gets chilly, so you go inside to finish reading, using a lamp with an ordinary 150-watt tungsten bulb. Looking back at Figure 7.3, we see that the outdoor light contains relatively more energy at the short-wavelength, "blue" end of the spectrum than does the indoor light, whose energy composition is biased toward the longer-wavelength, "yellow" end of the spectrum. If your color perception depended only on the light coming from a page of this book, the surface would appear somewhat yellow indoors (since indoors the page reflects more light that is normally called yellow than it does outdoors). Yet you don't notice the change. Why?

As you learned in Chapter 3, the visual system adjusts its sensitivity to the overall level of illumination—this process, called *light adaptation,* contributes to the eye's ability to function under a wide range of light levels (from twilight to bright sunlight). In effect, adaptation deemphasizes unchanging or steady stimulation by turning down the neural responses to that stimulation. Consequently, adaptation reduces differential physiological responses that are elicited by the spectral distribution of any illumination source. So, when you're exposed to the blue-rich outdoor light, adaptation diminishes your visual system's response to the short-wavelength portion of that light. When you're exposed to the red- and green-rich indoor light, adaptation reduces the response to long-wavelength light. Both effects tend to "homogenize" the visual responses under sunlight and indoor light, making those responses

Plasticity

more nearly alike than their different spectral distributions would suggest. Light adaptation, then, is one reason your book's pages don't change color as you shift from outdoors to indoors.

You can observe the consequences of the process of adaptation by performing this simple experiment. Get a pair of tinted sunglasses and, before putting them on, look at a white surface (for example, a wall or a book page) through one of the lenses while holding the glasses at arm's length. That small portion of the surface seen through the lens will appear tinted according to the color of that lens. Now put the sunglasses on, thereby tinting everything you're looking at. In just a few seconds, the tint will fade and the colors of everything you see—including the "white" surface—will look nearly the same as they did before you donned the glasses. Your visual system has adjusted its sensitivity to the new pattern of illumination reaching your eyes. When you take the glasses off, colors will look odd for a few seconds but, then, will quickly return to their normal appearance; vision, again, has adapted to the prevailing light condition.

You can also see the effect of adaptation in action using the Adapt and Test figures in Color Plate 7. Stare at the small plus mark in the center of the four colored objects in the left-hand figure—hold your fixation steady. After about 20 seconds shift your fixation to the plus mark in the center of the right-hand figure. You'll temporarily see colors where none existed before. These colored afterimages, as they're called, are attributable to adaptation. In this case, different regions of your eye have been adapted to different colors. Later in this chapter, we'll explain why the afterimages are the particular colors that they are.

But adaptation is not a complete explanation for color constancy (Webster and Mollon, 1995; Hulbert, 1999). Color contrast among objects and their backgrounds is a second important factor that promotes color constancy. Consider the textile in Color Plate 8, an antique Amish quilt made of wool patches whose colors are deeply saturated. The green and blue patches stand out in

sharp relief against the red background; in color parlance, both green and blue contrast strongly against red. The blue and green patches, however, are not so conspicuously different. When seen next to one another, those two colors generate weak color contrast. You can get a sense of color contrast by looking back at the color circle in Figure 7.7. Colors located close to one another on the circle are less contrasting than colors located far apart on the circle.

Color contrast is a property of visual objects that are near one another. It doesn't change much when the source of illumination changes. So if the visual system could compute color contrast among adjacent objects in a scene, it could exploit this source of information to preserve the color appearance of those objects under conditions of changing illumination. Recent research provides solid evidence that our visual system does exactly this. Kraft and Brainard (1999) showed that, despite large changes in illumination, color constancy remained relatively stable so long as color contrast within a scene was unchanged.

Kraft and Brainard distinguished two kinds of color contrast, local and global (you probably remember these terms from Chapter 5). Local color contrast refers to color differences between a single object and its immediate background; global color contrast refers to the differences between an object's color and the average color response across the entire scene. Each of these two sources of contrast information contributes to color constancy. For example, global color contrast between stimuli that are remote from one another can regulate the amount of local color contrast (Shevell and Wei, 1998; Barnes, Wei and Shevell, 1999).

In a related vein, Kraft and Brainard found that a scene's accessory objects can make unexpectedly strong contributions to color constancy. For example, objects with glossy surfaces, such as a porcelain vase, reflect highlights (recall Figure 2.15). These highlights provide mirror-like reflections of the light source itself, thereby providing a small "snapshot" of the wavelength distribution of the source.

Color constancy probably evolved to compensate for small variations in the broad wavelength distributions of natural light. As a result, when objects are illuminated by light with a restricted wavelength distribution, the compensation fails and color constancy can be defeated. Color Plate 9 shows some common objects illuminated by natural sunlight and by two different lights of restricted wavelength distributions. Note how, in the later cases, the objects take on highly unnatural colors, showing that color constancy works only under conditions of broadband illumination. Be warned that unscrupulous supermarkets exploit this limitation on color constancy. They can make their meat products look extra fresh (red) by illuminating them with light biased toward long wavelengths.

So far we've discussed illumination, surface reflectance and color contrast without really considering how the eye measures the relative amounts of light energy from different parts of the wavelength spectrum. Those measurements are crucial for any visual system that's going to specify object colors, and it is to those measurements that we now turn. Incidentally, the theory of trichromatic color vision that you're about to tackle represents one of the crowning achievements of vision science. It's the culmination of over a century's worth of research involving psychophysics, photochemistry, electrophysiology and molecular genetics. It is the only branch of science where the quality of human experience can be traced directly to short DNA sequences on a single chromosome (Mollon, 1992).

THE TRICHROMACY OF HUMAN VISION

The preceding sections reinforce the idea that color (a psychological experience) and light (a physical quantity) are connected in complex ways. Among those complexities, we learned that different combinations of wavelengths can yield the same color experience. Recall that neutral white can be produced by a mixture of orange and green or by a mixture of blue and yellow (both pairs constitute complementary colors). Such psychologically equivalent combinations—called metamers—indicate that the visual system confuses certain combinations of wavelengths with one another. The kinds of confusions that are observed provide important clues about how the eye encodes the wavelength composition of the light it receives. This encoding is initiated by photosensitive pigments in the photoreceptors, so this is where we should start. In the following sections, we'll concentrate on the cone photoreceptors, since they provide the substrate for color vision. To get things rolling, let's again adopt an engineer's perspective and ask how many different types of cone photoreceptors we'll need to produce an eye that can see the range of colors visible to humans.

A Design Decision: How Many Cone Pigments?

What If Eyes Had Only One Cone Pigment?
Every photopigment absorbs some wavelengths of light more efficiently than others. However, once absorbed, light of any wavelength initiates exactly the same chain of events in the visual receptor. Thus, the receptor makes no distinction as to the wavelength of the light absorbed. The response of the receptor conveys information about how much light has been absorbed, but the response conveys no information about the wavelength of the absorbed light. This is called the **univariance principle,** since a receptor's response can be summarized by a single number (one variable) that specifies the amount of light absorbed (Naka and Rushton, 1966). The univariance principle is key to understanding the photoreceptors' role in color perception. (Incidentally, the univariance principle also represents another case of the ambiguity inherent in the response of a single neuron, an issue discussed in Chapters 4 and 5.)

According to the univariance principle, an eye containing only one photopigment type is not

Neural

FIGURE 7.10
A one-pigment system.

able to discriminate one wavelength from another (see colors) because, with the proper adjustment of intensities, all wavelengths could be made to affect the receptor in exactly the same way. This is illustrated in Figure 7.10, which shows the absorption spectrum of a hypothetical single photopigment type. The curve summarizes the amount of incident light that the pigment would absorb at different wavelengths throughout the visible spectrum. These absorption values are expressed relative to absorption at the peak of the curve, which corresponds to about 550 nanometers and which we arbitrarily set at 100%.

You could think of this curve as a summary of the pigment's efficiency for absorbing light at different wavelengths. Note the photopigment's response to wavelengths *A* and *B:* it absorbs twice as much light (50 percent relative to the maximum) at wavelength *B* as it does at wavelength *A* (25 percent relative to the maximum). So, if equal amounts of *A* and *B* were incident on the photopigment, the response to B would be larger because more of wavelength *B* would be absorbed. However, equal amounts of *A* and *B* would be absorbed—and hence, yield equal responses—if twice as much *A* were incident on the photopigment, relative to *B*.

In fact, the intensities of many different wavelengths could be adjusted such that the amount of light actually absorbed by this pigment would be the same regardless of which wavelength was incident. This means, in other words, that many wavelengths would be metameric to one another. In addition, with proper adjustment of intensities, any combination of wavelengths, including white light, could be perfectly matched by any other wavelength or combination of wavelengths. So an eye with only one type of photopigment would treat all sorts of light mixtures as metameric, including many that the normal eye does not.

A person with just one cone pigment is unable to discriminate among wavelengths, and so cannot tell one color from another. Such a person, called a **monochromat** (meaning "one-colored"), sees everything as various shades of gray. (Incidentally, all of us are monochromats in dim light, because then we are forced to rely on the rod photoreceptors, which contain just one type of photopigment.)

What If Eyes Had Two Cone Pigments?   An eye with two distinct photopigments would be more discriminating than the one-pigment eye just described. Consider the consequences of having two photopigments such as those whose absorption spectra are shown in Figure 7.11. Again, since each photopigment obeys the univariance principle, either one of the pigments *on its own* conveys no information whatsoever about the wavelengths of light reaching the eye. However, when two different types of pigments act *in concert* they *do* provide some information about the wavelengths that are present. Let's see how.

First, note that when stimulated by light, a two-pigment system makes two statements, not one, about the amount of light energy absorbed. For any given wavelength, the statement (or response) of either pigment depends on how well that pigment absorbs light of that particular wavelength. By definition, two types of photopigments differ in how well they absorb light of various wavelengths, as summarized by their dif-

FIGURE 7.11
A two-pigment system.

gets more intense but wavelength does not change, the two responses will grow proportionately. Consequently, so long as wavelength is unchanged, the *relative* strengths of the two pigments' responses will remain constant. In summary, because the two pigment types have different absorption spectra, an eye with two pigment types extracts some usable wavelength information from light.

This two-pigment system can nonetheless be confused about wavelength, as the following example shows. Consider the response produced by the wavelength represented in the left panel of Figure 7.12 (see arrow). Note that this wavelength stimulates both pigments 1 and 2, yielding a small response in pigment 1 and a larger response in pigment 2. We shall express this pair of responses as a ratio, which for this wavelength would be 4:1. Now, the ratio for this pair of responses to a single wavelength can be duplicated by an appropriate combination of two wavelengths. This is illustrated in the right panel of Figure 7.12, where the effects of a mixture of two wavelengths are shown. Note that the resulting pair of responses, one from each pigment, stands in the same ratio (4:1) as the pair of responses elicited by the single wavelength in the left panel.

ferent absorption spectra (Figure 7.11). As a result, any single wavelength (for example, *A* in Fig. 7.11) will generate a *pair* of responses, one from each pigment. Note in this example that pigment 1 generates a larger response to *A* than does pigment 2. Of course, the magnitude of each pigment's response will also vary with light intensity, since more intense lights make more energy available for absorption. However, when light

FIGURE 7.12
A two-pigment system can be confused.

The owner of this eye, therefore, would confuse that single wavelength (left panel) with the mixture (right panel). These confusions, by the way, constitute failures of discrimination: two (or more) physically different stimuli look identical.

This eye is susceptible to color confusions (failures in discrimination) at other regions of the spectrum as well. Any wavelength or mixture of wavelengths (no matter how complex) will be represented by just a pair of signals. As a result, the effect of any wavelength or mixture of wavelengths can always be matched by just two wavelengths, provided the two are presented in the right proportions. Moreover, such matches can be produced using any of a large number of different pairs of wavelengths. An eye exhibiting these kinds of confusions is said to be **dichromatic** (meaning "two-colored"). Keep in mind, however, that not all wavelengths are confused. Unlike the one-pigment eye, a dichromatic eye retains certain information about the wavelength composition of light, and this information provides a basis for color discrimination. Indeed, all known mammals besides monkeys, apes and humans possess dichromatic color vision (Jacobs, 1993, Jacobs, Deegan and Neitz, 1998).

An eye with only two types of cone pigments will make one particularly interesting color confusion involving sunlight. (As you know, sunlight consists of nearly equal amounts of all wavelengths within the visible portion of the spectrum.) Like any other complex mixture of wavelengths, sunlight will be represented in this eye by a pair of responses, one from each pigment type. There also exists one specific wavelength of light that will produce exactly the same pair of responses. This means, therefore, that this one particular wavelength will be indistinguishable from sunlight. Looking at the curves in Figure 7.11, you should be able to figure out exactly where this wavelength falls along the spectrum. Since all other wavelengths will produce different pairs of responses, they will not be confused with sunlight. We can call the one wavelength that is confused the **neutral point** of the eye's spectral re-

FIGURE 7.13
A three-pigment system.

sponse. The existence of a single neutral point is the hallmark of a two-pigment eye. For most people, such a neutral point cannot be found, indicating that their eyes contain more than two cone pigments.

What If Eyes Had Three Cone Pigments?
So far we've seen that for a one-pigment eye any complex combination of wavelengths can be matched using just a single wavelength. Such an eye would be wholly color blind. We've also seen that a two-pigment eye can match any complex combination of wavelengths using two properly selected wavelengths. Such an eye would have some ability to discriminate the wavelength composition of light. Now you should be able to anticipate what happens if an eye contains three pigments, like those represented in Figure 7.13. Note that any wavelength (such as *A*) will produce a trio of responses, one from each photopigment. Moreover, this trio of responses cannot be mimicked by any other single wavelength. To mimic these responses would require the ability to vary the intensities of up to three different wavelengths (with some exceptions, to be explained in the next paragraph). Hence an eye containing a trio of photopigments is said to be **trichromatic** (meaning "three-colored"). Color

Plate 10 illustrates the variety of colors that can be produced by mixing just three colors. Note that each projector contains a transparency that creates a beam of a different color—one blue, one red, and one green. In the center, where all the beams overlap, your eye receives the reflected light from all three, and the result is white. Where only the red and green beams overlap, the light appears yellow. If the intensities of each beam were adjusted relative to one another, a host of intermediate colors could be generated.

The demonstration in Color Plate 10 does not require the particular trio of lights used there; many others would work equally well. But why *three* lights? If an eye contains three different cone photopigments, its response to any complex mixture of light can be represented by a trio of signals, one generated by each type of cone. To mimic this trio of signals, three independently adjustable lights are needed. Although any single wavelength will stimulate more than just one cone type, certain wavelengths do stimulate one type particularly well and the other types less well. A trio of wavelengths can be chosen so that each member of the trio elicits the largest response from a different one of the three pigments. We noted earlier that there are limitations to the matches that are possible with any set of three lights. To match any light, you need independent control of the response in each cone type. Because any single wavelength will stimulate all types of cones, three lights that have been chosen to match most colors will not be able to match many extremely saturated colors. To make those matches, a different set of lights would be required.

It has been known for some time that normal human vision is trichromatic. The idea that color perception depends on the responses of three different pigments is also quite old. Thomas Young, a British physician, is usually credited with articulating this theory first (1801/1948). Since the German physiologist Hermann Helmholtz developed the first detailed treatment of the same idea (1909/1962), the theory is usually known by both men's names, the **Young-Helmholtz theory.*** We're now ready to study some of the details of this theory. But first, consider what happens when there are more than three unique cone photopigments.

What if Eyes Had Four Cone Pigments? Imagine an eye that contains four different types of cones, each with its own unique absorption spectrum. By now you should be able to anticipate several "facts" about the color vision of the creature possessing this hypothetical eye. First, this creature would have even better color discrimination than humans and other trichromatic species. With four cone photopigments, the number of potential color confusions decreases. Moreover, this 4-pigment eye would require four unique wavelengths to perform the color matching task, not three, like we require. In fact, it appears that nature has provided some nonmammalian species—including some reptiles, birds and fish—with tetrachromatic vision (the prefix *tetra* means "four" in Greek). The best studied of these visually gifted creatures is the goldfish (Neumeyer, 1992), whose extra photopigment gives it sensitivity into the ultraviolet (very short wavelength) portion of the spectrum invisible to us human trichromats.

This raises a question: in the case of human vision, why did nature stop at just three cone types? (If you were a dichromat such as the cat, you'd ask why stop at just two cone types.) If more unique cone types give an eye greater color discriminability, why not upgrade to a goldfish-quality eye? For that matter, why stop at four?

Actually, there are several good reasons why trichromacy represents a good compromise. First, new cone types must arise from chance mutations in the genetic instructions specifying the

---

*In fairness to Thomas Young's genius it must be noted that Helmholtz originally rejected Young's theory and came only grudgingly to accept its validity (Hurvich and Jameson, 1949).

options contained in the photoreceptors (recall Chapter 2, where we discussed the molecular structure of photopigment). And those chance mutations are rare. Second, when mutations do occur, they would have little impact on color vision unless the postreceptor cells maintained some separation of responses generated by each of the mutated photopigments (Wässle, 1999). Otherwise, the postreceptor neurons would intermix the mutated pigments' responses with the normal ones, subverting the mutants' uniqueness. And, finally, that additional kernel of color information must have survival importance to the organism in which the mutation arose. The animal must be able to see things its competitors can not. Otherwise, the genetic instructions for synthesizing that novel photopigment would not be passed on to subsequent generations.

Given this sequence of very unlikely circumstances, it is remarkable that color vision has evolved at all. Trichromacy, in fact, represents a very efficient means for representing the behaviorally important surface colors in our natural environment. Just look at how many different colors we can distinguish! Of course there are some wavelength combinations that the human eye cannot discriminate from one another, as studies of metamers show. In the research laboratory, metamers are produced under conditions that afford strict control over the wavelength composition of stimuli. This kind of control never occurs in the natural environment, in which the visual system evolved. And it rarely occurs in everyday situations involving artificial illumination. In fact, mathematical analyses of natural surfaces and the wavelength distributions of typical illuminants reveal that trichromacy represents a very good solution to the problem of color vision: it provides an accurate description of surface colors under most conditions (Lennie and D'Zmura, 1988).

In a moment we will consider in more detail the genetic bases of color vision. But first we need to return to our trichromatic eyes and consider exactly what photopigments the three cone

types contain and how those cone types are distributed throughout the eye.

What Are the Three Cone Types?

Execute

For over a century, strong but indirect evidence suggested that the human eye contained three distinct cone types. But it wasn't until a few decades ago that the presence of those cones was confirmed and their spectral sensitivity was measured. Here's how that was accomplished.

The technique of directly measuring the light absorption of photopigments is aptly named **microspectrophotometry.** Consider each part of the term: *photometry* involves the measurement (*metron*) of light (*photos*); *spectro* indicates the spectrum (determining which wavelengths of light are present); and *micro* means "small." Hence, in the application to cone pigments, microspectrophotometry involves shining a small spot of light onto a single cone and determining, for various wavelengths, how much of that light is absorbed (MacNichol, 1964). The results obtained by studying cones in several human retinas are shown in Figure 7.14 (Dartnall, Bowmaker, and Mollon, 1983). The vertical axis portrays the amount of light absorbed, expressed as a percent-

FIGURE 7.14

Microspectrophotometric records from three cone types in the human eye. (Redrawn from Dartnall, Bowmaker, and Mollon, 1983.)

age of the light shone on the cone. The horizontal axis indicates the light's wavelength. To facilitate comparisons among pigments, each pigment's maximum absorption has been arbitrarily set equal to unity.

These absorption curves have several notable features. First of all, there are three different cone pigment types (one type per cone), as one would expect from experiments on color metamers. Each pigment type is most sensitive to light of a particular wavelength—approximately 430, 530, and 560 nanometers, respectively. Because of their peak sensitivities, these three cone types are referred to as short-wavelength sensitive (S cones), medium-wavelength sensitive (M cones), and long-wavelength sensitive (L cones). Notice that each cone pigment absorbs a broad range of wavelengths. As a result of this breadth, most lights—even those of only a single wavelength—stimulate more than just one class of cones. For example, stimulation in the region of 475 nanometers affects all three types. This breadth also means that the response of a single cone type provides no information about the wavelength(s) of light being absorbed. By itself, each pigment type is "color blind" (recall the univariance principle described earlier).

Each cone's photopigment comprises a membrane protein bound to retinal, which is a derivative of vitamin A. Photopigments are manufactured according to genetic instructions embodied in DNA sequences. Using techniques from molecular genetics, it has been possible to synthesize those cone pigment proteins in the laboratory from cloned DNA samples. By exposing molecules of each synthesized protein to light of different wavelength, one can measure the protein's absorption spectrum. When this is done with proteins that have been synthesized from human DNA, three distinct spectra show up, peaking at about 426, 530 and 557 nanometers (Merbs and Nathans, 1992). This remarkable technical achievement confirms some of what was already known about photopigments and genes, and sets the stage for identifying the de-

tails of the genetic "language" that controls cones' wavelength sensitivity.

Differences

Molecular biology has uncovered an unexpected twist in the trichromatic story: L-cones come in at least two varieties. Normal trichromatic humans, in fact, have one of two slightly different alternative types of L-cone pigment: one having its peak sensitivity at 552 nanometers and the other peaking at 557 nanometers. This genetically-based diversity reflects a difference of a single amino acid in the protein structures of the two kinds of L pigments (Merbs and Nathans, 1992). This tiny molecular difference, in turn, produces reliable differences in color perception. For example, when they mix lights that appear red and green in order to produce pure yellow, people with the 557 nanometer L-cone add more green to the mixture while those with the 552 nanometer L-cone add more red (Winderickx et al., 1992). This means that a given mixture of red and green looks different to these two groups of individuals.

Within a sample of several dozen people, the incidence of the two cone types turned out to be about 2:1 in favor of the 557 nanometer variety of L-cone (the variety shown in Figures 7.13 and 7.14). Inspired by these findings, there is a growing realization that people with normal color vision may have not one, but *many* versions of L- and M-cone pigments, produced by intergenic recombination in which, for example, portions of an L-pigment gene inherited from one's father is combined with portions of an M-pigment gene inherited from one's mother (Jacobs, 1996; Tovee, 1994; Neitz and Neitz, 1995).* These

---

*In some males, both types of L-pigment genes are expressed, creating patches of retina with one pigment type and patches with the other type (Neitz and Neitz, 1995).

For a long time it was believed that X chromosomes normally held just two photopigment genes, one for the M pigment and one for the L pigment. The use of sophisticated molecular biological techniques has undermined that assumption. In fact, a significant number of males have more than one L-pigment gene on the X-chromosome (Sjoberg et al., 1988). It is likely that a similar arrangement holds for M-pigment genes as well (Neitz, Neitz and Jacobs, 1993).

mistakes in DNA replication are promoted by the proximity and structural similarity of the L- and M-pigment genes.

A detailed knowledge of the connections between perception and events at a molecular level is both exciting and fascinating. As John Mollon (1992) put it, "Here is a case where a difference of a single nucleotide (unit of DNA) places people in distinct phenomenal worlds and where we know almost all the steps in the causal chain from gene to molecule to neural signals" (p. 378).

The Geography of the Cones

We've been considering the connection between color perception and the cones' absorption spectra. Let's focus now on other perceptually important facts about cone receptors. Knowing that the signals coming from the three cone types are important in color perception, we need to consider how these types are distributed across the retina. As you will see, the proportions of the three cone types vary from one retinal region to another, and color perception varies correspondingly.

Simply looking at retinal tissue under the microscope provides some clues about cone distribution, because the S cones are slightly different in shape than the L and M cones (Rodieck, 1998). Consequently, it's been known for some time that there are fewer S cones than L and M cones and, moreover, that S cones are altogether absent within the fovea. But it wasn't until very recently that the distributions of L and M cones could be visualized because those two cone types are indistinguishable anatomically.

It remained for Austin Roorda and David Williams (1999) of the University of Rochester to devise a way to reveal the spatial layout of S, M and L cones in the intact human eye. Using a sophisticated optical system, Roorda and Williams photographed the receptor mosaic with enough detail that individual cones could be seen. A series of these high-fidelity photographs was made immediately after exposing the eye to intense light that selectively stimulated each of the three

photopigments. An example of these remarkable results is shown in Color Plate 11. This represents about a 0.013 millimeter square patch of tissue located just to one side of the fovea of one eye (a tissue patch this size is slightly smaller than the period at the end of this sentence). Blue, green and red colored circles denote individual S, M and L cones, respectively. (Don't be misled: the colors in this photograph are simply used to earmark the cones. They are not actually colored in the eye.)

This patchwork of cones shows several remarkable features. First, a relatively small proportion of S cones are more or less irregularly scattered among larger numbers of L and M cones. Second, the L and M cones, too, are more or less randomly distributed within the mosaic of cone photoreceptors. One sees relatively large patches of retina comprised of only a single cone type.

What you can't see from this one photograph, however, are the significant individual differences Roorda and Williams found. In one person, L cones outnumbered M cones 4 to 1, while in a second person, L and M cones were equally numerous. Neither of these distributions necessarily represents an "abnormality." The genetic decision about whether a cone contains the L or the M photopigment is entirely statistical (Wang et al., 1999). In terms of the fine detail of the cone mosaic, it is quite likely that every person's geographical layout of L and M cones is unique.

Because color appearance depends on the signals generated by the various cone types, color vision varies from one part of your retina to another. To demonstrate regional variations in color vision, one must stimulate different, very small regions of the retina (recall Figure 3.29). Employing this strategy, Williams, MacLeod and Hayhoe (1981) presented tiny, brief, violet test flashes briefly superimposed on a steady yellow background, conditions that force an observer to rely on S cones to see the violet test stimulus. Measuring psychophysical thresholds at many different closely spaced regions on the retina, these investigators found pronounced variation in sensitivity from one region, presumably where an S cone existed, to another, immediately adjacent region where presumably there were no S cones. The wide variations in threshold were found to be consistent even with testing that extended more than a year. These experimental results confirm that single S cones are separated by fairly large stretches of the retina in which there are no S cones at all.

Illusion

In addition to light sensitivity, color appearance itself varies with the region stimulated. For example, a small light that appears greenish-blue when imaged slightly away from the fovea will appear pure green when imaged directly *on* the fovea. This change reflects the diminished presence of S cones at the center of the retina. In addition, as that same light is moved into the periphery of the retina—where cones are less numerous—the light's color becomes less conspicuous. To sustain color perception in the periphery requires enlarging the size of the stimulus, to compensate for the reduced density of cones. Far into the periphery, where cones are widely separated from one another, vision becomes achromatic ("without color"). Thus, when an object is seen out of the corner of your eye, you may recognize its shape, but it will appear colorless.

You can use Color Plate 8 to see the consequence of having so few S cones in your fovea. Look at a region of the photograph where there is a blue patch in the quilt. At normal reading distance, the image of the blue patch will not only cover the region free of S cones (your fovea) but will also extend into regions that do contain S cones (around your fovea). Now, prop the book up, back away from the page, and continue staring at the blue patch. As you get farther from the book, the image of the blue patch will get smaller on your retina, eventually shrinking so that it falls entirely within your fovea. As the image shrinks, the patch will cease to appear blue. Notice that at the same distance, though, the neighboring square continues to look green. This demonstration raises a paradox: when viewed from normal

reading distance, why doesn't the blue patch appear less blue in its center? For one thing, we seldom hold our eyes perfectly steady, which means that the images of small, blue objects rarely remain centered on the fovea. For another, we've seen that the brain has the propensity to "fill in" regions of objects that are obscured or that fall within the blindspot (recall Box 2.4).

The variation in color appearance with retinal region or image size has practical consequences. For example, if two stimuli containing precisely the same wavelengths differ in size or in retinal location, their color appearances will also differ. As a result, even the most faithful photographic reproduction of a scene is bound to look different from the scene itself (Hurvich, 1981). (Recall from Chapter 3's discussion of spatial resolution that the density of cone photoreceptors is one factor governing the eye's resolving power [acuity].) The large separations between S cones make it easy to understand why acuity with blue targets is much poorer than acuity with targets of other colors (Pokorny, Graham and Lanson, 1968; Williams, MacLeod and Hayhoe, 1981).

Because of their sparseness, S cones can also distort your perception of boundaries. And since boundaries contribute to the perceived shape of an object, the S cones can distort that perceived shape. Robert Boynton (1982) devised a powerful test stimulus that demonstrates this distortion, one version of which is given in Color Plate 12. Note first the pale yellow rectangle in the left half of the figure. The ink used to print the rectangle absorbs short-wavelength light and reflects longer wavelengths. This reflected light stimulates primarily M and L cones, hence its yellow appearance. However, the white paper around the rectangle reflects light more or less uniformly, thereby stimulating S as well as M and L cones. As a result, then, one side of the yellow-white boundary excites S cones while the other side does not.

To show how poorly the S cones register contour information, we've taken the same rectangle and drawn a squiggly black line around the outline of that rectangle. This is shown in the right half of Color Plate 12. Once again, prop the book open so you can see the color plate then walk slowly backward. You'll reach a distance at which the yellow-white boundary of the right-hand figure will appear squiggly rather than straight. The region outside the squiggly boundary appears white, while the region inside appears yellow. This means that some portions in and around the boundary that used to look white now look yellow, and vice versa. It is as if the yellow had spread outward toward the black squiggly line, and the white had spread inward. This spreading does not occur for all colors, only those differentially stimulating S cones on either side of a boundary.

In summary, then, the regional variations in the machinery of color vision underscore a theme running throughout this chapter: color is a subjective experience that cannot be predicted based solely on the wavelength composition of the light reflected to the eye. We once again hear echoes of Newton's famous dictum that the rays themselves are not colored.

THE EVOLUTION OF CONE PHOTOPIGMENTS

Near the beginning of this chapter we asked "Why is it important to see colors?" Let's revisit that question now, drawing on insights from recent work on how color vision evolved over millions of years. This evolutionary perspective frames some intriguing possibilities about the purpose of color vision.

The normal human eye, as you now know, contains four types of photopigments, rhodopsin (in the rods) and three different cone photopigments. Genes, which are the basic units of inheritance, carry molecular instructions that guide a cell's manufacture of proteins, the building blocks of every living cell. Each gene is a chain of several thousand units of deoxyribonucleic acid (DNA); these are the instructions for protein manufacture.

Jeremy Nathans (Johns Hopkins University) succeeded in isolating the genes responsible for instructing visual cells in the proper manufacture of S, M and L pigments. Nathans (1989) showed that the gene for the S pigment is carried on chromosome pair number 7, while the genes for M and L pigments lie head-to-tail, next to one another on the X-chromosome. S, M and L photopigments differ from one another because structurally different genes, and hence different instructions, control their manufacture. By analyzing the structural similarities among various genes and taking account of changes from mutation, one can create an evolutionary family tree (Jacobs, 1998). Two genes that are highly similar in structure are more likely to have been formed closer together in time than are two genes whose structures differ markedly.

Structural resemblances among the genes for rhodopsin and the three cone pigments suggest all four cone pigments evolved from some common ancestor (Nathans, 1989). Ninety-six percent of the DNA sequence in the M-pigment gene is identical to that in the L-pigment gene. Interestingly, the S-pigment gene shares 42% of its sequence with rhodopsin, and almost exactly the same proportion with each of the L- and M-pigment genes.

This pattern of structural resemblances, supplemented by information on the variations in color vision of humans, nonhuman primates and nonprimate mammals, suggests that long ago a single ancestor gene gave rise to all the modern photopigment genes. John Mollon argues that the original cone pigment probably had an absorption peak in the range 510 to 570 nanometers (Mollon, 1989). This would harmonize the pigment's peak absorption with the spectral peak of light from the sun.

As we've already discussed, however, an eye with just one cone cannot be said to possess color vision. Much later, about 500 million years ago, the S cone came into existence. Its addition to retinas already possessing the original 510 to 570 nanometer pigment gave birth to color vision. The relative responses of two different cone types made it possible to extract some wavelength information from the incoming light. Note though, that S cones conferred color vision that was only dichromatic.

Finally, about 40 to 60 million years ago, the original type of cone, with its peak between 510 and 570 nanometers, is thought to have duplicated and differentiated, giving rise to both the L pigment and the M pigment, which are found in apes, in some species of monkeys (such as baboons and rhesus monkeys), and in humans. With the addition of this third cone type, color vision in primates attained trichromacy.*

Differences

Mollon (1989) put these evolutionary facts together with various creatures' food preferences to refine an intriguing account of color vision's utility.** He proposed that our arboreal, primate ancestors developed a particular liking for certain nutritious fruits, especially orange and yellow ones. An eye with both L and M cones is particularly adept at detecting such fruits within green foliage.

A recent, detailed study of the red howler monkey (native to French Guiana) showed that its particular M and L cones were optimal for distinguishing that species' favorite fruits from the leaves of trees on which the fruit grows (Regan et al., 1998). Building on this connection between food preference and vision, Boycott and Wässle (1999) point out that trichromatic color vision could evolve only in a species whose eye and retina were already optimized for fine visual acu-

ity. Otherwise, mutations in the photopigments would never have a chance to communicate their unique messages to the brain. In an eye with only modest acuity, inputs from individual cone photoreceptors are spatially pooled, and the unique messages from a mutated cone pigment would forever be lost in the mix. It is intriguing to imagine that the world's colors appear as they do to us today because tens of millions of years ago our primate ancestors with excellent visual acuity received the gift of trichromacy as part of an implicit bargain with citrus trees: their fruit would nourish the primates, and by eating the fruit, the primates dispersed the seed of that fruit.

COLOR'S OPPONENT CHARACTER

We saw in Chapters 3 and 4 that information from the photoreceptors is transformed as it travels to the visual cortex. Messages from neighboring receptors are antagonistically organized into ON and OFF regions, which together comprise a neuron's receptive field. The characteristics of these receptive fields significantly affect the perception of visual form and brightness. So far in this chapter, we have concentrated on the initial stage of analysis, of color information, an analysis performed by the three cone types. We now need to consider how messages from these three cone types are organized and modified at subsequent stages of the visual system. We can get some idea of this organization by considering several phenomena of color vision, all of which point to an opponent linkage, pitting one color against another.

What Is the Evidence for Color Opponency?

One phenomenon that suggests some kind of opponent connection between colors is **color contrast.** Just as lightness contrast (described in Chapter 3) exaggerates lightness differences between adjacent objects, *color* contrast exaggerates their color differences (see Box 7.3). The major facts of color contrast have been known for

---

*Not all primates have trichromatic vision. In virtually all the "new world" primates, such as owl and spider monkeys and marmosets, males have just a single photopigment in the medium and long-wavelength portion of the spectrum, which makes them dichromatic; females, however, tend to be trichromatic (Tovee, 1994).

**The original version of this account should be credited to Stephen Polyak (1957), who discussed the evolutionary interdependence of colored fruits and primate color vision (p. 973). At the time Polyak was working, however, much less was known about the actual cone photopigments. Mollon's refinement of this account has benefited greatly from advances in color vision research.

BOX 7.3

COLOR CONTRAST

Illusion

You've probably had the experience of purchasing an article of clothing, such as a tie or a scarf, to go with an outfit in your closet. In the store, the tie or scarf looks neutral gray. But when you get home and try on the outfit, the article acquires a distinct color other than gray. Moreover, that distinct color seems to vary, depending on what outfit you wear it with. In other words, the color of the tie or scarf depends on what color is adjacent to it. This effect, demonstrated in Color Plate 13, is called *color contrast,* and it is a powerful influence in many everyday settings. The two squares marked by tiny black dots are identical in color, but the perceived difference in illumination makes them appear different. If you're skeptical that they are identical, get an index card or a piece of paper, cut two holes in it corresponding to the locations of these two portions of the image. Then, with the card or paper overlaid on the figure, you can view the two squares in isolation from their surrounding regions.

Some people have been able to capitalize on color contrast to enhance color perception. One such person was Michel Chevreul, director of the Gobelin Tapestry Works in Paris. Chevreul knew that interweaving just gray and red yarns could create tapestries that appeared to contain other colors as well, including distinct blue-green stripes—colors produced in the viewer's brain by color contrast. Chevreul developed a set of rules for ensuring that color contrast would have the effect his designers and weavers wanted. He went further, though, publishing a huge volume (1839/1967) that set out the basic rules of color harmony and contrast as they related to painting, interior decoration, printing, flower gardening, and dressmaking. In fact, the French Impressionist painters of the nineteenth century used Chevreul's book as a guide.

These principles anticipate the clever images devised by Edwin Land, the inventor of instant photography (the Polaroid camera) and synthetic polarizing material used in sunglasses and glare-reducing filters.* Land's published work on color vision contains many interesting demonstrations of color contrast. Let's consider a typical one here (Land, 1959).

Land took two black and white slides of the same scene. One slide (the "red record") was taken with a red filter in front of the camera. The other (the "green record") used a green filter. Using a pair of slide projectors, Land superimposed the two black and white slides on a screen. Not surprisingly, since the slides were black and white, the result was a black and white image of the original scene. The surprise came when Land placed a red filter in front of the projector containing the red record. The image on the screen now consisted of various amounts of red light (from the projector with the red filter) mixed with various amounts of white light (from the other projector). One might expect that the only colors perceptible would be white, grays, blacks, and various shades of red. However, the image on the screen produced a wide range of colors—for example, a blond-haired girl with pale blue eyes, a red coat, blue-green collar, and natural flesh tones. Where had all these colors come from?

Land's surprising range of colors sprang mostly from color contrast (Walls, 1960). For instance, the girl's collar appeared blue-green because it was surrounded by the red of her coat. This could be verified by looking at the image of the collar through a narrow tube, which blocked the surrounding region from view. Now the collar appeared colorless, rather than blue-green.

Though Land's color demonstrations were surprising, perhaps they should not have been. More than 60 years earlier, the French photographer Ducos du Hauron had demonstrated basically the same phenomenon (Judd, 1960). Although not entirely novel, Land's color demonstrations serve one very useful purpose. They are a vivid reminder of how important contrast is in the everyday experience of the colors of objects.

---

*A prolific inventor, Land earned 535 United States patents, second only to the number of patents given to another great inventor, Thomas Alva Edison (McElheny, 1999).

a very long time. More than four hundred years ago, Leonardo da Vinci, the famous painter, scientist, and engineer, discussed color contrast in his *Treatise on Painting:*

> *Of different colors equally perfect, that will appear most excellent which is seen near its direct contrary . . . blue near yellow; green near red: because each color is more distinctly seen, when opposed to its contrary, than to any other similar to it.* (Quoted in Birren, 1941, p. 135)

Strong interaction between the color of an object and the color of its surround suggests some sort of antagonistic linkages within the visual machinery that processes color information.

You've already experienced another phenomenon that suggests color opponency, when you used Plate 6 to induce colored afterimages. Try the exercise again, staring at the fixation mark in the left-hand adaptation figure for 20 seconds and then shifting your gaze to the fixation mark in the right-hand test figure. Note that the afterimage produced by the yellow patch appears blue, whereas the one produced by blue appears yellow. By the same token, the afterimage of the red patch appears green, and vice versa. These color afterimages are consistent with the idea that the visual system treats certain colors as opponent pairs.

In color experience, blue and yellow are mutually exclusive: an object may appear blue or an object may appear yellow, but an object never appears *both* blue and yellow at the same time. Similarly, red and green are mutually exclusive: an object never appears *both* red and green. Of course, other combinations of these four colors are not mutually exclusive: objects can be bluish-green or reddish-yellow. These observations suggest that the nervous system may treat red and green as one mutually antagonistic pair and blue and yellow as another such pair. These views were first articulated by Ewald Hering, a German physician. In the nineteenth century, Hering made important contributions to nerve physiology, binocular vision, the anatomy of the liver, and color vision. Unfortunately, Hering was of-

ten so far ahead of his time that his contributions could not be properly assimilated into then current scientific thought and were therefore either dismissed outright or misinterpreted (Hurvich, 1969). But Hering's views on color vision have been largely vindicated by subsequent discoveries.

Chromatic and Achromatic Systems

A combination of psychophysical and physiological studies has now established that signals from the three cone types are processed by one **achromatic system** and a pair of **chromatic systems.**

The neural connections thought to underlie these three systems are sketched out in Figure 7.15. For diagrammatic simplicity, the schematic designs of the various systems are shown separately, one in each panel of the figure. The boxes labeled "S cones," "M cones," and "L cones" represent the three cone types. Arrows emerging from any one of the boxes represent neural signals generated when cones of that type absorb light. Two different kinds of arrows are meant to suggest that the nervous system treats signals in two different ways, either adding them or taking their difference. When two signals are represented by solid arrows, the system adds those two signals together; when one signal is shown as a solid arrow and another is shown as a dashed arrow, the system takes the difference between those two signals.

Before going further into the details of this figure, we should remind you how the nervous system adds and subtracts. Recall, from Chapter 3, that addition is accomplished via spatial summation. This operation is carried out when one neuron sums the messages from other neurons. Recall also that subtraction can be accomplished via an antagonism between ON and OFF signals. This operation is carried out when one neuron takes the difference between messages received from other neurons. So although the nervous system doesn't have access to a calculator, it can certainly add and subtract signals.

Return now to the discussion of Figure 7.15, seeing first how the achromatic system is constructed.

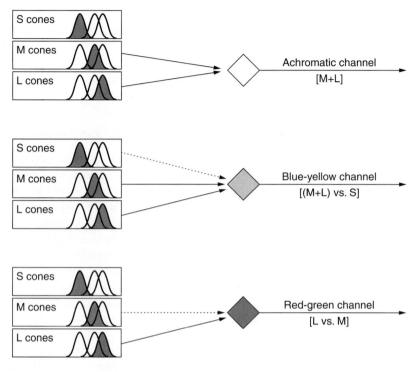

FIGURE 7.15
Chromatic and achromatic channels generated by combining the signals from three
cone types. The achromatic channel is represented in the top diagram, the blue-yellow
chromatic channel in the middle diagram, and the red-green chromatic channel in the
bottom diagram.

In the top panel, solid arrows indicate that the signals generated by M and L cones are added together. We can refer to the pathway carrying this
sum to the brain as a *channel* (a set of nerve fibers
bearing a common message). Activity in this
achromatic channel depends on the total excitation of M and L cones. There are various reasons
for imagining that activity in this channel determines an object's visibility. For example, the
shape of the photopic sensitivity curve (closely
related to visibility) can be predicted by taking a
sum of M and L cone responses (Smith and Pokorny, 1975; Werner et al., 1984). Note that by
adding together M and L cone signals, this achromatic channel actually discards the wavelength
information that it receives.

Turn now to Figure 7.15's two chromatic
channels.* According to the diagram, one of
these channels represents the *difference* between
S cone signals, on the one hand, and the *sum* of
M and L cone signals, on the other. This channel
signals the difference between short-wavelength
stimulation and stimulation throughout the
rest of the spectrum, so we'll refer to it as the
S−(M+L) channel.

_____

*Sometimes these channels are called the "blue-yellow" and
"red-green" channels. We have avoided these labels because,
although the labels are short and convenient, we prefer to re-
serve color names to describe experiences, not neural activity.

The other chromatic channel signals the *difference* between the stimulation of the M cones, on the one hand, and stimulation of L cones, on the other, which makes it the **M-L channel.**

To see Figure 7.15's implications, consider how the various channels might respond when an eye is stimulated by light that contains a wide range of wavelengths. This light, which appears white, would stimulate M and L cones to the same degree. As a result, the difference between their signals would be zero, resulting in no response in a channel that signalled the difference between those signals (the M-L channel). And this would be true regardless of the intensity of the light. Light that appears white would be similarly ineffective for the other chromatic channel, because that light excites its contributors equally well. Note, however, that the achromatic channel, which adds responses from M and L cones, would be much excited by this broadband light. In fact, the more intense this light, the greater the response in the achromatic channel.

The scheme outlined in Figure 7.15 gives a straightforward explanation of a puzzling observation mentioned earlier in this chapter. Recall that hues drawn from the region near the middle of the spectrum (where light looks yellow) appear less saturated than hues drawn from the ends of the spectrum (where lights look blue and red). But why should one hue look more saturated than another? The scheme in Figure 7.15 gives a simple answer. A hue will appear desaturated (washed out) if it produces a strong response in the achromatic channel and at least some response in one of the chromatic channels. Note that if light produces a response in the achromatic channel but none in either chromatic channel, it will appear completely desaturated—white or some shade of gray. In contrast, a highly saturated hue results when a strong chromatic response is accompanied by a weak achromatic response. In general, the perceived saturation produced by light of any wavelength can be predicted by taking the ratio of the chromatic response it evokes to the achromatic response it

evokes. For example, light that appears yellow will seem relatively desaturated because such wavelengths (in the vicinity of 580 nanometers) elicit a weak chromatic response but a strong achromatic one.

Opponent Processes and Efficiency of Coding

Execute

Many lines of evidence—behavioral, physiological, and anatomical—show that key attributes of color vision flow from its opponent-process organization. But what purpose is served by such a complex scheme? Although questions about the purpose of biological processes can never be answered unequivocally, it is instructive to speculate about the possible advantage vision gains from sorting signals into opponent streams.

Think first about the relations among the three types of cones found in the normal human eye. Because their absorption spectra overlap so much (see Figure 7.14), the cones will yield similar, though not identical, responses under many conditions. Computing the theoretical response of each cone to various representative natural objects, one discovers that responses of the cones are very highly correlated. The correlation is especially strong between the responses of M and L cones. So, under most circumstances, the nervous system gets little more information from analyzing both M and L cone signals than it would have gotten from analyzing just one. Because the nervous system has limited transmission and processing capacity, this considerable redundancy represents significant waste. But what are the alternatives? Theoretically, how could the redundancy be reduced?

To answer this question, Buchsbaum and Gottschalk (1983) analyzed statistically the responses generated by human cones while an eye viewed various natural scenes. From those responses, they derived a scheme that would minimize redundancy and allow the fibers in the optic nerve to carry as much color information as possible from retina to the brain. They found that a truly efficient arrangement would take the responses of the three cone types and transform them into three other signals. The converted signals, rather than the original ones, would be then fed to the brain. The best possible scheme turned out to be very much like the opponent-process system that we've been describing. When alternative designs are compared, the scheme illustrated in Figure 7.15, however complex it may seem, actually does make the best possible use of the biological hardware available.

The Physiological Basis of Opponency

Various details of the scheme in Figure 7.15 have been established by careful psychophysical studies (see Kaiser and Boynton, 1996, for details). But how does the nervous system accomplish the adding and subtracting implied by opponency? To seek an answer to this question, let's return to the lateral geniculate nucleus (LGN) described in chapter 4.

In some landmark work, Russell DeValois studied cells in the lateral geniculate nucleus of monkeys, whose trichromatic vision matches ours. He found that cells in the LGN could be divided into nonopponent and opponent types (DeValois and DeValois, 1975). The opponent neurons behaved as though they received opposing input from different types of cones. The essential details of DeValois' findings were later confirmed by Derrington, Krauskopf and Lennie's (1984) studies of neurons in the parvo cell layers of the monkey LGN. Let's consider each group in turn, starting with the nonopponent.*

When light was shown on the retina, some nonopponent LGN cells responded by increasing their activity (ON cells), while others responded by decreasing their activity (OFF cells). Cells of the ON type gave ON responses to *all* wavelengths, though more strongly to some wavelengths than to others. Similarly, OFF cells gave OFF responses to all wavelengths, but again, in varying strengths. Together, such cells could constitute the achromatic channel represented in Figure 7.15.

Cells of the opponent type behaved differently. In this group, any cell could give either an ON response *or* an OFF response, depending on the wavelength of light with which it was stimulated. For example, some cells would increase their responses when long-wavelength light was present but decrease their responses when short-wavelength was present. The opposite pattern was also found: reduced response with long-wavelength light and increased response with short-wavelength light. When light contained *both* long and short wavelengths, the ON and OFF responses tended to cancel each other and the cell gave little response. As far as the cell was concerned, the light never appeared.

If a cell gives an ON response in one portion of the spectrum and an OFF response in the other portion, there must be some transition wavelength at which the response changes from ON to OFF. DeValois found that opponent cells could be divided roughly into two groups, according to their transition wavelengths. For one group the transition occurred between the portion of the spectrum that appears green and the portion that appears red. Because these neurons seem to pit M-cone inputs against L-cone inputs, we can call them **M–L cells.** For the other group, the transition occurred between the portion of the spectrum that appears blue and the portion that appears yellow. Because they behaved as though S-cone signals were being pitted against signals from M- and L-cones, we can call these **S−(M+L) cells.** Note that these two groups of cells link different regions of the spectrum in an opponent fashion. Such linkages could be the re-

---

*Primate retinas also contain both spectrally opponent and spectrally nonopponent cells (Gouras and Zrenner, 1981). Presumably these retinal ganglion cells are the origin of the opponent and nonopponent LGN cells studied by DeValois.

alization of the two opponent channels schematized in Figure 7.15.*

We've already seen that the interplay between opponent and nonopponent channels can account for the way in which wavelength controls brightness and saturation. The interplay between these channels can account for other important phenomena of color perception, too. Using DeValois's results, we will consider some of these in detail. The curves in Figure 7.16 summarize some of DeValois's data. The curve labeled *R* represents the average response of M-L opponent cells to longer-wavelength light. Note that in such cells the response begins at about 600 nanometers and grows with increasing wavelength. The curve labeled *G* represents the average response of these same M-L opponent cells to shorter-wavelength light. Curves *Y* and *B* represent the responses of S−(M+L) opponent cells to longer and shorter wavelengths, respectively. How do these curves relate to color perception?

The simplest idea is that each curve corresponds to one particular color experience. For example, the *G* curve might correspond to the greenness evoked by various wavelengths. To examine the possible correspondence between the curves and color experience, let's consider the results of a color-naming experiment by Robert Boynton and James Gordon (1965). People were asked to name the color of briefly flashed lights

FIGURE 7.16
Responses of different LGN cells to light of various wavelengths. (Adapted from DeValois and DeValois, 1975.)

whose wavelength varied randomly across the spectrum. To help quantify these color names, people were asked to use only the names *blue, green, yellow, red* and various combinations of these names—such as *yellow-red* (meaning a red that was tinged with yellow).

The results are shown in Figure 7.17. The horizontal axis shows the wavelength of light, and the vertical axis shows the tendency to use a given color name in describing that wavelength. For example, the "green" curve reflects the use of the term *green* to describe color experience. Note that *green* is used to describe the visual effect of wavelengths ranging from about 470 to 600 nanometers. Toward the shorter-wavelength portion of this range, *green,* is modified by the term *blue.* In the longer-wavelength portion of the range, *green* is modified by the term *yellow.* The visual experience evoked by light of 510 nanometers is described solely as *green* (the "green" curve reaches its maximum at 510 nanometers). The use of *yellow* peaks at about 580 nanometers, and the use of *blue* at about 460. Note that the "red" curve consists of two segments—one at the right (longer wavelengths) and one at the left (shorter wave-

---

*Some researchers question whether all opponent cells can be put into just two distinct categories (Zrenner, 1983). Moreover, you should note that DeValois's experiments were performed by uniformly illuminating an LGN cell's receptive field with lights of different wavelength. Recall from Chapter 4, though, that each LGN receptive field is divisible into spatially distinct center and surround regions. More recently, physiologists have discovered that in some LGN cells, the center region of the receptive field responds best to one wavelength of light, while the surround region responds to a very different wavelength. So the color opponency derived by DeValois is really combined with the spatial opponency defined by the center/surround layout of the receptive field. Their spatially organized color opponency makes these cells ideal contributors to color contrast (Lennie, 1984).

FIGURE 7.17
Proportion of trials on which different color names are assigned to various wavelengths.

lengths). This is quite understandable, since very short wavelength light appears purple, a hue that can be produced by mixing lights that appear blue and red.

Note the general correspondence between Boynton and Gordon's color-naming results (Figure 7.17) and the physiological results from LGN opponent cells in the monkey (Figure 7.16). The use of the name *green* by humans seems to correspond quite well to the response of M-L opponent cells to shorter-wavelength light—the *G* curve in Figure 7.16. Similarly, the use of the name yellow resembles the *Y* curve in that figure. The correspondence is suggestive, but less satisfactory, between the use of the name *blue* and the *B* curve. Finally, at long wavelengths, the name *red* corresponds quite well to the *R* curve. However, the occasional use of the name *red* at short wavelengths has no counterpart in the way DeValois's cells responded. Nevertheless, there is, overall, a suggestive correspondence between color naming and the responses of opponent cells. Remember, though, that the LGN represents an intermediate stage in the neural pathways signalling color information (recall the K-cell and P-cell pathways discussed in chapters 3 and 4). So it would be incorrect to conclude that color naming is the exclusive province of the LGN. Rather the LGN imposes an opponent or-

...zation on color processing that is passed on ...gher stages and eventually reflected in our ...nses on perceptual tasks. This general correspondence between physiology and color naming, incidentally, dovetails with an idea presented early in this chapter: the major color categories— blue, green, yellow, and red—are universal and not simply a reflection of how people learn to use color terms.

Cortical Mechanisms of Color Vision

As described in Chapter 4, two pathways arising in the retina and passing through the LGN carry color signals to the cortex. One is the K-cell system which innervates cortical cells in the upper layers of V1. The other is the P-cell system which innervates cells in layer 4 of V1. Some believe that the K- and P-cell pathways split up the two opponent signals between them, each carrying one type of signal to the cortex (see the overview by Mollon, 1999), although the details of this scheme have yet to be verified.

What does seem clear is that V1 neurons carrying color information primarily innervate a series of visual areas collectively termed the temporal (or ventral) pathway (see Figure 4.19). Currently there is heated debate about which, if any, of these areas deserves the title "*the* color area." For example, some researchers advocate that area V4 is *the* color area, in part because neurons in this region of the monkey's brain respond to objects' color appearance, not simply to the wavelength composition of light reflected by objects. These neurons, in other words, seemed to be exhibiting color constancy (Zeki, 1980). More recent studies, however, reveal that color sensitive neurons of this variety are also present in other visual areas within the ventral pathway of the monkey's brain (see the review by Cowey and Heywood, 1997).

Several distinct human brain areas concerned with color vision have been identified using PET and fMRI techniques (see the review by Hadjikhani et al., 1998). Some of these areas, including V1 and V2 (Engel, Zhang and Wandell, 1997) are activated when people simply look at an array of colored patches. Other areas, however, are only activated when people attend to and identify colors (Gulyas and Roland, 1994). Given this widespread, task-dependent pattern of activations, is it reasonable to characterize any given brain area as *the* color area?

Ⓒ Clinical

Probably the most compelling piece of evidence for a specialized color area in the brain comes from the study of people suffering achromatopsia, the perceptual disorder characterized by loss of color vision from brain damage (introduced in Chapter 4). Because other aspects of vision remain normal in these individuals, it is natural to assume that the brain damage has destroyed a visual area indispensable for the experience of color. What follows is an abbreviated history of one individual in whom damage to the cerebral cortex produced substantial color vision deficiency. This case is particularly interesting because the damaged region has been pinpointed by neuroimaging. (A detailed description of this case has been given by Pearlman, Birch and Meadows, 1979.)

The patient was a man in his mid fifties who had been a customs inspector before he became ill. To get that job, he had taken a color vision test, which he had passed without difficulty. Following a stroke, he persistently claimed that he couldn't see colors. He likened the problem to watching a black-and-white movie. Although his general health and cognitive abilities remained sound, he was forced to take another job that did not require color judgments. In addition, his deficient color vision interfered with his personal daily routine. For instance, he had to rely on his wife to select his clothes, so as to avoid wearing weird color combinations, and he was unable to distinguish ripe from unripe fruit.

Following his stroke, this man retained good memory for colors, as evidenced by his ability to associate objects and colors. When shown a black and white outline drawing of familiar objects, he could readily say what color each *should* be. But when he attempted to color the outline drawing using felt-tip pens, he was unable to select the appropriate colors. An example of his results are shown in Color Plate 14. This page from a children's coloring book was colored (8 years after his stroke) using the pens shown in the upper part of the picture. He needed 30 minutes to complete this effort, spending most of this time comparing the various pens before selecting one. Despite the obvious color confusions evidenced in this picture, the man confidently stated that tomatoes should be red, carrots orange, and so on. He wasn't sure, though, whether he had actually selected the appropriate colors.

Other, more formal tests confirmed that this person possessed very poor color discrimination over the whole spectrum. In this respect, his performance differed from that of people with congenitally defective color vision. Congenital color blindness, as you will learn in a moment, usually involves color confusions within a restricted region of the spectrum. These forms of color blindness are present from birth and stem from a deficiency in a particular cone photopigment. In contrast, the person described here had perfectly normal color vision prior to his stroke. Moreover, the stroke affected only his *perception* of color—acuity and depth perception remained normal. Brain-scan images from this patient reveal damage within a region just in front of the primary visual cortex, in a position consistent with projections of the ventral pathway.

In recent years, equally intriguing cases of achromatopsia have been detailed, including the famous "color-blind" painter studied by neurologist Oliver Sacks (1995). In a review of these case studies, Cowey and Heywood (1997) conclude that the condition is indeed caused by damage to those portions of the occipital and temporal lobes that form the ventral pathway. They also point out, however, that at least some of these patients can still identify the shapes of objects and the direction of motion of objects even when those objects are defined solely by chromatic information. These observations led Cowey and Heywood to speculate that in cases of achromatopsia "perhaps only the information about wavelength that leads to conscious awareness of colour has been destroyed" (1997, p. 133).

From the still mysterious condition of achromatopsia, let's turn to another class of color deficiencies whose bases are much better understood.

ABNORMALITIES OF COLOR PERCEPTION

Clinical

Earlier you learned that within the normal population of trichromats, not everyone sees color in precisely the same way. A surface that appears pure yellow to you may have a slight greenish tint to your friend, all because the two of you have slightly different cone photopigments. Even more striking, though, are those individuals whose color vision deviates dramatically from the norm. People with such variations are described as "color deficient" (popularly, but wrongly, called "color blind"). Consideration of color deficiency enhances understanding of normal color vision and also reinforces Newton's insight, mentioned earlier, that "the rays are not coloured."

Color deficiency can take any of numerous different forms and can be either hereditary or acquired during an individual's lifetime. The prevalence of inherited color deficiency varies among populations. For example, 8 out of every 100 Caucasian males, 5 out of every 100 Asiatic males, and 3 out of every 100 African- and Native-American males are color deficient. Within all these groups, the incidence of color deficiency is much lower in females than in males. For instance, Caucasian females are ten times less likely to be color deficient than are males (Hurvich, 1981, p. 267).

Although color deficiency has probably been around for millions of years, the first recorded descriptions of the problem do not appear until the end of the eighteenth century. Among the first reports of color deficiency was one made by the English scientist John Dalton late in the eigh-

teenth century. You may recognize Dalton's name. He's the scientist responsible for developing the atomic theory, and the unit of molecular weight is named in his honor. Since Dalton was a person of considerable distinction, his description of his own "shortcoming" was all the more interesting and noteworthy. Dalton wrote of himself:

I was always of the opinion, though I might not mention it, that several colours were injudiciously named. . . . All crimsons appear to me to consist chiefly of dark blue: but many of them seem to have a tinge of dark brown. I have seen specimens of crimson, claret, and mud, which were very nearly alike. Crimson has a grave appearance, being the reverse of every shewy and splendid colour. Woolen yarn dyed crimson or dark blue is the same to me. (1798/1948, p. 102)

Dalton was a keen observer of his own experiences, but he had a very mistaken idea about the cause of his visual abnormality. He reckoned that the vitreous humour of his eye was tinted blue, thus absorbing longer wavelengths of light and, thereby, distorting his color perception. A postmortem dissection of Dalton's eyes, performed in accord with his prearranged request, demolished his own theory posthumously. His vitreous was normal for a man his age (Sharpe and Nordby, 1990). In fact, we now know that Dalton's odd color vision was rooted in his retina. About one hundred fifty years after Dalton's death, a team of molecular geneticists and psychologists working in England took a small tissue sample from Dalton's preserved eye and used the sample to identify Dalton's DNA sequence (Hunt et al., 1995). On the X-chromosome (where the genes for L and M cones reside), they found only genes specifying the opsin associated with the L cone. This makes it certain that while Dalton was alive, his eye lacked M-cone photopigments, which posthumously settles the diagnosis of Dalton's color deficiency.

There are several reasons why color deficiency such as Dalton's went unnoticed for so long. First, very few people are completely color blind, meaning that they can't see colors at all. The more common forms of color deficiency are not especially dramatic. These people do see color but in ways that differ from the norm. Second, many color-deficient people simply don't notice that their use of color names differs from that of other people. Third, most color-deficient people manage to compensate for their deficiency. When driving automobiles, people who cannot distinguish reds from greens may still know when to stop and when to go based on which light—top or bottom—is lit in a traffic signal. Also, a person who confuses reds and greens may be able to distinguish a red shirt from a green one because they differ in lightness (Jameson and Hurvich, 1978). Sometimes, though, lightness differences are not adequate substitutes for color. John Dalton, in fact, learned this to his dismay. A Quaker, Dalton was supposed to wear subdued clothing, preferably black. As a result, his friends were shocked when he paraded around in his crimson academic robes, believing that they were black.

Because color and lightness normally covary, special test materials must be designed so that lightness does not provide a clue to color. One of the most widely used color tests consists of a series of figures defined by dots differing from one another only in hue, not in lightness. Unless a person can distinguish the color of the dots defining the figure from the color of the dots defining the background, the figure will be invisible. For example, when the figure is red and the surround is green, people with normal color vision will be able to identify the figure whereas people who confuse reds and greens will not. As a consequence, the test picks out people who have one particular kind of color deficiency, one involving red-green confusions. To detect forms of color deficiency involving other confusions, colors other than red and green would have to be used for the figure and its surround.

Color Plate 15 shows a couple of test plates from the widely used Ishihara Color Blindness Test. Look at the two circular regions and note the digit or digits that you see within each. Viewers with normal color vision will see a single numeral

in the left-hand circle and two numerals in the right-hand circle. People who make red-green color confusions will have trouble seeing any numerals. Also, variant forms of red-green color blindness, which we'll discuss later, permit either only the left digit or only the right digits to be seen.

Now let's consider the origins of the color deficiencies themselves.

Congenital Color Deficiency

In some forms of congenital color deficiency the eye has the normal number of cones, but it performs as though it had fewer than three *types* of cones. In fact, this is exactly how color deficiency was explained by Helmholtz, one of the coauthors of the trichromatic color theory. We've already noted that an eye containing just two types of cones would be *dichromatic*. This means that the eye would require just two different wavelengths to match the appearance of any other wavelength. Since the normal, trichromatic eye—one with three types of cones—requires three different wavelengths to make such matches, many matches that are satisfactory to the dichromatic eye are unsatisfactory to a trichromatic one. For example, to a dichromat who is missing L cones, all three rectangles in Color Plate 16 appear to be of the same color. Unless you are that same type of dichromat, the rectangles won't look even vaguely alike.

Clinical

Although genetic mistakes can eliminate any one of the three cone types, they predominantly eliminate either M or L cones, not the S cones. When either M or L cones are missing, middle and long wavelengths will be confused with each other. However, all of these wavelengths will be distinguishable from short wavelengths. Dichromatic color deficiencies caused by the absence of either M or L cones are lumped together under the rubric *red-green deficiency*. This, incidentally, is the form of dichromacy John Dalton had.

In a much rarer form of dichromacy, S cones are missing. Here, lightness perception is unaffected because S cones make no contribution to perceived lightness, and discriminations among middle and long wavelengths are normal because M and L cones are unaffected.

People categorized as dichromats make another kind of color confusion characteristic of a two-cone eye. We pointed out earlier that eyes with only two cone types should experience a neutral point in the spectrum, a single wavelength that looks achromatic. People with dichromatic color vision show precisely such neutral points. However, the wavelength at which the neutral point occurs varies depending on their form of dichromacy.

In addition to dichromatic color deficiencies, there are other, even more common color abnormalities that we haven't mentioned. People with one of these common abnormalities have color vision that is an unusual form of trichromacy. These people are not dichromats. Their spectrum shows no neutral point, and matches that satisfy dichromats fail to satisfy them. Since they require three separate lights to match any hue they

can see, their color perception is trichromatic. However, their color matches will not look satisfactory to someone with normal trichromatic vision. Because in these instances color vision is trichromatic but anomalous, the condition is termed *anomalous trichromacy*. The anomaly arises from the abnormal absorption curve of one of the three cone pigments (Dartnall, Bowmaker and Mollon, 1983).

Figure 7.18 summarizes the discussion to this point, giving the technical names for various forms of color abnormality, the color confusions associated with each, and prevalence rates in North America and Western Europe (Alpern, 1981).

Congenital Supernormality?

The relative rarity of color blind females provides an important clue about the genetics of color vision, both normal and abnormal. Sex-linked patterns of inheritance, color defects included, implicate the X-chromosome, and mo-

Differences

NAME	CAUSE	CONSEQUENCES	PREVALENCE
DICHROMACIES			
Protanopia	Missing L-type pigment	Confuses 520–700 Has neutral point	M: 1.0% F: 0.02%
Deuteranopia	Missing M-type pigment	Confuses 530–700 Has neutral point	M: 1.1% F: 0.1%
Tritanopia	Missing S-type pigment	Confuses 445–480 Has neutral point	Very rare
ANOMALOUS TRICHROMACIES			
Protanomaly	Abnormal L-type pigment	Abnormal matches Poor discrimination*	M: 1.0% F: 0.02%
Deuteranomaly	Abnormal M-type pigment	Abnormal matches Poor discrimination*	M: 4.9% F: 0.04%

Note: "M" indicates males; "F" females. Wavelengths that are confused are given in nanometers. An asterisk (*) means that only some members of this group exhibit this problem.

FIGURE 7.18
Major genetic color deficiencies.

lecular biological studies have pinpointed locations on the X-chromosome where the critical DNA may be found. This same work raises an intriguing possibility, namely that some among us may actually possess color vision that is superior to the normal trichromatic variety. Here are the clues leading to that speculation.

Females have two X-chromosomes, one inherited from each parent, but males have only one X-chromosome, inherited from their mothers. Earlier we noted that anomalous trichromacy involves errors in the production of photopigments that are coded by genes on the X-chromosome. As a result, a male anomalous trichromat had to inherit the anomaly from his mother, who must have had an abnormal gene on one of her X-chromosomes. Suppose that her other X-chromosome was normal, meaning that it instructed the manufacture of normal M and L pigments. What can we say about the color vision of this female, who has one normal and one anomalous X-chromosome?

Early in any female's embryonic development, half of her X-chromosomes are inactivated permanently (Gardner and Sutherland, 1989). Which X-chromosome gets shut off in any cell seems to be random. But once an X-chromosome is inactivated, throughout the female's life that same X-chromosome remains inactive in every descendant cell. Inactivation serves an important developmental function. With twice as many X-chromosomes as males, females also have twice as many X-linked genes—and, potentially, instructions to produce twice as many X-linked proteins. Inactivation of half the X-chromosomes, then, maintains parity between the sexes.

Returning to the mother of the anomalous trichromat, random inactivation would, in different cells, turn off approximately half her normal X chromosomes and half her anomalous ones. Because different embryonic cells give rise to photoreceptors in disparate retinal regions, her retina would resemble a mosaic of different tiles, with normal regions interspersed among anomalous regions. Taking account of both normal and anomalous patches, her entire retina has four different photopigments: in one patch, normal S, M and L pigments, and in another patch, normal S, M (or L) pigments along with an anomalous pigment whose absorption peak is distinct from the others.

Mollon (1990) has speculated on the visual and evolutionary significance of four-pigment color vision in humans. In females with four photopigments, color vision might be as superior to the "normal" variety as the "normal" variety is to the color vision of a dichromat. Four-pigment color vision, described as *tetra*chromatic, might give certain females a real biological advantage, making it possible for them to recognize subtle color differences that so-called normals, male or female, could not. These tetrachromatic females might even be supernormal mothers because their extra-good color vision might enable them to spot subtle complexion changes when their children were becoming ill. But, Mollon conjectures, tetrachromatic vision's real evolutionary advantage would have come when our ancestors hunted for food. On such hunts, their superior color vision might have made valuable tribal leaders of these tetrachromatic females. It would have been they who guided the tribe toward sought-after ripening fruit on the trees of those prehistoric forests.*

Acquired Color Abnormalities

The color abnormalities just discussed are genetic in origin. But not all color vision problems are genetic; some fairly common ones are *acquired*. Since normal color perception depends on a whole series of neural events—starting in the retina and continuing back to the brain—disturbance in any part of the chain can alter

---

*Thompson, Palacios and Valera (1992) give an excellent treatment to several issues in color vision, including differences among color vision in various species and how evolution has shaped those differences.

color perception. You've already learned how brain damage can produce cortical color blindness, the condition termed achromatopsia. In this next section, we'll consider acquired color abnormalities in the eye.

Ocular Disorders   Some unfortunately common diseases, including glaucoma and diabetes, affect the integrity of S cones, thereby disturbing color vision (Adams et al., 1982). Diabetes often changes the structure of the eye in ways that can be seen using an ophthalmoscope: the retinal vasculature exhibits swellings and abnormal growth. Glaucoma is detected by measuring the pressure within the eye. By the time these conditions are discovered, permanent damage to the retina may have already occurred. For that reason, it is fortunate that abnormalities of color vision typically precede the appearance of notable structural changes in the eye. Color vision tests, if performed early enough in the progress of the disease, can be helpful in the diagnosis and treatment of glaucoma (Sample, Boynton and Weinreb, 1988) and diabetes (Zisman and Adams, 1982).

In both diseases, changes in color vision are retinal in origin. In other cases, however, acquired abnormalities of color vision can be caused by disturbances in the optic nerve rather than in the retina. For example, alcoholics frequently exhibit a reduced sensitivity to long wavelengths, causing reds to appear dark and desaturated. This change in color vision reflects a dietary deficiency. The typical alcoholic doesn't get sufficient vitamin B12 in his or her diet to ensure proper optic nerve function. Supplements of B12 restore normal color vision. Besides alcohol, certain toxins such as carbon disulfide (a substance used in the manufacture of insecticides and rubber) can disturb color vision. In each of these conditions, the onset of abnormal color vision can serve as an early warning of a threat to health.

Though the above forms of acquired color deficiency are relatively rare, there is another form that affects nearly everyone sooner or later. Once people reach about 50 years of age, the crystalline lens of the eye begins to accumulate a pigment that absorbs short-wavelength light more than it does the rest. This pigment might serve a useful function by screening out ultraviolet radiation that could damage the already fragile retinas of older people. However, because short wavelengths appear blue, the world's colors look different when seen through an older lens, which selectively reduces the short wavelength light that reaches the retina. Blues look darker and they tend to be confused with greens (Weale, 1982). The tendency of older people to confuse some blues and greens can have serious consequences. For example, an aging crystalline lens could cause someone to mistake one type of medicine tablet or capsule for another (Hurd and Blevins, 1984).

What Does the World Look Like to a "Color-Blind" Person?

D
Differences

We'll end this chapter with a question that naturally arises when one thinks about color vision: what do color-deficient people see? If you, like most people, enjoy trichromatic color vision, you'll wonder what colors are missing from the visual world of a dichromat. (Keep in mind that most mammals with color vision are dichromats.) And if you're one of those relatively rare human dichromats, don't you sometimes puzzle about what others are seeing that you don't?

These are tricky questions to answer. We can't rely on color vision tests for the answer, because these tests only tell us which particular colors cannot be distinguished one from another. Those tests tell us nothing about what the visible colors look like to a trichromat or a dichromat. Nor will we be able to know what colors look like by talking about our color experiences. An object that you and a friend both call "green" may appear quite different colorwise to the two of you. But since you've both learned to apply that color name to the object, you'll always agree what color to call it.

PLATE 1
See page 159. right hemisphere of the brain seen from two angles, with locations shown in color corresponding to key cerebral centers of the visual system.

PLATE 3
See page 264. Camouflaged hunter in tree

PLATE 2
See page 264. Color and b/w photos of girl with green patch on red sleeve

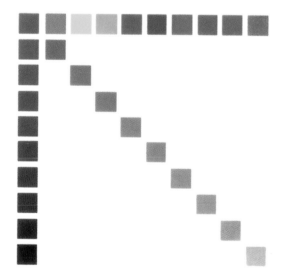

PLATE 4
See page 267. Hue, brightness and saturation

Common color names

| Violet | Indigo | Blue | Green | Yellow | Orange | Red |

425   500   550   600   650

Wavelength (nm)

PLATE 5
See page 274. Newton's seven color regions of the spectrum

PLATE 6
See page 276. Two views of a Close painting. ("Susan" Oil on Canvas 24 × 20" 1987 by Chuck Close. Courtesy Louis K. Meisel Gallery, New York. Photographer, Steve Lopez)

Adapt

Test

PLATE 7
See page 278. Two panel figure for inducing and seeing color adaptation

PLATE 8
See page 278. Amish quilt Irish Chain

PLATE 9
See page 279. Failure of color constancy

PLATE 10
See page 282. Mixture of colored light from three projectors

PLATE 11
See page 286. Roorda and Williams cone mosaic

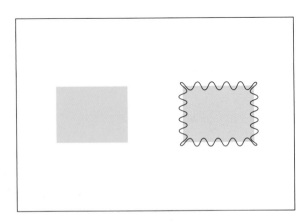

PLATE 12
See page 287. Boynton's yellow wiggle demo

PLATE 13
See page 290. - color contrast

PLATE 14
See page 297. -achromatopsia patient's drawing

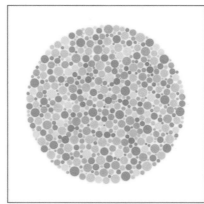

PLATE 15
See page 290. Ishihara color plates. The above has been reproduced from Ishihara's Test for Colour Blindness published by KANEHARA & Co., LTD., Tokyo, Japan, but tests for color blindness cannot be conducted with this material. For accurate testing, the original plate should be used.

PLATE 16
See page 299. Three colored squares that are indistinguishable in color to a r/g dichromat (current plate 12)

PLATE 17
See page 303. Dichromat simulation (reprinted from Nature)

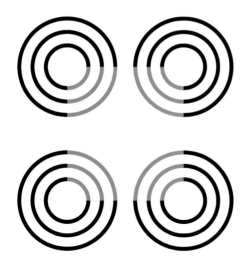

PLATE 18
See page 334.

We get some inkling of what it must be like to have deficient color vision by reading accounts by those color-deficient people who are unusually keen observers. The physician Robert Currier (1994), for example, has written a vivid account of his visual experiences as a red/green dichromat. From his words we can imagine how frustrating it would be to select clothes, match socks and try to read a colored text. An even more colorless world is experienced by individuals who are truly color blind, meaning they have only one type of cone photoreceptor. Nordby (1990) provides an autobiographical account of the everyday challenges created by this rare condition. But in the final analysis, these first-person accounts, too, boil down to descriptions of colors that are confused and those that are not. We can never know if Currier's *blue* is our *blue*.

A group of European investigators took a different approach to the question of color appearance (Vienot et al., 1995). Using digitized color images, they simulated what the world might look like to each of the three categories of dichromats. They began with a normal, digitized trichromatic picture, and divided the picture's color palette into two regions. The dividing line between these regions was the neutral point for the type of dichromacy being simulated. This neutral point varies, depending on whether it's the S, M or L-cone type that is missing. Next, the color of each pixel in the digitized original was replaced with one of two hues, with the substituted hue depending on whether the wavelength in the original picture is shorter than the neutral point or longer than the neutral point. For people lacking the L-type and M-type cone pigments, the two substitution colors corresponded to what we would call "blue" and "yellow" respectively. For people missing the S cone, the corresponding colors were "blue-green" and "pinkish red." Then, throughout the modified picture, the saturations of the two colors were adjusted according to which cone types were present in the simulated dichromat.

The results of this simulation applied to a photograph of a scene are shown in Color Plate 17. As you can see, the range of color experiences is compressed, and the colors of different objects in some parts of the scene are indiscriminable (for example, the flowers and leaves in the protanopes' view). As the team of individuals producing this picture acknowledges, the validity of this simulation rests on several assumptions. Still, the technique offers promise as a means for adjusting colors used on signs and video displays to insure that important visual information is seen by all people, normal and color deficient.

Postscript: In Color Plate 3 the camouflaged "animal" is an adult male outfitted in hunting attire whose color and patterns blend in with the branches and leaves. The hunter is standing erect, directly in front of the tree trunk.

SUMMARY AND PREVIEW

In this chapter we noted how ideas about color vision have developed over the past 300 years. We described the mechanisms of color vision, emphasizing that wavelength of light is first analyzed by three spectrally broad and widely overlapping cone photopigments and that the outcome of that analysis is then fed into chromatic and achromatic visual channels.

Unfortunately, science's success in explaining *how* people see color tends to obscure *why* they see color. Probably, the ability to perceive color developed to help creatures detect and discriminate objects in their environment. Because objects—artificial as well as natural—have characteristic pigments, they absorb and reflect light in characteristic ways. These patterns of spectral reflection make it advantageous to have color vision. An animal whose visual system retains information about the wavelength distribution of reflected light can more easily pick out objects from their backgrounds. Moreover, the colors of the surfaces of objects enable the animal to recognize what sort of objects it has encountered and what kinds of actions those objects call for.

In the next chapter we introduce the three-dimensional quality to vision, a quality that defines the presence, location and shapes of objects.

KEY TERMS

achromatic system
additive color mixture
brightness
chromatic system
color constancy
color contrast
color deficiency
complementary
composite light
detection
dichromatic
discrimination
habituation
hue
identification
isoluminant

M-L channel
M-L cells
microspectrophotometry
monochromat
neutral point
Newton's color circle
nonspectral colors
pure light
S−(M+L) channel
S−(M+L) cells
saturation
spectral colors
subtractive color mixture
trichromatic
univariance principle
Young-Helmholtz theory

CHAPTER 8

SEEING A THREE-DIMENSIONAL WORLD

The simple engraving in Figure 8.1 is one of the crowning artistic achievements of the ages. Albrecht Dürer (1471–1528) made this woodcut in 1525. This engraving is special because in it the artist succeeded in using perspective to portray a three-dimensional (3D) scene on a flat, two dimensional surface. Dürer's objects look solid, and their depth relations are unambiguous. When the scene is viewed from the appropriate vantage point, it looks real.

For centuries, the technique devised by Dürer and his contemporaries eluded every person who tried to portray a 3D scene. You may have seen pre-Renaissance paintings or drawings in which the sizes of the characters look wrong and the sense of depth is almost comical (see Figure 8.2). It wasn't until the discovery of linear perspective by Italian artists, during the 15th century, that this challenge—mapping a 3D scene onto a two-dimensional surface—was conquered. Although he did not make the discovery, Leonardo da Vinci

(1452–1519) described the technique with great clarity (see Figure 8.3):

> *Have a piece of glass as large as a half sheet of royal folio paper and set this firmly in front of your eyes, that is between your eye and the thing you want to draw; then place yourself at a distance of two thirds of an ell [a unit of measure equivalent to about 45"] from the glass, fixing your head with a mechanism in such a way that you cannot move it at all. Then shut or cover one eye and with a brush or drawing chalk draw upon the glass that which you see beyond it; then trace it on paper from the glass. (Argentieri, no date given, p. 436).*

Our visual systems constantly face the same challenge that confronts artists who struggle to imbue their work with depth and solidity. In fact, during the first few months of life, every human infant manages to master what artists took centuries to understand: how to create 3D impressions of the visual world from two-dimensional representations.

FIGURE 8.1
Woodcut by Albrecht Dürer illustrating perspective.
©Bettmann/CORBIS

FIGURE 8.2
Pre-Renaissance painters had trouble with perspective.
© San Francesco, Assisi/ET Archive, London/SuperStock

FIGURE 8.3
A method for generating a perspective drawing.

As you know, the optical image that triggers vision is formed on the back of the eye, the retina's two-dimensional "canvas." The locations of features within this retinal image can be specified in up/down and left/right two-dimensional Cartesian coordinates or, if you prefer, in two-dimensional polar coordinates specifying angles and magnitudes. But there's nothing in either of these coordinate systems to designate whether one object is nearer or farther than another. From the two-dimensional retinal image, the brain has to recover depth relations among objects. For that matter, each object's 3D shape also gets flattened into two dimensions, forcing the brain to come up with an educated guess about the solid object's true shape. The word *guess* is used in recognition of the fact that numerous possible 3D objects can produce a given two-dimensional shape on the retina. Stated in technical terms, vision must compute the shapes of objects using nonmetric* optical information contained in the two-dimensional retinal image. This chapter describes the information that the brain uses as it attempts to reconstruct the layout of solid objects in our 3D visual environment.

Being able to see 3D objects in depth provides obvious advantages: to interact with those objects (including other people) we need to know where they're located in 3D space and what their actual shapes are. Every time you drive a car, you're judging, again and again, the distances from you to other vehicles. These judgments must be made rapidly and automatically; you cannot take the time to calculate the locations and distances consciously. The same type of judgment is required numerous times a day—such as when you cross a street in traffic or when you reach for a cup on your desk. To react quickly and accurately requires you to know *where* the object is located in three-dimensional space. Your visual systems must register how far away the object is, an ability usually referred to as **depth perception,** and the direction in which it is located relative to yourself, which is called **egocentric direction.** Some creatures, such as bats, can use their ears to pick up information about direction and distance (Griffin, 1959), but for humans, the most reliable sources are visual ones.

EGOCENTRIC DIRECTION

When specifying an object's location in the environment, you can adopt one of two frames of

---

*Nonmetric implies that something has no measure, or units.

reference. One frame of reference specifies object location independent of the vantage point from which an object is viewed. This frame of reference is often called "**allocentric**" (Howard, 1982). You may say, for example, that the oak tree in your front yard is located 12 meters due north from the front door of your house. Expressed this way, the tree's location will be unambiguous regardless where in the front yard you're standing (or, for that matter, whether you're even standing in the yard at all). Or consider the layout of objects in your workspace. Expressed in allocentric coordinates, your computer video monitor may be located in the center of your desk, with the keyboard located 10 cm in front of the screen. Again, these allocentric spatial relations remain invariant regardless where you're sitting.

We can even specify parts of an object in relation to the whole, a so-called object-based frame of reference (which we talked about in Chapter 6). An object-based perspective is another example of an allocentric frame of reference because the coordinates are independent of the viewer's location. An allocentric frame of reference is obviously important when you want to instruct another person where to find things without that person's having to assume your particular viewing perspective. So, no matter where a viewer is standing or in which direction the viewer faces, it is true that the town center of Concord, Massachusetts, lies almost directly south of the Old North Bridge. Or, to take an interplanetary example, suppose you wanted to turn Sojourner's thousands of separate Martian images into a coherent description of the Martian landscape's layout. Such a description is best put in an allocentric frame of reference, independent of a viewer's perspective. So, we might describe the Twin Peaks, a pair of distinctive Martian mountains, as lying north of the boulder known as Yogi. Again, this is true no matter where Sojourner sits or in what direction it faces.

But for your own, immediate interactions with objects in the environment, a "viewer-centered" frame of reference is more convenient and more

meaningful. Here, we specify the location of an object in the environment relative to the viewer's current position. This is what we mean by the term *egocentric direction:* where things are located relative to your current viewing position. Thus, in a viewer-centered frame of reference, the video monitor is directly in front of you when you're working at the computer, but it's behind you when you turn completely around to talk with a friend.

With some effort, we can imagine viewing a scene from positions other than the one we currently occupy. And when tested, people are actually reasonably good at shifting their perspective using their imagination (Farrell and Robertson, 1998). But usually we're interested in where objects are located relative to where we are. Vision seems especially well designed to specify object locations in a viewer-centered framework (Tarr, 1995).

Egocentric direction can be specified in a two-dimensional coordinate system, where the two dimensions refer to up/down and left/right. Because this coordinate system is referenced to a person, the center of the coordinate system corresponds to the line of sight. Thus, when you stare at an object, that object's location defines "straight ahead" (see Figure 8.4), and the locations of other objects in the visual scene can be specified in reference to this fixated object.

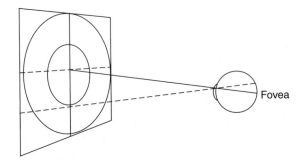

FIGURE 8.4
Egocentric direction can be specified in a two-dimensional coordinate system, with the observer's center of gaze defining the center of the system.

This two-dimensional layout of objects in the world is maintained in the images formed on the back of the eye. (Images of objects maintain their locations relative to one another.) Although the retinal image is inverted, with objects in the upper part of the visual field imaged on the lower part of the retina, and vice versa, the inverted image maintains all the two-dimensional positional information present in the real world. In other words, all the up/down and left/right information in the two-dimensional egocentric coordinate system is preserved in the "inverted" two-dimensional retinal image.

Neural

Now, you may recall from Chapter 4 that the mapping of the retina onto the cortex is topographic, meaning that neighboring regions on the retina are represented in neighboring regions of the cortex. As a result, the two-dimensional relations among objects in the world are maintained in the neural representations of objects in visual cortex. Thus, neural activity among cortical neurons devoted to the fovea specify the direction "straight ahead" and other egocentric directions by simply registering the activity among neurons whose receptive fields are displaced in the topographic cortical map relative to the foveal representation. Of course, objects situated to the left of the center of gaze create neural activity in the right hemisphere, and vice versa (recall Figures 4.2 and 4.3).

D
Differences

Just how accurate are we at pinpointing the locations of objects? Remarkably accurate, judging from the skills of experienced marksmen who can hit the center of a bullseye more than 90% of the time from considerable distances. On simple pointing tasks, even unpracticed human observers can accurately point in the direction of a single point of light in an otherwise dark room (Matin, 1986). Errors do creep in when a person who is looking straight ahead tries to point to some object in the periphery of vision. In this case, people consistently point too far into the periphery, overestimating how far off the line of sight the nonfixated object is located (Bock, 1993). Under ordinary conditions, we avoid this

potential source of error by looking directly at objects whose locations we are trying to judge.

When it comes to specifying the locations of objects relative to one another, we are unbelievably accurate under optimal conditions. Look at the five pairs of vertical lines in Figure 8.5. For each pair, can you judge the position—left versus right—of the upper line relative to the lower one? On tasks like this, people use **vernier acuity** to judge whether one line is offset relative to the other. People are able to make accurate judgments even when the lateral offset between lines is only about 5 seconds of arc. This amazingly small value is approximately equivalent to the width of a human hair viewed at arm's length. What makes this tiny value all the more remarkable is that it's about 6 times smaller than the diameter of a single cone photoreceptor in your eye. You're able, in other words, to resolve a lateral offset between two objects that is tinier than the spacing between adjacent cone photoreceptors in your eye. Human performance of this caliber is dubbed "hyperacuity" since it exceeds the spacing of receptors in the eye (*hyper* is from the Greek term meaning "above" or "beyond"; acuity is from the Latin word *acus* meaning "needle," something "sharp" or "pointed"). At present it's not known just how human vision achieves this level of spatial resolution, although an array

FIGURE 8.5
For each pair of lines, judge whether the top one is located to the left or right of the bottom one. You are using vernier acuity to perform this judgment.

of neighboring cones, in principle, does generate a spatial pattern of signals sufficient to specify vernier offsets at the limits of human acuity (Wandell, 1995). As Chapter 6 pointed out, vernier acuity improves with practice.

Attention to Location

Besides pinpointing objects' locations in visual space, we also have the knack to direct attention to locations in space, in anticipation of the appearance of an object. Visual location, in other words, provides a spatial framework for aiming attention, much like one would aim a spotlight to a given region on a theater stage. Normally when we shift our attention to a given location in space, we simultaneously shift our eye position to fixate on that location, aiming our fovea on it. But it's possible to shift our attention without redirecting our eyes. Try this. Hold your left hand at arm's length out to the left side of your head, where it can barely be seen in your peripheral field of view. Open your palm with all five fingers held upright. Now, carefully maintain fixation on the word printed in **bold** type and, at the same time mentally scrutinize your fingers. You've successfully dissociated fixation from attention.

Execute

Exploiting this ability to uncouple fixation and attention, Michael Posner (Posner, 1980; Posner, Snyder and Davidson, 1980) developed a simple but effective task for gauging the consequence of attending to a given spatial location. While keeping their eyes fixed on a central plus sign, observers watched for a spot of light that could appear either to the left or to the right of the fixation mark. Their task was to hit a button as soon as the "target" appeared. Observers responded quickly when they were cued ahead of time in which location the target would appear, compared to a condition where no cue was given. The cue enabled them to shift their attention to that location, without shifting their eyes. About twenty percent of the time, Posner purposefully cued the wrong position, meaning that the target appeared in the noncued location. On these trials,

observers were unusually slow in reacting to the presentation of the target, presumably because their attention was directed elsewhere.

Comparable experiments with monkeys showed the same fast response times when cues were valid and slower ones when cues were invalid. Researchers also found that visually activated neurons in the monkey's parietal lobe gave enhanced responses to a nonfixated stimulus when the monkey was attending to the location where the stimulus was presented (Bushnell, Goldberg and Robinson, 1981). Along with more recent findings by Robinson, Bowman and Kertzman (1995), this implicates the parietal lobe as the brain region in control of spatially selective visual attention. You may recall from Chapter 4 that the parietal lobe is a major component in the dorsal stream (or parietal pathway), responsible for specifying where objects are located in space and, hence, where our actions should be directed.

Turning the World Upside Down

Before we turn to depth perception, let's spend a few moments on one aspect of egocentric direction that has long intrigued researchers: upside down vision. As mentioned earlier, the optics of the eye invert the retinal image of the world. This inversion isn't a problem, though, because all spatial relations among objects are maintained. What we call "up" and "down" are completely relative, and we've lived with the same up/down coordinates throughout our lives. But specially constructed goggles can instantly change all that by turning the image of the world upside down (see Figure 8.6). The result of this sudden inversion of the image of the world is a series of changes in your vision and motor coordination.

In the past one hundred years, beginning with George Stratton (1897), various researchers turned the visual world upside down. In the most recent and thorough study, a group of German investigators had four volunteers wear inverting goggles for 8 to 10 consecutive days, with the goggles in place every waking moment (Linden

Execute

Plasticity

FIGURE 8.6
Inverting goggles turn the retinal images of the world upside down.

et al., 1999). While carefully monitored for their safety, the volunteers went about their normal, everyday activities, with as little assistance as necessary. Each volunteer took a battery of tests to assess motor skills and perceptual abilities. In only a few days, all volunteers could walk without assistance, even in crowded environments. And before the experiment ended each could ride a bicycle. The volunteers also learned to read and write, but they took an unusually long amount of time to assemble 3D objects from building blocks. Despite these signs of adaptation to image inversion, none of the four reported any recovered sense of upright vision. Throughout the entire experiment they always felt that either they or the world was upside down.

Researchers used neuroimaging to monitor the volunteers' brain activity, using wedge-shaped stimuli that isolated activity in either the upper or lower part of the visual field. Comparing brain activity before and after adaptation to image inversion showed no evidence that the retinotopic map had been affected by the adaptation. In other words, goggle-induced inversion of the retinal image produced no compensatory inversion of the map of the retina onto the visual cortex. Evidently, the successful adaptation of visuomotor function was mediated mainly by motor areas of the brain, not those mediating perception. Incidentally, once the goggles were removed all four participants rapidly readapted to normal visual input.

So it appears that *up* and *down* are irrevocably etched in our brains through years of visual experience. We don't know—and hopefully will never find out—what would happen if very young infants were reared with inverting goggles. It is known, though, that developing kittens reared with rotated images never adapt to this distortion, behaviorally or neurologically (Singer, Tretter and Yinon, 1979).

Plasticity

DEPTH PERCEPTION: THE THIRD DIMENSION

It is remarkable that human beings can make distance judgments at all, let alone accurate ones. As mentioned at the beginning of this chapter, the retinal images from which depth information is extracted are two-dimensional; they are inherently depthless. To dramatize this idea, imagine that we could take a snapshot of the image falling on the back of your eye. Like an individual frame in a motion picture, this photograph would consist of a complex distribution of contour and color. But all this information would be constrained to lie within the two-dimensional boundaries of the retinal image—depth is absent.

Fortunately for us, this photographic analogy is misleading. Unlike a photograph, the retinal image is continuously changing, because of our own movements and because of the movements of objects in the environment. These changes provide a rich source of depth information missing in a static snapshot. The photographic analogy also ignores the fact that the brain acquires depth information from *two* sources, the left *and* right eye. This binocular vision affords another useful source of depth information.

Sources of information about depth are sometimes referred to as *cues* to depth. Following this convention, we will also refer to *cues* to depth, but don't misunderstand what we mean by this term. It does not mean that depth perception results from conscious deliberation on your part. To see objects in depth, you don't respond to cues like an actor taking cues from a director. On the contrary, depth perception occurs effortlessly and without thought, despite being derived entirely from a two-dimensional image on the retina.

Accurate judgments of distance arise from the coordination of several different sources of information. In the normal environment, these various sources of depth information usually operate in harmony, yielding an unambiguous impression of three-dimensional space. But in the laboratory, it is possible to assess how potent various cues are by devising situations that put the cues into conflict with one another. In some instances, conflicting cues yield interesting visual illusions that provide insight into depth perception's normal operation.

Before surveying cues to depth, we need to clarify precisely what is meant by *depth perception* because this term can be used in two quite different ways. In one case, the term refers to the distance from an observer to an object. This is sometimes called **absolute distance.** To give an example from the sport of baseball, an outfielder attempting to throw out a base runner must judge the distance between himself and the base where the runner is headed. Shooting a basketball also entails judgments of absolute distance. Alternatively, the term *depth perception* may refer to the distance between one object and another or between different parts of a single object. This is known as **relative distance.** When trying to figure out which of two birds perched on a branch is closer to you, you're making a judgment involving relative distance. It's important to distinguish between these two types of depth perception because each is specified by different sources of optical information. Also, although the ability to judge absolute distance is useful behaviorally

(Rieser et al., 1990), that ability is much less precise than the ability to make judgments about relative depth (Graham, 1965).

James Cutting (1997) distinguishes among sources of depth information on the basis of the distance over which sources are most effective. He divides 3D space into three egocentric regions:

- Personal Space: the area within arm's reach (approximately 1.5 meters); contained within this immediate space would be the objects to be manipulated by a person, primarily using the hands.
- Action Space: the region beyond arm's length but within about 30 meters of your body; it is within this space that you're able to move about quickly, to make social contact with other people and throw something at a threatening enemy or to a sports teammate.
- Vista Space: the region within eyesight beyond action space; objects and events falling within vista space are useful for planning navigation, including approach or escape.

These regions and the activities they support, incidentally, are defined in terms of a person on foot; when traveling at high speeds, as in a car, action space extends far beyond 30 meters. Cutting has identified which depth cues work most effectively within these different regions of space. In covering these depth cues, we won't explicitly partition them among Cutting's three categories, but we will describe the conditions under which those cues are effective.

We are now ready to explore the various cues to depth that the visual system uses. We have divided these into two broad categories, **oculomotor cues** and **visual cues.** The oculomotor cues are actually *kinesthetic* in nature, meaning that the cue itself derives from the act of muscular contraction of either the muscle fibers controlling the focus of the lens or the fibers controlling the positions of the eyes in the head. The visual cues, so called because they are genuinely visual in nature, are subdivided into those that are available only when two eyes are used (*binocular cues*)

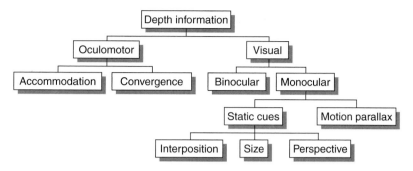

FIGURE 8.7
Major sources of depth information.

and those that are available when just one eye is used (*monocular cues*). Figure 8.7 summarizes the ways in which these types of cues to depth are related. As you will see, oculomotor cues are the only ones that provide unambiguous information about absolute distance, meaning that an oculomotor cue does not require supplementation by other cues. In contrast, any of the visual cues can provide good relative depth information, but in order to specify absolute distance they must be supplemented with other information.

OCULOMOTOR CUES TO DEPTH

Whenever you are looking at an object, your eyes are focused and converged by an amount that depends on the distance between you and the object. To be seen clearly, close objects require more accommodation and convergence than do objects farther away from you. Now suppose we were able to attach tiny gauges to the two sets of muscles involved in these two reflexes, strain gauges that could tell us how much the muscles were contracted (see panel A of Figure 8.8). By monitoring the degree of muscular contraction, we could compute either of two values: your angle of **convergence** or the amount of **accommodation** of the lenses of your eyes. Because these two values are related to the distance from your eyes to the object you are viewing, we

would then have a useful index of absolute distance. In other words, by monitoring your eye muscles, we could compute the distance from you to the object of regard. But before this same information could serve as a cue to depth for you, your visual nervous system would have to be able to sense the contractions of your eye muscles.

It is simple to show that convergence is accompanied by a sense of muscle strain. Starting with your index finger held up at arm's length, steadily move it toward your nose while keeping both eyes focused on your finger. As your finger moves closer to your nose, you can feel the increased strain as your eyes turn inward to maintain fixation. At the same time, your accommodation is increasing, too. The lens attempts to keep the image of your finger in sharp focus on your retina. In fact, these two motor responses—accommodation and convergence—usually operate in a yoked fashion, such that changes in one are accompanied by changes in the other.

There is potentially another source of information about the degree of accommodation and convergence. We could insert some measuring instrument along the neural pathway leading to the eye muscles (see panel B of Figure 8.8). Now we would be recording the strength of the command signals being *sent* to those muscles. In effect, we would be monitoring the instructions used to

Execute

A

Accommodation
strain gauge

B

FIGURE 8.8
Two possible schemes for registering oculomotor information.

steer accommodation and convergence. The signals flowing out to your muscles could furnish information about distance.

So far we have described how oculomotor cues *could* furnish information about distance. But can people judge distance under conditions where accommodation and convergence provide the only cues to depth? The answer is yes, but not very accurately and only within a limited range (Leibowitz and Moore, 1966; Wallach and Floor, 1971). When they are the only sources of distance information, do *both* cues—accommodation and convergence—contribute equally? To answer this question, let's consider the two cues individually, starting with accommodation.

In accommodation, you have a cue whose potentially effective range is necessarily limited. Whenever you focus on an object more than a few meters from you, the muscle controlling accommodation assumes its most relaxed state. So as a potential depth cue, accommodation would be useful only within the region of space immediately in front of you. Even within this small range, distance judgments based solely on accommodation are inaccurate (Heinemann, Tulving and Nachmias, 1959; Künnapas, 1968). So

we can dismiss accommodation as an effective source of depth information.

Turning to convergence, we find that it, too, operates over a limited range of distance, albeit more extended than accommodation. The convergence angle formed by your two eyes vanishes to zero when you are looking at objects from a distance of about 20 feet and beyond (assuming your eyes are looking straight ahead). For distances less than 20 feet (about 6 meters), however, observers can use convergence angle as a reliable depth cue, in the absence of other distance information (Grant, 1942).

On their own, then, the oculomotor cues play only a restricted role in depth perception. In fact, people rely much more heavily on visual cues to depth. It is to those cues that we now turn, beginning with the cue provided by looking at the world through two separate eyes.

BINOCULAR VISUAL DEPTH INFORMATION: STEREOPSIS

Chapter 2 pointed out that in humans, the two eyes look at much the same region of visual space. Only near the margins of the visual field is each eye's coverage exclusively monocular. The overlapping binocular field of view reflects the fact that both eyes are located in the front of the head. Within this region of binocular overlap, the eyes' lateral separation means that each eye views objects from a slightly different vantage point. As you're about to see, this binocular arrangement has important perceptual consequences.

To begin, why did nature position human eyes so as to provide two views of the world, particularly when each view largely duplicates the other? The answer is that this duplication has real advantages. By virtue of the slight differences, or *disparities,* between the views seen by the left and right eyes respectively, humans are able to discriminate extremely small differences in relative depth, differences that are very difficult to discriminate using either eye alone. You can demonstrate this for yourself by performing the following simple experiment.

Execute

Take two sharp pencils, one in each hand, and hold them at arm's length. Their tips should be separated by 10 centimeters or so and pointed toward one another. Now slowly bring the two pencils together in such a way that the two points are touching. First, try this several times with one eye closed, each time noting by how much, if any, the two miss each other. Next, repeat the exercise with both eyes open. You will probably find your accuracy much improved with binocular viewing. However, not *all* individuals benefit from using both eyes. Some 5 to 10 percent of the general population do no better with two eyes than they do with one. Why? The answer is given later in this chapter.

The perception of relative depth from binocular vision is called **stereopsis.** This word is derived from two Greek words: *stereos* meaning "solid," and *opsis* meaning "seeing." Stereopsis allows you to judge relative depth with great accuracy, and it also enables you to see objects that are invisible to either eye alone. These aspects of stereopsis are described in Box 8.1. We are now prepared to consider two aspects of stereopsis: the nature of the stimulus information specifying

stereopsis and the nature of the brain processes responsible for registering that information. Let's consider each problem separately.

Retinal Disparity

The two eyes look at objects in the world from slightly different angles. As a result, objects, particularly ones relatively close to you, do not appear exactly the same to your left eye and to your right eye. Ordinarily, however, you are unaware of differences between the left eye's view and the right eye's view. This is because the brain combines information from the two eyes in a way that obscures these differences. Only by looking at something alternately with one eye and then the other can you actually notice the differences between the two eyes' views. Take a moment to perform this simple exercise. Choose some object in front of you and look at it steadily using one eye and then the other. You should be able to see more of the left side of the object with your left eye, and more of the right side with your right eye.

While looking alternately through your two eyes, also pay special attention to the position of the object you are looking at. Compare it to the position of another, neighboring object that is located a little closer to you than the one you are looking at. To make this comparison, you may want to arrange some objects on a table. Alternatively, you can simply hold up your two index fingers in front of you at different distances from your nose. Either way, you will now see that the lateral separation between the two objects appears to change when you switch eyes.

Figure 8.9 illustrates this observation. These two photographs mimic the views seen by two eyes looking at a real scene from slightly different vantage points. These photographs were taken in succession, shifting the camera sideways by 65 millimeters (the typical distance between an adult human's two eyes) before taking the second photograph. Note that the separation between the two bottles is larger in the left-hand

BOX 8.1

COOPERATION BETWEEN THE TWO EYES

Of all visual abilities, none excels the keenness of stereopsis. Using binocular disparity information, humans can make exceedingly fine depth judgments that are utterly impossible when using just one eye. To illustrate, imagine that you are viewing a pair of pencils oriented vertically and placed side by side 1 meter away from you. At that distance, stereopsis would make it possible for you to tell whether one pencil was as little as 1 millimeter closer to you than its neighbor. From a distance of 1 meter, a 1-millimeter difference corresponds to a judgment accuracy of one-tenth of 1 percent. In this case, the resulting disparity between the two eyes' views is less than four ten-thousandths of a millimeter. This distance is many times smaller than the diameter of a single visual receptor in your eye!

Because of this extraordinary resolving power, stereopsis provides a very effective means for uncovering slight differences between a pair of pictures presented separately to the two eyes. For instance, imagine viewing a pair of one-dollar bills in a stereoscope (the familiar device used for presenting two pictures, one to each eye). If the two bills are identical down to the smallest detail, you will see a single, absolutely flat bill; there will exist no disparity to differentiate the two. But if the two bills differ, even slightly, the single, combined bill will no longer appear flat—portions of the bill will stand out in relief, due to retinal disparity produced by the slight differences. This stereoscopic technique has been used for identifying counterfeit currency, as well as tiny flaws in the electronic circuits in computers. Radiologists are also being encouraged to use stereoscopic images of biological tissue to enhance the conspicuity of breast tumors, which can be difficult to spot (May, 1994).

Stereopsis also provides an effective means for detecting camouflaged objects. Two views of a visual scene taken from different vantage points can reveal the presence of forms that are invisible from either vantage point alone. As an example, aerial photography of a landscape from two positions can disclose the presence and location of objects (such as military hardware) on the ground. Stereopsis also makes it possible for a predatory animal to spot its next meal even when the color and texture of the meal blends into the environment.

A most dramatic example of stereopsis' sleuth-like powers is provided by random-dot stereograms, an example of which is shown in Figure 8.13. Each eye's view consists of a random array of dots, with no hint of an object hidden therein. Yet, when the brain combines the two views, a figure in depth emerges. The technique used to create this kind of stereogram is simple (it is described in the text).

In contrast, the technique used by your brain to extract depth from such a stereogram must be quite complex. For this reason, you may be surprised to learn that infants as young as 4 months of age can see the depth in random-dot stereograms (Fox et al., 1980). Moreover, this form of stereopsis is not unique to humans. Monkeys (Bough, 1970), cats (Lehmkuhle and Fox, 1977) and falcons (Fox, Lehmkuhle and Bush, 1977) show evidence of being able to discriminate the depth portrayed in random-dot stereograms.

Incidentally, those popular "magic eye" posters seen in shopping malls, books and newspapers are based on the same geometric principles as the random-dot stereograms: a hidden "figure" is defined by clusters of small picture elements that have been shifted laterally in one portion of the poster. By crossing or by diverging your eyes, you allow your brain to discover those shifted dots and, hence, the figure they define (Thimbleby and Neesham, 1993).

picture than it is in the right-hand picture. This comes about because the two bottles were located at different distances from the camera at the time these pictures were taken. The difference in lateral separation between objects as seen by the left eye and by the right eye is called **retinal disparity;** it provides the information for stereoscopic depth perception.

The magnitude of the disparity, expressed in terms of lateral separation on the retina, depends

FIGURE 8.9
The lateral separation between two objects as it might appear to the left eye and to the right eye. (McGraw-Hill photo.)

on the distance between objects. If one object is much closer to the observer than the other, the resulting retinal disparity will be large. If one object is only slightly closer to the observer than the other, the disparity will be small. Figure 8.10 illustrates this geometrical principle.

This cue to depth, retinal disparity, arises whenever objects are located in front of *or* behind the object you are looking at. Of course, you can tell visually whether an object is nearer or farther than your point of fixation, which means that your visual nervous system distinguishes between the disparities produced by these two possibilities—objects nearer versus objects farther away. If an object lies farther from you than the object you're fixating on, the disparity between the two is said to be *uncrossed.* If an object is located closer to you than the one you are looking at, the disparity is said to be *crossed.* To remember this distinction easily, just keep in mind that with crossed disparity you would need to converge, or *cross,* your eyes in order to look di-

rectly at the nearer object. By the same token, you would diverge, or *uncross,* your eyes to shift your fixation to a more distant object.

So the type of disparity, crossed versus uncrossed, specifies whether objects are in front of or behind the point of fixation, while the magnitude of the disparity specifies the amount by which objects are separated in depth. It is important to remember that retinal disparity specifies the *relative* depth between two or more objects; it does not provide information about absolute depth. When you fixate on a single small spot of light in an otherwise empty field of view (such as the glow of a cigarette in a dark room), there is no disparity information to be used. Only the convergence angle of your eyes (an oculomotor cue) provides binocular information.

Objects in the visual field can also be situated so that they give rise to zero disparity—a disparity that is neither crossed nor uncrossed. In other words, the lateral separation between the objects seen through the left eye will be identical to the

FIGURE 8.10
Retinal disparity increases with the distance, in depth, between two objects.

separation between those objects seen through the right eye. As you should be able to deduce, zero disparity occurs when two or more objects are located at the same distance from the observer. Figure 8.11 illustrates this situation. In this case, the two bottles were located at the *same* distance from the observer. Images from such equidistant objects are said to fall on corresponding areas of the two eyes.*

The foveas of the two eyes represent one set of corresponding retinal areas. Whenever you look directly at an object, an image of that object will be formed on the fovea of your left eye and on the fovea of your right eye. In this case, we say that the images fall on corresponding retinal areas. In addition, there are numerous other sets of corresponding areas spread over the two retinas. By definition, these areas have zero disparity with respect to the two foveas. Therefore, objects casting images on these other, nondisparate retinal areas will be seen at the same depth as the object seen by the two foveas.

To clarify this point, try the following exercise. Take two pencils, one in each hand, and place one directly in front of you. While fixating on that pencil, position the other one so that it is several centimeters (about an inch) to one side but located *at the same perceived distance* from you as the pencil you are looking at. To accomplish this, you may want to move the nonfixated pencil back and forth *in depth* until it appears at exactly the right distance. By so doing, you are varying retinal disparity between uncrossed and crossed until you settle on what amounts to zero disparity. If you are very careful, the second pencil will be placed so that it too casts left and right eye images on corresponding retinal areas.

If you repeated this exercise, repositioning the nonfixated pencil farther to one side of the point of fixation, you could generate another point at which the nonfixated pencil appeared to lie the same distance from you as the fixated pencil. In so doing, you would have established another zero-disparity location. If you repeated this exer-

Execute

---

*There are actually several alternative ways to specify retinal correspondence (Howard and Rogers, 1995, Chapter 2), but for our purposes, the definition based on depth is the most appropriate.

Bottle 2 Bottle 1

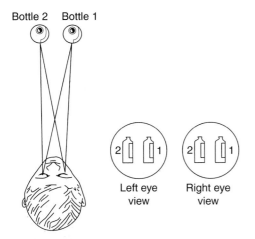

FIGURE 8.11
Zero disparity occurs when two objects are located at equal distances from the observer.

cise a number of times, all the resulting zero-disparity locations could be connected to form an imaginary plane called the **horopter** (see Figure 8.12). So long as you maintain fixation on some point in this plane, all objects located anywhere in the plane produce images on corresponding, or nondisparate, retinal areas. Objects closer to you than this plane yield crossed disparities, whereas objects farther from you than this plane yield uncrossed disparities.

This, then, is how retinal correspondence and retinal disparity are related to binocular depth perception. Considering that the geometry of this situation is relatively straightforward, it is surprising that it took so long before anyone fully appreciated that disparity supplied information about depth. From his writings, it is clear that Leonardo da Vinci realized that the two eyes see

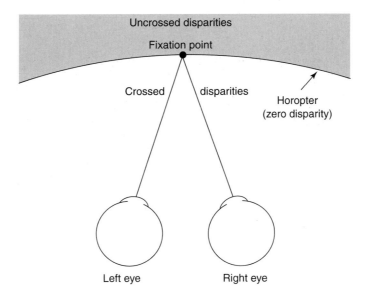

FIGURE 8.12
The horopter—an imaginary plane marking the positions of all objects located at the same perceived distance from the observer. Objects more distant than the point of fixation are said to produce uncrossed disparities (shaded area), whereas objects nearer than the point of fixation are said to produce crossed disparities (unshaded area). (The degree of curvature of the horopter plane varies somewhat with absolute viewing distance, for technical reasons we need not go into.)

slightly different portions of a solid, three-dimensional object, but he offered no descriptions of the detailed geometry of crossed and uncrossed disparity and no demonstrations of stereopsis. It remained for a British physicist, Charles Wheatstone (1838/1964), to provide the first proof that a vivid impression of stereoscopic depth could be created from two flat pictures (Wade, 1988).

Wheatstone's demonstration took the following form. On two cards, Wheatstone sketched a pair of outline drawings of a three-dimensional object. One drawing depicted the view of the object as seen by the left eye and the other drawing depicted the view of the object as seen by the right eye. He then looked at this pair of two-dimensional drawings using a **stereoscope,** a device Wheatstone invented to present the two drawings (which together constitute a *stereogram*) separately to the two eyes. He observed that the two drawings of the object perceptually merged, or fused, into one drawing. In addition, the fused drawing conveyed an amazing sense of relief, or three-dimensionality. Thus, by incorporating retinal disparity into his drawings, Wheatstone was able to recreate the three-dimensional appearance of an object—an effect that is lost in a single, two-dimensional picture. Wheatstone's novel observations demonstrated the potency of retinal disparity in producing depth perception.

Execute

At several places in this chapter you'll have opportunities to experience depth perception from stereo images like the ones invented by Wheatstone. But to enjoy these pictures, you need to learn how to "free fuse" a pair of stereo images. (The technique is called "free fusion" because you're able to bring two pictures into binocular alignment without having to use an optical device.) Box 8.2 teaches you how to manipulate your eye alignment to bring stereo pictures into binocular registration. Take a time-out right here and master the art of free fusion. But be patient. The brain has to learn to see depth in the more complicated random-dot stereograms, particularly those portraying complicated surfaces with hills, valleys and assorted curlicues (Julesz, 1971).

Upon first viewing a stereogram, it may take you several minutes of concentrated viewing to see depth. During this time, the previously hidden surfaces appear to grow, slowly rising out of the page. Moreover, it is impossible to speed up this process by telling or showing a person what to look for (Frisby and Clatworthy, 1975). However, just as with riding a bicycle, once you learn to see depth in one of these stereograms, you never completely forget how. Acquiring the ability to perceive depth in stereograms is another form of perceptual learning, like those discussed in Chapter 6.

So far, we have focused on stereopsis from a geometrical perspective. You have learned that objects nearer or farther than the plane of fixation project their retinal images on disparate regions of the two eyes. You have also learned that by mimicking these disparities in a stereogram (a pair of pictures), it is possible to create realistic stereoscopic depth artificially. Having defined the cues from which stereopsis *might* arise, let's consider what the visual system must be doing in order to exploit this depth cue of retinal disparity.

Matching the Left and Right Eyes' Views

Imagine for a moment that you were a machine, facing the same predicament that your brain normally encounters. Handed two slightly different two-dimensional pictures (left and right eye's retinal images) of various objects, you must recreate the way in which those objects are actually laid out in depth. To do this, you must use only the information contained in the two pictures. How would you proceed? Since there is a connection between objects' relative distances from one another and their disparate positions in the two pictures, you might first compute these disparities. This computation requires that you compare the two pictures, noting in each where particular objects are located. Before you could perform that computation, you would have to figure out which portion of one picture matched which portion of the other. Only then would it be

BOX 8.2

A LESSON IN FREE FUSION

According to a familiar saying, "Nothing in life is free." Well, you're about to acquire something that costs no more than a few minutes' practice: the ability to "free fuse" stereogram images and, consequently, experience 3D vision from two-dimensional images. (The ability is called *free* fusion because you're able to binocularly fuse two images free of any kind of optical device like a stereoscope.) We've already detailed the geometry of binocular disparity and described how a compelling sense of depth can be experienced when the two eyes view pictures of a visual scene taken from slightly different perspectives (such pictures are called stereograms). You're now going to learn how to deliver those two pictures separately to your two eyes. This ability, incidentally, is the same one needed to see depth in those popular "Magic Eye" posters.

Let's start with an easy pair of pictures and work up to other pairs that are more difficult and more entertaining. The accompanying pair of figures consists of a series of vertical lines. You may notice that the spacing between lines is slightly different in the two pictures, and our goal is for you to experience the perceptual consequence of that difference. To achieve this goal, you need to get one of the figures imaged in your right eye and the other imaged in your left eye. And you can do that by aiming your left eye at one figure and your right eye at the other.

Easier said than done? Try this. Place your index finger (it doesn't matter which one) on this page right between the two figures and stare right at that finger. Now very gradually move your finger away from the page straight toward your face, all the while maintaining fixation on the finger. Now here's the trick. At the same time you're staring at your finger pay atten-tion to the pair of figures. As you move your finger closer, you'll notice that the two gradually slide on top of one another. With patience, you'll find a distance for your finger where the two figures completely fuse. This happens because your eyes are now converged at a point that aims them at different parts of the page. Once you've found this point, hold your finger steady while concentrating on the superimposed figure. You should be able to see that some of the vertical lines are situated in depth relative to others. This depth effect is stereopsis.

Once you've mastered this lesson, you're ready to graduate to more complicated stereograms. Try the pair shown at the end of this box. Again, patience will pay dividends. Keep searching for the right degree of eye convergence that causes the two images to appear superimposed. As you practice this technique, you'll soon be able to dispense with the finger and simply cross your eyes at will to get the images aligned. The most difficult aspect of this maneuver is that your accommodation changes as you converge your eyes, thereby blurring the two images. To begin, then, practice free fusion in bright light conditions, when your pupils will be small and blur will be minimal.

Once you've got the hang of it, you'll be ready to try your new ability on the demonstration stereograms in this chapter. One final thing. Some people just find it impossible to cross their eyes and fuse stereograms. If you're experiencing this difficulty, try staring *through* the page of the book, as if you were looking at an imaginary object located 10 or so centimeters beyond the page. This, too, is a way to achieve free fusion, although this method reverses which eye sees which image and, consequently, flips the depth relations portrayed in the stereogram.

---

possible to measure positional disparities between the two pictures.

Neural

This exercise indicates that stereopsis really involves two steps: first, matched features must be identified in the two eyes (a matching problem); second, the magnitude and direction (crossed versus uncrossed) of the retinal dispari-ties between those features must be computed (disparity computation). Let's consider these two steps in turn.

First, to match features in the two retinal images, you must decide what constitutes a "feature." On the basis of intuition, the most plausible candidate would seem to be some recognizable

BOX 8.2 continued

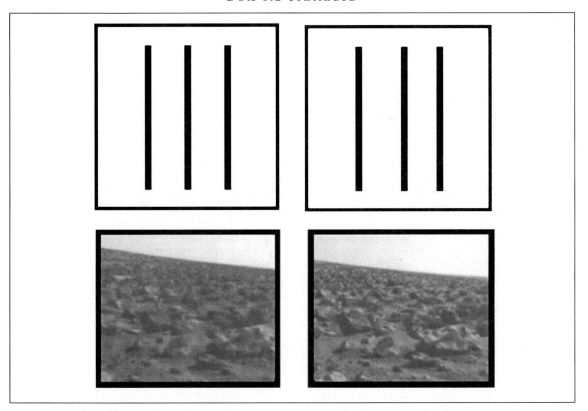

form, or pattern, appearing in both of the pictures. For instance, if one eye's view included your roommate's face, it would be a simple matter to locate that face in the other eye's view. According to this idea, each eye's image is analyzed separately, and the two are then brought together for purposes of matching recognizable features. However, this idea cannot be entirely correct, for there are instances where stereoscopic depth can be perceived from stereograms that contain no recognizable objects whatsoever. An example of one of these **random-dot stereograms** is shown in Figure 8.13. These ingenious visual figures were first developed by Bela Julesz (1971).

Both halves of this stereogram consist of nothing more than an array of black and white dots.

The two halves are identical with one exception. In one of the halves of the stereogram, a central subset of dots has been shifted laterally by several rows, as is illustrated schematically in the middle panel of Figure 8.13. This lateral displacement creates a retinal disparity between the two halves, in much the same way as would a speckled square held in front of an identically speckled background, as depicted in the bottom panel of Figure 8.13. Because the texture in the stereogram is completely random, it is impossible to pick out from either half of the stereogram alone which area will appear in depth when the two halves are viewed simultaneously. Once you've learned to free fuse stereo images (Box 8.2), you'll be able to use this technique to see

FIGURE 8.13

A random-dot stereogram. The two halves are identical, except that a central subset of dots has been shifted laterally. (The middle panel outines the section of shifted dots.) This lateral displacement creates retinal disparity and, thus, stereosopic depth (bottom panel).

your brain's remarkable ability to extract depth from these random-dot pictures.

Think for a moment about the confusing job confronting your brain as it tries to sort out the depth in this jumble of dots. Because each half of the stereogram is made up of nothing more than a random array of tiny dots, there are numerous dots in one eye's view that could match up with any single dot in the other eye's view. Despite this, the brain manages to find a satisfactory match between the two pictures, as is evidenced by the vivid illusion of depth produced by these pairs of random textures.

Thus random-dot stereograms disprove the theory that stereopsis results from an analysis of monocularly recognizable forms such as your roommate's face. But if not monocular forms, then what monocular features *does* the visual system match in order to compute disparity? Think back to earlier chapters where you learned that form perception initially involves analyzing a figure's orientation and size, or spatial frequency. The same features are involved in stereopsis, too. The evidence favoring this idea is rather complicated, so we are going to mention just a couple of relevant studies here. More thorough discussions of feature matching and stereopsis can be found in Blake and Wilson (1991).

Execute

It is possible to remove certain spatial frequencies from random-dot stereograms such as the one shown in Figure 8.14a. This process of removal is called *filtering*. When high spatial frequencies are removed from both halves of a stereogram, the dots are no longer sharply defined but instead appear blurred (see Figure 8.14b). Still, the phantom figure is easily seen to stand out in depth when these two blurred half-images are viewed stereoscopically (try free fusing the two images). By the same token, if just low spatial frequencies are removed from both halves of a stereogram (Figure 8.14c), depth may still be experienced, although with more difficulty. But if high spatial frequencies are removed from one half of the stereogram while low spatial frequencies are removed from the other (Figure 8.14d), stereopsis is abolished.

Instead, the two halves undergo **binocular rivalry,** such that only one picture or the other is visible at any one moment (see Box 8.3).

For stereopsis to be experienced, then, the spatial-frequency content of the two halves of a stereogram must overlap (Frisby and Mayhew, 1976). This implies that in order to compute disparity, the brain matches the two eyes' views, making use of sets of neurons responsive to limited bands of spatial frequencies (Yang and Blake, 1991). This strategy actually simplifies the matching problem, making it unnecessary to test all left-eye features against all right-eye features. The possible feature matches are restricted to the monocular image components at a given spatial scale. As you might deduce from Figure 8.14b, there are fewer possible "feature" matches in the pair of low spatial frequency images than there are in pairs of unfiltered images. The brain, consequently, can more quickly hone in on the correct set of matches. And once these have been established, feature matches for the higher spatial frequencies have been delimited to those within the boundaries established by the low frequency matches.

Recall from Chapter 5 that the brain also relies on neurons tuned to different spatial scales to support form perception. It is not surprising that form perception and stereopsis should utilize the same machinery, since both of them are designed to distinguish objects from their backgrounds (Marr, 1982). Because of the remarkable human ability to resolve small depth differences stereoscopically, the two eyes together can unearth objects buried in complex visual environments, objects that when viewed monocularly remain hidden from sight. In this respect, stereopsis effectively adds another dimension to form perception.

The Neural Basis of Stereopsis

So far we have considered the geometry of retinal disparity (the cue for stereopsis) and the matching features that seem to be used in the analysis of retinal disparity. But how does the

FIGURE 8.14

The two components of a random-dot stereogram (upper panel) with their spatial frequencies filtered to produce components containing only low spatial frequencies (LP), only high spatial frequencies (HP) and a "mixed" stereogram where one component is HP and the other is LP.

Illusion

BOX 8.3

COMPETITION BETWEEN THE TWO EYES

Charles Wheatstone, the discoverer of stereopsis, described another intriguing aspect of binocular vision. This second discovery concerned the perceptual outcome when one eye's view differs radically from its partner's view. Wheatstone's interesting observation can best be described by reference to the figure below.

Suppose you were to view these two dissimilar patterns separately with your two eyes in such a way that your left eye saw one set of diagonal lines while your right eye saw the other set. What would be the outcome? If the two were combined by simply superimposing one on the other, the result would be a sort of checkerboard pattern. Yet when these figures are viewed stereoscopically, thereby allowing your brain to perform the combination, the two certainly do not blend into a single, stable pattern resembling a checkerboard. Instead, a person sees portions of one pattern together with portions of the other, the net result resembling a mosaic of the two. Moreover, this mosaic changes over time, as regions of one eye's view replace regions of the other eye's view. (To experience this instability in perception for yourself, try free fusing these two orthogonal gratings or the pair of dissimilar pictures in Figure 8.14d.)

The resulting phenomenon is known as *binocular rivalry,* an appropriate term in view of the evident breakdown in cooperation between the two eyes. The occurrence of binocular rivalry indicates that the brain, in attempting to put together information from the two eyes, seeks to establish matches between features in the two eyes. When such matches are found, stable single vision and stereopsis result. But when satisfactory matches are impossible, the brain attends to portions of one eye's view at a time, ignoring or suppressing the corresponding portions of the other eye's view as though they were not there.

But how complete is this suppression of information during binocular rivalry? Is a person completely oblivious to new information presented to a region of the eye that is temporarily suppressed? To study this question, investigators have employed a "probe" technique whereby small visual targets (such as a word) are briefly flashed to a suppressed region; the observer's task is to report whether or not the probe target was noticed. The results are conclusive—during suppression, people fail to see targets that would normally be quite visible, including, for example, familiar names (Blake, 1988b). However, the eye is not completely blind to all visual stimulation

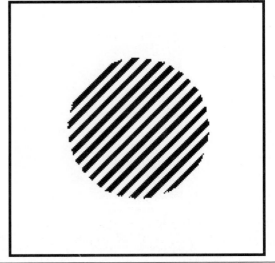

BOX 8.3 continued

during suppression. Abruptly increasing the brightness of a suppressed stimulus or suddenly moving it will cause the stimulus to become visible. Apparently, during suppression an eye's overall sensitivity, though reduced, is not totally abolished. While vision in the suppressed eye is erased from consciousness, some processing of information from that eye continues unabated (Blake, 1997).

What actually transpires within the visual system when one eye's stimulus dominates perception during rivalry? Nikos Logothetis and colleagues (Logothetis and Schall, 1991; Leopold and Logothetis, 1996) have identified several visual areas in the brain where the activity of neurons waxes and wanes in synchrony with fluctuations in left and right eye dominance. This tight coupling between perception and neural activity is most prominent in higher visual areas, including regions in the temporal lobe.

Since the two eyes normally view the same visual scene, you might wonder what binocular rivalry has to do with normal vision. When one object partially occludes a more distant object, one eye sees portions of that object that are screened from the other eye's view—there can be, in other words, unmatched image regions in the two eyes' views. As mentioned in the text, this is the geometrical principle first deduced by Leonardo da Vinci, and it has been studied in the laboratory by Nakayama and Shimojo (1990). These investigators provide clever demonstrations that the binocular visual system actually relies on information about interocular mismatches to figure out depth relations among objects.

brain actually do its feature matching and disparity computation? Certainly the entire process is not yet understood, but something is known about the neurobiological hardware involved in the initial stages of stereoscopic vision. Let's take a look at this hardware.

Neural

Recall from Chapter 4 that most visual cortical neurons receive input from both eyes, left and right. Each of these binocular neurons gives its largest response when the two eyes view the same stimulus. For instance, a particular binocular neuron that gives its most vigorous response when the left eye sees a vertical contour will respond best when the right eye sees a vertical contour too. The same holds for contour width, or size, as well as for the direction and speed of movement of a contour. In general, binocular neurons respond best when the two eyes view matched features (see the review by Gonzalez and Perez, 1998). This property, then, satisfies one of the requirements for the analysis of disparity information, namely, the matching of monocular features.

Binocular neurons have another property, one that satisfies the second requirement for stereopsis: these neurons are sensitive to retinal dispar-

ity. In particular, some binocular cells respond only when their preferred features appear at the *same* depth plane as the point of fixation. This is because the receptive fields for these binocular neurons are located on *corresponding* areas of the two eyes. These cells, in other words, would respond best to objects giving rise to zero disparity. Activity in such cells would serve to signal the presence of stimuli located *on* the horopter. Other binocular cells respond best to features that are imaged on noncorresponding, or disparate, areas of the two eyes. Cells of this type would be activated by objects located at depth planes other than the plane of fixation. Refer back to Figure 4.16 to see the layout of the receptive field of one of these so-called **disparity-selective cells.** As noted in Chapter 4, some cells prefer crossed disparities, whereas others prefer uncrossed disparities. Also, the amount of depth (disparity) giving the best response varies from cell to cell.

So it appears that these binocular neurons perform two of the operations necessary for stereopsis, feature matching and disparity computation. But can we be sure that these binocular neurons actually play a role in stereoscopic depth perception? One piece of evidence favoring such a role comes from studying cats who, while kittens, were allowed to see with only one eye at a time. The eyes were stimulated alternately by placing an opaque contact lens in one eye on one day and in the other eye on the next day. This rearing procedure effectively turns binocular neurons into monocular ones (Blakemore, 1976). When tested as adults, these animals were unable to perform binocular depth discriminations that were simple for normally reared cats (Blake and Hirsch, 1975; Packwood and Gordon, 1975). Because they lacked a normal array of binocular neurons, these cats were "blind" for stereopsis. Monkeys, too, lose stereopsis when early experience deprives them of coordinated, binocular use of the two eyes (Harwerth et al., 1997).

Recall our earlier comment that some people are stereoblind—unable to perceive depth from retinal disparity. By analogy with the stereoblind cats and stereoblind monkeys, we assume that this condition in humans stems from a lack of binocular neurons. Again, there is evidence to back up this assumption. For instance, when stereoblind people are tested on the tilt aftereffect described in Chapter 4, they show very little interocular transfer—adapting one eye has very little effect on judgments of line orientation when the nonadapted eye is tested (Mitchell and Ware, 1974). In contrast, people with good stereopsis show substantial interocular transfer, which, we assume, reflects adaptation of binocular neurons. The meager degree of interocular transfer in the stereoblind individual, then, probably reflects the paucity of binocular neurons in that person's brain.

The incidence of **stereoblindness** is estimated to be as high as 5 to 10 percent in the general population. As a rule, stereoblindness is associated with the presence of certain visual disorders during early childhood. The most common of these disorders is misalignment of the two eyes, a condition known as **strabismus,** or *squint.* People with this condition are unable to look at, or fixate on, the same object simultaneously with both eyes. Consequently, one eye's view rarely corre-

sponds with the other eye's view. To deal with this potentially confusing situation, the brain eventually suppresses one eye's view from visual consciousness, an outcome reminiscent of binocular rivalry. Box 8.4 describes this and similar conditions in more detail.

If left uncorrected, strabismus can lead not only to stereoblindness but also to amblyopia,* which, as you will recall from Chapter 4, is defined as a permanent reduction in the acuity of an eye not attributable to optical defects. Both amblyopia and stereoblindness can be prevented if eye misalignment is surgically corrected early in life, while normal binocular vision is still developing (Thorn et al., 1993). If correction is postponed until school age, the chances for attaining normal vision are significantly reduced (von Noorden, 1981; Banks, Aslin and Letson, 1975).

The discovery of disparity-sensitive cells three decades ago was an exciting first step toward an understanding of the neural basis of stereopsis (Barlow, Blakemore and Pettigrew, 1967). But, as several reviews of this work have pointed out (Blake and Wilson, 1991; Gonzalez and Perez, 1998; DeAngelis, 2000), the existence of disparity detectors leaves a number of questions about stereopsis unanswered.

For one thing, the perceived depth resulting from a given disparity depends on the absolute distance from your eyes to the object you are looking at. This can be demonstrated when an observer views a random-dot stereogram, such as the one in Figure 8.14a, from different distances. (Try this for yourself, using the free fusion technique you learned in Box 8.2.) The central square in the stereogram appears to move farther and farther in front of its background as viewing distance increases. Yet the disparity, expressed in angular terms, actually decreases as you view the

---

*Amblyopia can arise from causes other than eye misalignment. Other disorders producing amblyopia include marked differences in an uncorrected refractive error between the two eyes, closure of one eye due to lid paralysis or blurred vision in one eye due to a cataract in that eye.

BOX 8.4

COORDINATION BETWEEN THE TWO EYES

Like any other partners, our two eyes have to share the same viewpoint in order to get along. This means that movements of the eyes must be coordinated so that both eyes are always looking in the same direction. As you learned in Chapter 2, the eyes are guided in their movements by twelve extraocular muscles—six for each eye. Because the eye movement system is complex and dependent on fallible parts, things can and do go wrong. Here, we will consider some of the most common problems and their remedies, emphasizing extraocular dysfunctions that affect perception.

When most people look at an object, the two eyes both end up aimed at that object. For these people, the two eyes fixate together. This binocular fixation depends on the coordinated responses of the extraocular muscles that guide the two eyes. For various reasons, however, some people lack this coordination. For example, if one extraocular muscle is too short, it can exert too much pull on the eyeball, turning that eye in (toward the nose) or out (toward the ear). Chronic deviation of an eye is called *strabismus.* Often this is a congenital condition, which means that an infant may lack coordinated binocular vision early in life. Because strabismic eyes look in different directions, they send the brain conflicting messages, which may result in double vision, or **diplopia.** Alternatively, the brain may simply ignore, or suppress, one eye's view altogether; in this case, only one eye contributes to vision even though both are open. This latter condition resembles a chronic form of binocular rivalry (see Box 8.3).

Various therapies have been developed for strabismus. In cases where the deviation between the positions of the two eyes is relatively small, visual exercises may help to recoordinate the eyes. In more severe cases, surgical correction may be required. This usually involves removing a small portion of one or more of the extraocular muscles and then reattaching the muscles to the eyeball, so that the eyes line up. This procedure requires a high degree of skill, for altering the muscle by the wrong amount will leave the eyes still misaligned.

Other extraocular dysfunctions are less debilitating and less noticeable. When you do close work such as reading, your eyes must converge—each turns inward by the proper amount. Strong, constant convergence strains the muscles of the eye (Guth, 1981). Some people have difficulty converging their eyes, as you can discover for yourself. Stand facing a friend and ask him or her to keep both eyes on your finger as you move it slowly but directly toward a point between the eyes. Note how well your friend's eyes follow. Some people can keep both eyes fixated on the finger until it is within 1 or 2 centimeters of the nose; others will not be able to follow the finger after it is within 5 or 6 centimeters of the nose. As the finger approaches, one of their eyes may wander off. If you try this small experiment with several people, you'll be amazed at the individual differences. In addition, when someone is tired or has consumed too much alcohol, that person's eyes may be unable to converge normally.

People who have trouble binocularly fixating on close objects may experience eyestrain during prolonged reading. Eyestrain, in turn, can cause dizziness, headaches, and nausea, leading to reduced studying and hence poorer grades. Occasionally, college students suffer this kind of problem, called **convergence insufficiency,** while studying for final examinations. Amateur "psychologists" can do great harm by misdiagnosing this condition, thinking it is an aversion to studying or "a need to fail." In fact, the proper treatment is straightforward: prescription glasses, possibly supplemented with appropriate eye exercises. Reading will then become less of a strain, and higher grades may follow.

Execute

FIGURE 8.15
Photographs simulating what the left and right eyes see when you look at a book held several feet in front
of a bookshelf. Notice that the left eye can see objects occluded in the right eye's view, and vice versa.
© McGraw-Hill Higher Education, John Thoeming, photographer.

stereogram from afar. So, disparity alone does not specify depth; disparity must be supplemented by other distance information.

One potential supplementary source of distance information is convergence angle, the oculomotor cue discussed earlier in this chapter. We do know that the perceived depth associated with a given angular disparity does vary with convergence angle (Foley, 1980; Collett, Schwartz and Sobel, 1992). In addition to convergence angle, we also know that depth from stereopsis can be influenced by other visual cues, such as perceived slant specified by perspective or texture (Stevens and Brooks, 1988), two monocular sources of information about depth discussed later in this chapter.

We also should point out that binocular vision can produce what is termed partial occlusion, a special form of retinal disparity. When one object partially occludes another, more distant object, one eye will see portions of the more distant object that are invisible to the other eye. This geometric principle is illustrated in Figure 8.15. These two pictures simulate what your left and right eyes would see if you were to look at a book held at arm's length in front of a bookshelf. Notice that the left eye's view of the background includes books that are partially occluded from view by the right eye, and vice versa. These partial occlusions, an extreme form of retinal disparity, are readily interpreted by the brain as arising from depth differences between the foreground and background objects (Anderson, 1994). Partial occlusion, as mentioned earlier in this chapter, is the geometric principle Leonardo da Vinci identified in the 15th century.

This completes our survey of binocular stereopsis, the major source of binocular depth information. Keen as stereopsis is, though, it certainly is not the sole source of depth information. People can successfully perform visually guided tasks, such as landing an airplane (Grosslight et al., 1978), while using just one eye. And you can easily confirm that the world retains a real sense of depth even when one eye is closed. Rather than collapsing into a single, depthless plane, objects in the visual field continue to appear three-dimensional. This is possible because the monocular view of the world contains additional sources of information about depth. Let's consider these monocular cues.

MONOCULAR VISUAL DEPTH INFORMATION

Some monocular depth cues are based on principles of geometry, others are based on conditions of atmosphere and illumination, and still others arise from differential motion within the visual field. We do not refer to these as *monocular* cues because you have to shut one eye to experience them. On the contrary, monocular cues are readily available during binocular viewing. They're called *monocular* because these sources of depth information can be realized by either eye alone.

As we survey these various monocular cues, keep in mind that several of them were initially discovered by artists in their attempts to represent depth pictorially. Those pictorial cues we call *static* because they are available to a stationary observer viewing a motionless scene. The other monocular source of depth information is provided when an individual moves through the environment or when objects within the environment move relative to one another. We'll start with the static, pictorial cues discovered by artists.

Static Cues to Depth

Interposition When one object occludes, or obscures, part of another from view, as in Figure 8.16, the partially occluded object is automatically perceived as the more distant one. This cue is called **interposition,** and from the standpoint of pictorial representation, it is probably the most primitive. Young children often incorporate interposition into their simple drawings, even though they are unable to reproduce any other pictorial depth cues. Actually, there is evidence that by 7 months of age human infants can judge relative distance solely on the basis of interposition (Yonas, 1984).

FIGURE 8.16
Interposition: When one object obscures part of another, the obscured object is perceived as the more distant one.

On the other hand, brain damage during adulthood can abolish a person's ability to judge depth from interposition without affecting the ability to use other depth cues (Stevens, 1983). Interposition is such a strong depth cue that it can override retinal disparity when the two cues conflict (Kaufman, 1974). Moreover, the effectiveness of interposition is amplified when the surface of the occluding object contains high spatial frequency information, meaning that it appears to be finely textured (Brown and Weisstein, 1988).

Clinical

Perhaps the most compelling evidence for the potency of interposition are the so-called Kanisza figures mentioned in Chapters 1 and 4. Figure 1.8 showed an example of a Kanisza figure, and another version is shown in Figure 8.17A. As you can tell, these are drawings in which one object appears to partially occlude several others even though the boundaries of the nearer object are invisible. This illusory figure appears to have distinct edges where, in fact, none exist, and the entire figure is seen in front of objects that seem to be partially occluded. Descriptively speaking, the visual system seems to employ a kind of interpolation process whereby

Illusion

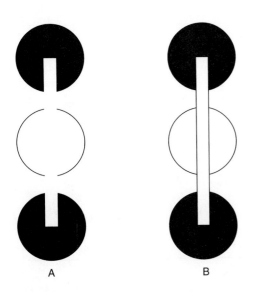

FIGURE 8.17
An illusory bar (drawing A) and a real bar (drawing B),
both of which activate neurons in Area V2 of the visual
cortex.

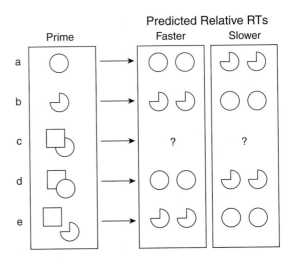

FIGURE 8.18
Test figures used by Sekuler and Palmer to study priming
and occlusion.

separate edges or contours in the same spatial
neighborhood are connected *if* this connection
can be formed by a simple line or curve and *if* the
operation is consistent with the principle of interposition.

But how does the visual system make the
seemingly complex decision to interpolate an object? As we saw in Chapter 4, there is evidence
(Peterhans and von der Heydt, 1991) that interpolation is accomplished by neurons in the visual
cortex that respond not only to real contours but
also to interpolated, illusory contours like the
ones forming the object in Figure 8.17A. These
cortical neurons perform an interesting new
operation—interpolation—that involves not only
boundary completion but depth ordering. The illusory figure appears in front of the real figures.

It is also worth noting that objects occluded by
a nearer figure are seen as complete, even though
portions of their surfaces are obscured by the
nearer object. Thus, in Figure 8.17, we perceive
the black circles as complete, not notched. In a
similar fashion, despite the occluding objects in

Figure 5.36, we saw a girl's entire face uninter-
rupted by horizontal and vertical gaps. The perception of occluded areas of an object is termed
amodal completion. How we are able to perceive
parts of objects that are occluded represents a challenging question (Kellman and Shipley, 1991).
Here again, the visual system seems to employ an
interpolation process to complete the portions of
the figure missing in the image. And as a study by
Allison Sekuler and Steve Palmer (1992) shows,
the process of completion takes some time to occur.

In that study, observers saw briefly-presented
pairs of simple geometric figures, and had to indicate as quickly as possible whether or not the
two figures were identical. Figure 8.18 shows a
few examples of Sekuler and Palmer's test pairs.
Just prior to each test pair, observers saw another
brief stimulus, called a *priming* stimulus, which
either did or didn't match the test pair. Examples
of priming figures are also shown in Figure 8.18.
When the priming stimulus included an object
that was identical to the test figures, observers responded "same" very quickly—the reaction time
between presentation of the test pair and observers' responses was short. When the priming

Execute

stimulus did not match the pair of test figures, re-action times were slower.

The stimulus-selective speed up in responses defines perceptual priming, which was discussed in Chapter 6. Sekuler and Palmer exploited prim-ing to determine the time necessary for percep-tion's "completion" of an object. Here's their logic. Suppose the prime figure consisted of a notched circle snuggled against a square (third row, Figure 8.18) and the test pair consisted of two circles. Would observers' reactions be fast, indicating that the notched circle had been seen as a whole circle partially occluded by the square? Or would reaction times be slower, because the notched circle didn't match the complete circles?

The result, it turned out, depended on the time elapsing between presentation of the prime figure and presentation of the test pair. When this inter-val between prime and test was very brief—just a twentieth of a second or so—observers gave rel-atively slow reaction times to the pair of circles. Evidently, within this brief period of time, the prime figure was not registered as a complete ob-ject that is partially occluded. But when the in-terval between prime and test was longer than two-tenths of a second, reaction times were fast, indicating that the prime figure had been regis-tered as a complete, partially occluded circle. From these and other, related conditions, Sekuler and Palmer concluded that perceptual representa-tion of a partially occluded object starts out as a mosaic-like snapshot of the object's individual pieces and, then, gradually evolves over time into a perceptually complete object.

Any discussion of interposition has to recog-nize the importance of **transparency,** a special case where a nonopaque object partially occludes another object. Under these conditions, people perceive the occluded object in its entirety, in-cluding the portions covered by what appears to be a transparent filter. For example, people have the strong tendency to see Figure 8.19A as a transparent, square filter in front of a surface composed of black and white checks. Yet look at Figure 8.19B and see what happens when we

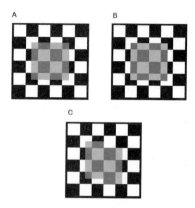

FIGURE 8.19
Perception of transparency depends on lightness relationships. See text for details.

simply interchange the two colors that comprise the central square region. That central region no longer looks like a separate, transparent object in front of the checkerboard. Instead, the checks themselves in the center of the checkerboard ap-pear to be different colors compared to their neighbors—the two shades of gray, in other words, are assigned to the surface of the checker-board, not to another object located in front of the checkerboard.

For decades researchers have been fascinated with transparency and have documented the con-ditions under which it's experienced. One key to perceiving transparency is the relationship of lightness values in the covered and the uncovered portions of the figure (Metelli, 1974). In a nut-shell, lightness values within the regions covered by the transparent filter must be intermediate to the lightness values of those regions where the filter isn't covering them. Comparing Figures 8.19A and 8.19B, you will see that this condition is satisfied in the left-hand figure but is not in the right-hand figure.

Another key is the spatial configuration of the gray portions—those parts must plausibly form a single object. Thus, in Figure 8.19C, it's more dif-ficult to see a transparent object because the bor-ders of the candidate regions don't form a square,

FIGURE 8.20
Stereo pairs in which a circle appears either transparent (when seen in front of the white cross) or opaque (when seen behind the white cross). To see these outcomes requires that you "free fuse" the two components by crossing your eyes (see text for details).

even though the individual gray levels are the appropriate values (Singh and Hoffman, 1998).

Execute

A region will also be perceived as transparent only if binocular disparity specifies that the region is in front of an occluded object (Nakayama, Shimojo and Ramachandran, 1990). Take a look at Figure 8.20, a stereogram containing the components for testing the contribution of stereopsis to the perception of transparency. Using the free-fusion technique (Box 8.2), binocularly combine the left and middle pictures. You should see a light gray, transparent object floating above a white cross drawn on a black background. Now take a look at what you see when the middle and right pictures are free fused. You'll see an opaque gray circle lying on a white background seen through a cross-shaped section cut out of a black surface. The only difference between these two conditions is the "sign" of the retinal disparity of the light gray regions relative to the rest of the figure. In one instance, the disparity is *crossed* and in the other it's *uncrossed* (recall the discussion of disparity earlier in this chapter).

Illusion

In some circumstances, interposition exerts another effect, which is also illustrated in Figure 8.20. When you saw the light gray regions floating in front of the white cross, you probably saw them forming a circular region of transparent material. Yet in the figures on the page, there is no gray color anywhere except at the white intersections. Your brain filled in the rest of the gray to complete the implied circle. Much of the circle,

then, consists of illusory contours (like those in Figure 8.17).

This filling-in process can also be seen without the aid of stereopsis. Look at Color Plate 14, which presents another configuration whose component parts imply transparency. Here, the semicircular blue portions of each set of circles seem to give the impression of blueness that spreads into the center of the figure. We see a faint bluish, semitransparent square resting on top of the four sets of circles. This illusory migration of color into neighboring regions is called **neon spreading,** since it resembles the glow one experiences when viewing neon lights. Neon spreading represents a form of interposition since one perceives a faintly colored surface resting in front of other objects (the circles, in this example). Moreover, neon spreading is related to illusory figures because the spreading color is confined to an area whose shape is insinuated by the semicircular blue contours. The boundaries of the shape, in other words, are defined by illusory contours.

All these phenomena—occlusion, amodal completion, illusory figures, transparency and neon spreading—entail the perception of depth relations among partially overlapping objects. They testify to the role of interposition in depth perception. Despite being a very strong depth cue, however, interposition by itself only specifies whether one object is nearer or more distant than another. It provides no quantitative information about the actual distance separating objects. For that information, additional cues are required.

Size Take a look at the series of squares in Figure 8.21. Note that the smaller squares appear to recede into the distance, implying that size influences perceived depth. Why should size and distance be related?

As the distance between you and an object varies, the size of the image of that object on your retina changes. This principle is true for any object viewed from any distance. Thus, if you are familiar with the size of an object, you can judge
Top-down

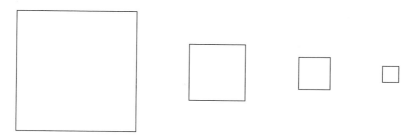

FIGURE 8.21
Size alone can influence perceived depth.

from the size of its retinal image how far away the object is. In fact, it has long been known that *familiar size* is an effective cue to distance in the absence of other information (Ittelson, 1951).

But the cue of retinal image size critically depends on knowing the correct size of the object. When you are confronted with an unfamiliar object and are provided with no clues as to its true physical size, retinal image size gives you no clear sense of the distance from you to that object. For instance, you may have trouble judging the size of the sculpture pictured in Figure 8.22 and therefore its distance from the camera. But if something familiar appears in the vicinity of that object (such as the pear in Figure 8.23), the perceived size of the unfamiliar object becomes obvious. (You are also now able to judge its distance from the camera.)

Interestingly, even prior knowledge about the true distance to an object may not be sufficient to support the perception of relative depth. In one study (Gruber and Dinnerstein, 1965), a person was shown a pair of squares in a lighted corridor. One square was located about 8 meters away and the other about 16 meters away. Because the farther square was physically twice as large as the nearer one, the two squares cast the same-sized images on the person's retina. Depth cues provided by the corridor and by the apparatus enabled the person to see clearly that the two squares were located at different distances. How-

FIGURE 8.22
How big is this object? It is difficult to judge the size of an unfamiliar object in the absence of supporting cues.

ever, when the lights were extinguished, the squares (which had been outlined with luminous paint), appeared to "come together" at a common depth, completely contradicting what the person *knew* about their real locations. This demonstration underscores the point made earlier, that depth cues are registered automatically, without conscious deliberation.

So far we have considered size as a determinant of perceived distance. But it is just as easy for perceived distance to influence apparent size. Looking at panel A of Figure 8.24, the girl on the right appears to be almost twice as big as the boy on the left. But in fact the two are really equal in size. This compelling illusion stems from the unusual construction of the room. As shown in

Illusion

FIGURE 8.23
The size of an unfamiliar object—and therefore its distance from you—becomes obvious when you see it in the vicinity of a familiar object, in this case a pear. (The unfamiliar object is a contemporary sculpture by Bruce Peebles.)

panel B of Figure 8.24, the left corner of the room is much farther away from the observer than the right corner. The floor-to-ceiling height as well as the sizes and shapes of the windows have been distorted to make the room appear rectangular, and hence normal, when viewed from a location directly in front of the room. The back wall looks perpendicular to the line of sight, with left and right corners appearing equidistant from the viewer. Actually, though, the person on the left is farther away than the one on the right. The visual angles subtended by the two children are therefore quite different. From the viewer's perspective, this means that the girl on the right is larger, since you have been fooled into believing that the difference in visual angles is *not* due to a difference in distance. Adelbert Ames, a lawyer turned scientist, devised this clever demonstration of perceived distance's influence on apparent size. In his honor, this sort of distorted structure is called an **Ames room** (Ittelson, 1952/1968).

Besides the Ames room, another visual phenomenon, the moon illusion, vividly demonstrates the interdependence of size and distance. You will have noticed that the moon, especially when full, appears much larger on the horizon than it does when overhead at its zenith. Of course, the actual size of the moon remains constant, as does its distance from the earth: the moon is 2,160 miles in diameter and 239,000 miles

FIGURE 8.24
The Ames room: A demonstration that perceived distance influences apparent size. (Baron Wolman/Woodfin Camp and Associates.)
© Baron Wolman/Woodfin Camp & Associates

away. This means that regardless of its position in the sky, the full moon casts a circular image about one-sixth of a millimeter in diameter on your retina. Why, then, does the apparent size of the moon change so strikingly?

One possible answer is that the moon's **perceived distance** varies with its heavenly position. Near the horizon, where there are many depth cues, the moon seems to be farther away than when it is at its zenith. This idea is illustrated in Figure 8.25. But we know that the size of its retinal image remains constant regardless of the moon's position in the sky. This produces something of a conflict: usually, when the distance from you to a single object changes, the size of the retinal image also changes. Yet, in the case of the moon, perceived distance *changes,* but retinal image size *remains constant.* And the only way for image size to remain constant when distance changes is for object size to change, too. With the moon illusion, when perceived distance is great (moon on the horizon), then perceived object size must be large. But when perceived distance is reduced (moon at its zenith), perceived object size is smaller. This relation between perceived depth of a fixed size retinal image is known as **Emmert's law,** and

the moon illusion is a prime example of this law at work.

Support for this idea comes from some classic experiments by Lloyd Kaufman and Irvin Rock (1962). They found that the normally large moon on the horizon shrank as soon as it was viewed through a small hole in a piece of opaque material. Looking at the moon through such a tiny hole eliminated distance cues provided by the horizon. You can easily replicate this finding by viewing the horizon moon monocularly through a small peephole made by clenching your fist.

Execute

Kaufman and Rock also discovered a way to make the normally small zenith moon appear large: they had observers view the moon through an artificial horizon drawn on a large sheet of clear plastic. Thus, by manipulating apparent distance, Rock and Kaufman could create the illusion or make it vanish. We should point out, however, that not everyone agrees with the theory that the moon illusion depends on perceived distance (Baird and Wagner, 1982; Baird, 1982; Iavecchia, Iavecchia and Roscoe, 1983; Enright, 1989). Perhaps these disagreements are not surprising. After all, people have been speculating about the moon illusion for more than two thousand years (Hershenson, 1989).

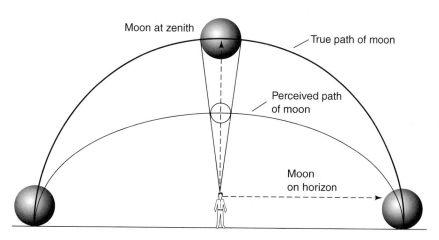

FIGURE 8.25
Explanation of the moon illusion based on perceived distance.

The Ames room and the moon illusion are just two of many visual illusions involving errors in perceived distance and size. After completing the roster of monocular depth cues, we will consider these other visual illusions in greater detail.

Perspective The term *perspective* refers to changes in the appearance of surfaces or objects as they recede in distance away from an observer. As mentioned in the introduction to this chapter, the geometry of visual perspective was developed during the fifteenth century by Italian artists. Here, we are concerned primarily with perspective from the perceptual, not the geometrical, standpoint, so it will not be necessary to discuss the geometry of perspective in any detail. Pirenne (1970) offers a well-illustrated account of that topic.

Let's begin with **linear perspective,** which we will illustrate with an example. Suppose you looked out a window at a neighboring building, the situation depicted in Figure 8.3A. Now imagine using a marking pen to trace the outline of the building onto the glass windowpane, being careful to hold your head still. You would be tracing the two-dimensional projection of this three-dimensional scene. The result—a *perspective drawing,* as it is called—would look something like the outline drawing shown in Figure 8.3B. Note that the outlines of the building are drawn in such a way that the lines converge. In reality, of course, the roof's top and bottom run parallel to each other. The observer sees them as converging and draws them this way because the roof recedes in depth away from the observation point. This convergence of lines is termed **linear perspective.** When pictorially portrayed, linear perspective generates a strong impression of depth.

As we saw in the Ames room (Figure 8.24), the impression of depth produced by linear perspective can be strong enough to cause physically similar objects to appear different in size. In that case, the room's distorted construction furnished perspective cues that misrepresented the actual layout of the room. Hence the sizes of the people

in the room were also distorted. Figure 8.26 provides another example of how perspective can influence perceived size. In fact, the perceived depth implied by linear perspective can be sufficiently robust to contradict depth information conveyed by retinal disparity (Stevens and Brooks, 1988), as mentioned earlier.

There is another consequence of viewing surfaces or planes that recede in depth. Most surfaces have a visible texture, such as the grain in wood or the irregularities in a sidewalk. So long as a surface is not perpendicular to your line of sight, the density of the surface's texture will appear to vary with distance. Examples of this are shown in Figure 8.27. This form of perspective has been called **texture gradient** by James J. Gibson, the first person to emphasize the saliency of this source of depth information.

According to Gibson (1950), texture gradients provide precise and unambiguous information about the distances and slants of surfaces, as well as about the sizes of objects located on those surfaces. Gibson also proposed that abrupt changes in texture gradient signal the presence of edges or corners. In Figure 8.28, note that the texture discontinuity implies the presence of a bend, or corner, in a continuous surface. Stevens (1981) provides a detailed description of the geometrical basis for determining distances from texture gradients.

Just how accurately can people derive depth information from texture patterns? Sinai, Ooi and He (1998) performed a simple but revealing experiment to answer this question. They had people stand outdoors and estimate the distance between themselves and an object located anywhere from 2 to 7 meters in front of them. Observers were quite accurate judging distance so long as the ground plane was uniformly textured with, for example, grass. But when the ground plane contained a gap—such as a ditch—that disrupted the texture plane, distances were seriously overestimated; the object appeared to be farther from the observer. Errors in judged distance were also made when the ground plane between the

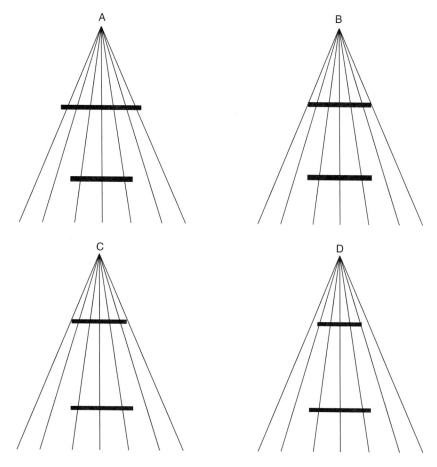

FIGURE 8.26
Linear perspective. In which one of the four perspective drawings (A, B, C or D) do the two thick horizontal lines appear equal in size? Use a ruler to discover the correct answer. This figure illustrates that linear perspective can cause objects whose sizes are really different to appear identical in size.

observer and the object was divided into two adjacent regions composed of distinctly different textures (grass and concrete). Based on their findings, Sinai, Ooi and He concluded that because human vision is adapted to terrestrial navigation, it relies heavily on a uniformly textured ground surface as a cue for spatial distance. Abrupt disruptions in the ground plane (a highly unusual situation in the natural environment), undermine this cue and, hence, perturb distance perception.

Continuing our list of perspective cues, you've probably noticed that objects in the distance are seen less clearly than those closer to you. This effect is called **aerial perspective,** and it occurs because light is scattered as it travels through atmosphere, especially if the air contains dust or excess moisture. This scattering of light reduces the contrast and, hence, blurs the clarity of objects' details. Naturally, light reflected from more distant objects must pass through more of this atmosphere than light reflected from nearby

Illusion

FIGURE 8.27
Texture gradients provide information about depth. (Frank Siteman/Stock, Boston.)
© Frank Sitman/Stock Boston

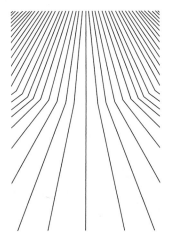

FIGURE 8.28
Texture discontinuity signals the presence of an edge or corner.

objects. As a consequence, more distant objects appear less distinct, or hazy, as you might say (see Figure 8.29).

Laboratory simulations show that reductions in the contrast of features in a picture cause those features to appear more distant. So reduced contrast from aerial perspective is an effective depth cue (O'Shea, Blackburn and Ono, 1994). In the absence of contrast reduction, blur can also serve as a depth cue (O'Shea, Sekuler and Govan, 1997). The cues of reduced contrast and blur can have perceptual consequences. Upon initially encountering conditions of extremely clean air (such as in the mountains), city dwellers accustomed to looking at the environment through congested atmosphere may seriously underestimate distances. Because atmospheric conditions vary greatly, when airline pilots attempt a visual landing, they must take account of aerial perspective as they try to judge distances.

Shading   Last in our list of static depth cues is **shading.** Look at the set of spherical objects in Figure 8.30. You probably see some of them as bumps protruding from the background (convex

bumps) and others as scooped out cavities (concave bumps). When you turn the book upside down, bumps change into cavities and vice versa. This demonstration raises two questions: What gives the spherical regions this three-dimensional quality? And why does the perceived depth reverse when the book is upside down? Starting with the first question, depth is perceived because the intensity gradient across each region resembles a shadow. Flat, two-dimensional surfaces don't cast shadows, so the visual system associates the implied shading with three-dimensional objects.

And why does the depth reverse? In natural environments, light always comes from above, a constraint that the visual system could exploit when deriving depth information from shading. So when the book is properly oriented, the unshaded regions point upward, implying that the spherical region is convex. But when the photograph is viewed upside down, the unshaded regions point downward, implying a concave spherical region (Ramachandran, 1988). Interestingly, this assumption about direction of illumination is made with reference to head orientation,

FIGURE 8.29
Try to identify the various depth cues in this photograph, "Relative Depth" by Dennis Markley. (Courtesy of Dennis Markley.)

Top-down

not gravitational orientation (Howard, Bergström and Masao, 1990). Viewing displays like Figure 8.30 upside down (such as through your legs) also reverses the depth relations.

A series of computer-generated scenes created by Daniel Kersten and colleagues dramatizes how potent shading is as a depth cue (Kersten, 1997; Kersten, Mamassian and Knill, 1997). Kersten's scenes demonstrate that perceived depth varies depending on the position of a shadow relative to the object casting the shadow. Figure 8.31 illustrates this dependence. If asked to judge which of the three squares seems to be hovering highest above the checkered background, people would agree it's the right-hand square, with the middle one next and the left-hand square closest to the background. The only source of informa-

tion triggering these vivid impressions of depth comes from the location of the fuzzy shadow relative to the square.

An even more compelling version of this demonstration is provided by an animation in which the fuzzy shadow moves back and forth over the checkered surface in the direction denoted in Figure 8.32. Even though it's only the shadow that actually moves, the white square appears to move up and down in depth relative to the checkered surface. Note that this is not the only possible interpretation of this sequence of events. The same shadow movement could have been produced by a stationary white square illuminated by a moving light source. However, we simply do not perceive the animation in this way. We always perceive the square moving in depth.

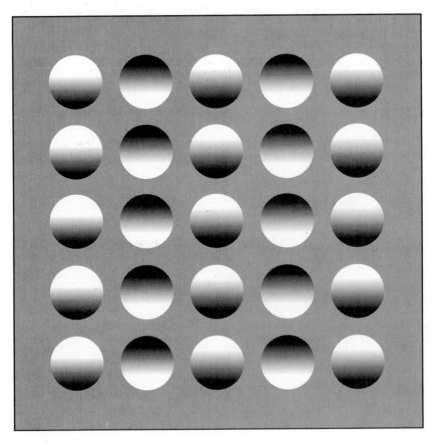

FIGURE 8.30
Shading as a cue to depth. Elements in the left, middle, and right columns appear to bulge
out of the background; elements in the remaining columns appear to be cavities. When the
book is turned upside down, the bulges become cavities and vice versa. Note that whatever
the page's orientation, top-to-bottom shading within an element determines its depth.

Evidently, our visual systems automatically assume that any light source producing a shadow is
stationary, a perfectly reasonable assumption in
the natural environment.

This completes our catalog of the static
monocular cues to depth. As noted earlier, artists
are able to use these cues to create an impression
of three dimensionality on a flat canvas. By way
of review, see if you can identify the various
static depth cues as they appear in the photograph
in Figure 8.29. There is, however, one very potent
source of monocular depth information that no

painting, etching or snapshot can ever capture,
and it's that depth cue to which we turn now.

Motion Parallax

Remember the Ames room demonstration in Figure 8.24, where static depth cues markedly distorted the perceived size of objects? To experience that illusion, you need to view the scene
from one specifically designated vantage point,
and you must hold your head perfectly still. Simply moving your head back and forth immedi-

FIGURE 8.31
Which one of these three squares is hovering farthest from the textured surface? (Reprinted with permission from Kersten, Mamassian and Knill, 1997.)

FIGURE 8.33
One situation in which motion parallax provides potent depth information. The arrows indicate the direction of relative apparent motion.

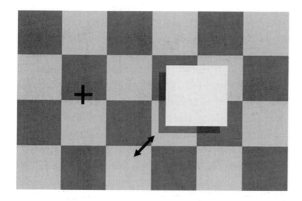

FIGURE 8.32
When an implied shadow moves laterally (denoted by arrows), one sees the stationary square appear to move up and down in depth relative to the textured surface. (Reprinted with permission from Kersten, Mamassian and Knill, 1997.)

ately reveals the true layout of the room and, consequently, you see the objects (people included) at their true sizes. Motion very quickly dispels misperceptions conveyed by static cues, and that's because motion introduces another, very potent source of depth information.

As you move about in the world, objects constantly shift position relative to one another within your field of view. This happens whenever you are walking, traveling in a car, or simply

turning your head to look at something. Next time you are a passenger in a car, notice how the world appears as you look out the window. Objects closer to you than the spot you're fixating on will appear to stream past in a direction *opposite* to the car's movement. More distant objects also seem to move, but at a more gradual speed and in the *same* direction as you are traveling. This complex flow of motion, illustrated in Figure 8.33, is an example of **motion parallax**—the relative apparent motion of objects within your field of view whenever you move—which provides a very effective cue to the relative depth of objects.

To take advantage of this cue, your entire body does not have to be moving: you can perceive depth from motion parallax by moving just your head. Take a moment to test this for yourself. Pick out an object in front of you and look at it with one eye closed. This eliminates retinal disparity as a possible cue. Now, while continuing to look at this object, move your head back and

Execute

forth in a sideways direction. Notice how other objects at different distances appear to move relative to the one you are looking at.

To experience this parallax effect again, hold your two index fingers at different distances in front of you and perform this exercise: with one eye closed, stare at one of your two fingers while moving your head back and forth. Again, you will see that one finger shifts in position, as if it were moving, relative to the other. The direction and speed of this shift depends on the distance between your two fingers and on the overall distance from you to your hands.

So far we have discussed situations in which the observer moves and objects in the world remain still. However, motion parallax is also effective in the complementary situation, when a *stationary* observer views a scene in which objects themselves move. For instance, imagine looking at clusters of leaves in a tree with one of your two eyes closed. When there is no wind, the still leaves seem to blend into a confusing array. But when stirred to life by a breeze, different groups of leaves stand out conspicuously in depth from one another. The movement of the leaves creates motion parallax information in the same way that movement of your head would.*

Motion pictures and television have made excellent use of depth from motion. For example, many of the special effects in *Star Trek* episodes and in the *Star Wars* movies rely heavily on the cue of motion parallax. And all video arcade games and other, more sophisticated virtual viewing environments exploit motion to create a compelling sense of three-dimensionality. Motion's

---

*Some perception researchers (for example, Cutting, 1997) distinguish between observer-induced motion parallax (where optical image motion is produced by a moving observer viewing stationary objects, sometimes called "motion perspective") and object-induced parallax (where a stationary viewer sees objects moving in the environment located at different depth planes, sometimes called "kinetic depth"). There is some justification for this distinction, since the former is very useful for self-navigation, while the latter is more useful for 3D shape perception.

potency is most vividly dramatized by computer-generated animations composed entirely of randomly arrayed clusters of dots. Viewing any single frame of the animation, you'd see nothing but a meaningless, random arrangement of dots. But when those dots undergo differential movement on the video screen, you see vivid 3D surfaces that can be quite complex in shape (Turner, Braunstein and Andersen, 1995). Here, the brain has literally created a 3D shape from motion, a capability discussed in more detail later.

Using motion parallax, people are quite good at judging whether one object is situated in front of or behind another one. In fact, relative depth judgments based on motion parallax are almost as accurate as those made using binocular disparity (Graham, 1965). This makes sense when you compare the geometrical bases of motion parallax and binocular disparity. Figure 8.34 shows two objects, *A* and *F,* being viewed from two vantage points, 1 and 2. Let's assume that fixation is always maintained on object *F* (for "fixation"). This means that at both vantage points the image of *F* will fall on the fovea. Because *A* is closer than *F,* the image of *A* will fall on one retinal area, *A1,* when *A* is viewed from vantage point 1; however, when *A* is viewed from vantage point 2, the image of *A* will fall on a different retinal area, *A2.* The distance between the retinal images produced by *A* and *F* varies from one vantage point to the other. At vantage point 1, the retinal images are separated by the distance between *F1* and *A1;* at vantage point 2, they are separated by a different amount, the distance between *F2* and *A2.* This variation in the retinal image distance between the images provides information about the distance between objects *A* and *F.*

There are two ways the situation shown in Figure 8.34 could arise. Vantage points 1 and 2 could represent the successive positions of a single eye as it moves from 1 to 2. In this case, the resulting variation in retinal image distances would be called *motion parallax.* Alternatively, vantage points 1 and 2 could represent the positions of left and right eyes. In this case, the variation in reti-

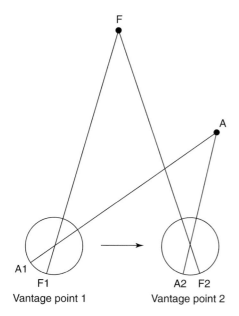

F

A

A1

F1

A2   F2

Vantage point 1   Vantage point 2

FIGURE 8.34
An illustration of the equivalence of retinal disparity and
motion parallax.

nal image distance would be called *retinal dis-parity*. In fact, if a single eye moves by 65 millimeters (the distance between your eyes), this movement produces a depth cue—motion parallax—that is equivalent to the cue produced by binocular viewing—retinal disparity.

There is another similarity between motion parallax and stereopsis. Recall from our discussion of random-dot stereograms how forms invisible to either eye alone could be synthesized from retinal disparity information. The same kind of synthesis of form can occur through motion parallax. In an ingenious set of experiments that have become classics, Brian Rogers and Maureen Graham (1979, 1984) asked observers to view a single array of random dots with just one eye (it is important to keep in mind that their stimuli were not stereograms and that viewing was monocular). The entire display consisted of about 2,000 dots, and a subset of dots could be displaced while the rest maintained their same positions. Figure 8.35 depicts one such display.

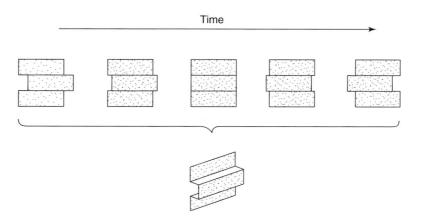

Time

FIGURE 8.35
Motion parallax, like stereopsis, can generate information about object form. The five panels in the top row depict changes over time in the position of a subset of dots in the display. These changes are produced either by the observer's head movements or by movement of the display itself. The bottom panel depicts the stable percept produced by either of these maneuvers. (Adapted from Rogers and Graham, 1979.)

In one condition, the displacement occurred whenever just the observer's head moved. In other words, moving the head from side to side caused the predesignated subset of dots to move relative to the rest. This condition would correspond to observer-induced motion. In a second condition, the observer held still while the display itself was moved, with the predesignated region of dots moving by an amount different from the rest. Rogers and Graham found that both forms of relative motion generated a clear, immediate impression of a surface standing out in depth from its background (as in the bottom panel of Figure 8.35). Moreover, so long as their heads or the display moved, observers could accurately describe the shape of this surface. But whenever both the observer's head and the display were stationary, the sensation of depth immediately vanished. Rogers and Graham's study clearly shows that motion parallax, like retinal disparity, can generate information about the shape and depth of objects, in the absence of all other cues. In fact, under some conditions, people cannot distinguish depth produced by motion from depth produced by binocular disparity because the two are so compellingly similar (Nawrot and Blake, 1993).

So, head motion with one eye generates the same kind of information generated by two eyes in a stationary head.* This raises an interesting question: Why is the visual system designed to provide two equally sensitive mechanisms for seeing objects in depth, one monocular and one binocular? Wouldn't it be safer to relocate the eyes on the side of the head, thereby achieving a panoramic view of the world? Then the consequent loss of disparity information could be compensated by the equally effective cue of motion parallax.

---

*Without even thinking about it, people with only one eye move their heads more when attempting to make depth judgments (Marotta et al., 1995). Presumably they are creating motion parallax information to compensate for the absence of stereopsis.

Differences

The key to this puzzle may have something to do with the type of animals that possess well-developed binocular vision. As a rule, these frontal-eyed animals are predators, who rely on stealth to capture their prey. Movements of the hunter's head or body could forewarn an intended victim, thereby costing the hunter a meal. So it may have been advantageous for predators to develop the capacity for stereopsis, a quieter but equally accurate means of depth perception. For humans whose hunting is confined to the supermarket, where there is no real concern about giving away one's whereabouts, motion parallax and stereopsis provide largely redundant information.

INTEGRATION OF DEPTH INFORMATION

The previous sections have described various sources of information specifying depth relations among objects and distances from a perceiver to those objects. As you should now be able to appreciate, the visual world is rich with depth information. How, then, are these multiple cues combined? Do we rely only on the most salient? Do some sources of depth information work better than others in particular circumstances? How are other aspects of vision influenced by depth information? Investigators are now beginning to address these questions, and this section provides an overview of some of the emerging answers.

One strategy for studying depth interactions entails varying the number of depth cues present in a display and asking how depth perception is affected. An excellent example of the application of this strategy comes from the work of Bruno and Cutting (1988). They tested all different combinations of four sources of depth information—size, interposition, motion and perspective—and measured the quality and the accuracy of depth for each combination. The results showed that these sources interacted additively, as if each source were processed separately and made its own unique contribution to depth perception. Bruno and Cutting speculate that the visual system is composed of different "minimodules," as they were termed, each devoted to one source of depth information. Conceivably, these mini-modules might relate to the multiplicity of specialized visual areas in the brain. In their studies, Bruno and Cutting varied the number of available cues, but these cues were never placed in conflict.

Execute

The strategy of pitting cues against one another has been employed in many other experiments (see, for example, Braunstein and Stern, 1980; Stevens and Brooks, 1988; Rogers and Collett, 1989). In essentially all cases, depth perception is degraded when cues conflict, implying that no single source of information dominates. In a related vein, it is possible to create displays in which one source of information (for example, perspective) generates ambiguous depth, meaning that the shape or configuration of a three-dimensional object can be seen in multiple, mutually exclusive ways.

A classic example of an ambiguous figure, the Necker cube, was shown in Chapter 1 (see Figure 1.3). The cube's configuration fluctuates over time as different components take turns being perceived as the front face of the cube. Either interpretation is consistent with the available perspective information specifying depth, so perception is unstable. However, the introduction of unambiguous disparity information stabilizes perception: the cube is seen in one perspective only. This strategy of disambiguating one source of depth information with another has been successfully applied to study other combinations of information as well (Dosher, Sperling and Wurst, 1986; Nawrot and Blake, 1991).

Finally, another strategy involves determining how depth information influences other aspects of vision, such as object recognition. To give an example, Nakayama, Shimojo and Silverman (1989) measured how well people could recognize faces when portions of the faces were missing. In one condition missing portions appeared to

A.   **B.**

FIGURE 8.36
A partially visible face as it would appear in front of (right-hand drawing) or behind (left-hand drawing) a surface. In Nakayama, Shimojo and Silverman (1989), stereopsis was used to place the face segments in depth relative to the surface. (Illustration courtesy of Ken Nakayama.)

be occluded by blank strips that appeared to be situated in front of the face (Figure 8.36A). A second condition displayed the same visible portions of the face only now they appeared as strips in front of a blank background (Figure 8.36B). Nakayama and colleagues used stereoscopic depth to manipulate the depth relations of the face regions and the blank regions. In the first condition observers perceived the head of a person partially occluded by venetian blinds; they had no difficulty recognizing the faces. But in the second condition recognition performance was seriously impaired, even though the number of face segments and the quality of the image remained the same. The fragments made no sense because the face no longer looked partially occluded. Using the stereo pairs in Figure 8.37, you can experience what the participants in this experiment saw. In this figure (an actual version of one used by Nakayama and colleagues), random speckles ("noise") have been added to the images to make recognition more difficult from the outset. Using this demonstration, notice how depth interpretation—occluded versus non-occluded—influences the perceptual organization of the face fragments.

FIGURE 8.37
Use the free-fusion technique (Box 8.2) to view the middle and left-hand pictures. The "strips" of face will appear "behind" the opaque, horizontal strips (as if the person were being viewed through venetian blinds). Next free-fuse the middle and righthand pictures. Now the face itself appears as strips or in front of the opaque strips. (Adapted from Nakayama, Shimojo and Silverman, 1989.)

DEPTH, ILLUSIONS AND SIZE CONSTANCY

In our discussion of static depth cues, we noted several perceptual errors that occur when people are confronted with misleading depth information. These errors involved distortions in perceived size, such as the moon's unusually large appearance when it is on the horizon. Several other, classic visual illusions are also characterized by misperceptions of size.

Examples of two of the better-known size illusions are given in Figure 8.38. In both cases, one portion of the figure appears larger than its partner, even though both are really identical in size. For over a century, psychologists have been fascinated by these illusions and have focused a great deal of research on testing various theories concerning their origins.

Let's conclude this chapter by considering one particular theory that, although not universally accepted, has endured over the years. This theory attributes errors in perceived size to the operation of monocular depth cues (Gregory, 1970). We'll call this the *depth theory,* and we'll introduce it with some examples.

Consider the left-hand illusion in Figure 8.38, known as the *Müller-Lyer illusion.* According to

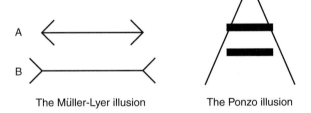

The Müller-Lyer illusion   The Ponzo illusion

FIGURE 8.38
Two size illusions.

the depth theory, the arrowheads on the ends of the vertical lines can be seen as angles formed by two intersecting surfaces. An example of this idea is shown in Figure 8.39. In both drawings, the vertical line represents the point of intersection, or the corner, formed by two surfaces. When the arrowheads point outward (as in B), the two surfaces appear slanted toward you. When they point inward (as in A), the surfaces appear to recede away from you. Why should the "corner" formed by the receding surfaces (inward-pointing arrowheads) appear longer than the one formed by the approaching surfaces (outward-pointing arrowheads)?

According to the depth theory, the answer is simple: because of the perspective cues supplied

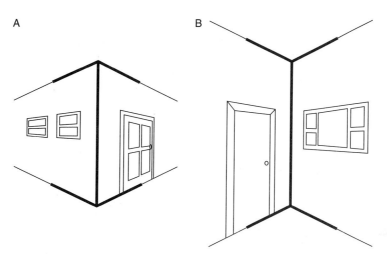

FIGURE 8.39
The Müller-Lyer illusion could arise from implied depth information.

by the arrowheads, the receding corner appears farther away than the approaching corner. At the same time, the retinal images of the two corners are identical in size. Now there is only one way objects at *different* distances can cast images of *equal* size: the farther object must actually be larger. In the case of the two vertical lines, the height of the corner formed by the receding surfaces (inward-pointing arrowheads) would have to be longer than the height of the one that is formed by the approaching surfaces (outward-pointing arrowheads). And this is exactly how it is perceived.

The same line of reasoning applies to the other size illusion illustrated in Figure 8.38, the *Ponzo illusion.* In this case, too, perspective cues imply that one region of the figure is located farther away than another. According to the depth theory, this distance information enters into judgments of the sizes of objects occupying these different regions. Note, again, that the apparently larger object is situated in that portion of the figure that appears farther away.

The depth theory, then, attributes size illusions to errors in perceived distance (Gregory, 1970). The theory is based on the observation that perceived size remains constant despite differences

in distance from the viewer and, hence, changes in the size of the retinal image cast. In other words, perceived size is *scaled* in terms of perceived distance, a process known as **size constancy.**

We call size constancy a scaling process because one unit of measure (retinal image size) is converted, or scaled, into another (perceived size). Road maps typically include scales that transform centimeters into kilometers (or inches into miles); the visual system contains a mechanism that scales image size into object size. It's crucial that retinal image size be scaled, since the size of the image of an object depends on how far away that object is. As a result, *unscaled retinal* image size would be a poor index of *object* size. Without size scaling, one would always be confused about the height of people, the width of doorways, the size of cars, and so on. The fact that one rarely errs in these kinds of judgments means that the visual system utilizes depth information in making size judgments.

Just how good is the visual system at estimating the true sizes of objects? In a classic study, Holway and Boring (1941) found that an observer's accuracy at judging a circle's size was almost flawless under conditions rich with depth information. But

Execute

as depth cues were progressively eliminated (for example, by requiring a person to close one eye), size judgments became increasingly dependent on retinal image size; the perceived size of the same object increased when the object was closer to the observer—a breakdown in size constancy.

In an interesting extension of Holway and Boring's study, Schiffman (1967) asked at what *distance* a familiar object would appear to be if all depth cues were removed. He found that in this case, observers judged distance on the basis of their memory about the true size of the familiar object. So, in the absence of other cues, remembered size can determine perceived distance.

Size constancy seems to occur automatically. This is evidenced by the fact that people are rarely aware of the size of their retinal images. Yet with appropriate instruction people can accurately judge the retinal size of an object, in effect ignoring information about distance (Gilinsky, 1955; Epstein, 1963).

You can verify this ability yourself. Hold up both thumbs with thumb nails facing you. Place them side by side approximately 20 centimeters (about 8 inches) from your eyes. They will look identical in size, as well they should. Next, extend one arm until that thumb is approximately 40 centimeters (about 16 inches) away, twice the distance of the other one. At first glance the two thumbs should continue to appear equivalent in size, even though the image size of the nearer one is now twice that of the farther one. This is what we mean by size constancy.

Now, while maintaining your thumbs at these different distances, move the farther one laterally until it appears just to the side of the nearer one. With one eye closed (to prevent double vision) and your head very steady, carefully compare the apparent size of the two thumbnails. Switching your attention from one to the other reveals that the closer thumbnail does look larger than the farther one. With this exercise you've managed to capture a glimpse of your retinal image. But notice how quickly this glimpse disappears once you open both eyes or move your head.

At present, we don't know exactly how the visual system performs this scaling process of size constancy, although there are some tantalizing clues from neurophysiology. Studying neurons in area V4 of monkeys, Dobbins and colleagues (1998) found cells that responded best to a bar of given size located at a particular distance from the monkey. When the bar was moved to a non-preferred distance, the cell's response dwindled, even if the size of the bar was adjusted to be identical in retinal image size to that used at the preferred distance. The cell, in other words, was responding to the actual size of the bar, taking distance into account; the cell was not just responding to the size of the image of the bar on the retina. Groups of neurons responding in this fashion could provide a substrate for size constancy (see also Trotter et al., [1992]). It remains to be learned how these V4 neurons acquire information about distance.

Neural

SUMMARY AND PREVIEW

This chapter has examined sources of information, monocular and binocular, used by perception to specify the 3D layout of objects in the visual environment. We have emphasized that 3D vision is computed automatically and effortlessly, without conscious deliberation. We have also seen that depth perception influences perceived size, resulting in size constancy as well as certain illusions of size. This connection between illusion and constancy should remind you of a similar connection seen earlier, for lightness perception (Chapter 3).

Although we have emphasized distance information in this chapter, depth cues' more general contribution should not be overlooked. As David Marr (1982) has pointed out, depth serves to define objects relative to their backgrounds—helping the viewer to distinguish those objects and appreciate their shapes. In the next chapter, we take up another aspect of vision—motion—that serves that same purpose in addition to others.

KEY TERMS

absolute distance
accommodation
aerial perspective
allocentric
amodal completion
Ames room
binocular rivalry
convergence
convergence insufficiency
depth perception
diplopia
disparity-selective cells
egocentric direction
Emmert's law
horopter
interposition
linear perspective

motion parallax
neon spreading
oculomotor cues
perceived distance
random-dot stereograms
relative distance
retinal disparity
shading
size constancy
stereoblindness
stereopsis
stereoscope
strabismus (or squint)
texture gradient
transparency
vernier acuity
visual cues

CHAPTER 9

ACTION AND THE PERCEPTION OF EVENTS

You are walking alone in the beautiful woods near Walden Pond, where the philosopher and environmentalist Henry David Thoreau lived and wrote in the 1840's. You are deep in thought, enjoying the gentle, warm breeze on this beautiful summer day. An occasional bird flies back and forth overhead; off to the side of the path, three Monarch butterflies hover around tall, purplish flowers.

Your reverie is interrupted when a small rabbit, frightened by your approach, bounds away. The rabbit, well-camouflaged by the way its coloration blended with the foliage, had been invisible to you. But the rabbit's movements broke the camouflage. You turn your gaze toward the motion but never get a good look at the creature. The hopping motion, however, tells the tale.

As this scenario illustrates, motion serves multiple perceptual purposes: detection (seeing something hop away), segregation (recognizing something move relative to its background),

guidance (turning toward the source of the motion), and identification (the hopping motion identified the object as a rabbit).

The neural processes responsible for perceived motion begin by extracting from the retinal image the spatial displacements of various environmental features over time. This defines motion as a spatio-temporal event. As you walked through the woods, a variety of spatio-temporal events were occurring simultaneously within different locations in your field of view. Some of those events (for example, the butterflies fluttering about the flowers) occurred in unison while others (for example, the scurrying rabbit) were unique. In addition, your own movements—eyes, head and body—were constantly producing spatio-temporal variations in the optical image on your retina. Somehow the visual system must sort the various local motions into sets of events that belong to different objects, putting together local motions that originate from one moving object, and segregating local motions that come from different events. The tasks of aggregating and segregating local signals may remind you of similar challenges that confront form perception (Chapters 5 and 6).

Clinical

The experience of motion, in all its various forms, is so integral to daily life that it is hard to imagine life without it. But in rare cases, individuals who have suffered certain kinds of brain damage can no longer perceive motion. To get some idea of what this would be like, consider this description of D. L., a woman who suffered extensive damage to the posterior portions of both hemispheres of her brain. Although D. L.'s visual acuity and form perception were normal, her experience of visual motion was drastically impaired.

> She had difficulty, for example, in pouring tea or coffee into a cup because the fluid appeared to be frozen, like a glacier. In addition, she could not stop pouring at the right time since she was unable to perceive the movement in the cup (or a pot) when the fluid rose. . . . In a room where more than two other people were walking she felt very insecure and unwell, and usually left the room immediately, because "people were suddenly here or there but I have not seen them moving." . . . She could not cross the street because of her inability to judge the speed of a car, but she could identify the car itself without difficulty. "When I'm looking at the car first, it seems far away. But then, when I want to cross the road, suddenly the car is very near." (Zihl, von Cramon and Mai, 1983, p. 315)

Today, nearly two decades after her brain was damaged, D. L.'s condition remains essentially unchanged, though she has developed some coping strategies. For example, she has learned to look away from a speaker's face when listening to that person talk; otherwise D. L. is distracted because the speaker's mouth never seems to move (Zihl, von Cramon Mai and Schmid, 1991; Campbell et al., 1997).

As you'll learn later, the damage to D. L.'s brain includes areas that are crucially involved in the perception of motion. D. L.'s peculiar, circumscribed visual deficit is yet another example of how the brain compartmentalizes different visual functions.

Being unable to see motion is frustrating and dangerous. Not only was D. L. unable to see the movements of other creatures and objects, she also had difficulty seeing the consequences of her own movements and actions. Her inability to judge when enough tea had been poured is a reminder that perceivers themselves cause many of the changes and movements that they perceive.

As you move about among the world's objects, such as the trees around Walden Pond, you see those objects from various perspectives. You also act on the world's objects, such as the rabbit you inadvertently frightened. Those actions influence what you will subsequently see. Thus, while your perceptions govern your actions, your actions in turn influence what you perceive, as Figure 1.1 denoted. Because actions are an integral part of visual perception, our discussion of the dynamic perceptual world has to consider what the perceiver *does* as well as what the perceiver *sees*. But let's begin our discussion of motion perception by considering one of the important things that motion does for us.

STRUCTURE FROM MOTION

We can derive vivid impressions of the 3D shape of an object from motion, an ability called the perception of **structure from motion (SFM).** To see what this entails, look at Figure 9.1. A wire clothes hanger has been bent and twisted into a meaningless three-dimensional shape. A light source is arranged so that the bent hanger casts a shadow on a piece of paper. When the wire is motionless, the shadow gives a viewer no idea of the hanger's shape. But when the wire begins to rotate, this movement makes its three-dimensional shape immediately obvious (Wallach and O'Connell, 1953). Perception of SFM can also be compellingly created using dynamic arrays of random dots generated under computer control on a video monitor (Figure 9.2).

FIGURE 9.1
Movement can provide information about form.

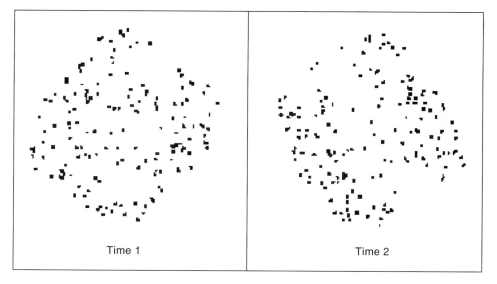

FIGURE 9.2
Two frames from an animation sequence depicting a transparent cube rotating about the vertical axis. The surface of the cube is textured with dots placed randomly over its six sides. From single frames, the shape and volume of the object are unknown, but when the display is shown as a movie, you would be able to tell the object's structure from its motion.

During the last decade, SFM perception has been intensively studied, with particular emphasis on the accuracy of form judgments that use SFM information (Norman and Lappin, 1992), the stimulus conditions that enable or limit SFM perception (Todd and Norman, 1991) and the neural circuits that make SFM possible (Nawrot and Blake, 1991; Andersen and Bradley, 1998).

BIOLOGICAL MOTION

Execute

One class of SFM events is important enough to merit particular attention: events that distinguish animate from inanimate objects. Imagine walking along the beach and spotting what looks like a clear, gooey substance. Something has probably been washed up by the tide, but you can't be sure whether or not it's alive. You watch it for a while, waiting for it to move. Finally, you notice some movement, but not the sort that suggests life. Instead, the gooey substance seems to be simply floating in response to the motions of incoming waves. There's something in its pattern of movement that signifies the object is not alive.

This seaside encounter demonstrates a couple of things. First, motion offers powerful clues about an object's biological status, whether something is living or not. The encounter is also a reminder that one kind of motion can be discriminated from another. When a creature's body moves *en masse,* that movement signifies something different than if its parts move relatively independent of one another.

Humans regularly watch the motion generated by biological creatures. This happens most commonly when we watch another person walk, run or dance. The motions we see tell us much more than just whether that person is alive or not; they may also reveal the person's sex and, perhaps, the individual's identity. Since this is a particularly important type of event perception, and since it provides some general lessons about motion perception, let's consider biological motion in some detail.

Recognizing Biological Motion

As a friend walks across the room, you are able to recognize that person even if you don't see the person's face. What characteristics of his or her gait allow you to recognize who it is? Gunnar Johansson, at the University of Uppsala in Sweden, was the first to study this question systematically (1975). Johansson began by determining the minimum information needed to recognize biological motion. Reasoning that the movement of the body's joints might convey particularly important information, Johansson attached tiny light bulbs to a person's hips, knees, ankles, shoulders, wrists, and elbows. This person was clothed entirely in black so that looking at the individual in a dark room, you would see only the small set of illuminated "dots." Johansson's aim was to eliminate all the familiar, nonmotion cues that might give away the fact that the figure underlying the dots was a person.

Figure 9.3 gives some idea of what people saw in Johansson's study. The pictures show lights attached to a person who is sitting very still on a chair. The person in panel A is seated with both feet on the ground; the person in panel B is also seated, but with legs crossed. Viewing the pictures without these clues, however, gives the viewer very little to go on. The lights appear to be a random collection of spots: they could be just about anything. Yet Johansson found that as soon as the person began to move, viewers recognized that it was a person. In other demonstrations, Johansson discovered that the same light bulbs were sufficient to reveal when a person was painting, riding a bicycle, or doing push-ups. The overall movements of the lights—and, more importantly, their movements relative to one another—conveyed this information in a most compelling way.

The following is an even more impressive demonstration of the potency of biological motion. Johansson outfitted two people with small light bulbs and had them dance in the dark. Figure 9.4 is a sample of frames taken from a motion picture Johansson made of the two people dancing. Since any single frame contains information only about space and none about time, examination of any one frame gives no clue about what you're looking at. However, even a brief section of the film, when projected at the proper speed, gives an almost instantaneous impression of two people dancing. It has been found, in addition, that this minimal information enables viewers to

A

B

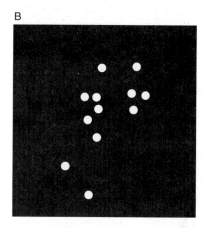

FIGURE 9.3
Each white dot is a light attached to some part of a person's body. (Drawings adapted from Johansson, 1975.)

identify whether an individual actor is a male or a female. (Males and females typically have different shoulder and hip widths and, consequently, as males walk, their bodies oscillate about a lower center of movement than do the bodies of females.) Viewers can recognize their own gait in such displays, as well as the gaits of friends (Cutting and Proffitt, 1981).

Structure from motion portrayed using these "points of light" is referred to as **point-light motion.** The perception of biological motion from just a few moving points of light is so compelling that digital artists, in collaboration with the distinguished contemporary choreographer Merce Cunningham, have exploited it to create effective, aesthetically-pleasing performances by computer-generated, virtual dancers, whose movements are represented only by points and swirls of light.*

---

*Commercial animators use similar techniques to produce delightful mismatches between an animated cartoon figure and its movements. For example, the movements of an actual adult human doing a series of somersaults can be extracted and used to control the animation of a cartoon baby. The result is a somersaulting or dancing baby. Such effects are arresting because viewers immediately recognize that the movements are inappropriate to the body executing them.

People who haven't seen firsthand Johansson's demonstrations or Cunningham's dances tend to get the wrong idea about what's involved. People assume that complex thought processes are used to deduce the activity conveyed by the complex movements of the small lights. But this assumption is wrong. The perception of biological motion actually occurs automatically. People do not have to puzzle over what they are seeing. The impression is as immediate as it is when viewing any other form of motion. In fact, viewing the moving lights for as little as 200 milliseconds is enough to enable a person to identify familiar biological motion without having been told what to expect (Johansson, von Hofsten and Jansson, 1980). Perception of biological motion persists even when the moving spots differ from one another in color, or when some spots are presented to one eye and the remainder are presented to the other eye (Ahlström, Blake and Ahlström, 1997).

It's clear that biological motion perception does not require sophisticated thought processes—cats (Blake, 1993) and very young infants can discriminate biological from nonbiological motion. Not only can infants tell the two types of motion apart, but they also have a distinct preference for motion that is biological in origin.

Differences

FIGURE 9.4
Frames from a movie of two people dancing in the dark with lights attached to parts of their bodies.
(Adapted from Johansson, 1975.)

358

Robert Fox and Cynthia McDaniel (1982) presented infants with two different motion patterns side by side on a television screen. Both biological and nonbiological motions were presented for several seconds. Following Johansson's method, each pattern consisted of some white dots against a dark background. One of the two patterns represented the joints of a human who was running. Dots in the other set moved randomly in all directions. An observer sitting near the television screen noted which side of the television screen the infants preferred to look at. By 4 months of age, infants showed a clear preference for biological rather than nonbiological motion.

Fox and McDaniel worried that their infants might have been responding not to the biological or nonbiological character of the motion but to how random or constrained the motion was. (Since arms and legs do not usually go flying in all directions, biological motion is more constrained than random motion.) So a second experiment was needed to verify that infants had not been responding to differences in the randomness of motion.

In their second experiment, Fox and McDaniel used a display with dots representing a human running in place paired with that same dotted motion pattern shown upside down. Again, infants preferred the biological motion pattern—the one presented right side up. (For a good analytic treatment of other studies of biological motion, particularly ones with infants, see Bertenthal, 1996.)

Execute

Studies of infants' responses to biological motion displays do not prove that the ability to recognize biological motion is innate. Those studies do, however, confirm that recognition of certain forms of biological motion does not require complex intellectual processing. Recent neuroimaging studies have revealed a brain region at the juncture of the parietal and temporal lobes that is specifically activated when people view point-light animation sequences, but is not activated by other animation sequences that involve nonbiological motion (Grossman et al., 2000).

From the perception of biological motion produced by watching other people, let's next turn to motion information that guides your own movements.

THE VISUAL GUIDANCE OF LOCOMOTION

Three centuries ago, the philosopher George Berkeley (1709/1950) had an intriguing idea about vision's main purpose, and it had to do with motion. He wrote that vision was designed to allow animals to "foresee . . . the damage or benefit which is likely to ensue, upon the application of their own bodies to this or that body which is at a distance" (p. 39). In other words, he believed that vision keeps creatures out of trouble, which certainly is true. When you move about in the world—walking, running, driving a car, or piloting an airplane—you'd better know *whether* you're going to collide with something, and if so, *when.* This knowledge allows you to change course, thereby avoiding harm. As Berkeley realized, vision guides movement and movement alters vision. Let's consider this interplay between vision and locomotion, starting with the visual information that allows you to steer your movements properly.

Finding the Right Direction

Most people move about easily, with a minimum number of collisions, even on crowded sidewalks. Obviously, humans exploit some source of information to locomote—to keep on course, and, if necessary, to change course when needed. But what exactly is that source of information, and how is it used? As you move about the world, the image on your retina changes with your movements. To take a simple example, as you move toward some stationary object, the image of that object on your retina expands. James Gibson, a leading perceptual theorist, pointed out that visual expansion could guide complicated and important movements of the body and head.

"To kiss someone," Gibson (1979) instructed, "magnify the face-form, if the facial expression is amiable, so as almost to fill the field of view. It is absolutely essential to keep one's eyes open so as to avoid collision. It is also wise to learn to discriminate those subtle [features] that specify amiability" (p. 233).

Neural

Kissing isn't the only activity that produces a flow of visual information. Think about what happens when you walk toward some object such as the door to a building. To appreciate how the retinal image changes in this situation, look at Figure 9.5. Each panel in the figure represents what you might see as you move toward the door. This changing pattern of stimulation is called **optic flow.** Note particularly how the view changes from one drawing to the next. Though a series of stills cannot fully capture the dynamic character of these changes, there are some important things that can be appreciated. The door you are looking at and walking toward always remains at the center of the field of view. Objects around the door— to its sides, above, and below—shift radially outward, flowing farther and farther into the periphery of the visual field. The center of this flow, known as its *focus,* allows you to steer yourself toward the door. You will successfully reach the door by keeping the door at the center of the outward optic flow.

Gibson proposed that the pattern of outward flow could be used to tell where one is headed and how to steer around obstacles. To test this idea, he filmed the view from the cockpit of an aircraft in flight and found that viewers of this film could identify the direction in which the plane was headed (Gibson, 1947).

There's a more general way to represent the optic flow produced in situations such as the one illustrated in Figure 9.5. Imagine that an observer is looking directly ahead and walking on a perfectly straight course through the environment. At any instant, the optical flow can be portrayed as a velocity field, where lines signify the instantaneous optical velocity of elements (the dots) in the environment (Figure 9.6). Each line's direction corresponds to the direction of optic flow at one point in the field; the length of the line corresponds to the instantaneous speed of the optic flow. The single vertical line sticking up from the "horizon" in Figure 9.6 represents the direction in which the observer is headed. So long as the direction of heading and the speed of forward motion are the same, this single diagram would be valid for the optical flow for a walker, a runner or a driver.

William Warren (1998) examined the accuracy with which observers use optic-flow information to judge the direction in which they're

FIGURE 9.5
Changes in the field of view as a person approaches a door.

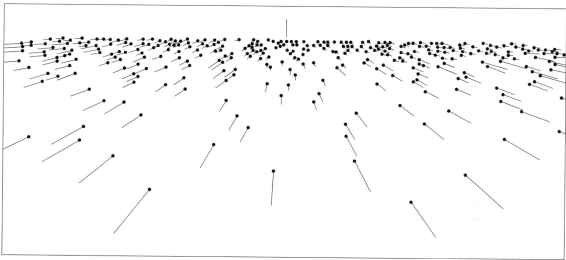

FIGURE 9.6
Instantaneous velocity field produced by an observer moving forward on a straight course parallel to a plane. The single vertical line poking up from the plane indicates the direction in which the observer is moving. Dots represent elements on the surface plane, and line segments indicate the velocity vector associated with each element. Vector orientation signifies the direction of the local optical flow; vector length signifies the speed of the flow. (After Warren, Morris, & Kalish, 1988.)

heading. In Warren's experiments, people were shown computer-generated displays that consisted of moving dots. The moving dots simulated the optic flow that would be generated on the retina as an individual walked in a particular direction. In each trial, the observer judged whether he or she appeared to be heading to the left or right of a stationary target located at various positions along the display's simulated horizon. Even with relatively few dots in the display, or with presentations lasting less than half a second, observers managed to achieve accuracy levels equal to what would be needed to guide high-speed locomotion.

In an important related experiment, Warren and associates used the same measurements with a group of older observers (age range 61 to 78 years) whose vision, despite their age, was quite good. Using displays that simulated speeds of locomotion from a slow walk (1 meter per second) through a fast run (3.8 meters per second), Warren, Blackwell and Morris (1989) found that at all speeds the older observers were only half as good

at judging direction as were young observers tested under the same conditions. Warren and his colleagues speculate that the diminished ability to judge direction of heading could contribute to age-related errors of locomotion and result in an increased incidence of falling accidents.

Patients with Alzheimer's disease, a progressive, degenerative disease of the brain, often have difficulty finding their way around their surroundings, even when those surroundings are familiar. Two groups of researchers have connected this difficulty to subnormal processing of information from the optic flow. If optic flow information, as Gibson hypothesized, helps us keep track of our heading, failure to process that information fully could produce spatial confusion and loss of one's bearings.

Rizzo and Nawrot (1998) showed that patients with mild to moderate Alzheimer's disease have particular trouble extracting form or shape information from stimuli in which the form is defined by movement (shape from motion). Moreover, some patients with Alzheimer's disease are impaired in

Clinical

extracting directional information from optic flow stimuli (Tetewsky and Duffy, 1999). Many of these same patients showed correspondingly poor performance on a test of spatial navigation (wayfinding) ability. Rizzo and colleagues (1997) tested Alzheimer's patients and non-Alzheimer control subjects in a realistic driving simulator scenario. Crashes and near-misses, which were especially prevalent among people with Alzheimer's disease, were linked to driver inattention and driver error.

The recent work on optic flow that you've just read about confirms Gibson's hypothesis of 50 years ago: visual information contained in optic flow can be used to determine heading during normal locomotion, ranging from slow walking (1 meter/second) to running (about 4 meters/second). So visual information can specify *where* you're going. But it's equally important to know *when* you're going to arrive (or collide). How does visual information help us do that?

Judging Your Time of Arrival

Differences

Perhaps you've watched seabirds diving for food. They fly along until a fish is spotted in the water below, then, without warning, they dive into the water at impressive speed. Often they get their fish. The whole process is a marvel to behold. Some species of birds add additional mystery to their performance: a split second before hitting the water's surface, these birds fold in their wings, streamlining their bodies and easing their entry into the water. Watching this performance, you'd think that somehow the bird knew exactly when it would hit the water. Though the bird doesn't have sophisticated navigational instruments, it performs this feat with precision and consistency (Lee and Reddish, 1981). Humans perform comparable, albeit less spectacular, feats whenever we walk, run, drive or catch a ball. What's the information that enables us to do these things?

Let's begin by considering the information that *might* be available to a creature who is approaching some stationary object in its environ-

ment. Figure 9.5 showed that as you approach an object—a door in that case—the image size of that object expands. If you are walking toward the door at a constant rate, the rate of expansion specifies the time to collision—the moment at which you will reach the door.

Suppose that at time t you're a certain distance, say D meters, away from the door. If you move at a steady rate (no acceleration), travel time is equal to travel distance divided by travel rate. So if your rate is R meters per second, and distance is D meters, then time to arrival will be D/R seconds. However, to solve this equation you must have good information about both distance and rate. How does the visual system get such information? It doesn't. Instead, as David Lee (1980) suggested, vision uses another, dynamic source of information about time to arrival—which makes it unnecessary to know either distance or rate.

Imagine you're 100 meters from a telephone pole when you start walking toward it at a rate of 1 meter per second. Suppose, further, that while walking, you look directly at a knothole on the pole. To simplify calculations, assume the knothole is 1 centimeter in diameter. Using simple trigonometry, we can calculate the size of the image cast by the knothole on your retina. We can also calculate how that retinal image changes moment by moment during the approach (the derivative of image size with respect to time).

Lee designated the *ratio* between the retinal image size and the rate of change in that image size at any given instant as tau. For the case we've been working with—approaching the telephone pole at a steady rate—tau is 1/100. By calculating tau, a visual system would also have the time to collision—time to collision (in seconds) is the reciprocal of tau. This kind of calculation is especially valuable because its outcome is independent of object size. So long as starting distance and rate of travel are constant, tau is constant, regardless of object size. If you started out just ten meters from the object, tau would be 1/10, and the time to collision would be the reciprocal of tau, or 10 seconds. If you approach the pole more rapidly, tau decreases and its reciprocal increases, again as the laws of physics suggest it should. For example, if you start 100 meters from the pole and jog toward it at 5 meters per second, tau is 1/20, which yields a collision time of 20 seconds.

The connection between imminent impact and rate of expansion of retinal image size holds for any moving creature that has its eyes open—including the diving birds mentioned earlier. The visual system carries out these complex computations so rapidly that resulting information about rate of expansion can be used to control the braking of an automobile (Lee, 1976), the split-second changes in gait that are needed when running across rough terrain (Warren, Young and Lee, 1986), or the various movements and adjustments of the hand that are required to catch a ball (Savelsbergh, Whiting and Bootsma, 1991). Lest you think of this coupling between optical expansion and action as something calculated and conscious, it's worth pointing out that people can succeed in these tasks even though they are not aware—or able to articulate—what they're doing (Savelsbergh, Whiting and Bootsma, 1991).

Incidentially, animals as dissimilar as fiddler crabs, chickens, monkeys and human infants, all behave as if they can compute tall, for they all try to avoid looming objects (Schiff, 1965). This is true even for newborn infants who have never before encountered a looming stimulus (Figure 9.7). Apparently, learning plays little role in this behavior.

Although tau may be helpful in many circumstances where we need to recognize collision time, that quantity cannot be our only cue to collision. In fact, tau fails under a number of conditions (Tresilian, 1999). For example, if the approach rate is not constant, tau evaluated at any single moment fails to give the correct collision time.

This same problem also undermines tau's usefulness as a predictor of vertical movement. Tau cannot correctly predict when a falling body will strike some surface because the body's rate of movement is not constant (due to gravity-induced acceleration). Additionally, with a very slow approach to an object, the rate of image expansion could become so small as to be undetectable by the visual system. In discussing tau's limitations, Tresilian (1999) identifies additional cues that compensate for tau's failures in various situations.

FIGURE 9.7
Most animals, including human infants, will try to avoid a looming stimulus, even when that stimulus is portrayed on a television screen.

Locomotion and Movement Without Vision

Although locomotion and other forms of movement through space tend to be visually guided, there are times when they can manage despite the absence of vision. With eyes closed, you can walk around with a fair degree of safety, at least for several seconds. You can also keep track of a moving object without constantly watching it. By visually sampling the object's trajectory every half second or so, you can track it pretty accurately. Or if you take a quick look at the objects on your desk, and then close your eyes, you can reach out and grasp any one of them with relative ease. Even if you miss, your hand will be fairly close to the intended position. Small errors tend to creep in during the final moments of actually trying to grasp the object; then vision seems especially important (Goodale, Pelisson and Prablanc, 1986).

Clinical

This dissociation between the initial, large movements of the hand and the final, smaller ones shows up dramatically in a neurological condition called **optic ataxia** (*ataxia* means a disorder of movement). Damasio and Benton (1979) examined a patient who had localized brain lesions resulting from a suicide attempt. One affected area, immediately in front of the visual cortex, integrates visual information about the hands and arms with proprioceptive information about the hands and arms. (**Proprioception** is the sensation-based awareness of where your limbs are.) When the patient's eyes were open, she had great difficulty reaching for objects—a cigarette or ashtray might be missed by several inches. She would begin to reach out in the right direction, but at the last second, her arm and hand would go astray. She then had to grope about for the object as though she were blind.

Her difficulties with visually guided reaching were not caused by impairment of her sense of touch: with her eyes closed, she had no trouble buttoning or unbuttoning garments or pointing to some part of her body. The impairments were also not caused by diminished vision. In fact, her

visual acuity was quite normal. Moreover, she had no trouble walking with her eyes open. The impairment seemed to be limited to fine hand movements performed under visual guidance. This rare disorder is a reminder of how crucial a role vision normally plays in guiding movements. It is also a reminder that a complete theory of vision must include the action that vision makes possible.

EYE MOVEMENTS: THEIR AIMS AND EFFECTS

There's no doubt that vision helps guide your exploration of the world around you. We've already discussed how vision guides one particular form of exploration, locomotion. Now let's turn to visual explorations that are made possible by small, rapid movements of the eye, rather than by larger, slower movements of limbs and the entire body.

Researchers use sophisticated instruments to track eye movements. The resulting eye movement records provide accurate information about where someone is looking at any given moment. (You saw one such record in Figure 6.2.) These instruments also track a viewer's shifts in gaze while inspecting a visual scene. From the resulting eye movement records, it is possible to deduce which aspects of the scene receive closest scrutiny.

In one application of this technique, Carmody, Kundel and Toto (1984) monitored the eye movements of radiologists who were examining x-rays for signs of tumors. Compared to the doctors' verbal reports of what they did as they examined the x-rays, their eye movements produced a richer, more comprehensive description of their strategies.

We will deal with two principal kinds of eye movements (Steinman, Kowler and Collewijn, 1990). To anticipate, one type is responsible for shifting your gaze rapidly from one object to another. Such eye movements include the ones you're making right now as you read this book. The other type of eye movement, whose speed may vary from pretty fast to quite slow, allows you to smoothly track a moving target, such as a golf ball that's just been putted toward the hole. We distinguish these two principal types of eye movements because each serves a distinct purpose, though they are usually coordinated with one another and depend upon different (but partially overlapping) neural circuits in the brain (Krauzlis and Stone, 1999).*

We'll also spend some time on the variety of smooth eye movements that help your eyes stay fixed on an object even when your head and body move about. You can experience this last type of movement by looking at the number at the top of this page while moving your head slowly back and forth. Anyone who watches your eyes during this maneuver will see them move in their orbits, compensating for the movement of your head.

Acquiring the Target

Consider an unpleasant situation that you may have experienced. (We've selected this situation because it is common and also because it involves both types of eye movements just mentioned.) Imagine that while reading, you suddenly spot out of the corner of your eye something scurrying across the floor. Your eyes swing rapidly away from what you've been reading toward the surprise visitor. This kind of high-speed eye movement is designed to shift the image of some potentially interesting object (the scurrying thing) from the periphery of the retina (where acuity is poor) to the fovea (where acuity is good). About one-fifth of a second after spotting the creature, your eyes begin to move. Almost instantly, they reach a very high speed of

movement (achieving velocities of almost 20 centimeters per second). Then, usually less than one-tenth of a second after they started to move, the eyes screech to a halt.

When the eyes move about in this way, they do so in abrupt jerks; as a result, eye movements of this type are called **saccades** (from the French verb *saccader,* meaning "to jerk"). The eye does not jerk, or saccade, only when it needs to fixate on some object out in the periphery. Anytime you shift your gaze from one object to another, your eye executes these jerky movements. For example, while you read this page your eyes are saccading from word to word, four or five times each second (recall our discussion of reading in Chapter 6). Because you shift your gaze thousands of times each hour, saccades can certainly lay claim to being your most commonly used instrument for visual exploration. Since you need to make so many saccades, it is fortunate that the eye muscles responsible for these saccades never become fatigued (Fuchs and Binder, 1983).

Saccadic Suppression In Chapter 2 you read that vision tends to be suppressed during a blink. A similar dampening of vision accompanies saccades. To experience this, stand in front of a mirror and watch the reflection of your eyes as you make saccades voluntarily. Allow your eyes to jump back and forth between two points several inches apart. Though you know that your eyes have moved, you never actually see that movement. This is a puzzle. Furthermore, during the saccade you don't experience blurred vision. Yet if you took a photograph with a camera that moved at the same rate your eyes moved, you'd get a very blurred, low-contrast picture (see Figure 9.8). Why, then, do you not experience impaired vision each time you execute a saccade?

Illusion

Perhaps the retinal image is changing so rapidly (see Box 9.1) that the motion can't even be perceived. After all, there is a lower threshold, a minimum velocity below which motion cannot be seen. For example, you cannot actually see the movement of a clock's minute hand even though

---

*The categories of eye movements introduced here have no bearing on the distinction, between conjective and vergence eye movements. That earlier distinction was based exclusively on the *direction* in which the eyes moved. In fact, one can have saccadic movements that are conjunctive or disjunctive; one can also have slower, smooth movements that are conjunctive or disjunctive.

FIGURE 9.8
Moving a camera while the shutter is open produces a blurred picture.

you know that it's moving. Perhaps, then, there is also an upper threshold, a maximum velocity above which you can't see motion. Such an upper threshold would limit ability to see the blur and motion that accompany saccades.

To test this suggestion, you'd have to move some object at a rate equal to the rate at which the eye would sweep across that object during a saccade. Can an observer see an object moving at this rate? To make sure that motion was being seen, you might ask the observer to identify the direction in which the object moved. It turns out that the ability to see the moving object depends on its size and contrast. Rapidly moving objects of low contrast are impossible to see. So are rapidly moving small objects, regardless of their contrast. However, large, rapidly moving objects can be seen if their contrast is sufficiently great (Burr and Ross, 1982). So rapid movement does not on its own preclude vision.

The rapid movement accompanying saccades is not seen because of visual masking. Masking

occurs when, immediately before and after each saccade, the eye momentarily fixates. Under normal viewing conditions, these fixations produce a stationary, patterned retinal image with abrupt onset and offset (Dodge, 1900). In the laboratory, masking can be precluded by measuring visibility against a nonpatterned, uniform background. However, even when this step is taken, some saccadic suppression remains.

Perceptual Stability   As you read this paragraph, each and every saccade shifts the page's retinal image, sometimes by quite a bit. You can mimic these retinal image shifts by keeping your eyes still (minimizing saccades) while quickly jiggling the page back and forth. Though the retinal image shifts around under both conditions, the perceptual consequences are very different. Somehow, when we make saccades the visual world appears to remain still, despite what's happening on the retina. So where does this remarkable perceptual stability come from? Specifi-

BOX 9.1

BLINKING, WINKING AND FLICKERING

In modern industrialized societies, people are immersed in lights that blink and flicker. Some of these lights, such as the flashing lights atop a police vehicle, try to capture attention. Others, like the flashing light at a railroad crossing, are designed to warn. For a flashing light to be effective, it must flicker at a rate that can be easily seen. If it flickers too rapidly or too slowly, the flicker will be imperceptible.

Much is known about the **critical flicker frequency (CFF)**—the highest rate of flicker that can be perceived as such. When this highest frequency is exceeded, the separate flashes of light blend together to yield the illusion of continuous light. Under the best conditions, the human CFF is around 60 Hz. (*Hz* the abbreviation for "hertz," is a unit of flicker rate equivalent to one on/off cycle per second.) In fact, this is why you cannot see the flicker from a typical fluorescent lamp. Although the lamp actually does flicker on and off at a rate of 60 Hz, you can't see the flicker because its rate exceeds your CFF. However, a bee looking at the same lamp could perceive the 60-Hz flicker, since the bee's CFF is around 300 Hz (Lythgoe, 1979).

Clinical

The CFF depends on many variables, including the light's intensity and size. In addition, CFF varies with location in the visual field. The rate of flicker of a large stimulus, such as a television set or a bank of fluorescent lights, may be too fast to be seen when you look at the stimulus directly, but may be highly visible when you look slightly away from it. You may have experienced this annoying peripheral flicker if you've been in a room where the fluorescent ceiling lights were functioning improperly.

In some individuals, seizures can be brought on by exposure to a flickering light. Individuals with this condition, called photoconvulsive epilepsy, have to be aware that seizures can be triggered by a strobe light in a disco, a malfunctioning television set or the flashing lights of video games (Ferrie et al., 1994). With a television, the likelihood of a seizure is enhanced by low frequency (50 Hz) video systems (like those used in Europe), by very bright images or by close viewing (Badinand-Hubert et al., 1998).*

Warning lights flicker at rates well below the CFF. Just how sensitive is the human visual system at these lower rates of flicker? Recall from Chapter 5 that human vision has an optimal spatial frequency—there is an object size that can be seen most easily. The same holds for temporal frequency—there is a rate of flicker that can be seen most easily, typically around 10 Hz.

---

*Chapter 6 noted the parallels between vision and visual imagery for scenes and static stimuli. These parallels may extend to flickering or moving stimuli. For example, some people with photoconvulsive epilepsy are able to induce seizures intentionally by generating mental images of appropriate flickering stimuli (Anyanwu, 1997).

---

cally, how does the visual system distinguish retinal motion due to eye movements from retinal motion due to object movement?

Researchers have proposed two different mechanisms to monitor eye movements. According to one view, the visual system tracks actual changes in the extraocular muscles. In the alternative view, the visual system tracks the command signals that go to the extraocular muscles. (These two alternatives were depicted schematically in Figure 8.8.)

The preponderance of behavioral evidence favors the second view. Additionally, physiological research has identified neural mechanisms that use the signals sent to the extraoculars to update the brain's representation of visual space (Duhamel, Colby and Goldberg, 1992). We will not review the literature here, but instead examine several conditions chosen to illustrate some basic principles. These conditions are outlined in Table 9.1.

To make predictions of what ought to be seen in each condition, we'll need some consistent

TABLE 9.1

Perceptual Consequences of Eye Movements

Test Conditions	Command Signals (C)	Eyes Move	Retinal Image Motion (R)	Experience (E) [C − R = E]
Normal; stable environment	Left (+1)	Left	Left (+1)	No motion [1 − 1 = 0]
Normal; stable environment	Right (−1)	Right	Right (−1)	No motion [(−1) − (−1) = 0]
Eye passively displaced left	None (0)	Left	Left (+1)	Right [0 − 1 = −1]
Eye paralyzed, person *wills* movement left	Left (+1)	None	None (0)	Left [1 − 0 = 1]
Environment translates left	None (0)	None	Right (−1)	Environment moves left [0 − (−1) = 1]

conventions about our descriptions of motion. Our convention assigns a value of +1 to leftward motion and value of −1 to rightward motion. This assignment applies to motion in the external world, to motion of the eyes, to retinal image motion, to the command signals that normally control the motion of the eyes and to perceived motion. In this convention, the absence of motion or a command signal has a value of 0. Finally, we assume that predictions concerning the perceived direction of motion should develop from a comparison between two quantities—the command signals to the extraocular muscles and the accompanying retinal image motion. To derive perceived direction, subtract the retinal image motion from the command signal (remembering to respect signs).

In the first two test conditions (normal) of Table 9.1, the observer decides to move the eyes leftward, across a stationary visual environment, and the eyes do as they're instructed. Subtracting the retinal image motion from the command signal yields zero (no perceived motion) in both cases. Now we come to a more interesting condition. To understand the third condition, close your left eye and gently tap your finger on the outer edge of your open right eye (being careful

not to poke your eye too hard). With each displacement of your eyeball, you should experience a jerky displacement of the world. As Table 9.1 suggests, this illusory motion occurs because there is retinal image motion in the absence of command signals to the extraocular muscles. The fourth condition is the most unusual; in it the eyes are paralyzed and, thus, prevented from obeying the command to move. Here, the observer *wills* a leftward eye movement, but none occurs, yet the world still seems to move leftward. Be sure that you work through the details of this condition in order to understand how it is related to the last condition described in the table.

This exercise underscores the complicated compensatory calculations performed by the visual system to achieve perceptual stability as the eyes move about.

Now that you understand something about saccadic eye movements, we can return once more to the creature we left scurrying across the floor. You visually captured that creature—acquired the target—by making a saccade. But the creature is still moving, so you've now got a different problem: keeping your eyes aimed at this moving object.

Staying on Target: Keeping Your Eye on the Ball

To pursue a moving target, the eyes behave very differently from the way they do when they make a saccade. During pursuit, they move smoothly, instead of with abrupt stops and starts. To guide the eyes' pursuit movements, the brain draws on two complementary sources of information. One source comprises sensory information derived from neurons that code the direction and speed of moving objects (recall Chapter 4). The other source is the observer's cognitive expectations about object motions that are about to occur (Kowler, 1989). Integrating both sensory signals and cognitive expectations, the brain sends commands to the extraocular muscles for guidance of **pursuit eye movements,** sometimes called **smooth eye movements.**

Unlike jerky saccades, pursuit movements are smooth. They are also not ballistic; the signals being sent to the extraocular muscles are constantly being updated and revised, thereby altering the speed and direction of the pursuit movements. Accurate pursuit is important. Only when the eye's movements match some object's movement will the image of that object be relatively stationary on the retina, which has the beneficial consequence of keeping that object sharply imaged on the fovea. If the pursuit is not accurate, the image will be blurred.

How well do pursuit movements actually match the movement of the object the eyes are pursuing? The answer depends on the speed of the moving target that the eyes have to follow (Murphy, 1978). When targets move slowly (less than one-third of a millimeter on the retina per second), eye movements match target movements almost perfectly. However, at higher target speeds, the eyes have increasing difficulty keeping up with target movement. This difficulty causes the target's image to slip on the retina.

Differences
Not everyone appreciates just how difficult it is to pursue a rapidly moving target with the eyes. Take baseball coaches, for instance; they're al-

ways exhorting batters to keep their eye on the ball, which turns out to be impossible to do (Ripoll and Fleurance, 1988). Baseball, like cricket, tennis and other sports involving rapidly moving balls, is a game of milliseconds.* A 10-millisecond error in a batter's swing is the difference between a hit over second base and foul along one of the foul lines (Kirkpatrick, 1963). The pitched ball zooms toward the batter at speeds approaching 50 meters per second, and as few as 500 milliseconds elapse between the pitcher's release and the ball's crossing the plate. But these conditions make it impossible to keep your eye on the ball. Using a realistic batting situation, Bahill and LaRitz (1984) measured the position of the batter's gaze over time. They found that experienced baseball players (including individuals in the major leagues) cannot accurately follow the path of a ball from the pitcher to home plate. Instead, a batter executes a predictive saccadic eye movement a fraction of a second after the ball leaves the pitcher's hand. The predictive saccade aims the batter's eyes at the position the batter predicts the ball will be when it reaches the plate. Contrary to the batter's intuition, then, it is impossible to keep one's eye on the ball throughout its entire travel from pitcher to home plate. Bahill and LaRitz found that really topnotch hitters can pursue the ball for more of its flight before having to resort to the inevitable predictive saccade.

You don't have to be a major league baseball player to see how hard it is to make your eyes move as you'd like them to. For example, although you can will your eyes to jump back and forth, you can't will them to move smoothly unless there is some smoothly moving object to track. To test this, ask a friend to track your finger as you move it slowly back and forth in front of his or her eyes. You'll see smooth pursuit eye

---

*Regan (1992) offers a detailed treatment of visual and cognitive factors in cricket, as well as a brief introduction to the sport itself.

movements. Now remove the actual tracking stimulus and ask the friend to continue moving the eyes as if tracking your moving finger. You'll see that, despite his or her best efforts, your friend's eyes move along in a series of little jerks.

Now that you've become familiar with several of motion perception's key features (and some of its quirks, described in Box 9.2), it is time to find out more about the neural circuits that make all this possible.

BUILDING DIRECTIONAL SELECTIVITY: SPACE-TIME RECEPTIVE FIELDS

N

Neural

Chapter Four introduced the idea of neural direction selectivity when it described how the responses of some cortical cells vary with the direction of motion within the cells' receptive fields. Each **direction-selective cell** responds most strongly to one preferred direction, but little (if at all) to motion in the opposite direction (see Figure 4.13). Because the preferred direction varies from cell to cell, the direction in which some object moves could be represented within the nervous system by the responses that object evokes in different cells. Before exploring the perceptual importance of direction-selective cells, we should clarify the origin of direction selectivity itself. How might one build a direction-selective cell?

To answer this question, Werner Reichardt (1961) proposed that neurons could be interconnected to create a small neural network that compared changes in the distribution of light within neighboring retinal regions. Figure 9.9 schematizes the basic building block of Reichardt's theory. In the left-hand panel, signals from two regions of the retina (α and β) are collected by neurons (shaded rectangles) and passed along to another neuron, labeled DS (for "directionally selective"). The DS neuron takes the inputs and multiplies them. As a result, a DS neuron's response is strongest when its two inputs have the

same light level and reach the DS neuron simultaneously. But note that on its way to the DS neuron, the input from region α is delayed by some time, call it Δt. As a result, in order for signals from α and β to arrive simultaneously at the DS neuron, the one from α must have a head start. Putting this another way, the DS neuron responds when the same pattern of light first strikes region α and then, some time later (equivalent to the Δt), strikes region β. A good stimulus would be an image that moved continuously across the retina from left to right, as represented by the arrow.

It's important to realize that this is not the only stimulus that would work. Certain, nonmoving stimuli would be equally as effective in stimulating the DS neuron. One example is a stationary light flashed briefly on region α and after Δt, on region β. Later, in the section on apparent motion, you'll see that such nonmoving stimuli dupe the visual system into treating them as though they had moved.

Returning to Figure 9.9, let's assign the label Δx to the distance separating retinal regions α and β. Defining this distance allows us to be more precise about the moving stimulus that elicits the strongest response from the DS neuron. Recall that an optimal stimulus strikes first α and then β, after delay Δt. In order to meet that requirement, the stimulus must move over distance Δx in a time of Δt. As you know, speed is distance divided by time (S = d/t). Therefore, the speed of the optimal stimulus is $\Delta x / \Delta t$. Given the proper direction, of course, this speed, which causes an image to fall first in region α and then, Δt later, in region β, will elicit a strong response from the DS neuron.

The middle panel of Figure 9.9 illustrates how one might construct a unit that would respond best to retinal image motion in the opposite direction, but with the same speed. Now look at the right-hand panel of Figure 9.9 and try to identify the motion that best stimulates the DS neuron. The *orientation* of the two input areas on the retina, together with the *elapsed time* of the delay, determine the direction to which the DS neuron will respond.

BOX 9.2

PERCEPTUAL ERRORS AND ACCIDENTS

Illusion

Motion perception can be a matter of life or death—literally. It can cause fatal accidents, and it can prevent them. To document this claim, we'll start with the dark side—collisions at railroad crossings.

According to the Federal Railroad Administration (1992), there are about 5,000 collisions each year between locomotives and other vehicles at railroad crossings in the United States. Most railroad crossings are protected by crossing gates and warning bells. In addition, locomotive engineers must sound a bell or horn as they approach a crossing. With all these precautions and the conspicuous nature of huge locomotives, how is it still possible that so many accidents occur? According to Herschel Leibowitz errors in motion perception are partly to blame (Leibowitz, 1983).

During an accident investigation, Leibowitz rode in the cab of a locomotive that retraced the route on which the accident had occurred. The trip took Leibowitz through an urban area with many gate crossings. He was astonished at the number of motorists who drove around the crossing gates and across the tracks in front of the oncoming train. The train crew, who saw this kind of thing every day, shrugged it off as "typical." Since automobiles don't fare too well in collisions with railroad trains, why do people take such chances? Leibowitz realized that although the locomotive's bulk made it easy to see, that same bulk would cause its speed to be seriously underestimated.

It has long been known that the size of an object and its apparent speed are inversely related. To study this relation, J. F. Brown (1931) asked people to adjust the speed of one square so that it appeared to move at the same speed as another square. When both squares were the same size, observers were very accurate in their adjustments. (Typically a mismatch in speed as small as 10 percent can be easily seen.) However, when the two squares differed in size, the accuracy of the matches was very low. When the squares differed in size, the larger one had to move faster than the small one in order to appear to move at the same rate. As a result, if the two squares moved at the same speed, the larger one seemed to be moving more slowly than the smaller one.

Leibowitz points out that a comparable phenomenon can be seen at just about any airport. All commercial jets, regardless of size, land at pretty much the same speed. However, wide-body planes (DC-10s or 747s) *appear* to land much more slowly than smaller planes. Leibowitz believes that the same kind of perceptual error causes motorists at railroad crossings to underestimate an oncoming train's speed, and thereby overestimate the time the train will take to reach the crossing.

Let's end on a happier note—the ability of motion perception to *prevent* accidents. Particularly dangerous spots in any highway system are the intersections called rotaries (roundabouts in the United Kingdom). To navigate safely through a rotary, a driver must slow down. But when motorists don't slow down enough, accidents often result. Because exhortations and warnings seemed to have little effect, Gordon Denton (1980) took a desperate step. He tricked motorists into believing their cars were traveling faster than they really were. His aim was to frighten motorists into slowing down.

Imagine a road with transverse stripes painted across the pavement. A motorist passing over these stripes will get a sense of how fast the car is traveling by the rate at which it passes the stripes. When the stripes are close together, she will pass them at a higher rate, causing her to overestimate her speed. Denton exploited this phenomenon by having white stripes painted across the roadway near the entrance to a rotary—the stripes near the rotary were more closely spaced than those farther away. As a result, motorists approaching the rotary erroneously perceived that they were speeding up. This misperception caused them to slow down. Preliminary tests with this simple and inexpensive scheme indicate that it works: accidents declined at over two-thirds of the rotaries on which such stripes had been painted. It's nice to know that illusions of motion perception can also save lives as well as take them.

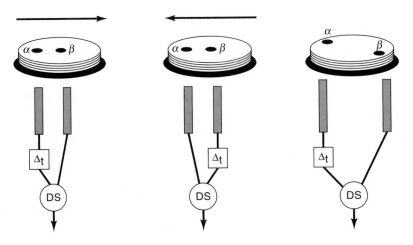

FIGURE 9.9
Schematic drawing of a direction-selective cell responsive to rightward motion (left-hand panel) and to leftward motion (middle panel). What would be the appropriate speed and direction of motion to activate the cell in the right-hand panel?

Note also in the right-hand panel that the two retinal areas α and β are farther apart than were the areas in the other panels. Assuming that Δt, the delay, has not changed, would the optimal stimulus move faster or slower than the previous cases? Finally, imagine a whole array of DS neurons. Suppose that each received signals from retinal regions separated by some distance, Δx, and suppose that each preferred some particular delay, Δt. If Δx and Δt varied from one DS neuron to another, each DS neuron would be optimally stimulated by a pattern moving in a particular direction and with a particular speed. Following tradition, we will describe such neurons as "directionally-selective," keeping in mind that their responses are controlled jointly by direction and speed.

Reichardt's account of DS mechanisms is built around a network that compares changes in the distribution of light within neighboring retinal regions. Although motion usually does arise from changes in light levels over space and time, other events, which do not entail changes in light level, can also give rise to motion. Events involving moving texture boundaries (waves of motion in a grain field), moving subjective con-

tours like those shown in Figure 4.1 (Ramachandran, Rao and Vidyasagar, 1973) or even moving, binocular-disparity discontinuities (ocean waves) can also trigger perception of motion in a given direction.

In the contemporary literature, motion defined by luminance variations over space/time has been dubbed *first-order* motion (meaning that the sensors register changes in luminance over time). Motion defined by other cues, such as texture differences, has been dubbed *second-order* motion (Chubb and Sperling, 1988; Smith, 1994; Sperling and Lu, 1998). In the case of second-order motion, the extraction of direction probably involves the same basic idea shown in Figure 9.9, but with different inputs to the comparison circuit.

Now that we're armed with an understanding of Reichardt's motion-extracting circuit, let's consider how this simple network can be "fooled" into seeing motion where it doesn't really exist.

APPARENT MOTION

Ordinarily, one's experience of motion seems fairly straightforward because that experience is

Illusion

grounded in the actual motion of an object. That rabbit you frightened near Walden Pond traveled several meters in a short time. As the rabbit moved, the image of it moved over your retina, so it's not surprising, thanks to neural intermediaries, that you experience the rabbit move. Conditions such as this require no explanation. You see motion because there *is* motion. And that motion is just what the motion-extracting circuits in Figure 9.9 are designed to register.

But evidently under certain circumstances those circuits can be tricked, because one can have a compelling experience of motion even when nothing in the world actually moves. Let's consider one such circumstance, known as **apparent motion.**

Apparent motion has become an important part of our lives. As Stuart Anstis points out,

> *The flashing lights on a cinema marquee, which seem to move inward toward the lobby and entice us to follow them, are an example of apparent movement. If we go in and watch the movie, we experience two hours of apparent movement: each movie frame projected on the screen is actually stationary whenever the projector is open. If we stay at home and watch TV instead, we are once again experiencing apparent movement. Films and TV, as they exist today, are possible only because of a quirk in our visual systems. (1978, p. 656)*

The visual system takes discrete and separate inputs (such as the separate frames of a movie) and knits them into an experience that is smooth and continuous. This is the "quirk" to which Anstis refers. We'll now focus on apparent movement because this quirk provides insights into how the visual system operates where there *is* genuine motion of the retinal image. (As we progress through this discussion, keep in mind the scheme for constructing direction-selective neurons in Figure 9.9.)

People have known about apparent motion for quite some time. For example, Sigmund Exner (1888) created brief but intense electrical sparks from two sources placed some distance apart. Observers judged which spark flashed first—the

one on the right or the one on the left. When the time delay between sparks was long, the judgment was easy; when the delay was short, the judgment became difficult. Exner found that about one-twenty-fifth of a second had to intervene between the two sparks before their order could be judged accurately.

Then Exner placed the two sources of sparks very close to each other. With short intervals between the two sparks, people saw apparent motion—a single spark moving from one location to the other. Exner then asked people to judge the direction of that apparent motion. Although these people needed delays of one-twenty-fifth of a second to judge the order of sparks that were some distance apart, they needed less than half that delay to judge the *direction* of movement. This experience of apparent movement could not have been *derived* from judging the sequence of flashes because the time interval separating the two flashes was too brief to allow for such a judgment. Instead, motion was experienced directly.

Next, Exner brought the two sparks so close together that they appeared as a single bright spark. When the twin sparks were flashed one after the other, the observer saw apparent motion. This experience of apparent movement could not have been *derived* from judging the positions of flashes because the flashes were so close together that they couldn't be distinguished. Again, motion was experienced directly.

Exner's observations led him to conclude that motion was a primary sensation in its own right, not some inference derived from comparing temporal order or spatial position. Keeping in mind that apparent motion is not an inference, let's consider the work of Max Wertheimer, the Gestalt psychologist mentioned in Chapter 5.

In one study, Wertheimer (1912/1961) briefly presented two spatially separated vertical lines in succession. What people saw depended on the delay that separated the two presentations. With long delays (greater than one-tenth of a second), one line appeared to succeed the other. In other words, the observer saw one line that came on and went off and then a second line that did the same. With very short delays between presentations (about one-fortieth of a second or less), the two lines appeared to come on and go off simultaneously. Perceptually there had been only a single presentation. With intermediate delays between presentation of the two lines (about one-twentieth of a second), a single line seemed to move smoothly from one position to the other. In other words, people saw apparent motion.

Next, Wertheimer arranged conditions so that the first line was seen by one eye and the second line was seen by the other eye. Even under these conditions of interocular stimulation, motion was again perceived. This suggests that the DS neurons giving rise to the perception of motion must be centrally located at or beyond the site where information from the eyes has been combined. Wertheimer devised a simple but effective demonstration of interocular apparent movement, one that you, too, can try.*

Hold a thin book in both hands and lean your forehead against the book's edge, as shown in Figure 9.10. Be sure to place your head so that one eye is on each side of the book. This allows you to use the book as a separator, making it easy to present different objects to the two eyes. Now, with your hands on opposite sides of the book, extend the index finger on each hand upward. Position the left hand so that its index finger can be seen by your left eye, and position your right hand so that its index finger can be seen by your right eye. Don't look directly at your fingers; instead, keep you gaze directed straight ahead at a point several inches beyond the far end of the book. Your fingers should be about 6 inches from your nose. Now comes the hard part. Rhythmically open and close alternate eyes. Though it may take a little practice, at the proper speed of

FIGURE 9.10
Setup for experiencing apparent motion.

alternation you'll have a strange and amusing experience: your finger will appear to jump back and forth as if it were moving through the interior of the book!

Wertheimer could not have known what we know today about cortical function. Thus, he mistakenly attributed apparent motion to a short-circuiting of current flow in the brain. Today, however, we believe that motion perception—including apparent motion—involves direction-selective neurons something like those schematized in Figure 9.9. DS neurons will respond vigorously to the successive presentation of two stationary lines, if the Δx and Δt values associated with those neurons correspond to the spatial separation and presentation delay between the lines. From the standpoint of the DS neurons, then, apparent motion and real motion constitute equivalent events.

The Correspondence Problem in Motion Perception

Apparent motion, besides implicating the operation of DS neurons, also highlights another question concerning motion perception that is easily overlooked when we think only about real motion in the natural environment: How does the visual system register that an object seen at one moment corresponds to the same object seen at another moment? After all, the finger example demonstrates that detecting correspondence over time is a prerequisite for motion perception.

---

*Sekuler (1996) discussed many other of Wertheimer's experiments, relating them to the modern research on motion perception.

We can highlight the nature of this prerequisite by comparing retinal images to photographic snapshots of the visual world. Suppose that you have two retinal "snapshots" that were taken a fraction of a second apart. Looking at the two snapshots, how would you determine whether a single object had moved? To accomplish this, you must determine which elements in one snapshot correspond to which elements in the other (this problem is reminiscent of the matching problem in stereopsis, discussed in Chapter 8). Now here's the problem: potentially, any small detail in one of the snapshots *might* correspond to any number of different details in the other.

This situation is illustrated by a simple display that has been widely used in work on apparent motion (see Figure 9.11). Here, two displays alternate, separated by a brief uniform field (not shown). The upper and lower panels both contain frames with a trio of large dots. Note that from frame 1 to frame 2, the trio of dots has shifted rightward. Before telling you what you would actually see, let's consider the possibilities, bearing in mind that what you'll see depends on the cor-

respondence that vision perceives in the trio of dots from frame to frame.

Panels 3 through 6 of Figure 9.11 illustrate two possible correspondences. Following the dotted lines from panel 3 to panel 4 shows that your visual system might pair dot *A* with dot *X*, dot *B* with dot *Y*, and dot *C* with dot *Z*. With these correspondences, you would see the entire group of dots moving rightward: *A* to *X*, *B* to *Y*, and *C* to *Z*. Following the dotted lines from panel 5 to panel 6 shows an alternate set of correspondences. Here, your visual system pairs dots *B* and *X*, dots *C* and *Y*, and dots *A* and *Z*. With this set of correspondences, you would see two stationary dots (since *B* and *X* occupy the same positions on successive frames, as do *C* and *Y*). At the same time, you would also see a third dot (*A* to *Z*) that moves all the way from the left end of the trio to the right end.

This simple, two-frame display is interesting because its ambiguity makes possible two different perceptions, depending on how the correspondence problem is solved. The apparent motion actually seen from such ambiguous displays

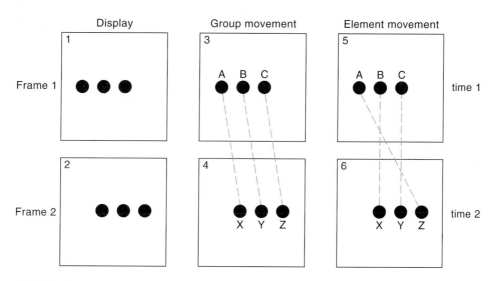

FIGURE 9.11
An illustration of the correspondence problem in motion perception.

reveals the rules used by the visual system to establish correspondences. Your actual perceptual experience is a choice from among the various sets of correspondences that *might* have been selected.

Illusion

What, then, do observers actually see when they're shown displays such as that depicted in panels 1 and 2 of Figure 9.11? How does the visual system solve the correspondence problem? The answer is, "It depends" (Pantle and Picciano, 1976; Pantle and Petersik, 1979). Under some conditions, observers see **group movement**—all three dots seem to move en masse (as in panels 3 to 4). Under other conditions, observers see **element movement**—the overlapping dots of each frame appear stationary while just the third dot moves back and forth from one end to the other (as in panels 5 to 6). When the interval between displays is long, or when the two displays are shown to different eyes, observers tend to see group movement. Such conditions seem to make it difficult for the visual system to carry out detailed, point-by-point comparisons of alternate displays. When the interval is short and the two displays are shown to the same eye, observers tend to see element movement. Such conditions facilitate detailed comparisons between displays.

Plasticity

These results demonstrate that vision can be flexible when it has to solve a problem of correspondence. But the world in which we live contains few situations in which correspondences are as ambiguous as those represented in Figure 9.11 or as those that have been generated in other studies (Lappin, Doner and Kottas, 1979; Ullman, 1979). The number of potential correspondences can be sharply reduced if the visual system takes advantage of regularities in the physical world (Marr, 1982; Ramachandran and Anstis, 1986). After all, the visual system evolved in a world consisting of objects that, because of their physical properties, are constrained to behave in certain ways: natural objects don't change color suddenly; natural objects are made of parts that are connected; the surface texture of natural objects tends to be uniform; natural objects, once in mo-

tion, tend to stay in motion; and solid objects cannot move through one another. Neurons in the visual system register these regularities. In so doing, the visual system is biased against unnatural solutions to the correspondence problem, favoring solutions that are consistent with the properties of real-world objects.

As an example, consider one consistency between apparent motion and the motion of natural objects. Objects in motion tend to obey Newton's First Law of Motion: once in motion, a body will continue in motion unless acted upon by an external force. In one demonstration of this law, Wertheimer alternated two visual features at a rate that he knew would produce apparent motion between them—such as a line at the left and a line at the right. As long as the alternation continued, the line appeared to travel back and forth. Then without warning to the viewer, he occluded one of the lines but kept presenting the remaining line at its appropriate times. Surprisingly, even though only one line was being exposed, it took a while for the apparent motion to cease. For three or four repetitions, the observer continued to see motion. These findings suggest that inertia works not only in the natural world but in the world of apparent motion as well.

Newton's First Law of Motion applies to all objects in the real world. So perhaps it's not surprising that the visual motion reflects such a general real-world property. But can properties that are far more specific, limited to particular objects, also influence the perception of motion? Maggie Shiffrar of Rutgers University and Jennifer Freyd of the University of Oregon (1990) proved that the answer is yes. In one of their experiments, two photographs of a human model were alternated in rapid succession. The photographs in each pair were identical except for the position of the model's hand or the position of a single limb. One set of photos, for example, showed the hand fully extended and rotated about the wrist in two different positions. To get a sense of this configuration, extend your right arm fully and directly in front of you; spread the fingers of

Top-down

FIGURE 9.12
Drawings based on one set of figures used to study biological plausibility's effect on apparent motion (Shiffrar and Freyd, 1990). When the stimuli are presented in alternation, the young man's hand appears to rotate about his wrist, either clockwise or counterclockwise. With a brief interval separating the two stimuli, the hand appears to rotate through a short, but biologically implausible arc; with a greater interval between stimuli, the hand appears to rotate in the opposite direction, over a path that is longer but biologically plausible.

that hand, palm facing forward. Rotate your wrist so that your fingers point leftward; seen from the front (as in a mirror) that could be one of the photos. To create the second photo of the stimulus pair, rotate the wrist as far it will go in the other direction, without moving your arm (for most people, the fingers will end up pointing downward or nearly so). These two bodily configurations are illustrated in Figure 9.12.

Before reading further, imagine what a person might see when there two views were alternated. In principle, alternation of these two views of the hand, wrist and arm could produce apparent motion along either of two quite different paths. One path represents a large rotation of the wrist (about 270 degrees); the other path represents a much shorter rotation (about 90 degrees or less). These paths differ not only in length but also in biological plausibility. The shorter path requires a rotation that is biologically impossible (unless the wrist were able to rotate through a full 360 degrees). Shiffrar and Freyd found that when the two photos alternated, with only a brief time

elapsing between them, people saw the shorter (biologically impossible) rotation. This result was not surprising; many previous studies had shown the visual system tends to resolve a choice between two paths in favor of the shorter one. With longer intervals between the photos, though, Shiffrar and Freyd's observers tended to see motion over the longer, but biologically plausible path. The visual system, then, can be influenced by the physical plausibility of particular stimulus transformations, provided that there is sufficient time for that influence to be registered.

So in these last few sections we have seen how a laboratory curiosity—apparent motion—actually reveals fundamental characteristics of normal motion perception. In this next section, we consider another curiosity about motion perception which, on the face of it, seems to imply a design flaw. In fact, however, this curiosity, like apparent motion, stems from the brain's clever solution to a complicated problem. In this case, the problem involves figuring out which pieces of a dynamic puzzle go together.

The Aperture Problem

Illusion

Because each DS neuron responds only to what is happening within its own receptive field, the signals from DS neurons are necessarily ambiguous. This ambiguity, now known as the aperture problem, was pointed out more than 60 years ago by the psychologist Hans Wallach (Wuerger, Shapley and Rubin, 1996). Figure 9.13 illustrates what Wallach had in mind. The circular area in the figure represents the receptive field of a directionally-selective neuron. Its preferred direction of move-

ment is rightward. As a large vertical bar moves rightward at an appropriate speed through the receptive field, the neuron responds strongly (Panel A). But this isn't the only direction of movement that will evoke such a response. So long as the vertical bar is large compared to the aperture (the receptive field), the same local spatio-temporal event—movement at the same velocity—could be generated by any number of other combinations of direction and speed, some of which are suggested in Panels B and C. This equivalence means that the neuron's response is inherently ambigu-

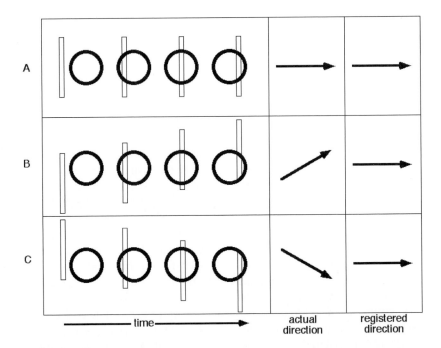

FIGURE 9.13
Illustration of the aperture problem: the ambiguity of directional information within the aperture of a receptive field. The circular area in the figure represents the receptive field of a directionally-selective neuron whose preferred direction of movement is rightward. As the vertical bar moves rightward through the receptive field, the neuron would signal rightward motion (A). However, movement of the bar downward and to the right (B) could generate the same rightward motion in the receptive field, as could movement upward and rightward (C). The equivalence of stimulation within the receptive field renders the neuron's response inherently ambiguous.

ous. Because the neuron's "view" of the world is limited to the confines of its receptive field, the neuron responds exactly the same way to each of these different velocities of movement. As a prelude to explaining the visual system's strategy for resolving this ambiguity, consider one side effect of this ambiguity.

Because the movement within a single receptive field can arise from distinctly different visual events, the door is opened to a variety of striking illusions of perceived motion. In these illusions, observers watch as a line or bar moves through an aperture whose shape strongly influences the perceived direction of movement. For example, suppose that an L-shaped aperture is cut out of a piece of paper (Figure 9.14A). Suppose also that a long oblique line (at 45 degrees) is placed behind the aperture and is moved steadily down and to the right. Viewers will first see an oblique line that moves straight downward, but once the line reaches the base of the L-shaped aperture, the

movement abruptly changes. Then viewers see an oblique line that moves rightward (9.14B). Wallach investigated this and several dozen, related aperture illusions (Wuerger, Shapley and Rubin, 1996). To see the basic elements of his approach, return to the L-shaped aperture.

Let's approximate the L-shaped aperture's upright portion by a series of circular receptive fields whose centers lie along a single vertical line (Figure 9.14C). An oblique, downward-moving line would traverse each field, one after another. But this pattern of stimulation could have arisen from any number of different stimulus scenarios. For example, it have been produced by several different, similarly-oriented lines, each of which traverses just one receptive field and then disappears, just as the next line appears at the top of the next receptive field and begins its descent. Or the same pattern of stimulation across all the receptive fields could have resulted, as it did in Wallach's demonstration, from a single line that moved from

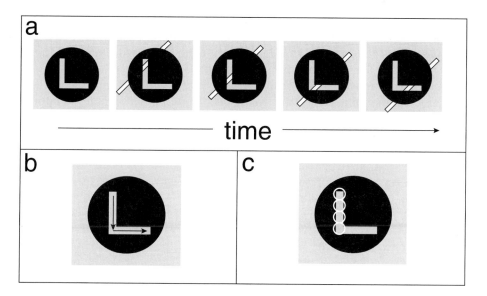

FIGURE 9.14

Upper row: Motion of an obliquely oriented line into, through, and then out of an L-shaped aperture. Lower row: At first, the line appears to move vertically downward; then, when the line enters the horizontally-oriented portion of the aperture, its apparent direction abruptly changes to horizontal. (After Wallach [1935], in Wuerger, Shapley and Rubin, 1996.)

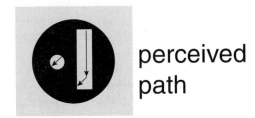

perceived
path

FIGURE 9.15
Upper row: A bar moves down and to the right, first into, through and then out of an elongated
vertical aperture that adjoins a small circular aperture. When the line first becomes visible, it is
seen only in the elongated aperture. As a result, influenced by the aperture shape, its motion is
directly downward (bottom row). Then, when it is visible in the circular aperture as well, the bar's
overall motion shifts to oblique. (After Wallach [1935], in Wuerger, Shapley and Rubin, 1996.)

top to bottom, entering and then exiting one receptive field after another in succession. How
does the visual system, given the limited information it has, choose which scenario is responsible
for that information? In the spirit of Gestalt psychology, Wallach proposed that the single perceptual choice made in such multiple-choice situations tends to be the simplest global motion. In
this case, then, people see a single line that moves
continuously rather than a series of successive
lines. With this idea in mind, you should be able
to deduce why, at the bottom of the L-shaped
aperture, the line appears to move rightward.

Figure 9.15 illustrates another of Wallach's
demonstrations, which shows how powerfully
the visual system favors a simple perceptual response when several responses are all possible.
Instead of a single aperture, there are two apertures, side by side, one a circle and the other a
vertically-oriented rectangle. When an oblique
line moves downward through only the rectangular aperture, people see downward motion—
just as they did with the vertical section of the
L-shaped aperture. When the oblique line moves
downward through only the circular aperture,
people see motion in a different direction—perpendicular to the orientation of the oblique line.
The interesting part of the demonstration comes
when the line is long enough to extend through
both apertures at once. As the line begins to
move downward, at first it is visible only in the
rectangle—and the perceived motion is downward. But when the line enters the circular aperture and is visible in both apertures simultaneously, the perceived direction in both apertures
abruptly shifts, and the line appears to slide
downward and to the left (as it would in the circular aperture alone). Presumably, this change
reflects the visual system's effort to treat the line
in both apertures as a single line moving in one
direction, rather than as two separate lines moving in different directions.

In another set of demonstrations, Wallach showed people figures composed of two different line gratings, like those shown in Figure 9.16A and B. When the two are superimposed, as in panels C and D, they generate a series of diamond-shaped structures. When the bars of the two gratings move downward at the same rate, the display's appearance fluctuates between a field of diamonds that move downward (panel C), and two line-gratings that move at different velocities, sliding over each other in the process (panel D). The relative potency of the two, alternative perceptual outcomes varies with a number of factors, Wallach found, including the angle between the two line gratings. (This bistability may remind you of the vase/face illusion illustrated in Figure 4.1 or the binocular rivalry phenomenon described in Box 8.3.)

This perceptual bistability points to something quite important about motion perception. Consider what the nervous system must do in order to parse the display into two gratings moving in different directions. This would seem to require mechanisms that can separate out the different directions within each local region. But to produce the alternative outcome—the moving diamond—the nervous system needs a second mechanism that collects dissimilar directional signals from regions across the display and binds those signals into coherent perceptual wholes rather than independent, isolated elements. This may sound challenging, but it is utterly necessary. As Oliver Braddick put it "we do not live in a world of independent fragments, but of objects and surfaces that move coherently" (1993, p. 263). What you saw in the case of object recognition (Chapter 6) also holds for motion perception: vision needs some way to combine velocity signals that belong to the same moving object. It also needs to separate velocity signals that do not belong together; signals that arise from different objects (Snowden and Verstraten, 1999). Obviously, the characteristics of the world mandate precisely the sort of complex behavior that Wallach demonstrated.

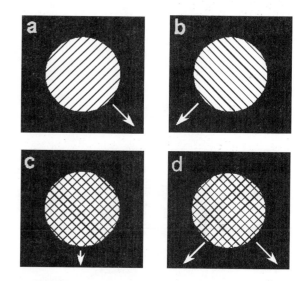

FIGURE 9.16
Superimposing two diagonal, moving gratings produces a diamond pattern whose motion is bistable. When either moving grating alone is present (panels A and B), it appears to move in a consistent direction, indicated by the arrow. However, when the two moving diagonal gratings are superimposed, they sometimes cohere to form a single, downward moving pattern (panel C) and, at other times, they appear to slide over one another in two different superimposed directions (panel D). (After Wallach [1935], in Wuerger, Shapley and Rubin, 1996.)

Wallach's motion demonstrations tell us that perceived motion is not determined solely by individual responses to the stimulus velocity generated within isolated, local regions of the field. Instead, similar local measurements of velocity are integrated, producing an overall response. This integration points to some place in the visual system at which the local velocity-related signals are brought together. In fact, such a combination of different signals is the nervous system's standard way to resolve neural ambiguity in the signals of individual neurons. When the response of one neuron is ambiguous, you have seen before that the nervous system can resolve the ambiguity by aggregating outputs from a number of differently-tuned neurons. We saw this earlier in color vision, for example. For visual motion, the nervous system reduces ambiguity about individual, local

FIGURE 9.17
Location of visual area MT (also known as V5) in the right hemisphere of the human brain. This region is located in approximately the same corresponding anatomical region of the left hemisphere. Using fMRI, area MT can be identified by comparing brain activation associated with viewing moving objects (such as dots) with that associated with viewing stationary objects.

spatio-temporal events by channeling outputs from the first stage of direction processing to a second stage of neural processing, involving higher-order neurons. To implement this strategy for motion processing, direction-selective neurons in V1 project forward (anterior) and upward (superior), synapsing on neurons in a small oval area on the brain's lateral surface near the junction of the occipital, parietal and temporal lobes (see Figure 9.17). This area goes by two different names: Area V5 and Area MT*. Receptive fields in area MT are considerably larger in size than

those in Area V1, implying that an array of spatially distributed V1 neurons contribute to the synthesis of individual MT receptive fields. Also, in Area V1 only a minority of neurons exhibit direction-selectivity, but in Area MT nearly every neuron is directionally selective.

Some neurons in MT receive input from V1 neurons with different preferred directions of motion. The result? The directional selectivity of these MT neurons differs qualitatively from that of their predecessors in V1. And these differences enhance the importance of MT's contribution to the perception of motion.

To see this, return to Wallach's demonstration with two overlaid, moving gratings. When similar two-component displays are imaged within the receptive fields of V1 neurons, the neurons tend to respond to the separate components. In the example shown in Figure 9.16, these direc-

*The abbreviation *MT* has been adopted in the belief that this area is the homologue in the human brain to area MT that has been carefully delineated in nonhuman primates. The preponderance of directionally-selective neurons in nonhuman primate Area MT has attracted much attention from researchers interested in motion perception.

tions would be obliquely downward to the right and left (panels A and B). But when the same displays are presented in the receptive fields of MT neurons, many of those cells respond to the motion, not of the components, but of the overall moving pattern (Movshon et al., 1986). In the case illustrated in Figure 9.16, this would be coherent motion directly downward. It is thought, then, that important aspects of motion perception arise from two stages of processing: one stage extracting local motion vectors, and a second stage sorting those vectors into object-related combinations. In the next section, we take a closer look at this second stage of processing, focusing in particular on the small but well-studied area MT.

Area MT's Special Role in Motion Processing

Neural

Converging lines of evidence implicate area MT in motion perception. We know, for instance, that damage to MT impairs motion perception. This is most dramatically shown in the motion-blind patient, D. L., whose symptoms were described early in this chapter. D. L.'s brain damage was centered in the area where MT is located. We also know that motion perception in normal individuals can be transiently impaired by a brief, strong pulse of magnetic energy applied to the region of the scalp overlying MT (Hotson et al., 1994; Beckers and Zeki, 1995; Walsh et al., 1998).* There is also evidence that neural signals channeled through area MT guide pursuit eye movements (Watamaniuk and Heinen 1999).

Execute

The role of the Area MT in motion perception has been fruitfully studied using one particular class of animation sequences: computer-generated displays consisting of moving dots. Such displays make it possible to control precisely the strength of motion signals present in animation sequences. Consider two extremes of dot motion, which we can designate *correlated* and *uncorrelated*. With

perfectly correlated motion, all dots move in the same direction (for example, either up or down). The right portion of Figure 9.18 ("100%") shows this arrangement. With uncorrelated motion, each dot can move in any direction and, consequently, dots appear to jiggle about randomly, moving like swirling snow. This stimulus, which is often described as "visual noise," is represented in the left portion of Figure 9.18 ("0%").

When human observers are tested with various mixtures of correlated and uncorrelated motions (such as in the middle portion of Figure 9.18), correlations of just 3 to 5 percent are strong enough to permit reliable discrimination of the motion's direction. Normal monkeys do equally well. But in monkeys in which area MT is damaged, direction of motion cannot be recognized until the correlation is about ten times stronger (Newsome and Paré, 1988). The motion-blind patient, D. L., shows an even more dramatic deficit in detecting motion in noise, presumably the result of damage to Area MT in her brain (Baker, Hess and Zihl, 1991).

MT's key role in motion perception was most dramatically shown in a study done by Salzman and colleagues (1992). This study took the novel approach of using tiny, localized electrical currents to induce a temporary change in the responses of selected MT units. These currents, which were not evoked by the visual stimulus, boosted the responses of particular directionally-selective neurons. The study began by establishing the direction preferences of various MT neurons. This purely physiological phase of the study was followed by a phase that was purely behavioral: while they viewed random dot displays, monkeys moved their eyes in one direction or another to signal the perceived direction of those displays. Finally, Salzman and colleagues combined behavior and physiology, eliciting perceptual judgments: (1) while electrical stimulation was being applied to particular MT neurons and (2) without accompanying electrical stimulation.

Electrical stimulation of neurons that share a direction preference biased the monkeys' perceptual judgments of random dot displays. The result

---

*Transcranial magnetic stimulation (TMS) was described in greater detail in Chapter 4.

Percentage correlation

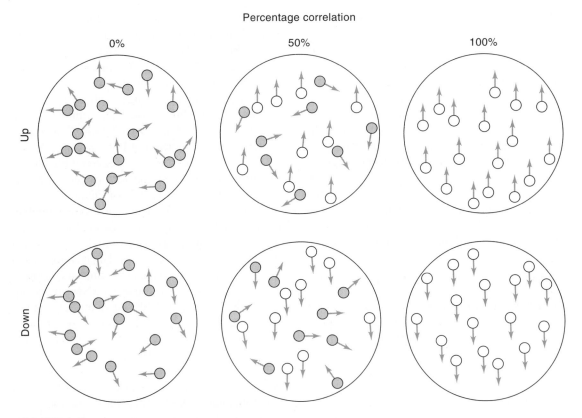

FIGURE 9.18

Schematic representation of a random-dot stimulus that can be used to measure motion thresholds. In each panel, the arrow indicates the direction in which the attached dot moves. In the two left-hand panels, there is 0 percent correlation among the movements of the various dots; they move in random directions. In the two right-hand panels, movements of all dots are 100 percent correlated, either up (as in the top panel) or down (as in the bottom panel). The middle panels represent an intermediate case: 50 percent of the dots move together, either up (top panel) or down (bottom panel). To make it easier for the reader to distinguish them, dots that move in an uncorrelated fashion are shown in gray; in the actual stimulus, all dots were identical.

was an increased likelihood that the display would appear to move in the direction preferred by the stimulated neurons. So, for example, direct stimulation of MT neurons that prefer leftward motion made it more likely that the display would appear to move in that direction. Direct stimulation of MT neurons was perceptually equivalent to an effect normally produced by a visual stimulus moving in a particular direction. As far as the brain is concerned, it doesn't matter

whether its neurons are responding to this unusual, direct electrical stimulation or to normal, visual stimulation.

Though neurons in Area MT certainly contribute to the perception of motion, don't get the idea that Area MT is the only place where neurons extract significant motion information. Actually, various aspects of motion perception depend upon the neural computations carried out in several different areas of the cortex. Normal motion perception depends upon activity distributed over many areas of the brain, each extracting somewhat different information from the retinal image.

To emphasize this point, consider the computations carried out in another region of the cortex, Area MST (MST stands for *medial superior temporal,* a label that indicates this area lies adjacent to and just above MT, *medial temporal).* Going back to the complex circuit shown in Figure 4.19 you may be able to find MST's two divisions, MSTd and MSTl (for dorsal and lateral, respectively), and confirm that both receive input from MT. In a way, MST's view of the world is shaped by MT.

To reinforce the notion that motion perception depends upon computations in multiple areas of the brain, consider the properties of some neurons in MST's dorsal division. Much of our understanding of MST and its contribution to motion perception comes from the work of Keiji Tanaka and his colleagues (Tanaka and Saito, 1989). Tanaka showed that neurons in MSTd have extremely large receptive fields, likely reflecting each neuron's input from many, spatially-dispersed neurons in MT. Moreover, MSTd neurons respond most strongly to stimuli that move in a characteristic fashion over large portions of the visual field. These preferred motions are quite different from the linear motions that V1 and MT neurons prefer. In MSTd, neurons respond strongly to stimulus expansion (or its opposite, contraction) or to stimulus rotation.

The stimuli preferred by two typical cells are shown schematically in panels A and B of Figure 9.19. The stimuli depicted here are spatially random dots, but strong responses could also be evoked by other figures, so long as they contained appropriate directional vectors. For example, expansion patterns, would evoke good responses from an MST expansion cell; a rotating spiral or other pattern would evoke good responses from an MST rotation neuron.

Additional experiments by Tanaka, Fukada and Saito (1989) show the likely origin of the stimulus preferences expressed by expansion neurons and rotation neurons. We have schematized these ori-

gins in Panels C (expansion) and D (rotation) of Figure 9.19. Every MST neuron receives input from several MT neurons, each of which has its own preference for motion in a particular direction (shown by the arrows). Although the diagrams show eight different input neurons, Tanaka and colleagues indicate that fewer would suffice, so long as their direction preferences were appropriate.

What value might these odd neural computations have for us? Why should our brains bother to register optical expansion or optical rotation? Think back to our earlier discussion about the visual guidance of locomotion. There, we noted the importance of variables such as optical expansion (looming) and tau. In a stable environment, forward locomotion produces expansion of the retinal image; as we saw earlier, that optical expansion carries information about time to collision. In the same environment, twisting your head from side to side, produces rotational motion on the retina.

Clinical

Signals from various MST neurons probably make crucial contributions to the visual guidance of locomotion. Evidence for this idea is given by Lucia Vaina (1998), who also describes two brain-injured patients who perform perfectly well on ordinary tests of motion perception—such as discrimination of direction—but seem unable to extract heading information from optic flow. For example, R. R., whose bilateral brain injury covered an area that included MST, performed normally on direction discrimination and speed judgments, although he

> frequently bumped into people, corners and things in his way, particularly into moving targets (e.g., people walking). He was unable to catch a ball or any object thrown directly to him, whatever its speed; although he could see the object and that it was moving. In the laboratory, he was unable to perceive radial motion and was very impaired on even the simplest heading tasks. (1998, p. 498)

COMMON FATE

When people whose vision is good are tested with random-dot stimuli, they can detect motion

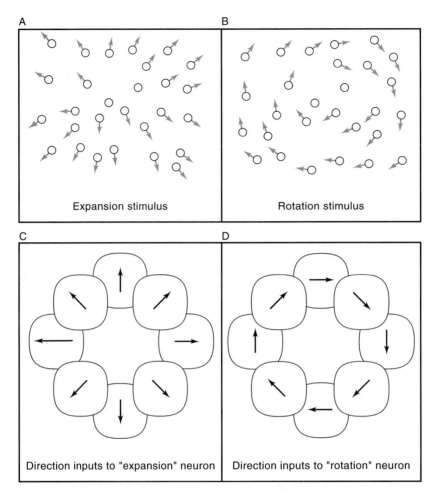

FIGURE 9.19
The two upper panels depict motion vectors associated with expansion (A) and rotation
(B). The two lower panels show possible inputs to a neutron selectively responsive to
expansion (C) or rotation (D).

with incredibly weak correlations among the
dots' movements. For example, despite the fact
that 97 to 98 percent of the displacements are totally random, people can see net motion when
just 2 to 3 percent of all the dots move coherently, in the same direction. But how does the visual system manage to pull such a weak signal (2
percent correlation) out of so much noise (98
percent noncorrelation)? Some theorists credit
special, synergistic interactions among neurons

(Williams, Phillips and Sekuler, 1986). The
guiding idea is that neurons that respond to similar directions of motion "cooperate" by amplifying one another's responses.

Neurons that respond to very different directions "compete," by inhibiting one another. As a
result, the effect of even a small amount of motion in a single direction gets amplified, and the
effect of other motions in many different, uncorrelated directions is diminished.

BOX 9.3

MOTION CAPTURE

Illusion

When we discussed various Gestalt principles in Chapter 6, we noted how they sometimes lead to revealing errors in perception. The same holds for the Law of Common Fate. Using computer animation techniques, Ramachandran and Cavanagh (1987) presented two different random-dot patterns in rapid alternation on the computer's display screen. Because the dots in the two patterns were unrelated to one another, this alternation caused the dots to appear to jump about randomly. Ramachandran and Cavanagh then superimposed a low-contrast, moving grating over the noisy display. The grating's motion immediately captured the random jumps of the dots—all the dots now seemed to move along with the grating as though the grating and dots formed a single object. The smooth motion of the grating "captured" the random motions of the dots.

Here's how you can see **motion capture** for yourself. Using a broad-tipped pen, create a grating by drawing a series of parallel lines on a sheet of cellophane or overhead transparency material (a marker such as a fluorescent highlighter with transparent ink works best). Then tune a television set to a channel that is not broadcasting; this will create a snowy effect much like the random motions that Ramachandran and Cavanagh's observers first saw. Place your homemade grating against the television screen and move it smoothly. You'll see that the television's bright spots, which formerly jumped about at random, now follow along quite tamely as the grating is moved. This compelling motion capture—an illusion in perception—exemplifies the principle of common fate.

Cooperative competitive interactions among direction-selective neurons might be important in another well-known perceptual phenomenon. It was long ago recognized that a perception of **global motion**—a general tendency to perceive motion in a given direction—emerges even though many individual motion vectors are random (Koffka, 1935). In other words, nearby elements or features tend to be seen as moving together. This phenomenon, which the Gestalt theorists called "the law of common fate," is just what one would expect from synergistic interactions among neurons tuned to similar directions (Yuille and Grzywacz, 1988). You can experience "common fate" for yourself when a light breeze blows the leaves of a tree. You can see the tree's net motion (in the direction of the breeze) despite the fact that each leaf also moves on its own. Or when smoke rises from a chimney, you can see the smoke's overall, net motion despite random, local perturbations in the plumes.

Like the Gestalt organizational principles discussed in Chapter 6, the **Law of Common Fate** may reflect how well our visual systems match the physical properties of the world in which we live. In our world, immediately adjacent regions in the visual field tend to belong to the same object. As a result, there is a correlated tendency for adjacent regions, when they do move, to move in similar directions (see Box 9.3). On the other hand, when adjacent regions fail to behave in this way, the visual system treats those adjacent regions as belonging to different objects (recall the discussion of motion parallax in Chapter 8).

Motion Adaptation

We are now ready to consider one of the fundamental properties of direction-selective neurons, a property that you've already seen in action in other domains of vision: neural adaptation. As we've done several times already in this chapter,

Plasticity

we'll introduce you to a phenomenon—adaptation, in this case—by considering a related, compelling illusion.

Suppose that for a minute or so you viewed motion in just one direction. Immediately after this period of adaptation, when you looked at a stationary object that would seem to move in a direction opposite the direction you'd been looking at. This is known as the **motion aftereffect** or sometimes as the **waterfall illusion,** since the illusion is often experienced after looking at a waterfall (Addams, 1834/1964). This illusion has a long history, dating back more than two millennia, to the observations of the Roman poet and philosopher Titus Lucretius Carus (Wade and Verstraten, 1998).

There's a good chance that you have already experienced this illusion of motion. Many naturally-occurring conditions have the potential to engender it. If you haven't, though, here is an easy way to generate a strong motion aftereffect. Some television programs and many movies have long "crawls"—the steadily moving list of people who were to blame for the show. To read the names, your eyes have to keep up with the crawl. Next time you see a crawl, though, forget about reading the names, and just keep your eyes fixed steadily on the center of the screen while the crawl goes by. Then, as soon as the crawl is over, you will experience illusory motion in a direction opposite to that of the crawl—this is the motion aftereffect.

Over the years a number of explanations have been advanced for this striking aftereffect, but most modern theories are based on two quite reasonable assumptions. These assumptions constitute psychophysical linking statements, assertions of particular connections between neural events and perceptual experiences. Mather and Harris (1998) frame the two psychophysical assertions this way:

> (1) perception of motion is mediated by some form of comparison between the responses of cells in the visual system sensitive to different directions; and (2) . . . following adaptation to a moving stimulus there is a change in the responsiveness of these cells, so that cells tuned to motion directions con-

gruent with the adapting stimulus show a reduction in response relative to cells tuned to other direction. (p. 157)

The first of these linking hypotheses may remind you of ideas you encountered earlier, particularly in the chapters on color vision and on spatial vision. The second of the linking hypotheses states an established fact about the effects of prolonged stimulation, namely that adaptation happens.

To see how such ideas might work in practice, imagine that when stationary contours are seen, direction-selective cells, regardless of their direction preference, generate approximately equal levels of spontaneous activity. Following prolonged exposure to a particular direction—say, downward—cells preferring downward motion will show little if any spontaneous activity, while cells responsive to upward motion show a normal level of spontaneous activity. This biased distribution of spontaneous activity following adaptation is similar to the activity distribution evoked by actual motion upward—hence the illusory upward motion. Note that the first of Mather and Harris's psychophysical linking statements does not specify what sort of comparison is made among neurons, and there is continuing disagreement about the details of that comparison (Barlow and Hill, 1963; Mather and Moulden, 1980; Hiris and Blake, 1992).*

Roger Tootell and colleagues (Tootell et al, 1995a; Tootell et al, 1995b) combined psychophysical and neuroimaging techniques to pinpoint one region of the human brain that certainly contributes to the motion aftereffect (MAE).

Execute

---

*The waterfall illusion is not the only case in which stationary objects appear to move. Have you ever noticed how the moon appears to move speedily across the sky as clouds pass in front of it? This is an example of **induced motion**—the real movement of the clouds causes illusory movement of the moon (Duncker, 1929/1938). Unlike the waterfall illusion, induced motion's physiological basis is not known.

They used computer-generated concentric rings with a fixation point in the center. The rings were programmed to expand, contract, or remain unchanged. Forty-second periods of expansion or contraction (sometimes both together) alternated with equally long periods during which the rings were stationary. As you might expect from your knowledge of the MAE, viewing an expanding pattern produced illusory contracting motion in a physically-stationary pattern, and viewing a contracting pattern produced illusory expansion. These aftereffects were quite powerful, lasting around 20 seconds after the cessation of real motion. During that period, the MAE became progressively weaker and finally ceased altogether.

In contrast to these powerful MAEs from unidirectional adaptation, alternation between expansion and contraction produced no MAE—the opposite directions canceled one another. The unidirectional adapting motion produced strong activation in several regions of observers' brains, but activation was by far the strongest in Area MT. When adapting motion ceased and was replaced by a stationary pattern, activation in MT continued but progressively diminished over about 20 seconds.

To visualize the connection between the time frame of the observers' experience of MAE and the time frame of the MAE-related fMRI signals, Tootell plotted the two phenomena on the same axes (Figure 9.20). The solid line in the graph is the MAE-related fMRI signal, which is essentially zero throughout the 40-second adapting period; the vertical dashed line indicates the time at which adaptation ceased. Notice that shortly after the end of adaptation, the MAE-related fMRI signal jumps up and then steadily declines, back down to zero. The open squares in the right half of the graph are measurements of MAE strength sampled at various times following adaptation. Note the striking similarity between the rate of decline in MAE-related fMRI signal (solid line) and the decline in MAE strength (open squares). This demonstrated link between MAE and activation in MT has been strengthened by He, Cohen and

FIGURE 9.20

The fMRI and psychophysical measures of MAE as a function of time after end of adaptation. After 40 seconds, the adapting motion was turned off. Shortly thereafter, both fMRI (solid curve) and psychophysical measures (square data points) give clear evidence of direction-specific activity that declines over time. To generate the psychophysical measure, participants adjusted a nulling motion, which canceled the apparent motion of the MAE. (Adapted from Tootell et al., 1995.)

Hu, (1998) and by Culham and colleagues, (1999). Incidentally, Tootell found that some areas other than MT also seem to show post-adaptation activation that may also be related to MAE. This activation outside MT is consistent with psychophysical observations suggesting that adaptation may occur in more than one site in the nervous system (Blake, 1995; Pantle, 1998; Thompson, 1998).

The MAE, then, probably results from a biased distribution of responses in direction-selective neurons, including neurons in MT. Let's examine another perceptual consequence of biased distributions, since it provides additional support for this way of thinking about the perceived direction of motion.

If an object's perceived direction of motion does depend on the distribution of activity in direction-selective neurons, it should be possible to alter a moving object's perceived direction by adapting some of those neurons. Levinson and Sekuler (1976) asked observers to judge the direction in which an array of bright dots traveled across a television screen. Prior to adaptation, judgments were accurate; upward moving dots, for example, were seen as moving upward. After adapting for several minutes to dots moving steadily in one direction, observers again judged the direction in which dots moved. When the dots moved steadily in a direction similar but not identical to the adaptation direction, the observers now made errors of judgment: the direction of motion of the dots always seemed to be shifted away from the adaptation direction. This phenomenon should remind you of the tilt aftereffect, demonstrated in Figure 4.23.

HIGHER-ORDER EFFECTS IN MOTION PERCEPTION

Top-down In Chapter 6 we distinguished between reflexive attention and purposeful attention. Sometimes purposeful attention is made possible by knowl-

edge about the relative likelihood that various objects and events will occur. In general, when observers are uncertain about what they may encounter, stimuli become harder to detect or recognize. In one study, Ball and Sekuler (1981) determined the ease with which people detected very dim dots that moved across a video screen. From trial to trial, the dots' direction of motion changed unpredictably. In addition, during half the trials, no dots at all were presented; the viewer saw just a blank screen (see panels A and B in Figure 9.21). The dots could be made so dim that a viewer had great difficulty telling whether or not any dots were present.

Ball and Sekuler measured the intensity threshold for detecting the dots under various conditions. Thresholds were initially determined simply by randomizing from trial to trial the direction in which the dots moved. Thresholds

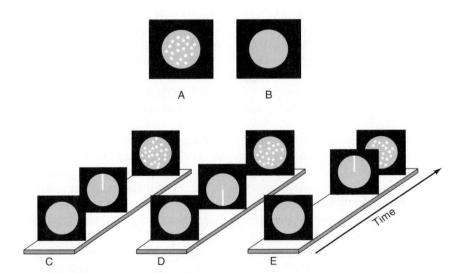

FIGURE 9.21
On any trial, Ball and Sekuler presented either dim dots (A) that could move in any direction or no dots (B). Panels C, D and E represent the sequence of events for different trials. The viewer first saw a blank screen. Then a cue (short white line) appeared, followed some time later by moving dots. The orientation of the short lines in panels C and E signifies upward motion; the orientation of the line in panel D signifies downward motion. The interval between cue and motion varied—the intervals represented in panels C and D are longer than the one represented in panel E.

were then measured with an explicit cue that reduced the viewer's uncertainty about direction of motion. As illustrated in Figure 9.21, this directional cue was a short line flashed very briefly at different times relative to the presentation of the dots. The orientation of the line indicated the direction in which the dots, if present at all, might move (recall that on half the trials, no dots at all were presented).

Ball and Sekuler made several noteworthy discoveries. First, when the orientation of the line corresponded exactly to the dots' direction of motion, the dots were easier to see—that is, the threshold was low. Second, the cue was not helpful unless it preceded the dots by about half a second or so, confirming that selective attention required some time to operate. Third, if the cue's orientation did not match the dots' direction precisely, but only approximated it, the cue could still lower the detection threshold, but not as much as when it was precisely accurate. Generally, the greater the discrepancy between the cue's orientation and the dots' direction of motion, the more difficult it was to see the moving dots. A cue that misdirects an observer's, attention to the wrong direction can be worse than no cue at all.

But how do directional cues or certainty about direction manage to exert the effect that they do? Cues or prior knowledge are not part of the stimulus, but they certainly do affect the response evoked by the stimulus. Obviously, some information extracted from the cue must be recoded into a format that can influence the subsequent processing of the test stimulus. After this recoding process, the nonmoving cue presumably is able to selectively boost responses in particular sets of directionally-selective neurons.

Execute

Recently, Shulman and colleagues (1999) extended Sekuler and Ball's study by measuring brain activity while people performed the cued-motion detection task. As before, the stationary cue, presented prior to the moving target, specified the direction of motion that people would see. The fMRI results showed that presenting the

nonmoving cue produced activation in brain areas including MT and nearby regions that normally respond to motion, as well as in some parietal lobe areas not normally responsive to motion. Together, these motion-sensitive and motion-insensitive areas constitute a neural circuit that encodes and holds instructions during the interval between the cue and the onset of motion.

So, prior information about the direction of motion temporarily boosts MT neurons that are responsive to that direction of motion (Treue and Maunsell, 1999; Treue and Trujillo, 1999). You can think of this internally-generated boost as equivalent to what happens when the responses of particular directionally-selective neurons are strengthened, either by the presentation of a strong visual stimulus or by direct electrical stimulation as in the study by Salzman and colleagues.

Earlier you read how prolonged inspection of a stimulus moving in one direction generated a motion aftereffect, illusory motion in a direction opposite to the adapting direction. Motion aftereffects can also be produced by stimuli comprising two superimposed directions of motion. Here, the resulting aftereffect is opposite the vector sum of the two adapting directions' (Riggs and Day, 1980; Verstraten, Fredericksen and van de Grind, 1994). Thus, for example, simultaneous adaptation to leftward and upward motions subsequently causes a stationary test figure to appear to drift down and to the right (the vector sum of the downward component and the rightward component).

When the two adapting components are unequal in strength—say, one component is higher in contrast than the other—the aftereffect direction shifts toward the stronger component, and the size of the shift tracks the inequality between stimulus components.

Instead of varying the relative contrasts of the two component adapting motions, Alais and Blake (1999) manipulated how much attention people paid to one of the components. In their experiments, people viewed a computer display

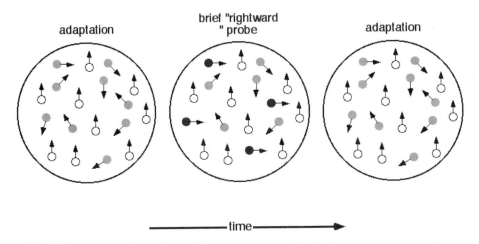

FIGURE 9.22
Schematic of stimulus conditions used by Alais and Blake (1999) to test attention's influence on motion adaptation. During most of the adaptation period, a subset of "adaptation" dots moved coherently upward (open circles in this figure) while the remaining "noise" dots moved incoherently in all directions (filled circles). Unpredictably, during the adaptation period a subset of the "noise" dots moved briefly rightward (black dots), and observers had to pay attention during adaptation to detect these brief episodes of rightward motion.

consisting of two superimposed fields of moving dots. Dots in one group all moved coherently in a single direction, shown as "upward" in Figure 9.22. Dots in the other group moved in random directions most of the time, producing no net directional drift. Every once in a while, a subset of the random dots joined forces to move in the same direction, shown as "rightward" in Figure 9.22. The proportion of dots moving rightward was only about 25%, making it necessary for observers to look carefully to detect their presence.

On some trials, observers were required to indicate when this weak coherent motion was present. On the remaining trials observers simply observed the same stimuli but did not have to perform the detection task and, therefore, did not have to attend selectively to the rightward motion. Alais and Blake reasoned that the first of these conditions—active viewing—would demand more attention than the second, passive viewing condition.

In the passive, control condition, brief insertions of weak rightward motion had little effect on MAE's direction. When observers had to attend to it, however, the inserted motion dramatically altered the aftereffects' direction, shifting it by about 20 degrees. This same shift, which was mediated solely by attention to a weak signal, was equivalent to the shift that would have been produced by a very powerful signal (motion with dots 70% correlated). So attention to motion in one direction boosted the response to that motion by almost threefold—making a 25% correlated stimulus as effective as one that was 70% correlated.

Extrapolating from the response of MT neurons to changes in stimulus correlation, Alais and Blake deduced that the attentional effects observed in humans were equivalent, on average, to what would be expected from a doubling in stimulus correlation in a nonattended stimulus. There's no doubt, then, that attention can exert a very powerful influence on perceived motion.

Attending to Objects That Are Not Really There

Top-down

When William James discussed varieties of attention, he noted that people could attend either to sensory stimuli, such as locations or objects, or to some "ideal or represented objects" (1890, p. 393). James was distinguishing between attention to a thing that was physically present and attention to an object that existed only in the mind, what we today might call a "virtual object." In the previous section, you read about attention's impact on perception of moving objects that were physically present. But as James intuited, attention can also influence perception of motion that exists only in the mind.

Some demonstrations of attention's influence on virtual moving objects use a procedure devised by Pylyshyn and Storm, (1988). The procedure assesses the ability to keep track, over time, of multiple, spatially-dispersed, independently moving targets. Roughly, the task resembles watching some crows feeding in a field, and then, when the crows fly off in different directions, keeping track of all of them.

A typical experiment on **multiple object tracking** consists of three phases: *target designation*, *movement*, and *probe*. These three phases are illustrated in Figure 9.23. Target designation began with the presentation of ten targets, such as discs, scattered about on a computer display. Then three, four or five of the ten discs, chosen randomly, blink several times. This informs the observer which discs will be targets for that trial. In the movement phase, all ten of the discs move about smoothly on the screen in various directions, each changing course unpredictably. After several seconds' movement, the trial's probe phase began. One of the ten discs is highlighted and the observer must report whether that one probe item had or had not been one of the designated targets.

Quality of performance is summarized by the proportion of trials with accurate reporting. Performance is most accurate when people have to keep track of fewer targets, say three rather than four or five. This is consistent with earlier findings that attention loses potency for any one item when additional items must also be attended to.

PHASES OF TRIAL

TARGET DESIGNATION (target discs blink)	MOVEMENT (discs move randomly, several seconds)	PROBE (one disc blinks)

— time ⟶

FIGURE 9.23

Display characteristics during a trial in a multiple-object tracking experiment. During phase 1 (*target designation*), several discs are singled out by a momentary brightening. During phase 2 (*movement*), all discs undergo a series of random movements. In phase 3 (*probe*), only one disc is brightened. Thereafter, the observer must judge whether the probe disc had or had not been among the target discs designated in phase 1. Under many conditions, the random movements of the discs make it difficult to track simultaneously all the designated target discs.

Steven Yantis (1992) examined how perceptual grouping contributes to multiple object tracking. This effort required several different ways of influencing perceptual grouping of the targets. For example, in one experiment, some targets were either chosen at random, while others were chosen for their strategic location within a simple geometric figure, such as a diamond. At the outset of the experiment, tracking performance was much better when the target was initially part of a geometric perceptual group. However, observers quickly learned to impose virtual groupings on elements that had not been part of the regular geometrical groupings, which erased any early boost from geometrical groupings.

Of course, grouping at the start of a trial is no help at trial's end (the probe phase) unless the grouping is maintained during the movement phase. By varying the targets' movements during a trial's movement phase, Yantis manipulated the likelihood that any existing grouping would be maintained.

In one condition, targets moved about randomly, which allowed one or more targets to occasionally cross over an opposite edge of the virtual polygon. This crisscrossing destroyed the original grouping, which undermined the coherence of the virtual polygon and caused elements to lose identity as designated targets in that virtual polygon.

In another condition, movements of targets were constrained, insuring that none ever crossed over an opposite edge of the virtual polygon. In this condition, movements of individual targets produced moment-to-moment fluctuations in the shape of a virtual figure that would be created by connecting those targets. But none of these fluctuations were drastic enough to destroy the convexity of the virtual polygon. Performance was distinctly better when target movement did not destroy the virtual polygon than when it did. This suggests that observers' attention creates (in the target designation phase) and maintains (in the movement phase) an updatable virtual object that is used (in the probe phase) to determine whether the probed target was or was not in the object.

To track multiple *moving* objects, the brain exploits neural circuits that are ordinarily devoted to a slightly different purpose, namely for shifting attention from one location in space to another. Culham and colleagues (1998) used fMRI to identify the brain circuits that participated in multiple object tracking. Their results provide a clear picture of how the brain manages this difficult task. Attentive tracking of multiple, independently moving objects is mediated by a network of areas that includes parietal and frontal regions (known to be responsible for eye movements and shifting attention between locations) and area MT and related regions, which you learned earlier are central regions for processing motion information. (Scholl provides a thoughtful review of the work on multiple object tracking.)

SUMMARY AND PREVIEW

This chapter emphasized motion perception's many, varied contributions, from defining the three-dimensional shape of moving objects and providing information that we use in locomoting, to guiding the eye movements that we use as we explore the world. The chapter described the neural basis of movement perception and the circuitry used to extract motion signals. It explained how limitations of this circuitry produced a dependence on configural properties, including the shape of the aperture within which an object moves. You read about two theoretically significant illusions of motion perception, namely apparent motion and motion aftereffect. After exploring parallels between the properties of natural events and the neural mechanisms designed to register those events, the chapter ended with a discussion of important higher-order influences on motion, including attention.

This chapter concludes our survey of visual qualities that enable you to appreciate the various biologically important aspects of the world. Next, we turn to other senses that also provide vital information about that world. We begin with the ear and hearing.

KEY TERMS

apparent motion
critical flicker frequency (CFF)
direction-selective cell
element movement
global motion
group movement
induced motion
Law of Common Fate
motion aftereffect
motion capture
multiple object tracking

optic ataxia
optic flow
point-light motion
proprioception
pursuit eye movements
saccades
smooth eye movements
structure from motion (SFM)
waterfall illusion

THE EAR AND AUDITORY SYSTEM

Close your eyes and listen carefully to the sounds all around you. Even in the quietest room, it's surprising how much there is to hear: an airplane flying overhead, people talking in the next room, that odd whirring noise made by your computer's hard drive. As you listen, try to identify what makes one sound different from another. It will be immediately obvious that different sounds seem to come from sources at different locations around you. You're probably able to pinpoint the locations of those sources with ease. Notice also how sounds may differ in loudness, ranging from the soft rustle of leaves on a tree to the piercing wail of a siren. Sounds vary in complexity, too. A birdsong may be composed of just a few pure notes, whereas the traffic on a busy street can generate a cacophony of a great many different sounds jumbled together.

Besides complexity, sounds can also differ in their cadences, or rhythms. Some sounds have a regularity that makes them recognizable, such as the sound of footsteps in the hallway. The tempo of those footsteps may even disclose who's coming, for people have characteristic strides whose rhythm is broadcast by their footsteps. In contrast, other sounds, such as the snap of a breaking twig or the slamming of a door, occur abruptly and without repetition.

Sounds can also possess emotional overtones. The hair-raising sound of fingernails being scraped across a chalkboard elicits a strong, immediate revulsion in almost any listener, whereas the soothing sound of flowing water is a universal tranquilizer.

So sounds have a number of characteristics that enable us to locate, identify and react to the objects or people from which they arise. For this reason, hearing plays a very important role in defining your perceptual world throughout your lifetime.

Often, you are able to *hear* things in your environment before you can see them. You rely heavily on hearing when it is dark or when an event occurs out of your field of view. Even when a sound source *is* readily visible, your behavioral reaction to it may depend on the nature of the sound it makes. Some grocery shoppers believe that a melon's ripeness can be judged only from the sound made by thumping it. A similar thumping technique is sometimes used by doctors to check for fluid accumulation within a patient's chest cavity.

Hearing provides the basis for many forms of social communication, particularly speech. Without the ability to hear voices, an individual must struggle heroically to remain in touch with the flow of social discourse. Perceptual appreciation of the world is diminished when hearing is lost, as any deaf person will testify (Noble, 1983).

In this chapter, we will examine the process of hearing, starting with the acoustic energy that carries auditory information, and progressing through what is known about the machinery of hearing. This coverage sets the stage for the next chapter, which considers sound recognition, sound localization and speech perception.

ACOUSTIC PROPERTIES OF SOUND

What Is Sound?

You've probably heard the old puzzle, "If a tree falls in the forest but no one is around to hear it, does it make a sound?"* The answer is quite simply no. The word *sound* refers to a perceptual experience, and that experience requires the presence of a perceiver, an organism with a properly outfitted nervous system. Without a perceiver, there is no sound, no matter how much energy was generated when that tree fell. Conversely, without that energy, there'd be nothing to hear, no matter how many perceivers are in the vicinity. With the distinction between sound—a *perceptual* quality—and energy—a *physical* quality—

firmly in mind, we can consider the physical basis of sound.

Sound is inaugurated when some mechanical disturbance produces vibrations. These vibrations are transmitted through some medium (usually air) in the form of tiny collisions among the molecules in that medium. If they are sufficiently strong when they arrive at your ears, these vibrations trigger a chain of events culminating in an auditory experience. All sounds, regardless of their nature, come to you this way. It's odd, but the strains of a symphony and the flush of a toilet share the same physical basis, a series of tiny molecular collisions. To understand this, let's consider sound and its properties in greater detail.

Whenever an object vibrates, or moves back and forth, it causes a disturbance within its surroundings. This disturbance takes the form of waves spreading outward from the source of vibration, and these waves possess and convey what is known as **acoustic energy.** They travel through the surrounding medium in a manner similar to the ripples produced when a pebble is tossed into a quiet pond (see Figure 10.1). Like ripples on a pond, sound waves require something to travel through—there can be no sound in empty space or in a perfect vacuum.

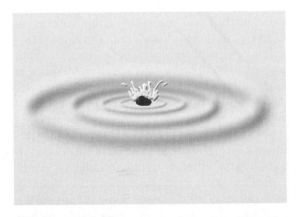

FIGURE 10.1
Sound waves resemble the ripples on a pond.

---

*Henry David Thoreau expressed the falling tree idea in a different, clever way when he wrote in his journal, "It takes a man to make a room silent" (cited in Merker, 1992, p. 59).

Execute

This was convincingly demonstrated in the seventeenth century by Robert Boyle, a British physicist and chemist. He placed an alarm bell inside a tightly sealed jar and used a vacuum pump to suck nearly all the air out of this jar. When the alarm went off, the bell "rang" but could not be heard because there were essentially no air molecules to carry the vibrations from the bell to the wall of the glass jar. After quickly pumping air back into the jar, Boyle could hear the bell. From this simple experiment, Boyle correctly concluded that air was made up of particles and that sound involved waves of energy traveling *through* these particles.

We could liken these acoustic pressure waves to the wave of motion produced by toppling a stack of dominoes lined up in a row. In this analogy, the individual dominoes represent individual air molecules. The pressure wave is transmitted by one domino bumping into another—a chain reaction propagated the length of the row of dominoes. For the analogy to be complete, however, each domino would have to return to its upright position after colliding with its neighbor, becoming available for participation in future chain reactions.

Though one usually thinks of air as the medium for carrying sound, pressure waves may also be transmitted through other media whose constituent molecules are sufficiently close together to collide with one another when they are set in motion and, at the same time, are sufficiently elastic to return to their original position following disturbance. In fact, the more densely these molecules are packed, the faster sound will travel through them. For instance, at room temperature, airborne sound travels 343 meters per second (or 1,130 feet per second) and slightly less when the air is colder. (The speed of sound is, of course, considerably slower than the speed of light—300,000 kilometers per second—which is why we see lightning before we hear the associated thunder.) In the denser medium of water, sound travels about 1,500 meters per second, almost five times faster than in air. With this differential in mind, imagine partially submerging your head at one end of a swimming pool so that one ear is under water while the other is above the water's surface in the air. A person at the other end of the pool now snaps her fingers on both hands, one below the water's surface and the other above. The resulting sound will arrive sooner at the ear underwater, probably causing you to hear two clicks. Sound moves even faster through steel, clipping along at over 5,000 meters per second. In general, sound travels more slowly in gases than in liquids, and more slowly in liquids than in solids.

Regardless of the medium through which it is propagated and regardless of the source, sound energy becomes weaker as it travels farther from its source. Yet while it is fading in strength, sound continues to travel at a constant speed, so long as it travels in the same medium. Thus, whether you whisper or shout at a nearby friend, the message will arrive at its destination in the same amount of time, albeit with a different degree of emphasis. This is true for just about all sounds—voices, musical notes and door bells.

As sound waves spread out from their source, they interact with one another as well as with objects in their paths. These interactions can actually be more complex than those involving light. For instance, a solid object casts a visual shadow if exposed to light shining from one direction. But most sounds can be heard with little noticeable change if a relatively small object is situated between the source of a sound and your ears. This happens because sound, unlike light, can travel around—and sometimes through—solid objects. Consequently, it is harder to shut out unwanted sounds than it is bothersome light—pulling a shade, for instance, may eliminate the glare from a nearby streetlamp, but it will not silence the noise of passing traffic.

When sound waves strike a surface, a portion of the sound waves bounce off the surface. These reflected sound waves are called **echoes,** and they can be used to compute the distance from a listener to a sound source. Knowing the speed at which sound travels, one can measure the time elapsing between production of a sound and reception of its echo. From this duration, it is simple to calculate how far away the reflecting surface is. This is the principle used in **sonar** (a term derived from the words **so**und **na**vigation **r**anging), a means for detecting objects underwater.

Although we're seldom aware of it, echoes actually have a distinct impact on what we hear. When echoes (reflected sound) collide with other, unreflected sound waves from the same source, these sounds interact by adding or subtracting their component.* The result of these interactions among sounds can be particularly conspicuous in enclosed spaces such as rooms and auditoriums. Depending on an auditorium's shape and design, for example, there may be some seats where sound is unnaturally loud and other seats where sound is considerably damped. In an acoustically "good" auditorium, these variations in sound quality are minimal. In fact, it's a real engineering challenge to design and construct auditoriums with superb acoustics. Despite great advances in the science of **acoustics** (the branch of physics concerned with sound), even the most thoughtfully designed structure may, in fact, fail to live up to its billing. The repeated modifications and the eventual complete reconstruction of New York's Avery Fisher Hall demonstrate how sound, particularly reflected sound, has the insidious knack of turning up where it is least expected while avoiding where it is *supposed* to go (Bliven, 1976).

Not all sound striking a surface is reflected— some acoustic energy is absorbed. The amount of sound absorbed depends on the surface material. Smooth plaster, for example, absorbs only 3 percent of the sound striking its surface, reflecting the rest as an echo. This is why your singing voice invariably sounds strongest within the con-

fines of a shower enclosure, particularly one with hard-tiled, reflecting walls. Nylon carpet, by comparison, absorbs about 25 percent of incident sound. As you can imagine, a room containing carpet, drapes, and stuffed furniture soaks up a lot of sound energy, thereby providing a rather dead listening environment. For the same reason, the acoustics in a concert hall vary with the season, depending on whether the audience is dressed in heavy winter clothing, which absorbs sound.

Special rooms called *anechoic chambers* create an environment devoid of echoes. The walls, floor, and ceiling of such rooms are made of porous foam wedges that absorb sound before it can be reflected to your ears. Consequently, you hear only the sounds emitted from the source itself, with no echoes. For instance, when you walk in an anechoic chamber, your footsteps sound quite unnatural, having a muffled, flat quality. This is because you are hearing the sounds of your footsteps unaccompanied by their usual echoes. In general, the dull, muted quality of sounds in an anechoic chamber underscores the contribution of echoes to the normal perception of sound.

Besides contributing to an appreciation of sound, echoes furnish information about objects from which sound is reflected. For one thing, the mere presence of an echo signals that some object besides the sound source must be present in your environment. And as explained earlier, by noting the time elapsing between the production of a sound and hearing its echo, it is possible to estimate the distance from the source to the reflecting object.

Differences

This information may be particularly useful if you produce the sound yourself, such as by yelling or clapping your hands. Some animals, including bats and porpoises, rely heavily on reflections of self-produced sound to navigate. We humans aren't consciously aware of self-produced echoes in our environment, except when we shout inside a large building (such as a cathedral) or in an enclosed area (such as a canyon). But, then, neither are we aware of the sensory information that stabilizes our posture.

---

*Strictly speaking, the waves themselves do not add and subtract. Instead the densities and velocities of the particles through which the waves travel interact to reinforce or cancel one another.

It is well established that blind people can utilize reflected sound—echoes—to guide their locomotion and to discriminate among materials such as glass, metal and wood. It is quite conceivable that echoes also help sighted individuals judge distance and recognize objects, without our being consciously aware of it (Stoffregen and Pittenger, 1995).

So far we have described the vibratory nature of sound waves and how they travel through a medium and reflect off surfaces. But to clearly understand hearing, we must study the ways that sound waves differ from one another. We begin with a thorough analysis of the physical properties of sound.

The Nature of Sound Waves

A sound source transmits acoustic information to a perceiver by means of molecules bumping into one another. You can neither see these molecular collisions nor feel them, except in unusual cases of very strong sound waves. To envision the behavior of sound waves, imagine the following setup. Suppose a very thin, lightweight thread is dangled in front of a loudspeaker, with the thread held at one end, leaving the other end free to move about. By measuring the amount the free end of the thread is deflected, you can gauge the strength of various sounds broadcast over the loudspeaker. This setup is depicted in Figure 10.2.

The tiny dots in front of the speaker represent individual air molecules. In the absence of sound energy, air molecules are more or less evenly distributed, as illustrated in panel A. As you may know, a loudspeaker produces sound by moving back and forth, an action that physically jostles air molecules in immediate contact with the speaker cone (the round portion of the unit that actually moves). When the speaker cone moves forward, it produces an increase in air pressure that, if one could see it, involves a bunching up, or compression, of air molecules. This is shown in panel B of Figure 10.2 as a heightened concentration of dots. These compressed air molecules, in turn, collide with their immediate neighbors, thereby projecting the increase in air pressure out from the speaker itself. This miniature "breeze" eventually

A   B   C

| | | |
| Uniform pressure, loudspeaker stationary | High pressure as loudspeaker moves toward thread | Low pressure as loudspeaker moves away from thread |

FIGURE 10.2
Sound waves consist of changes in air pressure.

strikes the thin thread, causing it to bend in a direction away from the speaker.

In the meantime, the loudspeaker cone has moved steadily back to its initial position. This creates a suctionlike action that spreads out, or rarifies, the air molecules, returning them to their initial density (normal air pressure). As shown in panel C, this rarefaction also travels outward, as air molecules are sucked into the area of decreased pressure. Eventually, this rarefaction pulls the thread back to its vertical position. Now suppose the speaker cone continues to move inward, further decreasing air pressure in the immediate vicinity of the cone. This partial vacuum travels outward and eventually sucks the thread in a direction toward the loudspeaker.

This bunching up and spreading out of air molecules, caused by mechanical displacement of the speaker, represent waves of high and low pressure. The air molecules themselves each move very little. It is the *wave* of pressure that travels steadily outward from the sound source. You might think back to the ripples on the surface of a pond (Figure 10.1). The water molecules in the pond, like air molecules, each move only a short distance when disturbed, but by colliding with their neighbors they transmit a wave of motion that can carry over great distances.

As illustrated in Figure 10.2, changes in the position of the thread reflect changes in air pressure radiating outward from the loudspeaker. Suppose we now graph the successive changes in the position of the thread occurring over time by tracing out the sound waves produced by the loudspeaker as its cone moves in and out in a cyclic fashion. Such a graph is shown in Figure 10.3. The horizontal axis plots time, and the vertical axis plots the thread's position relative to the loudspeaker. The dotted horizontal line shows the case where the thread is perfectly vertical, undisturbed by sound from the loudspeaker. Deviations from this level represent changes in the thread's position and, hence, changes in air pressure produced by movements of the loudspeaker. The height of the curve above or below the dot-

FIGURE 10.3
Change in thread position (representing air pressure) over time.

ted line indicates how much the thread deviates from vertical (the amount of change in air pressure). This deviation of the curve from the baseline level is known as **amplitude,** and it is determined by the distance over which the speaker moves. When this movement is tiny, the air pressure change is small and the amplitude of the wave is low (the curve labeled 1 in Figure 10.3). As you might guess, small-amplitude pressure waves give rise to weak sounds. But when the loudspeaker's movements are large, the change in air pressure, and hence, the wave amplitude, is great (the curve labeled 2). You would hear this as a loud sound. The peak of this pressure variation curve provides an index of the strength of the sound.

As air pressure changes proceed away from the source, the peak amplitude of the pressure wave gradually decreases. This property of sound propagation explains why a sound becomes fainter and, eventually, inaudible, as you move away from its source. Specifically, sound energy (just like light energy) falls off with the square of the distance between a listener and the sound source. Thus, for example, doubling the distance between your ear and a telephone receiver will produce a fourfold reduction in the sound energy reaching your ear. Sound amplitude is usually expressed in units called **decibels** (abbreviated **dB**); this unit of sound intensity is the "industry standard" and deserves more detailed description.

Sound level   The human ear can hear and distinguish sound over an enormous range of intensities. In this respect, the ear is comparable to the eye: both manage to handle energy levels that can differ by many orders of magnitude (each order of magnitude is a factor of 10). To get some idea of the energy levels confronted by your ears, look at Figure 10.4, a chart listing the intensity values characteristic of common sounds.

You will notice that these various sound intensities are scaled in decibel units. This is a *logarithmic* scale with a particular reference level of sound. The logarithmic nature of the scale makes it much easier to show a wide range of values on a single graph. Also, the logarithmic scale specifies sound level differences in terms of their ratio to one another, not simply in terms of their algebraic difference. This seems to describe more accurately the way one judges intensity differences. Let's consider the definition of a decibel (dB):

$$dB = 20 \log (p1/p0)$$

where $p1$ refers to the air pressure amplitude of the sound under consideration and $p0$ refers to a standard reference level of air pressure. This reference level is typically set at 20 microPascals (μPa), the approximate sound pressure of the softest sound that humans can detect. To signify when amplitudes are being given relative to this particular **sound pressure level (SPL),** we'll denote such amplitudes as dB_{SPL}. Under ideal conditions at that reference level, a sound in the neighborhood of 1,000 to 4,000 Hz is just barely audible.

Sometimes the decibel unit is used in a different way. Suppose that instead of expressing some sound relative to 20 μPa, we wish to compare the amplitudes of two sounds—say, a sound at 60 dB_{SPL} versus a sound at 35 dB_{SPL}. Here we can describe amplitudes relative to each other in terms of dB, omitting the subscript *SPL*. In this example, we would say that the two sounds differ by 25 dB.

With these definitions in mind, let's consider some of the entries in Figure 10.4. Note that

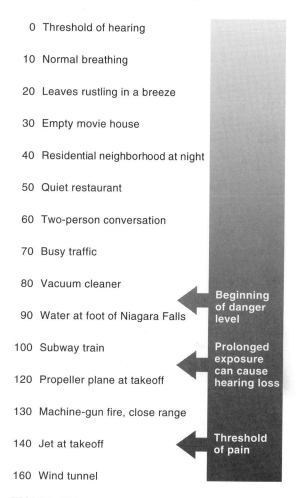

THE DECIBEL SCALE

0   Threshold of hearing

10   Normal breathing

20   Leaves rustling in a breeze

30   Empty movie house

40   Residential neighborhood at night

50   Quiet restaurant

60   Two-person conversation

70   Busy traffic

80   Vacuum cleaner

90   Water at foot of Niagara Falls — **Beginning of danger level**

100   Subway train

120   Propeller plane at takeoff — **Prolonged exposure can cause hearing loss**

130   Machine-gun fire, close range

140   Jet at takeoff — **Threshold of pain**

160   Wind tunnel

FIGURE 10.4
Sound intensity is expressed in units called decibels.

rustling leaves (or a quiet whisper) is 20 dB higher than the 0 dB_{SPL} reference level. This corresponds to a tenfold increase in sound pressure. A loud scream, in contrast, can reach 100 dB_{SPL}, which is 100,000 times more intense than the threshold, reference level. Sounds in excess of 130 dB_{SPL} can lead to an experience of pain, an adaptive sensation since it causes one reflexively to cover the ears, thereby protecting them from damage. We will discuss the consequences of exposure to loud noise in the following chapter.

Sound frequency   Returning to our loudspeaker example, let's next consider the effect of varying the rate at which the speaker moves back and forth. When the speaker's movements occur slowly over time, the peaks and troughs of the sound wave spread out, as shown in the left-hand portion of Figure 10.5. Rapid movements of the speaker, on the other hand, yield bunched-up peaks and troughs, as shown in the right-hand portion of Figure 10.5. When dealing with steady, cyclic variations such as those described here, one may specify the *frequency* of the sound. This refers to the number of times per second that air pressure undergoes a complete cycle from, say, high to low and back to high. The unit used to designate frequency is the **hertz** (abbreviated **Hz**).

Thus, for instance, in the case of a 500-Hz sound, a complete cycle of air pressure change (from compression to decompression and back) occurs in two-thousandths of a second, yielding 500 such cycles in one second. Think of frequency as the number of wave cycles passing a given point in one second.

You can also relate frequency to the *length* of a single wave. This refers to the distance from a point along one wave (such as its peak) to the cor-

responding point in the next wave. Considered in this way, a low-frequency sound wave would have a long wavelength, whereas a high-frequency wave would be short in length. Figure 10.6 illustrates the relation between wavelength and frequency. As you can see from this graph, a 400-Hz sound wave is about 3 feet in length, measuring from, say, the peak of one cycle to the peak of the next.

You probably recognize the waveforms shown in Figure 10.5 as sinusoids, waveforms discussed in Chapter 5 in relation to spatial vision. In the case of vision, recall that complex visual patterns (such as a checkerboard) can be described as the combination of certain spatial frequency components. This is why gratings of various spatial frequencies are so useful in the study of spatial vision. By the same token, complex sounds can be described as the combination of certain temporal frequencies, or **pure tones** as they are sometimes called. Analogues to sinusoidal gratings, pure tones represent sinusoidal changes in air pressure over time. Let's see how a more complicated waveform (and hence, a more complicated sound) may be described as the sum of certain sinusoidal frequencies of various amplitudes. We will develop this idea in several steps.

Think back to the loudspeaker example: what will happen when two or more tones are simulta-

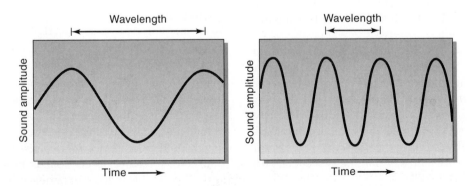

FIGURE 10.5
Rate of change in air pressure corresponds to sound's frequency.

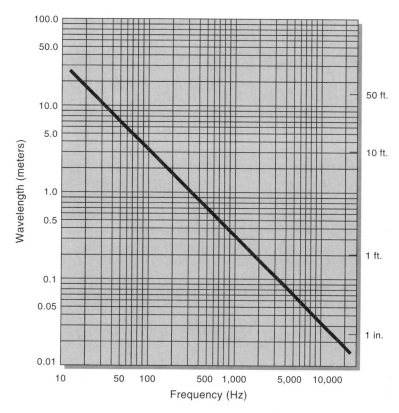

FIGURE 10.6
The relation between wavelength and frequency.

neously broadcast over the speaker? In this case, air molecules immediately in front of the cone will be influenced by several vibratory forces. As you continue adding more and more frequencies, you create more complex sound waves. Such waves will consist of the algebraic sum of the component frequencies, and the resulting waveform will quickly resemble a set of irregularly spaced peaks and valleys. One such example is shown in panel A of Figure 10.7. This irregular waveform depicts a complex change in air pressure over time. If enough components are added together *randomly,* the resultant sound may be heard as **noise.** In a way, noise is analogous to white light, which, as you learned in Chapter 7, contains light energy at all wavelengths of the visible spectrum. However, most sounds in the environment are complex, meaning their acoustic energy is composed of many frequencies. But they are not heard as noise (see panel B, Figure 10.7). This is because the constituent frequencies of most sounds have a certain temporal structure; unlike the frequencies in noise, they are not added together randomly.

In fact, very seldom does one encounter anything resembling pure tones in the natural environment, which is fortunate. If events and objects in nature were to broadcast their presence using pure tones only, one's ability to identify those objects and events via hearing would be seriously

Differences

A

Time ⟶

B

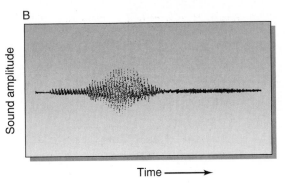

Time ⟶

FIGURE 10.7
Many different frequencies mixed together randomly can produce "noise," but when mixed together nonrandomly can produce a recognizable sound. These two examples of complex soundwaves would be perceptually quite distinct were you to listen to them.

limited because there are not enough discriminable tones to uniquely specify all the recognizable sounds important to us.

Because of their virtually unlimited range of unique structures, complex patterns of sound energy provide an enormous vocabulary for conveying biologically and socially relevant information. For instance, your ability to recognize a person's voice over the telephone stems from the unique "signature" provided by the package of frequencies composing that person's voice. Figure 10.8 shows two soundwaves produced by two different people uttering the same phrase. The soundwave on the top is associated with the utterance by a female, the one on the bottom, by a male. The specific frequencies and the rise and fall of the waveforms are discernably different for the two individuals, but you'd have no trouble understanding that both people were saying the same thing. Still, it is important to understand that all sounds, regardless of their duration or complexity, can be considered as the sum of many simple frequency components. As you're about to learn, early stages of the auditory system analyze complex sounds into their simpler frequency components.

FIGURE 10.8
Two sonograms showing soundwaves produced by a male and a female uttering the phrase "Where were you when the lights went out?"

THE AUDITORY SYSTEM: THE EAR

The human auditory system consists of the ears, a pair of auditory nerves, and portions of the brain. This section of the chapter is devoted to the ear, which is depicted in Figure 10.9. The top part of the figure shows a cutaway diagram of the right ear, and the bottom part schematically illustrates the operations performed by the three chambers of the ear. In this section, we will focus on the specifics of these initial stages of auditory processing. As we proceed, the terms appearing in the schematic flow diagram will become

clearer. You should mark this page and refer back to the diagram from time to time.

The Outer Ear

The most conspicuous part of the ear is the **pinna,** that shell-like flap gracing the side of your head. Some animals, such as cats, can rotate their pinnas in order to funnel sound into their ears. Human pinnas, though, are immobile; humans must turn the entire head to orient themselves toward sound. Still, the two pinnas are not useless vestiges. Their corrugations act like small reflecting surfaces that modify, or "color," the complexity of sound actually entering the ear (Batteau, 1967; Wightman and Kistler, 1998). The degree of coloration introduced by the pinnas depends on which direction sound is coming from. Sound originating straight ahead of you would be affected differently by the pinnas than would sound coming from a source behind you. So these ear flaps, besides providing a convenient support for eyeglasses, play a significant role in sound localization.

And because pinna shape varies so greatly among individuals, we each possess our own, unique "sound modulators" that we learn to hear with. We will consider the pinna's contribution to sound localization in greater detail in the next chapter.

Differences

After it is collected by each pinna, sound is channeled down the **auditory canal,** a slightly bent tube approximately 2.5 centimeters long and about 7 millimeters in diameter (the same diameter as that of a pencil, which you should not confirm yourself). Because of its dimensions, the auditory canal has a resonant frequency (see Box 10.1) around 3,000 Hz. As a consequence, sounds containing frequencies in this neighborhood are actually amplified several decibels or more (Tonndorf, 1988), which is one reason why human sensitivity to barely audible sounds is best around this frequency.

At the far end of the auditory canal, sound pressure comes in contact with the **eardrum (tympanic membrane).** This thin, oval-shaped membrane

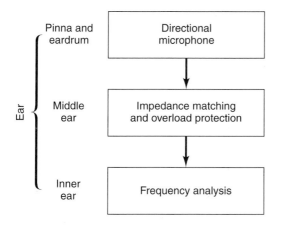

FIGURE 10.9

A schematic representation of the ear and the functions of its constituent parts.

BOX 10.1

RESONANT FREQUENCIES: IS IT LIVE OR IS IT . . . ?

During the 1980's an oft-played commercial on United States television showed a popular female singer shattering a crystal wine glass by singing a loud, high note. You'd never witness such an event in real life though. The unamplified human voice cannot produce sufficient volume—around 130 dB—to shatter a glass. Of course, some sounds are this intense or greater. Perhaps you have felt the window panes in a building rattle when there's a loud clap of thunder or an explosion. This raises the question: "how can sound produce vibrations in solid objects?"

All objects have a **resonant frequency,** defined as the frequency at which the object vibrates when set into motion. You've probably experienced the high-pitched ringing sound produced by striking a glass with a spoon. This clear, pure ringing sound corresponds to the resonant frequency of the glass, and it occurs because the molecules of the glass are vibrating back and forth at that frequency. Adding water to the glass causes those molecules to vibrate at a slower rate when you strike the glass with the spoon. The resonant frequency of the glass has been lowered. So long as the amount of water in the glass remains constant, its resonant frequency will stay the same. Regardless of how you set up vibrations in the glass, it will produce the same ringing sound. (Mozart actually composed a piece featuring a musician playing an array of glasses filled with different amounts of water: "Glass Armonica Adagio in C Minor and Rondo in C Major," K. 617.) Sound from another source may induce vibrations in the glass, so long as that inducing sound contains energy at the resonant frequency of the glass. For instance, by whistling the right note, you could produce a faint ringing sound from the glass. And if this inducing energy were sufficiently intense (such as an electronically-amplified pure tone), the vibrations set up in the glass could be sufficiently strong to shatter it.

Is this perhaps how the band of priests at the city of Jericho (in Joshua 6:1–20) managed to tumble that city's walls, by blasting their trumpets in unison? The sound energy needed to bring off that biblical feat would have to have been awesome. In fact, if true, the priests themselves would surely have been rendered instantly deaf from exposure to such intense sound. On a less spectacular scale, these induced vibrations, or *resonance,* explain why objects in your room may tremble sometimes when you turn up the volume on your stereo. In general, the resonant frequency of an object depends on the size and rigidity of the object.

We will discuss the relation between hearing and the frequency of sound in the next chapter, but at this point it would be helpful for you to have some idea of the subjective experience of different frequencies. To give a few examples, the tone called middle C has a frequency of 261.63 Hz; the faint, high whine produced by a television when the volume control is turned all the way down is 15,750 Hz; and adult human speech consists of frequencies ranging from 500 to 8,000 Hz.

vibrates when sound pressure waves strike it, and these resulting vibrations may be remarkably small. It has been estimated (Von Békésy and Rosenblith, 1951) that a soft whisper, with an intensity of about 20 dB_{SPL}, displaces the eardrum approximately 1/100-millionth of a centimeter, about the width of a single hydrogen molecule! Despite the almost infinitesimal size of this movement, you hear the whisper.

This exquisitely sensitive device, the eardrum, is actually quite sturdy; structurally it resembles an umbrella, with a frame of supporting ribs. In the human ear, the surface area of the tympanic membrane is approximately 68 mm^2, which is tiny by elephant standards (450 mm^2) but huge compared to the gerbil's eardrum (15 mm^2). Larger eardrums are better designed to handle low frequency sounds, but this comes at the ex-

pense of registering high frequency sounds.*
This is one reason why hearing acuity—indexed
by the highest audible frequency—is better in
smaller animals: eardrum area scales with body
size (Hemilä, Nummela and Reuter, 1995).

Together, the pinna and auditory canal constitute the *outer ear.* Referring back to Figure 10.9,
you can see that this portion of the auditory system functions like a directional microphone that
picks up sound and modifies it, depending on its
frequency content and locational source.

The Middle Ear

The eardrum forms the outer wall of a small, air-
filled chamber called the *middle ear.* In the middle ear, the vibrations impinging on the eardrum
are passed along to the **oval window,** which is
covered by another membrane, smaller than the
eardrum, that forms part of the inner wall of the
middle ear. Bridging the small gap between
eardrum and oval window are the **ossicles,** the
three smallest bones in the human body. Each of
the three ossicles is about the size of a single letter on this page. Their individual names reflect
their shapes (see Figure 10.10). First in this
chain, the **hammer** (technically called the
malleus) is attached at one end to the back side
of the eardrum. The other end of the hammer is
tightly bound by ligaments to the **anvil,** or **incus,**
the middle link in this chain of tiny bones. The
anvil, in turn, is secured to the **stirrup,** or **stapes,**
whose footplate is in turn anchored against the
oval window. Together the three ossicles transfer
vibrations from the eardrum to the oval window.

Differences

Like eardrums, the size of ossicles varies enormously among species. Considering just the hammer, in humans this structure weighs 28.5 milligrams (0.001 ounces), in the elephant it tips the
scales at 335 milligrams, and in the gerbil it

weighs just 1.15 milligrams. In general, the size of
the ossicles is proportional to the area of the
eardrum. Nummelä (1995) provides a comprehensive discussion of variations in middle ear size and
the effect of those variations on hearing ability.

The Role of the Ossicular Bridge   Why did
nature build a delicate bridge of tiny bones between these two membranes, the eardrum and the
oval window? Why not have airborne vibrations
impact directly on the oval window, doing away
with the intermediate chamber, the middle ear?
To appreciate the importance of the middle ear
and its ossicular bridge, let's consider how things
would sound if this chamber and series of tiny
bones were eliminated from the ear.

To begin, you need to realize that the inner ear,
the chamber located on the other side of the oval
window, is filled with fluid. Glen Wever (1978) discusses the evolutionary significance of the fluid-
filled inner ear, pointing out that it probably derives
from the aquatic environment of the amphibians
from which our species inherited our ears.

Because we are land dwellers, acoustic energy
is usually carried to our ears by *airborne* pressure
variations. Without the middle ear, these airborne
pressure changes would be pushing directly against
the oval window and, therefore, against the fluid
contained in the inner ear. Because its constituent
molecules are more densely packed, the fluid offers
more resistance to movement than does air. In other
words, more force is required to set up sound waves
in water than in air. This explains why when you
are under water you have trouble hearing sounds
that come from above the water—about 99 percent
of airborne sound is reflected when it strikes the
water's surface; only about 1 percent is absorbed
by the water (Evans, 1982a). This represents almost a 30-dB loss in sound energy. Referring back
to Figure 10.4, you can see that lowering sound intensity by 30 dB would definitely affect your hearing, wiping out altogether some routine sounds
(those listed as 30 dB$_{SPL}$ or less in intensity) and reducing the intensity of all others.

---

*For the same reasons, a large drum produces lower fre-
quency sounds than does a small one.

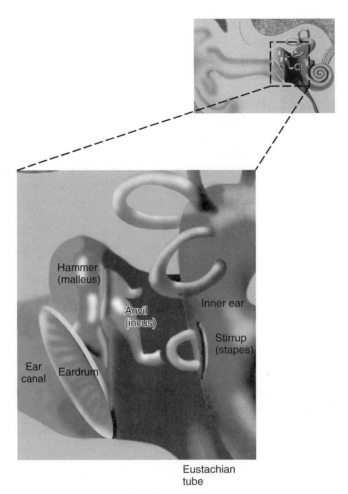

FIGURE 10.10
The middle ear.

So if your ear were to transfer vibrations directly from air to fluid, a great deal of sound energy would be lost. This potential loss in sound energy—or most of it—is partly avoided within the middle ear, however, because of the difference in surface area between the eardrum and the oval window. The oval window is roughly twenty times smaller in area than the eardrum. Consequently, the force applied on the oval window exerts considerably more pressure than the same amount of force applied to the eardrum. By funneling vibrations from the large eardrum down to the small oval window, sound energy is effec-

tively amplified. This funneling effect recovers about 23 dB of the impedance loss that is caused by passing from air to water. In addition, the three ossicular bones together act as a lever to amplify the force of the incoming pressure waves. Because it operates to overcome the impedance imposed by the fluid-filled inner ear, the middle ear is sometimes referred to as an impedance matching device.

For this impedance matching system to work efficiently, the average air pressure within the middle ear must equal the atmospheric pressure existing in the outside environment and, hence, within the auditory canal. This equivalence is maintained by the **Eustachian tube*** connecting the middle ear and the throat. Every time you swallow, this tube opens, allowing air either to enter or to leave the middle ear, depending on the outside air pressure. You can sometimes hear the consequences of this ventilation process, such as when your ears "pop" while riding an elevator, flying in an airplane or ascending a high mountain. Sudden increases or decreases in outside pressure (such as those experienced by scuba divers) can actually rupture the eardrum; this occurs when the pressure differential on the two sides of the membrane becomes too great.

The Acoustic Reflex   Before we conclude our discussion of this part of the ear, we also need to draw your attention to the protective role played by the *tensor tympani,* a small muscle attached to the eardrum, and the *stapedius,* a tiny muscle attached to the stapes bone. In the presence of loud sound, these muscles contract, thereby stiffening the eardrum and restricting the movement of the ossicles (Moller, 1974). These combined actions, called the **acoustic reflex,** dampen the sound vibrations passed from the outer ear to the inner ear. In this respect, the acoustic reflex acts like the damper pedal on a piano, the one that muffles the musical notes by limiting the vibrations of the piano's strings. But why should the ear contain a mechanism to dampen sound?

According to one popular theory, the acoustic reflex serves to protect the inner ear from intense stimulation that could otherwise damage the delicate receptor cells within the inner ear (Borg and Counter, 1989). Considered in this way, one can draw an analogy between the acoustic reflex and the pupillary light reflex (the constriction of the pupil in response to light). It is true that the acoustic reflex *does* reduce the intensity of sound transmission by as much as 30 dB (Evans, 1982a). However, it is primarily low-frequency sounds

that are damped by the acoustic reflex; high frequencies pass through the middle ear unattenuated. So as a protective device, the acoustic reflex is only partially successful. Moreover, the acoustic reflex takes about one-twentieth of a second to exert its shielding influence. Consequently, any sudden, intense sound, such as the explosion of a firecracker, can speed through the middle ear before the acoustic reflex can dampen the force of that sound. Incidentally, abrupt sounds such as this are called *transients,* and if too strong, they can produce a permanent loss in hearing; this is one reason that playing with explosives such as firecrackers can be dangerous. (Explosions, of course, were probably not part of the natural environment in which the human ear evolved; it is not surprising that the acoustic reflex is too sluggish to deal with these kinds of sharp transients.)

Another possible role for the acoustic reflex is suggested by the fact that it occurs whenever one talks or chews something—the same nerves that activate the facial muscles also trigger the acoustic reflex. You can easily experience the consequences of this by listening to a steady low-frequency sound such as the hum of a refrigerator motor while clenching and unclenching your teeth. The sound will seem fainter with teeth clenched, because this engages the acoustic reflex. This general observation has led to the theory that the acoustic reflex reduces the ears' sensitivity to self-produced sounds such as one's own voice. These sounds *do* consist primarily of low frequencies, which, as mentioned above, are the ones attenuated by the acoustic reflex. We leave it to you to figure out the advantage of de-emphasizing self-produced sounds.

The functions of the middle ear are summarized in Figure 10.9. Basically, it serves as an impedance matching device and as a circuit overload protector. With these roles established, we are now ready to migrate to the next stage in the auditory system, the inner ear. This is where mechanical vibrations are converted into electrical nerve impulses to be carried to the brain. Within the inner ear, the auditory system really gets down to the business of hearing.

---

*Named after its discoverer, Bartolomeo Eustachi, a sixteenth-century Italian anatomist (Hawkins, 1988).

The Inner Ear: The Cochlea

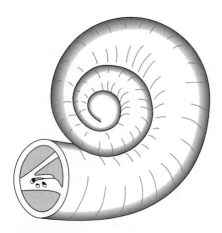

Neural

The *inner ear* consists of a series of hollow cavities, or labyrinths, carved into the temporal bone of the skull. One set of these cavities, the semicircular canals, is concerned with the maintenance of bodily posture and balance. In this chapter, however, our focus will be on the **cochlea** (from the Greek word for snail), a coiled, fluid-filled cavity containing the specialized receptors that place us in contact with the sounds in our environment. Vibrations of the oval window produce pressure changes in the fluid within the cochlea. These pressure changes cause movement of the sensitive receptor cells within the cochlea, providing the stimulus for their activity. To understand this process of sensory transduction, we need to examine more closely the structural detail of this tiny, pea-sized organ (a magnified schematic of which is shown in Figure 10.11).

The spiral-shaped cochlea is partitioned into three chambers, which are easier to visualize if you imagine the cochlea uncoiled, as shown in Figure 10.12. (To keep track of its arrangement, we shall refer to the end nearest the middle ear as the *base* and the end normally curled up in the center as the *apex.*) The three wedge-shaped chambers of the cochlea each have names: the vestibular canal, the cochlear duct and the tympanic canal.

The vestibular canal and cochlear duct are separated by one membrane, while the tympanic canal and the cochlear duct are separated by another membrane; this latter one is called the **basilar membrane,** and it plays a crucial role in the hearing process. The three chambers run parallel to one another the entire length of the cochlea, except right near the far end, at the apex. There the vestibular canal and the tympanic canal merge at a pinhole-sized passage.

Because these two chambers are continuous with each other, they contain the same fluid, similar in composition to spinal fluid. The middle chamber, the cochlear duct, contains a fluid that is chemically different from that filling the other two canals. This chemical difference between the two fluids plays a crucial role in the initial stage of hearing. For example, when the two fluids are intermixed (which can occur if the membrane separating them ruptures), hearing is impaired. Besides their apparent role in the hearing process, these fluids also take the place of blood in supplying all the nourishment for cells in the cochlea. Blood vessels, even tiny capillaries, are forbidden within this structure because their pulsations would create violent waves of sound pressure within the closed confines of the cochlea. This arrangement is reminiscent of the eye (Chapter 2), where blood vessels are routed around the fovea to avoid obstructing the image formed on this crucial part of the eye.

Except at two spots where it is covered by elastic material, the walls of the cochlea consist of hard, relatively shockproof bone. At the base of the cochlea, the vestibular canal is covered by the oval window, which, you will recall, is attached to the stapes (stirrup) on the side facing the middle ear. The tympanic canal is likewise covered at the base by the **round window,** another thin membrane that also covers a small opening into the middle ear.

These two elastic surfaces allow pressure to be distributed within the fluid-filled cochlea: when

FIGURE 10.11
The cochlea.

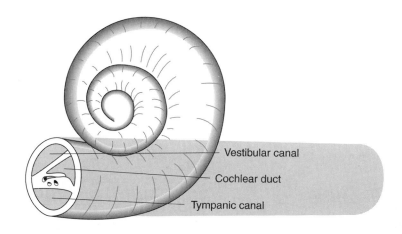

Vestibular canal
Cochlear duct
Tympanic canal

Stapes
Oval window
Membrane
Organ of Corti
Basilar membrane
Round window

FIGURE 10.12
A section of an uncoiled cochlea.

the oval window is pushed inward by the stapes, the round window bulges outward to compensate (see Figure 10.12). This compensation is possible because the two chambers, the vestibular and tympanic canals, are linked. How, though, does the fluid-borne pressure wave generated by the stapes at the oval window give rise to hearing?

To answer this question, we must look more closely at the cochlear duct and, in particular, at the complex structure, the **organ of Corti,** situated inside it. (The structure is named after the Italian anatomist Alfonso Corti, who first described it,

in 1851.) The organ of Corti is the receptor organ where neural impulses are generated in response to vibrations passing through the fluid environment of the inner ear. In other words, the organ of Corti transforms mechanical vibrations into neural messages that are sent on to the brain. To understand this process of sensory transduction, let's take a close look at the organ of Corti.

The Organ of Corti   Pictured schematically in Figure 10.13, the organ of Corti sits snugly on top of the basilar membrane (recall that this is the

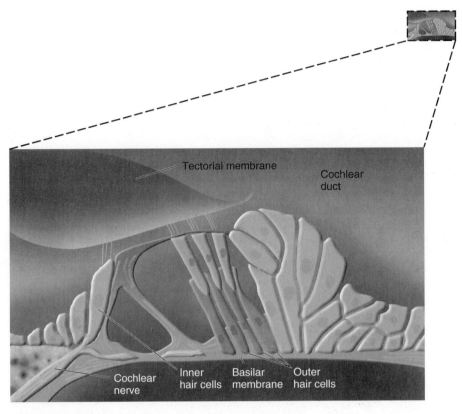

FIGURE 10.13
The organ of Corti.

membrane separating the cochlear duct and the tympanic canal), and it runs the full length of the cochlear duct. The following are the major components of the organ of Corti: a layer of supporting cells resting on the basilar membrane, rows of hair cells sticking up from the supporting cells, and an awninglike membrane, the **tectorial membrane,** arching over the hair cells.

Notice a few things about this arrangement. First, structures called hair cells extend up into the fluid within the cochlear duct. Second, the tectorial membrane that arches over the structure contacts the tops of some of these hair cells. Finally, note that because the tectorial membrane is attached at only one end, it can move independently of the basilar membrane. Let's focus more closely

on the hair cells, for they hold the key to the transduction of fluid vibrations into nerve impulses.

Hair Cells and Sensory Transduction   The ear is similar to the eye, in that both organs contain two different types of receptor cells. The eye, as you learned, contains rods and cones. These two classes of photoreceptors are different in shape and in retinal distribution, and they are involved in different aspects of visual perception (recall chapters 2 and 3). The ear's receptors, the **hair cells,** are equally distinctive anatomically and functionally. In all, there are about 15,500 hair cells within a single ear, with this total divisible into two distinct groups. One group, the **inner hair cells (IHC),** is situated on the basilar membrane close to where the tectorial membrane is attached to the wall of the cochlear duct (see the lower right-hand part of Figure 10.13). Numbering about 3,500, these inner hair cells line up in a single row that runs the length of the basilar membrane. The 12,000 or so **outer hair cells (OHC),** in contrast, line up in anywhere from three to five rows. Let's first look at the anatomical distinctions between the two and then consider their functional differences.

Drawings of an IHC and an OHC are shown in Figure 10.14. Note that each IHC is shaped something like a flask, and each is surrounded by supporting cells. Each OHC, in contrast, is more cylindrical in shape, and each is surrounded by fluid. Both the inner and the outer hair cells terminate in tiny bristles called **cilia.**

Figure 10.15 shows a section of the basilar membrane photographed through an electron microscope—in this top-down view, you can actually see the single row of IHCs and multiple

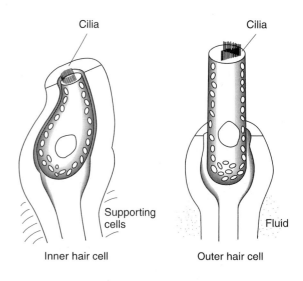

FIGURE 10.14
Schematic drawings of an inner hair cell and an outer hair cell.

FIGURE 10.15
Electron microscope photographs of the cilia of the multiple rows of outer hair cells and the single row of inner hair cells. The two pictures on the right show a single OHC and IHC in greater magnification. (Photograph courtesy of David Lim.)

rows of OHCs; shown in the right part of the Figure are magnified views of each cell type. The most prominent structures visible in these photographs are the brush-like cilia shown sticking up from the tops of the hair cells. Ordinarily these structures would be covered by the overlying tectorial membrane but, to make this photo, the tectorial membrane was removed.

It used to be thought that cilia from *all* the hair cells actually made contact with the tectorial membrane. Now, however, it is recognized that only cilia from the OHCs actually touch the tectorial membrane (Nobili, Mammano and Ashmore, 1998). Bending of the cilia constitutes *the* crucial early event in the process that leads to hearing, for it is this event which triggers the electrical signals that travel from the ear to the brain. Let's take a look, then, at how airborne sound ends up producing this crucial event, the bending of the cilia.

As you will recall, airborne vibrations are picked up by the external ear and converted into a mechanical, pistonlike action by the ossicles of the middle ear. Because it is attached to the stapes, the oval window receives these mechanical displacements and passes them in the form of pressure waves into the fluids of the cochlea's vestibular and tympanic canals. As the pressure waves travel through these chambers, they cause waves of displacement along the basilar membrane. The tectorial membrane also moves slightly in response to these pressure waves, but it tends to move in directions that are different from the movement of the basilar membrane. These opposing motions cause the cilia of the hair cells on the basilar membrane to bend, like tiny clumps of seaweed swept back and forth by invisible underwater currents. This bending triggers electrical changes within the hair cells (Russell, 1987). These electrical changes in the hair cell cause it to release a chemical transmitter substance, which is picked up by auditory nerve fibers that make synaptic contact with the hair cells at their base (the portion of the hair cells op-

posite the cilia). These fibers, in turn, carry electrical impulses from the cochlea to the central nervous system. It is truly remarkable that such microscopic movements of thin membranes, tiny bones and hairs inaugurate a process—hearing—that can have such an enormous impact on one's feelings and behaviors.

With this sequence of events in mind, let's return for a moment to the two classes of hair cells. As already pointed out, the IHCs and OHCs differ in number (3,500 versus 12,000) and in location along the basilar membrane. In addition, these two classes of hair cells also differ in the pattern of their connections to the approximately 30,000 auditory nerve fibers that carry messages from the cochlea to the brain. The more numerous OHCs make sparse contact with the auditory nerve; only about 5 percent of the auditory nerve fibers receive signals from the OHCs. The remaining 95 percent of the fibers get their information from the IHCs, the smaller of the two cell populations. To draw an analogy, it is as if the telephone company took 30,000 phone lines and divided them up so that 1,500 were devoted to the entire population of Boston while 28,500 were devoted to the much smaller population of suburban Concord. Why should the more numerous OHCs have so little control over the signals traveling along the auditory nerve? According to recent thinking (Nobili, Mammano and Ashmore, 1998), the IHCs are the principal actors in the sensory drama that unfolds in the ear, with the OHCs playing an important supporting role. Here's how the idea goes.

To begin, remember that the cilia of the OHCs are actually attached to the overhanging tectorial membrane. It is now thought that when electric currents are set up in the OHCs, their cilia produce a motor response—they have miniature muscle-like elements (actin filaments) that contract and expand the cilia along their longitudinal axes. Suppose that an acoustic disturbance causes maximal vibration at some place along the basilar membrane. As the OHCs at that place ride up and down, their cilia, which are attached to the tectorial membrane, are stretched and relaxed. This sets up an alternating current within the hair cells. The alternating current, in turn, stimulates the OHC cilia to contract and expand, causing them to behave like small motors that pull and push the tectorial membrane. This motorlike action of the OHCs on the tectorial membrane amplifies and concentrates displacement of the basilar membrane created by the back and forth movement of fluid within the cochlea. These amplified movements, in turn, cause the cilia of the IHCs to be displaced by a greater amount than they would have without the extra boost provided by the contractions of the OHC cilia. As a result, the OHCs, despite their minor *direct* contribution to information carried by the auditory nerve, are very important to the hearing process.* (It should be noted, by the way, that these amplifying actions must be accomplished at a molecular level. Ordinary mechanical actions such as contraction and elongation of muscles could not occur rapidly enough to accomplish the task carried out by the OHCs.)

In a later section, we will learn more about the auditory consequences of this amplification process. But first, there is one important step in this process of sensory transduction that was sidestepped: How do the vibrations traveling within the cochlear fluid affect the basilar membrane? Because the hair cells ride on the basilar membrane, the membrane's reactions to fluid vibrations determine which hair cells are stimulated and, hence, which nerve fibers will be activated. To fill in this missing step, let's turn our attention to the basilar membrane, the thin-walled membrane separating the tympanic canal from the cochlear duct (see figures 10.12 and 10.13).

The Basilar Membrane Much of what is known today about the basilar membrane comes from work by Georg von Békésy, a Hungarian scientist who was awarded the Nobel Prize in 1961 for his research on the ear. To appreciate Békésy's contributions, you need to be familiar with the two major theories describing the way that pressure waves in the cochlear fluid affect the basilar membrane. Both theories were originally formulated in the nineteenth century, before anyone could observe the basilar membrane in action. The opposing theories, called the *temporal theory** and the *place theory,* form the background for Békésy's important work.

The Temporal Theory The **temporal theory** proposes that the temporal structure defining sound is represented in temporal fluctuations in firing rates of auditory nerve fibers. According to this idea, the stapes taps out a series of beats on the oval window, and the entire basilar membrane dances along.

Neural

William Rutherford, a nineteenth-century English physicist, was the temporal theory's first proponent. He likened the basilar membrane to the diaphragm inside a telephone receiver. Because it is thin and light, the diaphragm moves back and forth in response to the sound waves of your voice. These movements are converted into electrical current that is carried along a telephone line. And the current eventually produces the same pattern of movements in the listening diaphragm of another person's telephone receiver, thereby reproducing the sounds of your voice. Rutherford believed that the basilar membrane behaved in a comparable fashion, vibrating as a unit at a rate that matched the sound stimulus. In

---

*Acting as amplifiers and tuners, the OHCs primarily modify the mechanical environment of the IHCs. Strictly speaking, the IHCs are the only true sensory receptors for hearing. In this sense, the analogy to rod and cone photoreceptors is not helpful.

---

*Temporal theory has also been referred to as "frequency theory" since sound frequency is represented in the frequency of neural impulses. However, contemporary hearing scientists prefer the phrase "temporal theory" to avoid any confusion with "place theory," which relates location along the basilar membrane with sound frequency.

turn, this vibration produced in the auditory nerve a train of impulses whose rate mimicked the frequency with which the entire basilar membrane was vibrating. According to Rutherford's idea, then, a 500-Hz tone would yield 500 nerve impulses per second, while a 1,200-Hz tone would yield 1,200 impulses per second.

Several things are wrong with this theory. For one thing, the basilar membrane is not like a diaphragm in a telephone. The basilar membrane varies in width and in stiffness from one end to the other. As a result, the basilar membrane, unlike a diaphragm, cannot vibrate uniformly over its entire length. (Yost [2000] and Nobili, Mammano and Ashmore [1998] give particularly clear explanations of why this is physically impossible.) There is another problem, too, with Rutherford's version of the temporal theory. Single auditory nerve fibers cannot match the performance of a telephone line, because neurons cannot fire repetitively at rates beyond 1,000 impulses per second. Yet we can hear tones whose frequency greatly exceeds this value. So the neural signal required by Rutherford's theory cannot be realized by individual fibers.

This limitation in firing rate could be surmounted if separate nerve fibers fired not in unison but in a staggered fashion. For instance, two fibers each firing at 1,000 impulses per second in combination could produce 2,000 impulses per second if those impulses were appropriately interleaved (Figure 10.16). This modification of the temporal theory, known as the *volley theory,* was proposed by Wever and Bray (1937), who also described some fascinating findings in support of temporal theory (see Box 10.2). Also, the volley theory, unlike Rutherford's temporal theory, does not assume that the basilar membrane acts like a telephone diaphragm. It does, however, require that some higher neuron add the interleaved neural impulses from the fibers responding near their limits of activity. How this neuron could overcome its upper limit of firing rate was never specified by proponents of volley theory. We will have more to say about the volley theory in our

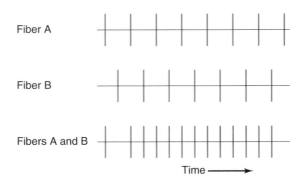

FIGURE 10.16
Two fibers firing regularly but asynchronously.

discussion of pitch perception in the next chapter. But let's return now to the basilar membrane and consider the temporal theory's chief opponent, the *place theory.*

The Place Theory   The **place theory** maintains that different frequencies of vibration of the cochlear fluid disturb different regions of the basilar membrane. These different regions of disturbance, in turn, activate different hair cells and hence, different auditory nerve fibers. You can see where this theory gets its name—frequency information is encoded according to the location, or *place,* along the basilar membrane disturbed by fluid vibration.

The most notable early proponent of the place theory was Hermann von Helmholtz,* whose ideas on color vision we discussed in Chapter 7. Helmholtz's theory was inspired by the fact that the basilar membrane is narrow at the base of the cochlea and broad at the apex. This layout reminded Helmholtz of the variation in the length

---

*Helmholtz's towering scientific reputation did not guarantee automatic acceptance of his theory. For example, one of his many competitors attacked Helmholtz's theory as "the product of a great mind in an hour of weakness" (Wever, 1949, p. 76).

BOX 10.2

A PECULIAR SORT OF MICROPHONE

Execute

Imagine walking into a radio studio to find a newscaster speaking into the ear of a live cat. Even more astounding, imagine *hearing* the newscaster's voice being broadcast over a loudspeaker in the room! As far-fetched as it sounds, this kind of demonstration has actually been performed (Cohen, 1969). Moreover, the demonstration works using other animals besides a cat. Your own ear would work just fine. Here is how this unusual sound system works.

An electrode placed near the site where the auditory nerve exits the cochlea will pick up an electrical signal arising within the cochlea. This electrical signal results from the high concentration of certain positively charged chemicals within the cochlea's fluid. As the hair cells of the inner ear bend in response to pressure waves within those fluids, the electrical signal changes.

When plotted on a graph, this change in electrical potential mirrors the change in the amplitude of the sound wave presented to the ear. For example, playing a 500-Hz pure tone sound into the ear yields a 500-Hz sinusoidal variation in electrical potential. If this electrically recorded cochlear potential is now fed into an amplifier and then passed to a loudspeaker, you will hear the 500-Hz tone with essentially no distortion: it will be indistinguishable from the original tone played into the ear.

In fact, *any* sound stimulus, such as someone's voice or a passage of music, entering the ear can be faithfully reproduced in this fashion. The ear is behaving exactly like a microphone. Both devices convert airborne pressure waves into an electrical signal whose temporal waveform closely parallels the stimulus waveform. For this reason the electrical potential recorded from the cochlea has been termed the *cochlear microphonic.*

When it was first discovered by Wever and Bray in 1930, the cochlear microphonic was thought to originate from the auditory nerve. This would have meant that the frequency of nerve impulses in the auditory nerve exactly followed the input frequency of sound. If correct, this interpretation would have provided strong support for the temporal theory described in the discussion of the basilar membrane. However, later experiments proved that the cochlear microphonic can be recorded even when the nerve itself is temporarily deadened by an anesthetic. These findings ruled out the auditory nerve as the source of the cochlear microphonic. Instead, it appears that the outer hair cells are the generators of the cochlear microphonic. This would explain why damage to the outer hair cells diminishes the cochlear microphonic (Davis et al., 1958), whereas damage to the inner hair cells leaves this electrical signal unaffected (Dallos and Cheatham, 1976).

FIGURE 10.18
Békésy's mechanical model of the cochlea.

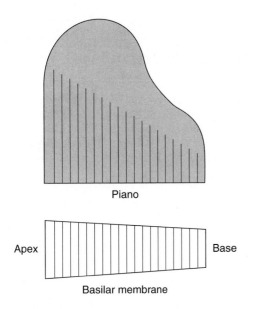

FIGURE 10.17
The basilar membrane's tapered shape resembles the layout of a piano's strings.

of strings of a piano (Figure 10.17), which led him to propose that the basilar membrane was composed of distinct fibers that individually stretched across its width. Because of the basilar membrane's tapered shape, fibers at one end would be longer than those at the other, just like piano strings. According to Helmholtz, vibrations within the cochlear fluid would set into motion only those "strings" of the basilar membrane that were tuned to the frequencies at which the fluid vibrated. In other words, fibers of the basilar membrane would vibrate in the same way that piano strings can be induced to vibrate when you sing a loud note. This is the principle of resonance discussed in Box 10.1.

While based on solid physical principles, Helmholtz's place theory was flawed in several respects. For one thing, subsequent anatomical work showed that the basilar membrane is not composed of separate fibers capable of resonating individually. Rather than a set of piano strings, the basilar membrane looks more like a

continuous strip of rubber. Moreover, the basilar membrane is not under tension, like piano strings; it is relatively slack. So the resonance portion of Helmholtz's theory proved incorrect, but his idea that different *places* along the basilar membrane respond to different frequencies *did* survive. In fact, it is this idea that Békésy's work so elegantly substantiated, and it is to his work that we now turn.

Traveling Waves   Békésy realized that the essential difference between the place and frequency theories lay in how each thought the basilar membrane vibrated in response to different frequencies. Of course, the simplest way to settle the issue would have been to observe the membrane's movements, but this was technically difficult in the late 1920s when Békésy became interested in the problem. Nonetheless, Békésy knew that the thickness of the basilar membrane varied along its length, being thinner (and, hence, more flexible) at the end near the apex. Armed with this knowledge, he built a simplified, mechanical model of the cochlea, so he could directly observe the behavior of an enlarged replica of the basilar membrane (Békésy, 1960).

For the tympanic and vestibular canals he used a brass tube with a small rubber cap stretched over each end; these caps represented the oval and round windows. He cut a narrow slot along the length of the entire tube and covered this slot with a rubber "membrane" whose thickness was tapered from one end to the other; this represented the basilar membrane. For the stapes he substituted a small mallet placed against the rubber cap on one end of the tube; this mallet was vibrated by a tuning fork. A drawing of Békésy's large-scale cochlea is shown in Figure 10.18.

To observe the behavior of his mechanical model, Békésy lightly rested his forearm on a small ridge secured to the rubber membrane over its entire length; vibrations at different points along the rubber membrane were accurately transmitted to the corresponding points along the ridge. When a pure tone was produced by striking

Execute

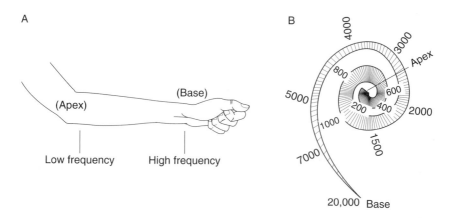

FIGURE 10.19
Summary of the results of Békésy's experiment.

the tuning fork, Békésy felt, via the ridge, the rubber membrane vibrating against his arm at one particular spot (see panel A of Figure 10.19). By testing with tuning forks that produced different frequencies, he discovered that the location of this tingling spot depended on the frequency with which the tuning fork vibrated the "oval window." With higher frequencies, this tingle occurred near his wrist, a place on the membrane corresponding to the more rigid end closest to the stapes. Lower frequencies, in contrast, yielded a tingle nearer his elbow, the region of the membrane corresponding to the more flexible end near the apex.

In panel A of Figure 10.19 you can see the relation between a pure-tone frequency and the point along Békésy's mechanical model where that frequency yields its peak vibration. Translating Békésy's results to the actual basilar membrane—a much smaller, coiled structure—yields the scaled diagram in panel B of Figure 10.19. This diagram reveals the various points along the basilar membrane that maximally vibrate to a particular sound frequency.

Békésy's ingenious demonstration therefore strongly favored the place theory. Subsequently, Békésy went on to confirm this conclusion using other, more precise techniques, including direct visualization of the human basilar membrane, using a microscope. He explained the connection between the point of maximum vibration along the basilar membrane and sound frequency in the following way. The fluctuations in fluid pressure produced by the pistonlike movements of the stapes set up a **traveling wave** along the basilar membrane itself.

To envision what is meant by a *traveling wave,* think of what happens when you flick one end of a rope whose other end is tied to, say, a pole. You see a wave of motion traveling the length of the rope. Unlike a rope, though, the basilar membrane varies in thickness and width along its length. If you were to flick the basilar membrane, the resulting wave of motion would actually grow in amplitude as it traveled away from you. But this wave would reach peak amplitude and then rapidly collapse, never getting to the other end. An example of this kind of traveling wave is illustrated in Figure 10.20.

In this figure, the basilar membrane is drawn as if uncoiled and viewed from the side. Thus, in each panel the horizontal axis represents the length of the basilar membrane, with its base at the left and its apex at the right. Each separate panel shows the profile of the basilar membrane at a different instant in time. You might imagine these as successive snapshots of the basilar membrane taken just after you have flicked it as you would a rope. (Flicking it corresponds to the

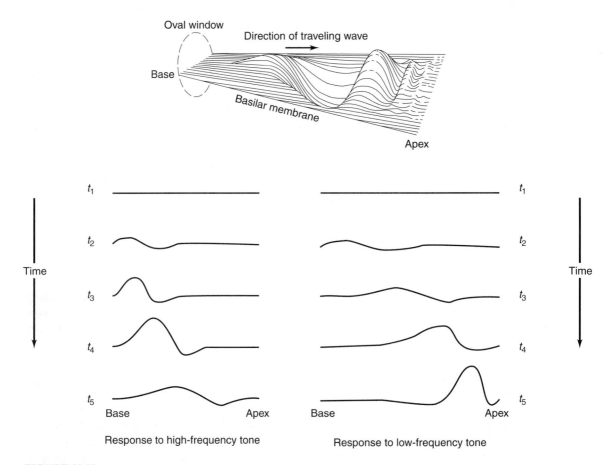

FIGURE 10.20

The top drawing shows a traveling wave deforming the basilar membrane. The set of curves below at the left represents the response of the basilar membrane over time to a high-frequency tone. The curves at the right represent the basilar membrane's response over time to a low-frequency tone.

stapes's tapping against the oval window, setting up waves of motion in the fluid of the cochlea.) As the wave progresses down the membrane over time, note how it grows in size, reaches a peak, and then rather abruptly disappears. The place along the basilar membrane where this peak occurs depends on how rapidly you flicked the basilar membrane. This idea can be seen by comparing the traveling waves depicted in the left panel of the figure to those depicted in the right panel. Note that in the series on the left, the traveling wave reaches its peak nearer the base, while in the series on the right it reaches its peak nearer the apex. The waves in the left-hand series were produced by a high-frequency tone, those in the right-hand series by a low frequency tone.

The peak of the traveling wave, you should understand, represents a place where the basilar membrane flexes up and down, which is why Békésy felt a tingling spot on his forearm when he tested his mechanical cochlea. This flexion in the actual basilar membrane means that hair cells riding on this portion of the membrane will be displaced further—and their cilia bent more—

than elsewhere along the membrane. In turn, these highly bent cilia will activate their associated hair cells. In other words, each vibration frequency will cause the basilar membrane to flex maximally at one particular location, thereby maximally stimulating a characteristic group of hair cells. This arrangement is so orderly that if you were told which hair cells had been maximally stimulated, you would be able to deduce the sound frequency that had produced that stimulation. This orderly layout of frequency over the length of the basilar membrane is known as **tonotopic organization.**

Neural

The behavior of traveling waves also suggests how intensity information is registered by the basilar membrane. For a given frequency, the intensity of the sound will determine the amplitude, or height, of the peak of the traveling wave. Increases in the amplitude of these movements of the basilar membrane will cause the cilia to bend more, leading to greater stimulation of the hair cells, a larger neural response, and ultimately an increase in perceived loudness. Increases in the amplitude of these movements also enlarge the spread of the displaced region along the basilar membrane, which in turn alters the pattern of hair cells stimulated. The perceptual consequences of these changes in the basilar membrane's response to different frequencies and intensities will be discussed in the next chapter.

This gives you a bird's-eye view of the workings of the inner ear. Referring back to Figure 10.9, you can now understand why the inner ear is characterized as a frequency-selective sound transducer. We call it "frequency selective" because, by virtue of its mechanical properties, the inner ear breaks up incoming sound into its component frequencies. Incidentally, the design of this marvelous but delicate mechanical system—including the inner and outer hair cells and the tectorial and basilar membranes—is implemented following genetic instructions, and these instructions are subject to mutations.

Clinical

In fact, several forms of hearing loss can be traced to specific genetic abnormalities (Steel

and Brown, 1998). For example, a single gene on chromosome 11 controls the production of a protein that is instrumental in fabrication of the tectorial membrane. Hearing impairment in some individuals can be traced directly to mutations in this gene. Other forms of hearing impairment can be traced to mutations in a gene that controls the length and the stiffness of the cilia projecting out of the hair cells.

In the last section of this chapter, we will survey what happens to the signals from the hair cells as they are routed to the brain via the auditory nerve. But before leaving the inner ear, we want to describe one of the cochlea's really unusual properties, its ability to *generate* sounds on its own. These so-called **cochlear emissions** represent one of the most intriguing discoveries about hearing in the past several decades. While they play no role in your experience of the auditory world, they are probably a byproduct of the important amplification role of the OHCs.

Sounds Emitted by the Cochlea   The cochlea is built to receive sound and convert it into neural impulses, and it does this exquisitely. But in addition, the cochlea is capable of actually *generating* sound energy that is transmitted back through the middle ear and into the outer ear where this sound energy can be picked up by a microphone (Kemp, 1979). First, we will describe where these "emitted sounds" come from. Then we will tell you why they occur.

The chain of events stretching from the outer ear to the inner ear should be familiar to you by now:

airborne sound → movement of the eardrum → movement of the ossicles → movement of the oval window → fluid-borne pressure waves → displacement of basilar membrane → stimulation of hair cells

But there is no reason why many of these events could not occur in the reverse sequence. After all, the cochlea consists of moving parts suspended in fluid, and any time those parts move, they will create waves within the cochlear fluid. To illustrate, imagine that you are *inside* the cochlea moving your arms back and forth, splashing about as if you were in a swimming pool. Your movements would disturb the cochlear fluid, setting up waves within it that would spread throughout the volume of the fluid. Because the cochlea (your miniature swimming pool) is a sealed container, these waves will eventually push against the oval window from the inner side. Since the oval window is attached to the stapes, this push would be felt by the stapes and passed in reverse through the other two attached bones in the ossicular chain. The hammer, as a result, would be pushed against the inner side of the eardrum. This pressure would in turn cause the eardrum to flex back and forth slightly, displacing air molecules within the auditory canal. The eardrum, in other words, would behave just like the cone on a loudspeaker (recall Figure 10.2)—movements of the eardrum would create air pressure changes within the ear canal. If these air pressure changes were sufficiently robust, they could actually be *heard* by someone in the vicinity of the ear from which the acoustic energy was being emitted. So you can see that movements of any of the structures within the cochlea could set up the reverse chain of events, causing sound energy to be reflected back into the world.

Differences

The reverse sequence of events just described actually occurs. Sensitive microphones placed within the auditory canal of the human ear are able to record what are called "spontaneous emissions" (Kemp, 1979). These emissions consist of acoustic energy in the absence of an external stimulus—they originate from within the ear. Such spontaneous sounds can range up to 20 dB$_{SPL}$ in intensity, a level well within the audible range, if the background is quiet (refer to Figure 10.4). They tend to consist of energy within a relatively narrow band of frequencies, implying that the cause of the emitted sounds is localized on the tonotopically organized Basilar membrane.

This condition is not rare or abnormal. By one count (Zurek, 1981), spontaneously emitted sound can be measured from the ears of about two-thirds of the people sampled, though the measured frequency and intensity level varies from person to person (see Figure 10.21). There is a tendency for these spontaneous acoustic emissions to be more prevalent and stronger in females than in males (McFadden, 1998).

These emitted sounds can have bizarre consequences. In some cases, although the emitted sound cannot be heard by the source (the person emitting the sound), it *can* be heard by someone else nearby (McFadden, 1982); these emitted sounds are heard as high-pitched tones. You might try listening for emitted sounds from a friend's ear. In a quiet setting, place your ear close to your friend's and notice whether you hear a steady, faint tone. If you do, have your friend move away from your ear and notice whether you still hear the tone. If the tone persists, it must be originating either from an external source or from within your own ear. But if the tone becomes inaudible when your friend moves, you very likely were hearing an emitted sound from your friend's ear. Incidentally, emitted sounds have been measured from the ears of many species of birds and mammals, including dogs and cats (McFadden, 1982), so you need not limit your experiment to humans.

Emitted sounds can also be measured immediately following stimulation of the ear by a briefly presented sound such as a click.* Rather than being spontaneous, these sounds emitted in response to clicks are more like echoes in response to the brief acoustic event. But the echo analogy is misleading, for these emitted sounds aren't simply acoustic energy bouncing off the eardrum back to the recording microphone. Instead, they arise from the fluid-filled cochlea. If the real evoking click consists of

---

*The evoking sound has to be brief, so that the recording microphone in the auditory canal can pick up the relatively weak emitted sound against an otherwise quiet background. If the evoking sound continues, its energy and influence within the cochlea swamp any trace of an emitted sound.

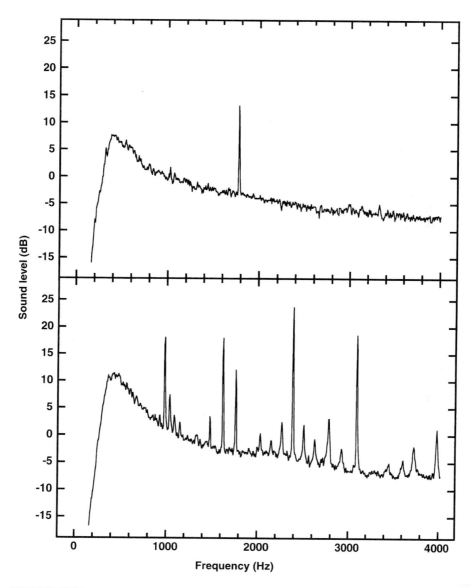

FIGURE 10.21

Otoacoustic emissions measured from two different ears show differences in frequency content. (Adapted from McFadden, 1998.)

high-frequency energy, the emitted sound arrives at the microphone earlier than when the evoking click consists of low-frequency energy. Looking back to figures 10.19 and 10.20, this makes sense, for the region of the basilar membrane registering high-frequency sound is closer to the eardrum and, hence, to the recording microphone.

Most auditory experts now believe these sounds—both emitted and evoked—can be traced to the amplifying actions of the OHCs. Recall that the OHCs behave like tiny motors, amplifying the wave actions in the fluid of the cochlea in response to sound. When that sound is brief (like a click), these motorlike actions of the OHCs continue briefly after the offset of the click. They behave, in other words, like tiny post-click tremors, setting up the reverse sequence of events described above.

In the case of spontaneously emitted sounds, the amplification process seems to involve self-induced reverberations within the OHCs. Because the middle and inner ears are so delicately designed to amplify and transduce mechanical displacements, it takes very little motion within the cochlea to trigger the chain of events leading to emitted sounds. And the amplification by the OHCs involves molecular movements at least as large as those capable of producing a sensation of hearing. (Recall that motion displacement as small as the diameter of a single hydrogen atom can be heard.) It is ironic that nature has designed an ear so sensitive that it can transmit the effects of the mechanical movements produced by its own parts!*

But if our ears generate sound energy all the time, why don't we hear that sound? One reason is that we are rarely in environments quiet enough for faint sounds to be heard: the normal sounds of the world mask emitted sounds. Moreover, we tend to adapt to a continuous, steady sound, rendering it inaudible. Now despite having said this, there are individuals who *do* experience illusory sounds, meaning that an auditory sensation is experienced in the absence of an external stimulus. This condition is described in the next section.

Tinnitus   It is not uncommon for people to experience a sort of humming or ringing sound

coming from within their ears, in the absence of an external sound source. This condition, termed **tinnitus,** may be limited to one ear only, or it can be heard in both ears. Perceptually, tinnitus is comparable to the ringing in the ears you may have experienced immediately following an abrupt, loud sound such as an explosion. In the case of tinnitus, however, the experience is persistent. It is estimated that 35 percent of people experience tinnitus at some point in their lives. Fortunately, many people adapt to this self-produced ringing, just as we all adapt to a steady hum from an external source such as a refrigerator motor. For others, however, tinnitus can be sufficiently annoying to produce anxiety or even depression. Although you should not try this, tinnitus can be temporarily induced by ingesting a large dose of aspirin (Stypulkowski, 1990). In fact, patients who take aspirin to relieve arthritis symptoms are sometimes instructed to moderate their aspirin intake so as to keep tinnitus at bay.

It is natural to assume that someone with tinnitus is merely hearing the spontaneously emitted sound from his or her own ear. While this may be true in a few cases (Wilson and Sutton, 1981), most instances of tinnitus are traceable to neural degeneration (Tonndorf, 1987; Coles and Hallam, 1987). As a rule, the ringing experienced with tinnitus has a characteristic frequency for any given individual. This frequency, however, typically does *not* correspond to the frequency recorded as spontaneous emission from that individual's ear. Moreover, a large dose of aspirin, which *induces* tinnitus, can *eliminate* spontaneous emitted sounds (McFadden, Plattsmier and Pasanen, 1984). These observations underscore the distinction between emitted sounds and tinnitus.

Brain mapping techniques applied to humans reveal that the neural representation of sounds in the auditory cortex—that portion of the brain devoted to hearing—is altered in people who develop chronic tinnitus (Mühlnickel et al., 1998). These findings suggest that tinnitus results from a

Execute

---

*Hearing tests based on the measurement of emitted sounds are currently under development (Allen and Neely, 1992). These should be particularly useful for assessing hearing in individuals, such as newborn infants, who are unable to respond verbally on conventional hearing tests.

reorganization of the auditory cortex in response to selective damage in the cochlea, damage that deprives the brain of sounds within a fairly narrow range of frequencies. We will return to this point later, when we discuss the neural representation of sound frequency in the auditory cortex.

THE AUDITORY SYSTEM: THE AUDITORY PATHWAYS

Neural

As you have learned, the cochlea converts sound energy (pressure waves) into the only form of information understandable by the brain, neural impulses. This neural information is carried out of the inner ear by the **auditory nerve,** which consists of approximately 30,000 nerve fibers (individual axons) arising from each ear. The auditory nerve branches into several different pathways that eventually reconverge within the auditory cortex (the region on the side of your brain that would be covered if you put your hand over your ear).

These various pathways seem designed to process different aspects of auditory information (Rauschecker, 1998). One pathway contains neurons whose response properties enable them to specify *where* sound is coming from. Another pathway contains neurons that analyze information necessary for identifying *what* the sound is. In other words, the auditory system contains specialized neural analyzers for locating and identifying sound sources within the auditory environment. (This division of labor within the auditory pathways is reminiscent of the situation with vision, where the dorsal and ventral pathways analyze *where* objects are located and *what* those objects are, respectively.)

Figure 10.22 gives an overview of the pathways originating from the left auditory nerve and the right auditory nerve; the right ear has been omitted for clarity. In the drawing, the dark lines represent pathways from the inner ear, to thalamic nuclei and on to the brain. At each structure along this route, neurons make synaptic contact with the next set of neurons in the pathway; the

pathways are not a single bundle of fibers passing from ear to cortex.

Top-down

Not shown in the drawing are the neural projections *from* midbrain structures *back* to the inner ear. These feedback projections are called **efferent fibers.** One set of efferent fibers originates in the medial portion (*medial* means toward the center of the brain) of the superior olivary complex (the region of the brain labeled Superior olive in Figure 10.22). These fibers make synaptic contacts with cell bodies of the OHCs. Activity in this feedback pathway modulates cochlear output, probably by dampening the effect of the OHCs on the IHCs. (Recall that the OHCs exaggerate the wave actions in the fluid of the cochlea in response to sound, thereby strengthening stimulation of the IHCs.)

A second set of efferent fibers originates in the lateral portion of the superior olivary complex (*lateral* means toward the side of the brain), and projects to auditory nerve fibers at the point where those fibers make contact with the IHCs. Their role in the hearing process is currently unknown (Dallos, Popper and Fay, 1996).

We will not trace the flow of information through the maze of pathways depicted in Figure 10.22. Interested readers may consult the particularly clear description of these pathways given by Hackney (1987). Instead, we'll summarize several aspects of auditory information that the neurons seem to be processing. Our aim is to highlight neural properties that bear on perceptual aspects of hearing to be discussed in the next chapter.

This final section of the chapter is divided into three subsections. The first summarizes the properties of neurons comprising the auditory nerve. The two remaining subsections focus on the neural analysis of the cues for sound localization (where) and the cues for sound identification (what). In the course of our discussion, you will see a similarity between auditory neural processing and visual neural processing: at successively higher stages, individual neurons become increasingly more discriminating about the sounds that activate them.

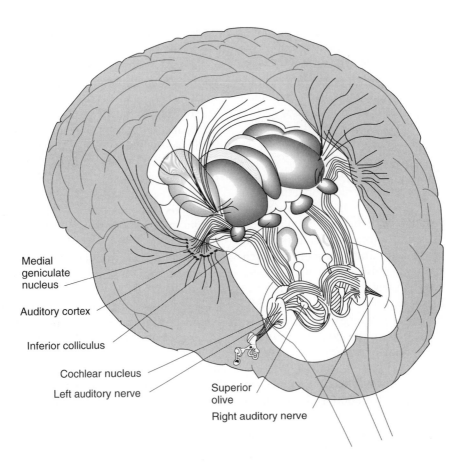

Medial
geniculate
nucleus

Auditory cortex

Inferior colliculus

Cochlear nucleus

Left auditory nerve

Superior
olive

Right auditory nerve

FIGURE 10.22
An overview of the auditory pathways.

Neural

The Auditory Nerve

Approximately 30,000 individual fibers make up the auditory nerve. These fibers are the axons of nerve cells located in the inner ear. As detailed in an earlier section, about 95 percent of these fibers carry information picked up from just the IHCs (which total only about 3,500), while the remaining 5 percent or so are devoted to input from the OHCs (which total about 12,000). This means, then, that single IHCs are each innervated by many auditory nerve fibers.

The locations at which auditory nerve fibers contact a single IHC are arranged systematically around the circumference of the hair cell (Liberman, 1982). On the side of the IHC facing the rows of OHCs (refer back to Figure 10.15), contact is made with fibers exhibiting high rates of spontaneous activity. On the opposite side of the IHC are fibers with relatively low spontaneous activity. The remaining locations around an IHC are innervated by fibers with intermediate levels of spontaneous activity. This arrangement is summarized in Figure 10.23. In a moment, we will return to these three classes of auditory nerve fibers, pointing out another, functionally important distinction among them. But first, let's consider the responses of these fibers to sound stimulation.

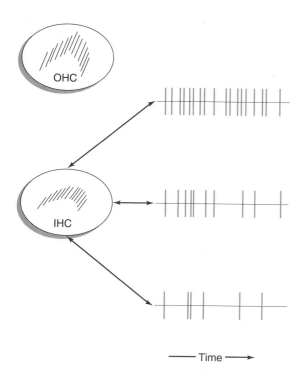

Spontaneous neural activity

FIGURE 10.23
Spontaneous activity of auditory nerve fibers varies depending on which portion of the IHC they innervate. The three traces depict spontaneous neural impulses over time: activity in the top trace is "high"; in the middle trace, "medium"; and in the lower trace, "low."

By recording the electrical impulses from many individual fibers, physiologists have determined what kinds of sound stimuli must be presented to the ear to activate those fibers. As mentioned in the previous paragraph, fibers of the auditory nerve, like retinal ganglion cells of the eye, are active even when no stimulus is present. Therefore, to register its presence, a sound must alter this spontaneously occurring, random neural chatter. In auditory nerve fibers, sound is registered by a temporary increase in firing rate. However, not just any sound stimulus will do. For any given fiber, there is a limited range of pure-tone frequencies that can evoke a response.

Execute

Moreover, within this limited range not all frequencies are equally effective. We will illustrate these observations using the following example.

Suppose we measure the number of impulses that pure tones produce in a single auditory nerve fiber. Suppose further that we make such measurements for pure tones of various frequencies (Hz) and intensities (dB). (Keep in mind that a pure tone has a sinusoidal waveform.) For each frequency, we will determine the *minimum* intensity needed to produce a noticeable increase in that fiber's spontaneous level of activity. The resulting intensity value will constitute that fiber's threshold for detecting that frequency. We refer to this intensity as the threshold because at lower intensities the fiber behaves as if the tone were not presented at all—the fiber is "deaf" to all weaker intensities. Such a **threshold intensity** is determined for a number of frequencies. Plotting the resulting thresholds for an individual fiber would yield a graph like the one shown in Figure 10.24.

There are a couple of points to note in this graph. At the very lowest intensity, this particular fiber responds only to a 5,000-Hz tone (abbreviated 5 kHz). This value, then, constitutes this fiber's preferred, or *characteristic,* frequency. At this quiet sound level, no other tone produces activity in the fiber. But as we increase the sound intensity, previously ineffective frequencies begin to produce measurable increases in the fiber's activity. In other words, the fiber has different intensity thresholds for different frequencies. The entire curve in Figure 10.24 describes what is called the **frequency tuning curve** for that fiber.

When this sort of analysis is applied to many different auditory nerve fibers, the result is a family of tuning curves like those illustrated in Figure 10.25. Note that different fibers possess different characteristic frequencies. Some respond best to low frequencies, others to medium frequencies, and still others to high frequencies. As a group, then, the auditory fibers cover a large range of frequencies. Note, too, that all fibers—regardless of characteristic frequency—exhibit asymmetric tuning curves. The reduction in neural responsiveness

FIGURE 10.24

A graph of the threshold intensities (frequency tuning curve) for a single auditory nerve fiber. (Courtesy of Evan Relkin.)

(change in sensitivity) is much sharper at frequencies *higher* than the characteristic frequency. This means, therefore, that small changes in frequency can make big differences in the neural activity of nerve fibers.

The frequency tuning of any auditory nerve fiber depends on the location, along the basilar membrane, of the receptor cells (typically IHCs) from which the fiber collects information. Recall that different sound frequencies produce traveling waves that peak at different places along the basilar membrane. As you might guess, each fiber's characteristic frequency is determined by where along the basilar membrane that fiber makes contact with hair cells. Fibers originating from the apex of the cochlea (the low-frequency region, see Figure 10.19) respond to low frequencies, whereas fibers from the base (the high-frequency region) "prefer" higher frequencies.

This idea of representing a stimulus dimension within an array of tuned neurons should be familiar to you by now. We saw the same principle at work in the visual system: visual cells are tuned for size, orientation, retinal disparity, and so on. In effect, tuned cells make a particular statement about the nature of a stimulus. In the case of the auditory nerve, individual nerve fibers are able to signal the occurrence of a tone whose frequency falls within a limited range of frequencies. Within this range, however, a fiber's activity increases with sound *intensity* (a property we will discuss shortly). Consequently, within this limited range, the fiber's response is wholly ambiguous: any number of different frequencies could produce the same neural response if their intensities were adjusted properly. So looking just at the firing rate of a particular fiber, we could never be certain which frequency had stimulated it. (This is the same sort of ambiguity problem discussed in Chapters 4 and 5.)

We don't want to give you the impression that auditory fibers respond only to pure tones. In fact, an auditory fiber will respond vigorously to *any* complex sound just so long as that sound contains at least some energy within that fiber's frequency range. To illustrate, the sound produced when you snap your fingers is *broadband*—that is, it contains many different frequencies. So, too, is the static heard when you dial a radio between stations. Either of these broadband sounds would activate a number of frequency-tuned fibers. Any particular fiber, however, would "hear" (respond to) only those frequency components of the complex sound to which it was tuned.

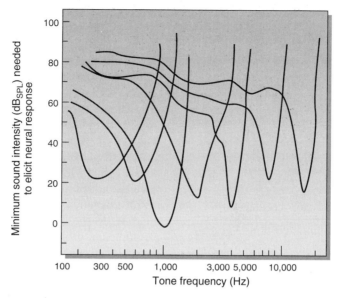

FIGURE 10.25
Frequency tuning curves for a number of different auditory nerve fibers. (Courtesy of Evan Relkin.)

So far our description of auditory fibers has focused on their frequency selectivity, as reflected in their threshold response profile. Before moving to higher levels of auditory processing, let's take a look at two other characteristic features of auditory nerve fiber responses. One feature is the way a fiber responds to sound levels above its threshold.

Imagine recording the discharge rate from the fiber whose tuning curve is shown in Figure 10.24. Suppose that we use a 5-kHz tone, that fiber's preferred frequency. As the tuning curve indicates, an intensity of 20 dB$_{SPL}$ will produce a barely discernible elevation in the fiber's activity level—this represents that cell's threshold. Now suppose we plot the discharge level produced by increasingly higher sound intensities of the 5-kHz tone. The result would be a graph like the solid line in the top portion of Figure 10.26.

As you can see, between about 20 dB$_{SPL}$ and 60 dB$_{SPL}$, the fiber's activity steadily grows as the sound level increases. Above 60 dB$_{SPL}$,

however, the fiber's activity level flattens out. Higher intensities of the tone all produce the same neural response. This so-called *saturation effect,* typical of auditory nerve fibers, means that the fiber has a limited range over which it can signal the intensity level of a given frequency. Hence, firing rate provides an *im*perfect representation of sound level—distinguishable differences in sound intensity (for instance, 80 dB$_{SPL}$ versus 120 dB$_{SPL}$) produce indistinguishable neural responses.

Suppose we repeat these intensity/response measurements on another auditory nerve fiber, also one tuned to 5-kHz. Now we might generate a curve like that shown in the bottom portion of Figure 10.26. Notice that this fiber's spontaneous level is lower, its threshold level is higher, and it responds to more intense levels before saturating. These two different fibers—which share a characteristic frequency—correspond to two of the three different innervation patterns previously described. (An example of the third fiber type

FIGURE 10.26

The neural activity of an auditory nerve fiber increases as the sound level increases, until a saturation point is reached. The graph at the top shows a fiber with high spontaneous activity, low threshold, and low saturation level; the graph at the bottom shows a fiber with low spontaneous activity, high threshold, and high saturation level. The fiber whose activity is shown in the top graph would innervate the IHC on the side facing toward the OHC; the one shown in the bottom would innervate the IHC on the side facing away from the OHC (recall figure 10.23).

would simply fall midway between the two shown in Figure 10.26.)

Recall that some fibers making synaptic contact with an IHC have low spontaneous activity, others have intermediate spontaneous activity and still others have high spontaneous activity. The spontaneous level of activity is closely related to the location around the IHC where the fibers innervate the IHC (recall Figure 10.23). We now see that these three categories of fibers have different

thresholds and different saturation intensities. These differences will prove important when we discuss hearing thresholds and loudness perception in the next chapter.

Besides variations in responsiveness with intensity, another significant property of auditory nerve fibers is their response to continuous, prolonged stimulation. When a sound of constant intensity is presented continuously, the level of activity evoked by that sound declines over time, but does not diminish to zero. This change in response is called **adaptation.** As described in Chapter 4, neural adaptation is a common property of sensory neurons. In the case of hearing, this adaptation phenomenon probably has something to do with the gradual reduction in loudness you experience when listening to a steady sound, such as the hum created by the fan on your computer.

This gives an overview of the response properties of auditory nerve fibers, the brain's sole link to the sounds in the environment. The train of neural impulses carried by the auditory nerves from the left and right ears provides the ingredients for all aspects of hearing. Subsequent auditory processing must utilize information contained within these impulses. In the two following sections, you will see how this neural information is utilized for sound localization and for sound identification.

Beyond the Auditory Nerve: Sound Localization

Having two ears enables you to localize sounds. This section discusses how the processing of information within the auditory system makes such localization possible.

Neural

Binaural neurons   Looking back at Figure 10.22, note that the left auditory nerve projects to the **cochlear nucleus** on the left side of the brain, while the right auditory nerve projects to the cochlear nucleus on the right side of the brain. Thus, at this first stage in the auditory chain, information from the two ears remains segregated. Sound delivered to just the left ear (stimulation that is **monaural,** meaning "one ear") will activate cells in the left cochlear nucleus, but have no effect on those in the right cochlear nucleus. Exactly the opposite is true for monaural stimulation delivered to the right ear.

However, at processing stages beyond the cochlear nucleus (superior olive, inferior colliculus, and higher), the auditory system becomes **binaural** ("both ears"), meaning that these higher stages receive neural input from the left ear *and* the right ear. (This property should remind you of the binocular visual cells discussed in Chapters 4 and 8.)

Some binaural neurons can be activated by sound presented to either ear; others are activated by sound presented to one ear but inhibited by sound presented to the other ear. Neurons in the former category—the purely excitatory neurons—tend to prefer low-frequency sound, whereas those in the other category—the excitatory/inhibitory neurons—prefer higher frequencies (Dabak and Johnson, 1992). Some binaural neurons even have a different characteristic frequency for the left versus the right ear (Mendelson, 1992), and they respond to sound sources moving at particular speeds (Ahissar, Bergman and Vaadia, 1992).

It is now commonly believed that these binaural cells register information about the location of a sound source relative to the head. To understand how these binaural cells work, you first need to be familiar with the two chief cues available for sound localization. In both of these cues, the sounds received by the two ears are compared, which is why the cues are called **binaural cues.** Let's take a moment to discuss them here, to provide some context for understanding the operations of binaural neurons. We'll go into more detail on these cues in the next chapter.

Interaural time Imagine keeping your head still and listening to a sound originating from a source located at various positions in front of and to either side of your head. (Try snapping your fingers while holding your hand at arm's length

at various positions around your head.) When the sound source lies straight ahead (a *midline* source), the sound energy reaching your two ears will be identical: the air pressure waves will arrive at the two ears at precisely the same time. Now suppose that a sound source is located to your left, away from the midline. In this case, the sound wave from the lateralized source will arrive at your closer ear, the left one, slightly before reaching your farther ear, the right one. This difference in time of arrival of sound at the two ears is called **interaural time difference,** and under certain conditions it provides a potent cue for sound localization.

How might the auditory nervous system register interaural time differences? Do neurons exist that can compute time differences between the two ears? The answer is yes—neurons at several levels in the auditory pathways are sensitive to small binaural time disparities (Masterton and Imig, 1984; Knudsen, du Lac and Esterly, 1987). For example, certain cells in the superior olivary nucleus, often called the "superior olive" (see Figure 10.22), respond maximally when the left ear receives sound slightly before the right ear does, whereas other cells respond best when the right ear receives sound slightly before the left. The interaural time delay that gives the best response varies from cell to cell. But by what means are these interaural delays actually created at the level of binaural cells? The answer, which is elegant yet simple, was proposed decades ago by Jeffress (1948) and more recently substantiated by physiological measurements.

Here's how it seems to work. As you already know, the axon is the neural process carrying impulses from one end of a cell (usually the cell body) to the other (the synaptic zone), where those impulses trigger chemical communication with the next set of neurons in a pathway. A neuron with a short axon conveys impulses to its recipient neurons in a shorter period of time than does a neuron with a longer axon because the impulse travels over a shorter distance. Axon length, in other words, governs the time elapsing

FIGURE 10.27
Schematic drawings showing how interaural time differences from a
lateralized sound source could be registered by a binaural cell
receiving inputs from cells whose axons differ in length.

between the generation of neural impulses and
the delivery of the "message" conveyed by those
impulses to the next set of neurons.

Now imagine a binaural neuron that receives
input from two cells whose axons *differ* in length,
one axonal path being shorter than the other (see
drawing A in Figure 10.27). With this in mind,
what will happen if both input neurons are activated at precisely the same time? The input cell
with the shorter axon will get its message to the
binaural cell sooner than will the input cell with
the longer axon, with the disparity in time of arrival at the binaural neuron depending on the
magnitude of the difference in axon length between the two input neurons.

Given these two input neurons, what would be
necessary to insure that the binaural neuron received *simultaneous* inputs from both? To accomplish this, the input neuron with the longer axon
would have to be activated *prior to* activation of the
input neuron with the shorter axon; the time disparity between activations would have to match the
disparity associated with their conduction times.
We could, in other words, compensate for the axon
length differences by introducing an appropriate
delay between activation of the two input cells.

How could we create these differences in activation time? The answer is simple: place the

sound source at a location where the interaural
time difference creates this exact activation delay. (This scheme, by the way, is similar in purpose but not implementation to the delay-line circuit described in Chapter 9 to account for
direction-selective motion perception.)

This, then, is the essence of the **delay line** theory proposed by Jeffress (1948). Different binaural neurons receive inputs from pairs of cells, one
activated by sound presented to the left ear and the
other by sound presented to the right ear. For any
given binaural cell, its pair of input cells has a
characteristic time delay, governed by the difference in axon length. The binaural neurons respond
maximally upon simultaneous stimulation by the
input cells. But to achieve this simultaneity, the
left- and right-ear input cells must be activated at
slightly *different* times. In general, registration of
sounds located to the left of the midline would require that the left-ear input cell have the longer
axon (to compensate for the left ear's receiving the
sound first), as depicted in Figure 10.27A; sounds
located to the right would require the opposite
arrangement (Figure 10.27B).

To register particular locations to the left or to
the right, the disparity in axonal length could
vary among pairs of cells, which means that different binaural neurons would respond best to

different interaural time differences. Actually, there are several means by which impulse conduction delays could be introduced, besides variations in axon length, but the essence of the idea remains the same: binaural neurons with different preferred interaural delays signal different sound locations. Recent physiological work confirms that the auditory system has such a mechanism in place (Carr and Konishi, 1988), and theoretical work has aimed at refining the Jeffress model (Dabak and Johnson, 1992).

Interaural intensity differences   There is a second potential source of information specifying sound location: sound energy arriving at the two ears from a single source will be more intense at the ear located nearest the source. This **interaural intensity difference** arises primarily from the "occluding" effect produced by the head. When sound energy passes through a dense barrier—such as your head—some sound energy is usually lost. Thus, for a lateralized sound source, a portion of its sound energy will be blocked from reaching the farther ear because the head stands in the way. The head produces what is called a *sound shadow,* a weakening of the intensity of sound at the more distant ear. This binaural difference in sound intensity provides another cue for sound localization. Of course, when the source is located equidistant from the two ears—for instance straight ahead—the interaural intensity difference will be zero.

The auditory nervous system appears to capitalize on this source of location information as well. Neurons have been discovered that respond best when the two ears receive slightly different intensities, some preferring the stronger intensity in the right ear and others preferring the stronger intensity in the left ear (Wise and Irvine, 1985; Manley, Koppl and Konishi, 1988). These binaural neurons, incidentally, are found at different neural sites than those registering interaural time differences (Knudsen and Konishi, 1978). Moreover, binaural cells sensitive to interaural intensity tend to fall into the excitatory/inhibitory cat-

egory, meaning that the input from one ear is excitatory and the input from the other is inhibitory. In fact, the algebraic subtraction of inhibition from excitation—an operation easily performed by a binaural cell—accounts for a given cell's preferred interaural intensity difference (Manley et al., 1988)

Binaural cells and sound localization   To reiterate, most binaural cells respond best to a sound arising from a particular location. For example, some binaural cells respond best to a source located close to the midline, while other cells respond best to sounds arising from various points to one side or the other of the midline. In effect, each binaural cell "listens" for sound within a fairly restricted region of auditory space. This region of space constitutes the neuron's receptive field, the area in space where a sound must be located in order to stimulate that neuron. As an aggregate, these cells provide a neural map of auditory space (King and Moore, 1991; Fitzpatrick et al., 1997). In the human brain, evidence for spatial maps of sound location has come from brain imaging studies (reviewed by Rauschecker, 1998).

Neural

There are several reasons for thinking that binaural cells of this sort are involved in sound localization. For one thing, placing an earplug in one ear causes sounds to be mislocalized. Under this condition, sound seems to originate not from the actual location of the source, but from a location displaced toward the unplugged ear. This makes sense. Plugging an ear reduces sound intensity received by that ear. Plugging one ear also produces a shift in the receptive fields of binaural neurons, by an amount and direction predicted from errors in sound localization (Knudsen and Konishi, 1980). This systematic shift in the receptive field locations of binaural neurons reinforces the idea that these neurons encode the location of sound in space.

Illusion

There is another reason for believing this idea. Not all species of mammals possess the kind of binaural neurons just described. In particular, the size of the superior olive varies greatly from one

Differences

species to another. This structure is one of the brain structures containing binaural neurons. Bruce Masterton tested the abilities of different species to localize sound (Masterton et al., 1975). The animals were trained to listen for a short tone that came from one of two loudspeakers, one located to the animal's left and the other located to the animal's right. The tone informed the animal which way to go, left or right, in order to obtain a drink of water. Masterton found that cats and tree shrews, both of which have sizable superior olives, could perform this task with ease. However, hedgehogs and rats, who have a much smaller superior olive, made numerous errors, indicating an inability to localize sound accurately. Masterton's behavioral study reinforces the idea that binaural neurons of the superior olive are responsible for analyzing interaural cues for sound localization.

Plasticity

Experience also plays an important role in the development of the neural connections responsible for registering locations of sounds in space (Knudsen, 1998). As mentioned above, hearing loss in one ear causes compensatory shifts in auditory receptive fields, in response to the altered interaural timing and interaural intensity cues (Knudsen and Brainard, 1995). In addition, when vision cannot be used for locating objects, the spatial acuity of binaural neurons is enhanced. That is, when an animal must rely on binaural hearing as its sole source of spatial information, neurons in some auditory regions of the brain become unusually sharply "tuned" for particular locations (Korte and Rauschecker, 1993). As you might expect, these animals exhibit extra good sound localization ability when tested behaviorally (Rauschecker and Kniepert, 1994). There are reasons to believe that humans, too, can develop extra keen spatial acuity when forced to rely on hearing without sight, and we will consider that evidence in the next chapter.

This concludes our overview of how the auditory system processes information about *where* a sound originates. We have left out important facts about sound localization, but those will be cov-

ered in Chapter 11 when we return to binaural hearing. For now, though, let's consider how the auditory system processes information about the identity of a sound: *what* it is that's being heard.

Beyond the Auditory Nerve: Sound Identification

Recall that any fiber in the auditory nerve responds to a limited range of frequencies, a range that defines the fiber's frequency tuning. The responses of such fibers to more complex sounds (such as noise or a vocalization) can be simply predicted from each fiber's tuning curve. Moving from the auditory nerve to more central processing stages (for example, the cochlear nucleus), cells continue to respond to tones of certain frequencies, but the range of frequencies over which any given cell responds becomes narrower. Thus, over the first several stages of the auditory system, tuning curves become more selective for frequency.

In addition, information destined for the auditory cortex passes through the **medial geniculate nucleus** (see Figure 10.22). This structure, the analogue to the LGN in vision, also receives input from the reticular activating system, which was introduced in Chapter 4. So again, an organism's level of arousal probably modulates auditory sensitivity by means of neural influences occurring within the medial geniculate nucleus. Cells in the medial geniculate nucleus, in turn, send projections to the **primary auditory cortex** located in the temporal lobe of the brain.

Within the primary auditory cortex, frequency is organized tonotopically, meaning that the frequency selectivity of neurons changes systematically within this cortical region. There is, in other **Neural** words, an auditory cortical map that mirrors the tonotopic organization of the basilar membrane. (In a sense, this tonotopic frequency map is analogous to the retinotopic map in visual cortex.) Moreover, this auditory map exhibits a form of cortical magnification since there are more neurons tuned to mid-frequencies than to either higher or lower values. Incidentally, this is the region of the frequency spectrum responsible for carrying human speech information.

The primary auditory cortex (sometimes termed area A1) is flanked by additional brain areas responsive to acoustic signals (Rauschecker, 1998). Neurons in these nonprimary areas, however, tend to respond rather weakly to pure-tone sounds. Rather than being "interested" in the frequency or intensity of sounds, these neurons, instead, respond best to more complicated, biologically significant sounds. To give just a few examples, some cortical neurons fail to respond to any steady tone but do respond vigorously to a tone that changes in frequency. For some of these neurons, the frequency change must be in a particular direction, either up or down. One sound whose frequency goes up is the "Hmmm?" sound you make when you don't understand something (try it). A sound whose frequency goes down is the sound you make when you yawn (try it). In general, frequency changes are responsible for the voice inflections during speech; without these inflections, the voice has a flat, monotone character.

Other cortical neurons respond only to complex "kissing" sounds that resemble the noise often used when calling a dog. In animals that utilize vocalizations to communicate, the auditory cortex contains neurons specifically responsive to individual vocalizations. Such cells often fail to respond to tones or clicks and, instead, are activated only by a certain "call" that forms part of that animal's natural vocabulary. For instance, in several regions outside the primary auditory cortex of the macaque monkey, some neurons are activated exclusively by "cooing" sounds, other neurons activated only by "barks" and still others activated only by "grunts" (Rauschecker, Tian and Hauser, 1995). Each of these natural vocalizations conveys a particular message within the repertoire of calls made by the monkey. It is interesting that these neurons are found in regions of the monkey's temporal lobe which, in humans, corresponds to areas associated with speech perception.

Many cortical neurons, then, unlike those at lower levels of the auditory system, respond to more *abstract* features of sound—features that identify the sound source itself, not just the constituent frequencies of that sound. This is why damage to the auditory cortex impairs performance on tasks where an animal must discriminate between complex sounds but spares performance on tasks involving the detection or discrimination of simple tones.

Insight into cortical processing of auditory information in humans has come from several sources. One is application of the neuroimaging techniques, which reveal regions of the human brain active during specific tasks. We know, for example, that the human auditory cortex is organized tonotopically, which, you will recall, means that different tone frequencies are represented in a spatially ordered map (Wessinger et al., 1997). Thus, listening to a low-pitched tone activates a distinctly different region of your auditory cortex than does a high-pitched tone. People with tinnitus—the experience of a tone-like sound in the absence of a real sound—exhibit distorted tonotopic maps in the auditory cortex that exaggerate the neural representation of the frequency associated with the "illusory" pitch (Mühlnickel et al., 1998). This distorted representation, it is thought, results from abnormal auditory experience associated with partial hearing loss (Rauschecker, 1999).

Execute

Plasticity

But why does hearing loss produce phantom sounds? Damage to a restricted portion of the cochlea produces an auditory "deaf spot" in the individual's hearing: tones normally signalled by that portion of the cochlea are no longer registered by the inner ear and, therefore, are no longer heard (we will discuss this form of hearing loss in greater detail in the next chapter). Consequently, neurons in the brain responsive to those lost tones are deprived of their normal inputs, even though the deprived neurons are themselves healthy. Over time, those neurons develop responsiveness to neighboring tone frequencies that are still audible (that is, frequencies to which the cochlea still responds). The tone frequencies

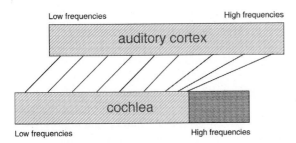

Low frequencies   High frequencies
auditory cortex
cochlea
Low frequencies   High frequencies

FIGURE 10.28

Schematic of cortical reorganization following cochlear damage. What happens when a portion of the cochlea signalling high-frequency sound is damaged? Regions of the tonotopically organized auditory cortex that normally receive input from this high-frequency portion of the cochlea are instead innervated by fibers from neighboring, healthy portions of the cochlea. Those cortical neurons still respond as if high-frequency sound were presented, even though their inputs are from parts of the cochlea responsive to lower frequencies. (Adapted from Rauschecker, 1999.)

neighboring those associated with the hearing loss expand their neural representations within the auditory cortex.

This expansion is the neural basis for the cortical "distortion" supposedly associated with tinnitus: a central, cortical distortion arising in response to neural events on the periphery of the auditory system. This hypothesis is illustrated schematically in Figure 10.28. Presumably, a phantom tone is heard in the absence of auditory input because of chronic increased spontaneous activity in this region of the tonotopic map (Rauschecker, 1999). Tinnitus thus represents an intriguing example of neural plasticity—the brain's ability to alter its connectivity in response to longterm changes in sensory input.

Brain imaging has revealed other interesting facts about the organization of auditory portions of the human brain. Listening to speech sounds activates regions in the temporal lobe and regions near the junction of temporal and parietal lobes (Petersen et al., 1988), with activation being most pronounced in the left hemisphere (Johnsrude et al., 1997). There is also evidence that attention directed to spoken words modulates the extent and

focus of activity in these areas (Hari, 1989). Musical sounds, in contrast, activate regions in a different portion of the temporal cortex, and predominantly in the right hemisphere of the brain (Zatorre, Evans and Meyer, 1994).

Clinical

Studies of brain-damaged patients provide another source of information about the auditory cortex in humans. The clinical literature on brain damage and hearing is too extensive to review here; interested readers should see Tanaka and colleagues (1991). Suffice it to say that damage to different portions of the auditory pathways creates different kinds of hearing losses, ranging from temporary deficits in the ability to hear tones to permanent inability to identify previously familiar sounds.

There are even auditory analogs to blindsight and to akinetopsia, the syndromes described in Chapter 4. Tanaka and colleagues (1991) describe two patients who exhibited seriously impaired hearing from extensive, bilateral damage to brain structures in the auditory cortex, but whose ears and auditory nerves were intact. Despite their **cortical deafness,** these patients sometimes behaviorally reacted to a sound—such as a door slamming—while denying any experience of that sound. This suggests that neural pathways subserving the auditory reflexes, such as turning the head toward a sound source, are different from those involved in awareness and identification of the source.

As for the analog to akinetoposia (motion blindness), Griffiths and colleagues (1996) described a patient with a right hemisphere stroke who was unable to perceive the movement of a sound source when that movement was specified by changing interaural time cues or changing interaural intensity cues. Normal listeners, in comparison, clearly hear sounds moving within the environment when these cues are present. The patient's brain damage included posterior parts of the parietal cortex, an area involved in spatial localization.

This completes our survey of sound, the ear and the auditory pathways. The stage is now set for consideration of hearing, the next chapter's topic.

SUMMARY AND PREVIEW

This chapter has described the physical events that give rise to the experience of sound. These events are captured by the ears, transformed into neural events by the hair cells and analyzed by neurons especially designed for frequency and sound location. Throughout this chapter we've largely avoided discussing the perceptual consequences of this sequence of events. But now that you know something about the auditory system's machinery, we're ready to consider the accomplishment that this machinery makes possible: hearing.

KEY TERMS

acoustic energy
acoustic reflex
acoustics
adaptation
amplitude
anvil (incus)
auditory canal
auditory nerve
basilar membrane
binaural
binaural cues
cilia
cochlea
cochlear emissions
cochlear nucleus
cortical deafness
decibels (dB)
delay line

eardrum (tympanic membrane)
echoes
efferent fibers
Eustachian tube
frequency tuning curve
hair cells
hammer (malleus)
hertz (Hz)
inner hair cells (IHC)
interaural intensity difference
interaural time difference
medial geniculate nucleus
monaural
noise
organ of Corti
ossicles
outer hair cells (OHC)

oval window
pinna
place theory
primary auditory cortex
pure tones
resonant frequency
round window
sonar (sound navigation ranging)
sound pressure level (SPL)
stirrup (stapes)
tectorial membrane
temporal theory
threshold intensity
tinnitus
tonotopic organization
traveling wave

CHAPTER 11

HEARING AND LISTENING

Do blind people hear better than sighted individuals? Does listening to loud music damage one's hearing? How do you manage to ignore the hubbub at a noisy party while at the same time picking out and listening to a familiar voice? These are just a few of the questions we shall consider in this chapter on hearing and listening. Because the auditory system's properties are crucial to any account of hearing, much of the discussion here is grounded in the material you read in the previous chapter.

Sounds are with us all the time. They're impossible to escape. In fact, you were listening to sounds before you were born. The intrauterine environment may not be as noisy as New York's Times Square, but maternal sounds, such as a mother's heartbeat, breathing, speaking or singing voice and even the gurgles of her tummy,* make the uterus anything but quiet. And these sounds have an impact because by about the twenty-eighth week after conception, a human fetus shows clear responses to sounds, and grows increasingly sensitive to sound through the remainder of the pregnancy and beyond (Ruben, 1992). Prenatal exposure to sound may explain why soon after birth, an infant will preferentially orient toward the sound of its mother's voice. The infant has gained familiarity with this very special voice by listening to it for months prior to birth.

It's impossible to estimate how many different sounds we can recognize, but the average person's auditory repertoire is huge, growing larger over time. Just think of all the people you know fairly well. Their voices are sufficiently imprinted in your mind's ear that you can typically recognize them in an instant over the telephone.

---

*The medical term for a tummy gurgle is *borborygmus,* one of the oddest sounding words in the English language. It sounds odd because it is an onomatopoeia, a word made up to imitate some sound, in this case a stomach gurgle. Incidentally, a borborygmus is produced by gas squeezing through the intestines' liquid contents.

FIGURE 11.1
Each soundwave wave corresponds to a unique acoustic event.

Famous voices, too, are acoustically etched in our minds, to the extent that we immediately know when we're listening to the recorded voice of, say, Mike Tyson (the boxer), Bill Clinton (former President of the United States) or Marge Simpson (Bart's mother).

Besides the sounds of voices, we're intimately familiar with countless musical tunes and animal sounds, not to mention the miscellaneous sounds associated with life's everyday events: walking, sneezing, laughing, scratching, typing, tearing open an envelope, knocking on a door or kissing a loved one. Sounds are generated when objects rub against one another or when one object hits another. Those sounds tell us something about the nature of those objects. Thus, we're able to "hear" the shapes of objects when they're struck by a hammer (Kunkler-Peck and Turvey, 2000). We can judge when a vessel being filled with water is nearly full based only on the sound produced by that action (Cabe and Pittenger, 2000). And, of course, sounds are invaluable in being able to tell us about objects and events we cannot see, such as the rattle of a loose screw inside an

appliance or the increased pitch of a clogged vacuum cleaner. These days computers exploit sounds to signal the arrival of e-mail and to characterize all sorts of "desktop" actions, such as opening applications and deleting files.

It's amazing that this huge spectrum of auditory events comes to us courtesy of only about 15,000 tiny hair cells in each ear and approximately 30,000 fibers in each auditory nerve. This feat is all the more remarkable when we consider the acoustic signal that inaugurates the process of hearing.

Take a look at the array of acoustic waveforms shown in Figure 11.1. These are samples of some common, easily recognized sounds. These waveforms, which summarize the signals available to the ears, appear as a jumble of different frequencies varying in amplitude and times of onset and offset. Just looking at the waveforms, it's impossible to associate a given sound wave with a specific event. Yet the ear and auditory portions of the brain accomplish this feat accurately and effortlessly.

What's even more remarkable is that hearing works quite well even when we encounter many sound sources all at once. Stop and think about it. The ear typically receives a stream of acoustic energy from a multitude of environmental sources, and the energy from those sources sums to form a single, complex sound arriving at the ear. To appreciate this fact, think about attending a symphony performance. Without effort, you can pick out and listen to the melody line carried by, say, the woodwinds and then easily shift attention to the harmonic strains of the violins. It is possible, in other words, to hear the separate instruments even though their separate voices blend into one complex acoustic stream arriving at your ears. Or imagine chatting with a friend at a noisy baseball game. The acoustic environment includes applause, music, shouts from popcorn vendors, cheers of neighboring fans and, of personal interest to you, your companion's voice. Amidst the jumbled din, you can pick out your friend's voice from all the rest.

Let's begin our exploration of hearing and listening by considering the range of sound frequencies audible to humans since these frequencies define the boundaries of auditory perception.

THE RANGE AND LIMITS OF HEARING

The range of audible sound frequencies is analogous to the range of visible spatial frequencies (see Chapter 5). In like fashion, the eyes and ears register a fairly wide but definitely limited range of visual and auditory information. Because this range is limited, our perceptual world is limited.

Execute

For hearing, the range of audible frequencies is determined by measuring the minimum intensity, or amplitude, necessary to just barely detect tones of various frequencies. These measurements are made in a quiet environment, with no other sounds present. Test tones are typically delivered over earphones or through a loudspeaker. The minimum intensity value is referred to as the **threshold intensity.** Values below this threshold intensity cannot be heard, whereas intensities higher than this can be heard. (The Appendix

gives a detailed discussion of techniques for measuring thresholds.) The threshold intensity for each of a number of tone frequencies can be plotted on a graph like the one in Figure 11.2.

Curves like this are called **audibility functions (AFs).** They summarize the range of frequencies audible to the human ear. The analogy between an AF and a contrast-sensitivity function for spatial vision should be obvious—both express variations in threshold performance over a range of frequencies. Notice that the threshold of hearing varies with the frequency of sound: in the middle frequencies, far less intensity is needed to make a tone audible than in the low and high frequencies.

In this figure, intensity values are expressed in terms of decibels (dB_{SPL}), with the value of $0\ dB_{SPL}$ assigned to the weakest intensity that can be heard at any frequency (recall Figure 10.4). In this case, tones in the neighborhood of 2,500 Hz require the least intensity to be heard. As a result, their threshold is expressed as $0\ dB_{SPL}$ and all other threshold values are expressed relative to this value. Thus, to hear a 200-Hz tone, its intensity must be 40 dB higher than the intensity needed to hear a 2,500-Hz tone.

To provide some points of reference, the lowest key on a standard piano produces a musical note whose primary frequency is 27.5 Hz, the note produced by middle C is 261.63 Hz, and the top note on the piano is 4,186 Hz. A sound of very high frequency can be produced by turning on a television set but leaving the volume turned all the way down. This generates a high-pitched whine about 16,000 Hz (16 kHz).

At its best, the human ear is extraordinarily sensitive: the intensity required to hear a 2,500-Hz tone is hardly any greater than the amplitude of vibrations associated with the random movements of air molecules! This incredible performance testifies to what a masterpiece of engineering the ears are. All the more remarkable in view of the fact that this very sensitive device is not harmed by sounds several million times more intense. On top of this, human beings can hear a

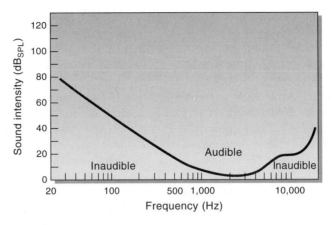

FIGURE 11.2
An ability function (AF) showing the range of tone frequencies
audible to a normal young adult.

wide range of frequencies: most people can detect frequencies as low as 20 Hz, which is heard
as a very low rumble. Young people can detect
frequencies as high as 20,000 Hz. To get this
much performance out of a device so sensitive
represents a real design feat.

The performance summarized in Figure 11.2
represents the range of hearing for the normal
young adult. This curve is remarkably consistent
across individuals, so much so that deviations
from this norm usually signify some type of impairment in the peripheral auditory system, either
in the ear or in the auditory nerve. Abnormal AFs
are *not* commonly associated with disorders of
the central auditory nervous system. Central neural disorders lead to other kinds of hearing loss,
some of which we'll mention later in this chapter.
For now, let's consider some of the conditions
that can produce abnormal AFs (higher than normal, pure-tone thresholds) and the perceptual
consequences of those abnormalities.

HEARING LOSS

Hannah Merker, an author and professor of creative
writing, became deaf after a skiing accident during
her young adulthood. She writes about her loss.

As an adult, losing most of my hearing . . . was akin
to being adrift in a fog where the edges of nearby
land, other fog-bound craft, are barely visible. You
know something is there but definition is vague. . . .
You are aware yet cut off, alone in a scary isolation.
The world is running forward and you cannot keep
up. That is what it is like to be severely hearing impaired. (1992, pp. 66–67)

As Figure 11.3 documents, the incidence of
hearing loss is high, especially in the older population. An estimated 28 million Americans suffer
some loss of hearing, making this the most common of all physical disabilities (Nadol, 1993).
Within that large group, about 2 million suffer
profound deafness, meaning a complete inability
to hear. As Hannah Merker's words reveal, people who become completely deaf after years of
normal hearing find the experience frightening
and isolating. Since everyday sounds keep us in
touch with the environment, loss of hearing iso-
lates the totally deaf person not only from the
voices of others but also from the security of
life's background hum. Helen Keller poignantly
described that isolated world this way:

Clinical

I am just as deaf as I am blind. The problems of
deafness are deeper and more complex, if not more
important, than those of blindness. Deafness is a

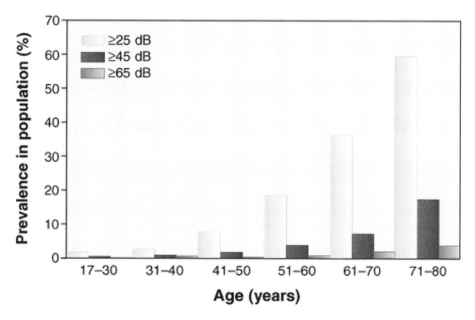

FIGURE 11.3

The incidence of hearing loss increases with age. For each age group, the three histograms correspond to varying degrees of hearing loss expressed in decibel units.

much worse misfortune. For it means the loss of the most vital stimulus—the sound of the voice that brings language, sets thoughts astir and keeps us in the intellectual company of [others]. . . . I have found deafness to be a much greater handicap than blindness. (cited in Ackerman, 1990, p. 191)

In legal terms, a person is said to be totally deaf when speech sounds cannot be heard at intensities less than 82 dB_{SPL} (the intensity of ordinary speech is around 60 dB_{SPL}). The term *hearing impairment*—a more inclusive term—refers to any loss in auditory sensitivity relative to the hearing ability of the normal young adult (as summarized by the AF in Figure 11.2).

But when does hearing loss become debilitating? The ability to comprehend speech effortlessly is compromised by a 25 dB hearing loss (recall from Chapter 10 that the decibel is the unit of measurement of sound loudness). To experience what this loss sounds like, place your palms tightly over your ears and notice how muffled

sounds become. This maneuver produces about a 25 dB reduction in sound intensity within the range of frequencies contained in speech (see Figure 11.4).

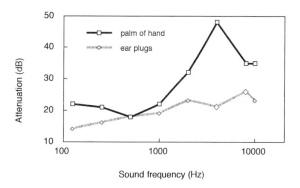

FIGURE 11.4

Graph showing reduction in sound intensity when you cover your ears with the palms of your hand or when you insert standard ear plugs.

All hearing impairments can be divided into two categories: conduction loss and sensory/neural loss. **Conduction loss** stems from some disorder within the outer or middle ear, those portions of the auditory system involved in mechanically transmitting (conducting) sound energy to the receptors in the inner ear. Hearing disorders originating in these peripheral stages of the auditory system typically involve an overall reduction in sensitivity to sounds of all frequencies.

Sensory/neural loss originates within the inner ear or in the auditory portion of the brain. The associated hearing loss may extend over the entire range of audible frequencies or over only a portion of that range. Let's consider some of the more common causes of the two categories of hearing loss, starting with conduction losses.

Conduction Hearing Loss and Possible Remedies

Conduction loss can be caused by excessive build-up of ear wax* in the canal of the outer ear. Simply cleaning out the plugged-up canal cures the problem. In other cases, however, the problem is more serious. Infection can cause fluid to build up in the middle ear, and if the Eustachian tube (the middle ear's pressure regulator) becomes inflamed, middle ear pressure can rupture the eardrum. Infection can also spread to the bony chamber housing the middle ear, leading to bone disease that must be treated surgically. Today, the use of antibiotics usually clears up ear infections before the symptoms reach these dangerous stages.

Middle ear infection, known as otitis media, is the most common cause of conductive hearing loss in children. During the first year or two of life, the auditory system's proper neural development requires normal acoustic input. Because

otitis media interferes with that input, children who have had recurrent bouts of otitis media, particularly during the first year of life, can exhibit long-lasting deficits in hearing-related function (Mody et al., 1999).

There is another type of conduction disorder that affects the middle ear, and this condition is not remedied by drugs. Called **otosclerosis,** this disorder involves the gradual immobilization of the stapes, the last of the tiny middle-ear bones that form the ossicular bridge between the outside world and the inner ear. Recall that the stapes (stirrup) is the bone actually responsible for transmitting sound vibrations to the oval window, which in turn sets up pressure waves within the cochlear fluids. Hence, when the stapes becomes immobile, the bridge to the inner ear is destroyed. The stapes becomes immobilized by a steady accumulation of a spongy substance near the foot of this bone. This spongy substance eventually hardens, cementing the stapes in a rigid position. No one understands what triggers this disease, but it tends to occur in young adults and more often in females than in males. Fortunately, the disease can be treated. Using a surgical microscope to guide their movements, ear surgeons can remove the immobile stapes and replace it with a plastic substitute. So long as other portions of the ear have not been affected by the disease, this surgery can restore hearing to normal levels.

Otosclerosis is a progressive disease that, in time, may spread to the cochlea. In these cases, surgery to replace the stapes cannot restore hearing to normal levels. It is important, therefore, for the physician to know beforehand whether a candidate for stapes surgery also suffers hearing loss due to cochlear pathology. But how can a physician determine functional status when the immobile stapes blocks sound's normal route to the cochlea?

The answer turns out to be rather easy. Sound has an alternate route to the cochlea, through the bones of the skull. You have probably noticed how loud the dentist's drill sounds when it con-

---

*Known in polite circles by its proper name, *cerumen,* this waxy substance provides important lubrication for the tympanic membrane.

tacts one of your teeth. This is because vibrations from the drill are transmitted from your tooth to your skull. The cochlea, remember, is the coiled cavity formed within the bone of the skull. Thus, when vibrations are introduced into the skull, those vibrations reach the cochlea, and if they are sufficiently strong, they set up pressure waves in the cochlear fluids. Those pressure waves behave just like the ones reaching the cochlea through the ear. They set up ripples along the basilar membrane, causing you to experience those bone-transmitted vibrations as sound.

This is called hearing by **bone conduction.** Every time you speak, part of what you hear is the sound of your voice transmitted via bone conduction. That's why a tape recording of your voice sounds strange to you but not to others. Listening to the recording, you hear your voice without the normal contribution from bone conduction ("Yes, that's what your voice really sounds like to others").

Sounds are not as loud when carried via bone conduction as when conveyed through the ear because this alternate route includes no mechanism like the ossicles for amplifying sound energy. For this reason, pure-tone thresholds measured through the skull of a person with good hearing are roughly 30 dB higher than those measured using tones delivered to the ear. Incidentally, to measure pure-tone thresholds for bone conduction hearing, a metal tuning fork is set into vibration and placed firmly against the bone just behind the ear. To return, then, to the question of whether to operate on a patient with otosclerosis: if that person's bone conduction thresholds are near normal, then the cochlea must be unaffected by the disease. Then surgery should be successful in restoring the world of sound to the patient.

Sensory/Neural Loss

Anything that harms the cochlea (which houses the receptors for hearing) or the auditory nerve will adversely impact hearing. This section outlines several conditions that can have such an impact.

Age and Hearing Loss The most common, perhaps inevitable, cause of hearing loss is age. In industrial societies, people gradually lose sensitivity to high frequencies, a condition known as **presbycusis** (from the Greek words *presbus,* meaning "old," and *akouo,* meaning "hearing"). This selective high-frequency deafness begins at a surprisingly early age. According to one survey (Davis and Silverman, 1960), most people 30 years old are unable to hear frequencies above 15,000 Hz; and by 50 years of age, hearing is impossible beyond 12,000 Hz. Aging's progressive assault on high-frequency hearing can eventually encroach upon the range of frequencies present in normal speech (Frisina and Frisina, 1997). For any given age group, men tend to exhibit a larger degree of hearing loss than women (Corso, 1981). These figures represent average values and therefore do not invariably apply to all people.

Differences

Békésy, whose pioneering work on the cochlea was discussed in Chapter 10, believed that age-related hearing loss resulted from the cochlea's loss of elasticity, which diminished its ability to transmit traveling waves. Some contemporary researchers believe that presbycusis results from changes in the vasculature of the cochlea—changes that restrict the blood supply to the delicate neural elements in the inner ear, presumably leading to chronic ischemia that starves these elements. Still others feel that cumulative exposure to loud noise may contribute to the steady loss of hearing with age. This noise exposure hypothesis receives some support from cross-cultural studies that show normal hearing levels in 70-year-old African tribal people living in natural environments unpolluted by noise (Bergman, 1966). Whether their immunity to hearing loss is attributable to their quiet environment, or to other factors such as diet or genetics, remains undetermined. Whatever the cause, those of us living in modern societies better become resigned to a steady loss in hearing with age.

Noise Exposure and Hearing Loss All too commonly, hearing loss results from exposure to

Plasticity

very loud noise. In most instances, the cause can be traced to damage of the fine receptor structures in the inner ear. For instance, the acoustic energy from explosions—in combat or in industrial accidents—can produce sudden, permanent deafness as a result of trauma to the organ of Corti. Even the explosion of a single 2-inch firecracker can cause a major loss in hearing (Ward and Glorig, 1961). Comparable hearing losses have been reported in people exposed to the noise of gunfire, such as hunters (Taylor and Williams, 1966), people in the armed forces, and actors in western movies. Included in this last group of hearing-impaired individuals is former United States President Ronald Reagan, whose hearing loss dates back to his days as an actor (Reagan, 1990).

All the cases just mentioned involve sudden explosive noises, but this certainly is not the only type of sound that can damage the inner ear and, hence, lead to hearing loss. Sustained loud noises can also lead to permanent hearing loss. Astronauts and cosmonauts are susceptible to noise-induced hearing loss because the noise level aboard a space shuttle is comparable to a continuously grinding garbage disposal. Medical authorities point to loud music and headphones as contributors to the high incidence of hearing loss among people in their late teens and early twenties (which by some estimates approaches 60 percent of that age group). In response to these concerns, manufacturers include literature with each pair of headphones, warning of the potential hazards to hearing. One manufacturer has gone so far as to install a warning light on its portable cassette players to indicate when the volume exceeds safe listening levels.

The loud, amplified music often encountered at rock concerts and clubs can also cause permanent hearing loss. In one study of this effect (Hanson and Fearn, 1975), pure-tone thresholds were measured in two groups of college students. One group consisted of people who attended at least one rock concert each month, while the other group consisted of people who never attended rock concerts. At all frequencies tested,

which spanned the range 500 to 8,000 Hz, "attenders" had higher thresholds (that is, pure tones had to be more intense in order for attenders to hear them). Differences between the groups were small, averaging just a couple of decibels, but they were consistent. The regular attenders, incidentally, were entirely unaware of their deficits, and they had no complaints about their hearing.

Besides members of their audiences, pop musicians can develop hearing loss from their chronic exposure to amplified music (Axelsson and Lindgren, 1978). This effect is far from universal (Axelsson, Eliasson and Israelsson, 1995), however, and seems to be no more severe than sound-induced hearing losses experienced by classical musicians (Royster, Royster and Killion, 1991). By the way, can you guess which ear of violinists tends to have the greater hearing loss? If you can't, think of the instrument's usual position in the violinist's hands, and remember that the musician's head generates a sound shadow.

Chronic noise exposure also represents a serious occupational hazard for individuals who work in such environments as mechanized assembly plants, airports, and construction sites. Chronic exposure to the squeals of farm animals can also damage hearing (Kristensen and Gimsing, 1988). It is well documented that unprotected workers in noisy environments suffer permanent increases in pure-tone thresholds, with the magnitude of the loss related to length of time on the job (Nixon and Glorig, 1961; Taylor, 1965). Moreover, high noise levels in industrial settings are associated with higher accident rates, presumably because noise makes it more difficult to hear warning signals such as whistles or shouts (Wilkins and Acton, 1982). Aware of these deleterious effects of noise (and their likely legal liability in such instances), more industries attempt to shield their workers from harmful noise. This shielding can consist of earplugs (which can reduce noise levels by up to 30 dB: see Figure 11.4) and, where possible, sound-attenuating enclosures for workers.

Clinical

Even people who work and play in quieter everyday environments often experience noises such as the roar of a motorcycle or the wail of a siren. On an ordinary day, the average sound level on a Manhattan street approaches 100 dB$_{SPL}$, and inside a subway tunnel, even this level is exceeded when trains pass through a station. But you don't need to go to a busy city to experience a noisy environment. You can do this in the "quiet" of your own home. Ordinary household appliances can generate surprising levels of noise: a dishwasher can produce 60 dB$_{SPL}$ of sound, a vacuum cleaner 75 dB$_{SPL}$ and an innocent-looking garbage disposal can exceed 100 dB$_{SPL}$ when it is chewing on hard objects such as bones. While these sound levels won't lead to *permanent* deafness, they are sufficiently loud to elevate your threshold for hearing *temporarily* after cessation of the noise. This transitory reduction in hearing sensitivity following noise exposure is aptly called a **temporary threshold shift.** The phenomenon has been thoroughly studied under laboratory conditions. We'll just mention some of the highlights and implications of that work.

In general, sound levels in excess of 60 dB$_{SPL}$ can produce temporary threshold shifts if the duration of exposure is several hours or longer. The actual threshold shifts can vary from just a few decibels, which for all practical purposes is unnoticeable, to complete deafness. As you might guess, the size of the shift depends on the level and duration of the inducing noise. The length of time it takes for thresholds to return to normal also varies, depending on the strength and duration of noise exposure. Recovery can occur within only a few hours when the noise is modest, but it can take several days to recover following exposure to severe noise. You may have noticed a temporary threshold shift after attending a loud party or a boisterous football game—normally-audible sounds such as your own footsteps may temporarily fall below your elevated threshold.

For unknown reasons, women seem to exhibit smaller threshold shifts than men when the inducing noise consists of *low* frequencies. Thus,

after a male and female have been listening to the romantic roar of the ocean for some time, she may be able to hear his passionate whispers, just barely, but he won't be able to make out her whispered replies. However, just the opposite is true when the inducing noise consists of *high* frequencies. Now men exhibit smaller threshold shifts than women (Ward, 1966, 1968). So if our hypothetical couple had been listening for some time to the strains of Wagner sung by a lusty soprano, the female of the couple would be at a temporary disadvantage when it came to communicating in whispers.

Drugs and Hearing Loss   Several widely consumed drugs can have deleterious effects on hearing. One is nicotine. Chronic cigarette smokers have higher pure-tone thresholds than nonsmokers of the same age, and this loss is most pronounced at higher frequencies (Zelman, 1973). The loss is probably traceable to poor circulation, since nicotine narrows the ear's blood vessels and makes the ear's blood pressure irregular. These circulatory effects, in turn, reduce the blood supply to the cochlea.

Another common drug that affects hearing is aspirin which, when taken in large doses, can produce a temporary hearing loss (McCabe and Dey, 1965). A person taking 4 to 8 grams of aspirin per day is likely to experience anywhere from a 10- to 40-dB shift in pure-tone thresholds, with the loss often more pronounced at higher frequencies. This hearing loss persists as long as aspirin is taken, and normal hearing returns within a day or two after the person ceases to take the aspirin. Since one tablet usually contains one-fourth of a gram of aspirin, hearing won't be affected by taking a couple of aspirin. The aspirin dose that can produce hearing loss (4 to 8 grams) is the typical prescription dose for people with rheumatoid arthritis. The temporary hearing loss induced by aspirin is often accompanied by **tinnitus,** the high-pitched ringing in the ears we described in the previous chapter. The tinnitus, too, disappears once the consumption of aspirin ceases. It is thought that aspirin produces this effect by temporarily disabling the amplification function performed by the OHCs.

Dennis McFadden of the University of Texas found that aspirin makes people more vulnerable to the effects of noise (McFadden and Plattsmier, 1983). In his study, McFadden exposed paid volunteers to a 2,500-Hz tone for 10 minutes. The tone's intensity was adjusted to yield around a 14-dB threshold shift. The intensity of the tone required to produce such a shift was in the neighborhood of 100 dB$_{SPL}$. McFadden divided his volunteers into two groups, giving one group 1.95 grams of aspirin and the other, 3.9 grams. The volunteers took the aspirin every day for several days. At the end of this period, he once again exposed them to the loud tone and then retested their pure-tone thresholds. Some people who were given the higher dosage of aspirin (3.9 grams) suffered a hearing loss that was almost twice what they had suffered initially. In addition, it took them longer to recover from the noise exposure, although they eventually did. People who got the smaller dose (1.95 grams) showed neither of these effects. McFadden's results imply that people routinely exposed to loud sounds should restrict their intake of aspirin or, better yet, find a substitute pain reliever. It should be noted that this study and its conclusions speak only to the question of temporary shifts in threshold, not permanent hearing loss.

Some Perceptual Consequences of Impaired Hearing

Clinical

So far we have focused on some of the things that cause pure-tone hearing losses, either temporary or permanent. To appreciate the perceptual consequences of such losses, you need some idea of the frequencies and intensities of sound in your everyday environment. Take, for example, the ringing sound made by a typical telephone, a routine sound we all rely on. Suppose that the acoustic energy associated with the sound lies between 4,000 and 8,000 Hz, and that its sound

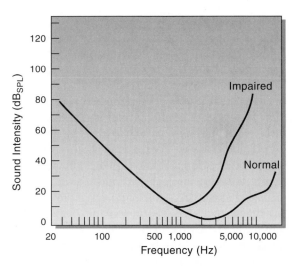

FIGURE 11.5
An AF of an individual with about a 50-dB hearing loss in the middle and upper frequency range.

level is somewhere around 70 dB$_{SPL}$. (The actual distribution of acoustic energy varies from one type of telephone to another.) Suppose also that a person with the abnormal AF shown in Figure 11.5 is expecting a phone call. As you can see, this person suffers about a 50-dB hearing loss in the mid- and upper-frequency range, the region where much of the bell's sound lies. Will this person be able to hear the phone ringing?

As mentioned in the previous chapter, sound intensity falls off with the square of the distance between the source and the listener. So in order to hear the phone's ring, this hearing-impaired person must be within about 8 feet of the phone. Beyond this distance, the sound may be too weak to be heard. This analysis assumes ideal conditions—no distracting noises and no large objects such as walls or doors to intercept the phone's acoustic energy before it reaches the ears. Incidentally, people with normal hearing would have no trouble hearing such a bell, even over distances of several hundred feet or through walls and doors.

Let's continue with this example by assuming that the hearing-impaired person manages to hear the phone and answers it. Will that person have difficulty understanding the voice on the other end of the line? To find out, we must know something about the frequency content of human speech. Figure 11.6 shows the region of the frequency spectrum responsible for conveying speech sounds. Note that acoustic energy in speech spans the range from 250 Hz to about 8,000 Hz. As the diagram shows, vowel sounds consist primarily of low frequencies while consonants cover very nearly the entire range. Of the consonant sounds, the nasal ones (such as *m*) are the lowest in frequency and the fricatives (such as *f*) are the highest. In terms of their relative intensities, vowel sounds tend to be stronger than consonants, meaning that at normal speaking levels, vowels produce larger variations in sound-wave pressure.

Armed with this information, consider the plight of the hearing-impaired individual whose AF is depicted in Figure 11.5. To understand how a telephone conversation will sound in such a case, let's first examine how the telephone itself alters the frequency composition of the voice it transmits. Modern telephones transmit frequencies only up to about 4,000 Hz, which means that the very highest frequencies contained in normal speech are missing during a phone conversation. Since people are easily able to carry on a phone conversation, these omitted frequencies must be unnecessary for speech comprehension.

For our hearing-impaired person, though, more is missing than just these high frequencies. Even picking up speech frequencies that *are* available over the phone is a problem. This particular person's pattern of hearing loss means that some of the consonants (especially those such as /t/ and /d/ will be heard as mere whispers, if at all. (The slashes, / /, indicate that we are referring to the sounds of these characters, not to their names as letters of the alphabet.) These consonants, in fact, are some of the most important ingredients in speech. So a person with an AF of the type shown in Figure 11.5 will have difficulty hearing some of the environment's most important sounds, those of human speech. Simple words such as *time* and

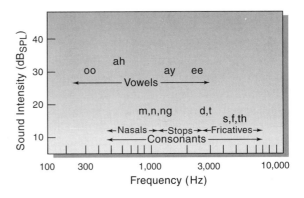

FIGURE 11.6
The region of the sound spectrum responsible for conveying speech sounds. Vowel sounds are primarily of low frequency; consonants cover almost the entire range.

dime may be mistaken for one another, which in turn may make whole sentences confusing.

Clearly, then, a person does not need to be totally deaf in order to experience the frustrations of unintelligible speech. In a way, the plight of hearing-impaired people is particularly difficult since they hear speech sounds but are confused by the meanings. No wonder some hard-of-hearing people, including the elderly as well as young children with congenital hearing impairments (Hindley, 1997), find it easier simply to avoid social encounters.

People with good hearing can gain some understanding of the disturbing consequences of impaired hearing by wearing ear plugs for a few hours. Those who have done so testify to the psychological importance of nonverbal sounds (Eriksson-Mangold and Erlandsson, 1984). You should try this disquieting exercise yourself. In a sports or drug store you can purchase inexpensive ear plugs producing a 30 dB reduction in sound level. Note that a 30 dB hearing loss is sufficient to interfere with speech perception (Nadol, 1993).

Compensating for Hearing Loss

Hearing Aids For those suffering mild to moderate hearing loss, simply amplifying the acoustic signal by wearing a hearing aid may provide some help, assuming the person learns to use the device correctly and uses it regularly (Tesch-Römer, 1997). Hearing aids convert sound into electrical signals, amplifying those signals by up to 60 dB, and then converting the amplified signals back into sound energy. Good hearing aids are designed to amplify mainly those frequencies necessary for adequate speech comprehension, 250 to 4,000 Hz. Thus, other sounds, such as music, may seem distorted (much like nonspeech sounds heard over a telephone).

Although not as effective as a modern electronic hearing aid, the simplest, most popular hearing aid is the hand. When the hand is cupped and placed behind the pinna, extra sound waves are funneled into the ear, raising the intensity by as much as 6 dB. Actually, any device or action signalling that an individual is hearing impaired improves hearing, for other people tend to speak louder if a listener is thought to have impaired hearing. Even a string dangling from one's ear can serve as an effective hearing aid (Gregory 1992).

Cochlear Implants   Unfortunately, there are conditions in which hearing is completely lost, leaving the person with no sound perception whatsoever. In these cases, hearing aids are useless. If complete deafness results from destruction of the auditory nerve or auditory portions of the brain, there is currently nothing that can be done to relieve the condition. However, if deafness results from damage to the cochlea's hair cells and if the rest of the auditory system remains intact, there is hope for some recovery of auditory perception. A series of tiny electrodes can be surgically implanted in the cochlea itself and used to activate auditory nerve fibers directly. Called a **cochlear implant,** this tiny device can be a highly useful substitute for the nonfunctioning hair cells. By appropriate adjustment of the timing and level of electrical current passed through the array of electrodes, auditory nerve fiber stimulation can produce an experience of sound. The patient will experience sound sensations that vary in pitch, depending on where

along the cochlea stimulation is delivered, and on the timing of the pulses.

To attain functional hearing, the person with the implant wears a small microphone that picks up sounds in the environment. Those sounds are transmitted to an electronic sound processor (a small digital chip) that separates sound signals into different bands of frequencies. These, in turn, are converted into patterns of electrical stimulation of particular sets of electrodes in an array whose tips are in contact with auditory nerve fibers. Cochlear implants don't come close to restoring normal hearing, but they do allow profoundly deaf individuals, including congenitally deaf children, to achieve modest levels of speech recognition (Miyamoto et al., 1997; Svirsky et al., 2000). These auditory protheses have been successfully implanted in more than 30,000 deaf patients of all ages (Nicolelis, 2001).

A recent neurophysiological study showed that congenitally deaf cats outfitted with cochlear implants had larger auditory portions of the brain and generated stronger, more effective neural signals, compared to deaf littermates who did not receive implants (Klinke et al., 1999). This important finding suggests that cochlear implants in congenitally deaf humans may work best when implanted early in life, while the brain's connections are highly malleable (Rauschecker, 1999; Lee et al., 2001).

The technology involved in cochlear implants is still in its infancy, and the effectiveness of these prosthetic devices will undoubtedly improve as better circuitry and stimulating arrays are developed. Newer implants can produce very rapid temporal variations in stimulation rate, thereby crudely simulating speech's variations in temporal structure (Shannon, 1995). Despite their ability to open the doors of hearing to the profoundly deaf, cochlear implants are not without controversy. In particular, some people strenuously object that cochlear implants in young, congenitally deaf children supplant other methods of communication available to the deaf, including American Sign Language and other sign languages. As a consequence, they argue, the child is isolated from the

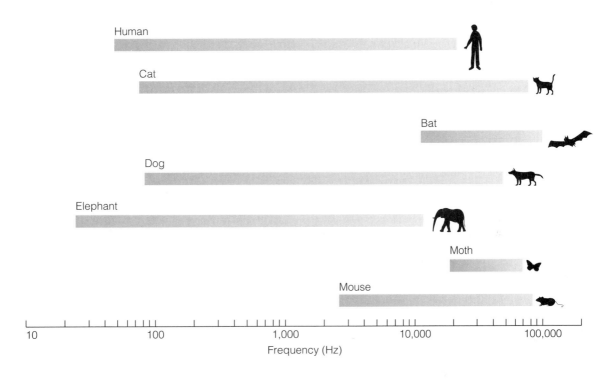

FIGURE 11.7
The range of sound frequencies audible to various species at a fixed intensity of 60 dB$_{SPL}$. (Data for the moth from Fullard and Barclay, 1980; data for all other species from Heffner and Heffner, 1985.)

deaf community as well as from the hearing community. Dolnick (1993) provides an evenhanded discussion of both sides of the argument.

Maybe the day will come when damaged hair cells can be replaced by newly grown, normal ones. Researchers are currently working on regenerating auditory hair cells using neurochemical agents that stimulate cell growth (Lefebvre et al., 1993). At the same time, tantalizing clues are emerging about the genetic instructions that initiate and inhibit cell growth. Such discoveries may eventually lead to interventions that halt or reverse auditory hair cell degeneration (Steel, 1998).

The Range of Hearing in Animals

Differences

Audibility function reveals important aspects of an individual's perceptual world. The same point can be made by comparing the AFs of different animal species. Look at Figure 11.7. Each horizontal bar shows the range of frequencies audible to a particular species. As you can see, there is quite a diversity among animals. Many members of the animal kingdom can hear sounds outside the limits of the human ear (Fay, 1988). For example, dogs have no trouble hearing the high frequencies emitted by a device called a dog whistle, although those frequencies are at the upper limits of the human ear.

One sound that no human will ever hear is the stream of very high frequencies that bats emit. This acoustic energy bounces off objects in the bat's flight path and then echo back to the bat. As Figure 11.7 indicates, bats are able to hear these frequencies, and they use them to navigate (Griffin, 1959; Suga, 1990). As an aside, bats would deafen themselves if they heard their high frequency screeches as they are emitted. To avoid this catastrophe, the bat's ear contains a built-in mechanism that very briefly shuts down the middle ear while the screech is emitted. Then, in a fraction of a second, the ear returns to its normal sensitivity, allowing the bat to hear and react to the echoes from the screech.

So far we have concentrated on normal and abnormal hearing in humans and in animals as specified by pure-tone thresholds measured under quiet conditions. Of course, most of the sounds one usually encounters are heard against some background level of noise. As it turns out, pure-tone thresholds measured in the presence of noise reveal fundamentally important properties of hearing, properties that relate to the registration of different sound frequencies. So let's turn now to consideration of this widely studied problem.

NOISE MASKING AND CRITICAL BANDS

Execute

From common, everyday experiences, you're already familiar with the phenomenon known as auditory **masking.** It happens whenever some background noise makes it more difficult for you to hear a weak sound. Imagine listening for the phone to ring in the next room while you're taking a shower. The steady noise of the water makes the ring much harder to hear. Or think about listening to your car radio while driving on a busy expressway. To hear your radio, you must crank up the volume to compensate for the road noises.

When auditory masking is studied in the laboratory, investigators often use pure tones and specially crafted forms of background noise. As you would expect, the detection threshold for a pure tone is elevated when that tone is presented coincident with noise. This elevation in threshold constitutes auditory masking. The magnitude of masking can be conveniently expressed as the difference between masked and unmasked thresholds. The magnitude of masking varies with the noise level, which makes sense intuitively: intense noise yields greater masking

(greater threshold elevation) than does moderate noise. But another, equally important determinant of masking effectiveness is the frequency content of the noise relative to the tone. This relation deserves careful analysis, for it reveals important properties of the neural processes underlying hearing.

To explore this point, we need to develop some notation. In the examples that follow, the listener has one, fixed task: to detect a pure tone of a given frequencey—call that frequency Hz_t—presented either alone or in the presence of noise. In the last chapter, noise was characterized as a complex of sound composed of energy at many different frequencies. When noise contains energy at all audible frequencies it is called **broadband noise** and, perceptually, it resembles the sound made by a steady waterfall. The diagram in the middle panel of Figure 11.8 pictorially represents the energy spectrum of broadband noise, with the area under the rectangle defining the frequencies present in the noise. In the laboratory, unlike in nature, the intensity of broadband noise can be systematically varied, which would correspond to varying the height of the rectangle in the graph. (In fact, energy levels in noise vary randomly within limits from moment to moment; the rectangular shape shown in the drawings is meant to depict the average noise level over time.)

In the lab, it is also possible to restrict the range of frequencies contained within the noise by passing the noise through an electronic filter; alternatively, a computer can be used to synthesize noise of specified frequency content. Using either technique, suppose we remove energy from the low- and high-frequency ends of the broadband noise spectrum. This form of energy filtering creates what is called **bandpass noise.** Pictorially, this reduces the width of the rectangle (see the graphs in the left and right panels of Figure 11.8). Perceptually it makes the noise sound different in quality and reduced in intensity. It is possible to vary systematically the width of bandpass noise while keeping the center of the distribution at the same point along the frequency spectrum. This noise

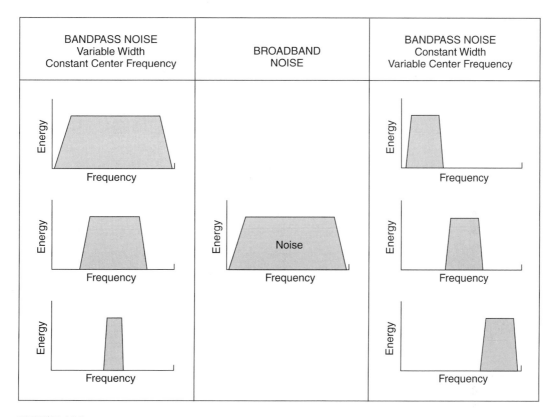

FIGURE 11.8
Schematics of the frequency distribution of acoustic energy content of noise—the shaded area in each drawing represents the presence of energy. The middle panel shows broadband noise—energy covering the entire audible spectrum. The two side panels show noise from which energy at low and high frequencies has been removed. This form of filtering produces what is called bandpass noise. The spectra in the left-hand panel show three examples of bandpass noise whose bandwidth varies and whose center frequency remains constant. The spectra in the right-hand panel show noise whose bandwidth remains constant and whose center frequency varies.

center point is called the **center frequency.** Examples of this type of bandpass filtering are shown in the left-hand column. Alternatively, it is possible to keep the width of the noise constant but vary its center frequency, in effect moving the noise package along the horizontal axis. Examples of this type of filtering are shown in the right-hand column of Figure 11.8.

With these concepts in mind, let's see how the detectability of a pure tone of frequency Hz_t might be affected by various kinds of noise. First, suppose we again measure the threshold for a test

tone of Hz_t while varying the bandwidth of the bandpass noise and holding the noise's center frequency constant at the frequency of the test, Hz_t (the manipulation depicted in the left-hand column of Figure 11.8). The result would look something like the graph in the upper panel of Figure 11.9, which plots threshold elevation against noise bandwidth; the inset serves as a reminder that the noise center frequency matches the tone frequency. The far left-hand value represents the threshold measured in the absence of noise—the unmasked threshold.

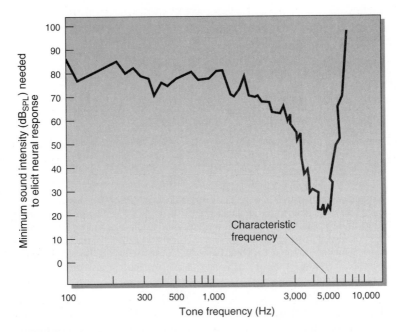

FIGURE 11.9

Upper panel: Hypothetical result from a noise masking experiment. Intensity thresholds for detection of a given pure-tone frequency are plotted as the function of the width of bandpass noise within which the tone must be detected. Threshold increases with noise bandwidth, up to a critical band beyond which threshold remains constant even though noise energy increases. Upper panel inset: Schematics of narrow and wide bandpass noise used in hypothetical experiment; note that noise is centered about Hz_t. Lower panel: Tuning curve for an auditory nerve fiber maximally responsive to the test frequency used in the masking experiment. The activity level in this fiber will increase as the bandwidth of the noise is increased, as long as the added frequencies fall within the tuning curve of the fiber. Frequencies outside this curve will have no effect on the fiber's activity.

Once noise is introduced, the tone is harder to hear, as indicated by the steady increase in threshold. Widening the bandwidth of the noise produces greater and greater threshold elevation, which makes sense because the tone must be detected in the presence of more and more noise energy. Significantly, though, there is a critical bandwidth beyond which threshold is not further elevated even though additional energy is added to the noise and it sounds louder. This indicates, then, that only a limited portion of the energy in broadband noise acts to mask a tone. This effective portion was termed the **critical band** by Fletcher (1940). Why should noise energy outside the critical band have no influence on the audibility of a tone? What, in other words, is the basis for the critical band?

A clue to the answer appears in figures 10.24 and 10.25, which show tuning curves for auditory nerve fibers. One of those curves is reproduced in the bottom panel of Figure 11.9, the curve for a fiber whose characteristic frequency (the one to which it is most sensitive) corresponds to Hz_t (the test frequency used in the hypothetical masking experiment). Since this fiber is the most sensitive to the test frequency, it mediates pure-tone detection at threshold. Of course, the fiber will also be activated neurally by noise, if that noise contains energy at frequencies to which the fiber responds.

The presence of noise, then, creates a background of elevated neural activity against which the neural activity arising from the tone must be discriminated. To produce a signal discriminable from this background noise, the tone's intensity must be higher than when the background noise is absent. The stronger the influence of the noise on the fiber's activity, the more intense the tone must be to create a signal audible within this noise.

With this in mind, think again about the result depicted in the upper panel of Figure 11.9. Presumably, the magnitude of masking increases with bandwidth because widening the bandpass noise adds more and more frequencies that stimulate the fibers mediating detection of the tone.* Increasing the bandwidth, in other words, in-

creases the fiber's background activity, making it harder to detect the tone. But at some point, additional frequencies associated with wider bandwidths fall outside the tuning curve for the fiber and, therefore, have no further effect on its background activity. At this point, there is no further elevation in threshold; masking remains constant.

Following this line of reasoning, then, the inflection point in the masking function defines the frequency limits, or tuning width, of the fiber(s) used for detection of the tone. (We use the term *fiber(s)* to denote that detection of a pure tone is probably based on activity within a set of fibers, not a single fiber, all with the same preferred frequency.) Adding more frequencies activates other fibers with different characteristic frequencies, causing the noise to get louder and to sound richer in quality. But those additional frequencies fall outside the critical bandwidth of the fiber(s) responsive to the test. This notion of the critical band in hearing should remind you of the spatial frequency channels described in Chapter 5 and measured using an adaptation procedure analogous to the masking technique described here.

Suppose we repeat the masking experiment, this time using bandpass noise of constant width but varying center frequency (the manipulation depicted in the right-hand column of Figure 11.8). Results from this procedure resemble an inverted U-shaped curve. When the center frequency of the noise is well below the test frequency, the noise is audible but ineffective as a masker. Presumably, none of the noise energy stimulates the neuron(s) responsive to the test. Not until the noise begins to encroach upon the tuning curve of the detecting neuron(s) will threshold increase, and masking will grow to a maximum as more and more of the noise stimulates these neuron(s). As the center

---

*Nerve fibers alone, of course, are not responsible for detection of tones; activity in auditory nerve fibers is passed on to neurons at higher stages in the auditory pathways which participate in hearing. But it is reasonable to consider the effects of noise on auditory nerve fibers, for masking effects arising at this level will be transmitted to higher levels.

frequency of the noise exceeds this maximum, less of the noise falls within the critical bandwidth. Masking is reduced until, finally, the threshold equals the unmasked level. So varying the center frequency of bandpass noise also generates evidence for a critical band in hearing.

These two examples portray the essence of the critical band: the detection of pure tones by neural processes tuned for frequency. Both employed bandpass noise and both involved varying the intensity of the test tone to measure its threshold.

There are many variations on this masking procedure. Some experiments, for instance, employ different filtering regimes for producing the masking noise, such as removing frequencies from the *center* of the noise spectrum, not its extremes, thereby producing a notch in the energy spectrum. In other experiments, the intensity of the noise, not the tone, is varied to find the level that just barely masks a pure tone of fixed intensity. In still other experiments, a brief interval of time is inserted between the onset of the tone and the onset of the masking noise. While the details of the resulting masking curves vary with the particulars of these experiments, the general conclusion remains unchanged: noise is effective as a mask only when it contains frequencies at or near the frequency of the test tone (see Moore [1986] for a thorough review of the auditory masking literature).

In some (but not all) these experiments, the resulting masking curves—masking strength as the function of the frequency content of the noise—resemble the tuning curves of auditory nerve fibers. For instance, a tone of given frequency is more effectively masked by noise whose frequency composition is a bit lower than the tone compared to noise composed of frequencies higher than the tone. The critical band, in other words, appears more broadly tuned on the low-frequency side. This asymmetry in masking effectiveness dovetails nicely with the asymmetric shape of auditory nerve tuning curves (recall Figure 10.24).

The importance of the critical band cannot be overstated. It plays a pivotal role in theories of tone detection, loudness perception and pitch discrimination. Critical bands in hearing represent an important, initial stage of auditory processing potentially related to the function of the cochlea and the auditory nerve.

In these next several sections, we'll survey characteristics of sounds—loudness, pitch and timbre—that contribute to a hearer's ability to specify the identity and location of various sounds.

LOUDNESS PERCEPTION AND DISCRIMINATION

How Loud Is Loud?

Everyone knows what is meant by **loudness**—it's your subjective impression of the intensity of sound. And most people would have no trouble agreeing whether one sound is louder than another, indicating that we all employ the concept of loudness in the same way. Yet despite this agreement, there is no way to compare each other's impressions of loudness directly. Loudness remains a subjective experience that cannot be measured with an instrument. Instead, we must rely on language to talk about the perception of loudness. By the same token, there is no way to determine whether your judgment of a sound's loudness is right or wrong, for there is no right or wrong answer—a sound's loudness *is* whatever you experience.

Execute

These constraints immediately raise a barrier against attempts to study loudness perception. Fortunately, psychologists have gotten around this limitation by devising effective procedures for measuring perceived sensory magnitude, including loudness. As applied to hearing, one of these procedures requires the person to adjust the loudness of one sound until it is equivalent to the loudness of another; this method is called **loudness matching.** Another method treats the perceiver as a measuring instrument capable of assigning numbers to sounds in proportion to their loudness; this method is generally known as

magnitude estimation. More details on those procedures are given in the Appendix. The following summarizes some key features of loudness perception.

First, loudness depends on the frequency content of the sound being heard. At a given intensity level, the loudness of a very high frequency sound will be less than the loudness of a medium frequency sound of the same dB$_{SPL}$ level. And, comparably, the loudness of low frequency tones tends to be less than that of medium frequency tones. The relation between loudness and frequency is shown in Figure 11.10, which shows a family of curves, each one summarizing the intensity levels that make tones of different frequencies sound equal in loudness (Fletcher and Munson, 1933). Such curves are called **equal loudness contours,** and they are produced simply by having listeners adjust the loudness values of a set of tones until they all match the loudness of a reference tone. Notice, at least for moderately loud sounds, that low frequencies tend to

sound weaker than higher frequencies of the same intensity. Manufacturers of audio equipment know this, and they design their amplifiers to allow listeners to give low frequencies a little extra boost in intensity. Such amplifiers typically have a "loudness" switch on the front of the unit, to let the listener choose the desired amount of low-frequency boost.

The curves in Figure 11.10 tell us how the loudness of one tone compares with the loudness of others. What these curves don't tell us is just how loud a given tone sounds, and how that tone's loudness varies with intensity. Does doubling the intensity of a sound double its loudness? To answer this kind of question, we can ask listeners to assign numbers to tones of different intensity levels, making sure that those numbers are proportional to the tone's loudness. This is the *magnitude estimation* technique we mentioned above. When these measurements are performed, we find that doubling sound intensity does *not* double loudness. Instead, loudness increases by

FIGURE 11.10
Equal loudness contours.

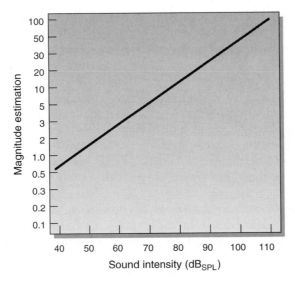

FIGURE 11.11
The growth of loudness plotted on logarithmic axes.

only about 60 percent. To double the loudness of a sound, its intensity must be approximately tripled, which corresponds to about a 10-dB increase in intensity. This means, for example, that two people singing at the top of their lungs will not sound twice as loud as one of them singing alone. Instead, the duet's singing will sound about 1.6 times louder than a solo. To double the loudness produced by one singer requires adding two additional singers.

Figure 11.11 graphically illustrates the relation between loudness and intensity. Note that both variables are scaled logarithmically. (Recall from the previous chapter that the decibel is a logarithmic unit.) Notice that the slope of the line is less than 1.0, reflecting the fact that loudness grows more slowly than intensity, as described above. (The Appendix further discusses magnitude estimation, including its application to senses other than hearing.) Incidentally, the measurement of loudness is not limited to pure tones. People are also able to rate the loudness of sounds consisting of many frequencies (Zwicker and Scharf, 1965), including noise—which, as

you learned in the previous chapter, consists of all audible frequencies. As a rule, the loudness of complex sounds can be predicted by adding up the loudness contributions from the component frequencies, making allowance for the ability of one sound to reduce, or mask, the loudness of others.

Neural Bases of Loudness Perception

What happens within the auditory system as the loudness of a sound varies? What, in other words, is the neural code for loudness? The most obvious answer is that the discharge rate of auditory neurons increases with sound level, and this constitutes the information for loudness. After all, we did learn in the last chapter that the activity of auditory neurons increases with intensity (recall Figure 10.26). However, while discharge rate is probably involved in the coding of loudness, it alone cannot be the whole explanation (Zeng and Shannon, 1994; Relkin and Doucet, 1997). The reason is that auditory nerve fibers increase their firing rate over a limited range of sound intensities; this range typically covers only about 40 dB (Kiang, 1968). Yet one can hear variations in the loudness of sounds over a much larger range, around 120 dB. So one's range of loudness perception exceeds the range that can be coded by individual neurons.

The nervous system has two ways to overcome the relatively limited range of individual neurons. First, as we pointed out in Chapter 10, different neurons operate over different levels of sound intensity. One set of neurons, for instance, responds to intensity changes ranging from 20 dB_{SPL} to 60 dB_{SPL}, another set responds to intensity changes ranging from 40 dB_{SPL} to 80 dB_{SPL} and a third, to intensities ranging from 60 dB_{SPL} to 100 dB_{SPL}. As you can see, each *set* covers only a 40-dB range, but as a *population* the neurons would then span an 80-dB range of intensities.

Neurons responsive to different intensity ranges would be fairly simple to "construct." It could be done by adjusting the intensity level where different neurons first start to respond. As pointed out in Chapter 10, physiological evidence points to the existence of three categories of auditory nerve fibers, distinguished by their different threshold intensities and their different points of contact on the IHCs. For the coding of loudness information, then, one way to overcome the limited range of individual neurons is to design them to operate within different intensity ranges.

There is a second possible way that increasing sound levels may produce greater and greater neural activity, and this has to do with the tuning curves for individual auditory nerve fibers. Recall that single fibers respond to a limited range of temporal frequencies, with the preferred frequency varying from fiber to fiber (see Figure 10.24). At weak sound levels, the only fibers to respond will be those whose preferred frequencies match the frequencies contained in the sound; fibers preferring other frequencies will be unresponsive at these low sound levels. However, it is possible to recruit some of those fibers into activity by raising the sound level. At higher levels, the sound (though it does not contain those

fibers' preferred frequencies) *will* produce activity in such fibers because their tuning curves do encompass frequencies contained in the sound. We caught a hint of this spread of activity in the previous chapter, where it was noted that more intense sounds caused the traveling wave to spread out over a larger region of the basilar membrane. This is tantamount to recruiting more and more nerve fibers into action at higher and higher sound levels.

Loudness Discrimination

We turn next to loudness discrimination: the ability to tell whether one sound is louder than another. This sort of judgment can be of practical importance. Imagine, for instance, that your roommate next door is playing his stereo so loudly that you can't study. You beg him to turn it down a little, and he says he will. Just by listening, how do you tell if your roommate has kept his promise? Of course, you would have no trouble hearing a large drop in intensity, but what if the drop was more subtle? How sharp is your ability to discriminate intensity changes, and what transpires within your auditory system when you make such a discrimination?

In the laboratory, intensity discrimination can be measured by varying the intensity of a tone very gradually until a person first notices that it has gotten louder. This minimum necessary increase in intensity specifies the person's **discrimination threshold.** Although the actual value of the threshold varies, depending on the details of the experiment, people typically require about a 1- to 2-dB increase in intensity to be able to notice any increase in loudness.

A listener probably achieves such keen performance by detecting an increment in the level of neural activity produced by the tone. In the example above, the most informative neural activity would arise within that subset of neurons maximally responsive to the tone's frequency. For instance, if the tone is 1,000 Hz, the listener should monitor neurons whose center frequency is 1,000 Hz (recall our discussion of the critical band in the previous section).

But in real life, most sounds are more complex than the pure tones used in this example. Sometimes a complex set of frequencies changes its intensities in unison, and that change must be heard in the midst of many other frequency components whose intensities are also changing. For example, an alert driver can tell that a truck's engine is malfunctioning when its high-pitched whine becomes louder than the other sounds made by the truck. In effect, the driver hears a change in the intensity of one set of frequencies (the high-pitched whine) in the midst of other sounds. The driver's perceptual task is complicated. When driven slowly, all the truck's sounds—high-pitched whine included— are weak; when driven faster, all the sounds are louder. A number of years ago, David Green offered a compelling explanation of how people detect such intensity changes in the midst of other changeable components.

Green (1982) acknowledges that if a listener only has to detect the intensity changes of a single tone heard against an unvarying background, the traditional view is correct: only one subset of neurons needs to be monitored, namely those tuned to the frequency of the varying intensity tone. But when other frequencies are present and their intensities are also changing from one moment to the next (as in the truck driver's situation), Green believes, a more complex process comes into play. This process uses neural information about the *relative* activity across different subsets of neurons. Green calls this process **profile analysis** because the relative neural response to various frequency bands could be represented graphically as a profile. According to Green, in an acoustically rich environment the listener picks up intensity changes by detecting a variation in the profile of activity. (This idea should be familiar to you from our discussions of orientation, spatial frequency, color and motion perception.) To see where Green's view came from, let's consider two of his experiments.

In one experiment, Green, Kidd and Picardi (1983) created a complex sound consisting of twenty-one different tones, ranging in frequency from 300 to 3,000 Hz, all played simultaneously. He presented this set of tones twice on each trial. In one presentation, all twenty-one tones were identical in intensity; in the other presentation, the intensity of one tone (1,000 Hz) was slightly greater than the intensity of the other twenty tones. The listener's task was to identify the interval in which the 1,000-Hz tone had been incremented.

Green made the task even more difficult by randomizing the *overall* intensity of the package of tones from one presentation to the next. For example, in the first presentation all the tones might be 20 dB_{SPL} in intensity, while in the second presentation they might all be 50 dB_{SPL}. The exception, of course, was the 1,000-Hz tone, which was slightly more intense than its companions during one of the two presentations. Though the 1,000-Hz tone would be incremented *relative* to the rest, its *absolute* level of intensity would provide no clue whatever to the interval in which it had been incremented. This procedure made it impossible for the listener to base a judgment on the amount of neural activity produced by the 1,000 Hz alone. The listener was forced to compare the activity produced by the 1,000-Hz tone to the activity produced by its companions.

Execute

Using these complex tones, Green determined the minimum increment of the 1,000-Hz tone that could be heard. Despite having to rely on *relative* intensity information alone, listeners were able to detect remarkably small increments in loudness. In fact, in some instances, the detectable increment in the complex sound was about as small as that measured for the 1,000-Hz tone on its own.

In the second experiment, Green and his colleagues varied the number of different tones that accompanied the 1,000-Hz tone. Starting with a very few companion tones, Green found that adding additional tones actually *improved* a listener's ability to hear small increments in the 1,000-Hz tone. Presumably, the additional tones sharpened the definition of the neural activity profile utilized by the listener. These results and others (Green and Nguyen, 1988) show how useful profile analysis might be in explaining hearing performance in certain real-life situations.

Loudness and intensity discrimination alone seldom allow you to identify a sound source. You also need information about the frequencies composing that sound. This brings us to the topic of pitch perception.

PITCH PERCEPTION

What Is Pitch?

Pitch—like loudness—is an entirely subjective experience. Unlike loudness, however, which can be related systematically to intensity, pitch has no single physical dimension to which it corresponds. Different sorts of sounds, both simple and complex, can have the quality of pitch. Generally speaking, **pitch** refers to that aspect of hearing that allows sounds to be ordered from low to high. A few examples will help, starting with relatively simple tones.

Perhaps you have seen a set of metal tuning forks. Each fork varies in size, which means that when struck against a hard surface, each fork vibrates at a different frequency, producing what is called a pure tone. The perceptual quality associated with these different frequencies we call *pitch*. A tuning fork that vibrates at a low frequency, such as 500 Hz, will sound lower in pitch than a tuning fork that vibrates at a higher frequency, say, 1,000 Hz.

A set of crystal glasses filled with different amounts of water will also generate pure tones when struck lightly. In this case, a glass that is almost filled to the top with water will produce a lower-pitched tone than the same-sized glass containing just a little water. Again, these differences in pitch are associated with different frequencies of vibration, as determined by the volume of water filling the glass. In fact, using enough glasses you can create a sufficient num-

ber of different tones to play a tune. (As mentioned in Chapter 10, Mozart composed a piece—"Glass Armonica Adagio in C Minor and Rondo in C Major" (K. 617)—for a string ensemble and crystal glasses!)

The notes played on a musical instrument will also give you some appreciation of the relation between frequency and pitch, even though an instrument's sound is not a genuine pure tone. (We'll tell you why in a moment.) Take, for example, the piano. Each and every note on a properly tuned piano produces a sound of predominantly one frequency; that frequency is called the **fundamental frequency.** As you probably know, a musical note on the piano is produced when a small hammer strikes a string, causing it to vibrate. Strings differ in length, and the shorter ones vibrate more rapidly than the longer ones. Consequently, the shorter strings (which are struck by keys located toward the right-hand end of the keyboard) produce higher-pitched notes than the longer strings (which are struck by keys toward the left-hand end of the keyboard).

Figure 11.12 shows the fundamental frequencies associated with the notes on a piano's keyboard. *Frequency* changes in regular steps (or intervals) as you move from the low notes at the far left of the piano to the high ones at the far right. *Pitch*—your perception of the musical sounds produced by those keys—changes in the same step-wise fashion. Played in sequence from left to right, the notes are heard as the steps on the musical scale. The range of frequencies produced by a piano, 27.5 Hz to 4,186 Hz, is narrower than the total range of frequencies audible to the ear of a young adult (20 Hz to 20,000 Hz). Still, the notes on keyboard instruments such as the piano should give you some idea of how pitch changes with frequency, at least for periodic sounds like musical notes. Incidentally, the ability to discriminate tones on the basis of frequency alone appears to be one that improves with practice. That practice effect can be traced to changes within the auditory cortex, as described in Box 11.1.

FIGURE 11.12
The fundamental frequencies associated with the notes on a piano's keyboard.

Pitch and Frequency Are Not Synonymous
So far we have treated pitch and frequency as though they were two sides of the same coin. In reality, however, the two are dissociable. In some conditions, tones of fixed frequency sound different in pitch. For instance, the loudness of a pure tone influences that tone's pitch. You can experience this yourself by comparing the pitch of a vibrating tuning fork held at arm's length to the pitch of that same tuning fork held close to your ear. Held close to your ear, the tuning fork's note will of course sound louder, but you'll also hear that its pitch changes, too. For instance, a tuning fork vibrating at 300 Hz sounds lower in pitch as intensity increases, even though its frequency remains constant. In contrast, a tuning fork vibrating at 3,000 Hz sounds higher in pitch as intensity increases.

The pitch of a pure tone of fixed frequency may also vary when that tone is heard within a background of noise. In particular, noise composed of frequencies lower than a tone cause the pitch of the tone to appear higher than it does

when heard on its own; noise higher in frequency than the tone causes its pitch to sound lower.

One of the most intriguing dissociations between pitch and frequency is the perception of the **missing fundamental.** To explain this phenomenon requires introducing the concept of **harmonics,** which can be accomplished most easily with an example. Any musical note played on an instrument produces not only a fundamental frequency but also a unique set of additional frequency components called harmonics. These harmonics arise because the object producing the sound (a string, a wooden reed, and so forth) has multiple resonant frequencies (recall Box 10.1). To illustrate, Figure 11.13 shows the frequency components produced by a piano when middle C is played. (Each vertical line in the graph means that the instrument is producing sound energy at that frequency. The height of the line indicates the amount of energy, or intensity, present in that frequency.) The fundamental frequency, represented by the bold vertical line, is 261 Hz, and if asked to select a tuning fork whose pitch matched that

BOX 11.1

PRACTICE ALTERS THE BRAIN

Plasticity

In earlier chapters you read how visual abilities improve with practice. The same is true of hearing. It is well known, for example, that experience helps people improve their accuracy in tuning musical instruments (Platt and Racine, 1985). We now have an idea about the neural concomitant of this practice effect. A recent study of auditory training revealed remarkable plasticity in both frequency discrimination and the trainee's brain. Attempting to train monkeys to make finer discriminations of frequency, Recanzone, Schreiner and Merzenich (1993) gauged improvement behaviorally and then used physiological techniques to examine possible changes accompanying the improvement. During the behavioral phase of the study, tones were presented as a series of pairs. For most pairs, the tones were of the same frequency. Whenever the tones differed in frequency, the monkey signaled recognition of the difference by lifting its hand from a key. Monkeys were trained to discriminate a standard frequency from one that was slightly different. For example, several monkeys were trained to discriminate a tone of 5,000 Hz from one somewhat higher. Over many trials, the monkeys were trained with several different standard frequencies, learning, for each, to discriminate it from a higher frequency. Performance was described in terms of the discrimination threshold, the smallest difference reliably detected by the monkey (see Appendix). During the course of training, frequency discrimination improved by as much as fivefold. Moreover, improvement was restricted to the training frequency. So, for example, if the monkey were being trained with a standard of 8,000 Hz, there would be no improvement of the threshold at 2,000 Hz.

The physiological phase of the study examined responses of neurons in the monkey's auditory cortex while various tones were being presented to the monkey's ear. In normal, untrained monkeys the auditory cortex contains a frequency map, with neurons tuned to different frequencies occupying different regions of the cortex. In monkeys who had been trained, there were also maps, but Recanzone and colleagues found the regions of the map devoted to the trained frequencies to be greatly expanded. In fact, the size of these regions correlated strongly with the monkeys' behavioral thresholds: larger areas were associated with lower thresholds for frequency discrimination. This relation between cortical area and perceptual function is reminiscent of cortical magnification (Chapter 4), wherein areas of the retina with greater spatial resolving power are represented over larger areas of the visual cortex. Here, in the auditory system, the amount of cortex devoted to particular frequencies apparently grew as frequency discrimination improved for those frequencies.

Not every monkey in Recanzone's study exhibited cortical changes. Monkeys who listened passively to the training stimuli but did not have to make any discrimination showed little if any change in the auditory cortex. Training requires more than passive listening; the stimuli must be relevant to the animal's behavior.

Neuroimaging studies point to the same kind of plasticity in auditory portions of the human brain. In highly skilled musicians, the cortical representation of musical tones is enlarged by approximately 25 percent when compared to the tonotopic maps in the brains of nonmusicians (Pantev et al., 1998). Musical experience has an additional impact on the brains of musicians who make their music by conducting orchestras. A conductor faces special challenges, attending to the whole orchestra and to its various sections, but at the same time hearing individual musicians within each section. For example, during rehearsal a conductor may need to identify which one of an orchestra's 20 violinists played the wrong note. This requires an extraordinary ability to attend to sounds originating at the same time from a wide range of locations and directions. An ERP study has shown that locations of sound sources in peripheral auditory space are much more differentiated in the brains of professional conductors than they are in the brains of non-musicians or in musicians who are not conductors (Münte et al., 2001). These results demonstrate that extensive sensory experience leaves lasting marks on sensory areas of the brain and expands one's sensory abilities.

FIGURE 11.13
Acoustic energy is produced at multiple, harmonically related frequencies when a
given note is played on the piano (or any other musical instrument). This particular
set of frequencies is associated with middle C.

associated with middle C, you would select one that produced this frequency. But suppose we played a sound containing exactly these same higher harmonics but omitted this fundamental. What would be the pitch of this missing fundamental sound? Surprisingly, the pitch remains that associated with middle C, even though there is no acoustic energy at 261 Hz. This demonstration, which works for various sorts of sounds including musical notes and the human voice, represents a dramatic dissociation of pitch from frequency.

It's easy to experience the missing fundamental phenomenon for yourself: just listen to music on an inexpensive tape player or radio. The tiny speakers in such devices typically do not reproduce the lower frequency sound components at all. Still, you're able to hear these low frequency musical notes, courtesy of your auditory system's ability to synthesize them using information contained in their higher harmonics.

The phenomenon of the missing fundamental implies that pitch is determined by the pattern of

harmonics associated with a sound, not simply its fundamental frequency. A given type of musical instrument, by the way, generates harmonic patterns that are unique to that instrument. These unique harmonic patterns endow an instrument with its characteristic sound, or **timbre.** The ability to identify various instruments based on sound alone rests on their differences in timbre. For example, look at Figure 11.14 and compare the set frequency components produced when a guitar and an alto saxophone play the same note—one with a fundamental frequency of 196 Hz. Notice that the two instruments, while producing notes equivalent in pitch, are generating different patterns of harmonics (the vertical lines to the right of the fundamental). These so-called "overtones" enable you to tell the guitar note from the one sounded by the saxophone. Here is another dissociation between frequency and pitch: the two instruments are producing markedly different patterns of frequencies, yet both create the same pitch quality.

FIGURE 11.14

The various frequency components when a guitar and an alto saxophone play the same note. Here the note has a fundamental frequency of 196 Hz. (Adapted from Olson, 1967.)

The sound quality associated with pure tones and musical notes is often referred to as *tonal pitch*. But the sensation of pitch isn't confined to these so-called periodic sounds composed of energy harmonically placed throughout the frequency spectrum. Complex, aperiodic sounds such as the whine of an engine or a person's voice have a pitch-like quality, which is termed *nontonal pitch*. Even broadband noise can generate a sensation of pitch when its intensity waxes and wanes regularly over time (a form of intensity variation known as amplitude modulation). We mention these examples of nontonal pitch and illusory pitch because they bear on the question of the neural basis of pitch perception, the topic of the next section.

The Neural Bases of Pitch Perception

Neural

What happens in the auditory system when you perceive a sound as having a particular pitch? To answer this question, think back to the last chapter and the material on the inner ear and the auditory nerve. Recall that the basilar membrane moves up and down in response to sounds impinging on the eardrum, with the crest of this displacement depending on the sound's frequency. This displacement bends the hair cells, and this bending, in turn, triggers neural activity within the portion of the auditory nerve that innervates those hair cells. So what happens when sounds of varying degrees of complexity are heard? Let's start with the simplest situation, listening to a single pure tone.

When the ear is presented with a pure tone, one portion of the basilar membrane will be maximally displaced, a limited set of hair cells will be disturbed and a subset of auditory nerve fibers will be activated. The frequency of a tone could be registered, therefore, by which set of nerve fibers is currently most active. As you will recall from the last chapter, such a theory is referred to as a *place theory;* it has several things in its favor. First, damage to a limited portion of the basilar membrane causes a loss in the ability to hear certain frequencies. The frequencies affected depend on the region of the membrane damaged, as predicted by the place theory (Crowe, Guild and Polvost, 1934). Also consistent with the place theory are the results from a study in which an array of small stimulating electrodes was implanted in one cochlea of a 36-year-old man whose hearing had progressively deteriorated to the point of deafness (McDermott and McKay, 1997). This patient was particularly adept at pitch judgments since, prior to his loss, he had received training in musical instrument tuning. When mild electric current was applied to a single electrode, the man reported hearing a single tone. Different electrodes evoked tone sensations that differed in pitch. Presumably, different electrodes were contacting different fibers in the auditory nerve.

Consequently, the ability of different electrodes to evoke different pitches strengthens the presumed link between activity in individual nerve fibers and pure-tone hearing.

Some aspects of pitch perception, however, cannot be explained by place theory. For instance, frequencies below 1,000 Hz produce a broad pattern of displacement along the basilar membrane. Because of this broad displacement, there is no specific place where the basilar membrane bulges maximally. Yet you have no trouble accurately identifying the pitch of these low-frequency tones. Moreover, a sensation of pitch can be produced by taking a sample of broadband noise, introducing a slight time delay and adding the delayed noise together with the original. The summed noise contains energy at all frequencies, yet we hear a pitch determined by the slight time delay (Yost, Patterson and Sheft, 1996). So, apparently, pitch perception for pure tones depends on something besides place coding.

As an alternative to place, the auditory system could use the firing rate of auditory nerve fibers to register low-frequency information. As you will recall from the previous chapter, this form of neural coding is known as the *temporal theory*. The idea here is that nerve fibers discharge periodically in synchrony with the frequency of the stimulating tone. According to the temporal theory, then, the pitch of a tone corresponds to the periodic firing of nerve fibers. And indeed, nerve fibers can fire in synchrony with tones of moderately low frequency (Rose et al., 1967). Fibers can behave, in other words, like metronomes, generating impulses in time to the frequency of a tone. Thus, information about the tone's pitch could be conveyed by the temporal pattern of fiber activity.

So working in tandem, temporal theory and place theory could convert acoustic signals into the requisite neural signals carrying information about pitch. Those signals would consist of unique patterns of activation over the entire basilar membrane and, by extension, within the ensemble of auditory nerve fibers. (Recall that this idea of ensemble coding of sensory attributes was introduced in Chapter 4, in regard to visual coding of

contour orientation.) These patterns of activation would, in turn, produce patterns of activation within the tonotopically organized neurons of the auditory cortex. Functional neuroimaging techniques have identified areas in the temporal lobe of the human brain, immediately adjacent to primary auditory cortex, that are uniquely activated during pitch perception (Griffiths et al., 1998).

Having discussed the possible neural basis of pitch perception, let's now turn to another question about pitch perception, one concerning individual differences in the ability to identify the pitch of a tone.

Perfect Pitch and Tone Deafness

Some individuals have what is called **perfect pitch**—the ability to vocally reproduce any musical note requested or to name any note that is played. Such individuals are encountered in musical circles, although even among musicians the ability is quite rare (Vernon, 1977). One of the most renowned people with perfect pitch was Wolfgang Amadeus Mozart. It was claimed he could tell when the violin he was playing was tuned differently from one he had played the day before, even if those violins were mistuned by no more than "half a quarter of a tone" (Stevens and Warshofsky, 1965). Because it tends to run in families, perfect pitch used to be regarded as genetic in origin (Seashore, 1938).

This evidence alone, however, is equivocal— family members with perfect pitch are very likely to be musicians and would have received lots of exposure to musical notes, the only kind of sound in nature that allows the development of perfect ptich. More convincing evidence for a genetic component comes from a recent study by Drayna et al, 2001. They found that one component of pitch perception ability is more strongly correlated in identical twins than in fraternal twins, even though both sets of twins presumably would have had comparable exposure to music.

According to one theory, all individuals are born with perfect pitch, but it is trained out of them early in life (Ward, 1970). This unlearning occurs because people are trained to ignore absolute pitch and to attend, instead, to the relations among various pitches. To give an example, you recognize a familiar melody such as "Pop Goes the Weasel" regardless of the key in which it is played. Hence, you perceive a melody not as a specific sequence of notes but rather as a particular relation among notes. In other words, you attend to pitch relations and not to absolute pitch. While this discourages the retention of any ability for perfect pitch you may have had as a youngster, it enables you to enjoy the same musical melodies played or sung in different keys. In this regard, it is noteworthy that people with perfect pitch frequently complain that it is disquieting to listen to a piece of music played in an unusual key—the piece sounds "wrong" (Terhardt and Ward, 1982). Box 11.2 describes additional interesting work on melody perception.

Besides perfect pitch, there is a more common ability known as **relative pitch**—people with relative pitch can identify tonal intervals very accurately, although they are not so accurate at naming the particular notes making up that interval. You can think of tonal intervals in terms of the steps of the musical scale. In particular, a tonal interval is defined by the number of steps that separate a pair of notes. For instance, the first two notes of "My Bonnie Lies over the Ocean" define a larger interval than do the first two notes of "Greensleeves." To be able to recognize and label all these various intervals means you have relative pitch. Many musicians have this ability (Siegel and Siegel, 1977).

Our discussion of pitch perception led to the conclusion that a sound source is defined perceptually by the profile of component frequencies that it produces. This sets the stage for our next question: What stimulus properties promote the perceptual grouping of the constituent frequencies of a given sound source? An answer to this question is crucial for understanding how sounds are recognized.

BOX 11.2

WHAT IS A MELODY?

You don't have to be a musician to recognize musical melodies; that's an ability that comes naturally to just about everyone. Moreover, musicians or not, most people can recognize a familiar melody when it is played in different keys, or on different instruments or when it is sung by different voices. In these cases, the particular notes differ, but the melody remains the same. Just as different type fonts can be used to print the same sentence, different notes can produce the same melody. We hear melodies not as specific sets of notes but as particular relations, or patterns, among notes.

But what aspects of a melody unite musical notes into a pattern? Is it the rise and fall in the pitch of successive notes—the property known technically as **melody contour?** Does it have something to do with the size of the intervals between successive notes? To answer this question, Dowling and Fujitani (1971) asked college undergraduates—most of whom had no musical training—to identify some familiar melodies including "Yankee Doodle," "Oh, Susannah," "Twinkle, Twinkle, Little Star," "Good King Wenceslaus," and "Auld Lang Syne." Each tune was tape-recorded while being performed on the same wind instrument, in the same key and at the same tempo. Listeners correctly identified undistorted versions of the melodies 99 percent of the time, confirming that the melodies were indeed well known. But how did listeners do when these melodies were distorted?

Dowling and Fujitani tried several different forms of distortion. In one condition, the *absolute* size of the intervals between notes was altered, but the *relative* size of the intervals remained the same. To illustrate, consider the first three notes of a verse from "Oh, Susannah" (see the accompanying diagram). In the unadulterated version, notes 1 and 2 are separated by one whole tone, as are notes 2 and 3. In the

BOX 11.2 continued

first distorted version, notes 1 and 2 are separated by two whole tones, as are notes 2 and
3. Hence, in the distorted version, the absolute size of the intervals has been altered
but the relative size remains unchanged.
Note, too, that the pitch contour remains the
same: in both versions, the second note is
higher than the first, and the third note is
higher than the second. Upon hearing
melodies distorted in this way, listeners could
correctly identify the tune 66 percent of the
time. This decline in performance indicates
that absolute interval size (the property distorted in this condition) does contribute to defining a
melody. Still, this property isn't absolutely crucial—
relative interval size and pitch contour provide
enough information for listeners to distinguish one
melody from others some of the time.

Undistorted   Distortion 1   Distortion 2

In a second condition, only the pitch contour was
preserved. With this more severe form of distortion,
the sequence of notes moved up and down in pitch in
the same manner as they did in the normal version,
but the size of the intervals between notes in the distorted version was unrelated to the size of the intervals in the original. An example of this form of distortion, applied to "Oh, Susannah" appears in the
musical staff at the far right (distortion 2). Listeners
still managed to identify the melody 59 percent of
the time. So pitch contour, all by itself, does provide
some information for identifying melodies.

In their final condition, Dowling and Fujitani distorted even the pitch contour. The only thing left
undistorted was the first note in each measure. With

just this scant information to go on, people were not
able to recognize the melodies.

Another salient aspect of melody is its rhythm. To
appreciate rhythm's salience, have a friend pick one
of the five tunes mentioned above and then clap out
the rhythm of that tune—no humming, singing,
whistling, just clapping. You'll be surprised how
easy it is to identify which melody you're "hearing."
Good examples of rhythm's contribution to melody
come from classical music. One is Franz Liszt's
short piece for piano and orchestra, "Totentanz"
("Dance of Death"). It is an amazing example of the
musical variety that can be achieved simply by altering the speed and rhythm of one theme. The piece
consists of thirty variations on the same theme, the
medieval "Dies Irae," and each variation makes its
own unique musical statement. An attentive listener
should have no trouble hearing the same melody running throughout the piece. Liszt's composition beau-
tifully demonstrates how changes in rhythm alone
can influence your perception of a melody.

SOUND RECOGNITION: JUDGING *WHAT* THE SOURCE OF A SOUND IS

Perceptual Organization of the Auditory Stream

As pointed out earlier, at any one moment our
ears receive a tangle of intermixed acoustic disturbances, which arise from the environment's
myriad sound sources. Yet from this tangled

acoustic stream we manage to hear individual auditory events, each perceptually associated with a
particular external source. Look at the waveform
in Figure 11.15. It's a graphic representation of
the acoustic energy associated with a brief musical excerpt in which tenor Luciano Pavarotti
sings while accompanied by the London Philhar-
monic Orchestra (he's performing the haunting
"Nessun dorma" from Puccini's opera *Turandot*).

FIGURE 11.15
Complex soundwave generated by tenor Luciano Pavarotti singing while an orchestra plays in the background. This excerpt lasts about 4 seconds.

When you listen to the musical passage, this waveform is all your auditory system has to work with. Yet, from visual inspection it's impossible to tell which parts of the complex waveform are Pavarotti and which are the instruments of the orchestra. Using just this stream of acoustic energy, your ears and brain have no trouble sorting out the various sound sources contributing to this lovely song.

The auditory system, then, manages to segregate complex sound fields into separate **auditory images,** as they're known. How the ear and brain perceptually organize the components in this auditory stream has become a problem of intense interest to those studying hearing (Bregman, 1990; Yost, 1991). From the outset, realize that this problem of auditory grouping has analogs in vision, smell and taste. In all the senses, the nervous system must organize complex sensory inputs into separate perceptual events and objects. However, each modality has at its disposal unique stimulus properties that make this process of perceptual organization possible. Early in this century, the Gestalt psychologists investigated organizing principles that promote segregation of a visual scene into distinct objects and events (some of those principles were outlined in Chapter 6). In the last decade or so, scientists interested in hearing have posed a comparable question: What are the properties that promote perceptual grouping in hearing? Some important ones are summarized in the following sections.

Common Spectral Content   We know that the inner ear parses the auditory stream into component frequencies, so it is natural to wonder whether frequency content could determine perceptual grouping. Perhaps, the reasoning goes, acoustic energy activating one set of frequency tuned neurons is attributed to a single sound source, one that is perceptually distinct from the source associated with acoustic energy activating a different set of fibers. Construed in this way, the detectability of a test tone heard against a background of noise is impaired because the tone is perceptually combined with the noise to form a single perceptual event. But when the frequency spectrum of the noise is sufficiently removed from the tone's frequency, the tone stands out as a separate acoustic event and is, therefore, easily detected.

Bregman (1990) devised a number of demonstrations showing how the auditory system tends to group and sort inputs according to their frequency. Here's a brief description of one such demonstration. Bregman created a multitone sequence comprising the notes of a familiar nursery rhyme song, "Mary Had a Little Lamb." Inserted between each of Mary's notes were other notes chosen randomly from the same range of tones. When this new "hybrid" sequence of notes was played for them, people could not hear "Mary." She was hidden among random notes of similar average frequency.

Subsequently, the sequence was repeated with random, camouflaging notes drawn from a set of notes situated one octave higher in frequency than the notes comprising Mary's tune. Now "Mary Had a Little Lamb" was clearly audible. Why? The random notes in this second presentation differed in average frequency from Mary's notes, making it easy for the auditory system to segregate the two sets of notes into two streams, each grouped according to frequency proximity. This grouping of tones according to proximity in frequency is reminiscent of the Gestalt principle of grouping by visual proximity (recall Figure 5.38).

Common spectral content, while effective in some instances, cannot be the entire explanation for auditory grouping. In the natural environment, different sound sources produce frequency spectra with considerable overlap. The spectra associated with two females talking at the same time, for instance, are highly similar. Yet a third person would have no difficulty distinguishing the two speakers based on voice alone. Clearly information other than spectral content must also be supporting perceptual grouping.

Common Time Course   If you examine the acoustic disturbance generated by some sound source, you'll find that the disturbance's frequencies fluctuate together over time. For example, the frequencies come on together when the disturbance begins, and those frequencies disappear together when the disturbance ends. In between, variations in intensity tend to match for different frequency components of the disturbance. Your voice is a good example because your utterances comprise a rich package of many different acoustic frequencies. As you speak, the components in this package of energy rise and fall in unison, and when you're finished the offsets of the constituent frequencies exactly coincide. In effect, frequency components from the same sound source form a cohesive unit, all members following the same pattern of change. In this respect, the frequency components from a sound source are like sailors in a boat: although individual sailors differ in size and appearance, all

undergo the same up and down motions, as the boat rides the waves. This common fate links the individual sailors into a single entity called a "crew." Likewise, common fate could be one way that the auditory system registers which frequencies belong together, meaning that they come from the same source.

Evidently common temporal fate does play a role in perceptual unification, for people have trouble identifying sound sources from recordings heard without temporal modulation (McAdams, 1984). And when one frequency component within a set of frequencies is slightly out of temporal synchrony with the rest, it seems to arise from a separate source (Bregman and Pinker, 1978). It's even possible to produce recognizable speech sounds using temporal fluctuations of broadband noise whose frequency content bears no relation to those speech sounds (Shannon et al., 1995).

But temporal synchrony alone cannot be sufficient, for we can easily pick out a single individual singing in unison in a quartet even though the temporal modulations of the voices of all four are essentially identical. Moreover, common temporal fate is of limited use in situations where frequency content, not just intensity, varies over time (one such situation is listening to). So, what other source of acoustic information make it possible to segregate one singer's voice from the rest?

Spectral Harmonics   Another factor influencing whether frequency components seem to originate from a single sound source is the harmonic relations of those components. Frequencies that are multiples of one another are said to be harmonically related. For instance, playing the A string on a violin generates acoustic energy at the frequencies 440, 880, and 1,320 Hz; as you can see, the two higher frequencies are multiples of the fundamental frequency, which means they are harmonically related. Recall that harmonically related frequencies comprise *pitch*. In general, harmonic tones tend to group together much more readily than do nonharmonic tones (de Boer, 1956). In this regard, it is significant that many relevant sounds in the environment, especially speech and music, are made up of harmonically related frequencies. To give one example, automobile horns on newer model cars honk at F-sharp and A-sharp, a harmonically related pair that is judged pleasing to the ear (Garfield, 1983).

Familiarity Remember Bregman's listeners who failed to hear the tune "Mary Had a Little Lamb" among distracting tones that overlapped Mary's notes in frequency? Their inability could be "cured" very easily: first listen to the tune on its own. Now, armed with this knowledge of what to listen for, people could hear Mary's tune among the noise of overlapping notes. In other words, prior experience with sound sources strongly influences your ability to segment a complex auditory stream.

Top-down

Here's an example you may be familiar with. Try to listen to the voice of a single speaker among a group of individuals all talking in a foreign language unfamiliar to you. It's nearly impossible, and that's because your auditory system hasn't learned to parse this complex array of unfamiliar sounds. If the people were speaking in English, you'd have little trouble picking out one voice from among the group. McFadden and Callaway (1999) studied the role of familiarity in the laboratory by having listeners discriminate small changes in one component of a simple 6-tone sound. When the tones comprised a musical chord, small changes were readily discerned, but when the tones formed nonchords, changes were more difficult to hear. McFadden and Callaway's listeners were also better at detecting removal of small bands of frequencies from speech signals when the speech sounds were played in their familiar, forward direction compared to when the speech sounds were played backward. In a similar vein, errors in musical performance are much less conspicuous when those errors are melodically or harmonically related to the musical passage. The familiar context of a musical piece hides the errors (Repp, 1996).

Familiarity grows with experience, implying that the auditory system possesses a degree of plasticity when it comes to parsing complex acoustic signals. We know that infants spend the first few months of their lives becoming familiar with the sounds populating their environment, especially the vocalizations of those around them. Moreover to facilitate this learning process, mothers unwittingly accentuate phonetic characteristics of speech that define words and word boundaries when speaking to their infant babies (Kuhl et al., 1997).

There is one other rich source of information that promotes perceptual grouping of constituent frequencies into a coherent sound source, and that is information specifying sound location. By tagging where in space sound energy arises, it is possible to group frequencies arising from that single location and, thereby, define a single sound source. The next section is devoted to this problem of sound localization.

SOUND LOCALIZATION: JUDGING *WHERE* A SOUND ORIGINATES

Hearing involves more than just recognizing sounds. One also has a sense of the direction from which those sounds are coming. This ability to perceive the location of sounds in space—termed **sound localization**—can be as important as the capacity to identify those sounds. What good is it to recognize the scream of a firetruck's siren if one cannot tell from which direction it is approaching? How frustrating it would be for a parent to hear the frightened cries of a lost child and yet be unable to pinpoint the origins of those cries. Fortunately, hearing does have a distinct spatial quality—sounds always appear to come from somewhere. Moreover, perceiving a sound's location occurs effortlessly and automatically, as common experience tells you. In fact, even newborn infants will turn their eyes toward the source of a sound (Butterworth and Castillo, 1976; Wertheimer, 1961); sound localization is a perceptual ability present from the day of birth. This

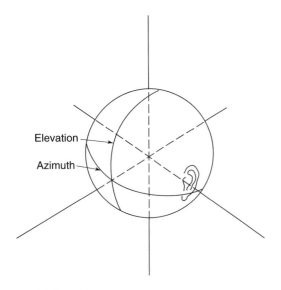

FIGURE 11.16
Sound location is specified in terms of azimuth (position
along the horizontal plane) and elevation (position along a
vertical plane).

section discusses the auditory information that en-
dows sounds with this quality of spatial location.

From the outset, keep in mind that there is *no*
inherent spatial information in the acoustic signals arriving at an ear. In vision, of course,
left/right and up/down spatial relations are faithfully retained in the optical image formed on the
retina. But in hearing, there is simply nothing contained in the acoustic image that corresponds to
these relative locations. Spatial coordinates must
be computed from available auditory information.

In specifying spatial location of sounds, the
terms *azimuth* and *elevation* will sometimes be
used (see Figure 11.16). Azimuth refers to the
horizontal direction of a sound relative to the listener's head; elevation refers to the vertical direction of the sound relative to the head. As you
will learn, these two coordinates seem to be specified by different sources of information.

One thing seems clear: accurate sound localization is best when we can listen to sounds using
both ears. Working together, the ears, like the eyes,

enable one to locate objects in three-dimensional
space. As people with unilateral hearing loss will
testify (Wilmington, Gray and Jahrsdoerfer,
1994), sound localization using just one ear can
be difficult.* From the previous chapter, you already have some idea about the information afforded by listening with two ears: sound waves
from the same source arriving at the two ears may
differ in intensity and in time of arrival, depending on the location of that source relative to the
head. The following sections discuss both these
sources of binaural information in greater detail
and inquire about their effectiveness. We should
stress one point. When tested on binaural sound
localization tasks, listeners never actually hear
differences in intensity between the two ears. Nor
can they tell that sound arrives at one ear ahead of
the other. Instead, listeners hear a single sound
originating from a particular direction relative to
straight ahead.

Interaural Intensity Differences

Figure 11.17 summarizes how **interaural intensity difference (IID)** varies with the azimuth of a
sound source. These data were obtained by positioning a sound source at various points around
the horizontal plane of an artificial head outfitted
with microphones in each "ear" (Shaw, 1974).
The vertical axis plots the intensity difference between the sounds arriving at the two ears. The horizontal axis plots the position, or azimuth, of the
sound source relative to the straight ahead position. Two curves are shown, one using a 6,000-Hz
tone and the other using a 200-Hz tone. Notice
that when the high-frequency (6,000 Hz) tone is
located to the side of the head, the interaural intensity difference grows to more than 20 dB.

---

*Briefly presented sounds are particularly difficult to local-
ize when using just one ear, but monaural localization performance improves significantly with long, continuous
sounds. Under these conditions, people can turn their heads,
which modulates the intensity of the monaural sound, providing additional information specifying location (Perrott,
Ambarsoom and Tucker, 1987).

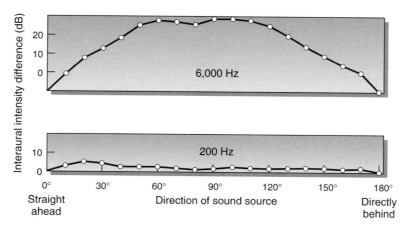

FIGURE 11.17

Sound intensity at the two ears varies with the location of the sound source. This variation in interaural intensity difference depends on frequency. (Data from Shaw, 1974.)

Notice also that for each and every IID (values on the vertical axis), there are *multiple* distinct locations (on the horizontal axis) where a sound source could produce that intensity difference. Take, for example, sound originating from a location directly behind the head. As Figure 11.17 shows, this location yields an IID value of zero. Yet the same value—zero—occurs when the sound originates from a location straight in front of the head. Besides this pair of sound source locations, there are other positions where IID provides ambiguous information. Since distinctly different spatial locations can produce the same information about interaural intensity, that ambiguous information could lead to confusions about the location of a sound source. These confusions can in fact occur, but we'll postpone describing why until we have completed our review of the binaural cues for sound localization. For now, let's continue our examination of Figure 11.17.

As the 200-Hz curve indicates, IIDs are much less pronounced when the sound source consists of low frequencies. This means that IID is a less potent cue for low-frequency sounds than it is for high-frequency sounds. There is a simple reason why the intensities of low frequencies are so sim-

ilar at the two ears. With low-frequency sounds, the wavelength of the sound wave is actually longer than the diameter of the head, which is about 20 centimeters. For the sake of comparison, the length between successive peaks of a 900-Hz tone is approximately 40 centimeters, double the head's diameter. The head, in other words, is too small to interfere with propogation of low-frequency sound waves. Because they are unimpeded by the head, these low-frequency waves lose nothing in the way of intensity from one side of the head to the other. High frequencies, however, are more effectively blocked by the head. Their waves are too small to avoid the shadowing effect of the head. Consequently, the head more effectively blocks sound waves of high frequency from reaching the farther ear, thus weakening their intensity at that ear. Because of this physical property of sound, IIDs associated with high-frequency sounds will be larger than those associated with low-frequency sounds; in fact, IID falls to zero at frequencies below 1,000 Hz.

Think for a moment what this means for species whose head sizes differ from ours. In particular, small heads (such as a mouse's) will generate very little "shadowing" effect, meaning that

IIDs will be vanishingly small for frequencies where IIDs are potent for us.

Next let's review the other binaural source of localization information, **interaural time difference (ITD).**

Interaural Time Differences

Figure 11.18 summarizes how the time of arrival of a sound at the two ears varies with the location of the sound source relative to the head. These measurements were made in much the same way as the ones described above, only using brief clicks as sound stimuli in this case (Shaw, 1974). The horizontal axis again plots the azimuth of the sound source; the vertical axis, the difference in time of arrival of the sound at the two ears. As this graph shows, a sound coming from somewhere off to the side of the head strikes one ear before the other. The largest difference in time of arrival occurs when the sound source is located directly to the side of the head, in which case the ITD is somewhere around 600–800 μsec (1 μsec equals one-millionth of a second); the precise value depends on the size of the head. Sounds located just slightly to the left or the right of the straight ahead position produce ITD values as

small as 10–20 μsec. Listeners can discriminate, however, among these slight differences in location, indicating that the auditory system is remarkably sensitive to ITD information.

As with the case of interaural intensity differences, interaural time differences can be potentially ambiguous: the same values of time difference (vertical axis) can be produced by sources in multiple, different locations (horizontal axis). For instance, a zero interaural time difference could arise from a source located either directly ahead of the listener, directly behind or anywhere on the median plane connecting these two points.

The Cone of Confusion

In a moment, we will look at results from experiments that have examined how well people are able to localize sounds in auditory space. First, however, it will be helpful to point out a fundamental limitation in the information provided by IID and IIT, the two binaural sources of location information. For any given IID or IIT, there is a family of potential spatial locations which could generate that interaural difference. To a first approximation, the surface describing these points of ambiguity (constant IID or constant IIT) corresponds to a cone and, for this reason, the set of ambiguous locations is termed the **cone of confusion** (Woodworth, 1938). You should understand that different values of IID and IIT have different associated cones of confusion; one exemplar is shown in Figure 11.19.

This concept of the cone of confusion is important, for it means that neither IID nor IIT provides *unique* information about sound location. Based on IID or IIT alone, listeners should have difficulty distinguishing sound sources located anywhere on this hypothetical surface. To the extent that listeners unambiguously localize a sound when provided with a given interaural difference, there must be additional information available to specify, or disambiguate, exactly where on the associated cone of confusion the sound source resides.

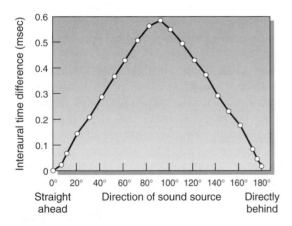

FIGURE 11.18
The time of arrival of sound at the two ears varies with the location of the sound source. (Data from Shaw, 1974.)

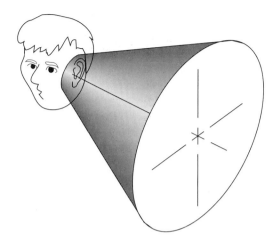

FIGURE 11.19
The cone of confusion, a conical surface defining locations where a sound source would produce the same value of interaural time difference or the same value of interaural intensity difference.

Given this description of IIT and IID and the potential points of confusion, just how well *do* people perform on localization tasks?

The Effectiveness of Interaural Time and Intensity Differences

The classic study of sound localization was performed by Stevens and Newman (1934), and their results highlight several major points about IIT and ITD. For their experiment, Stevens and Newman seated a listener on the roof of a building at Harvard University. This outdoor setting eliminated sound reflections from walls and ceilings. To minimize disturbance from extraneous sounds, data were collected during the wee hours of the morning. Extending out from the listener's chair was a long metal arm that could rotate around the listener's head in the horizontal plane at ear level. Thus, they varied azimuth while holding elevation constant. Attached to the end of this mechanical arm was a loudspeaker that could play pure tones of various frequencies. Listeners sat blindfolded with head held very still. They

were instructed to point in the direction from which the sound seemed to originate, and the measure of sound localization was accuracy in reporting position. For tones below 1,000 Hz, localization accuracy was high. But for tones between 2,000 and 4,000 Hz, errors became increasingly frequent. At still higher frequencies, performance again improved, eventually becoming as good as it had been with low frequencies. Stevens and Newman took these results as support for the **duplex theory** of sound localization, which says listeners use one source of information (IIT) to localize low-frequency sounds and a different source of information (IID) to localize high-frequency sounds. Presumably, the transitions in performance corresponded to shifts in the cue used to make localization judgments. The high error rates at intermediate frequencies indicate that this is a region where neither time nor intensity is particularly effective.

Following the experiment by Stevens and Newman, there have been many other studies of sound localization. Some have used an array of loudspeakers surrounding a listener sitting in an anechoic chamber (Wightman and Kistler, 1980; Oldfield and Parker, 1984a, 1984b). Sound is played from different speakers, and the listener indicates where the sound comes from. In other experiments, listeners have been outfitted with headphones* through which sounds are played (Mills, 1960; Jeffress and Taylor, 1961). In general, the results from all these experiments support the conclusions reached by Stevens and Newman: sound localization depends on interaural time differences at *low* frequencies and on interaural intensity differences at *high* frequencies.

---

*Headphones have the advantage of allowing the experimenter to vary interaural time and interaural intensity independently, making it possible to examine the effectiveness of the two cues separately. Headphones have the disadvantage of producing a sound sensation localized within the head, not in the external environment. Consequently, headphone studies typically ask listeners to judge the lateralization of sound—whether it comes from the left or from the right of midline.

In most ordinary listening situations, sounds consist of both high and low frequencies, which means both sources of information, time differences and intensity differences, are available for localizing those sounds. Wightman and colleagues (1989) believe that ITD dominates in this situation.

Plasticity

Incidentally, people blind from birth are better at sound localization than sighted individuals (Lessard et al., 1998; Ashmead et al., 1998). Blind people's superior localization ability might be connected to an activity-dependent sharpened tuning in neurons that code spatial location. This sharpening could result from heightened reliance on sound as a spatial cue. Recall from Chapter 10 that neurons in the auditory cortex become sharply "tuned" for given locations when animals are forced to rely on hearing to get around (Korte and Rauschecker, 1993). Indirect evidence points to a similar sharpening in human cerebral cortex (Röder et al., 1999). It is also possible that brain areas normally devoted to vision are appropriated for hearing in blind individuals, providing more neural territory for registration of auditory space. This possibility is not as far-fetched as it sounds at first. It has been shown that occipital regions of the brain normally devoted to vision can be activated by auditory stimuli in blind people (Alho 1993; Leclerc 2000). Similar results are found with people who did not lose their vision until they were teenagers which shows that even mature brains can undergo experience-dependent reorganization (Kujala, 1997).

Sound (Mis) Localization

People do make errors in sound localization experiments, and those errors tend to be most common at particular positions in auditory space. As you might guess, those positions include the ones where information about interaural time and interaural intensity is ambiguous. Two such positions were mentioned earlier, straight ahead and straight behind. Sounds from either of these positions arrive at the two ears simultaneously and

with equivalent intensity. So it is not surprising that sounds arising from these two positions are sometimes mislocalized, especially when the sound consists of a narrow band of frequencies (Butler, 1986); broadband noise yields fewer front/back confusions (Makous and Middlebrooks, 1990) and the presence of sound reflecting surfaces helps, too (Guski, 1990). Besides directly in front and directly behind, there are many other positions in space where time and intensity cues are also ambiguous; these constitute the cones of confusion described earlier.

Design Features That Minimize Mislocalization Errors   In view of these multiple points of potential confusion, it is surprising that people don't mistake the direction of sounds more often than they do. In fact, there are two reasons why you normally are not confused about the location of sounds. The first reason has to do with *head movements.* In sound localization experiments involving an array of speakers, the listener's head remains in a fixed position. Ordinarily, though, you are free to move your head when listening to a sound, and these head movements can eliminate potential confusion arising from ambiguous localization cues. To illustrate, imagine hearing a sound from a source located directly behind your head. While interaural time and intensity information is momentarily ambiguous, you can eliminate this ambiguity simply by turning your head in either direction. The sound source will no longer be symmetrically located between your two ears, and the available localization information will now specify the sound's location unambiguously. Moving your head changes the pattern of interaural differences set up by a stationary sound source, thereby clearing up any initial confusion about where a sound comes from. Note, however, that head movements are effective in eliminating ambiguity only if the sound is of sufficient duration to allow you to listen to it while turning your head; head movements are too slow to help localize brief sounds, such as the snap of a twig (Pollack and Rose, 1967).

Execute

A second factor that minimizes the incidence of localization errors has to do with the *pinnas*. Without them, people have more trouble judging the locations of sound sources (Burger, 1958). You can demonstrate this for yourself by performing the following test. While you are blindfolded, have a friend stand close enough to you that he can snap his fingers at various positions around your head. See how well you can guess where that sound comes from. Now repeat this test while wearing earmuffs or a set of headphones, either of which largely eliminate any contribution from the pinnas. While still able to hear the sound, you'll find it more difficult to pinpoint exactly where the finger-snap originates, especially when that sound originates from either directly in front of you or directly behind you. This simple exercise demonstrates that the pinnas make it easier to locate sound.

But why is that so? It is thought that the pinnas aid localization because sound bounces around in the folds of the pinnas before entering the ear canals. The number and direction of the bounces depends on the direction from which the sound originated. The pinnas, in other words, alter the frequency spectrum of the acoustic signal entering the external canal, imposing a unique "spectral signature" that specifies the direction from which that sound arrived at the ear (Batteau, 1967; Kulkarni and Colburn, 1998). The auditory system, in turn, manages to "read" that signature, thereby avoiding any ambiguity about the location of the source of that sound wave.

Pinna cues would be particularly useful for specifying the vertical location of a sound source—its elevation—because binaural cues are plagued by ambiguity in this dimension. In fact, listeners are able to determine the elevation of a source with some accuracy. Oldfield and Parker (1986) compared monaural to binaural localization performance for brief bursts of noise positioned at various locations throughout the auditory field. For elevation judgments, the two conditions were very similar, implying that pinna cues (the only source of information available in the monaural condition) specify a source's elevation. For azimuth judgments, however, listeners performed quite well with two ears but poorly when forced to use one ear only. This disparity between monaural and binaural performance implies that IID and ITD are the primary sources of information for judgments of azimuth (but see Butler, Humanski and Musicant, 1990). Middlebrooks and Green (1991) provide a comprehensive review of the localization literature, especially studies bearing on the question of information supporting judgments of azimuth and elevation.

Because the size and shape of the pinnas vary so much from person to person, this labeled information about a sound's direction should be highly specific to one's own ears. Thus, if you and a friend were to trade pinnas, your ability to localize sound might be impaired. Such an impairment has actually been demonstrated by Fred Wightman and Doris Kistler (Wightman and Kistler, 1989a,b). They placed a tiny microphone inside each ear canal of a person and recorded sounds originating from speakers located at various positions around the person's head. Because of the microphone's position, the sounds it picked up had already been influenced by the person's pinna. These measurements confirmed that a given sound is affected differently by different shaped pinnae—each pinna imposes its own unique signature on the incoming sound (Figure 11.20).

Differences

Wightman and Kistler also had people judge the location of the sounds, and as expected, few errors were made except for the ambiguous sound locations we mentioned earlier. Wightman and Kistler collected localization judgments and ear canal recordings from several people. They then played back those recorded sounds over headphones and had the same people once again make localization judgments. Listening to the sounds that had been recorded through their own ears, people had no trouble accurately localizing sounds. But when listening to sounds that had been recorded through someone else's ears, people were less accurate at localization.

FIGURE 11.20

Soundwave recordings made from the ears of two different individuals listening to broadband sound broadcast from a speaker located at different elevations in front of the head. The curves plot the degree to which the soundwaves were altered by the pinna (values of 0 denote no alteration). The solid curves correspond to the ear on the left and the dotted curves to the ear on the right. Although the incoming soundwaves were always identical, the individual's pinna altered the frequency spectrum of the sound. (Fred Wightman.)

Sound localization is also impaired when flexible plastic material is molded into the cavaties of a person's outer ears, thereby altering the pinnas' reflecting surfaces (Hofman, van Riswick and van Opstal, 1998). When the plugs are worn continuously for six weeks, performance returns to normal, implying that the listener has learned to hear through his/her modified ears. Remarkably, the person exhibits perfectly normal sound localization when the plugs are removed, suggesting that the original "pinna signature" remained in sensory memory, peacefully co-existing with the newly-learned signature.

Illusion

Mislocalization: Sound Heard Through Headphones This discussion of the role of head movements and the pinnas in sound localization raises an interesting point. You've probably listened to music in stereophonic sound over a set of headphones. If so, you know that the sounds usually seem to originate from various places *within* your head, not from external locations. At this point you should be able to figure out why stereophonic music heard over headphones sounds the way it does. Typically, music is recorded from an array of many microphones placed at various positions around the musicians. Furthermore, technicians then combine the signals from those microphones to achieve whatever sound balance they desire. So by the time it reaches your ears over the headphones, the sound bears little resemblance to the binaural stimulus you would have heard in person.

Using just two microphones, recordings can be made that mimic what would be heard live. Music recorded in this manner and heard over headphones *does* seem to emanate from out in space and not within your head (Koenig, 1950; Belendiuk and Butler, 1978). Even then, however, you must hold your head still for the illusion to be compelling. Here's why. The microphones were stationary at the time the recording was made, so the reproduced sound carries none of the changes in interaural time or intensity that would be produced by head movements. When

you do move your head, the brain receives contradictory information: the vestibular system (the one responsible for signaling head orientation) informs your brain of your head movement but the auditory system does not report an associated change in interaural time or intensity. These contradictory messages reduce the otherwise compelling illusion that sounds heard over a headphone appear to come from out in space. Auditory researchers are now trying to devise a computer-controlled headphone system that senses the direction and magnitude of head turns and immediately alters the IID, ITD and pinna spectra in the stereo signals fed into the headphones. This technique would allow a computer to generate compelling and realistic acoustic experiences of virtual sound fields over headphones worn by a freely moving head. For example, a listener at home or in the office could experience all the sounds associated with a stroll through some remote environment, complete with subtle variations in IID, ITD and pinna spectra produced by changes in the listener's head position.

Mislocalization: Ears Versus Eyes There are other instances where sound is incorrectly localized. In these instances mislocalization stems from contradictory information provided by the eyes versus the ears. In movie theaters, speakers are usually positioned on either side of the screen, yet we hear the sounds coming from the appropriate sources pictured on the screen. Another example of this kind of mislocalization is ventriloquism—speech is perceived to come from the mouth of the dummy, when, of course, it comes from the still mouth of the ventriloquist. Both of these examples underscore vision's dominance over hearing when it comes to specifying the location of events (Welch and Warren, 1980).

Probably the most convincing proof of vision's dominance is provided by the *pseudophone*—the odd-looking listening device pictured in Figure 11.21. The pseudophone effectively interchanges input to the two ears, causing the left ear to hear what would normally

FIGURE 11.21
A pseudophone reverses the inputs to the two ears.

be heard by the right, and vice versa. What this binaural swap does to sound localization depends on whether you listen with eyes open or closed (Young, 1928). Imagine that you are wearing a pseudophone and are sitting between two friends, a male to your left and a female to your right. They are arguing. With your eyes closed, the male's voice will sound as though it were coming from your right and the female's voice from your left. Although wrong, this way of hearing the two voices is not surprising; it is caused by the reversing mechanism of the pseudophone. What is surprising, however, is what you hear with your eyes open. Now the male's voice will seem to originate from your left and the female's voice from your right. While this corresponds to the true seating arrangement, your brain has to *ignore* interaural time and intensity cues to arrive at this perception. Your brain, in other words, believes your eyes, not your ears.

In a way, this bias toward vision makes some sense. For one thing, sounds can bounce off solid surfaces and be reflected to your ears in the form of echoes. Hence, the direction from which sound arrives at your ears may not always correspond to the actual location of the sound source. The same is not true of vision—the light reflected from an object travels in a straight line to your eye. Thus, the principles of optics ensure that the light arriving at your eyes reliably specifies an object's actual location.

Physics offers another reason why your brain may trust your eyes more than your ears—sound travels much more slowly than light. Consequently, the sounds from a distant object (such as an airplane in flight) can belie the true position of that object, whereas the light from that object almost never lies. Considered together, these properties of light and sound may have encouraged the brain to rely more on vision for localization. But, as the next section discusses, there may still be an intriguing link between eyes and ears when it comes to localization.

Do the Eyes Control Sound Localization Accuracy? Accuracy of sound localization varies widely from one species of animal to another. Heffner and Heffner (1992) surveyed the species' lifestyles and anatomies in an attempt to discover what factors govern sound localization ability. Two related factors stood out; surprisingly, both had to do with vision. Species with panoramic vision—eyes located on the sides of the head—exhibit relatively crude acuity for localizing sounds; these species, incidentally, tend to be prey, meaning they are hunted by predators. Species with narrow visual fields—both eyes located in the front of the head—exhibit superior localization acuity; these species are typically predators. Prey species also tend to have regions of maximum acuity* extending over larger portions of the retina than do predatory species (see Figure 11.22). From Chapter 9 you will remember that one purpose of eye movements is to direct the region of highest acuity to the object of regard. If that region of high acuity covers a large region of the retina, eye movements need not be as precise. Small, concentrated regions of high acuity, in contrast, require the eyes to be very accurately directed at the object of regard.

---

*For each species, the region of maximum acuity was determined by assessing retinal ganglion cell density. You may want to look back to Chapter 3 refresh your memory about the relation ganglion cell density and acuity.

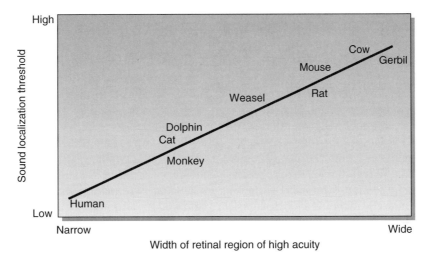

FIGURE 11.22
Graph showing sound localization acuity as a function of the size of the high acuity retinal region estimated from ganglion cell density. (Adapted from Heffner and Heffner, 1992.)

So what does this have to do with sound localization? We know that sounds can reflexively trigger head movements toward the source (Thurlow and Runge, 1967) and that head movements also serve to direct the eyes to an object of regard. Putting two and two together, Heffner and Heffner (1992) proposed that sound localization operates to guide the eyes to a source of interest. If eye movement accuracy is crucial (as it is with frontally placed eyes with narrow regions of high acuity), sound localization ability must also be good. But if eye movements need not be precise (because the area of maximum acuity is more extensive, as it is in animals with panoramic vision), sounds need not be localized with great accuracy. This putative linkage between eye movements and sound localization is further strengthened by physiological evidence showing that neurons in certain brain structures, including the superior colliculus, may be activated by either visual patterns or sounds (see p. 129, Chapter 4).

Heffner and Heffner note that this relation applies only to terrestrial animals that don't rely on echo location. They conjecture that a major role for hearing is to direct visual attention to sound producing objects of potential interest within the environment.

SOUND LOCALIZATION: JUDGING THE DISTANCE OF A SOUND SOURCE

So far our discussion of localization has concentrated on the horizontal and vertical positions of sound sources. But there's another dimension to sound location, and that's the distance between the listener and the sound (*absolute distance* to use the term introduced in Chapter 8). How good are we at judging distance based on sound alone?

When tested outdoors, people tend to *underestimate* the distance between themselves and a sound source, but this error is reduced if people are allowed to walk blindfolded toward the source (Ashmead, Davis and Northington, 1995). People in this free-field situation probably rely on the loudness of the source, since loudness depends on intensity and intensity varies with the square of the distance between the listener and the source. However, loudness is not a particularly reliable cue for a stationary listener unless the person is familiar with the source and knows how loud it typically sounds. If the listener is allowed to move relative to the source (or if the source moves relative to a stationary listener), the rate of change in loudness provides some distance information.

Indoors, people are pretty good at judging sound source distance (Mershon and Bowers, 1979). Here listeners can utilize a cue that is independent of the loudness of the source: comparing the sound energy reaching the ears directly from the source to the reverberant energy reaching the ears after reflection from solid surfaces such as room walls (Bronkhorst and Houtgast, 1999). When sounds containing this reverberation cue are synthesized and heard over headphones, listeners are very accurate at judging the apparent distance of the virtual sound, so long as the simulated environment contains many reflecting surfaces.

The Cocktail Party Effect: Masking and Unmasking Sound

Being able to spatially localize sound sources makes it easier to pick out and attend to one sound from among many in a noisy environment. Because this skill is often required at loud parties, it is aptly called the **cocktail party effect.** Here's how this phenomenon is brought from everyday experience into the laboratory.

Imagine wearing headphones and having an audible tone delivered to your left ear only. Now suppose noise is also delivered over the headphones to that same ear, with its intensity adjusted so that you are no longer able to hear the tone; the noise, in other words, masks the tone. Finally, suppose the same amount of noise is added to the other ear as well, the one *not* receiving the tone. Ironically, this additional noise in the other ear actually unmasks the previously masked tone, making it audible once again. The difference in the tone's audibility with and without noise to the other ear defines the **binaural masking-level difference (BMLD),** which is a measure of **binaural unmasking.**

Besides unmasking the tone, adding noise to the other ear does something else as well—it seems to place that tone and the noise in different locations. With the tone and noise going to the left ear only, both are localized at that ear. But noise introduced to the right ear pairs with the noise already going to the left ear. This now causes the noise to be localized in the center of the head, no longer in the same position as the tone. In other words, when the noise and tone coincide in apparent location, masking is strong; when the two are separated, masking is weak. Binaural unmasking illustrates, then, how localization of sounds can promote perceptual segregation of acoustic events.

Binaural unmasking enables you to focus on one person's voice in the presence of competing conversations elsewhere in a room. However, you are not totally oblivious to those other conversations. If your name happens to be mentioned in one of those conversations, your attention will be drawn to what is being said. This implies that your auditory system continues to analyze unattended sounds. Researchers interested in selective attention have studied this phenomenon by presenting different, unrelated messages separately to the two ears to learn what aspects of an unattended message are registered in the absence of attention (Moray, 1959).

PERCEPTION OF SPEECH SOUNDS

Animals, including people, seem compelled to make sounds, and they will use just about any device at their disposal to do so. Woodpeckers drum their beaks against trees, rattlesnakes shake their tails, gorillas beat their chests, grasshoppers scrape their legs together and termites grind their mandibles. The variety of resulting sounds is remarkable, ranging from the happy melodies of the robin to the mournful calls of the humpback whale; from the faint, rhythmic ticking of a beetle to the piercing shriek of a baboon. While some of these biological sounds may just be idle chatter to break the silence, most serve to communicate messages to friends and to foes. Obviously, then, for the sender's messages to be effective, those messages must be received by the other party. In nature, this is one of auditory perception's primary jobs, enabling animals to hear what others have to say.

Of all nature's creatures, humans have developed the largest repertoire of sounds. Human beings can make sounds using various parts of their bodies, including their hands, their feet, and of course their vocal apparatus. Not satisfied with these means, they have also invented devices to assist them in making sounds—musical instruments, sirens, doorbells and all sorts of other noise makers. But among the many ways that humans have of producing sound, speech is undoubtedly the most important. It used to be commonly believed that the capacity to produce and to perceive speech sounds, more than anything else, set *Homo sapiens* apart from all other creatures. However, as we learn more about the language capabilities of nonhuman species such as the dolphin and the chimpanzee, it becomes necessary to question this belief that language is the hallmark of the human species. Nonetheless, there is no denying that speech, the vehicle of language, has been of paramount importance in the biological and cultural evolution of our own species.

The study of speech encompasses several disciplines, ranging from neurology to linguistics. Each discipline analyzes speech from a particular perspective. For instance, the neurologist might be interested in the neuromuscular mechanisms responsible for the production of speech. Here the emphasis would be on the components of the vocal tract and on the motor areas of the brain that guide the movements of those components. In contrast, a linguist might focus on the structure of grammar. Here the emphasis would be less on the hardware of speech and more on the rules governing the formation and interpretation of sentences.

Where does auditory perception fit into this picture? Obviously, to understand a verbal utter-ance you must be able to hear the associated sounds. So speech perception must take into account the initial stages of hearing, those involved in the reception and processing of sound waves; these are the stages discussed earlier in this chapter and in the previous one. In addition, however, speech perception entails more complex auditory processing. Spoken words are composed of sounds whose acoustic properties are special. In this final section we will summarize some of the major findings concerning the auditory processing of speech sounds.

The Sounds of Speech

Let's begin by considering the acoustical properties of speech sounds, since these define the relevant information that the auditory system must process in order for speech to be perceived. Speech sounds are produced when air from the lungs is forced through the vocal folds,* a pair of elastic membranes stretched across the upper part of the air passage from the lungs. Passage of air through the vocal folds causes them to vibrate, just like the reed on a wind instrument. The vibrating portion of male vocal folds are 60 percent longer, on average, than their female counterparts. This means that male folds vibrate at a lower frequency than do female folds. This is a major reason why the pitch of a typical male voice is lower than the typical female voice.

The airborne vibrations produced by the vocal folds, in turn, are modified by changes in the shape of the throat, mouth, lips and nasal cavity. These components of speech production are intricately innervated by complex sets of muscles that can execute hundreds of articulatory actions per second (Handel, 1989). These actions result in the vowel and consonant sounds that make up speech. Each of these sounds results from a particular positioning of the elements of the vocal tract. Take a moment to voice slowly several of

---

*Vocal folds are commonly called vocal cords.

the vowels and consonants, paying attention to the position of your lips, teeth, tongue and throat. Notice how these positions differ for various vowels and consonants, which is why they sound different from one another.*

Not all sound differences are important, though. For example, sound differences associated with regional accents in the United States usually don't prevent people from understanding one another. Sound differences that are important are ones that actually change the meaning of an utterance. Any sound that can produce such a change is called a **phoneme.** Phonemes are the distinctive features of speech—they form the vocabulary of sounds used in a language, and different languages make use of different phonemic sounds. When speaking at a normal pace, we produce about 12 phonemes per second, and we can comprehend speech at rates up to around 50 phonemes per second (Werker and Tees, 1992). To understand speech perception requires knowing how phonemes are processed by the auditory system. A good first step is to understand the acoustical properties of phonemes.

Any phoneme contains acoustic energy at a number of different frequencies. It is impractical, therefore, to define phonemes the way we defined pure tones. Instead, hearing specialists use what is called a sound **spectrogram** to characterize speech sounds. A sound spectrogram is a graph showing the amount of acoustic energy at various frequencies over time. To illustrate, the sound spectrogram shown in Figure 11.23 shows a "picture" of the speech energy produced when a person uttered the word "spike." The vertical axis plots sound frequency and the horizontal axis represents time. Spelled out underneath the horizontal axis is the word "spike," indicating when in time each of its phonemes was uttered. The dark portions of the graph denote the distri-

---

*As we speak, we hear our own vocalizations, and what we hear influences how we speak. Speakers receiving perturbed versions of their own speech alter the production to compensate for the perturbations. (Houde and Jordan, 1998.)

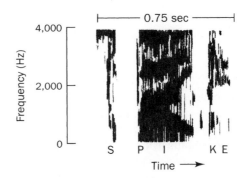

FIGURE 11.23
A sound spectrogram of the utterance "spike."

bution of acoustic energy produced by that utterance; the degree of darkness is proportional to the amount of that energy.

Note that the hiss of the consonant *s* consists of energy distributed over a fairly wide range of frequencies, as indicated by the wide band of darkness above that letter. There is a brief period of silence between /s/ and /p/, seen in the sound spectrogram as an absence of acoustic energy. The vowel *i* consists of several bands of acoustic energy, which in the sound spectrogram looks like a group of worms located above the letter *i*. Note that during the course of this utterance, one of these bands of frequencies dips down. This corresponds to the drop in the pitch of your voice when you say the phoneme /i/. (Listen to your voice as you speak this vowel.) In other words, the sound spectrogram also depicts the intonation of your speech.

The sound spectrogram neatly summarizes the acoustic properties of speech sounds. As Figure 11.24 illustrates, sound spectrograms can be created for sentences as well as words. The beauty of the sound spectrogram is that it depicts the entire package of frequencies making up each and every phoneme in an utterance, and it shows how those frequencies change over time. The sound spectrogram visually depicts the transitions and irregularities that characterize different speech sounds. Because an individual's voice reflects the

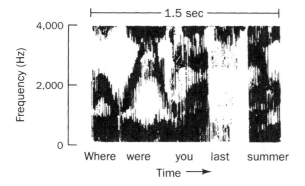

FIGURE 11.24
A sound spectrogram of a sentence. Note the longer time scale in this spectrogram relative to the one in Figure 10.21.

many distinctive features of that person's own vocal apparatus and speech intonation, a sound spectrogram of a voice may be as unique as an individual's fingerprint (Kertsa, 1962). But unlike fingerprints, an individual's spectrogram changes with age, coincident with noticeable changes in the sound of the aging person's voice (Liss, Weismer and Rosenbek, 1990). Incidentally, the spectrographic analysis of sound can also be applied to nonspeech sounds such as the cries made by infants (Green, Jones and Gustafson, 1987), the vocalizations made by animals (Seyfarth and Cheney, 1984) and the characteristic sounds of male and female footsteps (Li, Logan and Pastore, 1991). It is even possible to create a spectrographic picture of the chilling sound of fingernails scraped over a chalkboard (Halpern, Blake and Hillenbrand, 1986)!

Armed with this powerful tool for describing the acoustic properties of speech sounds, let's turn to how the auditory system responds to these properties.

The Neural Analysis of Speech Sounds

Neural

We'll start by thinking about how speech sounds might be represented within the fibers of the auditory nerve which, as you know, respond to narrow ranges of sound frequencies. Each fiber, in

other words, "listens" for the presence of particular frequencies in the sound wave arriving at the ear, and different fibers "listen" for different frequencies. With this in mind, look back at the spectrogram shown in Figure 11.23. You could envision points along the axis labeled "Frequency" as representing auditory nerve fibers. Fibers that respond to low frequencies would be situated at the bottom of the axis, while fibers that respond to high frequencies would be situated at the top. Thought of in this way, distance along the vertical axis would correspond to distance along the basilar membrane. The horizontal axis would still correspond to time. The changes in the degree of darkness within the spectrogram would now correspond to the amount of neural activity within various nerve fibers.

This way of thinking about nerve fiber activity was introduced by Nelson Kiang (1975), who called the resulting plot of neural activity a **neurogram.** For a given utterance, such as the word "spike," there is a close correspondence between the pattern of acoustic energy in the sound spectrogram and the pattern of neural activity in the neurogram. This correspondence merely confirms that the ear and the auditory nerve perform a frequency analysis on the incoming sound. This cannot be the whole story of speech perception, though. For one thing, there are instances where speech sounds that are perceived as equivalent produce distinctly different sound spectrograms. To give an example, the sound spectrogram representing a particular consonant can vary depending on what vowel happens to follow that consonant. This point is illustrated in Figure 11.25, which shows the spectrographic representations of two utterances, /di/ and /du/. Notice how the transition corresponding to the /d/ sound rises in one case (/du/) but falls in the other (/di/). Yet in both instances, we hear the same /d/ sound. And these variations in the sound spectrogram are registered in the pattern of activity across different fibers; for example, different fibers are activated by /di/ as opposed to /du/. Nonetheless, the same consonant is heard. This happens because when the brain

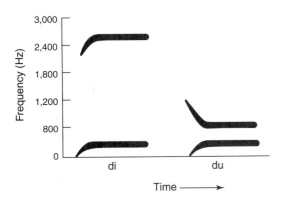

FIGURE 11.25
Spectrogram of the utterances /di/ and /du/. (Adapted from
Werker and Tees, 1992.)

processes speech sounds it registers crucial information about the *transitions* from consonants to
vowels (Kaukoranta, Hari and Lounasmaa, 1988).
These transitions, incidentally, look like the dips
and rises seen in the sound spectrograms of Figures 11.23 and 11.24.

There's another reason why one must look beyond the auditory nerve for the analysis of speech
sounds, and this has to do with the variability of
speech sounds. The acoustic features of human
speech differ from person to person, which is
why it is easy to identify people just by hearing
their voices. Yet despite these individual differences in speech acoustics, we usually have no
trouble understanding what people are saying,
even when they speak in whispered voice (Tartter, 1991). This invariance of perception despite
variability in the stimulus is a form of constancy,
analogous to size constancy (Chapter 8) and
color constancy (Chapter 7) in vision.

So when the brain interprets utterances, it uses
more than just the specific frequency components in speech sound. In fact, speech experts
vigorously debate whether perception of speech
sounds entails processes fundamentally different
from those involved in the analysis of other, nonspeech auditory events (Mattingly and Liberman,
1988). Werker and Tees (1992) summarize this

debate, which is presently unresolved. From neurological case studies, we know that speech perception (Phillips and Farmer, 1990) and voice
identification (Lancker, Kreiman and Cummings, 1989) depend crucially on neural activity
in specific areas of the brain. Damage to those areas produce selective losses in speech perception,
leaving other aspects of hearing intact. This implies that the *brain,* not just the auditory nerve
fibers, contains specialized machinery essential
for speech perception.

To look for brain events related to the processing of speech sounds, physiologists have
recorded activity from neurons in the auditory
cortex of monkeys who listen to human speech
sounds through headphones (Steinschneider,
Arezzo and Vaughn, 1982). You might wonder
what neural activity in a monkey's brain could
tell anyone about perception of human speech
sounds. However, these physiologists feel justi-
fied in generalizing their results from monkeys to
humans because monkeys can discriminate the
same speech sounds as humans (Sinnott et al.,
1976). Without going into details, the results can
be summarized as follows. A number of perceptually significant acoustic properties of human
speech affect the responses of neurons in the auditory portion of the brain. These properties include (1) the time elapsing between the release of
the lips and the start of sound production (the
property enabling you to distinguish between
such syllables as /pa/ and /ba/); (2) the acoustical
context of a sound (such as whether a particular
vowel is preceded by one consonant or another);
and (3) the rate of frequency changes (an important feature distinguishing certain vowels from
one another).

A number of laboratories have used functional
neuroimaging to identify areas in the human brain
uniquely responsive to speech sounds (Fitch,
Miller and Tallal, 1997). In agreement with studies of patients with brain damage, regions in the
temporal lobe and frontal lobe are activated when
people are engaged in a phoneme discrimination
task. Among those areas, however, there is a sub-

Execute

division of labor: brain regions responsive to speech sounds entailing rapid acoustic changes, such as consonant and vowel syllables, are different from those responsive to sounds that do not involve rapid changes in acoustic energy, such as steady-state vowels (for example, /o/). Brain activations in response to speech sounds tend to be stronger in the left hemisphere (Gootjes et al., 1999), which also squares with neurological case studies showing a strong tendency for stroke-related language impairments to be associated with left-hemisphere damage.

Factors Influencing Speech Perception

The Role of Feature Detection in Speech Perception

We've just seen that the auditory system of the monkey contains neurons that respond to perceptually relevant portions of human speech sounds. These neurons are located in a region of the monkey's brain that, when damaged, makes it difficult for the monkey to discriminate human speech sounds (Dewson, Pribram and Lynch, 1969). Damage to comparable regions of the human brain also produces deficits in speech perception (Marin, 1976). This parallel between monkeys and humans makes it tempting to believe that the human brain also contains neurons responsive to distinctive features of speech. But how could one go about testing this idea?

Think back to Chapter 4, where we described selective adaptation as a procedure for confirming the existence of visual neurons responsive to lines of different orientations. In that case, staring at lines of one orientation temporarily caused lines of a neighboring orientation to appear tilted away from their true orientation. This visual aftereffect presumably results from the reduced responsiveness of orientation-selective neurons.

The same line of reasoning has been applied in the search for neurons specially designed for analysis of human speech sounds. Eimas and Corbit (1973), were the first to do this. Using an electronic speech synthesizer, they generated consonant sounds such as /b/, /p/, /t/, and /d/. In-

cluded among these consonant sounds were some that were ambiguous, meaning that they might sound like /t/ one time and /d/ the next. These ambiguous sounds, in other words, seemed to lie at the boundary between two unambiguous phonemic categories. Eimas and Corbit had people listen to an unambiguous consonant such as /d/ repeated over and over for several minutes. Following this period of adaptation, people listened to the previously ambiguous consonant, the one that used to sound sometimes like /t/ and other times like /d/. No longer did this consonant sound ambiguous—now it more clearly sounded like /t/ and not like the adapted consonant /d/.

Eimas and Corbit concluded that repeated exposure to one consonant had temporarily fatigued a set of detectors responsive to the distinctive features of that consonant while those feature detectors responsive to other consonants remained at full strength. Thus, following adaptation, the ambiguous consonant produced more activity within the set of unadapted feature detectors than within the adapted set. Consequently, listeners heard the consonant sound signaled by the unadapted set of feature detectors. The findings of Eimas and Corbit, along with more recent results using the selective adaptation procedure (Samuel, 1989), point to the existence of neural feature detectors responsive to speech sounds. But this still cannot be the entire story of speech perception. There are two other important factors that govern how the sounds of speech (the ones signaled by feature detectors) will actually be heard by a listener: the context in which those sounds occur and the perceived boundaries between speech sounds. Let's consider these two factors in turn.

The Role of Context in Speech Perception

Top-down

Figure 11.26 illustrates a well-known principle: perception of a stimulus depends on the context in which that stimulus appears. The two center circles are equal in diameter, but one is perceived as larger than the other because of the surrounding dots. The same principle applies in the case of

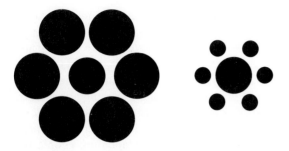

FIGURE 11.26
Context influences perception. Are the center dots in these two figures really different sizes, as they appear to be?

speech perception: how a given speech sound is perceived depends on the context in which it is heard. Speech context can be defined by any of several sources. One source is the phonetic information occurring closely in time; this influence was illustrated in the /di/ versus /du/ example in Figure 11.25. At a more abstract level, the *topic* of a conversation can itself provide a context for perceiving speech sounds. This form of context is amusingly illustrated by a catchy tune popular during the 1940s. Phonetically speaking, the first several measures go:

Marzi doats n doze edoats n lidul lamzey divey. . . .

Now to those of you who've never heard this song (popularized by Bing Crosby and the Andrew Sisters), this string of "words" may sound like make-believe speech. But in fact the words refer to the eating habits of several familiar hoofed animals. Still puzzled? Try repeating the words quickly, paying close attention to the sounds, not the letters. Once you hear the verse as it was meant to be perceived, you'll be able to hear it no other way. Knowing what the song's verses are about will influence what the words sound like to you.

In the case of the nonsense verse, context was provided by the general theme of the song. Speech perception can be influenced by other types of context, too. For instance, the same utterance can sound quite different depending on the *rapidity* with which words preceding that utterance are spoken. To give an example, a syllable may sound like /ba/ when it occurs within the context of a slowly spoken phrase but may sound like /pa/ when occurring within the same phrase rapidly spoken (Summerfield, 1975).

The same thing can happen with words in a sentence, as shown by Ladefoged and Broadbent (1957). They tape-recorded multiple versions of the sentence "Please say what this word is," with each version having a different, characteristic cadence. Different versions of the sentence sounded as if it were spoken by different speakers. Listeners heard the different versions of the sentence,* and following each presentation they heard a single word uttered either with the same cadence as the immediately preceding sentence or with one of the other five possible cadences. Listeners simply had to identify the last word. People listening to these recordings frequently misidentified the last word when its cadence differed from that of the preceding phrase. For instance, the same physical utterance was heard as "bit" when preceded by one sentence version and as "bet" when preceded by another. This demonstrates just how powerfully context can influence speech perception.

In the examples just cited, the context shaping the perception of speech sounds was provided by other speech sounds. As the following classic experiment shows, *visual cues* can also influence what a verbal utterance sounds like. Harry McGurk and John MacDonald did an experiment in which they put auditory information about a spoken word in conflict with visual information about that word (McGurk and MacDonald, 1976). They had people watch a film of a young woman who was repeating various syllables. In

---

*The different versions of the sentence were produced by varying the amount of energy in certain regions of the frequency spectrum. Technically speaking, this manipulation alters the formant structure of the speech signal. Perceptually, this manipulation produces utterances that are readily identifiable as the same sentence, but sound as though they were pronounced by different individuals.

some segments of the film, the audio cue (sound-track) and the visual cue (lip movement) corresponded to the same syllable. But in other segments, the soundtrack for one syllable was dubbed onto the lip movements for another syllable. People reported the syllable accurately when just the sound was heard, and they were able to name the syllable being spoken when just the lip movements were seen with no accompanying sound. (This latter observation merely confirms that people are pretty good at lip reading.) However, people made some very interesting mistakes while watching the dubbed film. One type of mistake involved hearing entirely new syllables, ones corresponding neither to those on the soundtrack nor to those articulated by the speaker's lips. For example, when the syllable /ba/ was dubbed onto lip movements for /ga/, nearly all people reported hearing /da/. In other instances, people heard the syllable formed by the lip movements, not the one actually sounded. This demonstration of vision's strong influence on speech perception is now known as the **McGurk effect,** in honor of one of its discoverers.

The McGurk effect is not limited to single syllables. Also using a dubbing procedure, Barbara Dodd (1977) found that people sometimes heard the word "towel" when the sound of a voice saying "tough" was dubbed over the lip movements for "hole." This influence of vision on speech perception is reduced, incidentally, when the face is shown upside down (Massaro and Cohen, 1996), which is not so surprising considering the deleterious effect of inversion on face recognition (recall Chapter 6).

In an interesting twist on this procedure, Massaro and Egan (1996) had people judge the emotion—angry versus happy—of a computer-generated "talking" head whose facial expressions and voice intonation could be independently varied. On trials when the affective connotation of the voice agreed with that of the facial expression, people always correctly judged the emotion of the talking head. On trials when the two cues were in conflict—for example, the face signaled "happy"

while the voice implied "anger"—people over-whelmingly went with the facial expression.

These dubbing experiments show that vision provides complementary information about speech. This is fortunate because people often talk to one another in noisy environments where speech sounds are obscured. Visual information accompanying lip movements can improve speech intelligibility in these situations (Summerfield, 1992). You may be surprised to learn, incidentally, that infants 18 to 20 weeks old can recognize correspondence between the auditory and visual components of speech (Kuhl and Meltzoff, 1982). In an experiment to test for this ability, infants viewed a pair of film sequences projected side by side at the same time. Both films depicted a woman's face as she repeated a vowel sound, one vowel for one film and a different vowel for the other. The soundtrack corresponding to one of the two faces was broadcast from a speaker located midway between the two motion pictures. By monitoring the infant's direction of gaze, it was determined that infants preferred to look at the face whose lip movements matched the sound. This indicates that by 5 months of age infants can detect the correspondence between speech sounds and the lip movements necessary to produce those sounds.

We don't know the details of how the brain integrates visual and auditory information about speech, but some tantalizing clues have come from a neuroimaging study (Calvert et al., 1997). Regions of brain activity were monitored while people watched video-taped sequences of a face silently mouthing words. Not surprisingly, visual areas of the brain, including area MT (recall chapters 4 and 9), were activated. The surprising results, however, were the strong activations in primary auditory cortex and neighboring auditory brain regions known to be involved in registering auditory signals including speech sounds. Moreover, vision's ability to activate auditory cortex was limited to facial movements associated with speaking. Other, nonlinguistic movements such as chewing did not activate those areas.

Given vision's influence on speech perception, shouldn't blind people have difficulty in comprehending speech, especially in noisy environments? Paradoxically, just the opposite is true. When asked to discriminate spoken numbers, words, and sentences heard against a background of noise, blind high school students outperformed their sighted classmates (Niemeyer and Starlinger, 1981). This seems to imply that blind individuals hear better than sighted individuals. However, on simpler hearing tests, such as loudness discrimination, the two groups of students were comparable. This latter result suggests that the blind students' advantage in speech comprehension reflects superior performance by their brains rather than by their ears or auditory nerves.

Next let's look at two other important factors that govern how verbal utterances actually sound, namely the perceived boundaries between words and the intonation, or pitch, of the voice as words are spoken.

The Role of Speech Boundaries and Intonation in Speech Perception Listening to conversational speech, one usually has no trouble distinguishing words from one another—boundaries seem to exist between words. These boundaries, however, are an illusion. A sound spectrogram of a sentence spoken at a normal, conversational speed shows relatively few identifiable pauses between words and no beginnings or endings to the syllables that comprise those words (look back at Figure 11.24). In fact, if one speech sound had to be completed before the next was generated, talking would take forever. So, the boundaries perceived between words have no counterpart in the acoustic signals reaching the ears. Awareness of the paucity of word boundaries occurs when listening to a conversation in an unfamiliar foreign language. In this case, it is difficult to tell where one word ends and another begins—sentences seem to consist of unbroken strings of sounds, with few demarcations to set off one word from the next. Of course, to someone familiar with that

language, those individual words are as distinct as the English words you hear during ordinary conversation. What, then, causes speech sounds to be grouped into separate words?

For one thing, listeners rely on the context of a conversation to help establish those boundaries. An example of this effect of context was provided by the nonsense song introduced earlier. Once you discovered what the song was about, the continuous phrase "marzeydoats" sounded instead like "mares eat oats." In the absence of context information, one sometimes errs in establishing boundaries between words, leading to misperceived speech. *New York Times* columnist William Safire (1979) related a particularly amusing instance of misplaced word boundaries. Upon first hearing "the girl with kaleidoscope eyes," a phrase from a Beatles tune, someone thought that the line went "the girl with colitis goes by." Anyone not familiar with the subject of "Lucy in the Sky with Diamonds," the song in which the verse appears, could make such a mistake.

When distinct *pauses* do occur in speech, listeners naturally interpret those pauses as the completion of a clause or of a sentence. These pauses thus serve to inform a listener that it is appropriate to take a turn talking. Pauses, in other words, operate like traffic signals, controlling the flow of conversation between people. For most individuals, the arrival of an intended pause is signaled by a drop in the pitch of the voice. Listen to your voice drop at the end as you speak the sentence "It's ready." Figure 11.27 illustrates this pattern of intonation. A drop in voice pitch signals your listeners that you are through speaking. However, some individuals have a pattern of speaking in which pause signals (drops in voice pitch) occur *before* completion of a sentence. A listener hearing these extraneous pause signals may be confused—the pause signals invite the listener to become the speaker when in fact the other person may not have finished talking.

As you can imagine, people whose speech is punctuated with inappropriate pause signals are inadvertently interrupted quite frequently. One

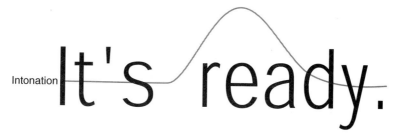

FIGURE 11.27
The continuous line depicts the pattern of intonation as you utter this declarative sentence.

FIGURE 11.28
The continuous line depicts the pattern of intonation as you utter this question.

such individual is Margaret Thatcher, the former Prime Minister of Great Britain. A trio of British psychologists, Geoffrey Beattie, Anne Cutler and Mark Pearson (1982), were intrigued by how often Thatcher seemed to be interrupted during interviews and during debate in Parliament. By analyzing sound transcripts from a television interview with the prime minister, these psychologists discovered that the inflections in Thatcher's speaking voice included frequent drops in voice pitch in the *middle* of her sentences. In other words, Thatcher unwittingly signalled listeners that she had finished talking when in fact she has more to say.

Next let's consider the voice intonation accompanying verbalized questions. Listen to the inflection in your voice as you speak the sentence "Is it ready?" Notice how the pitch of your voice rises at the end (see Figure 11.28), in contrast to the falling pitch that characterizes the end of a de-

clarative sentence. Besides signaling the end of a sentence, then, the voice intonation at the end indicates whether that sentence was declarative or interrogative.

Voice intonation, or prosody as it is sometimes called, is also a prime source of information for identifying a speaker based on voice alone. All of us, including newborn infants (DeCasper and Fifer, 1980), are quite good at voice recognition. Evidently the neural machinery responsible for this ability is located in the right hemisphere, for patients with damage to the right parietal cortex (but not the left) exhibit deficits in voice perception, a condition termed **phonagnosia.** This syndrome should not be confused with deficits in speech comprehension, which is typically associated with left hemisphere damage (Evans, 1982b; Corina, Vaid and Bellugi, 1992). People suffering phonagnosia can understand what is being said but cannot recognize the speaker, even if that speaker is highly familiar (Lancker et al., 1989).

Voice intonation indicates even more than this. During conversation, one also relies on voice intonation as an index of the speaker's mood. Excitement, whether from enthusiasm or anger, is characterized by marked swings in intonation, whereas calm and boredom are typically signaled by flat, relatively unchanging intonation of the voice. You would be surprised how much information can be conveyed just by humming your sentences—in other words, using only pitch changes to convey a message. Next time you answer the phone, see how long you can carry on a "conversation" using hummed speech. You'll gain an appreciation of intonation's role in speech perception.

Fine Temporal Structure in Language-Based Learning Impairments

Like other aspects of hearing, speech perception is fundamentally about registering and discriminating rapid, abrupt changes in acoustic energy over time. Such fluctuations constitute what is called "fine temporal structure." Your ability to discriminate the phonemes /da/ and /ga/ hinges on the fidelity with which your ear and brain represent acoustic fluctuations associated with those speech sounds. If those rapid fluctuations were eliminated from the acoustic signal, the phonemes would become indiscriminable. Similarly, if the ear or brain were unable to register these finely timed acoustic fluctuations because of a neurological disorder, speech perception would be impaired.

In fact, approximately 5 percent of children have serious difficulties understanding spoken language, even though their hearing sensitivity expressed in terms of the AF is normal. They are not "hearing impaired" in the usual clinical sense. Instead, they are *perceptually* speech impaired. They can hear but cannot understand. For at least some of these children the problem stems from an in-

ability to discriminate transient acoustic features associated with speech sounds (Tallal and Piercy, 1973; Kraus et al., 1996). These children are described as having a **language-based learning impairment (LLI).** When tested in the laboratory, children with LLI experience difficulty distinguishing two brief tones occurring in close temporal proximity, and they have problems segregating tone signals from noise even when the tone and noise are presented successively in time (Wright et al., 1997). The children behave as though their brain failed to separate successive inputs, instead fusing those inputs into a single sound.

Fortunately, the brain, including the auditory cortex, is modifiable, as we've seen at several points in this and the previous chapter. Thus, in LLI children it possible to ameliorate their speech perception through simple training regimes. Michael Merzenich and colleagues (1996) devised a multimedia computer game in which success depends upon a player's reactions to various multitone sounds. During initial training, the timing of these acoustic sequences was adjusted to levels where the children could easily succeed, thereby receiving prizes for "winning." After a series of trials, the timing was shortened as the children improved. All the children who participated in the training steadily improved at the game and, more importantly, these gains transferred to speech discrimination and language comprehension tests (Tallal et al., 1996). These improvements were observed after only 10 hours of practice distributed over 20 days, and the gains were still evident 6 weeks after training. Merzenich, Tallal and their colleagues are currently field-testing a simple, computer-based training regime on thousands of children. Efforts are also underway to devise temporal processing tests that can be administered during the first year of an infant's life. The goal is to enable earlier intervention to prevent LLI. This work represents a remarkable synthesis of basic auditory science and clinical audiology, grounded in neurophysiological evidence on brain plasticity.

Plasticity

SUMMARY AND PREVIEW

These last two chapters have merely scratched the surface of one of perception's most highly developed areas of research, hearing. Acoustics and hearing were among the first fields of study to develop quantitative measures for describing their subject. These developments date back to the early Greeks, who showed experimentally that pitch was related to the length of a vibrating string. Hearing researchers were also among the first to come up with experimental techniques (such as direct scaling) for measuring perceptual reactions to sensory stimulation. These measurements were necessary in order to know what acoustic events actually sound like in terms of loudness, pitch, and so forth. Contemporary research in hearing has made possible a very sophisticated understanding of the initial mechanical and neural events that eventually culminate in auditory perception. Still many of hearing's mysteries remain to be solved, including that very special case of hearing, speech perception.

We are now ready to consider a trio of senses, touch, taste, and smell, that play subtle but important roles in our everyday lives.

KEY TERMS

audibility function (AF)
auditory images
bandpass noise
binaural masking-level difference (BMLD)
binaural unmasking
bone conduction
broadband noise
center frequency
cochlear implant
cocktail party effect
conduction loss
cone of confusion
critical band
discrimination threshold
duplex theory
equal loudness contours
fundamental frequency
harmonics
interaural intensity difference (IID)
interaural time difference (ITD)
language-based learning impairment (LLI)
loudness
loudness matching
magnitude estimation
masking

McGurk effect
melody contour
missing fundamental
neurogram
otosclerosis
perfect pitch
phoneme
phonagnosia
pitch
presbycusis
profile analysis
relative pitch
sensory/neural loss
sound localization
spectrogram
temporary threshold shift
threshold intensity
timbre
tinnitus

CHAPTER 12

TOUCH

Courtesy of a late-night thunderstorm, your house is plunged into total darkness. Seeking a source of illumination, you fumble around on the shelves of a closet trying to find a flashlight. You explore one object after another with your hands, using your fingers to "look" for telltale signs of the flashlight. Rejecting a box of laundry detergent ("wrong shape"), a can of spray paint ("surface is too smooth") and a piece of lead pipe ("too heavy"), you finally grasp the flashlight and locate its on/off switch. All of this was accomplished courtesy of your sense of touch. (Alas, if your flashlight is like ours, the batteries are probably dead.)

This hypothetical scenario underscores an important lesson: although we depend heavily on vision to detect and recognize objects, the sense of touch makes a distinctive contribution of its own. Touch helps us identify nearby objects by giving us information about the shape, size and weight of those objects. Touch also reveals a surface's texture and mechanical consistency, two

characteristics that may not be visually obvious. For example, subtle perceptual differences in qualities such as roughness, smoothness or fuzziness correspond to physical differences in the textures of objects. Similarly, perceptual differences in softness, hardness and elasticity arise from differences in how readily different objects can be compressed. Interestingly, these judgments don't even require direct contact between the hand and the object. Many of these tactile qualities can be perceived using a hand-held rod to explore the surfaces of objects (Barac-Cikoja and Turvey, 1991).

To appreciate touch's importance, imagine living in a world devoid of tactile stimulation. While for most of us the thought is unimaginable, some people find themselves in exactly such a world. Some patients suffering from multiple sclerosis (a disease affecting the insulating sheath surrounding nerve fiber axons) find it impossible to identify objects by touch; to find their keys in their pocket, for example, they must empty the pocket and inspect its contents visually. (Later in this chapter, we'll give other examples of deficiencies in touch perception resulting from brain damage.)

Touch aids object identification, but it does much more, such as playing a major role in development and in social interactions. Dating back to Harlow and Harlow's (1966) classic work with infant monkeys, animal studies have shown that early touch deprivation stunts growth, both physical and social. In rats, for example, the mother's regular grooming of her newborn pups stimulates secretion of growth hormone in the infants; without touch to trigger this secretion, growth is retarded. Touch *per se* is the key factor here. Secretion of growth hormone in newborn rats is triggered by vigorous, repetitive stroking with a paintbrush (which simulates the normal action of the mother's tongue). Pups receiving this surrogate touch grow at normal rates.

Research on premature human infants implies that touch exerts the same therapeutic effect in our species. Diane Ackerman, in her delightful book *The Natural History of the Senses* (1990), describes studies showing that premature human infants ("preemies") gain weight more quickly if they are systematically stroked or massaged. In addition, stroked infants seem to be more alert, sounder sleepers and, subsequently, more advanced cognitively. And infant stroking is something parents, especially mothers, are adept at. In fact, a mother resonates to the distinctive feel of her own newborn infant. Merely stroking the hands or cheeks of various infants is enough to tell the mother which infant is hers (Kaitz 1992).

Touch makes another important contribution to our lives: it is a universal means of social communication. We shake hands with acquaintances, we embrace close friends and family members, we affectionately tickle an infant,* we massage the temples of a distressed companion, we caress the skin of a loved one—all of these forms of communication are tactile and all convey specific messages. Some of these touch messages are common to our entire species, no doubt, but oth-

ers are culturally specific. In Thailand, for example, the top of a female's head is strictly taboo; merely to touch her head constitutes a sexual advance. In many cultures, western cultures included, touch exchanges between individuals follow unwritten rules of status: the initiator of physical contact is the individual of higher status, and violations of this ritual can be socially awkward. (To confirm this awkwardness, the next chance you have give a high political or religious leader whom you do not know a friendly pat on the back.)

In a way, touch can be construed as the most reliable of the sensory modalities. When the senses conflict, touch is usually the ultimate arbiter. Imagine reaching out to grasp an object that you see, only to find nothing there. After the initial astonishment, you'd probably decide that it was your visual system that had been misled. Touch, in other words, seems more trustworthy than sight. Or imagine, in the middle of the day, bumping into an object that you could feel but could not see. Again, you'd probably doubt your sense of sight, not your sense of touch. The eighteenth-century Irish cleric and philosopher George Berkeley believed that vision was initially unreliable until its messages were calibrated and interpreted by the more reliable sense of touch. Based on common experience, then, the aphorism "seeing is believing" might be rephrased as "feeling is believing." It is appropriate, though, to say that sometimes we "lose touch with reality."

Touch sensations can arise from stimulation just about anywhere on the body's surface. Indeed, the skin can be characterized as one large

---

*Tickling is that unique form of tactile stimulation that often elicits paradoxical reactions: laughter and reflexive withdrawl. It has long been a puzzle, incidentally, why a person does not evoke these reactions when tickling oneself. The brain seems to know who's doing the tickling and discounts the effect when stimulation is self-produced (Carlsson et al., 2000). People also reflexively react when they believe they are being tickled by a machine, so it's not necessary that the tickler be another person (Harris and Christenfeld, 1999).

receptor surface for the sense of touch (Sherrick and Cholewiak, 1986). But most often when you touch an object, your hand is the organ of stimulation. The English neurologist Hughlings Jackson paid homage to the wonderful and complex abilities of the human hand by calling it "the most intelligent part of the body." The remarkable Helen Keller, who became both blind and deaf less than two years after birth, put it this way:

> My hand is to me what your hearing and sight together are to you. In large measure we travel the same highways, read the same books, speak the same language, yet our experiences are different. All my coming and goings turn on the hand as on a pivot. It is the hand that binds me to the world of men and women. (1904/1908, p. 5).

The skin on a human hand contains thousands of **mechanoreceptors** (receptors sensitive to mechanical pressure or deformation of the skin), as well as a complex set of muscles that make it possible for the fingers to explore an object's shape, texture and firmness.

Whether exploring the overall shape of an object or the fine spatial details of the object's surface, the hand and the finger pads convey the most useful tactile information about that object. In this respect, the hand is analogous to the eye's fovea, the region of the retina associated with keenest visual acuity (Johnson and Lamb, 1981). There is, however, a flaw in this analogy: foveal vision is most acute when the eye is relatively stationary, but touch acuity is best when the fingers move over the object of regard. David Katz (1925), a pioneer of touch research, noted that holding the fingers very still on some surface dulled the ability to sense that surface's spatial features. As Katz noted, moving your fingers across a surface reveals important characteristics about that surface's detailed topography, characteristics that are missed when the fingers are immobile.

It's easy to verify Katz's claim. Think about what happens when you pick up a peach. Upon first grasping it, you can feel the fuzziness of the peach's skin. But if you're careful not to move your fingers over the surface of the peach, the sensation of fuzziness quickly disappears. Only by moving your fingers will the true surface quality of the fruit reappear. As you'll learn, this improvement in tactile sensitivity probably reflects the activation of a set of touch receptors that are relatively inactive when stationary fingers make contact with an immobile object.

TOUCH'S DIVERSE QUALITIES

Touch experiences are triggered by some mechanical disturbance of the skin produced by physical contact with an object. However, the precise nature of that mechanical disturbance varies depending on the physical properties of the object contacted and on the way in which you explore the object tactually. To illustrate what we mean, consider three highly simplified, but representative, cases.

First, suppose you're trying to judge the *firmness* of an object by squeezing it with your fingers. Because a hard object won't yield much to the pressure, the skin on your fingertips will be compressed, not the object. (Imagine squeezing a rock.) A soft object, however, offers less resistance, so the skin will be compressed relatively little. (Imagine squeezing a marshmallow.) Receptors capable of registering the degree of skin compression could, therefore, furnish information about the firmness of an object.

Execute

Next, suppose you're trying to learn something about the *shape* of some small object. Holding it between thumb and forefinger, you roll the object back and forth over your fingertips, searching for clues. If it's smooth and round like a pea, the object will exert more or less the same forces against your skin at all times. But if it has sharp, irregular edges like a tooth, the object will produce abrupt changes in pressure against your skin. In both cases, moving fingertips have translated the object's shape into a characteristic sequence of skin deformations. Receptors capable of registering the sequence of deformations could provide useful information about the shape, and hence, the identity of the object. Shape information could also come from the changes in the position of your fingers as you explore the surface of any three-dimensional object. Because your finger movements mirror the object's topography, receptors in the joints of the fingers can signal object shape.

Finally, imagine comparing the *smoothness* of two brands of bedsheets. As you may know, rough sheets typically have fewer threads per unit area than do smooth sheets. This means that rough sheets have larger gaps between neighboring threads. These gaps aren't conspicuous visually, however, so you're better off rubbing your fingers over the two sheets to compare their smoothness. But what actually happens when you make this comparison?

When you rub a finger over a piece of woven fabric such as a bedsheet, the skin's flexibility allows minute sections of skin to be pushed partway into the spaces between the fabric's threads. These small movements of the skin can be thought of as undulations whose frequency mimics the coarseness of the fabric. So touch receptors that register the frequency of skin undulations could provide information about an object's roughness or smoothness.

Here, then, are some distinct perceptual qualities produced by tactile stimulation; each quality corresponds to some physical property of objects. In a moment, we'll see that the skin contains several different types of receptors sensitive to mechanical deformation of the skin. Some of these mechanoreceptors are well designed to register information about the roughness of a surface, while others are suited for signaling the firmness of an object. But before considering touch receptors and other physiological aspects of touch, let's examine some of touch's capacities.

SENSITIVITY AND ACUITY OF TOUCH

How can one measure touch sensitivity? An old method still used today was developed in 1896 by Max Von Frey, a German neurologist. Von Frey took hairs of various diameters and lengths and glued each one to the end of a small stick. Von Frey realized that when the hair was pressed against the skin, it would exert only so much pressure before it bent. Since the pressure needed to bend a hair depended on its length and diameter, each hair could produce a characteristic maximum pressure and no more. So, for example, a short, thick hair would produce greater pressure than a long, thin hair.

Applying these calibrated hair-probes to several parts of the body, von Frey determined the weakest pressure that could be felt. He discovered that different parts of the body vary dramatically in their tactile sensitivity. For example, the lips and, to a lesser extent, the fingertips are exquisitely sensitive to touch; in contrast, sensitivity is dull on the back and stomach (Geldard, 1972). Interestingly, for any given area of the body, females are generally more sensitive to light touch than are males (Weinstein, 1968). It is also well known that touch sensitivity is dulled when the skin is cooled (Stevens, 1979), in part because the skin (and hence the receptors housed in the skin) is less pliant at colder temperatures.

Besides von Frey hairs, a stiff probe that vibrates the skin can also be used to measure tactile sensitivity (Verillo, 1962; Van Doren, Pelli and Verillo, 1987). Sensitivity to vibrotactile stimulation is best for vibration frequencies around 200 Hz (200 fluctuations in pressure per second). For very low frequency vibrations (in the range of 10 to 30 Hz), sensitivity measured using a large tactile probe is much poorer than when measured using a tiny probe (Gescheider 1985). Regardless of probe size, though, the region of the body exhibiting greatest sensitivity to vibration is not the fingertips, but the palm. (We will return to this matter of probe size in the section on touch receptors.)

Vibrotactile stimulation has several important practical uses. Deficits in vibrotactile sensitivity provide early warning signs of peripheral nerve dysfunction associated with exposure to environ-

Clinical

mental toxins (Arezzo, Schaumburg and Petersen, 1983). Vibrotactile sensitivity is also compromised in patients with chronic pain localized in the facial muscles that control chewing, a result suggesting the involvement of central nervous system dysfunction in this disturbing condition (Hollins 1996). Vibrotactile stimulation can also be used to present sound information, including speech, to deaf people (Weisenberger and Miller, 1987). Several research groups have developed miniature devices that convert acoustic energy into patterns of vibrotactile stimulation. When such a device is worn on a wrist band, different sounds are translated into different patterns of stimulation on the wrist. The vibrotactile stimulation, which is felt as a rapid sequence of taps on the skin, emphasizes the acoustic transients at the onset and offset of a sound. When those sounds are spoken words and sentences, the wearer of the device finds it easier to segment the speech stream, which in turn facilitates lip reading.

Differences

It is also possible to measure a different capacity of touch, **touch acuity.** For decades this was done using the two-point threshold test (see Figure 12.1). To understand this test, imagine using the two points on a drawing compass to stimulate neighboring regions on the skin. How close together can you bring the two points before they meld perceptually into one? This minimum separation is called the two-point threshold. Extensive measurements of two-point thresholds have been made over many different places on the body (Weinstein, 1968). When a finger pad is tested, separations as small as 2 millimeters can be reliably discriminated; on the forearm, the distinguishable separation is closer to 30 millimeters; and on the back, the minimally discriminable distance grows to 70 millimeters. This form of acuity deteriorates markedly with age, although much more so in some individuals compared to others (Stevens and Patterson, 1995). Although the scientific and clinical literature on touch is full of two-threshold measurements, the validity of data generated by the procedure has

FIGURE 12.1
Drawing of an apparatus for two-point threshold test. Apparatus is being pressed against extended fingertip.

been questioned. For one thing, the two-point threshold seriously underestimates spatial acuity (Craig and Rollman, 1999; Craig and Johnson, 2000). In place of two-point thresholds, investigators have turned to measurements of grating orientation discrimination, a technique we will describe in a moment.

Places on the body that have keen touch acuity tend also to be places where touch sensitivity is greatest. Those same places also exhibit superior **localization ability:** when a stimulus is applied to the skin within such an area, the location touched can be judged quite accurately. As will become clear in a moment, these acute, highly sensitive areas of the skin contain densely packed mechanoreceptors. Moreover, these supersensitive skin regions enjoy a disproportionately large representation in the cerebral cortex.

Localization of Tactile Stimulation

Top-down

Although regional variations in touch localization and touch acuity are correlated, the two tactile abilities differ in one important way: the ability to discriminate the relative locations of two probes impressed on the skin is considerably *better* than spatial resolution measured by the two-point technique described above. To explore this performance disparity, Jack Loomis, of the University of California at Santa Barbara, used tactile probes fashioned from metal sheets with raised dots on them (Loomis, 1981). One type of stimulus, illustrated in panel A of Figure 12.2, used two raised dots separated by varying amounts to remeasure spatial resolution. The smallest resolvable separation between two dots was 2.8 millimeters; dots closer together were indistinguishable from a single dot. In contrast, tactile judgments of *relative* position were highly acute. To measure this relative acuity, Loomis used a single raised dot presented at various distances either left or right of a reference line embossed in the metal (see panel B of Figure 12.2). With this stimulus, lateral displacements as small as 0.17 millimeter could be detected. Note that this value is many times smaller than the results of the two-point threshold method. To explain the discrepancy between two-point discrimination and discrimination of relative position, Loomis proposed that localization of a point, and hence discrimination of relative position, is governed by the relative responses in an array of receptors. This kind of cross-fiber code, as we've encountered elsewhere in this book, could represent target location to an accuracy beyond what might be produced by a single receptor operating alone.

Execute

Since our ability to judge the position of one point relative to another is so acute, you might expect that we would also be good at judging where on the body we're touched. Surprisingly, this expectation is wrong: localization shows large, consistent errors. Two touch researchers, Frank Geldard and Carl Sherrick, explored these mislocalizations using research methods that they likened to a party game (Geldard and Sherrick, 1986). For example, consider a game in which one child lightly touches another child's arm with a pencil. The second child, whose gaze is averted, must indicate exactly where the pencil touched. If you've tried this game, you know how

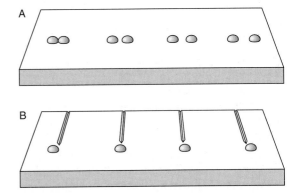

FIGURE 12.2
Stimuli used to measure the smallest resolvable separation (A) and smallest detectable lateral displacement (B). From left to right in panel A, small raised bumps in each pair grow progressively farther apart. These stimuli can be used to determine the minimum *separation* that the fingertip can just discern. From left to right in panel B, the bump in each pair shifts systematically from the line's left to its right. These stimuli can be used to determine the smallest lateral *displacement*. In an actual experiment, stimuli would be presented randomly rather than in the systematic progressions illustrated here.

far off the judgment can be; if you haven't tried it, do. Embarrassingly large errors are the rule as much as the exception.

In a related game, you can "write" on someone's bare back or palm, tracing a letter or a word with a finger or the eraser end of a pencil (Heller, 1986). So long as the person can't see the tracing in progress, he or she will find it difficult to tell what you've "written." Part of the difficulty comes from mislocalizing various parts of the letter or word. The task can be made even more difficult by frequently lifting the finger or pencil while "writing." These frequent interruptions play on the touch system's tendency to lose track of absolute spatial location.

Perception of Surface Texture by Touch

Objects often have distinctive texture surfaces that serve as a tactile signature for the object. This texture signature is determined by physical

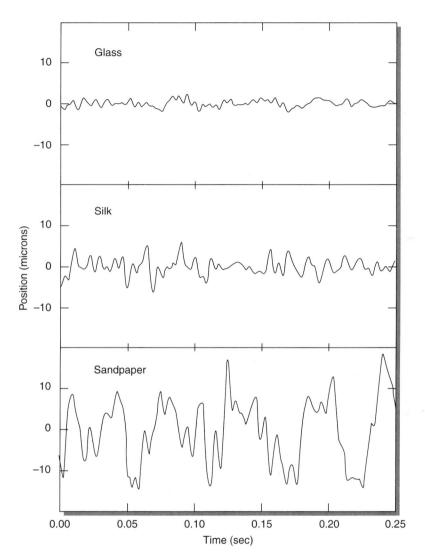

FIGURE 12.3
These three graphs show the skin displacement (in microns) produced by stroking glass, silk and sandpaper. (Adapted from Hollins, Delemos and Goble, 1996.)

characteristics of the object's surface. Think about a sheet of sandpaper, a silk scarf and a drinking glass, three distinctly different textures. Figure 12.3 shows the actual recorded patterns of vibrations produced on the skin's surface as each of these textures was stroked at a constant rate. The glass produces relatively minor fluctu-

ations in skin displacement at a fairly constant frequency. The silk produces greater periodic fluctuations in skin displacement, with the frequency of fluctuations corresponding to the weave of the fabric. The irregular texture of the sandpaper, in comparison, produces more rapid, irregular displacements of the skin. Incidentally, these displacement waveforms can be decomposed into a set of sine-wave fluctuations in displacement energy, using the same Fourier techniques described in chapters 5 and 10. These recordings confirm that movement of the skin over an uneven surface generates a unique "texture" signature of that surface. And common experience tells us that people are quite adept at identifying objects from surface texture alone. By using texture information, the sense of touch allows us to make subtle distinctions among objects.

Execute

Everyday objects don't really lend themselves to the systematic study of surface texture. Instead, we need specially manufactured objects whose physical properties can be specified quantitatively and varied over a large range. Recall that Chapter 5, on spatial vision, extolled the virtues of one particular type of artificial test target, the grating pattern. Gratings have been successfully used in touch research, too. In the case of touch, the gratings are formed by regularly spaced grooves carefully cut into a metal plate or a plastic sheet (see Figure 12.4). A plate containing many grooves per unit area constitutes a high spatial frequency grating; in fact, the grooves can be spaced so close together that the spatial undulations are not even felt, so the surface feels smooth.

So how closely a series of grooves is spaced defines the tactile grating's spatial frequency. The depth of the grooves can be varied as well. When the grooves are extremely *shallow,* the surface will tend to feel smoother than when the grooves are deeper. The depth of the grooves in a tactile grating corresponds to the contrast in a visual grating. Humans can resolve high spatial frequencies with peak-to-peak gaps as small as 0.95 millimeters (Van Boven and Johnson, 1994). In a medium spatial frequency tactile grating with broader peak-to-peak gaps, the undulations are more apparent and the surface feels bumpy. Finally, when the spatial frequency is low and each groove is very wide, the undulations again become harder to sense.

Differences

Imagine running your fingers across one tactile grating and then another to judge which one

FIGURE 12.4
Drawing of two tactile gratings differing in spatial frequency.

is higher in spatial frequency. You'd be able to discriminate between spatial frequencies differing by as little as 3 percent (Lederman and Taylor, 1972). Obviously, then, you could easily tell the difference between wide-wale and narrow-wale corduroy fabric by touch alone. The same stimulus dimension, roughness, also influences affective responses. People tend to find smoothly textured fabrics, such as silk, more pleasant to touch than coarse fabrics, such as burlap (Gwosdow et al., 1986). Incidentally, blind individuals are no better than sighted people when it comes to touch acuity measured with tactile gratings, but they are better at discriminating very small offsets in the spatial arrangement of raised dots of the sort used for Braille reading (Grant, Thiagarajah and Sathian, 2000). With practice, though, sighted individuals can achieve the same touch acuity as that shown by blind individuals. Later in this chapter we'll learn how practice improves touch acuity.

The ability to discriminate different degrees of roughness does not depend critically on the particular way in which the fingers are moved over the object's surface, just so long as the fingers do move. But there's a puzzle here. Moving your finger gradually over a surface generates slow modulations in the pressure exerted on your skin, but moving your fingers quickly over that same surface produces rapid modulations in pressure. That you perceive the surface as having constant roughness regardless of how you inspect it implies that information from touch receptors is referenced to information about the motions of your hand.

The ability to resolve fine spatial detail with the fingers does depend on the orientation of the spatial frequency grooves relative to the orientation of the finger (Essock, Krebs and Prather, 1992). Tactile grating resolution is best when the grating's undulations run perpendicular to the long axis of the finger (as shown in Figure 12.4). This finding is reminiscent of the oblique effect in vision, described in Chapter 5, where acuity was best for horizontal and vertical orientations. In the case of touch, however, only one orientation shows superior acuity.

Are all fingers of the hand equally good when it comes to tactile acuity? With continued use, the fingers develop calluses (a thickened keratin layer of the epidermis, the skin's outermost layer). A callus on the fingertip reduces the skin's elasticity and, according to Lederman (1976), should reduce perceived roughness by damping the pressure changes in the skin produced by surface roughness. Lederman asked people how often they used their various fingers to touch objects. She found that the index finger was used most often, the ring finger least often, with the middle finger coming out in the middle. If the degree of callus varies with frequency of finger use, a surface ought to feel least rough with the index finger and most rough with the ring finger. Though it takes carefully controlled experimen-

tation to really verify the prediction, you can check Lederman's conclusion for yourself: one after another, use each of those three fingers to examine the texture of the skin on your cheek. If you're like the participants in Lederman's experiment, your cheek will seem rougher to your ring finger than to your index finger. You can modify the experiment somewhat to confirm also that absolute touch sensitivity is greatest on the tip of your ring finger.

Why should perceived roughness and tactile sensitivity be influenced by the elasticity of the skin on the fingers? We'll postpone answering that question until we get to our discussion of the specialized tactile receptors located just underneath the surface of the skin. Meantime, you now know why professional safecrackers file their finger pads before going about their business.

Reading with the Fingertips

Most elevators in public buildings have small clusters of raised "pimples" next to the numerals designating each floor of the building. As you probably know, these tiny bumps are Braille representations of the numerals, and if you're like most people you've probably explored what they feel like to your fingers. To an inexperienced person, these characters feel like a random collection of bumps. But those bumps are just as meaningful to a blind person as the letters on a page are to a sighted person.

The Braille system was invented in the early 1800s by Louis Braille when he was just 16 (Braille was blind from childhood).* **Braille** symbols are formed within units of space known as cells, with each cell consisting of six raised

Clinical

*Braille's inspiration came from a system that was supposed to allow soldiers to communicate silently and without light on the nighttime battlefield. That system, invented by a French artillery officer, represented various letters by means of 12 raised dots arranged on a grid. This scheme failed because of its complexity; with raised dots in 12 possible positions, it was difficult to write the characters, let alone read them (Boorstin, 1985, p. 538).

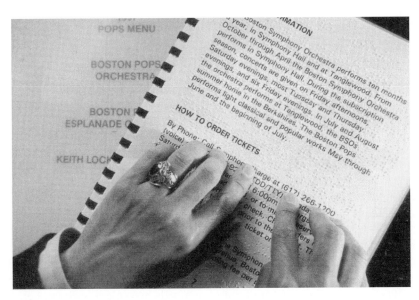

FIGURE 12.5
This person is reading Braille.

dots arranged in two parallel rows of three dots each. Sixty-four different combinations are possible using one or more of these six dots. A given cell can represent a letter, a number, a punctuation mark or even a whole word (for example, the letter *y* denotes the word *you* in a more advanced version of Braille). People literate in Braille can read the characters at 60 to 120 words per minute by moving their fingers over the dots (Figure 12.5). For decades special typewriters were used to produce embossed Braille code, but today computer programs and portable Braille notepads allow individuals to save and edit their work as well as print the embossed code to paper.

Braille's usefulness is not limited to portraying alphanumeric characters; it's equally good at representing musical notation. As a result, blind musicians no longer have to learn pieces by rote memory but, instead, can "sight read" from music scores portrayed using patterns of tiny bumps. While opening new doors for musical expression to the blind, the process of producing these scores was very time-consuming, which limited the range of available scores. That limitation was overcome, however, by the development of software that transcribes MIDI files (the standard notation used for computer transcription of musical scores) into their Braille equivalents. This software, dubbed GOODFEEL, was conceived and developed by blind trumpeter Bill McCann.

Let's take a look at some Braille representations of letters. Panel A of Figure 12.6 shows letters of the alphabet, which can be raised, or embossed, on the paper. Panel B shows the same characters portrayed in Braille. Using the fingers, it's much easier to read text written in Braille letters than it is to read text written in embossed (raised) Roman letters. Readers of Braille, it turns out, tend to confuse different embossed characters, which slows reading in the same way that a typed page with many typographical errors slows visual reading. This interesting outcome would not have surprised the inventor of the Braille system. When Louis Braille was a student at the Royal Institute for the Young Blind in Paris, the director of the Institute insisted that his sightless students read from texts written with embossed letters. Louis Braille himself found the

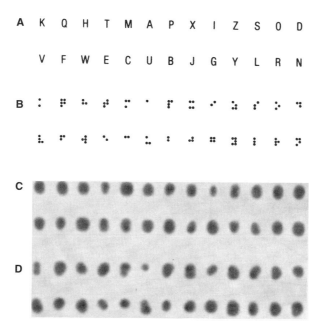

FIGURE 12.6
Panel A shows the letters of the alphabet. Panel B shows the letters Braille characters. Panel D shows the same Braille characters after blurring. Panel C shows embossed Roman characters (as in panel A) with the same blurring as in panel D. (After Loomis, 1981.)

embossed alphabet difficult to read, which provoked his search for an alternative that did not use alphabetic characters (Boorstin, 1985). The widespread use of the Braille system today attests to his success.

But why are embossed letters so much harder to read with the fingers than are Braille characters? Perhaps, you might think, that with the fingers, continuous lines are harder to follow than raised patterns of dots. But that's not the answer. Instead, as Loomis (1981) showed, the answer lies with the skin's limited ability to pick up fine spatial detail. If you press against the skin with a very thin probe, the probe deforms not just the skin it touches directly, but a fairly wide, neighboring area of skin as well. This spread of effect reflects the mechanical properties of the skin. It can be thought of as mechanical blurring, analo-

gous to the optical blurring discussed in earlier chapters. Like its optical counterpart, mechanical blurring eliminates a stimulus' high spatial frequencies (fine details), reducing the stimulus to a smeared version of itself. When fingertips touch the embossed letters, the resulting loss of detail is analogous to the loss of high spatial frequency information in a blurred photograph (see Figure 2.16). Loomis realized that loss of high frequency information would probably have a differential impact upon the discriminability of embossed letters and Braille characters. Embossed letters are made up of continuous contours and, in some cases, fairly small changes in those contours are crucial to the letters' identities. In contrast, Braille characters are made from spatially coarse elements that would be little changed by blurring.

Panels C and D of Figure 12.6 help you appreciate what Loomis had in mind. The visual blur introduced into these panels is meant to simulate the mechanical blur produced by the fingertips. Note that blurring leaves the Braille letters fairly distinct (panel D), while comparable blur renders many of the embossed letters indistinguishable (panel C). For example, after blurring, the Braille *O* and *D* remain visually distinct, but similar blurring renders the embossed *O* and *D* impossible to distinguish. The low frequency information available to the skin from different Braille characters is more discriminable than the low frequency information available from embossed letters. Loomis (1990) has expanded his original insight to create a formal, quantitative model of character recognition and legibility for both tactile and visual characters.

Of course, enlarging the embossed letters would compensate for the limited spatial resolution of the fingers, but this enlargement of letter size would reduce the amount of text that could be imprinted on a page of tactile text, making it impossible for one letter to fit on a single fingertip. Braille characters represent a good compromise between size and resolution.

Books, particularly textbooks, for visually impaired persons often must include drawings and diagrams. Typically such illustrations are created using a computer-controlled stylus that embosses the appropriate pattern on stiff paper. The resulting raised "image" can be read by moving the fingertip over it. However, embossed figures are notoriously difficult to interpret; even common objects presented in the form of raised images are recognized tactually only after great effort and considerable time. (These same drawings would have been recognized immediately by a sighted individual actually looking at the embossed figure.)

Why this disparity between vision and touch? It was probably not a matter of the fingertip's limited spatial resolution. In fact, blurring simple line drawings so as to simulate "blurring" by the fingertips, has little effect on visual recognition (Loomis, Klatzky and Lederman, 1991). The an-

swer probably has more to do with the contrasting ways in which the eye and the fingers collect sensory data.

When you look at a scene or a drawing, the eye extracts visual information simultaneously from a large area. When you use a fingertip to scan an embossed version of the same scene or drawing, at any one moment you're sampling a very restricted portion of the whole figure. In order to recognize or appreciate the embossed representation, those small, momentary samples must be somehow pieced together, and this places a large burden on a person's short-term memory.

To decide whether the fingertip's narrow field of view was to blame for the difficulty of deciphering embossed material, Loomis, Klatzky and Lederman (1991) handicapped vision so that, like tactual input, vision's input would comprise a series of spatially-restricted samples. The stimuli, for both vision and touch, were simple line drawings of common objects such as a key, a hammer and a pair of glasses. The person's task for both vision and for touch was to identify the object. For tactual recognition, people used either a single fingertip or the tips of two adjacent fingers to scan embossed versions of the drawings. For visual recognition, the drawing, presented on a computer display, was first blurred in order to match the finger's low spatial resolution. Additionally, to limit vision's sampling area, only a small section of each drawing was visible at any moment, in the center of the computer screen. The size of this area was adjusted to equalize the sampling areas of vision and touch. Expressed as a proportion of the whole drawing, the visible section's area equalled the fraction of the tactual version that would stimulate either a single fingertip or two fingertips (matching the tactual test conditions). Of course, a moving fingertip does not touch just one single part of the drawing. Over time, the fingertip scans many different parts of the drawing. In order to imitate this scanning, during visual testing various parts of the stimulus were made visible. As the individual moved a stylus on the surface of electronic tablet,

Execute

the computer sensed the stylus' position and displayed the corresponding section of the drawing that corresponded to that position. For example, moving the stylus to the upper left corner of the tablet caused the upper left corner of the drawing to come into view.

The results were unequivocal. With the larger of the two apertures, visual recognition was vastly superior to tactual recognition. But when vision was limited to sampling the drawings in the smaller bites, analogous to the sampling area of a single finger, visual recognition and tactual recognition were equally poor.

Perception of Surface Temperature

Besides sensing an object's roughness or smoothness when you touch it, you often also feel the warmth or coolness of an object's surface. This is because objects have their own characteristic "thermal conductivity"—the rate at which a surface draws heat away from a hand that's touching the surface. Surfaces such as cement and stainless steel seem cold to the touch because they have high thermal conductivities. Surfaces such as plastic and cloth seem warm to the touch because they have low thermal conductivities. This perception of surface temperature of an object has been termed "touch temperature," to distinguish it from the perceived temperature of the ambient environment (Gibson, 1966).

Execute

But what determines touch temperature? The temperature of your skin normally falls right around 33°C, with small variations depending on time of day and your state of health. When you touch an object, the temperature of the area of skin in contact with the object shifts in the direction of the temperature of the object's surface. So when an object feels warm or cool, it is the gradient in temperature between that object and your skin that you perceive, not the actual temperature of the object. This is the basis for a well-known illusion of touch temperature: a surface at room temperature will feel hot to a cool finger but cool to a hot finger. You can easily experience this il-

lusion by placing one hand in a container of hot water and the other hand in cold water. Now place both hands in the same container of tepid water and note the disparity in perceived temperature between the hands. People are actually quite good at detecting even slight deviations from "physiological zero," the temperature that seems neither warm nor cold (Kenshalo, 1972).

The rate of change in skin temperature also influences a surface's perceived hardness. Thus metal at room temperature feels cooler than wood at room temperature because the hard metal surface is a better conductor of heat, including the heat from your skin. Temperature also modifies the perceived weight of an object, as you can experience by performing the following simple experiment. Place a coin on a piece of ice (to cool it) while maintaining another similar coin at room temperature. Now place both coins on the underside of your bare forearm. You should find that the cool coin feels heavier than the neutral coin (Stevens, 1979). This observation suggests that peripheral nerve fibers responsive to pressure are also activated by thermal stimulation.

We're actually surprisingly poor at localizing thermal stimulation in the absence of tactile stimulation (meaning actual deformation of the skin). When Cain (1973) focused a radiant heat source on the front or the back of the torso of volunteers, he found that they often had no idea *where* on their skin the heat had been focused, even though the sensation of heat itself was vivid. In general, people are more sensitive to cool stimulation than to warmth, with sensitivity to both thermal sensations decreasing with age (Stevens and Choo, 1998). Brain imaging studies reveal that somatosensory stimulation yielding sensations of "warmth" activate different (but neighboring) brain areas from those activated by "cool" stimulation (Craig and Rollman, 1999). If thermal stimulation is sufficiently intense to cause pain, a region of the brain known as the anterior cingulate cortex is also activated (Craig et al., 1996). This brain region, located near the very front of the brain underneath the frontal lobes, is intimately involved in the control of affective reactions, including pain.

Mental Set and Tactile Sensitivity

Execute

During everyday activities, you sometimes unexpectedly touch—or are touched by—some object. A mosquito lights on your earlobe, a friend taps you on the shoulder, your hand accidentally bumps a glass while reaching for the salt shaker. It's impossible to be certain when or where you're liable to be touched. What are the perceptual consequences of uncertainty about the source and location of tactile stimulation?

This question has been addressed by James Craig (1985) who asked how well people could divide attention among several potential sites of tactile stimulation on the fingers and hand. Stimuli in Craig's experiment consisted of 108 blunt pins arranged in a rectangular array 6 columns wide by 18 rows high (see Figure 12.7). This array was pressed against the person's finger pad, and each pin could be made to vibrate independently at 230 Hz. A computer controlled which pins vibrated and which ones were still. By varying which subset of pins actually vibrated, different spatial patterns of stimulation could be presented to the person's finger. For example, the computer could present tactile patterns that corresponded to different letters of the alphabet.

In one experiment, Craig examined whether uncertainty about location of tactile stimulation influenced a person's ability to identify the pattern of stimulation. With the person's left hand resting on the array of blunt pins, tactile vibrations were delivered simultaneously to both the index finger and the middle finger. In each trial two different tactile letters were delivered, one to the index finger and one to the middle finger. Following each brief presentation, the person had to identify the letter delivered to a particular finger. Craig tested people under two conditions. In one, the person was instructed before stimulation which finger to pay attention to, while in the other, the person was informed only after stimu-

FIGURE 12.7
Two views of Craig's tactile stimulator.

lation. People were much more accurate in identifying the tactile letter when they knew in advance which finger to attend to.

In a second experiment, Craig studied whether people could integrate tactile information from adjacent fingers. On some trials the vibrotactile pattern was presented to a single finger, while on other trials the pattern was distributed over two adjacent fingers. Craig predicted that spreading the pattern over two fingers would force a person to shift attention quickly from one finger to another, which would diminish performance. As Craig expected, identification was significantly better when the entire vibrotactile pattern was delivered to one finger. In general, Craig's work shows that uncertainty about the location of tactile stimulation makes it more difficult to identify the stimulus.

Execute

At times, uncertainty about touch is more than a mere nuisance; it is a matter of life or death. Each year, more than 35,000 women in North America die of breast cancer. Thousands of these deaths could have been prevented if women had simply examined their own breasts for telltale lumps and changes. But it's not enough just to know that you *ought* to do these monthly self-examinations. There are many different ways to tackle a self-examination, and most of them are wrong. Part of the problem seems to be uncertainty about what to "look" for (recall Figure 6.26).

Clinical

Unfortunately, native skill in examining one's breasts varies widely among women. Physicians' skills in examining patient's breasts also varies considerably (Fletcher, O'Malley and Bunce, 1985). Because perception can often be improved by training (a phenomenon called *perceptual learning*), it is natural to ask what sort of training would improve skill in breast self-examination. Combining basic information about touch sensitivity with an understanding of perceptual learning, some researchers developed a highly successful method for teaching women the right way to conduct a self-examination.

Execute

Virtually all studies of perception begin with the proper choice of stimulus. So before they could study breast examination, Bloom and colleagues (1982) had to develop artificial breasts that felt natural to the touch. These breast models, made of a silicone material covered with a membrane that mimics the feel of skin, allowed the researchers to study the ease with which simulated tumors (lumps inserted into the model) could be detected. When volunteers palpated the models, detectability improved systematically with increases in lump size, as expected. Practice made it possible to detect smaller lumps. Moreover, the improved ability was retained even after a layoff of several months. Simply reading about the procedure had no effect. Apparently, improvement depends on the actual tactile experience.

In one particularly effective program, trainees first learn to distinguish the feel of normal breast tissue from the feel of tissue containing some typical tumors. Trainees are taught to move their finger pads in small circles, first in one spot and then in another, eventually covering the entire breast. Of course, lumps can form anywhere in the breast from just below the skin to quite deep inside. By systematically varying the pressure that they apply, trainees learn to detect relatively superficial lumps (with light pressure) or deeper lumps (with stronger pressure).

Box 12.1 describes other strategies for overcoming the handicap imposed by uncertainty. The effects of certainty show up as changes in brain activity. Merely anticipating stimulation of a particular finger increases the metabolic activity in the region of the brain that represents that finger (Roland, 1976). Additionally, in at least one area of the brain, the temporal cortex, some cells distinguish clearly between tactile stimuli that are expected and those that are not. These cells respond strongly when the animal's skin is touched unexpectedly but fail to respond to the same touch if the animal has been able to see that touch was impending (Mistlin and Perrett, 1990).

Having considered some of the psychophysics of touch perception, we're now ready to turn our attention to the neural hardware responsible for registering and processing tactile information. To give you a brief overview, mechanical disturbances of the skin are registered by several different kinds of specialized receptors located in various layers of the skin. Afferents from these receptors carry neural impulses evoked by tactile stimulation into the spinal cord, where those impulses are passed to fibers that ascend to the brain. Within the brain, touch information is processed in several specialized cortical regions that contain maps of the surface of the body.

In our discussions of the other senses, we always started with the receptors and progressed to the afferent fibers and finally to the associated sensory areas of the brain. In the case of touch, however, it makes more sense to begin by looking at the nerve fibers that carry touch information to the brain. We'll then backtrack to discuss the receptors that innervate those fibers. We are adopting this approach because the functional roles of touch receptors are easier to appreciate if you first know something about the different classes of afferent nerve fibers associated with touch.

SEEING WITH THE HANDS

Sometimes a person who is both deaf and blind will put his hands on a speaker's face. This laying on of hands is part of the blind and deaf person's effort to understand what is being said. The object is to sense the vibrations produced by the speaker's lips, throat and jaw. Helen Keller wrote eloquently of all that she could learn from her hands:

> By placing my hand on a person's lips and throat, I gain an idea of many specific vibrations, and interpret them: a boy's chuckle, a man's "Whew!" of surprise, the "Hem!" of annoyance or perplexity, the moan of pain, a scream, a whisper, a rasp, a sob, a choke, and a gasp. The utterances of animals, though wordless, are eloquent to me—the cat's purr, its mew, its angry, jerky, scolding spit; the dog's bow-wow of warning or of joyous welcome, its yelp of despair, and its contented snore. (1908, p. 570)

This stratagem allows experienced practitioners to gain remarkably good comprehension of speech, particularly when words are spoken at a moderate tempo. Obviously, when using this technique, the deaf and blind person must divide attention among several sites of stimulation on the hands and fingers.

As described in the text, dividing attention among different regions of the hand impairs tactile perception. How is it, then, that deaf and blind people pick up the tactile stimulation from speech so well? Just as puzzling, a blind and deaf person will often place a second hand on the speaker's face if he or she is having difficulty understanding what is being said. This maneuver, though seemingly doubling attentional demands, improves comprehension. A clue to this paradoxical observation comes from another of Craig's findings.

There are two ways to partition vibrotactile stimulation between pairs of fingers. The pattern of tactile stimulation can be divided between two adjacent fingers on the same hand or the pattern can be divided between one finger on one hand and one finger on the other hand. Surprisingly, Craig has shown that the two-handed condition yields better identification than the one-handed condition. In fact, performance on the two-handed condition is comparable to that measured when the vibrotactile stimulus is delivered to a single finger to which the person is attending.

Why does bilateral stimulation work so effectively? As you will learn shortly, information from the left hand is processed primarily in the right hemisphere of the brain, while information from the right hand is processed primarily in the left hemisphere. Craig's paradoxical result may imply that each hemisphere has its own attentional resources and that the deleterious consequence of uncertainty only occurs when a single hemisphere must process multiple tactile inputs.

For simplicity, we concentrate on receptors located in (and fibers originating from) the hand. The hand contains just about every type of mechanoreceptor and afferent fiber found anywhere on the body's surface. And as already pointed out, the hand is the principal organ of touch.

PHYSIOLOGY OF TOUCH

Touch Fibers

Information about tactile stimulation of the hand is passed to the spinal cord via two separate nerves, the ulnar nerve and the median nerve. Like all other nerves, these two consist of many axons, or fibers as they're sometimes called. In the ulnar and median nerves, the axons originate from various regions of the hand. The median nerve, as its name suggests, runs down the middle of the arm, branching out to innervate part of the palm, all the thumb, all the index finger, all the middle finger and that half of the fourth finger adjacent to the middle finger (Figure 12.8). The ulnar nerve takes its name from the ulna, a large bone in the forearm extending from elbow to wrist

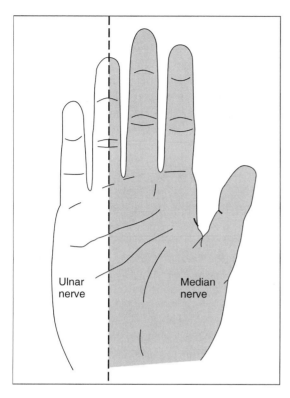

FIGURE 12.8
Innervation pattern of median and ulnar nerves.

Top-down

on the outside part of the arm. Fibers in the ulnar nerve conduct messages from touch receptors in the rest of the palm, the whole of the little finger and the adjacent half of the fourth finger.

Each individual fiber signals when a particular region of the skin has been touched. This fact was established by Edgar Adrian (later Lord Adrian) and Yngve Zotterman (1926), who recorded neural activity from individual fibers while applying tactile stimulation to the skin. The area of skin within which stimuli can influence a fiber's activity constitutes that fiber's *receptive field.* You should see the analogy between a touch fiber's receptive field and a visual neuron's receptive field (the area of retina within which light affects activity of the neuron).

Following Adrian and Zotterman's classic work, many other physiologists have studied the responses of touch fibers in a variety of species. Of course, when recording neural activity in a nonhuman species, a physiologist doesn't know what kinds of touch sensations are being evoked by the tactile stimuli. This limitation has been overcome in some important experiments performed on humans. Ake Vallbo and Karl-Erik Hagbarth, Swedish neurophysiologists, developed a method for inserting a microelectrode directly into the median nerve of an awake human volunteer. Experimental access to the nerve is easy, since it is relatively close to the skin's surface. Applying touch stimuli to various parts of the hand, Vallbo and Hagbarth (1968) located the receptive field of each of the single nerve fibers from which they recorded.

By analyzing the fibers' patterns of response to various stimuli applied to the skin, Vallbo and Hagbarth found that fibers carrying touch information from the human palm and fingertips could be put into one of four categories. These four categories were defined on the basis of the sharpness of the boundaries of each fiber's receptive field and on the fiber's pattern of activity over time. As you'll see, differences in spatial and temporal response properties enable each class of fibers to signal something unique about sources of stimulation within their receptive fields.

Temporal Properties   Imagine lightly pressing a small probe against the skin and maintaining that pressure for a brief time. Recording the activity in many different fibers to this stimulation, Vallbo and Hagbarth identified two types of fibers. Some fibers responded when the probe was first applied to the skin and continued to respond more or less constantly so long as the pressure was maintained. Fibers of this type are called **slowly adapting (SA) fibers.** Other fibers responded only when the probe was first applied to the skin; these fibers also gave a brief, strong response when the probe was removed. Fibers in this category are called **rapidly adapting (RA) fibers.** These first two categories of somatosensory fibers can be distinguished by their responses over time to constant stimulation.

Top-down

Spatial Properties Now suppose the probe is used to map a receptive field by stimulating a series of neighboring points on the skin. The spatial layout of the receptive fields reveals that both SA and RA fibers come in two types. Fibers of one type, **punctate fibers,** possess small receptive fields with sharply defined boundaries. Their fields tend to be oval in shape and encompass anywhere from four to ten of the closely spaced ridges that cover the palm and finger pads. Within this small region, sensitivity is approximately uniform.

The other type, **diffuse fibers,** have large receptive fields with ill-defined boundaries. Receptive fields of diffuse fibers sometimes cover a whole finger or the greater part of the palm. Because of their large size and blurred boundaries, these diffuse fibers are ill-suited for detailed spatial discrimination.

Four Fiber Groups Combining the two types of temporal responses with the two types of spatial properties yields four fiber types: SA-diffuse, SA-punctate, RA-diffuse and RA-punctate. Each of these four types may deliver a distinct message to the central nervous system, since each is best at signaling the presence of a particular kind of tactile stimulation.* This widely accepted view is commonly referred to as the "four-channel" model of mechanoreception.

Fiber Activity and the Experiences

One approach to functional differences among types of fibers compares responses evoked in each type by stimulation of restricted regions of the skin. Adjusting the temporal pattern of stimulation applied to this single location on an immobile

fingertip mimics the effect of moving a fingertip across some pattern, such as an embossed letter. For instance, if a fingertip moved horizontally across the middle of an embossed letter *o*, the finger would be stimulated twice, separated by an interval that reflected both the width of the letter and the speed of fingertip movement. In this way, researchers have recorded afferent fibers' responses to various embossed letters, to determine how faithfully the fibers register the spatial details of the letters (Johnson and Hsiao, 1992; Phillips, Johansson and Johnson, 1992). When the stimuli were raised dots comprising Braille characters, responses within SA-punctate afferents did an excellent job of reproducing the spatial detail of the characters. RA-punctate fibers were a distant second in fidelity of reproduction, with fibers in the other two classes failing almost completely (meaning that their responses to different letters gave no clues as to what the letters were). This strongly suggests that SA-punctate fibers carry the primary information for tactual form and roughness perception.

We could conjecture about the functional significance of different fiber types based on their response properties. But there are two more direct ways to get at the question of functional significance. One is to have a person describe what is felt when a stimulus is applied to the skin during a recording experiment. Keep in mind, of course, that the stimulus used to evoke neural activity in a single fiber actually activates many more fibers than just the one under study. Thus, the person's description of that stimulus is not solely attributable to activity in that single fiber (Torebjork, Vallbo and Ochoa, 1987). The other technique is to stimulate the nerve fiber directly and have the person describe what is felt. Let's consider some results obtained using these two strategies.

Execute

Neural Responses and Perceptual Judgments Evoked by Tactile Stimulation

While stimulating a person's hand with weak tactile probes, Johansson and Vallbo (1979) mea-

---

*From various alternatives, we've adopted this set of names for the four fiber groups because they are descriptive and relatively easy to remember. One alternative scheme uses the terms SA-I, SA-II, RA and PC to stand for what we term SA-punctate, SA-diffuse, RA-punctate and RA-diffuse, respectively (Johnson and Hsiao, 1992). As you'll see later, the PC system takes its name from Pacinian corpuscle, the receptor from which that system arises.

sured the activity in individual fibers and at the same time had the person report whether or not a sensation of touch was felt. When a barely detectable touch probe was applied to the glabrous (smooth, hairless) skin of the hand, RA fibers reliably responded but SA fibers were silent. Activation of SA fibers required a considerably stronger tactile stimulus. This implies that sensitivity to very light touch is mediated by RA fibers.

Of course, the sense of touch is designed to do more than signal weak, near-threshold tactile stimulation. What kinds of fiber activity are produced by more forceful touch stimulation? Localized indentation of the skin is one common source of stimulation. Such indentation occurs, for example, when you place a finger against your chin while thinking. And, of course, applying greater pressure with the finger produces a stronger sensation of touch on your chin. Suppose that psychophysical and electrophysiological measures are taken while calibrated amounts of pressure are applied to the skin with a tactile probe. The psychophysical measures could be verbal ratings, that is, magnitude estimates (see Appendix), and the electrophysiological measures could consist of changes in the activity of touch fibers. When this kind of experiment is done, the person's verbal ratings are most closely mirrored by activity in the SA fibers: the growth in response with tactical pressure roughly parallels the increase in magnitude estimation ratings made by the person. This finding with humans is reminiscent of earlier work on monkeys by Mountcastle, Talbot and Kornhuber (1966), who found that SA fibers registered information about touch intensity. We should note, though, that psychophysical and neural responses at the level of nerve fibers are not perfectly correlated, suggesting an important role for subsequent processing (Vallbo and Johansson, 1984).

Touch Qualities Evoked by Nerve Stimulation

If a given fiber is signaling something fairly specific about a touch sensation, then directly acti-

vating that fiber with mild electric current should produce an illusory version of that sensation at a particular location on the skin. (We would term such a sensation "illusory" because there would be no real object in contact with the skin causing that fiber to respond.) The location of the illusory touch would correspond to the location of the stimulated fiber's receptive field, and the quality of the sensation would tell us something about the information signaled by that fiber (Johansson and Vallbo, 1983).

Stimulation of an SA fiber produces a qualitatively different sensation than does stimulation of an RA fiber. When an SA fiber is stimulated electrically, one typically reports a sensation of light, uniform pressure. This can be likened to the pressure of a soft brush held steadily against the skin. When an RA unit is electrically stimulated, the person reports a kind of buzzing or vibration on the skin. You can get some idea of this feeling by rubbing your fingers across the grooves of a long-playing record or the fine mesh of a window screen.

In general, electrical stimulation studies support the idea that SA and RA fibers carry different sorts of information from touch stimuli. There is also evidence that certain types of losses in touch sensitivity resulting from the prolonged operation of vibrating power tools (such as a jackhammer) can be related to damage within particular touch fiber types (Brammer and Verillo, 1988; Taylor, 1988).

We are now ready to look more peripherally, at the different types of mechanoreceptors housed in the skin. Each afferent fiber terminates in at least one receptor and carries touch information from that receptor to the central nervous system. Again, remember that the distinguishing characteristics of fiber types reflect structural differences in the receptors that innervate those fibers. The same is true for the other senses. For example, some individual fibers in the auditory nerve respond best to high-frequency acoustic disturbances, while other fibers respond best to low-frequency acoustic disturbances. These response differences are not inherent in the fibers themselves. They reflect the different regions of the basilar membrane from which the fibers receive their input. The same principle applies to the touch fibers, which is why it is important to look at the structural details of the mechanoreceptors.

Receptors for Touch

The smooth, hairless portion of the skin on your hand contains four different types of mechanoreceptors, together numbering about 17,000 (Johansson and Vallbo, 1983). As mentioned above, each receptor type is associated with nerve fibers that have distinctly different response characteristics: either RA-diffuse, RA-punctate, SA-diffuse or SA-punctate. The receptors themselves are remarkably diverse in their structure and complexity, and this diversity shapes the functional specificity of different fiber types.

Mechanoreceptors are transducers that respond to indentation or pressure on the skin. Some types of receptors are surrounded by a specialized capsule filled with a compressible liquid or gel. The capsule's shape, size and location determine which kinds of touch stimuli will affect the receptor within that capsule. Consider, for example, a receptor housed within a large, oval-shaped capsule situated in the skin with its long axis parallel to the skin's surface. This capsule's receptor would respond to deformation anywhere along the fairly large area of skin over the capsule. If, however, an oval capsule had its long axis oriented perpendicular to the surface of the skin, tactile stimulation would have to occur within a more circumscribed area to activate the enclosed receptor.

The skin of the fingertips and palm, the touch-sensitive regions emphasized here, contain two types of encapsulated receptors. The two are **Meissner corpuscles** (in the upper layer of the skin) and **Pacinian corpuscles** (located in the lower layer of the skin). Figure 12.9 depicts these structures and shows their typical locations within the skin. It is believed that the Meissner and Pacinian corpuscles are innervated by RA type fibers. Also shown in Figure 12.9 are two

other, nonencapsulated mechanoreceptors, the **Merkel disks** and the **Ruffini endings.** These two receptor types, which lie at intermediate depths within the skin, are innervated by SA type fibers. Next, we look more closely at each of these receptor types, starting with the one located most superficially in the skin.

Meissner Corpuscles   Lying just below the surface of the skin, each Meissner corpuscle is tucked into small papillae that line the grooves in the skin of the palm and fingers. The capsule is oriented with its long axis perpendicular to the skin's surface. In humans, anywhere from two to six RA-punctate type nerve fibers enter a single Meissner corpuscle. Because this afferent unit adapts rapidly, it responds best to transient stimulation such as that produced when something rubs against the skin or when the finger is moved over the surface of an object.

The fingertips of young, preteen individuals contain forty to fifty Meissner corpuscles per square millimeter; by age 50, the number of corpuscles has dropped fourfold, to around only ten per millimeter. The rate at which corpuscles are lost correlates well with the age-related loss in touch sensitivity for small probes (Thornbury and Mistretta, 1981).

Merkel Disks   Moving just a little deeper into the skin, we next encounter the Merkel disks. This class of mechanoreceptor, usually found in groups of five to ten, is innervated by afferent fibers of the SA-punctate type. It is believed that these units are active when the skin is stimulated by the steady pressure of a small object.

Ruffini Endings   Ruffini endings lie deeper in the skin and are elongated parallel to the skin's surface. Each individual Ruffini cell is innervated by a single afferent fiber, and neighboring cells may share a single fiber. This convergence of input is analogous to the situation in the eye, where several rod photoreceptors provide input to a single retinal ganglion cell. And as you may remember, spatial convergence operates in the in-

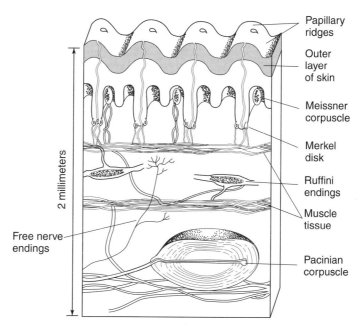

Papillary ridges

Outer layer of skin

Meissner corpuscle

Merkel disk

Ruffini endings

Muscle tissue

Pacinian corpuscle

Free nerve endings

2 millimeters

FIGURE 12.9
Cross section through skin of a primate finger pad showing the location of specialized nerve fiber terminals. (After Darian-Smith, 1985.)

terest of enhanced sensitivity, at the expense of spatial resolution.

The fibers innervating Ruffini endings are of the SA-diffuse type, and it is believed that these neural units provide information about steady pressure on the skin. Because they are also sensitive to stretching of the skin, these SA-diffuse units are active when fingers and other joints move, thereby stretching the skin.

Pacinian Corpuscles These are the largest, least numerous, and most deeply situated of the mechanoreceptors. Each corpuscle is innervated by a single fiber of the RA-diffuse type. Like the Ruffini endings, a Pacinian corpuscle has a long axis that is parallel to the surface of the skin.

Pacinian corpuscles are extremely sensitive to touch. Minute indentations of the fingertip trigger neural impulses in a Pacinian corpuscle. Take a moment to blow as gently as you can on the palm of your hand. The light feeling of the air on

your skin most likely originates in the response of Pacinian corpuscles. If you maintain a steady but gentle airflow to your palm, the sensation will diminish or cease altogether. The response adapts rapidly. In the laboratory, investigators isolate the Pacinian corpuscle system by testing touch sensitivity to relatively large tactile probes vibrating at high frequencies (Gescheider et al., 1985).

Because Pacinian corpuscles are located relatively deep in the skin, deformation anywhere within a large area of the skin can affect a single corpuscle, resulting in a spatially diffuse sensitivity. In fact, a single Pacinian corpuscle can have a receptive field as large as several square centimeters. However, these deeply situated receptors provide only crude information about the location of tactile stimulation.

Free Nerve Endings The skin, both glabrous and hairy, also contains **free nerve endings**—fine, hairlike structures that form a lacey net throughout the layers of the skin (see Figure 12.9). In hairy skin, the free nerve endings wind around the base of hair follicles so that slight bending of a hair will trigger neural impulses in these tactile afferent units. These free nerve endings are also richly distributed throughout mucous regions of the skin, such as that forming the lips and the genital region. They are also found in the cornea of the eye and, as you'll learn in the next chapter, in the nose and mouth. Later in this chapter you'll see the role these receptors play in pain perception.

Clinical

We've now completed our overview of touch's peripheral sensory hardware and are ready to trace the pathways that the touch fibers travel to the spinal cord and up into the brain. We should point out that touch, unlike any of the other sensory systems, is distributed over the entire surface of the body. This means that many different afferent nerve fibers entering the spinal cord up and down its length provide the input to touch centers in the brain. This multitude of inputs stands in marked contrast to other modalities, where just one pair of cranial nerves (for example, left and right auditory nerves) or at most three pairs of cranial nerves (the facial glossopharyngeal and vagus nerves innervating the tongue and mouth) convey information from peripheral organs to the central nervous system. Consequently, damage to one of the many touch nerves causes a loss of sensitivity that is confined to just that portion of the body innervated by that nerve. With other modalities, damage to the associated nerve fiber results in a more devastating, widespread loss in sensitivity. For a chilling description of what it would be like to lose all touch sensitivity, read *Pride and a Daily Marathon* (Cole, 1995), an account of a person's struggles to deal with the devastating consequences of a viral infection that destroyed all his large-diameter touch fibers.

Ascending Pathway for Touch

Afferent touch fibers enter the dorsal, or back, side of the spinal cord. Inside the spinal cord,

these afferent fibers make synaptic contact with two major classes of neurons. One class, called interneurons, synapse onto motor neurons, whose axons exit the spinal cord and travel to muscles located in the vicinity of the body where the afferent fibers originated (see panel A of Figure 12.10). This small circuit of afferent/interneuron/motor neurons mediates reflex reactions such as the immediate withdrawal of the hand when it is pricked by a sharp object. The other class of spinal cord neurons that receive touch input travel upward to the brain, carrying input to particular regions in the brain stem. These neurons comprise the so-called lemniscal pathway. A second, phylogenetically older pathway, the spinothalamic tract, carries information about pain and temperature. Because of its importance to touch perception, we will concentrate on the lemniscal pathway (lemniscus means "band" or "bundle").

As panel B of Figure 12.10 shows, axons in the lemniscal pathway project to nuclei in the brain stem. After synapsing, fibers in this pathway cross over the midline, projecting to thalamic nuclei on the opposite side of the brain. At the level of the thalamus, neurons receiving inputs from the superficial and deeper receptors in the skin are segregated. As a result, one set of thalamic neurons responds like the RA-punctate and SA-punctate fibers (the fibers innervating the superficial receptors), while another set responds like RA-diffuse and SA-diffuse fibers (the fibers innervating the deeper receptors). Both sets of thalamic neurons send axons to the parietal lobe of the somatosensory cortex, an area of the cerebral cortex largely devoted to sensory analysis of touch information.

We won't go into more detail on the pathways and nuclei interposed between the primary afferent touch fibers and the somatosensory cortex of the cerebrum. The interested student can read about this material in Mountcastle (1984) or Kaas (1987). Instead, we will move straight to the somatosensory cortex, that region of the brain whose location is shown in Figure 12.11.

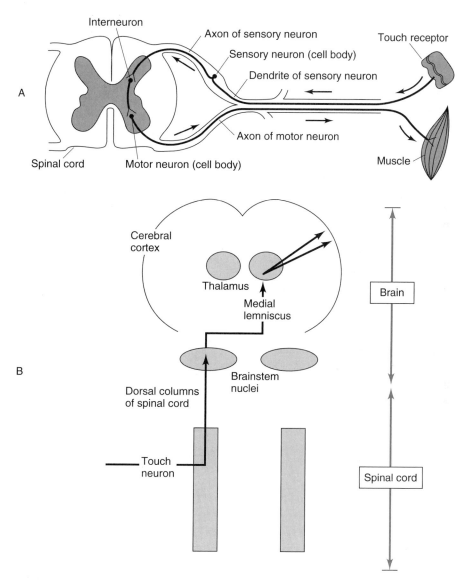

FIGURE 12.10
Panel A is a diagram of the spinal reflex arc mediating response to touch. Panel B is a diagram of the ascending lemniscal somatosensory pathway.

Somatosensory Cortex

Clinical

The chapters on vision and hearing showed that incoming sensory information is assembled in the brain and converted into biologically meaningful representations of objects. The same is true for touch. Just as for vision and hearing, brain damage can destroy a person's ability to recognize objects through touch, even though that person has normal touch sensitivity (meaning that he/she can tell when the hand is in contact with an object).

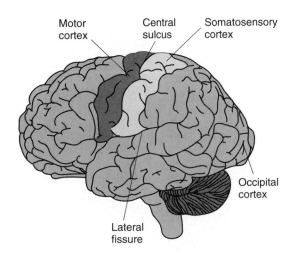

Motor
cortex

Central
sulcus

Somatosensory
cortex

Occipital
cortex

Lateral
fissure

Anterior   Posterior

FIGURE 12.11
Drawing of human cerebral cortex as seen from the brain's
left side. The somatosensory cortex, which receives and
processes touch information, is shown in light gray; the
neighboring motor cortex, shown in dark gray, controls
voluntary, or nonreflexive, movements. Also shown are two
major landmarks on the brain's surface: the central sulcus, a
long furrow that divides sensory from motor cortex; and the
lateral fissure, which separates the brain's temporal lobe
(below the fissure) from its frontal and parietal lobes (above
the fissure).

This condition is termed **tactile agnosia** (Reed
and Caselli, 1994), and it is associated with damage to the somatosensory portions of the brain.

Arrangement of Major Cortical Divisions
The somatosensory cortex consists of several
neighboring, functionally distinct areas whose interconnections are complex and only partially understood. Consider, for example, the two major areas, the so-called first and second somatosensory
areas, S-I and S-II. Although both receive touch
information from the thalamus, S-II also receives
input from S-I. So S-II's analysis of touch incorporates information that's been filtered through
S-I (Kaas, 1987). This constitutes one kind of parallel processing, with cross talk between neurons

at the same level. This arrangement is widely used
throughout the cortex, not just in somatosensory
processing (Sheperd, 1988). Still, we can discern
something of a hierarchy among areas devoted to
somatosensory information. For example, S-II receives much of its input from S-I but returns little,
if any (Pons et al., 1987).

In each hemisphere of the cerebral cortex, S-I
receives information arising from the contralateral side of the body and face. This is because of
the crossover within the lemniscal pathway (see
Figure 12.10). Thus, S-I neurons in the left hemisphere have their receptive fields on the right side
of the body, and vice versa. Generally, neighboring areas of the body are represented within
neighboring regions of the cortex. The body, in
other words, is mapped topographically onto somatosensory cortex. However, some regions of
the body, notably the hands and lips, receive exaggerated representation, with a relatively large
amount of cortical tissue devoted to touch information from these relatively small regions. This
distortion in the somatosensory body map is reminiscent of the magnified cortical representation
of the fovea of the eye. Just as the fovea provides
detailed spatial acuity, our fingers provide the
most detailed information about the quality and
location of tactile stimulation. The various parts
of the body are represented by different aggre-
gates of neurons in S-I, thus forming a topographic map of the body onto the somatosensory
cortex. Neighboring areas of the body tend to be
represented within neighboring regions of the
cortex, with some notable exceptions. Figure
12.12 shows how the different regions of the
body are "mapped" topographically onto the somatosensory cortex.

Cortical Representation of Body Surface

Cortical Magnification Not all body parts enjoy equally expansive representations within the
somatosensory cortex. Instead, each species accentuates, or magnifies, the distribution of neural
tissue for those body parts that are most impor-

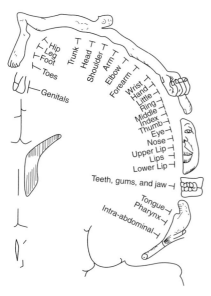

FIGURE 12.12
Different regions of the somatosensory cortex process tactile information from different parts of the body, with these regions forming a "map" of the body surface on the cortical surface.

FIGURE 12.13
A disproportionately large volume of cortical tissue is devoted to certain parts of the body, including the hands and mouth.

tant to members of that species. In many mammals, about half the S-I is devoted to information from the head. In tree shrews and opossums, the nose is emphasized; rats emphasize their whiskers, while the brains of squirrels and rabbits concentrate on the lips. Figure 12.13 illustrates those parts of the body that are exaggerated within the somatosensory representation of the human body. This bizarre caricature, termed the *homunculus,* has large hands and lips, denoting the cortex's disproportionately large neural representation of these body parts.

The sizes of the receptive fields of neurons in S-I also vary with the fields' locations on the body's surface. Specifically, cortical neurons activated by stimulation of the fingers and the lips have very small receptive fields compared to neurons devoted to, say, the back (Werner and Whitsel, 1973). Not surprisingly, touch acuity is best in the fingers and lips. In higher primates the entire region known as S-I contains multiple maps

of the body. Each map occupies a strip that runs nearly vertically downward from the top of the brain. The contralateral foot is represented in the upper portion of each map and the head is represented in the lower portion. The details of this layout vary somewhat from species to species and sometimes even between members of the same species (Merzenich et al., 1987). As we'll see later, these differences among individuals in the same species provide important clues about the developmental processes that shape the cortical representations of the body surface.

Cortical Maps   Look again at Figure 12.12. Although neighboring neurons within the somatosensory cortex do tend to represent adjacent areas of the body, overall, the cortical maps only roughly resemble the body's actual topography. For one thing, a given map may be interrupted at many different locations (Kaas, 1987). Because of these discontinuities, contiguous areas of the body may be represented in noncontiguous parts of the map or widely separated areas of the body may be represented in neighboring cortical locales. In some cortical maps, for example, neurons representing the hand are sandwiched between neurons representing the back of the head and neurons representing the front of the head.

For historical reasons, the most anterior (forward) of S-I's four strips is known as Area 3a; the most posterior (rear) strip is known as Area 2, with Areas 3b and 1 laying between. Actually, the four strips, or maps, can be grouped into two sets: neurons in Areas 3b and 1 (the middle strips) respond most vigorously when sites on the skin are touched lightly. They receive inputs, via the thalamus, primarily from the most superficial skin receptors that innervate the RA-punctate and SA-punctate fibers. Neurons in Areas 3a and 2 (the most anterior and most posterior strips) respond poorly, if at all, to light touch on the skin. Instead, they respond strongly either when particular joints are moved—such as the joints of the fingers—or when other structures deep beneath the skin's surface, for example, tendons and muscles, are stimulated. These areas receive inputs, again via the thalamus, primarily from the more deeply situated skin receptors that innervate the RA-diffuse and SA-diffuse fibers.

There's at least a rough correspondence between the receptive field locations of neurons in each strip and the receptive field locations of neurons in adjacent strips. So neurons in Area 3b that represent the skin on a particular fingertip are near the neurons in Area 3a that represent the tendons and muscles of that same finger.

Turning briefly to S-II, we find that here the neurons also comprise a map of the body. However, for comparable regions of the body, neurons in S-II have somewhat larger receptive fields than their S-I counterparts. Also, the representations of the hands and lips are less exaggerated in S-II than in S-I.

Compared to the receptive fields of touch fibers, the receptive fields of cortical neurons tend to be more complex. Take two examples of this greater complexity. Certain cortical neurons respond most strongly only when an edge of *particular orientation* lies within the neuron's receptive field. This neuron would respond when the skin pressed against an edge of one orientation but would give little or no response if the skin pressed against an edge of very different orientation. The optimal edge orientation varies from cell to cell. (This may remind you of the orientation-tuned visual cortical neurons described in Chapter 4.) Other neurons, particularly in the posterior strips of S-I, respond most strongly when an object moves *in a particular direction* across the skin. Some neurons give a brisk response when a brush is moved along a finger's long axis or a finger is moved lengthwise across the brush. These same neurons give no response when the brush is moved across the finger or when the finger is moved across the object. Such neurons could provide information during active touch (Warren, Hamalainen and Gardner, 1986).

Speculations About Cortical Organization

We have stressed the resemblances between the somatosensory cortex's organization and the organization of the visual cortex. Recall that in vision, different subregions, such as V1, V4 and MT, seem to be specialized for processing particular kinds of visual information. Analogously, some regions of the somatosensory cortex handle information from the superficial layers of the skin, while neighboring regions process information from deeper in the skin, as well as from tendons and muscles. What's the purpose, though, of this complex arrangement? What purpose is served by the multiple adjacent maps, such as the maps in Areas 3a and 3b? Although no one can yet say for certain, it may be useful to sketch out some possible answers.

Each individual mechanoreceptor in the skin yields information about just a small portion of the hand. Clearly, then, the appreciation of an object's overall shape, size and texture requires integration of responses from a large population of receptors (Warren, Hamalainen and Gardner, 1986). Particularly important may be the integration of information about touch and muscle position. Suppose, for example, with eyes closed, you run a fingertip slowly over a grainy wood surface. As the finger moves across the surface, various cortical neurons respond with some frequency of firing. One might imagine that the frequency of the neuron's response reflected, or coded, the surface's grain—the average distance between ridges in the wood's microstructure. In this scheme, a high firing rate might signal that the elements in the wood's grain were quite closely spaced. However, the same neuronal firing rate could have been produced by moving the fingertip more rapidly across a grain with widely spaced elements. As a result, the neural signal provides ambiguous information about objects and their properties (Darian-Smith et al., 1984). In order to disambiguate the signal, information about the finger's own movements must enter into the neural equation.

Movement is not the only factor that can introduce ambiguity. Take a nonmoving finger that is pressing against some surface. The receptor response might reflect the depth of the surface's microelements, its scratches, grain or what have you, but again, the response is ambiguous. Any given response could be produced by a finger that pressed lightly against a deeply structured surface (such as sandpaper with very large grains) or by a finger that pressed more strongly against a finely structured surface (such as sandpaper with very small grains). Again, to disambiguate the receptors' responses, the brain must calibrate the receptor response against the force with which the fingers are pressing.

In both examples, information from touch receptors becomes a useful guide to the properties of object surfaces only when that information is combined with information from receptors deeper in the skin, receptors that signal the state of tendons and muscles. There's good reason, then, for neurons in S-I that signal the responses of superficial mechanoreceptors to adjoin neurons that signal the responses of deeper mechanoreceptors. Adjacency could facilitate the coordination of disambiguating neural computations.

ACTIVE TOUCH: HAPTICS

Usually, when you touch something or someone, you don't simply plop your hand or fingers down and leave them still. Think what happens when you inspect a tomato in the produce market, trying to decide whether to buy it. As you reach for it, your fingers conform to the general shape of the tomato even before you grasp. Once you've lifted the tomato, you begin examining its surface with your fingers, looking for irregularities. At the same time you squeeze it gently to assess the tomato's ripeness. You are using your fingers actively to explore this object.

Feedback from touch receptors controls the fingers' pressure on the tomato. Initial contact generates touch signals that guide subsequent finger movements; those finger movements, in turn, generate updated touch signals. You can especially appreciate the importance of this feedback system when it doesn't work. For instance, when cold has numbed your fingers, it's hard to manipulate delicate objects. This makes complex activities, such as sewing or tying one's shoes, difficult. Even walking becomes tough without touch feedback, as you've undoubtedly experienced when your foot has fallen asleep (Sillar and Roberts, 1988).

A foot that's fallen asleep is usually a minor, temporary inconvenience. But when diminished touch results from damage to the brain, its impact can be devastating. In some patients, an interruption of the brain's blood supply (a cerebrovascular accident, or stroke) selectively damages the somatosensory cortex, leaving motor function unimpaired. When this selective brain damage diminishes touch feedback from a hand, the patient simply stops using the affected hand for even the most basic everyday activities such as eating or drinking. Ironically, this disuse has further consequences: deterioration of the hand's motor function, which may previously have been spared (Dannenbaum and Dykes, 1988).

For every one of us, finger, limb and body movements are essential parts of life. Guided by

Clinical

perception, these actions can change the objects being touched, and consequently, can change perception itself (Gibson, 1966). The importance of active touch has been confirmed by recent studies of activity in the human brain using neuro-imaging techniques (Ginsberg et al., 1987).

The hand is an extraordinarily gifted instrument for exploration. When this instrument is used to explore an object, information from the skin's touch receptors is actually coordinated or combined with a second kind of information, called **kinesthesis.** Kinesthesis receptors are in the muscles, tendons and joints. These receptors give us information about the movement and position of our limbs. Suppose with eyes closed, you pick up a small, complex object and explore it with your fingers. As fingers encounter the various parts of that object, touch receptors signal the properties of those parts. At the same time, kinesthesis provides information about the location of the hand and how the fingers are positioned relative to one another. (This positional information is sometimes referred to as **proprioception.**) As a result, touch information can be related, moment by moment, to the hand and finger positions where that touch information was acquired. Kinesthesis provides a coordinate system in which various touch experiences can be integrated.

An analogy may be helpful. Imagine an automated vehicle exploring the surface of another planet (recall Sojourner from Chapter 6). As the vehicle roams about, it sends information back to scientists on earth about the things it encounters. Unless the scientists know the precise location of the vehicle, on a moment-to-moment basis, they will be unable to meld the information they receive into a coherent representation of the planet's surface. Kinesthesis is analogous to information about the changing location of the vehicle. Without kinesthesis, touch receptors in the exploring hand would provide a series of signals about object properties, but those signals could not be translated into a representation of the object being explored. There would be no way to re-late touch signals to the position of the hand on the object. Because the coordination of touch and kinesthetic information is so important, a special term, **haptics** (from the Greek word meaning "to touch"), is reserved for sensory information that depends upon both touch and kinesthesis. We say, therefore, that as the hand explores an object, that exploration generates neither touch information nor kinesthetic information alone, but haptic information.

As Gibson (1966) pointed out, our haptic capacities, particularly those of the hand, tend to go unrecognized because they are overshadowed by the hand's extraordinary motor skills and because visual input is usually dominant. But, if visual input is precluded, people remain surprisingly good at recognizing objects using haptic information alone. For example, Klatzky, Lederman and Metzger (1985) asked blindfolded subjects to identify one hundred different common objects by means of haptic information. Performance was fast and highly accurate.

When people explore objects with their hands, the hand movements are not random, but highly predictable. So, with a small unknown object for example, an observer usually begins the exploration by enclosing the object with the fingers and palm. Lederman and Klatzky (1987) identified several different kinds of stereotyped hand movements, which they termed "exploratory procedures," or EPs. Figure 12.14 depicts the most important of these. Results from a series of related experiments allowed Lederman and Klatzky (1990) to discover the haptic purposes served by these EPs.

Execute

Here's how they went about it. From earlier work, Lederman and Klatzky knew which stimulus characteristics made it possible for people to discriminate objects haptically. These included texture, temperature, hardness, weight, size, shape and component motion (movements of an object's parts). Armed with a list of such characteristics, Lederman and Klatzky began by asking people to imagine handling an object, such as a pencil, and deciding whether this object was a

FIGURE 12.14
Principal exploratory procedures used in haptic examination of objects. Each term in parentheses indicates the stimulus feature most likely to be recognized by the corresponding exploratory procedure. (From Lederman, 1990, as adapted from Lederman and Klatzky, 1987.)

member of some class of objects, say writing implements. For 57 different classes of objects and their members, people identified the haptic properties used to decide about category membership. Sticking with the pencil example, observers reported that *shape* was crucial in identifying a pencil as a writing implement; that *texture* al-

lowed them to identify a crayon as a writing implement; and that *size* allowed them to identify a pencil as a used rather than a new.

Knowing the characteristic properties for various haptic discriminations, Lederman and Klatzky next tested the role of EPs in extracting those properties. Switching from an imagined discrimination to the real thing, a new group of individuals handled unseen objects one at a time and judged, for each, whether or not it was a member of some class. For example, an observer given a pencil had to state whether it was a writing utensil. On other trials, the person was asked whether the pencil was new or was used. Videotapes revealed that on about 80 percent of all trials, observers began by enclosing the test object with fingers curved and then lifting it (see Figure 12.14). These exploratory procedures provide gross information that was usually insufficient to permit a conclusion. Therefore they were usually followed by one or more additional EPs. The selection of a follow-up EP mirrored the property that would be most helpful in deciding category membership. (Recall that this property, for each pair of objects, had been gleaned from the judgments of other people.) For example, if shape were a distinguishing property, people tended to follow the object's contour with their fingers (see Figure 12.14); if texture were most important, people moved their fingers back and forth across the object's surface (see Figure 12.14). Haptic exploration, then, is driven by observers' knowledge of object properties.

From these and related experiments, Lederman and Klatzky (1987) derived two additional characteristics of the EPs: generality and duration. Though each EP was best suited for extracting information about a particular object property, many EPs provided subsidiary information about one or more additional properties. This allowed Lederman to rank the EP's on the generality of the information, primary and subsidiary, that each gave. Lederman found also that EPs varied dramatically in how long each took to execute. Interestingly, these two measures—generality and duration—tended to be inversely related. One EP, enclosure, offered good generality and rapid execution. Not coincidentally, that one EP typically inaugurated each and every exploratory sequence in Klatzky and Lederman's experiment.

The analysis of EPs has been extended to children blind from birth (Landau, 1991). In all cases studied, performance by blind children on tasks involving judgments of spatial configurations of objects was similar to that of sighted children tested while blindfolded. Landau concludes, "Visual experience is not necessary for the early development of the capacity to explore objects or layouts, the capacity to assemble haptic and kinesthetic information about objects into a unified representation, or the capacity to transform these representations in ways important to mature human spatial cognition" (1991, p. 176).

But if vision is not crucial for object representation, what is its role? Outside the laboratory, observers explore and characterize objects in terms of their visual appearance as well as by means of haptic exploration. How is the chore shared between these two sources of information? This question interests not only students of perception but also engineers who must design robots that can operate in distant environments (the moon, for instance) or handle dangerous objects and substances (radioactive material, for example). Suppose the robots have both visual and haptic capacities. Under what conditions should one be used in preference to the other? When do *we* use one in preference to the other?

Because of the relative speed with which various EP's are executed, haptics is best suited to extract information about properties related to an object's material—its hardness, its temperature, its surface texture—and least suited as a source for the object's geometric properties—its shape. Lederman, Klatzky and Pawluk (1992) note that choice of test stimuli can make haptics seem ineffective compared to vision. In particular, imagine having to sort differently-shaped, three-dimensional objects all made of the same material. Here, compared to vision, haptics would be slow. Conversely, if the objects were identical in shape but varied only in hardness or in temperature, vision would do poorly compared to haptics. The lesson, then, is that haptics and vision provide complementary sources of information.

Haptics and touch play important roles in another area: both guide skilled motor acts, particularly the grasp and manipulation of objects.

Suppose you reach for and pick up a delicate object. Your fingers must exert enough force to hold the object without its slipping but not so much force that the object breaks. The classic demonstration of this tradeoff is the robot hand that tries to pick up a raw egg. One approach is to adjust the force of the grip using information from touch receptors in the fingertips. Lederman, Klatzky and Pawluk (1992) summarize physiological studies that demonstrate the contributions of various touch receptors during different stages of reaching and grasping.

The intimate connection between touch and exploratory motor behavior is mirrored by the proximity of touch areas and motor areas in the cerebral cortex. The area of the brain responsible for activating the muscles of the body, the so-called *motor cortex,* lies immediately adjacent and anterior to the somatosensory cortex (recall Figure 12.11). This adjacency simplifies interconnections between these areas and facilitates the coordination of exploratory, grasping and other manipulatory movements needed in active touch.

There is evidence that different regions of the somatosensory cortex control different aspects of active touch. This is most directly shown by temporarily inactivating various localized regions of somatosensory cortex and measuring the behavioral consequences. In one such study, physiologists at the Toho University School of Medicine in Tokyo injected minute amounts of muscimol, a neurotransmitter antagonist, into the finger regions of a monkey brain S-I (Hikosaka et al., 1985). Before and after various injections, Hikosaka and colleagues tested a monkey's ability to detect and extract small pieces of food embedded in the holes of a wooden block (in most tests, the monkey's eyes were blindfolded). When the chemical had been injected into Area 3b, the monkey could put its fingers into the hole but seemed unable to detect the presence of food in the hole, even after actually touching the food. This constitutes a sensory deficit. But injections to Area 2 of S-I, presumably a later stage of cortical processing, produced a very different type of deficit.* The monkey's excited behavior showed that the food had been detected, but the animal was unable to move its fingers in the coordinated way needed to extract the food. Other studies, involving permanent lesions to restricted areas of S-I (Randolph and Semmes, 1974) and S-II (Carlson and Burton, 1988), support the idea that these different areas play a crucial role in various aspects of touch.

Besides informing us about the particulars of an object we're in tactile contact with, neurons in these somatosensory areas of the brain also participate in forming short-term memories of recently handled objects, as Zhou and Fuster (1996) documented. In their study, monkeys were trained to explore a textured object with one hand for a few seconds, to remember the shape and texture of the object, and then to use the same hand to select that object from several alternatives presented several seconds later. Recording from single neurons with receptive fields located on the hand being used by the monkey, Zhou and Fuster found that about half these neurons in somatosensory cortex kept on responding during the interval between the initial touch period and the test period. So these neurons not only analyze the tactile features of objects but also maintain a neural image of those features in short-term memory. Presumably this neural image can then guide subsequent motor responses to that object.

Recall from Chapter 4 that the visual pathways appear to be subdivided into specialized processing streams. One of those streams is responsible for directing and guiding our activities such as orienting toward and reaching for objects of interest. That processing stream is associated with the parietal lobe which, as you've just learned, is also intimately involved in tactile perception. It is not surprising, therefore, that vision and touch jointly control the ability to grasp and

---

*We describe Area 2 as "later" than Area 3b because some of Area 2's input comes from Area 3b, but the reverse does not seem to be true.

lift objects. Think back to that tomato that you were considering at the produce market. Initially, vision guided your hand to the object and controlled the conformation of your fingers as you prepared to grasp it. But once you made contact with the tomato, your sense of touch took over, using friction and force to gauge the strength of your grasp. Memory, too, was playing a role, informing you ahead of time what to expect when grasping the tomato. Actually, humans are pretty good at adjusting their grasp in a manner appropriate for an object using sight alone or using touch alone (Jenmalm and Johansson, 1997). But working together, these two sources of information coded in the parietal lobe make grasp decisions faster and more accurately.

Clinical

In humans, damage to these parietal regions produces a remarkable condition called **unilateral neglect.** In this condition, a patient may fail to attend to one side of the body, ignoring it as though it didn't even exist. For example, the neurologist MacDonald Critchley described one patient who reproved his own arm, protesting: "You bloody bastard! It's a lost soul, this bloody thing. It keeps following me around. It gets in my way when I read. I find my hand up by my face, waving about" (1979, p. 118). The ownership of the troublesome, wandering arm was denied by the patient despite contrary evidence from the sense of touch.

Phantom Limb

Clinical

In unilateral neglect, people may deny ownership of one of their limbs; a limb that is objectively present is subjectively ignored. The reverse situation can also occur, in which a person feels a limb that is objectively not present. This is the bizarre condition known as **phantom limb,** where an amputee has the compelling sense that an amputed limb is still attached to his or her body (Melzack, 1992). V. S. Ramachandran (Ramachandran and Blakeslee, 1998) vividly describes one such patient:

> As a result of this gruesome mishap [a motorcycle accident], Tom lost his left arm just above the el-

bow. . . . In the weeks afterward, even though he knew his arm was gone, Tom could still feel its ghostly presence below the elbow. He could wiggle each "finger," "reach out" and "grab" objects that were within arm's reach. Indeed, his phantom arm seemed to be able to do anything that the real arm would have done automatically, such as warding off blows, breaking falls or patting his little brother on the back. (pp. 21–22)

It used to be thought that phantom limb was a psychiatric disorder, a form of hysteria triggered by the traumatic loss of the limb. But now it's generally believed that these illusory bodily sensations arise from reorganization of the "touch" map in the parietal lobe of the brain (Melzack, 1992; Ramachandran and Blakeslee, 1998). The portion of the cortical map devoted to the missing limb comes to be innervated by other portions of the body, most likely those body regions with cortical representations neighboring those of the missing limb. Thus, for example, the patient Tom reported sensation in his missing limb when Ramachandran lightly stroked Tom's cheek with a cotton swab. (The face region of the somatosensory cortex is located adjacent to the hand region.)

The worst aspect of phantom limbs is the excruciating pain that seems to be localized in the limb or in specific parts of the limb. For example, Melzack (1992) mentions that after leg or foot amputation, patients feel that their toes are being "seared by a red-hot poker." Although researchers are actively pursuing a number of leads, there is now no sure way to alleviate such pain.

The discussion of phantom limb syndrome sets the stage for the final two topics of this chapter, pain perception and neural plasticity in the somatosensory system.

PAIN PERCEPTION

Pain is an unusually difficult sensory experience to study, for the simple reason that people have trouble verbalizing what pain really is and how intense it feels. According to the official definition given by the International Association for the

Clinical

Study of Pain (Merskey and Bogduk, 1994), pain is "an unpleasant sensory or emotional experience associated with actual or potential tissue damage." While capturing the general character of pain, that definition fails to capture the individual, subjective character of the experience. Pain, in fact, depends significantly on the specific instigating condition, the person's previous history with painful stimulation, and the sufferer's mental state. Whatever the particulars of pain, it is widely accepted that pain constitutes a biologically important "warning signal" of tissue damage. Thus, the threshold for acute, painful stimulation, whether it's produced by heat or by mechanical pressure, corresponds closely to the stimulus intensity level at which the skin and underlying tissue become susceptible to injury.

Chronic pain, such as that associated with a bruised muscle or a broken bone, has the beneficial effect of discouraging continued use of the affected body part, thereby facilitating recovery. Chronic internal pain with no obvious origin usually forewarns of illness or disease. So pain does have its adaptive purpose. Still, there is nothing more debilitating than chronic pain, as anyone who suffers painful migraine headaches will testify. Billions of dollars are spent annually in pursuit of pain relief, and the treatment of pain raises grave ethical issues about patient's rights, quality of life, assisted suicide and capital punishment.

In this section, we'll not do justice to the huge literature on pain and its management, but we will provide an overview of some of the perceptual and neurophysiological aspects of pain. Excellent reviews of pain-related findings can be found in Jessell and Kelly (1991), Wall and Melzack (1994) and Craig and Rollman (1999).

Neural Pathways for Pain Signals

Research on pain perception faces a unique challenge: There is simply no way to know whether one person's pain resembles the pain someone else experiences. It's difficult to gauge the qual-ity and intensity of any painful experience. Of course, this could be said for other sensory experiences as well. Is your red the same as mine? But in the case of the other senses—hearing, seeing, taste, smell and touch—we can point to an evoking "stimulus" that reliably accompanies a perceptual experience. In the case of pain, however, this is sometimes impossible. Pain is defined exclusively by the subjective report of the individual experiencing it.

Some common forms of acute pain (such as that experienced when you accidentally prick yourself with a pin) are generated by abrupt, strong stimulation of the skin's mechanoreceptors. These painful experiences can be eliminated by anesthetics that dull the responsiveness of mechanoreceptors or their associated afferent fibers (thank goodness for Novacaine when visiting the dentist). Other forms of pain (such as that associated with arthritis) are more chronic and result from damage to bodily tissue. Different drugs are needed in order to deal with different aspects of pain (Hunt and Mantyh, 2001). So, pain that originates in damage to the skin can be targeted by a drug that acts peripherally, reducing signals from the skin's pain receptors. Antiinflammatory agents are examples of such drugs. However, to address pain's psychological unpleasantness and distress, a centrally-acting drug, such as an opiate, may be called for.

Management of chronic pain presents a special challenge, for the most effective pharmacological treatments tend to lose their potency with increased use, while at the same time presenting the possibility of addiction. Molecular biologists are working hard to formulate effective drugs that do not have these drawbacks. For now, though, pain therapists focus heavily on behavioral strategies for managing chronic pain. As we'll see in a moment, some of those strategies could be effective because they recruit "top-down" cognitive control over neural events signalling pain.

To study pain in the laboratory requires the ability to induce the experience and to measure it. A number of different rating scales have been

E

Execute

developed for assessing the intensity and un-pleasantness of pain. Some of those scales ask the individual to assign numbers to their experi-ence of pain, often using behavioral indices to calibrate the numerical scale (for example, "As-sign the number 10 if you must immediately seek relief"). Alternatively, investigators can gauge pain using reflex reactions such as hand withdrawal, pupil dilation and galvanic skin re-sponse. These are particularly useful when studying pain in nonhumans. In recent years, in-vestigators have also used somatosensory evoked potentials (recorded from the scalp) and neuroimaging techniques to assess neural con-comitants of pain sensations.

To study pain experimentally, researchers have developed techniques for provoking cali-brated painful sensations in human and animal subjects. One technique is to apply a chemical ir-ritant to the surface of the skin. One popular irri-tant is capsaicin, the "hot" ingredient in chili pep-pers. (If you've ever touched your eyes or other mucous tissues after handling chili peppers, you're familiar with capsaicin's potency.) An-other technique involves applying a controlled degree of mechanical force to the skin using a hard, sharp object. A third technique employs a focused beam of radiant energy to generate ex-treme warmth on a restricted region of the skin.

Neural Stimulation from any of these noxious proce-dures can generate neural activity within a specific class of receptors within the skin known as **noci-ceptors.** These are found among the free nerve endings located near the surface of the skin (noci-ceptors registering information about temperature extremes) as well as within the subcutaneous fat below the skin's surface (nociceptors registering information about sharp, punctate stimulation). Neural messages from the nociceptors, in turn, are carried by specialized nerve fibers that travel from the skin to the dorsal parts of the spinal cord (see Figure 12.15). These fibers are divisible into two groups, the "slow-conducting" fibers and the "fast-conducting" fibers. Both sets of fibers have relatively high "thresholds," meaning that they are

activated only in response to rather intense levels of stimulation, levels well above that required sim-ply to detect the presence of a tactile stimulus. Once their threshold has been exceeded, slow-fiber responses increase as stimulation intensifies. However, these slow fibers respond more weakly to intense stimulation if they are activated several seconds before the intense stimulation. These fibers, in other words, seem to be responsive to the relative level of intense stimulation. Fast fibers have response thresholds that are even higher than the slow fibers, and they show long-term hyper-sensitivity following prolonged noxious stimula-tion to the skin. Slow fibers may be involved in hy-peralgesia, the heightened discomfort produced by stimulation delivered to an already painful region of the skin. (Imagine the painful sensation you might experience if you brushed a burned region of your hand against some object.)

Nociceptive fibers project to a circumscribed region of the thalamus, a cluster of nuclei that re-lays sensory information from the periphery to the cortex (recall the LGN in vision). Pain's thal-amic relay is situated laterally in the posterior portion of the thalamus (Craig et al., 1994). The neurons in this thalamic region, in turn, project to several regions of the brain, including the so-matosensory cortex and regions in the frontal

FIGURE 12.15
Two types of nerve fibers carrying pain information enter the spinal cord via the dorsal root.

cortex associated with the limbic system (those brain areas involved in affective reactions).

A recent neuroimaging study shows convincingly that these different brain regions are responsible for representing different perceptual aspects of painful experiences. Rainville and colleagues (1997) used PET to measure the distribution of brain activity evoked by exposing human volunteers to noxious thermal stimulation. The interesting twist to this study was the use of hypnosis to manipulate the perceived unpleasantness generated by a constant level of stimulation. Pain-related activation was found in S-I and S-II in the parietal lobe, regardless of the perceived unpleasantness of that stimulation. However, activation in limbic sites including the anterior cingulate cortex was modulated by the hypnotic suggestion, with more unpleasant experiences associated with greater activation. This dissociation between perceived intensity and perceived unpleasantness dovetails nicely with clinical reports that people with brain damage to these frontal lobe regions report that noxious stimulation, while feeling painful, isn't particularly bothersome (Fields, 1987; Treede et al., 1999).

The Gate Control Theory of Pain

The single most influential theory of pain perception is Melzack and Wall's **gate control theory** of pain, which builds on the idea of multiple interacting fiber pathways. (You should be able to see the link between this model and the "fast" and "slow" nociceptive fibers discussed above.) An overview of this theory is diagrammed in Figure 12.16. Three groups of nerve fibers make synaptic contact with a group of cells located in the spinal cord (labelled "T-cells" in the figure): fast-conducting nociceptive fibers, slow-conducting nociceptive fibers and fast-conducting fibers that carry information about touch but not pain. The T-cells, when active, transmit (thus the label *T*) pain signals up the spinal cord to the brain, culminating in the experience of pain. Also located in the spinal cord is a cluster of neurons (technically,

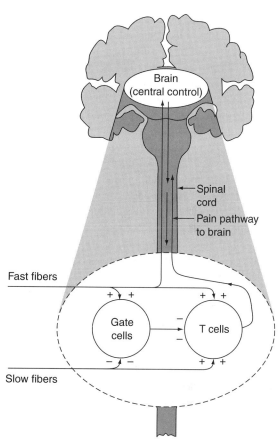

FIGURE 12.16
Schematic of the gate control theory of pain.

a nucleus) that constitutes the "gate." When activated, this nucleus inhibits the T-cells and, therefore, suppresses the communication of T-cell signals to the brain. The key to the model resides in the differential effect of the fast- and slow-conducting fibers on the "gate" itself. The fast-conducting fibers excite the neurons forming the gate, and the slow-conducting fibers inhibit the gate neurons.

To see how the model works, consider what happens when your skin lightly touches the handle of a cool pan sitting on the stove. This event would immediately stimulate the fast "touch" fibers, which have a lower threshold than the slow "pain" fibers. This activates the gate neurons which, in turn, would inhibit the T neurons. The result? You painlessly experience the feel of the handle. But suppose the pan itself was quite hot, handle included. Now the slow-conducting fibers with their higher threshold for activation would be excited, and this would simultaneously inhibit the gate neurons and activate the T-neurons. The result? Now you feel not only the handle but also the pain associated with it.

Top-down

According to this model, pain messages originating in the T-cells can also be blocked by fibers originating in the brain and projecting back down to the gate portion in the spinal cord. These fibers allow "top-down"control over pain perception. This aspect of the model is confirmed by clinical experience. It is well established that surgical patients require lower doses of pain killers when they have been told ahead of time what to expect during the procedure and have been trained to relax before and during surgery. These patients are also released from the hospital several days earlier than those not receiving pain management training. Also related to the "top-down" control of pain is the so-called placebo effect, whereby a patient experiences less pain following ingestion of a "painkiller" that, in fact, contains no active ingredients. The mere expectation of pain relief is sometimes sufficient to produce the desired effect. You can imagine how these expectations might enable the patient unwittingly to activate "top-down" influences that shut the spinal cord's pain gate. Box 12.2 describes some additional facts and myths about pain perception.

We will complete our survey of touch with the topic of cortical plasticity: modification of the brain's representation of the sense of touch in response to use and disuse.

PLASTICITY IN THE SOMATOSENSORY CORTEX

Plasticity

For decades it was thought that sensory maps in the brain were shaped by experiences very early in life but thereafter remained fixed in size and composition. During the 1980's and 1990's, how-

ever, converging lines of evidence forced abandonment of that view. Instead, it is now recognized that throughout life the somatosensory cortex remains malleable, or plastic, and that cortical connections adjust over time to changes in afferent input. This research has intriguing implications for the uniqueness of every human being. But before turning to such implications, we must consider the research itself.

Origins of Plasticity

The study of plasticity within the somatosensory cortex was stimulated by Vernon Mountcastle's theory of cortical development (Mountcastle, 1984). Mountcastle depicts the cortex as a dynamic, self-organizing system of interconnected neurons. Neurons in a given region of the brain can *potentially* form an enormously large number of synapses with other neurons, many more synapses than are *actually* formed. Presumably, afferent fibers coming into the somatosensory cortex from the thalamus compete for contact with—and control over—neurons in the somatosensory cortex. Only a fraction of all possible synapses actually survives this competition. What determines which fibers will win the competition? What controls the selection of particular synapses to be activated from among the horde of potential synapses? In basic terms, the theory claims that the most active inputs win, with less active inputs becoming dormant.

To evaluate Mountcastle's theory, one must study the events that influence the development and maintenance of connections between cortical neurons and their incoming afferent fibers. This problem has been the focus of research by Michael Merzenich and his colleagues (Merzenich, 1987; Buonomano and Marzenich, 1998). Merzenich began by mapping cortical locations that represent touch information from the fingers and hands of adult monkeys. These finger and hand "maps" in the somatosensory cortex turned out to be remarkably plastic, even in adult animals. Though the maps' broad outlines remain

BOX 12.2

SOME FACTS—AND MYTHS—ABOUT PAIN

The English writer and wit Samuel Johnson said, "The mind is seldom quickened to very vigorous operations but by pain, or the dread of pain." With characteristic insight, Johnson reminded his readers of the obvious: pain, or even the mere anticipation of pain, has the propensity to seize the mind. Anyone scheduled to have a root canal, a tetanus shot or a spanking can relate to this maxim. Researchers have identified some brain circuits that mediate the dread and fear that are evoked by the anticipation of pain (Price, 2000). Pain is not an experience we relish, and we're terribly uncomfortable even watching someone else suffer pain. (One of the most agonizing moments in cinematic history occurs during the scene in "Marathon Man" where we watch Dustin Hoffman writhing in pain as he is tortured by having a hole drilled in his tooth.) Because pain is so salient and, alas, so inevitable, humans have tried countless measures to relieve pain. Here, we summarize some of those palliatives, both successful ones and failures.

Acupuncture   For people raised in contemporary Western culture, with its emphasis on medical science, it's hard to imagine how the insertion of fine needles into specific sites on the body could alleviate pain. Yet centuries of practice document that **acupuncture** works. The acupuncture maps that guided the ancient Chinese pain healers are still accurate today. For some pain sites, the needle insertion point is within the immediate neighborhood, while for others the insertion point is quite remote from the pain site.

Western science has advanced several explanations for the **analgesia** (elimination of pain) produced by acupuncture. On one account, acupuncture stimulates the release of **endorphins,** naturally occurring morphine-like chemicals produced by our bodies. These chemicals, acting on specialized receptors in the brain, are able to quell painful sensations. Our bodies naturally produce endorphins, particularly under conditions of stress.

Centuries ago humans discovered natural substances—most notably opium and heroin—that

reduce pain and instigate feelings of euphoria. Those substances stimulate the same receptors as those designed to respond to endorphins. A brain on drugs isn't doing anything it wasn't designed to do. It's just doing it when it shouldn't be.

A second, alternative account of acupuncture's analgesic effect posits that the needle stimulates slow conducting nociceptive fibers, thereby "closing" the pain gate.

Whatever explanation eventually proves correct, there is no quarreling with thousands of years of success: when administered by an experienced practitioner, acupuncture can work.

Inducing Pain to Relieve Pain   In the text we mentioned that capsaicin—the active ingredient in hot peppers—was a sure-fire means for inducing pain when it comes in contact with the skin or mucous membrane. Ironically, capsaicin is also an effective agent for ameliorating pain. Following exposure to capsaicin, the experience of acute, burning pain gradually wanes. If a second exposure to capsaicin occurs after the burning sensation from a previous exposure has dissipated, your experience of pain is actually muted again. Capsaicin, in other words, elevates the threshold for pain in areas to which it has previously been applied (Berger et al., 1995). Moreover, this moderating effect generalizes to other painful stimuli as well. Thus, an individual's pain tolerance can be gradually elevated by increasing the capsaicin concentration in a series of repeated applications. Currently capsaicin treatment is being tested for use in cases of heartburn, some forms of itching, sunburns and rheumatism.

Pain and the Weather   In 1887 the American Journal of Medical Science published a case report of an amputee who experienced pain in his phantom limb (the condition described earlier in the text). The patient's pain varied with the weather, being most severe when an approaching storm produced a drop in barometric pressure (Shutty et al., 1992). Subsequent clinical reports suggested that arthritis sufferers also

BOX 12.2 continued

experienced heightened pain when the barometric pressure dropped. More recently, surveys of patients suffering chronic pain have confirmed that changes in temperature and humidity elevate self ratings of pain. It is conceivable that changes in temperature and/or humidity cause tendons, muscles and scar tissue to expand and contract, thereby exacerbating pain. While the exact mechanisms remain obscure, there does seem to be truth to the aphorism, "Aches and pains, coming rains." Contrary to popular belief, though, pain is not entirely relieved by living in a mild climate—seasonal changes still trigger surges in pain (Jamison, 1996).

The Pain of Execution   The VIII Amendment to the Constitution of the United States explicitly prohibits the use of "cruel and unusual punishment." Advocates of capital punishment argue that death by execution could be seen as extreme, but it does not constitute cruelty because, they argue, the person being executed does not feel pain. This argument, however, may be flawed. In an article not for the squeamish, Hillman (1993) argues that all forms of execution other than lethal intravenous injection induce severe pain in the dying individual. For starters, initial attempts at execution are not always success-

ful, leaving the prisoner injured and suffering until the procedure is successfully completed. And even when death results on the first try, the death is often not instantaneous. With electrocution, for example, a person experiences severe burns and, perhaps, asphyxiation and heart fibrillation. It may take many seconds before the individual loses consciousness, and in the meantime, he or she is very likely to be experiencing excruciating pain. Even the procedure of beheading (which is still practiced in some countries in Africa and in the Middle East) may entail a conscious experience of pain. The human brain maintains enough oxygen for metabolism to persist for seconds after the blood supply is severed. And animal experiments show that the brain continues to function for many seconds after its blood supply is interrupted. It is hard to imagine the experiences one might have during those few seconds immediately following decapitation.

Hillman points out that the absence of signs of extreme suffering cannot be taken as evidence that pain isn't being experienced. Restraints may mask some of those signs, and those signs may be mistakenly attributed to the act of dying itself. The widely held view that executions are painless and, therefore, humane rests on flimsy evidence.

fixed, their details could be altered by experience. In one study, Merzenich surgically joined the skin from two adjacent fingers without disturbing the receptors or nerve fibers lying within the skin. This delicate surgical procedure turns previously separate fingers into a single functional unit—anything that happens to one finger also happens to the other. They move as one, and they receive touch information as one.

The procedure had extraordinary consequences. After the newly joined fingers were used for a few weeks, previously sharp boundaries between the maps for the two digits had dissolved, leaving a single cortical representation

for the two-finger combination. Moreover, neurons that used to have receptive fields on just one of the digits now had receptive fields extending across both fingers. Next, Merzenich surgically redivided the fingers, restoring them to their normal state. After the fingers were used for a while, the cortical representations of the two fingers again became distinct and separate. The details of the somatosensory map, therefore, are created in response to experience, and can be modified by altered sensory input even in adulthood (Wall, 1988). Box 12.3 discusses some behavioral observations on humans that suggest the human brain is capable of analogous remapping.

BOX 12.3

ILLUSIONS OF TOUCH: KEEP YOUR FINGERS CROSSED

Illusion

The oldest known illusion of touch was described by Aristotle nearly 2,500 years ago. Suppose that you cross two adjacent fingers and then touch an object, such as a pen, with both crossed fingertips at the same time. It will feel like you're touching two pens, not one. Fabrizio Benedetti, an Italian psychologist, performed several ingenious studies of this ancient phenomenon (1985, 1986). Benedetti started with a puzzle. Suppose, with your fingers *not* crossed and held slightly apart, you touch that same pen with both fingertips. Now, even though two fingertips are being stimulated (as before), you feel only one pen. Why does the illusion fail under this situation?

Benedetti reasoned from an analogy to vision. Under most conditions, when the image of an object stimulates both retinas, we see a single object. This singleness of vision occurs because the two monocular images are normally formed on matching areas of the two eyes. When, however, those images are formed on nonmatching areas, double vision is experienced—a person sees two objects, not one. Benedetti applied the same reasoning to explain Aristotle's illusion. He hypothesized that we experience perceptual doubling whenever two receptor points (fingertips or retinal loci) not normally stimulated by a single object are stimulated by that object. In the case of touch, if matching sites on adjacent fingers, say the index and middle finger, are touched simultaneously, a single object is felt; however, if the same stimulus is somehow applied to nonadjacent fingers, say the index and fourth fingers, there is an illusory experience of two objects. Note that Benedetti's hypothesis puts visual doubling and touch doubling in a common framework.

Benedetti tested his idea by trying to produce **diplesthesia** (doubled touch) without having to cross the fingers. He used a specially designed clamp to press and hold together volunteers' third and fourth fingers. By changing the amount of pressure on the sides of the fingers, Benedetti was able to displace the fingers' skin by amounts ranging from 3 to 12 millimeters. He then touched the tips of the clamped fingers with either a single sphere or two spheres joined together. The volunteer reported whether he or she felt one or two objects. Benedetti found that a 4- to 6-millimeter displacement of the skin—without finger crossing—can produce a strong illusory doubling of touch sensations.

Extending these observations, Benedetti (1991) used prolonged bandaging to simulate amputation of the middle finger. The bandaged finger was immobilized, and thus excluded from the hand's exploratory and manipulatory activities. In order to grasp or manipulate an object (say, a pen) the remaining, working fingers had to be used in unusual pairings. For example, people wrote with the pen held between the thumb, index and fourth finger (instead of thumb, index and third finger). These unusual arrangement subjected some pairs of fingers to what was quite rare for them before the "amputation": simultaneous stimulation by a single object.

Six months of bandaging brought dramatic changes in diplethesia. For example, the index and fourth fingers now responded as though they were actually adjacent; simultaneous touch of these new partners no longer produced diplethesia. One hypothesis is that these perceptual changes reflect some kind of reorganization within the cortical representation of the hand. Such reorganization has been demonstrated by other investigators. Pascual-Leone and Torres (1993) recorded ERPs evoked in the human somatosensory cortex by stimulation of the fingers of Braille readers and nonreaders. With Braille readers, who presumably make greater use of their fingertips for fine discriminations, stimulation of the fingertips evoked electrical responses from a larger portion of the cortex than did equivalent stimulation of the non-Braille readers less-used fingertips. Related signs of human cortical reorganization have been reported by Braun et al. (2000). So after 2,500 years, we are finally beginning to understand the puzzle that Aristotle presented to us.

Plasticity

Up to now we've only talked about cortical reorganization in response to some rearrangement of the fingers, an event that is pretty exotic. Analogous changes in the somatosensory cortex follow from conditions much closer to our own experience. Coordinated behavioral and physiological studies reveal that discrimination of subtle differences in touch stimulation improves dramatically with practice, and that this improvement is accompanied by changes in the somatosensory cortex. Recanzone and colleagues (1992a) applied a vibrating stimulator to one spot on a monkey's fingertip. From a series of stimuli, the monkey had to identify the one stimulus that vibrated at a frequency slightly different from the others. Over time, the monkeys were able to make increasingly fine discriminations. Although adjacent, nonpracticed fingers, showed some slight improvement as well, the effects on the trained digit were far more impressive, suggesting the practice's effects were localized. Recanzone and colleagues (1992b) studied the somatosensory cortex in these same monkeys. Prolonged training produced several changes, including an increase in the area devoted to the trained region of the monkey's finger and an heightened crispness and consistency in responding to the vibration stimulus.

Plasticity

    This story of cortical plasticity has another intriguing twist. Changes in organization within the somatosensory cortex induced by training do not occur automatically. If the monkey's finger is stimulated but the animal doesn't have to discriminate one touch stimulus from another, there is very little improvement in performance and correspondingly little change in the somatosensory cortex (Recanzone 1992b).* The brain

changes only if the monkey pays attention to the stimulated finger. By some means, currently unknown, plasticity of cortical maps is modulated by the behavioral state of an organism.

Plasticity in the Human Brain

Is the human brain comparably malleable in response to training? One way to answer this question is to consider people who use their sense of touch in radically different ways from most of us. Are their brains organized differently? Consider professional musicians who play the violin. As you can imagine, they spend countless hours practicing their fingering using the left hand, with the right hand used primarily for bowing. Does the dexterous left hand of a violin player appropriate greater than normal brain representation because of this unique experience?

To find out, a group of German neuroscientists (Elbert et al., 1995) used PET neuroimaging to measure brain activity while the fingers on a person's left and right hand were being stimulated. In nonmusicians, the left hand and right hands exhibited comparably sized representations within the somatosensory regions of the right and left hemispheres, respectively. But in musicians who relied greatly on the left hand, that hand's touch representation was much larger than that of the right hand. In other words, the brain's touch map had changed in response to the individual's tactile experiences. Moreover, musicians who began their training early in life had larger left-hand brain maps than did musicians who postponed their training a number of years. Evidently, early onset of string playing recruits more brain cells to serve the touch sensors in the critical, left hand's fingers.

As you might expect, Braille readers also show an enlarged cortical representation within the S-I region associated with their reading fingers (see the review by Hamilton and Pascual-Leone, 1998). But not all Braille readers use the same technique, and these individual differences in technique have interesting cortical conse-

---

*The monkeys who did not have to make touch discriminations were actively distracted from attending to what happened on their fingers. These monkeys were serving simultaneously in a second study, on behavioral and physiological effects of practice in making auditory discriminations (Recanzone, Schreiner and Merzenich, 1993). Those results were described earlier in Chapter 10.

quences. Some Braille readers use just a single finger, others use fingers on each hand, in concert. This latter technique entails prolonged simultaneous and coordinated use of fingers that ordinarily would not be used together. And this reading-related synchronized activity alters the brain's normal orderly representation of the fingers, much as binding fingers together would (Sterr et al., 1998).

Some Possible Clinical Applications

Clinical

These results may help to shape new therapies for use with humans whose touch sensitivity has been diminished by damage to the somatosensory cortex. Dannenbaum and Dykes (1988) have developed a unique rehabilitation strategy, drawing heavily upon Merzenich's work with monkeys. The therapy, which seems quite promising, reeducates one component of touch at a time. To promote reorganization of a damaged somatosensory cortex, Dannenbaum and Dykes encourage the patients to practice skills such as recognizing the presence of rough objects applied to the skin, appreciating the direction in which an object sweeps across the skin, discriminating shapes and making progressively finer and more accurate localization of touch stimuli. With specific stimulation repeated time and time again, the well-motivated patients who have been studied thus far showed substantial improvement in touch and manipulation of objects.

Whatever their ultimate impact on rehabilitation therapy, Merzenich's findings with monkeys are certainly intriguing. But one must be careful not to misconstrue them. The modifications resulting from altered sensory input in adult animals occurred within the microstructure of neighboring touch maps; the gross boundaries of the somatosensory area were not affected by experience. Moreover, at least some of these cortical changes are responses to growth of new connections within subcortical structures that provide input to the cortex (Kaas, Florence and Jain, 1999). So, it would be wrong to conclude

from Merzenich's studies that one area of the adult brain can always take over the function of another. In the *mature* nervous system, the boundaries separating different areas of the brain (for example, the somatosensory cortex and the motor cortex) become fixed and are not subject to change. Only the details of maps within those areas can be reshaped by experience.*

Having qualified the extent of plasticity in the adult brain, we should also point out that there is much greater cortical flexibility in the *immature* nervous system (Kaas, 1991). Studies with animals show that the neuroanatomical and physiological response properties of neurons in various areas can be remarkably reshaped. For example, axons forming the optic nerve from the eye can be encouraged to sprout neural connections into auditory portions of the brain, if the normal target regions for those optic nerve fibers is destroyed (Sur, Garraghty and Roe, 1988). Fascinating evidence for wholesale cortical reorganization in humans comes from a study of brain activations in congenitally blind individuals who are experienced Braille readers (Sadato et al., 1996). In sighted people, tactile stimulation activates the somatosensory cortex but not the visual cortex in the occipital lobe. However, in experienced, blind Braille readers the visual cortex is also activated as those blind individuals use their fingers to "read" Braille characters. The occipital lobe, in other words, has been recruited into the process of tactile perception.

There's another piece of evidence pointing to the same conclusion (Cohen et al., 1997). Recall

---

*The inflexibility of the mature cortex does not mean that large-scale neural reorganization will *never* be possible. Once researchers figure out what neurochemical events promote plasticity in early life, it may be possible to artificially reinstate those events in adulthood, thereby reawakening cortical plasticity. This possibility offers great hope for rehabilitation of individuals suffering stroke and spinal cord injuries. At the same time, this reawakening process must be carefully focused, for major cortical reorganization could also have detrimental consequences such as disrupted perceptual processing and erased learning (Kaas, Florence and Jain, 1999).

from Chapter 4 the TMS technique, whereby brief pulses of magnetic energy applied to a person's scalp temporarily scramble neural activity in that region of the brain in the immediate vicinity of the pulse. This technique was employed with blind individuals who were seasoned Braille readers. TMS pulses delivered to their occipital cortex while they read either Braille or embossed Roman letters produced temporary disruptions in their reading comprehension. In sighted individuals, TMS applied over the occipital lobe had no effect on the sense of touch. This remarkable finding, together with the PET activation study described earlier, imply that cortical areas can be recruited to roles outside of their usual function, at least when the conditions sponsoring that recruitment (such as blindness) arise early in life. These findings offer new hope for the development of interventions that could accelerate the adjustment to blindness (Hamilton and Pascual-Leone, 1998).

Aside from their possible clinical significance, these findings on cortical plasticity carry profound philosophical implications. Human perception, cognition, personality and behavior are all shaped by the billions of connections within the brain, and these connections now appear to be dynamically modified in response to experience. These modifications would be tailored to your particular lifetime experiences, virtually guaranteeing that the connections in your brain are different from the connections in other human brains. Could these differences among brains, then, be responsible, at least in part, for the real differences among people?

As you can see, these speculations bear on some truly fundamental issues, including human identity and human diversity. It's exciting even to imagine that in our own lifetimes these basic, long-standing, and perplexing philosophical issues may finally be resolved.

SUMMARY AND PREVIEW

In this chapter we explored how the sense of touch, working primarily through that remarkable sensory organ, the human hand, is capable of fast, highly accurate and subtle discriminations. We discovered that touch owes part of its success to the information it gets from sets of touch receptors whose different characteristics create diverse and complementary perspectives on the world that lies at our fingertips. An equally great part of its success seems to come, though, from the unique information created by the hand's own skilled and highly purposeful exploration of the world. The intimate relationships between man-

ual exploration and the resulting sensory response reminded us of the pervasive connections between perception and action. We also learned about pain—touch's "dark" side. We saw that pain is a complex sensory experience with intensive and affective overtones. Finally, we saw how controlled, intensive practice could alter cortical organization even into adulthood.

In the next chapter we turn to taste and smell, senses that are important not only as channels for information about the world, but also as providers of particular delight and pleasure.

KEY TERMS

acupuncture
analgesia
Braille
diffuse fibers
displethesia
endorphins
free nerve endings
gate control theory
haptics
kinesthesis
localization ability
mechanoreceptors
Meissner corpuscles

Merkel disks
nociceptors
Pacinian corpuscles
phantom limb
proprioception
punctate fibers
rapidly adapting (RA) fibers
Ruffini endings
slowly adapting (SA) fibers
tactile agnosia
touch acuity
unilateral neglect

CHAPTER 13

SMELL AND TASTE

One of the greatest philosophers of the eighteenth century—Immanuel Kant—would probably have told you not to read this chapter. He had no respect for smell and taste, believing that these senses produced information that was much inferior to what the other senses offered. For example, Kant (1798/1978) singled smell out as *the* sense that was "most dispensable." The sense of smell, he asserted, was not worth cultivating because disgusting odors outnumbered pleasant ones (especially in crowded places), and even when we do come across something fragrant, "the pleasure coming from the sense of smell cannot be other than fleeting and transitory" (p. 46). In Kant's view, taste was only barely more valuable, mainly because eating and drinking promotes sociability.

Kant is not alone in denigrating taste and smell as "lower" or "minor" senses, but this designation is arbitrary. Though people do rely heavily on their eyes and ears to guide their everyday activities, the "minor senses" provide crucially impor-

tant information. The smell of smoke, for instance, can signal a dangerous fire, and the foul taste of spoiled food can prevent ingestion of harmful substances. In fact, many animal species depend almost exclusively on taste and smell to tell them about their world. Figure 13.1 shows one example: the star-nosed mole's vaunted senses of smell and touch allow it to live in the dark, safe confines of underground burrows, with virtually no need for eyes (Catania, 2000). Humans may not rely on taste and smell as much as other creatures do, but taste and smell certainly do contribute significantly to our ability to detect and recognize objects in the environment. One thing you will certainly take away from this chapter is a far healthier respect for your nose and your tongue, and the brain machinery responsible for interpreting sensory signals from those organs.

Taste and smell are often referred to by their technical names, *gustation* (from the Latin *gustare,* meaning "to taste") and *olfaction* (from the Latin *olfacere,* meaning "to smell"). They are

FIGURE 13.1
The star-nosed mole, a mammal for whom the sense of smell is paramount. (Photograph courtesy of Ken Catania).

sometimes lumped together as the "chemical senses" because receptors housed in the nose and on the tongue register the presence of chemical substances. These chemical substances are analogous to light energy that strikes the photoreceptors of the eye. But as this book has emphasized, you see *objects,* not *light.* By the same token, your experience of taste and smell is about *objects* and *substances,* not *chemicals.* So taste and smell serve precisely the same purposes as vision and hearing: all of them provide behaviorally-relevant information about the environment so that animals can take action appropriate to that environment.

Although all the senses work toward a common goal, something sets taste and smell apart. The sensations arising from stimulation of the tongue and nose can take on a uniquely pleasurable, sometimes sensual, quality. Sunsets may look beautiful and symphonies may sound enrapturing, but their pleasures are less compelling and immediate than the aroma and taste of, say, freshly-baked chocolate chip cookies. On the other hand, few sights or sounds are as repulsive as a really putrid smell or foul taste. When there's an annoying song on the radio, you can usually manage to ignore it. But try to ignore the stench of a stopped-up toilet. Similarly, merely thinking hard about the taste of some food that made you sick once can nauseate you all over again. Thus, in addition to their roles as sources of information, taste and smell wield a powerful emotional impact.

There is a sizable and rapidly growing body of perceptual, physiological, molecular and genetic studies of taste and smell, and in this chapter we will discuss some of the key findings. Although the two chemical senses are intimately intertwined, for ease of exposition we'll consider them separately, starting with smell.

THE SENSE OF SMELL

Smells are with us all the time. From the aroma of your first cup of coffee in the morning to the smell of clean sheets as you doze off at night, you are awash in a sea of odors. Smells enhance the enjoyment of food (which is why appetite decreases when a cold stops up the nose). You can verify this for yourself. While holding your nose so that you cannot smell what is put into your

Execute

mouth, compare the tastes of a piece of apple and a piece of raw potato. You'll be astonished to find that on the basis of taste alone, the two are very similar. Odors also influence the ways you spend your money. How often have you walked near a bakery and been enticed inside by the smells wafting into the street? It is said that some bakeries vent their ovens out to the sidewalk, using the aroma of fresh bread purposely to lure customers inside (Winter, 1976). Besides the natural smells of the bakery, some businesses also use artificially created odors to influence people's buying habits. For example, plastic briefcases are impregnated with leather scent to enhance their appeal to prospective buyers. And the market value of a second-hand car increases if it's been sprayed with "new car" smell. Real estate agents like to have a pot of coffee brewing when a house is being shown, for the aroma is said to convey a sense of "home" to the potential buyer.

Differences

In their zeal to make their products smell good, manufacturers sometimes go too far, altering the products in ways that defeat smell's function as a warning system. Take, for instance, the smell of ordinary laundry bleach (hypochlorite bleach). As you probably know, bleach has a highly unpleasant, pungent smell which most people can't tolerate. Bleach's offensive odor, however, warns people—even people too young to read the label or people whose eyesight makes its hard to read the label—that this stuff is not good to ingest. And, according to a study by de Wijk and Cain (1994), the warning is effective. These smell scientists asked people to sniff a sample of hypochlorite bleach and make two judgments: identify the sample and judge whether it is safe to drink. The results from their elderly volunteers (average age 76 years) were the most informative. These individuals identified the sample as bleach just 24 percent of the time, but they correctly categorized it as not drinkable 71 percent of the time. So bleach's unpleasant smell worked fairly well to communicate, "Don't ingest me," even when someone didn't know for sure what the stuff was. But, un-

fortunately, some manufacturers have resorted to adding an artificial "fresh" scent to mask bleach's pungency. When de Wijk and Cain tested samples of this *scented* bleach, elderly participants correctly identified it as bleach only 5 percent of the time. Even worse, 71 percent of the time these people made the potentially lethal mistake of classifying the bleach as drinkable. Obviously, this misuse of artificial scent could be very dangerous.

People's behavior is influence by many other smells besides those of foods, cars, briefcases and bleach. TV commercials constantly remind us that our own bodies are major sources of odor. Advertisers exhort us to buy products that will modify those odors, as well as create new ones: deodorants, perfumes, after-shave lotions and mouthwashes. In this pursuit, vast amounts of money are spent every year. Like it or not, you continually give off a invisible cloud of unique smells. Your odors constitute a smell signature so distinctive that a trained hound can track your scent amid the "noise" of odors from other people. Only the scents of identical twins seem to confuse such well-trained hounds (Kalmus, 1955). But dogs are not the only creatures that can exploit scent for tracking. Some humans—the Botocudos* of eastern Brazil and some aboriginal peoples on the Malay peninsula—are reputed to hunt by following their prey's scent (Titchener, 1915). Though few people in industrialized societies perform similar feats, they do have some primitive abilities to use scents for distinguishing people from one another, as the following experiments demonstrate.

If you had to judge whether another person was male or female on the basis of smell alone, do you think you could? The answer appears to be yes. Patricia Wallace (1977) tested whether college students could discriminate male from female just

---

*In the case of the Botocudos, occasionally the prey they tracked was probably human; the Botocudos were reputed to practice cannibalism.

by smelling a person's hand. While blindfolded, a student sniffed a hand held one-half inch from the student's nose. The male and female individuals whose hands served as test stimuli had washed thoroughly before the test session and then worn a disposable plastic glove for 15 minutes prior to testing, to promote perspiration. Wallace found that subjects could tell male from female hands, with over 80 percent accuracy. Furthermore, female sniffers were better at the task than were male sniffers.

In addition to using the smell from sweaty hands, people can also accurately use breath odor to judge the gender of the breather. Richard Doty and coworkers at the University of Pennsylvania had male and female college students judge the breath odor of breath donors who were seated opposite them. A partition prevented judges from seeing the donors (Figure 13.2). By inserting their noses into a plastic funnel, judges could inhale the breath of the donors, who were exhaling through a glass tube connected to the funnel. Donors were told not to eat spicy food the day before testing, and they were not permitted to wear odorous cosmetic products. Most judges scored better than chance (50 percent) at identifying the donor's gender, with female judges outperforming their male counterparts (Doty et al., 1982). Doty and colleagues also had judges rate breath odors for pleasantness and intensity. Breath odors of males were rated on the average as less pleasant and more intense than the breath odors of females.

The most remarkable individual acuity for body odor was evidenced by a blind woman who worked in the laundry of an asylum in Hartford, Connecticut. As described by William James (1890, vol. 1, pp. 509–510), this woman could sort the laundry of individual inmates on the basis of smell alone, and that was after the clothes had been washed! Less dramatic but impressive nonetheless is the performance of people in the dirty shirt study by Mark Russel, a British psychologist (1976). He had twenty-nine first-year college students bathe with clear water and then

FIGURE 13.2
Setup for measuring gender identification based on breath odor.

don nondescript T-shirts that they wore for the next 24 hours, during which they used no perfume or deodorant. At the end of this period, the T-shirts were collected and individually placed in sealed containers. The same students were now presented with three containers, one with their own shirt, one with the T-shirt worn by an unknown female, and one with the T-shirt worn by an unknown male. Of 29 people, 22 picked out their own T-shirt—a level of performance well above chance. Moreover, the same proportion of people correctly identified which of the remaining two T-shirts belonged to a male and which belonged to a female. Male odors were described as "musky," while female odors were described as "sweet."

Our smell recognition abilities are not limited to the odors from other humans. Wells and Hepper (2000) asked twenty-six dog owners to smell a pair of dog blankets that were contained in separate, opaque plastic bags. One plastic bag contained a blanket that had been used by that owner's dog when it slept; the other plastic bag contained the bedding blanket used by another dog, which was unfamiliar to the participant. Using smell alone, nearly 90 percent of the participants correctly identified the odor of their own dog. But before taking this performance as proof that people could recognize the distinctive smell of their own dogs, several control measurements were needed. For example, Wells and Hepper were concerned that the remarkable performance they had observed might come from a recognition not of the dog's odor, but of the odor of the household in which the dog lived. To control for this possibility, the same twenty-six people were re-tested, but with household odors not connected to their own or anyone else's pets. Now, each participant smelled a new pair of unseen blankets: one impregnated with the odors from the participant's home, the other carried odors from the home of another of the participants. The twenty six people performed only slightly better than chance in recognizing the odor of their own home—performance far worse than shown in recognizing their own dog's odor. The researchers concluded that "we are highly capable of identifying our so-called 'best friend' by smell."

One of the most remarkable things about smell is its ability to evoke old memories. A whiff of cedar triggers comforting remembrances of the chest in which your grandmother kept her blankets; the scent from a carnation vividly recalls the wonders of a senior prom; and the smell of suntan lotion immediately transports you to the beach. Some people have developed a huge repertoire of odor memories and rely on them in their profession. Skilled perfumers, for example, can discriminate hundreds of aromas, many quite subtle. Physicians can exploit their own noses as diagnostic tools, using a patient's odors as clues for detecting disease. In fact, many medical disorders have characteristic odors. To give some examples, typhoid creates a smell like that of freshly baked, brown bread; yellow fever victims

smell like a butcher shop; and kidney failure creates an ammonia-like odor. (A table of diseases that produce distinctive odors can be found in Smith, Smith and Levinson, 1982.)

Clinical

One little known disorder produces a strong odor of rotting fish in peoples' breath and sweat (Mitchell 1996). The inherited disorder, called trimethylaminuria, involves a breakdown in the liver's ability to oxidize one of the normal products of food metabolism. Although a low-protein diet helps some victims, there is no known cure. Unfortunately, today, thirty years after the disorder was first identified in the medical literature, few doctors and nurses know about it. As a result, people with this disorder can spend years looking for an explanation of their strange body odor. As Christensen (1999) notes, "They often acquire a long list of inaccurate diagnoses ranging from poor hygiene to psychiatric problems. These people may withdraw from the outside world to avoid ridicule or try to mask their odor with strong perfumes and cigarettes. Many of those with disorder also report symptoms of depression."

Mammals send and receive dozens of different types of odor messages (Doty, 1986), ranging from distress signals to age appraisal. For many animals, mate selection and identification are solely governed by odor. Typically, the females of these species emit sensuous scents called **pheromones** from specialized glands. These scents can be detected by potential mates. Among such species is the male cabbage moth, an insect whose antennae can sense minute concentrations of the scent released from a sexually receptive female cabbage moth many miles away (Lerner et al., 1990).

The understanding of chemical sex signals has allowed scientists to exploit other species' pheromones. For example, agricultural biologists use pheromones to control some harmful insects. With sex attractants as bait, unsuspecting harmful insects can be lured into traps. Pheromones can also be exploited for the eating pleasure of humans. Certain female pigs are trained to hunt truffles, a fungus highly prized by many gourmets. These sows can sniff out truffles buried as much as a meter below ground, and once the truffles are located, the animals root furiously to unearth them. Sows exert all that energy, rooting furiously for a piece of fungus, because truffles give off a musklike odor highly similar to the scent secreted by male pigs during mating behavior. So the sow's intense interest in truffles is a misdirected, purely sexual one (Claus, Hoppen and Karg, 1981).

It is natural to wonder whether sexual behavior of our own species is influenced by smell. Do humans use pheromones to send sexually tinged olfactory messages? Certainly the perfume industry would have us believe the answer is yes, but the evidence, while suggestive, is inconclusive. Case studies do disclose that people with serious smell disorders frequently report disinterest in sex (Henkin, 1982), but firm experimental data are lacking. It's clear, however, that odor signals play a role in the synchronization of menstrual cycles of women who live together over many months (Graham and McGrew, 1980).

Differences

Besides promoting sexual arousal in animals, smells are often employed as defensive weapons. If you've ever experienced the rank odor of a skunk's discharge, you can certainly appreciate how that odor would ward off enemies (and friends as well). Numerous animal species employ glandular secretions to mark their territories, often engaging in seemingly bizarre behaviors to ensure that their odor signatures are conspicuous (Macdonald and Brown, 1985). For example, the oribi (a small African antelope) uses scent glands just below its eyes to mark blades of grass with a dollop of oribi scent. It may look odd to see an animal rub its face in the grass, but from the oribi's perspective this maneuver makes perfect sense.

Odors also guide animals in their search for food, whether it is the bee attracted to the fragrance of flowering plants or the vulture picking up the scent of a dead animal. Some seabirds can locate food sources far from land, with no visual landmarks to guide them. They use smell to detect airborne dimethyl sulfide given off by their prey in the ocean below (Malakoff, 1999). In fact, humans' overwhelming reliance on eyes and ears to guide vital activities may be fairly unique, since many other animals depend heavily on their noses for such guidance. Indeed, if we were writing this perception book for an audience of nonhuman animals, particularly nonprimates, we'd have to revise it drastically. Instead of emphasizing seeing and hearing, the vast bulk of the book would have to address the most pressing concern of the nonhuman world—the sense of smell.

The Stimulus for Smell

Let's start with the basics, asking what physical properties give various substances the power to evoke sensations of odor. As you'll see, the answers are complex. First, to be odorous, a substance must be *volatile*—that is, it must give off vapors. This requirement has practical consequences. For example, because heated soup gives off more vapors than cold soup, hot soup smells more inviting. It used to be thought that these volatile molecules had to be airborne to be smelled. According to this view, substances suspended in liquid would be odorless even when they were in direct contact with the nose's odor receptors. Even if you submerged yourself in a pool of perfume, you would smell nothing. Ernst Weber, the nineteenth century physiologist, actually performed a version of this experiment, the results of which, he thought, confirmed this view. With his head upside down, Weber poured perfume into his own nostrils, and he smelled nothing (Boring, 1942). It's now thought, however, that the perfume, which probably contained alcohol, may have damaged the receptors in Weber's nose, so that he couldn't smell anything at all. In fact, there's good proof that smell is not restricted to airborne molecules: fish can use olfaction to follow scent trails in water (Barinaga, 1999).

Earlier, in discussing vision and hearing, we noted that stimulation reaching the eye or striking the ear usually comprises an aggregate of information from several different sources. Similarly,

Neural

many natural odors, such as those given off by flowers, fruits or by your body, reflect mixtures of many different types of molecules. The identities and relative proportions of those molecules comprise the signature of the odor's source, for example a particular variety of flower. We also noted that the perception of distinct objects requires the nervous system to segregate the complex incoming aggregate into the perceptual components emanating from each particular object. The same is true for olfaction. When you smell an object some distance away, you are responding to odorant molecules carried your way by air currents whose direction and speed are utterly unpredictable. As a result, the sample of odorant molecules reaching your nose can vary dramatically from one moment to another, even when the object of smell does not change. Also, along the path to your nose, the air currents pass over many different objects, picking up multitudes of odorant. So except for the carefully controlled conditions created in the laboratory, the air you inhale at any given moment contains odorant molecules donated by a variety of objects. To identify any single odorant source, the olfactory system must segregate the mixture into its constituents. Fluctuations in the direction and speed of air currents complicate the situation further: any single airborne odorant is presented to your nose in concentrations and in combinations that vary greatly over time. Despite these complexities, the olfactory system does manage to identify the sources of odors. (Laurent, 1999, presents an excellent analysis of the challenges that confront the first stages of processing in the olfactory system.)

One prerequisite for smell is that the volatile molecules be soluble in fat, because the receptor cells in the nose that capture volatile molecules are surrounded by fatlike materials. When odorous molecules are fat soluble, they can be absorbed by substances containing fat. This explains why uncovered butter on one shelf of the refrigerator takes on the smell of uncovered tuna fish sitting on another shelf. At the same time, not all volatile and fat-soluble substances are odorous. Additional chemical properties common to all odorous substances, such as atomic weight, must also be factors (Wright, 1966); identifying these properties remains a challenge. This challenge is closely related to the problem of odor classification, a topic we consider next.

The Classification of Odors

As Chapter 7 explained, the understanding of color vision was really launched when Newton devised a scheme for describing the relations among different colors (the color circle). Following Newton's work, there emerged some consensus about the categories of color. It has been widely assumed that odors, too, should fall into distinct categories, comparable in their uniqueness to blue, green, yellow and red. Knowledge of these odor categories would pave the way for determining the molecular properties common to members of various perceptual categories. But attempts to identify odor categories have foundered (Wise, Olsson and Cain, 2000). Here are several, better-known odor categorization schemes, and their shortcomings.

Execute

The idea of categorizing odors dates back to the ancient Greeks, most notably Aristotle, who classified odors as either pungent, succulent, acid or astringent. Odor classification took on real urgency in the seventeenth and eighteenth centuries, when people were convinced that bad odors were associated with disease and epidemics. By understanding various "families" of odors, they expected to eliminate those that posed danger to health, or so people believed (Corbin, 1986).

Probably the best-known system is Hans Henning's (1916) smell prism, a geometric system similar in spirit to Newton's color circle. Henning's geometric model was meant to depict the "principal" odors, that is basic odors from which all other odors could be generated. Henning used two procedures to determine the number of principal odors. First, he instructed volunteers to use

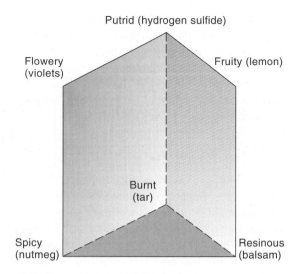

FIGURE 13.3
Henning's smell prism.

verbal labels to describe various scents presented one at a time. Second, he gave people sets of odorous substances and instructed them to line up the substances according to the similarity of their smells (Gamble, 1921). In all, Henning tested well over 400 different odorous substances. Using these sets of judgments, Henning constructed a three-dimensional form—a triangular prism (shown in Figure 13.3)—whose surfaces were meant to reflect people's judgments of odor similarity. Particular odors corresponded to points on the surface of the prism, with nearby points corresponding to odors that were judged similar. Odors were confined to the surfaces and edges of the prism; its interior was considered hollow, meaning that points inside the prism were not used to describe an odor.

To Henning, odors near his prism's corners seemed to have unique qualities. They could be described using a single verbal label (shown in Figure 13.3). To give you some idea of substances that evoke these six principal odors, a substance representative of each odor is given in parentheses. Odors located anywhere other than the corners of the prism—that is, either on an

edge or on the plane of one surface—could not be described using a single verbal label. But such noncorner odors could be described by some *combination* of principal qualities represented by the labels at the corners. For example, the smell associated with pine was located along the edge midway between *fruity* and *resinous,* implying that the odor of pine possesses both of those qualities. Pine was located where it is on the prism because of its similarity to lemon and balsam. Similarly the smell of garlic was located on the surface bounded by *flowery, fruity, resinous* and *spicy,* implying that the odor of garlic possesses all four of those qualities. Again, garlic was placed at that point on the prism because Henning considered its odor similar to the odors of violet, lemon, balsam and nutmeg.

Henning's scheme purported to show how odors on the edges or surfaces of the smell prism resemble odors at the prism's corners. This does not mean, however, that a mixture of odors from the corners could produce odors on other parts of the prism. Although pine is similar in smell to both balsam and lemon, it cannot be synthesized by a mixture of these two. In fact, "the resulting odor tends to be a unique percept blend in which both components can be smelled" (Engen, 1982). In this sense, odor shares the analytic character of pitch perception rather than the synthetic character of color perception. For example, when you simultaneously sound a D and an F on the piano, you can hear the individual components in the chord; however, when you mix red and green lights, the result is a synthesis (yellow) in which the two component identities are lost.

Henning's model is appealing for precisely the same reason that Newton's color circle is appealing: both provide a simple, geometrical description of sensory experiences. The accuracy of geometric models is easy to test because they make clear predictions. And many predictions from Henning's smell prism have not been confirmed. One major problem is that most people find it impossible to classify odors using just six categories, which implies that Henning may have underestimated the number of principal odors. Henning can also be faulted for using a small number of highly trained subjects and for eschewing quantitative analysis of his data. In staunch defense of his procedures, Henning bragged that "the critical introspection of trained psychologists is more valuable than statistics taken on all the students in the University, and the statistical procedure, about which science in America has raved so much, has by no means the precision of a *qualitative* analysis" (Henning, 1916; from a translation by Gamble, 1921).

Following Henning's work, other researchers have also tried to group odors according to qualitative similarities (for example, Crocker and Henderson, 1927). Most of these categorization schemes have begun with a series of semantic descriptors to be used as odor qualities—descriptors such as *sweet, flowery, fruity, burned,* and so forth. Whatever odor categories emerge, however, are constrained right from the start. They've got to conform to the specific descriptors chosen by the researcher in the first place. Moreover, there are reasons to question how reliably people can use verbal labels to describe their olfactory sensations (Davis, 1977). The constraints imposed by the descriptors, as well as the difficulty of using any label at all, would distort any classification scheme based on predefined verbal labels.

Execute

Multidimensional scaling (MDS), a technique described in the Appendix, sidesteps these problems. This technique was used by Susan Schiffman (1974) to study odor classification. Instead of using descriptor terms for various odors, a person merely compares different odors, numerically rating their similarity to one another. These similarity ratings are then used to place odors within a geometric framework called an odor space. Odors are arranged within the odor space in such a way that the distances separating odors reflect the rated similarity or dissimilarity of those odors. Odors rated as highly similar (such as cinnamon and ginger) would be placed near each other in an odor space, while odors judged to be dissimilar (such as vanilla and tur-

pentine) would be located far apart. As you can see, the concept of an "odor space" is reminiscent of Henning's smell prism—both arrange odorous substances in a geometric form based on perceptual similarity. However, the rules for generating an odor space by means of MDS differ from Henning's approach. MDS uses objective numerical procedures to create a geometric arrangement that represents judged similarities among odors; Henning based his arrangement on his own subjective smell impressions.

Besides objectivity, the procedures used in multidimensional scaling offer another advantage. The experimenter does not constrain the number of possible dimensions ahead of time. Instead, statistical analyses of the similarity ratings determine the number of dimensions needed to place odors in the odor space. (You can think of the dimensions as axes defining the coordinates of a geometrical space, like the Cartesian coordinates that define the two-dimensional space you're familiar with from plane geometry.)

In using multidimensional scaling, Schiffman found that just two dimensions adequately described the relations among a wide variety of odorous substances. Figure 13.4 replots some of Schiffman's analysis. Look at the various odors in this odor space, and note their relative positions. You'll probably agree that the nearby entries smell more alike than do the widely separated ones. How can one interpret the two dimensions that Schiffman's work uncovered? To answer this question, Schiffman examined the adjectives people use to describe the odors. She found that proceeding from left to right in Figure 13.4, odors tended to shade from pleasant (such as vanillin) to unpleasant (such as hydrogen sulfide). It is not too surprising that one strong dimension of odor perception has this hedonic quality, for odors so often trigger either approach (pleasant) or avoidance (unpleasant). Proceeding from top to bottom, however, Schiffman was unable to find any systematic progression in the adjectives used to describe the odors. This finding suggests that this dimension of odor experience

FIGURE 13.4
An odor space, showing the relations among various odors as defined by multidimensional scaling.
(Adapted from Schiffman, 1974.)

does not correlate with any simple psychological dimension for which there are linguistic descriptors. To what, then, might the ordering in the odor space correspond?

Schiffman (1974) asked whether perceptually similar odors might have some molecular property in common, such as the size or shape of the odorant molecules. The discovery of molecular similarities among perceptually comparable odors might furnish important clues about how odorous substances affect receptor cells in the nose. Schiffman considered several molecular characteristics in an attempt to uncover what physical properties, if any, similar smells have in common. Examining the molecular shapes of various substances, she found no relation between the shapes of various compounds and the odors produced by those compounds. This finding, incidentally, seems to contradict one theory of odor perception. John Amoore (1970), a noted olfactory scientist, proposed that a molecule's shape determines which odor receptor it is able to stimulate. This theory has been characterized as the lock-and-key model, since the molecule "unlocks" the receptor only if the shape of the molecule matches that of the receptor. According to this theory, molecules that look alike (in terms of

the arrangement of their constituent atoms) should also smell alike. Wise, Olsson and Cain (2000) offer a critical review of various attempts to categorize odors and to link categories to molecular properties.

Before continuing the discussion of odor perception, we should consider the olfactory system's front-end, the olfactory receptor cells that capture the volatile molecules from odorous substances. The properties of these receptor cells shape the world of smell.

THE ANATOMY AND PHYSIOLOGY OF SMELL

The stimulus for smell consists of airborne molecules, or vapors. The act of inhaling pulls these vapors into the nostrils and circulates them through the nasal cavity, a hollow region inside the nose where the olfactory (smell) receptors are located (see Figure 13.5). Exhaling expels the vapors back into the air. Sniffing or sneezing hastens these processes. The average sniff lasts about 400 msec and draws about 200 cc of air into the nose (Cain, 1992). Each sniff sucks air into the nose and speeds its circulation through the nasal cavity. Sniffing is comparable to cup-

FIGURE 13.5
A cutaway section of a human head, showing the routes taken by air inhaled into the mouth and nasal cavity.

ping your ear to help you hear a faint sound; sniffing is also the olfactory system's main way to explore the environment. Sneezing, in contrast, represents a reflexive clearing of the nostrils, an action comparable to covering your ears to muffle a loud sound.

With most odorant molecules, optimum odor detection occurs when odorant-laden air flows through the nose at about 30 liters per minute. Interestingly, when you intentionally sniff to check out some particular odor, 30 liters per minute is about the flow that you produce without even thinking about it (Laing, 1983). A good hard sniff draws an extra-large volume of air—and therefore an extra large volume of odorant—into the nasal passages. You might imagine, therefore, that such a sniff would boost perceived intensity of that odorant, but according to Teghtsoonian and colleagues (1978) that does not happen: odor intensity remains constant regardless of the vigor of a sniff. Teghtsoonian and colleagues called

this phenomenon **odor constancy,** because the perceived strength of an odor remains constant despite sharp variations in flow rate. You can see the similarity between this phenomenon and form constancy (Chapter 5), color constancy (Chapter 7) and size constancy (Chapter 8). In all these instances, perception of objects in the world remains constant despite changes in the energy impinging on the receptors. To explain odor constancy, Teghtsoonian and his colleagues suggested that the olfactory system recognizes when the increase in flow rate results from a natural sniff, and then calibrates the perception of intensity to take this factor into account. Sniff-associated brain activation could be the basis for this hypothesized calibration. Sniff-induced airflow, even when the inhaled air is free of odorous vapors, produces rhythmic activation—sniff for sniff—in several regions of the cerebral cortex, probably because of the somatosensory stimulation produced by the flow (Sobel et al., 1998).

Odor-bearing vapors normally enter the nostrils and then wend their way up the nasal passages. However, they can also reach the nasal cavity backwards, coming into the mouth and circulating up the throat through a chimney-like passage leading to the smell receptors. Both routes—via the nostrils or the throat—lead to the same place, the olfactory receptors in the nasal cavity. However, vapors from a substance in the mouth may not smell the same as vapors brought into the nose from the same substance. With training, though, people can learn to identify these backdoor odors with good success (Pierce and Halpern, 1996). Box 13.1 describes some differences between the smell of food when you sniff it and the smell of food when it is already inside your mouth.

BOX 13.1

IS OLFACTION A DUAL SENSE?

Have you noticed that some foods smell almost repulsive before you get them into your mouth, but once you start eating them they are enjoyable? Certain strong cheeses, such as Limburger and Roquefort, are good examples of this disparity between odor and flavor. Yet what is referred to as *flavor* is largely the smell associated with the food as it is chewed. This is known from the fact that foods lose their flavor when olfactory cues are eliminated during eating (such as when you have a head cold). How is it, then, that the same food can generate two distinct odor experiences, depending on whether you are sniffing the food or eating it?

Paul Rozin, a psychologist at the University of Pennsylvania, suspected this happened because olfaction is a dual sense—that is, olfaction has to acquire two sets of information: information about objects in the external world and information about objects within the mouth. According to Rozin (1982), these two types of information have different behavioral consequences. Airborne odors arriving through the nostrils can come from a host of objects and events—other people, animals, plants, fire and so on—only some of which have anything to do with eating. Behavioral reactions to these odors depend on identifying the source of the odor (Gibson, 1966). In this sense, olfaction serves the same interests as vision and hearing, identifying relevant objects and events in the environment. But olfaction's role changes during eating, after food has been selected and introduced into the mouth. Now odors become part of the flavor complex that also includes taste, temperature and palatability. Rozin believes that these two different contexts (odor in the mouth versus odor outside the body) are registered by the olfactory nervous system and give rise to distinctly different perceptual experiences.

Rozin figured that if odor did have different perceptual properties in the mouth versus outside the mouth, people should have trouble recognizing odor through the mouth if their previous experience with the odor was just through the nose. To test this hypothesis, Rozin came up with a set of unfamiliar odors and flavors by mixing together various exotic fruit juices and soups. He then taught blindfolded people to identify these various mixtures on the basis of their odors; each mixture was assigned a number for purposes of identification. Once these individuals had learned the procedure, Rozin asked them to identify the same mixtures delivered directly to the mouth through a plastic tube. In this way, any contribution of odor inhaled through the nostrils was eliminated; odor information came entirely from aromas passing up the throat to the olfactory receptors. The results were clear—people made many errors in identifying the mixtures, and they reported that the flavors were impossible to recognize. Evidently, the same substance smells different, depending on whether it is in the external world or in the mouth. This would explain why you may dislike the flavor of things (such as coffee) that smell appealing and also why you can enjoy eating foods that smell foul, such as Morbier cheese from France or the pungent Norweigian delicacy, lutefisk. Without prodding, most people would never get around to giving such off-putting foods a try.

Most of the air entering the nostrils and mouth ends up flowing down the throat to the lungs. However, some wisps of air do rise up from the mouth into the nasal cavity, where they circulate around a series of baffles formed by three bones located in the nasal cavity (see Figure 13.5). As air circulates through this series of baffles, it is warmed and humidified, and debris such as dust is removed by tiny hairs lining the nasal cavity. The entire process has been likened to an air-conditioning system that improves smell acuity. As you can imagine, when your nose is congested, the passages of the nasal cavity are narrowed, limiting the amount of odorous vapors that can reach the smell receptors. This is why your sense of smell is dulled when a cold clogs up your nasal cavities. This nasal blockage can be chronic in individuals who have nasal polyps.

Actually, the two nostrils appear to work in alternating shifts, a phenomenon called the **nasal cycle.** At any given time, the mucous lining in one nostril is more engorged than that of the other nostril, which narrows the nasal passage and creates greater resistance to the inflow of air. This alternating constriction of the nasal passages is under control of the autonomic nervous system and therefore occurs unconsciously. You can easily confirm the dominance of one nostril by holding a mirror just under your nose midway between the two nostrils. Then notice how the two pools of condensation (produced by exhalation) differ in size. Nostril dominance normally switches every 2 to 3 hours (Keuning, 1968).

We've described how vapors are introduced into the nose and how they circulate inside the nasal cavities. Now let's consider how neural elements turn these vapors into perception of an odor. The receptor cells that register the presence of odorous molecules sit on a patch of tissue called the **olfactory epithelium.** As you can see in Figure 13.5, the olfactory epithelium forms part of the ceiling of the nasal cavity. There are actually two patches of olfactory epithelium, one at the top of each nasal cavity. Each patch of tissue is about the diameter of a dime, but much thinner.

Figure 13.6 shows an enlarged drawing of an olfactory epithelium. Note the structure labeled **olfactory sensory neuron (OSN),** which is a bipolar (double-ended) nerve cell that captures odorant molecules and initiates the neural signals for smell. At one end, this bipolar nerve cell has a single dendrite that terminates in a number of tiny cilia. At its opposite end, the nerve cell terminates in a single axon that, together with the

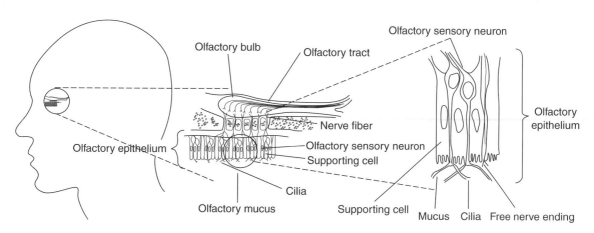

FIGURE 13.6
The olfactory epithelium (enlarged to show detail).

axons of several neighboring nerve cells, thread through one of the perforations in the ethmoid bone.* The ethmoid is a spongy, relatively thin bone that comprises the roof of the nasal cavity and the septum (the wall separating the left and right nasal passages). Once the axons have passed through this bone, they form a synapse with neurons in the olfactory bulb.

The typical human nose contains somewhere between 40 and 50 million olfactory sensory neurons. In contrast, a dog's nose has about 10 to 20 times more, which partly accounts for dogs' legendary ability to track someone, even hours after the individual has passed by. Notice also in Figure 13.6 the structure labeled **free nerve ending.** Although these nerve fibers do not themselves give rise to odor sensations, they do strongly influence the perception of odors, as we'll see later. But for now let's continue focusing on the olfactory sensory neurons.

Several things set olfactory sensory neurons apart from receptor neurons in the eye and ear. OSNs, unlike photoreceptors and hair cells, are genuine neurons, with all the basic structural elements of neurons—cell bodies, short dendrites and long axons. Because of their structure, OSNs do two jobs at once: transduce chemical stimulation into neural impulses and carry those impulses to the brain along their axons (which make up the **olfactory nerve**). In vision, hearing and taste, the two jobs are farmed out to different types of cells. For smell, the only neurons in the brain that actually come in contact with the outside world are those located in the nasal cavity.

OSNs have very short lives, about 5 to 8 weeks. When they die, they are replaced (Graziadei, 1973; Moulton, 1974). As a result of this turnover, by the time you read these words, you've already gone through countless generations of OSNs, and the olfactory neurons cur-

rently at work in your nose are relative newcomers to the job. This turnover of neurons is even more remarkable considering that as each new OSN matures, its axon must grow an appreciable distance to reach its target site in the olfactory bulb of the brain. And once there, each axon presumably must form connections that effectively duplicate those that were carried out by its predecessor. If the original connections were not duplicated, substances might not smell the same from one month to the next.

Some people believe that the cyclical turnover of OSNs may have something important to do with reduced sensitivity to an odor following prolonged exposure to that odor, a phenomenon well documented in the environmental health literature (Ahlstrom et al., 1986). To appreciate how this might come about, you'll need to know a little more about the structure of the olfactory sensory neurons, in particular the cilia that extend from an OSN into the mucous lining of the nose.

Extending from the dendritic end of each olfactory sensory neuron are clumps of **cilia**—thin, hairlike structures that are suspended in a thin layer of mucous that coats the nasal cavity. The receptor sites for olfaction are imbedded in the membrane of these cilia. To reach these receptor sites, molecules of odorant must pass from the inhaled air into the nasal cavity's mucous layer. Odorants are aided in this process by olfactory binding proteins (Snyder et al., 1989; Anholt, 1991). An olfactory binding protein, as its name implies, has a chemical affinity for a great many different odorants. It traps and concentrates odorous molecules, transporting them into the nasal mucous, where they potentially make contact with receptors. This process is illustrated schematically in Figure 13.7. The receptors on an OSN's cilia are long protein molecules that weave back and forth through the ciliary membrane. Over a hundred different varieties of olfactory receptor proteins have been identified in humans. Each member of this large family of protein receptors: 1) crisscrosses the membranes of host cells exactly seven times; 2) employs the

---

The word *ethmoid* is derived from a Greek word meaning "strainer or sieve," aptly describing this porous, perforated bone.

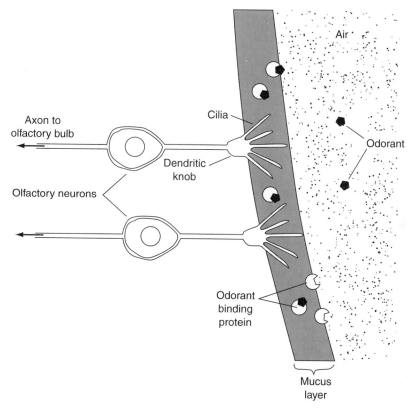

FIGURE 13.7

Odorants received at the olfactory epithelium are picked up by specialized proteins and transported to receptor sites on the cilia. (Adapted from Levitan and Kaczmarek, 1991.)

same basic mechanisms for initiating signals; and 3) shares some common, characteristic sequences of amino acids.*

The steps to the perception of an odor begin when odorant molecules bind to specific sites on the receptor proteins. This process is a sophisticated, molecular version of a lock and key. To understand the specificity of a key's operation—why one key opens a lock, while another doesn't—you have to understand the lock's internal mechanism,

how its individual tumblers interact with the key's notches and grooves. The same is true for the specificity of odor receptors. To understand why one odorant molecule will be absorbed by certain receptor proteins but another molecule won't, you have to understand something about the interaction between receptor and odorant.

The binding sites on a receptor protein are pockets created by the twists and bends of a protein as its chain folds itself up into its preferred three-dimensional structure. Differences among the amino acid strings that comprise any protein guarantee that the protein will have a unique three-dimensional structure, different from that of any other protein. As a result, the size, shape

---

*These olfactory receptors have a structural resemblance to the protein portions of rod and cone pigments, and many chemical receptors in the brain, including those for serotonin and dopamine (Shepherd and Firestein, 1991; Buck, 1992).

and chemical attraction of any protein's binding sites will also be unique to that protein. An odorant molecule typically forms a number of individually-weak bonds to many different sites on the receptor protein. Because any single bond is electrically weak, a stable connection between receptor and odorant requires a large number of such bonds. And because individual bonds can only be made when the active sites on both receptor and odorant are very close together, the number of bonds that are formed depends on the "fit" between receptor and odorant.

When an odorant molecule has firmly docked with its matching receptor protein, the receptor triggers a series of molecular events that, in rapid succession, recruit several different chemical intermediaries within the olfactory receptor neuron (Lindner and Gilman, 1992). The last of these intermediaries is an enzyme that triggers electrical changes in the cell membrane. At this point, the capture of an odorant molecule has been transduced into an electrical signal.

Although it is difficult to make a definitive test of the idea, most researchers assume a given olfactory sensory neuron contains just one type of receptor protein. If a nose lacks a particular olfactory receptor protein, that nose will be unable to detect the odorous molecule(s) that would be captured by that receptor protein. The term **anosmia** (literally, "without smell") is used to describe a complete inability to smell. When anosmia is partial, that is, restricted to a particular class of smells, the condition is termed **specific anosmia.** Most commonly, this condition can be traced to the absence of specific receptor proteins. Temporary anosmia (a temporary, reversible loss in odor sensitivity) results when the cilia are damaged, as they can be by certain toxic chemicals or drugs. Once new cilia grow, odor sensitivity returns. Although normal, healthy humans can distinguish among a great many different odors, judging by the standards of other species, members of our species are relatively anosmic—insensitive to a great many odors that other animals can detect and identify.

Differences

Earlier we alluded to one possible reason for humans' impoverished sense of smell, our small olfactory epithelia. But that is not the whole story. Compared to most mammals, the human genome contains relatively few olfactory receptor genes— between 500 and 750 (Mombaerts, 1999). Even if everything else were perfect, this paucity guarantees that humans would have a reduced number and variety of olfactory receptor proteins and would, therefore, be insensitive to many potential odorant molecules. But everything else is far from perfect. At least half of all human olfactory receptor genes are defective (Rouquier, Blancher and Giorgi, 2000). Thus, proteins encoded by these defective genes are unable to absorb odorant molecules, which further undermines human olfaction (Sharon et al., 1999).

Now that we've seen how odorant molecules dock with olfactory receptors and how olfactory signals are triggered, we can move to the next step in neural coding of odor quality. We can ask, "How are the various qualities of odor represented in the firing patterns of neurons of the olfactory system? What neural responses make it possible for us to distinguish, say, the smell of lemons from that of limes?"

Neural Coding of Odor Quality by Olfactory Fibers   You've already learned something about how qualitative aspects of a stimulus are represented in other senses. Recall from Chapter 10 Neural that each fiber in the auditory nerve responds to a certain range of frequencies, giving the strongest response to one particular frequency. Likewise, each fiber in the optic nerve prefers contours of a particular size and, for some, a particular color. Again, the preferred size or color varies from fiber to fiber. In those modalities, then, different subcategories of sensory fibers carry information about different sensory qualities. As a group, olfactory nerve fibers (the axons of the olfactory receptors) do *not* behave in this discriminating, specialized fashion. The vast majority of olfactory nerve fibers respond to a host of different odors, many bearing no qualitative similarity to one another (Kauer, 1991). To be sure, individual fibers don't indiscriminately respond to all possible odors. There must be (and is) some degree of response specificity. But the range of effective odorants is quite large for any given nerve fiber. There is nother resembling the specialization evident in auditory and visual nerves. Consequently, individual olfactory fibers can signal that some odorous substance is present, but no single olfactory fiber provides unequivocal information about *what* that substance is.

By and large the olfactory nerve does not treat an odorant as some combination of basic components each separately registered by specialized cells. Nor, for that matter, does there appear to be anything in the olfactory fibers like the center/surround antagonism characteristic of visual receptive fields. And there is nothing comparable in the olfactory epithelium to the tonotopic organization of the basilar membrane and the auditory nerve. Simply stated, nature seems to have worked out a unique form of sensory coding within the olfactory system, and to understand more about that code we must direct our attention to the next stages of processing, in the olfactory bulb and the olfactory cortex.

The Olfactory Pathways So far the discussion has focused on the olfactory epithelium and the receptor neurons embedded in that tissue. The rest of the olfactory system consists of the **olfactory bulb** (which receives all the input from the olfactory nerve) and the **olfactory brain** (a cluster of neural structures receiving projections from the olfactory bulb). Structurally, the olfactory bulb bears a superficial resemblance to the retina, in that it has several layers of cells laterally interconnected (see the upperhand panel in Figure 13.8). Based on the response properties of neurons in the bulb, however, it is clear that these two structures—the retina and the olfactory bulb—function quite differently.

For one thing, the incoming axons from the olfactory epithelium activate neurons in the receiving stage of the bulb rather diffusely (those

"second-order" neurons receiving this diffuse afferent input are concentrated in clusters called *glomeruli*). There is not any obvious kind of corresponding topographic, spatial map of the epithelium in the bulb. There is, though, enormous convergence at this anatomical stage. It is estimated that there are 1,000 receptor cell axons for each second-order neuron in the bulb. Consequently, very weak neural signals, originating in many different olfactory neurons and carried by olfactory nerve fibers, can be added together within the bulb to create reliable responses to minute concentrations of an odorant (Duchamp-Viret, Duchamp and Vitouroux, 1989).

It is generally believed that odor quality is coded by the spatial *pattern* of neural activity across the entire olfactory bulb (Freeman, 1991; Kauer, 1991)—an idea reminiscent of the profile theory described in Chapter 4. On this view, virtually all neurons in the bulb contribute to the registration of odor quality; there are no specialized neurons that signal, say, the fragrance of a rose. Support for this view comes from studies in which a map of neural activity was created using a technique that measures the uptake of a radioactive molecule that concentrates selectively in brain regions high in metabolic rate. Different odorants produce characteristic, reliable patterns of metabolic activity within the bulb, but these patterns are rather globally distributed over the structure and are not confined to local clusters of cells (reviewed by Buck, 1996).

The activity of neurons in the olfactory bulb is also shaped by two other important aspects of an odorant. First, neural activity varies throughout the phase of the inhalation cycle, being greatest at the end of each inhalation. Second, neuronal activity in the bulb depends on level of emotional arousal. If an animal is hungry, thirsty, sexually aroused or fearful, neural responsiveness is enhanced.

The olfactory bulb's output is carried by axons arising from several, morphologically distinct classes of neurons in the bulb. Those axons project to the olfactory cortex, which is located below the anterior portion of the frontal lobe.

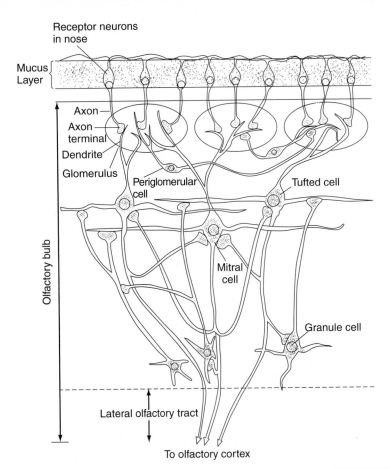

Receptor neurons
in nose

Mucus
Layer

Olfactory bulb

Axon
Axon
terminal
Dendrite
Glomerulus
Periglomerular
cell

Tufted cell

Mitral
cell

Granule cell

Lateral olfactory tract

To olfactory cortex

A.

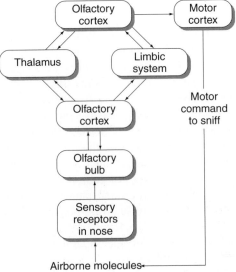

Olfactory
cortex → Motor
cortex

Thalamus

Limbic
system

Olfactory
cortex

Motor
command
to sniff

Olfactory
bulb

Sensory
receptors
in nose

Airborne molecules

FIGURE 13.8
A. A schematic drawing of the multiple layers of
the olfactory bulb. **B.** A flow diagram of the
pathway constituting the olfactory system.

558

B.

The olfactory cortex communicates with several other areas of the brain, including structures in the limbic system (see the bottom panel in Figure 13.8). This latter connection is noteworthy, for the limbic system, which is phylogenetically quite old, is central to emotional responses. It is thought that the emotion-evoking capacity of odors arises from two-way links between the olfactory and limbic systems.

There have only been a few physiological studies of neurons in the olfactory cortex. To date, efforts to identify an "odortopic" organization in the cortex (that is, an organized map of different odors represented by different neurons) have failed (Greer, 1991). It is known, though, that people with damage to the olfactory cortex can have difficulty detecting and/or identifying odors (see the review by Richardson and Zucco, 1989), indicating that those regions are critically involved in processing olfactory information. As described above, any given type of odorant molecule usually evokes a broadly distributed, characteristic pattern of activity within the olfactory bulb. Of course, the air we ordinarily breath carries numerous odorant molecules associated with different odor sources. So, the olfactory cortex is receiving from the bulb a complicated pattern of activity associated with this montage of odorant molecules. Researchers are just beginning to grapple with the problem of how the brain's olfactory regions extract appropriate invariant responses from what must be the fluctuating and unpredictable neural responses triggered by the wide variety of odorants that are present (Hopfield, 1991; Laurent, 1999).

Neural Representation of Odor Intensity
The previous section focused on odor quality—the difference, for example, between the odor of a banana and peanut butter. Another dimension of odor perception, of course, is the intensity of a given odor. Odor intensity depends on the concentration of the airborne molecules along with the amount of odorant actually reaching the receptors in the olfactory epithelium. (A given concentration is going to smell weaker when your nose is stuffed up.) Not surprisingly, the nervous system registers information about concentration in the firing rate of neurons responsive to an odor: weak odors elicit fewer neural impulses than strong odors. This property seems to hold at all levels of the olfactory system, from the receptor cells to the cortex. To complicate the picture, though, people can experience changes in the *quality* of an odorant (even chemically pure ones) with intensity variations alone (Gross-Isseroff and Lancet, 1988). So odor intensity and odor quality are not independent dimensions.

Building a Better Nose   For years, people have dreamed about the possibilities of electronic noses ("e-noses"). A highly accurate "e-nose" would be able to check for important telltale odors hour after hour, never growing tired, and, when needed, would never complain about being sent to sniff around in dangerous places where the atmosphere is potentially damaging to biological noses. As far as medical diagnosis is concerned, this sensitive e-nose would never forget to check a patient's breath and body odors for crucial signs of illness (recall our earlier discussion of odors and diseases). Now dreams have become a reality: e-noses have been built and tested. One particularly advanced e-nose is available commercially from a company, Cyrano Sciences (named after Cyrano de Bergerac, a fictional character whose nose is certainly the most prominent organ of smell in all of literature). Unlike Cyrano de Bergerac's fictional, but biological nose, Cyrano Sciences' electronic nose on a chip is small. But despite its size, this e-nose is extremely good at identifying a wide range of odorants (Freund and Lewis, 1995). Although it contains only electronics and specially-designed synthetic molecules, the e-nose operates much like its biological counterpart.

Execute

One current model of this "nose on a chip" contains about three dozen different odorant-absorbing polymers, large molecules synthesized to absorb vapors of different kinds. Each polymer absorbs a particular range of odorants, in a manner analogous to the odorant-absorbing protein molecules on olfactory receptor neurons. Just like an olfactory receptor protein, a given synthetic polymer absorbs a number of different odorants, and, again, like the nose's receptor molecules, various synthetic polymers in the e-nose are specialized for absorbing different sets of odorants.

When a polymer sensor comes into contact with one of the vapor molecules it was designed to absorb, the polymer undergoes a sponge-like expansion. This expansion alters the electrical resistance of a conductive, substrate to which the polymer is fused. So each odorant produces a characteristic set of changes in electrical resistance across the array of synthetic polymers. Any odorant—or at least a good many different odorants—generates a distinctive cross-molecule absorption profile. The nose chip contains an electronic neural network that can be trained to assign unique labels to various odorants to which the chip is exposed. Incidentally, this entire process—from odor presentation to identification—takes less than a second. And the nose on a chip needs no sleep, never needs feeding, does a competent job every time and is ready to go anywhere and smell anything, for as long as needed. Eventually, e-noses will stand silent guard at airport security checkpoints; they will monitor the quality of seafood and poultry products, helping to ensure food safety; they will inhabit new refrigerators, where they'll sound the alarm when food becomes tainted; they will sniff out buried landmines, and do many other vital jobs. (Perkins [2000] identifies additional current and future uses for such artificial noses.)

As good as all this sounds, however, don't think about trading in your perfectly fine biological nose for one of these electronic models quite yet. Remember the discussion, earlier in the chapter, of the limitations created by the human genome's relatively few working olfactory genes? Well, however limited the genome might be, the number of functional genes and receptor proteins in a normal human nose dwarfs the several dozen sensors used by the nose on a chip.

Our receptors have been tuned by evolution to pick up the myriad vaporous molecules that are behaviorally important for us. The nose on a chip, in comparison, senses a very limited range of odorants. Still, the technology and its applications are fascinating and will get better over time.

Having surveyed the biological bases of the olfactory system, we are now prepared to consider the perception of odors.

Odor Perception

Odor Detection   Admittedly, the human sense of smell is rather dull compared to that of other species such as the dog. Still, the human nose is remarkably sensitive. For instance, people can detect ethyl mercaptan (a foul-smelling substance) in concentrations as minute as 1 part per 50 billion parts of air. This performance rivals that of the most sensitive laboratory instruments available for measuring tiny concentrations of molecules. Such sensitivity is all the more impressive when you realize that only a small fraction of the odor molecules in this minute concentration actually reaches the olfactory receptors in the top of the nasal cavity. During normal breathing, only about 2 percent of the odorous molecules entering the nostrils actually make it to the receptors; the remaining molecules are absorbed by the receptor free lining inside the nose.

Olfactory sensitivity varies greatly from odor to odor. For example, the substance mentioned above, mercaptan, can be detected at a concentration 10 million times less than that needed to smell carbon tetrachloride, a liquid sometimes used in dry-cleaning fluid (Wenger, Jones and Jones, 1956). Because people are so sensitive to mercaptan, it is added to natural gas—which is odorless but toxic—to warn of gas leaks (Cain and Turk, 1985). One account of this remarkable sensitivity assigns a crucial role to a substance we mentioned earlier, the olfactory binding protein (Snyder et al., 1989). This protein, which is found only in nasal tissue, is created by a gland located toward the very rear of the nose. A duct carries the protein toward the tip of the nose where, every time you inhale, molecules of the protein are mixed into the incoming air. The protein in the newly inspired air traps molecules of potential odorants and carries these bound molecules to the olfactory receptors. The olfactory binding protein is very well suited to enhance sensitivity; it has at least some affinity for virtually all odorants. Moreover, although only a few odorants have been studied thus far, this protein has the greatest affinity for odorant molecules to which the human nose is most sensitive.

Besides molecular properties, odor sensitivity also depends on a number of other factors, including time of day, age and gender. In particular, people are generally able to detect weak odors better in the morning than in the evening (Stone and Pryor, 1967); elderly people are less sensitive than young adults (Cain and Gent, 1991; Schiffman, 1997); and females are more sensitive, on average, than males (Koelega and Koster, 1974). Because of these age and sex differences in smell acuity, some people may be put off by body odors that others are unaware of. Your own experiences in social settings probably confirm this observation. Your experiences may also lead you to believe that your sensitivity to odors increases when you are hungry. But this belief is questionable. Some experiments confirm this belief (Schneider and Wolf, 1955), while others call it into question (Furchtgott and Friedman, 1960). Consistent with popular belief, however, smokers *are* less sensitive to odors than nonsmokers (Ahlstrom et al., 1987). This dulled odor sensitivity is also found in nonsmokers who live or work with individuals who are heavy smokers (Ahlstrom et al., 1987).

Earlier we pointed out that the two nostrils seem to work in shifts, with one drawing in more air than its more engorged fellow nostril. As a consequence of this difference in air flow, the two nostrils should have different odor detection thresholds. After all, a higher flow rate means more odorant molecules will be available in the nostril. To test this straightforward prediction, Noam Sobel and colleagues at Stanford Univer-

sity (Sobel et al., 2000) measured thresholds for two odorants, vanillin (a pleasant-smelling odorant) and propionic acid (an acrid-smelling odorant); thresholds for both odorants were measured for each nostril separately. Contrary to expectation, peoples' ability to detect low levels of these odorants did not differ between the engorged, low-flow-rate nostril, and the more open, high-flow-rate nostril. This curious result was explained, though, by measures of peoples' sniffs taken while they were trying to detect the odorants. Sobel discovered that volunteers sniffed longer when they were working only with their low flow rate nostril, and made shorter sniffs when only their more open nostril was being tested. This variation in sniffing equated the total volume of odorant-carrying air that moved through the two nostrils. To clinch this point, Sobel repeated the experiment, this time keeping sniff duration constant. Now, odorant detection thresholds were higher in the engorged nostril than in the open nostril, as it should be, if thresholds depended on how many odorant molecules are available to be absorbed by receptors. Incidentally, we don't encourage unnecessary sniffing (which can annoy people around you), but when it's important to detect some weak source of smell, a long, steady sniff can come in very handy.

Odor Identification   Having bragged about the sensitivity of the human nose, we must qualify what we mean by *sensitivity*. The remarkable performance described above refers to the ability to *detect* the presence of a faint odor, not the ability to *identify* the odor. In fact, at near-threshold concentrations, people can *smell* an odor without being able to *identify* the odor. Here's an illustration of this point (Engen, 1960). When people are given three empty test tubes and a fourth test tube containing an extremely dilute odor, people can accurately select the tube that "smells different" from the others. But using the same set of stimuli, they make many errors when instructed to pick the test tube that contains some named odor ("pick the tube containing menthol"). So people

Execute

behave as if they have two thresholds, one for detecting the presence of an odor and a second, higher threshold for identifying what that odor is.

For some odorous substances, part of the identification problem may stem from a substance's bistability. Such substances can elicit two different qualitative experiences that fluctuate over time. (A visual example of bistable perception is the vase/face figure shown in Figure 4.1c.) For instance, the compound dihydromyrcenol (which is related to turpentine) sometimes has a citrus-like odor and other times a woody odor. Lawless, Glatter and Hohn (1991) were able to bias people's descriptions of this substance by also having the people smell an odorant that was unambiguously woody (such as pine) or unambiguously citrus-like (such as lemon oil). After smelling citrus, people said the ambiguous compound smelled woody; after smelling the woody odor, the compound smelled like citrus. This shift in perception is not attributable to sensory adaptation, for it did not matter whether the unambiguous stimulus was sniffed before or after sniffing dihydromyrcenol. This context-dependent change in odor identifica-

tion could be exploited for creative menu planning using dishes with multiple aroma components, such as curried chicken. And when serving wine, it is possible to give a fruity wine such as a German Riesling either an acidic or a floral bouquet, depending on its accompaniment.

Most odorous substances, though, elicit their own characteristic odor qualities regardless of context. Still, individuals differ greatly in their ability to identify (or attach labels to) various odors. Odor identification has been measured in two large studies: one, a sample of about 2,000 people ranging in age from 5 to 99 years (Doty et al., 1984), and the other, a survey of more than a million readers of a popular magazine (Wysocki, Pierce and Gilbert, 1991). The two studies agree. Overall, females are significantly better at odor identification than males, with the best performances exhibited by individuals ranging in age from the mid-twenties to late-forties (see Figure 13.9). Some people beyond their sixties show marked impairments in the ability to identify odors, which may explain why elderly people sometimes complain about the blandness of food;

Differences

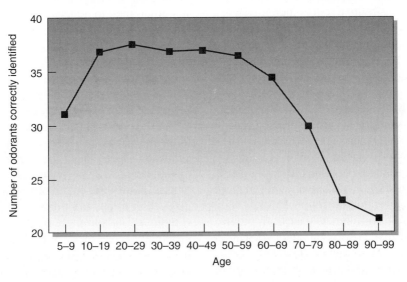

FIGURE 13.9
Ability to identify odors varies with age.

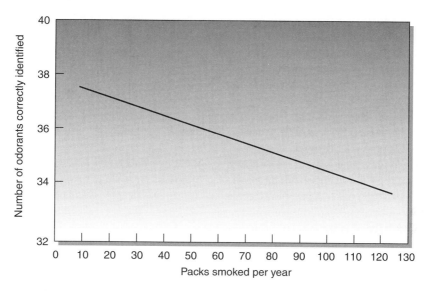

FIGURE 13.10
Ability to identify odors is impaired by cigarette smoking.

after all, smell is an essential component in the enjoyment of food. It should be noted, though, that odor identification performance is much more variable among the elderly: some people in their 70s or older perform as well as middle-aged individuals.

Age and gender are important, but they are not the only factors that influence one's ability to identify odors. For example, tobacco smoking impairs the ability to identify odors, as the graph in Figure 13.10 documents. The longer the history of smoking, the greater the number of errors on a standardized odor identification test (Frye, Doty and Schwartz, 1989). Fortunately, cessation of smoking promotes recovery. Ambient air quality, too, affects odor perception. Individuals working in plants manufacturing vaporous chemicals may experience long-term impairments in olfactory identification (Schwartz et al., 1989). People living in cities with poor ambient air quality have difficulty identifying at least some odors compared to matched samples of people from cities with generally better air quality (Wysocki, Pierce and Gilbert, 1991). These deficits associ-

ated with smoking and air quality may be related to structural changes at the receptor sites on the olfactory cilia, which become altered with chronic exposure to particular odorants.

Murphy and Cain (1986) found that blind adults are significantly better at odor identification than comparably aged sighted individuals. Perhaps, then, odor identification should be thought of as a skill that can be sharpened with the enforced practice required without vision. Indeed, even in sighted individuals, practice with feedback improves the ability to identify odors. Desor and Beauchamp (1974) tested people's ability to name thirty-two common odorous objects contained in individual opaque jars. After sniffing the jar, the person guessed what the object was and rated the familiarity of the odor. Some smells—such as coffee, paint and banana—were readily identified and were also rated as highly familiar. Other smells—including ham, cigar and crayon—were incorrectly identified by most people; these odors were also rated as less familiar. Desor and Beauchamp then went through the series again, this time providing people with the correct answer when they

564

made errors. With practice, everyone was able to name each of the thirty-two odors correctly. Furthermore, the same people were trained on an additional set of thirty-two new odors, and with practice they were able to identify all sixty-four odors with few errors.

Although practice improves odor identification, it does not help everybody to the same degree. For example, practice seems to benefit females more than males, as Figure 13.11 shows. This graph summarizes the results from an experiment where Cain (1982) asked male and female college students to identify each of the eighty common odorous stimuli listed in the figure. Each person went through the set of stimuli several times, with feedback provided after every trial. Students of both genders improved with practice on this task, but the females consistently outperformed the males on just about all odorous stimuli. Each bar in Figure 13.11 summarizes identification performance for a particular stimulus. Stimuli in the upper portion of the figure (such as coffee) were readily identified, while stimuli toward the lower portion (such as cough syrup) were difficult to identify. Unshaded bars indicate female superiority at identifying that odorant, while shaded bars indicate male superiority. The length of the bar denotes the size of the sex difference in odor identification. For instance, males were much better than females at identifying Brut brand aftershave lotion, but only marginally better at identifying the smell of mothballs. Females were much better than males at identifying coconut, but only slightly better at identifying peanut butter. As the overwhelming number of unshaded bars indicates, females are generally better at this task than males.

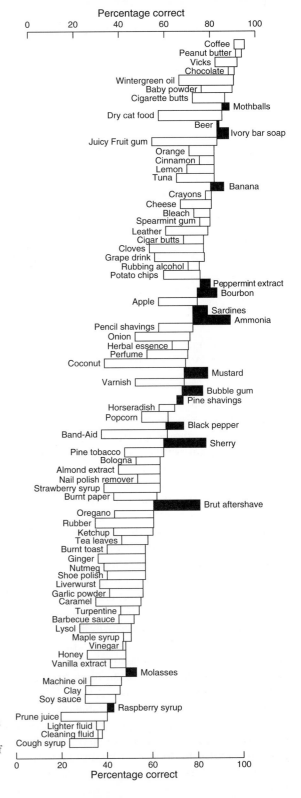

FIGURE 13.11

Odor identification for eighty common stimuli, arranged from top to bottom in order of ease of identification. Unshaded bars indicate the superior ability of female subjects to identify a particular stimulus; shaded bars indicate the superior ability of male subjects. (Redrawn with permission from Cain, 1982.)

The origin of these sex differences is not yet known; nonetheless, it is clear that both sexes do benefit from practice.

Next on our list of important determinant of odor identity is stimulus salience. This is dramatically demonstrated by the abilities of mothers to recognize their newborns by smell alone after less than 1 hour of postnatal exposure to the infant (Kaitz et al., 1987). This olfactory link between mother and infant occurs in a variety of species besides humans, and there is evidence that this adaptive reaction coincides with structural and neurochemical changes in the olfactory bulb (Kendrick, Levy and Keverne, 1992). Apparently newborn infants also rely heavily on olfaction to recognize their mothers. Porter (1991) provides an excellent review of findings on the role of odor perception in mother infant relationships. Related to this issue, Schaal (1988) has reviewed the literature on the development of olfaction in infants and children, concluding that from birth onward, infants are quite good at detecting and discriminating odors. What does seem to change, according to Schaal, are infant's hedonic reactions to odors—it may take several years for children to develop aversions to some odors that adults judge to be offensive.

Related to salience is the influence of familiarity, which also impacts the ability to name an odor. Older individuals, though generally poorer at odor identification than young people, *do* show superior recall for substances that have been in use for a long time. For instance, older adults have little trouble recognizing the smell of vinegar and coffee, odorants that older persons have been exposed to since youth. In comparison, epoxy and hair conditioner stump older adults but not youngsters (Wood and Harkins, 1987). At the other end of the age continuum, newborn infants exposed for about a day to an artificial odorant preferentially orient to that odorant two weeks later when it is paired with a novel one (Davis and Porter, 1991). This olfactory familiarization probably underlies infants' ability to recognize their mothers by smell.

Illusion

But if experience with odors starts to build from the very first days of our lives, why are adults relatively poor at identifying odors, even ones that they've experienced over and over? Of course, odors are typically associated with information from other senses, information that unambiguously identifies the source of those odors. For instance, a citrus-like aroma is usually accompanied by the sight of a lemon. But in odor identification tasks, people have only the sense of smell to go on. Even healthy, young females may get fewer than half the items correct. The problem is not one of discrimination: people find it easy to judge correctly whether two odors are the same versus different. The problem involves *naming* individual odors. In other words, the link between odors and their verbal descriptions is weak (Engen, 1987). This inability to name a familiar odor has been aptly termed the **tip of the nose phenomenon** (Lawless and Engen, 1977). If the problem is indeed one of retrieving odor names from memory, then prompting with verbal clues should help identify odors. And it does. Several researchers (Davis, 1981; Zellner, Bartoli and Eckard, 1991) have found that merely providing people with a color name related to an odor (such as *yellow* when lemon was being sniffed) is sufficient to trigger correct identification.

Odor Concentrations Besides having characteristic qualities, odorous substances also vary in the *intensity* of those qualities. Intensity, as you might guess, depends on the concentration level of odorous molecules. A common misconception about the sense of smell concerns people's alleged poor ability to judge differences in odor concentrations. Until recently, it was generally thought that people require about a 25 percent difference in odor concentration before they can tell that one sample of an odor is stronger than another sample of that same odor. (This implies that a bouquet of five flowers would smell no stronger than a bouquet of four flowers, since they differ by only 20 percent.) Compared to vision and hearing (where difference thresholds are on the order of 10 percent), this represents dull sensitivity indeed. However, William Cain (1977) has shown that this dismal performance does not reflect some inferiority of the olfactory nervous system; instead, the poor performance stems from the moment-to-moment variability in the amount of odorous vapor delivered to the olfactory receptor cells. Remember, only a small fraction of these vapors actually reach these cells. Taking account of variability in effective odor concentration, Cain found that concentration differences as small as 7 percent are discriminable. This places the nose in the same league with the eye and the ear as a judge of intensity differences. (Thus, if their fragrance was delivered through Cain's experimental apparatus, five flowers *would* consistently smell stronger than four.)

Execute

Recall the description of magnitude scaling in Chapter 11 and in the Appendix. In a typical application of that procedure, people are asked to assign numbers to sounds according to their loudness. Comparable scaling measurements have been made for perceived odor intensity. As with loudness, odor intensity grows as a power function of concentration. Although the values vary from odor to odor, many odors give exponents in the neighborhood of 0.6, indicating that perceived odor intensity grows gradually relative to increasing concentration. To illustrate, doubling odor concentration produces only about a 50 percent increase in perceived intensity, not 100 percent (the value associated with an exponent of 1.0). As a result, a bouquet of ten flowers will not smell twice as strong as a bouquet of five flowers; to smell twice as strong as five flowers, a bouquet would have to consist of seventeen flowers. Interestingly, intensity ratings can be affected by color. Zellner and Kautz (1990) found that some odorous substances smell stronger when the sniffed liquid substance is colored (for instance red, in the case of strawberry). Evidently, simple conditioning cannot explain this finding, since enhanced odor intensity was found even with inappropriate color/odor combinations (for instance, red lemon).

Why is it important to be able to judge the concentration of an odor? Suppose you walk into your room and smell a foul odor. You can't see where it's coming from so you have to rely on your sense of smell to guide you to the source. You move around trying to locate where the smell becomes stronger. Because the concentration of airborne odorant molecules decreases with distance from the molecules' source, as you move in a direction that increases the odor's concentration you'll ultimately come to the source of the odor. Many animals use exactly this strategy when tracking prey or when following an odor trail to a potential mate (recall the cabbage moth mentioned earlier in this chapter).

The Common Chemical Sense   While we're on the subject of odor concentrations, we should note that most odors judged pleasant at moderate concentrations lose their attractiveness at high concentrations. This is why sales clerks in a store's cosmetics department always urges customers to allow a dab of perfume time to dilute before smelling it. One reason intense odors can be overpowering has to do with the free nerve endings in the olfactory epithelium (a look back at Figure 13.6 will refresh your memory). Such free nerve endings are not limited to the nasal mucosa. They are found in all of the body's mucous membranes—the conjunctiva lining the eye as well as the mucous membranes of the mouth, respiratory tract, anus and genitals. Because of their free nerve endings, each of these membranes is very sensitive to potentially irritating chemicals (Cometto-Muñiz and Cain, 1996). The nose's free nerve endings can be stimulated by just about any volatile substance of moderately high concentration. They are the receptors for what is known as the **common chemical sense.** This common chemical sense is responsible for the *feeling* that accompanies certain smells— such as the coolness of menthol or the tingle in your nose when you burp. Even the crisp, invigorating "smell" of fresh mountain air (which itself has no odor) comes from stimulation of the

N
Neural

common chemical sense, by ozone in the mountain air. In fact, just about any volatile substance can elicit this "feeling" in the nose if the concentration of that substance is high enough. In the case of some substances, stimulation of the common chemical sense produces a burning sensation that causes you reflexively to hold your breath (a gasp reflex) and turn your head away from the source of stimulation. If you've ever inhaled ammonia fumes, you know what this gasp reflex is like.

Not all people have equally-sensitive common chemical senses. For example, cigarette smokers are less sensitive than nonsmokers. For smokers, the inhaled concentration of a potentially irritating substance must be about 25 percent higher than that of nonsmokers to elicit a reflexive change in breathing pattern (Cometto-Muñiz and Cain, 1982). Smokers, then, have a diminished system to warn them of dangerous chemicals. Elderly people also show reduced sensitivity to nasal irritants that stimulate the common chemical sense (Stevens and Cain, 1986). And, as you might guess by now, males are less sensitive than females (Garcia-Medina and Cain, 1982). Some people completely lose their common chemical sense from damage to the trigeminal nerve carrying information from the nose's free nerve endings to the brain. In these individuals, harsh chemical substances elicit *no* reaction when inhaled.

The common chemical sense warns us of the presence of potentially irritating substances. However, its operation is not limited to dangerous concentration levels. In fact, even at nonirritating levels of stimulation, the common chemical sense influences the perception of odor. In an experiment by Cain and Murphy (1980), participants sniffed amyl butyrate (a fruity-smelling substance) and then rated the perceived intensity of the odor. Mixed in with the odorant were various amounts of carbon dioxide. (Carbon dioxide is a gas that does *not* stimulate olfactory receptors but *does* stimulate the free nerve endings in the nose. Hence, it has no odor; but because it stimulates the common chemical sense, it elicits

FIGURE 13.12

Stimulation of the common chemical sense (using carbon dioxide) affects one's perception of odor (amylbutyrate).

a pungent sensation when inhaled.) Figure 13.12 shows that stimulation of the common chemical sense influenced people's judgments of odor intensity. The vertical axis plots the perceived odor intensity of the amyl butyrate and the horizontal axis shows the concentration of the odorless carbon dioxide. Note that increasing the concentration of carbon dioxide, which by itself could not be smelled, reduced the perceived intensity of the amyl butyrate. Even though the actual concentration of amyl butyrate remained constant, its smell changed from pleasant and fruity (at low levels of carbon dioxide) to pungent and irritating (at high levels of carbon dioxide). People also rated how irritating the "smell" seemed. As expected, higher concentrations of the odorless carbon dioxide gas were judged more irritating. However, the pungency of the carbon dioxide was lessened when more amyl butyrate was mixed in with it. The interaction between odor and the common chemical sense works both ways: each influences the perception of the other. Clearly, the common chemical sense adds an important ingredient to our experience of odorous substances.

Illusion

As noted above, the common chemical sense reflects responses generated by free nerve endings in the nose. These chemically-sensitive free nerve endings abound in all mucous membranes. Significant concentrations of certain airborne chemicals can irritate exposed membranes, not only in the nose, but in the eye and respiratory tract as well. This may explain some cases of what is known as "sick building syndrome." Although this syndrome likely has multiple causes, one of them may be that new carpets, upholstery, adhesives or plastic laminate furnishings emit volatile organic compounds, including formaldehyde. The compounds irritate free nerve endings in exposed mucous membranes, causing coughing and throat irritation, tearing, headache and unpleasant, tingling sensations in the nose. When the air in "sick" buildings is analyzed, just as often as not, no single volatile organic compound is found at high enough concentration to be worrisome. Does this mean that the complaints of eye, nose and throat irritation are merely excuses to get out of work? Or that the complainers are hypochondriacs?

According to Cometto-Muñiz, Cain and Hudnell (1997), when several volatile organic components are mixed, their individual effects sum. These researchers measured how mixtures of various volatile organic compounds affected the common chemical sense. To avoid contamination from people's smelling the stimuli, they worked with anosmic volunteers. Cometto-Muñiz and colleagues discovered that mixtures of such compounds could produce strong effects, even though individual components of the mixtures were at sufficiently low concentration to have no effect on their own. There is a lesson here, we believe, for environmental engineers who assess the quality of air in allegedly sick buildings.

Turning back to the topic of odor perception, let's consider *anosmia,* which, as you read earlier, is a loss of ability to perceive odors.

C

Clinical

Disorders of Smell Deficiencies in hearing and seeing are usually easy to detect because people depend so much on sight and sound to guide their everyday activities. Deficiencies in odor perception, in comparison, often go unnoticed. Though hard to imagine, some individuals are completely unable to distinguish odorless, pure air from strong concentrations of odorous substances. A blow to the head is a frequent cause of this "odor blindness," or anosmia (Varney, 1988). In such cases, anosmia often proves to be temporary, suggesting that the olfactory receptors or their axons had been damaged (recall that these neurons can regenerate). Anosmia may also be acquired from inhaling caustic agents such as lead, zinc sulfate or cocaine. These, too, are believed to injure the olfactory receptors, which is why smell sensitivity may recover after exposure to the caustic agent ceases. Reduced odor sensitivity and identification performance are also observed in patients with Alzheimer's disease (Resek, 1987). Here, impaired odor perception probably results from the degeneration of neurons in the olfactory epithelium (Talamo et al., 1989). Schiffman (1983) reviews the various causes of anosmia.

Sometimes anosmia does not involve a complete loss of ability to smell, but is instead restricted to particular odorants. Here, a person shows normal sensitivity to some odors but abnormally poor or no sensitivity to others. These are the specific anosmias we mentioned earlier, and they are more common than you might think. For example, 3 percent of the U.S. population have trouble smelling the odor of sweat, 12 percent have diminished sensitivity to musky odors, and 47 percent have trouble smelling the odor of urine (Amoore, 1991).

Losing one's sense of smell has serious consequences (Toller, 1999). Individuals with acquired anosmia claim that eating is no longer pleasurable, and these people show a loss of both appetite and weight (Schechter and Henkin, 1974). There is even speculation that anosmia may dull one's sexual drive (Bobrow, Money and Lewis, 1971). This possibility is not entirely far-fetched. As mentioned in the beginning of the chapter, animals heavily rely on odor to motivate and guide their sexual behavior. And certainly, the large sums of money spent on perfume, not to mention the erotic nature of many perfume commercials, suggest a connection between the nose and sexual behavior.

Before leaving our discussion of smell disorders, this seems a good place to mention **odor hallucinations**—the experiencing of odors for which there is no physical stimulus. Odor hallucinations are sometimes associated with brain tumors (Douek, 1974). They are also a common complaint of people diagnosed as mentally ill (Rubert, Hollender and Mehrhof, 1961). But don't assume that odor hallucinations necessarily indicate brain damage or mental illness. People sometimes describe sensing strange, metallic odors when they have the flu or other viral diseases (Schiffman, 1983). This effect is thought to result from a virus having damaged cells in the olfactory epithelium. In any event, you needn't become alarmed when you experience some olfactory hallucination; it is often difficult to distinguish real odors from imaginary ones, since the source of an odor may not be obvious. How many times have you searched your house trying to discover where that "funny smell" was coming from?

Plasticity

Adaptation to Odors As you walk into the lobby of a movie theater, you are confronted by the aroma of fresh popcorn. Driven by this lovely smell, you rush to get in line to buy some. But by the time you reach the counter, the aroma seems to have faded considerably. This exemplifies how exposure to an odor decreases sensitivity to that odor—a phenomenon called **odor adaptation.** Certain occupations depend crucially on odor adaptation—sewer workers, for instance, can carry out their jobs without being bothered by the stench of their surroundings. Odor adaptation also means that people cease to be aware of their own body odors or the odors permeating their immediate surroundings. As Freud (1930/1961) observed, "in spite of all man's developmental ad-

vances, he scarcely finds the smell of his own excreta repulsive, but only that of other people's" (p. 54). Thus, we usually rely on others for information about our own odors, a widely exploited theme in advertising for deodorant, mouthwash and soap.

Odor adaptation has been studied in the laboratory, and the results confirm what experience suggests (see Halpern, 1983). Following even prolonged exposure to an odor, one never *completely* loses the sensitivity to that odor. Instead, its perceived intensity steadily decreases with continued exposure, eventually falling to about 30 percent of its initial level (Cain, 1978). (This is why some people can tolerate wearing an overpowering amount of perfume or aftershave. Their noses have adapted to the strong fragrance that others wince at.) If an odor's concentration is weak to begin with, it may be impossible to detect that weak odor following adaptation to a strong concentration of the same odor.

Recovery from exposure to an odor takes just a few minutes unless the adaptation odor was quite strong, in which case an hour or more may be required for complete recovery (Berglund et al., 1971). There is also anecdotal evidence for an ultralong-term adaptation effect, whereby individuals develop a chronic insensitivity to odors common to their work environment. Even when they report to work first thing in the morning, after hours away, they fail to smell odors that visitors readily sense. The adaptation of these workers carries over from one day to the next. At the same time, these individuals exhibit normal sensitivity to odors not peculiar to their workplace; so they have not completely lost their sense of smell. Moreover, upon returning to work following a short vacation, they are initially able to sense the odors that their colleagues on the job cannot sense. After a few days on the job, however, they again become insensitive to those odors. Gesteland (1986) has speculated that these long-term losses in odor sensitivity may be related to the growth processes in the olfactory receptor cells that we described earlier. Perhaps chronic exposure to a limited set of odors affects receptor cells responsive to that set of odors, and several weeks away from that environment are needed to allow the spoiled cells to be replaced with fresh ones.

This explanation probably does not apply, however, to short-term adaptation, where brief exposure to an odor temporarily lessens your sensitivity to it. In this latter case, the process responsible for adaptation probably occurs within the brain, not in the nose. One reason for believing this is that you can adapt one nostril to an odor (keeping the other one closed) and then measure a loss in odor sensitivity using just the unadapted nostril (Zwaardemaker, 1895, cited in Engen, 1982). Since this nostril was closed during adaptation, the olfactory receptors associated with the nostril received no stimulation. Nonetheless, your perception of odors introduced into this nostril are still dulled, indicating that the process underlying the loss in sensitivity occurs in the brain, not in the receptor cells. However, the physiology of postreceptor adaptation is poorly understood.

Execute

So far we have considered situations where an odor's perceived strength is reduced by prior exposure to strong concentrations of that same odor. In some cases, though, a temporary loss in sensitivity to one odor can be produced by exposure to a different odor—a phenomenon called **cross-adaptation.** As you might expect, odors that tend to smell alike (such as nail polish remover and airplane model glue) usually show a large degree of cross-adaptation: exposure to one reduces your sensitivity to the other. If you spend several minutes sniffing perfume samples at the cosmetic counter, don't be surprised if the fragrance you're already wearing seems temporarily to have worn off; sniffing perfumes similar to your own lessens your sensitivity to the one you're wearing. Dissimilar odors, in contrast, do not influence each other nearly so much (Moncrieff, 1956). Thus, sniffing perfume samples will not subsequently affect your ability to appreciate the aroma of coffee.

You can experience cross-adaptation by performing the following simple experiment. First, take a sniff of a lemon and get an idea of the intensity of its aroma. Now hold a spoon of peanut butter close to your nose for a minute or so, adapting to its smell. Then quickly take another whiff of the lemon. You will find the lemon's fragrance just as strong as before. Next adapt for a minute to a lime held under your nose, and then again sniff the lemon. This time you will find the lemon's fragrance noticeably weakened. A lesson to learn from this exercise is that your appreciation of food during a multicourse meal depends on the order in which the foods are served. This is particularly true for foods with similar aromas. For instance, cheese with a strong, overpowering smell (such as Roquefort) should not be served before one with a more delicate aroma (such as Gouda).

Initially, it was hoped that cross-adaptation would provide a method for odor classification. Presumably, odors stimulating the same receptors should exhibit maximum cross-adaptation, while odors stimulating different receptors should show little or no cross-adaptation. While this sounds reasonable, the results are confusing. In particular, cross-adaptation is sometimes asymmetrical: adaptation to odor A may strongly influence your perception of odor B, but adaptation to odor B may exert hardly any effect on the smell of odor A (Cain and Engen, 1969). This outcome suggests that cross-adaptation is not strictly due to receptor adaptation. Moreover, odors that exhibit marked cross-adaptation sometimes bear no molecular resemblance to each other. Cross-adaptation, like short-term adaptation in general, then, does not appear to result from fatigue of the olfactory receptors.

Odor Mixtures   Besides cross-adaptation, different odors can affect one another when mixed together in inhaled air. For example, a meal may generate a bouquet of aromas whose interactions give rise to a unique and very pleasing experience. Odor mixture also underlies the success of commercial air fresheners sold to cover up house odors. In effect, these products exploit the ability of one odor to mask another, by "swamping" the offensive odor with an even stronger pine or floral scent. These products should be distinguished from true deodorizers, which act by actually removing odorous molecules from the air or by preventing the production of odorous molecules in the first place (the mechanism employed in some underarm deodorants).

As indicated before, the nose seems able to sort out and identify a mixture's various odors. This is why you can identify many of the food ingredients that went into some complex dish simply from the smell of that dish. In this sense, the nose's behavior resembles the ear's ability to single out one pitch from a musical chord; the nose does not behave like the eye, which sometimes loses track of the individual hues making up a mixture. However, a person's judgments of an odor mixture cannot be predicted on the basis of the simple addition of the two components. For instance, two different odorants of moderate intensity added together may not yield an intense mixture; this failure of addition is termed **mixture suppression,** and its physiological basis is not well understood (Derby, Ache and Kennel, 1985; Laing, 1988). (For a full discussion of odor mixture, see Engen, 1982).

Top-down

Odors and Memory Even when people cannot identify some odor, they are often able to say with confidence whether or not they have smelled it before. This suggests that odors can reach back into memory (see Box 13.2). For Helen Keller, who was blind and deaf from infancy, smell was

> a potent wizard that transports us across thousands of miles and all the years we have lived. The odors of fruits waft to me in my southern home, to my childhood frolics in the peach orchard. Other odors, instantaneous and fleeting, cause my heart to dilate joyously or contract with remembered grief. (1908, p. 574)

Odors can certainly be potent reminders of the past. They effortlessly call up memories, particu-

larly memories that were laid down long ago (Schab, 1991; Chu and Downes, 2000). But can memories call up odors? The answer seems to be no. Most people have great difficulty *imagining* what an odor smells like, even a very familiar one. Can you, for instance, conjure up the smell of a rose? Of course you recognize its fragrance when you actually encounter a rose, but recalling such a smell seems very difficult. Isn't it odd that one can readily hum tunes in one's head, can vividly picture a scene in the mind's eye, but cannot recreate in the mind a remembered smell? Perhaps, during the course of evolution, the sense of smell became fully developed before consciousness came on the scene. And perhaps, as a result, the olfactory system does not have access to the neural machinery needed to imagine odors consciously in the absence of the objects that normally evoke them. But emotional arousal seems quite able to trigger odor memories, probably from the intimate connections between the olfactory system and the limbic system. The so-called "smell of fear" may have neurological reality.

We'll close this section on olfaction by considering a vestigial portion of the olfactory system that may be connected to sexual arousal.

Sex and the Nose Earlier in this chapter we discussed pheromones, those special odor messages that signal sexual receptivity. Many mammalian noses have specialized sensory structures designed solely for picking up airborne chemical signals that mediate sexual attraction, including nonodorous chemicals (Taylor, 1994). These structures, called vomeronasal organs (VNOs), are embedded in the vomer bone, which is located at the junction of the nasal septum (the partition separating the two nostrils) and the hard palate of the roof of the mouth (see Figure 13.13). Notice that the VNO's location is different from that of the olfactory epithelium, which houses the olfactory sensory neurons. In humans, the VNO resembles two very small dimples about 2 millimeters deep on the floor of the nostrils. These structures can actually be seen with the naked

Differences

BOX 13.2

SMELL, TASTE AND LITERATURE

Languages have limited vocabularies for describing smell and taste experiences. Though it's fairly easy to describe what you see and hear, smell and taste are another matter (Bedichek, 1960). This places a special hardship on authors who want to communicate their character's smell and taste experiences. Fortunately, good writers rise above the apparent limitations of language. When you read a work in which smell and taste play a key part, you are reminded how important these "inarticulate senses" really are. To illustrate, let's consider some samples of writing in which authors have managed to give these inarticulate senses a voice of their own.

Smell can evoke memories long-buried and obscure; the same thing can happen in the case of taste. Probably the best-known literary description of this phenomenon comes from Marcel Proust's *Swann's Way.* In the book's overture, the narrator muses that it's impossible to recapture one's past merely by trying to think about it. True recapture requires that you reexperience the *sensations* that you felt originally. And he then goes on to provide an eloquent example of this idea. While the narrator is visiting his mother, she notices that he is cold and gives him a cup of tea and some little cakes called *petites madeleines.* Without thinking, he drinks some of the tea, into which cake crumbs have fallen. Immediately, he finds himself overcome with an "all-powerful joy," but he doesn't understand why. Then it strikes him: the taste was one he had experienced years before, as a young boy in the little French village of Combray.

> In that moment all the flowers in our garden and in M. Swann's park, and the water-lilies on the Vivonne and the good folk of the village and their little dwellings and the parish church and the whole of Combray and of its surroundings, taking their proper shapes and growing solid, sprang into being, town and gardens alike, from my cup of tea. (Proust, 1928, p. 58)

The whole of Proust's novel builds on his remembrances of things that happened in Combray. As a re-

sult, the whole work has roots in the taste of those few tea-soaked cake crumbs. What a powerful jolt to the memory! To honor the author who turned a bunch of cake crumbs into such beauty, researchers have given his name to the Proust phenomenon: "the ability of odors spontaneously to cue autobiographical memories that are highly vivid, affectively toned and very old" (Chu and Downes, 2000, p. 111).

Proust showed that a writer who wants to create truly convincing and complete lives cannot ignore smell and taste. James Joyce understood this as well as any writer of the past hundred years. In his masterpiece, *Ulysses,* Joyce frequently used smells to reach into the minds of various characters. You may know that various episodes in *Ulysses* emphasize different organs of the human body, with the so-called Nausicaä episode highlighting the eye and the nose. This episode takes place just after sunset on a June evening in 1904. Leopold Bloom, the middle-aged Dubliner around whose comings and goings the book revolves, is walking along the beach, trying to clear his head. Bloom finds himself attracted to Gerty MacDowell, a young woman who's sitting on some rocks near the beach. Although they never even speak, Bloom is infatuated. When she leaves, Gerty waves her perfumed handkerchief at Bloom. The scent reaches Bloom, triggering thoughts of Gerty and of his wife, Molly as well.

> Wait. Hm. Hm. Yes. That's her perfume. Why she waved her hand. I leave you to think of me when I'm far away on the pillow. What is it? Heliotrope? No, hyacinth? Hm. Roses, I think. She'd like scent of that with a little jessamine mixed. Her high notes and her low notes. At the dance night she met him, dance of the hours. Heat brought it out. She was wearing her black and it had the perfume of the time before. . . . Mysterious thing too. Why did I smell it only now? Took its time in coming like herself, slow but sure. Suppose it's ever so many millions of tiny grains blown across. . . . Clings to everything she takes off. Vamp of her stockings. Warm shoe. Stays. Drawers: little

BOX 13.2 continued

kick, taking them off. Byby till next time. Also the cat likes to sniff in her shift on the bed. Know her smell in a thousand. Bathwater too. Reminds me of strawberries and cream. (1922/1934, p. 368)

Another great writer with a special appreciation of the chemical senses was Jonathan Swift, the eighteenth-century English satirist. His most widely-read book is *Travels into Several Remote Nations of the World, a Letter from Captain Gulliver to His Cousin Sympson,* commonly known as *Gulliver's Travels.* In that book, Swift paints a dramatic portrait of adaptation to the smells of a highly unusual environment. In the fourth and final journey related in *Gulliver's Travels,* Lemuel Gulliver finds himself marooned on an island ruled by the noble Houyhnhnms, a race of intelligent, honest, socially-advanced horses. The island is also populated by a nasty, degenerate breed of barbaric, human-like creatures, Yahoos, whom the Houyhnhnms shun and whom Gulliver abhors. After living very happily among the horse-like Houyhnhnms for more than three years, learning their language and developing great admiration for their culture, Gulliver must leave the island and return to England and the home and family that he had once loved. In Gulliver's words:

As soon as I entered the House, my Wife took me in her Arms, and kissed me, at which having not been used to the Touch of that odious Animal for so many Years, I fell in a Swoon for almost an Hour. At the time I am writing it is Five Years since my last Return to England: During the first Year I could not endure my Wife or Children in my Presence, the very Smell of them was intolerable, much less could I suffer them to eat in the same Room. To this hour they dare not presume to touch my Bread, or drink out of the same Cup, neither was I ever able to let one of them take me by the Hand. The first Money I laid out was to buy two young Stone-Horses, which I keep in a good Stable, and next to them the Groom is

my greatest Favourite; for I feel my Spirits revived by the Smell he contracts in the Stable. My Horses understand me tolerably well; I converse with them at least four Hours every Day. They are Strangers to Bridle or Saddle, they in great Amity with me, and Friendship to each other. (1827/1890, p. 331)

There are many other literary examples that give proper respect to the power of taste or smell, and no list, however short, could fail to mention *Perfume,* a novel by Patrick Süsskind (1985) set in the eighteenth century. *Perfume's* central character and narrator, Jean Baptiste Grenouille, was born with no body scent of his own, but with a nose that had truly incredible sensitivity to odor. His unusual olfactory powers allow him to rely on his nose rather than his ears and eyes. Grenouille creates scents that bend other people to his will and satisfy his depraved appetites. In fact, when he sums up his infancy and early childhood, he does so in olfactory terms.

"(H)e first conjured up those that were earliest and most remote: the hostile, steaming vapors of Madame Gaillard's bedroom, the bone-dry leathery bouquet of her hands, the vinegary breath of Father Terrier, the hysterical, hot maternal sweat of Bussie, the wet nurse, the carrion stench of the Cemetiere des Innocents, the homicidal stench of his mother"

Grenouille bemoans ordinary human language's inability to express the subtleties of odors, but of course most people's sense of smell is so mediocre, that there is no real reason for language to express what only Grenouille could experience. The late Kurt Cobain and his band Nirvana, paid musical homage to Grenouille in the song "Scentless Apprentice."

These literary nuggets illustrate how writers at diverse times and in various places have woven smell and taste into their work. These samples are a reminder of how impoverished one's perceptual world would be without these "inarticulate senses."

FIGURE 13.13
The vomeronasal organ is located at the junction of the nasal septum.

eye, using a flashlight and a device that spreads open the nostril. It used to be thought that the VNO was present in infants but degenerated by adulthood. More recent evidence, however, clearly shows that the VNO is present throughout life. Moreover, we know that the VNO in human adults generates electrical signals in response to compounds that produce no response in the olfactory epithelium.

Most of what is known about the anatomy and physiology of the VNO system comes from studies of nonhuman mammals. Just like olfactory sensory neurons, cells in the VNO contain specialized receptors to which certain classes of volatile molecules readily bind. But VNO neural messages are carried to the brain by their own special nerve fibers, and these fibers bypass the olfactory bulb, innervating the accessory olfactory bulb instead. From there, the VNO pathway projects to the limbic system (which seems logical for a sensory channel concerned with sex). Damage

to the VNO system in nonhumans produces distinct disturbances in their sexual behavior.

Perfume companies would like to think that the VNO system is charged and ready for action in humans. Indeed, some companies have designed scents that include compounds explicitly tailored for the VNO. At present, however, the effectiveness of these perfumes remain questionable. Indeed, there is no firm evidence showing that VNO activity affects human sexual arousal and behavior. So for the time being, the link between sex and smell in humans remains tantalizing but unproven.

On this note we'll end our discussion of smell and move on to its companion sense, taste.

THE SENSE OF TASTE

We say of food, "This tastes good" or "I like the taste of that." But taste determines not only how much we like or dislike some food, but also whether we will eat it at all. In effect, the tongue and mouth (assisted by the nose) are designed to ensure that nutritious substances are eaten while noxious ones are not. Living in a civilized environment, one seldom needs to rely on taste to gauge edibility—if the grocer sells it or the restaurant serves it, we assume it must be safe to eat. Taste serves mainly to define our preferences among a large group of commercially available edible foods. Still, taste provides a bounty of perceptual experiences and therefore deserves to be studied.

Technically, the term *taste* refers to sensations produced when various substances dissolved in saliva penetrate the taste buds on the tongue and surfaces of the mouth. If you were to drop a pinch of sugar onto the tip of your tongue, the resulting sensation would constitute what most people call "taste." But when you actually eat something, you experience much more than taste alone: you also have an immediate appreciation of the food's temperature, texture and consistency (Gibson, 1966). All these sources of information combine with the substance's taste to form a complex of sensations known as **flavor.** Although the remainder of this chapter is concerned with the taste component of flavor, keep in mind that these other sources of information also contribute to one's enjoyment of food.

Our discussion of taste will follow the same general outline used in the discussion of smell. We'll describe the stimulus for taste, consider the question of taste categories, provide a brief overview of the anatomy and physiology of the gustatory system, and then take up the question of taste sensitivity. Finally, we'll explore interactions between taste and smell.

The Stimulus for Taste

To be tasted, a substance must be *soluble:* it must dissolve in saliva. This prerequisite for taste explains why you cannot *taste* the difference between a plastic spoon and a stainless steel spoon—neither material dissolves in saliva.

Moreover, food seems tasteless when the mouth contains insufficient saliva because saliva transports taste solutions to the receptors within the tongue and mouth. The salivary glands, incidentally, produce in the neighborhood of 740 cubic centimeters (25 ounces) of fluid daily, most of it during eating. Some food substances, particularly those containing citric acid, promote copious salivary secretion, while others, such as glucose, stimulate less. Besides aiding in digestion, saliva contains ingredients that prevent erosion of tooth enamel and eliminate bacteria in the oral cavity. In chemical composition, saliva closely resembles salt water, although the sodium content of saliva varies from one person to the next (Bradley, 1991). In fact, when you taste someone else's saliva you can actually detect the difference in sodium content (Bartoshuk, 1980), which we'll leave to the intellectually curious to confirm.

The Classification of Tastes

Systematic analysis of taste dates back at least 2,400 years, to Aristotle's claim that there were seven fundamental taste qualities: sweet, sour, salty, bitter, pungent, harsh and, finally, astringent. He took these fundamental qualities to be the building blocks out of which all more complex qualities could be synthesized. In the centuries following Aristotle, other fundamental taste qualities were added to the list (such as viscous and fatty) while others were dropped (Bartoshuk, 1978). By the early nineteenth century the list had shrunk to the four categories that most people are familiar with today: sweet, sour, salty and bitter. (Incidentally, the person who formalized the four-taste idea was Henning [1916]), the same man responsible for the odor classification scheme we discussed earlier.)

In 1908 Kikunae Ikeda, of the Imperial University in Tokyo, argued that another taste quality should be added to sweet, sour, salty and bitter. From seaweed, Ikeda extracted a substance that evoked a unique taste whose quality he described with the Japanese word *umami.** Although at the time it got little attention in the West, Ikeda's work has recently attracted considerable interest, and has now gained much credibility. Several factors lie behind this belated recognition of Ikeda's work: first, the increased Western interest in Asian cuisines, many of which use substances that produce umami taste (Lindemann, 2000); second, the identification of cortical subregions in which neurons seem to be specialized for umami taste (Rolls, 2000); and third, recent identification of umami-related receptors on the tongue (Chaudhari, Landin and Roper, 2000). Despite this addition, however, there remains considerable disagreement about what the fundamental taste qualities are, or even whether the very concept of fundamental taste qualities is really meaningful.

Neural

Robert Erickson (1980) took an interesting approach to the notion of fundamental taste qualities. He gave people taste solutions consisting of one or more of the so-called primary tastes and asked those people to judge whether they perceived "one" or "more than one" taste quality. For comparison, Erickson asked for the same judgment about auditory tones presented either alone or in a chord (that is, as simultaneously-sounded multiple tones). As expected, a single tone was always judged as one, and multiple tones were always judged as more than one. This confirms the analytical nature of pitch perception: identification of one tone is possible in the presence of another. The results with the taste solutions were quite different. Solutions composed of a single component were sometimes judged as more than one, whereas multi-component solutions were sometimes judged as one. Moreover, people were often unable to identify whether a mixture contained a particular component, even when they could reliably identify that component in isolation. For instance, quinine (a bitter-tasting substance) was easily recognized on its own. But

when mixed with sucrose (which, of course, is sweet), the quinine in the mixture was unrecognizable. These findings led Erickson to conclude that complex tastes are *not* analyzed into primary components but instead take on their own, unique quality, which may give little hint of their ingredients (Erickson, 1982). Putting this another way, when they are presented in mixtures, taste-producing substances (tastants) interact with one another in exceedingly complex ways. It seems that each tastant's perceptual effect modifies, and in turn is modified by, the perceptual effects of other components in the mixture.

This issue of fundamental taste categories is far from settled. Many taste researchers are reluctant to give up the idea of primary taste qualities, and after 2,400 years, the debate over how many primaries there are is as heated as ever. For the moment, though, we'll set aside the question of primaries and proceed to a less controversial, more enlightening topic, the neural mechanisms of taste perception.

The Anatomy and Physiology of Taste

The Taste Receptors   Let's begin by taking a tour of the tongue and the inside of the mouth. The tongue consists mainly of muscle covered with mucous membrane. To see taste's basic terrain take a careful look at your tongue in a mirror. Notice that it is covered with little bumps. These bumps are called **papillae** (from the Latin *papula,* meaning "pimple"). When viewed from the side (see Figure 13.14), they resemble regularly spaced columns separated by channels. The walls of the papillae are lined with tiny structures, called **taste buds,** that are shaped like garlic bulbs. These taste buds house the receptor cells responsible for registering the presence of chemical substances. Not all the papillae scattered over your tongue contain taste buds. Those in the center of the tongue have none, which is why food confined to this area has no taste. The center of the tongue is analogous to the blind spot in the eye: both are devoid of receptors. There's

---

This word does not have a precise equivalent in English, but the words *savory* or *meaty* are often used.

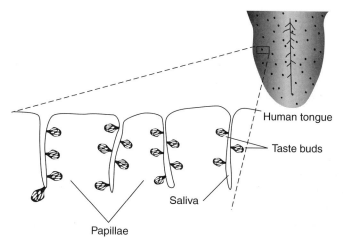

FIGURE 13.14
A side view of the tongue's papillae.

another parallel. Under normal conditions, you don't usually notice the blind spot because the brain fills it in; similarly, you don't usually notice the tongue's "blind spot." In fact, taste sensations appear to originate from the mouth's entire surface, including from regions with no receptors (Todrank and Bartoshuk, 1991). Moreover, when the taste information from an entire side of the tongue is blocked, for example by a virus, there is no change in everyday experiences of taste (Pfaffmann and Bartoshuk, 1989, 1990).

Taste buds are not restricted to the tongue: the throat, the roof of the mouth and the inside of the cheeks all have taste buds, though they are not housed in papillae. Some animals have structures similar to taste buds on parts of their bodies other than the tongue and inside of the mouth. Fish, who live in a watery equivalent of saliva, have taste receptors scattered over the surface of their bodies. And certain insects have taste receptors on their feet, enabling them to taste the surfaces they walk over.

Human papillae that contain taste buds have anywhere from several hundred buds down to just a single bud (Bradley, 1979), with a grand total of something like 6,000 taste buds distributed throughout the inside of the *average* human mouth. We stress average, because the total number of buds varies dramatically among individuals. One count from the tongues of healthy, college-age volunteers showed a fourteenfold difference within the sample (Miller and Reedy, 1990). Moreover, participants with the highest taste bud counts rated taste solutions of a given concentration as more intense than did participants with the fewest taste buds.

The density of taste buds also varies with age. Infants start out life with relatively few taste buds, but during childhood the number steadily increases to the numbers cited above. Around age 40, the trend reverses and the overall number of taste buds declines (Cowart, 1981). This decline may account for much of the well-documented loss of taste sensitivity in the elderly (Schiffman, 1983).

Like the olfactory receptors, taste buds are constantly degenerating and being replaced by new ones (Beidler and Smallman, 1965). The life expectancy of an individual taste bud is only about 10 days. Hence, throughout your lifetime there is a continuous, rapid turnover within the large population of taste buds. Unlike olfactory cells, however, taste buds do not have axons that

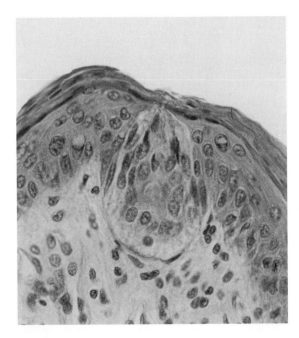

FIGURE 13.15
An individual taste bud. (Photograph courtesy of Inglis Miller.)

project to the brain. In a moment, we'll see how taste information is carried to the brain. Now, though, take a closer look at one of these short-lived but very important cells.

Figure 13.15 illustrates what an individual taste bud looks like under the microscope (buds are too small for the unaided eye to see). Each bud contains an average of fifty individual taste receptor cells, arranged within the bud like the individual cloves that make up a head of garlic. Sprouting from the end of each taste receptor cell

is a slender, threadlike structure called the *microvillus*. A clump of these "threads" juts into a tiny opening in the wall of the taste bud, which of course is bathed in saliva. Several different types of saliva-borne chemical stimuli can contact the microvilli and produce a change in the taste bud's electrical state. The types of stimuli with this power are listed in Table 13.1 (below). Notice that types of taste stimuli differ in size, and in the kind of taste quality that they tend to evoke.

Sensory transduction—a taste bud's conversion of chemical into electrical energy—involves mechanisms that vary with stimulus type. For example, some ions are thought to enter the receptor membrane and directly alter the cell's electrical potential. In contrast, when an amino acid or complex molecule is the chemical stimulus, the movement of that chemical stimulus to a bud's microvilli triggers a cascade of events inside the cell. These resemble the intracellular events in olfactory or visual transduction (Roper, 1992).

Neighboring taste buds appear to be electrically coupled via intermediary neurons, an arrangement that could promote interactions among receptors. Although the function of these connections is unknown, comparable kinds of circuitry in the retina serve to sharpen differences in activity between neighboring neural elements (Ratliff, 1965). Mucous secretions from supporting cells in taste buds wash excess stimulus substances away from the vicinity of the taste bud. This cleaning action is analogous to that described in the case of the olfactory epithelium. But because the tongue's self-cleansing is rela-

Neural

TABLE 13.1
Stimuli for Taste Categories

Stimulus	Stimulus size	Examples	Taste
Ion	Small	Sodium ions, Potassium ions	Salty, sour
Amino acid	Medium	Glutamate	Umami
Complex molecule	Large	Glucose, quinine	Sweet, bitter

tively slow, aftertastes linger after you have swallowed or spit out what was in your mouth.

Inside a papilla, taste receptor cells make contact with nerve fibers innervating the tongue. Remember that taste receptors themselves do not have axons to send messages to the brain; like photoreceptors, they must pass their messages on to neurons that in turn carry neural impulses to higher centers. Taste buds in the tongue and mouth are innervated by no less than three distinct cranial nerves, and a single taste bud may be innervated by more than one nerve (Keverne, 1982). We'll not go into which nerves innervate which regions of the tongue and mouth, but keep in mind that taste information arrives at the brain over several different communication lines. Moreover, these communication lines are hooked to a population of receptor cells whose members are constantly dying and being replaced.

So far we've considered the tongue's receptors. Can we relate the responses of specific receptors to specific taste qualities? For decades, textbooks gave a mistaken impression that particular taste sensations were associated with different regions on the tongue. It was customary to show a "tongue map" with sweet on the tip, salt on the front edges, sour along the edges toward the back of the tongue and bitter on the midline of the back. But those maps apply only to the ability to identify very weak solutions. Different regions of the tongue may be differentially sensitive to weak concentrations of different tastes (Collings, 1974), but at higher concentrations, various taste sensations can be elicited from nearly any place on the tongue. Taste qualities, then, are intermingled over the tongue; they are not uniquely identified with taste buds at particular locations.

To finish the survey of the tongue's receptors we should take note of the pain receptor that's responsible for the burning sensation you get from eating a hot pepper. This receptor registers the presence of capsaicin, the active ingredient in peppers that we mentioned in Chapter 12. Using molecular biological techniques, Caterina and colleagues (2000) created a strain of genetically altered mice that lack this class of receptor. The result? These altered mice readily drink capsaicin-laced water that normal mice find noxious. (People who liberally pour Tabasco sauce on their food or who eat whole chili peppers in a Mexican restaurant may have something in common genetically with these mutant mice.) These genetically altered mice also show little reaction to direct injection of capsaicin under their skin, whereas normal mice scratch and lick at the injection site as if experiencing discomfort. These findings suggest that the genes controlling manufacture of capsaicin-sensitive receptors on the tongue may also be involved in the creation of pain receptors elsewhere in the body.

Having looked at the taste receptors, let's now consider how messages generated by those receptors are represented in nerve fibers carrying information from the taste receptors to the brain.

The Taste Pathways Individual taste fibers exhibit a low, sustained discharge even when no taste substances are present on the tongue. When a substance is introduced, a fiber's activity increases by an amount that depends both on the nature of the substance and on its concentration. Most individual fibers respond to several different taste substances. For instance, one particular fiber might respond to both acids and salts. If individual nerve fibers are not selective for a particular taste, that fiber cannot unambiguously specify a particular taste quality. How, then, can the brain know which taste substance was actually present? This question of uniqueness in taste coding is reminiscent of the same issue in olfaction.

To answer this question, Carl Pfaffmann (1955) proposed the **cross-fiber theory** of taste quality. His powerful insight was that taste quality is represented in the *pattern* of activity across a population of taste fibers (see also Erickson 1968, 1984). Of course, such a pattern theory could work only if taste fibers responded better to some substances than to others. If every fiber responded to the same extent to *all* taste substances, the cross-fiber pattern of activity would be equivalent for all substances as well. In fact, although most neurons in the taste system are responsive to several taste stimuli, each responds best to a particular taste substance (Frank, 1973). So these neurons can be said to respond selectively to different taste substances. This selectivity of response means that information about taste quality can be coded by the pattern of activity within an ensemble of fibers, as the cross-fiber theory requires.

The tastes produced by various substances differ not only in quality but also in intensity, depending on the concentration of the substance and on how sensitive the tongue is to that substance. Most taste experts believe that intensity is signaled by the level of activity within individual fibers, since firing rate increases with the concentration of the stimulating solution. Moreover, if the same solution remains on the tongue for several seconds, a fiber's activity quickly decreases from its initial level, to a somewhat lower one. You might suspect that this drop in neural activity explains why your sense of taste is dulled by repeated sampling of the same food or drink. However, this can't be the entire story, for adaptation of taste sensations may take anywhere from several seconds to a few minutes. Instead of adaptation, the decreased response of taste fibers probably serves a specific function—getting the tongue ready for new tastes. Here's why this is important.

Recall that taste judgments allow you to gauge the edibility of food. Taste judgments can be made with astonishing speed: you can identify the taste of what you're eating within the first second of tasting it (Kelling and Halpern, 1987). So after this initial identification, it's less important to continue tasting what you've been tasting than it is to get ready for new tastes. And getting ready for new tastes requires letting the activity in the nerve fibers settle back to a level where they can once again signal the presence of a new substance. Neural adaptation of the kind exhibited by nerve fibers thus makes detection of these

changes in taste quality possible (Ludel, 1978). This property of adaptation is particularly important in such sensory modalities as taste, where any one fiber usually carries information about several different stimulus qualities.

Nerve fibers carry taste-related information from the tongue to nuclei in the brainstem. The axons of brainstem neurons then funnel taste-related information upward, along two different pathways, which mediate different aspects of taste perception. One of these pathways runs through the thalamus, a way station for every sense except olfaction. Thalamic neurons, in turn, project to the primary taste area, in the cerebral cortex. This region is the taste analogue to the visual cortex and the auditory cortex. Activity within this area of the brain is crucial for being able to identity a taste or judge a taste's intensity. In humans, damage to the primary taste area knocks out these abilities (Pritchard, 1991). Moreover, direct electrical stimulation of this region elicits taste experiences in people who are awake while undergoing brain surgery, (Penfield and Faulk, 1955). The best estimate places the primary taste area in the parietal lobe, adjacent to the tongue and mouth's representation in the somatosensory cortex, which you read about in Chapter 12.*

The brain's other cortical region for taste, the secondary taste area, is found in the in the frontal cortex, right above the orbits that house the eyes (in the orbito-frontal cortex). This region of the brain constitutes part of the limbic system, whose importance in emotional reactions we mentioned in the discussion of smell. Neurons in the secondary taste area signal taste attributes that have a clear behavioral relevance, in particular the reward

---

*The exact location and boundaries of the primary taste area have been difficult to pin down, partly because taste stimuli also stimulate the touch system, which can stymie attempts to localize brain responses to taste alone. This complication can be reduced by keeping touch stimulation constant, for example by embedding a tastant solution momentarily into a constant, steady stream of water (Kobayakawa et al., 1999).

value of what is being tasted. The orbito-frontal cortex is a general repository of information about behaviorally-relevant dimensions of stimulation associated with taste and other sensory modalities. Using fMRI to characterize patterns of brain activation, Francis and colleagues (1999) demonstrated that adjacent neighborhoods in orbito-frontal cortex respond to pleasant taste (glucose in moderate concentrations), pleasant smell (vanillin) and pleasant touch (light stroking of the skin with a piece of velvet). The link is that all these stimuli share a common hedonic dimension, pleasantness. Pleasant stimulation, via different sensory systems, activates the fronto-orbital cortex. This convergence of pleasant stimulation is behaviorally significant because this area of the brain is strongly involved in emotion.

If neurons in this secondary taste area were actually signalling the potential reward value of some ingested substance, those signals should vary with what the animal had eaten most recently. If you've just eaten several pieces of mushroom pizza and feel sated, you might not want any more pizza. But the attractiveness of say, a slice of watermelon, might be unaffected; your satiety is food specific. Some neurons in the secondary taste area reflect an animal's recent history with particular tastes. Prolonged exposure to one particular taste quality, say umami, diminishes the normal responsiveness of neurons that are selectively responsive to that quality (Rolls et al., 1998). Under ordinary conditions, food-specific satiety depends not just on the food's taste, but on its smell as well (Mennella and Beauchamp, 1999; O'Doherty et al., 2000). As you'll see later in the chapter, specific satiety plays a key role in the development of food preferences.

Sensitivity to Taste

Detection and Identification The variation in taste sensitivity across the tongue (Collings, 1974) has already been mentioned. Now we will consider some other factors that influence the ability to taste substances in weak concentra-

tions. Actually, right at the limit of sensitivity, where the presence of a substance is barely detectable, it is very difficult to identify a taste (McBurney, 1978). To confirm this point, try the following experiment. Fill three identical glasses with equal amounts of water. (The water should be at room temperature.) Place a few grains of sugar in one and a few grains of salt in another and stir both thoroughly. Don't add anything to the water in the third glass. While you keep your eyes closed, have a friend hand you each glass one at a time. Take a sip from each and see if you can pick out the one containing plain water. To do this requires merely *detecting* that the other two contain "something." Next, try to pick the glass containing sugar and the one containing salt. This task requires *identifying* the tastes. If you were sufficiently frugal in the amounts you added to each glass, this task should be difficult if not impossible. Realizing that you can succeed just by guessing, see how many times you are correct over a series of ten trials. For this demonstration to work, you may need to use less salt than sugar in the solutions. The reason is that a salt solution can be detected at one-third the concentration necessary for the detection of sugar, when the solutions are at room temperature.

For most people, the highest sensitivity is to bitter, so if you repeated the taste detection test using quinine you'd have to add just a minute quantity to the water. Some people, however, have difficulty tasting bitter substances. In 1931, Arthur Fox, an industrial chemist synthesized a compound called phenylthiocarbamide (PTC). Some PTC powder got into the air and finally found its way into the nose of one of Fox's colleagues. The colleague complained that Fox's creation was very bitter and tasted awful, but Fox couldn't taste anything at all. Testing still other colleagues, Fox found some people could and others could not experience PTC's bitter taste. We know now that for about two out of every three people, PTC tastes bitter, but the remaining people hardly detect any taste at all. This divergence in sensitivity to bitter is true for other substances, including 6-*n*-propylthiouracil,

Differences

known as PROP, and others as you'll see later. In all these substances, atoms of nitrogen, carbon and sulphur are linked in a characteristic molecular structure.

Studies of taste ability within different families show that sensitivity to the bitterness of PTC or PROP is genetically determined. Individuals to whom PTC doesn't taste bitter ("nontasters," as they've been called) have two recessive genes for this trait; those who are sensitive to the bitter ("tasters") have one or two dominant genes for the trait. (Inexpensive paper strips impregnated with PTC are readily available from science supply firms; you might want to purchase some to test yourself and friends.)*

Neither PTC nor PROP are commonly found in food, so inability to taste them is inconsequential in practical terms. However, Linda Bartoshuk and colleagues found that tasters and nontasters also differ in their responses to a number of less exotic bitter substances (Miller and Bartoshuk, 1991), including caffeine (one of the bitter ingredients in coffee). In fact, the caffeine in a typical cup of coffee is not perceived as bitter by nontasters, although it is by tasters (Hall et al., 1975). This means, then, that a cup of black coffee will seem more bitter to some people than to others. Some individuals who add lots of sugar and cream to their coffee may be tasters who are struggling to tone down a degree of bitterness that nontasters never experience.

During her research on the genetics and psychophysics of taste, Bartoshuk realized that not all tasters were equal. In particular, some people who could taste PTC or PROP found it so bitter that they began to choke and gag, an extreme response; other people could taste the bitterness, but found it far less intense. About 25 percent of people tested lack sensitivity to the taste of PTC/PROP; an equal percentage show extreme sensitivity to that taste;

the remaining people, 50 percent of those tested, are tasters, but of a less moderate persuasion. To distinguish people with extreme sensitivity from ordinary tasters, Bartoshuk dubbed people with high sensitivity "supertasters."

Such differences in taste sensitivity can be traced to the tongues of the people tested. When Bartoshuk inspected people's tongues closely, she discovered dramatic differences among the numbers of papillae on the tongues of nontasters, tasters and supertasters. Generally speaking, the tongue of the average supertaster has more than twice as many papillae—and hence more taste buds—than does the tongue of the average nontaster.

Execute

To perform your own version of Bartoshuk's observations, you'll need six items: a cotton swab, a good desk lamp, some blue food dye, a small magnifying glass, a gummed reinforcement of the kind used on loose-leaf pages and, hardest to come by, a supply of cooperative, trusting experimental volunteers. Ask one of the volunteers to stick out his or her tongue, while you glue the reinforcement on it, just back from the tongue's tip. Now, with the cotton swab put a small bit of blue food dye into the hole in the reinforcement's center. Be careful not to use too much food dye; you don't want the color to run. Now carefully remove the reinforcement; with the magnifying glass and desk lamp, you should see a bunch of tiny pink circles on a background of blue. Each pink circle is a papilla. From a count of the papilla in that small circular area, you can predict, with very good accuracy, how the tongue's owner would respond to bitter substances like PTC/PROP. If you counted fewer than 20 papillae, odds are that the person is a nontaster; if you counted more than 40 papillae, you can bet the person is a supertaster, someone extremely sensitive to PTC/PROP. Papillae counts between these two levels, that is, between 20 and 40, make it likely the person is a taster. If you make such measurements on a number of people, there's no doubt that you will be astonished by the differences, and you'll never again look at tongues the same way.

---

*A warning: people with phenylketonuria, an inherited metabolic disorder, should under no circumstances be exposed to PTC.

An individual's status, as taster, supertaster or nontaster, contributes to liking or disliking certain foods. One of this book's authors (RS) is inordinately fond of unsweetened grapefruit juice, a beverage that not everyone loves as he does. In fact, some people actually shudder at grapefruit juice's bitterness. What makes RS different is his nontaster status—to him, grapefruit juice is not bitter. The ingredient that makes grapefruit juice seem bitter to most people is a bioflavonoid* called naringin. In laboratory tests, people who respond strongly to the taste of PTC or PROP find naringin solutions bitter, and they try to avoid drinking grapefruit juice (Drewnowski, Henderson and Shore, 1997). Orange juice, incidentally, contains no naringin, so when tasters and nontasters are tested with that citrus beverage, the two groups do not differ in preference.

On rare occasions, an individual's taste preferences change from a private matter to a public, political one. Take the case of vegetables like broccoli and brussel sprouts. Such vegetables are touted as containing powerful anticancer agents, but many people avoid them assiduously. One reason could be that to supertasters these vegetables have a strong bitter taste.** Although that might be an explanation, chances are it's not the only one. In 1990, George H. W. Bush stunned farmers and public health officials by asserting that "I do not like broccoli. And I haven't liked it since I was a little kid and my mother made me eat it. And I'm President of the United States and I'm not going to eat any more broccoli!"

Bush's offhand comment stimulated some taste researchers to speculate that Bush was a supertaster. But until the supertaster hypothesis is verified or disconfirmed by direct measurement, it would be prudent to entertain alternatives. Look at Bush's entire pronouncement, particularly the part about his mother. Sometimes people shun particular foods because their parents were too heavy-handed in "encouraging" progeny to consume those foods. A child's taster status and parental overzealousness could go hand in hand. A child whose taste buds tell him that this green stuff is "yucky" may require extra strong encouragement to consume it, which further diminishes the palatability of that green stuff, and so on.

In previous chapters you learned that attention and expectation can influence the detectability of weak sensory stimulation, and earlier in this chapter you read how expectation can influence perception of odor. Taste sensitivity also benefits from these kinds of "top-down" influences, as researchers at Yale University recently demonstrated. Using a forced-choice procedure (see Appendix), Marks and Wheeler (1998) measured detection thresholds for sucrose (which tastes sweet) and citric acid (which tastes sour). In each trial, a person had two samples: one, deionized water* and the other, a dilute solution of either sucrose or citric acid. The person's task was to identify which of the two samples contained the dilute tastant. The person did not have to identify the taste or in any other way try to distinguish sweet from sour. Throughout the trials, Marks and Wheeler were careful to present the deionized water and dilute tastant randomly.

In some blocks of trials, people knew ahead of time that sucrose would be the dilute substance presented in 75 percent of the trials, with citric acid being presented in the remaining 25 percent of the trials. In other blocks, people knew that citric acid was three times as likely as sucrose. This maneuver, Marks and Wheeler reasoned, should

---

*Bioflavonoids like naringin are important for good health, which is why nutritionists urge people to eat plants containing them. When taken into the body, bioflavonoids contribute to good blood circulation by maintaining the structural integrity of small blood vessels.

**To accommodate people for whom broccoli is too bitter to eat, plant scientists recently bred a new vegetable called broccolini. This cross between broccoli and kale has a milder and sweeter taste than broccoli.

---

*As its name suggests, *deionized* water is water from which ions have been removed. Because such ions can impart subtle but detectable taste to water, their removal renders the water as tasteless as possible.

direct peoples' attention to sucrose when it was more likely and to citric acid when it was more likely. Throughout a given testing session, concentrations of both solutions were very near the detection threshold, meaning that people had to work to pick out which solution was the tastant and which was merely water. Remember: People did not have to judge which solution they were tasting; all they had to do was discriminate tasteless water from a weak taste solution. The result? People could detect weaker concentrations of a given solution when they were anticipating presentation of that solution. So, for example, thresholds for detecting sucrose in blocks of sucrose-dominant trials were lower than they were when the citric acid was dominant. As in other sensory modalities, foreknowledge of the likelihood of a given substance seems to direct your attention to subtle cues registering the presence of that substance, the consequence being improved detection performance.

In Marks and Wheeler's study, the experimenters made sure that all solutions came to room temperature (21° C) before being used. The reason for such care, which is typical in good experiments on taste, is that sensitivity varies markedly with temperature. Moreover, different taste substances are not equally affected by temperature, as illustrated in Figure 13.16. Note that bitter substances become more difficult to detect at higher temperatures, whereas sensitivity to sweet increases with temperature. Think what this tells you about the effect of temperature on the taste of various foods and drinks. For instance, wine advertisements that urge you to serve their product well chilled may be trying to hide its sweet taste, a common fault with cheap or immature wines. The variations in sensitivity shown in Figure 13.16 also underscore an important rule for cooking: if you season food on the basis of taste, the final seasoning should be done only after the dish has reached serving temperature.

Is there anything to the folk wisdom that your ability to taste is better when you're hungry? The results of one study (Moore, Linker and Purcell,

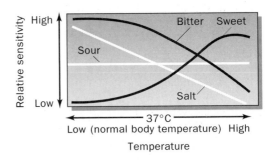

FIGURE 13.16
The effect of temperature on taste.

1965) suggests the answer is no, if by "ability to taste" one means detecting very weak solutions. The study did find, though, that taste sensitivity was better in the afternoon than in the morning, which may explain why people *think* their sense of taste is keener when they're hungry. Another misconception about taste concerns the dulling effects of smoking on taste sensitivity. Here, too, the evidence contradicts folk wisdom—regular smokers are just as good as nonsmokers at correctly identifying taste solutions (McBurney and Moskat, 1975). So why do reformed smokers often claim that food tastes better since they quit? Remember that flavor consists of several mouth-related sensations, and taste is only one of them. Perhaps the reformed smoker's enhanced pleasure from food comes from one of these other sources. For example, smokers are less able to appreciate the pungency of odors (Cometto-Muñiz and Cain, 1984), and pungency is a sensation produced by a number of spices used in cooking (Rozin, 1978).

As in the case of odor identification, human females are better at taste identification than males (Meiselman and Dzendolet, 1967). Though the reasons for female superiority are not yet understood, there seems no doubt that females are better equipped to appreciate food as far as taste and smell are concerned.

Discriminating Taste Intensity   So far we've focused on various aspects of the ability to detect

Execute

and identify different solutions. Now let's consider how good people are at judging differences in concentration of a single taste substance—another kind of judgment needed in the preparation of food. To get some idea of the difficulty of such judgments, you should try a modification of the taste experiment that introduced this section. This time fill three large glasses with clear water and place one teaspoon of sugar in the first glass, one and one-quarter teaspoons of sugar in the second and one and one-half teaspoons of sugar in the third. After stirring, have someone else rearrange the glasses so that you don't know which is which but the other person does. Now try to rank them in order of sugar concentration. This will measure your ability to judge differences in taste concentration.

Although this ability has not been studied thoroughly, available results indicate that people require a difference of about 15 to 25 percent in order to determine that one solution is stronger than another (McBurney, 1978). On the basis of these numbers, you should just barely be able to pick out the weakest of the three sugar solutions but will probably be unable to discriminate between the remaining two. The fact that people can discriminate concentration changes in the neighborhood of 15 to 25 percent has implications for cooking: to improve a dish's taste by adding more of some ingredient, add just enough to increase the total amount by about 25 percent each time. This will ensure that you don't suddenly add too much. Given taste's importance in the enjoyment of food, it is too bad that measuring cups and measuring spoons used in cooking can't be calibrated in psychophysical threshold units.

Taste Adaptation and Modification   Outside the taste laboratory, people rarely ingest substances in very weak, near threshold concentrations, and moreover, hardly ever are those substances encountered in isolation. When you eat, your palate is typically bathed in a whole complex of taste substances. So it is of interest to study how the taste of one substance is influenced by the presence of other substances. Such influences can take two forms: (1) the taste of a substance may be weakened by prior exposure to that same substance—the familiar process of **adaptation;** and (2) the taste of a substance may be altered in quality by another substance—a process called **modification.** Let's start with adaptation.

Execute

You can demonstrate taste adaptation for yourself in the following way. Fill four glasses with equal amounts of water. Now take a freshly sliced lemon and carefully squeeze one drop of juice into one glass, two drops into the second and the remaining juice into the third (this is the adaptation solution). Thoroughly stir all three solutions. Keep the fourth glass free of lemon—it should contain water only. In this demonstration you should keep track of which glass is which (you may want to number them). Now take a sip of the first solution, the one containing a single drop of lemon juice. You should be able to detect a slightly sour taste (sour is the predominant taste of pure lemon juice), especially in comparison to the neutral taste of water only. Next sip the two-drop solution and compare it to water only. As it is twice as strong, this solution should taste more sour than the one-drop solution, and certainly different from water only.

Now adapt your tongue to sour—take enough of the concentrated solution into your mouth to cover your tongue. Don't swallow it; instead, roll it around in your mouth for about 30 seconds, then spit it out. Now once again sip the two dilute solutions, again comparing them to water only. You should find that the sour taste of both is considerably weaker—perhaps too weak to distinguish from the taste of water only. Wait a few minutes and then repeat this part of the test. You'll find that your sensitivity recovers rather quickly.

This demonstration merely confirms that taste—just like vision, hearing and smell—shows adaptation. As the previous section pointed out, this decline in taste sensitivity cannot be caused entirely by the reduced responsiveness of taste fibers. The time course of fiber adaptation is much too short to account for the adaptation of taste sensations. This latter form of adaptation must take place along one of the neural pathways discussed earlier, but exactly where is a mystery (see Gillan, 1984).

Suppose you had adapted to a strong solution of *salt* water and then were tested on the dilute solutions of lemon. Recall that cross-adaptation provides a way to test whether different substances stimulate the same neural elements. You would find that adaptation to salty has essentially no effect on your ability to taste sour. The same would be true if you were to adapt to sweet and then test your sensitivity to sour. In general, cross-adaptation works only when the adapting substance is similar in quality to the test substance (McBurney and Gent, 1979; Bartoshuk, 1974). Thus, you'd find your sensitivity to dilute solutions of lemon temporarily reduced if you were first to eat a sour pickle, since these two share the quality *sour.* The quality *bitter* seems to be an exception to this rule: sensitivity to bitter substances can be reduced by adaptation to a different taste, sour (McBurney, Smith and Shick, 1972). In all, though, the results from cross-adaptation studies generally point to the existence of distinct taste qualities.

Modification, the second form of taste interaction, occurs when exposure to one substance subsequently alters the taste of another substance. Several of these so-called "taste illusions" have been described by Bartoshuk (1974; Bartoshuk et al., 1969). One that might be familiar to you involves fresh artichokes—after eating this delicacy, people find that other foods and drinks, including plain water, tend to have a sweet taste. (Actually, this is but one example of taste aftereffects involving water; Box 12.3 describes others that you can easily experience.) Another intriguing taste illusion is produced by the leaves of the *Gymnema sylvestre* plant, found in India and Africa. Eating the leaves or drinking tea made from those leaves temporarily abolishes the sweet taste of sugar. In fact, following exposure to *Gymnema sylvestre,* sugar crystals on the

tongue are indistinguishable from grains of sand. Salt, in contrast, retains its taste—proof that *Gymnema sylvestre* doesn't simply wipe out the entire sense of taste.

Another, equally exotic taste modifier comes from *Synsepalum dulcificum,* a shrub native to tropical West Africa. Popularly called "miracle fruit," the large, scarlet berries from this amazing plant impart an intensely sweet taste to even the sourest foods, such as lemons. Moreover, this sweetening aftereffect lasts about an hour after eating just a small amount of miracle fruit. This could provide a novel way to reduce your intake of sugar—you could fool your tongue into believing that food was sweet without adding sugar. While it's not known exactly how miracle fruit works, it is known that it alters the responsiveness of taste fibers (Brouwer et al., 1983). Following exposure of the tongue to miracle fruit's active ingredient, fibers normally responsive to sweet substances but not to sour ones develop a temporary sensitivity to sour. In other words, these nerve fibers temporarily behave as though sour were sweet. After about an hour, these fibers return to their normal state, once again ignoring sour. And an hour is also about how long the taste illusion persists. Incidentally, the sweet taste caused by miracle fruit can be abruptly abolished by tasting *Gymnema sylvestre,* the leaf that destroys the taste of sugar. Here's a case where one illusion can be used to combat another.

There's one taste modifier that everyone is familiar with: toothpaste. You've probably had the annoying experience of finding that the taste of your morning fruit juice has been ruined because you had just brushed your teeth. This cross-adaptation occurs because toothpaste contains an ingredient that temporarily reduces the sweetness of sugar, which makes the acid in the juice taste extra sour (Bartoshuk, 1980).

Illusion

Taste Mixtures   So far our discussion has focused on altering one taste by exposure to another. Next, let's consider what happens when two or more taste substances are mixed together

BOX 13.3

THE TASTE OF WATER: AN AFTEREFFECT

Illusion

You would probably agree that water doesn't seem to have any particular taste, aside from the faint mineral taste found in some tap water. Yet by adapting your tongue to different substances, you can make taste-less water take on various, distinct tastes. This phenomenon—"water taste"—is somewhat similar to the negative color afterimages described in Chapter 7. With water, however, the taste aftereffect is not organized in an opponent fashion. This will become apparent when you do the following experiment.

Obtain a bottle of distilled water for this experiment. Distilled water has no mineral taste whatsoever (you should confirm this for yourself). Pour a glass full of distilled water—this will be the test stimulus. Next, fill three other glasses with water (the tap variety will do) and add a teaspoon of salt to one, a teaspoon of lemon juice to the second and a teaspoon of sugar to the third—these are the adaptation stimuli. Be sure each is well stirred. Begin by taking a sip of the distilled water, just to remind yourself what "no taste" tastes like.

Then take a mouthful of the salty solution and roll it around in your mouth for about 30 seconds. At the end of this adaptation period, spit out the saltywater and take a sip of the distilled water. The previously tasteless liquid will now have a noticeable sour/bitter taste. Once this aftertaste has worn off (when the distilled water again has no taste), adapt to the sour (lemon) solution for 30 seconds. Now you will find that the same distilled water tastes faintly sweet. When this taste aftereffect has worn off, adapt to the sweet solution. This time distilled water will take on a sour taste.

Can you see the similarity between this taste aftereffect and the negative color afterimages you experienced from Color Plate 7. In the case of color, a white surface took on the hue that was dependent on the adaptation color. In the case of taste, the distilled water plays the same role as the white surface—both represent a neutral stimulus that becomes temporarily "shaded" by adaptation.

There is, however, a real difference between colored afterimages and water taste aftereffects. With color, adaptation obeys an opponent rule: adapting to red makes white look green, whereas adapting to green makes white look red; blue and yellow are comparably related. With taste, adaptation is not reciprocal: adaptation to salty makes water taste sour, but adaptation to sour makes water taste sweet, not salty. Similar, nonreciprocal aftereffects are found in the case of bitter (which you can most easily produce using unsweetened quinine water). Bitter makes distilled water taste sweet, but as you experienced, adapting to sweet makes distilled water taste sour, not bitter. All of this implies that taste does not involve opponent process mechanisms such as those implicated in color vision (McBurney, Smith and Shick, 1972). It also implies that the taste of water must be changing all the time during the course of a meal, since you are constantly adapting your tongue to different taste substances. Even the salt in your own saliva can act as a mild adaptation stimulus. Because you've adapted to your own saliva, when you sip distilled water it may appear to have a slightly sour taste.

(which occurs routinely when one cooks). Everyone knows that it's possible to tone down the taste of one substance by adding another. This is one reason why people add sugar to coffee, to mask its bitter taste. This reduction of one taste sensation by another is called **taste suppression,** and it seems to be a general property of taste mixtures

(Bartoshuk, 1975; Gillan, 1982). But what do taste mixtures actually taste like? Is taste analogous to color vision, where two component hues (for instance red and green) can create an entirely new hue (yellow)? Or is taste more like hearing, where two tones played together maintain their individuality?

The answer to this interesting and important question is not clear. McBurney (1978) maintains that new qualities are not produced by the mixture of taste components. According to this view, lemon juice with sugar added may taste both sour and sweet; but it won't taste salty or anything else new. This outcome is reminiscent of the situation in hearing, not color vision. Schiffman and Erickson (1980), however, report that sometimes a mixture will produce an unexpected taste, one not usually associated with the taste of any of the components. Such a result would be in line with the behavior of color vision, not hearing.

How does one reconcile these seemingly contradictory observations? Part of the problem stems from the inherently subjective nature of these perceptual judgments. In effect, people must be introspective on their taste sensations, decomposing the mixture into its constituents. (To see how difficult this is, try analyzing the tastes evoked by each dish in your next meal.) Introspection, however, is not a simple task, and it is subject to all sorts of extraneous influences, such as the instructions given to people. As an alternative, people could be asked to "construct" a taste mixture that matches the taste(s) of a solution mixed by the experimenter. Such an experiment would be analogous to the metameric color-matching experiments described in Chapter 7. However, performing such a taste-matching experiment requires some idea of what components should be provided for the mixture. And this brings us back to the question raised at the outset regarding the existence of basic taste qualities. At present, this question represents the fundamental issue in taste research, and until it is resolved, we'll have to be content enjoying what we eat without knowing exactly what we are tasting.

Taste Preferences

Differences

Liking and disliking are not usually thought of as natural properties of sensory stimulation. There seems to be nothing inherently sad about the color blue, for example. Taste may be an exception, however. People can reliably rate various tastes along a spectrum of pleasant to unpleasant, and in general, one person's ratings are likely to agree with another's. Bitter is usually judged unpleasant, while sweet, at least in low concentrations, is rated pleasant. Such judgments are called **taste hedonics** (*hedonic* is derived from the Greek word meaning "pleasure"). Some taste experts believe that these hedonic qualities stem from biological factors governing food selection. Organisms ranging from insects to primates, (human beings included), crave sweet substances. This may be adaptive, since sugars are easily detected nutrients common in plants (Ramirez, 1990). Bitter is typically associated with toxic substances, which would explain why nearly all animals show an aversion to bitter substances. In fact, some plant and animal species capitalize on this universal aversion by having evolved a bitter-tasting skin themselves, a characteristic that wards off potential predators (Gittleman and Harvey, 1980).

Plasticity

As you saw when we discussed former President George H. W. Bush's aversion to broccoli, different factors influence taste preferences (and aversions). The next few paragraphs explore a few of these: familiarity, genetics, age and the visual characteristics of foods. Familiarity's impact on preference is especially intriguing because it can be both subtle and extremely long-lasting. Here's one demonstration. For many years, the bottled milk specially formulated for German infants has been lightly flavored with vanillin, probably to improve milk's palatability. Researchers in Münich recently realized that this situation presented a perfect opportunity to study how familiarity altered preference (Haller et al., 1999). Would some infants' early exposure to vanillin-flavored milk have any long-term consequences for their taste preferences? To answer this question, Haller and colleagues asked 133 adult visitors to an environmental fair whether they had been breast-fed or bottle-fed as newborns. Thirty of the respondents said they'd been bottle-fed, the rest, breast-fed. Each respondent was given two samples of ketchup, a food not usually linked to vanillin. One of the samples was ordinary, pure ketchup; the other sample was doctored with a small amount of vanillin (1 part vanillin per 2000 parts ketchup). This low concentration made the vanillin just barely detectable and too weak to be accurately identified. The participants tasted the two samples in random order, naming their preferences.

Of people who had been breast-fed (n=103), about two out of three preferred the pure ketchup. Of people who had been bottle-fed (n=30), the preference ratio was reversed: about two thirds of these people preferred the ketchup sample that had been doctored. Presumably, this latter group had been exposed as infants to vanillin. Although we wish that the study had included more participants,* particularly in the bottle-fed category, it does suggest that early experience with particular tastes can have very long-term consequences for adult food preference. Some of the study participants were in their forties and fifties, which puts that important early experience four or five decades behind them. Incidentally, this enduring preference does not depend upon infants' ability to label with words what they experienced while they drank milk. Use of special infant formula usually ends well before children learn to speak.

Earlier we mentioned that sensitivity to certain bitter substances, including PROP and PTC, varies with one's genetic makeup. This genetic heterogeneity produces a corresponding heterogeneity in preferences for particular foods. Generally, tasters and supertasters have more finicky food preferences, expressing dislike for a greater number of foods (Fischer et al., 1961; Glanville and Kaplan, 1965). Anliker and colleagues (1991) summarize this body of work, noting that adults with normal bitter sensitivity tend to avoid certain strong-tasting foods, including sauer-kraut, turnips, spinach and strong cheese. (Anliker and colleagues also extended these observations to the preferences of tasters and nontasters among young children, ages 5 to 7 years.) Although food preferences are governed by many factors, including social and cultural ones, genetic differences in taste sensitivity have a clear influence as well.

We should note that a natural aversion to bitter taste can be overcome, as evidenced by the almost universal enjoyment of beverages like beer, coffee and quinine water. And just as natural aversions can be conquered, unnatural ones can be *acquired* (Garcia and Koelling, 1966; Garb and Stunkard, 1974). Extreme nausea following ingestion of some food is a sure bet to cause an animal to reject that food the next time it is available. This phenomenon, called **conditioned taste aversion,** is an extremely potent method for discouraging predators from disturbing farm animals such as chickens and sheep. One meal of sheep meat laced with lithium chloride (a chemical that induces violent nausea) will dissuade a coyote from going near the source of that meat in the future. By the same token, one night of heavy indulgence in whiskey is enough to discourage many people from drinking whiskey, at least in the near future.

Sweet tastes are usually thought of as pleasant, but extremely sweet food or drink can be unpleasant. For a variety of sweet substances, pleasantness increases with concentration up to a point, after which the substance becomes more and more unpleasant. Moskowitz (1978) calls this transition point the *bliss point*—the concentration yielding the highest hedonic rating. As you might expect, young children have a higher bliss point than adults (De Graaf and Zandstra, 1999), which explains why advertisements for highly sweetened breakfast cereals in the United States are aimed at a very young audience. Contrary to expectation, however, some obese individuals actually have a lower bliss point than do people of normal weight (Grinker and Hirsch, 1972), although this finding does not hold for all sweet substances (Drewnowski, Grinker and Hirsch, 1982).

---

*The study has another limitation: It assumes that participants knew and accurately reported whether they'd been breast- or bottle-fed.

Top-down

Besides concentration levels, a food's color can also influence how much people like its taste. One study (Duncker, 1939) had people rate the taste of white chocolate and brown chocolate, and they did this while either blindfolded or not. With their eyes open, people judged the white chocolate as weak in taste, whereas the blindfolded group liked it just as much as the brown chocolate. The same pattern of results has been found for fruit-flavored beverages and cake (DuBose, Cardello and Maller, 1980). The food industry, aware of the influence of color on taste perception, often adds color to products. Margarine, for instance, is naturally very pale but is dyed yellow to mimic the color of real butter. Likewise, orange food coloring is added to many orange juice products, and this strategy improves the flavor scores of these products (see Pangborn, 1960). To convince yourself of the potent effect color has on taste perception, just add green food coloring to milk and see how it tastes.

Clinical

Related to the issue of taste preference is **sensory-specific satiety,** the reduction in the pleasurable sensory quality of a particular food as it is being eaten (Rolls, 1986). Suppose a moderately hungry person rates the pleasantness of the taste, smell and texture of some food. Following this initial rating, imagine the individual gets a meal that includes the previously rated food, and immediately following the meal the person again rates the food's pleasantness. The postmeal ratings will be lower than the premeal ratings, even though the food itself has not had time to be digested. Evidently it is the sensory quality of the food itself, not its nutritional consequences, that produces the reduced hedonic response to the food. Moreover, this satiety effect is specific to the food items consumed during the meal—foods that were not eaten do not have lowered pleasantness (Rolls, Duijvenvoorde and Rolls, 1984).

The specificity of satiety means that relatively more food may be eaten during a meal that consists of many different foods served over several courses. Understanding sensory-specific satiety

may shed light on eating disorders such as bulimia (Drewnowski 1987), the condition where an individual engages in an eating binge followed by fasting or self-induced vomiting. Rodin and colleagues (1990) found that bulimic patients continued to rate sweet substances as pleasant even after ingesting a healthy dose of glucose dissolved in water; nonbulimics, in contrast, found the sweet substance less pleasant after ingestion of glucose. Rodin and colleagues speculate that bulimics may engage in food binges because they fail to experience a reduction in its pleasantness during the course of eating.

The general topic of taste preferences is a fascinating one. There is much interesting material that cannot be presented here for lack of space. Those interested in that material should consult Rozin (1979). In addition, there are several informative articles on cross-cultural studies of taste perception and preference (Johns and Keen, 1985; Bertino and Chan, 1986).

THE INTERACTION BETWEEN TASTE AND SMELL

Several times in this chapter we have stressed the role played by odor in what we usually think of as taste. Holding your nostrils closed while you eat dramatically demonstrates this role. One study found that the ability to identify food substances is severely hampered when odor perception is eliminated (Mozel et al., 1969). In this study, twenty-one familiar substances were individually liquified in a blender and dropped one by one onto a person's tongue from an eye-dropper; the person's task was to name each food. The results, summarized in Figure 13.17, show the percentages of people tested who could identify each of the twenty-one substances. The shaded bars give the results when the odor of the solution could be smelled; the unshaded bars give the results when odors were blocked from reaching the olfactory epithelium. Obviously, smell improved performance greatly. In fact, for several very familiar substances, including coffee,

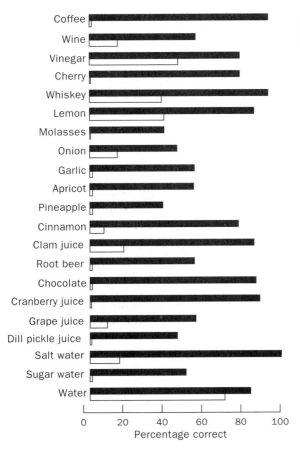

FIGURE 13.17
The percentages of people who could identify a substance dropped onto their tongues when they could smell the solution (shaded bars) and when they were prevented from smelling the solution (unshaded bars). (Adapted from Mozel et al., 1969.)

garlic and chocolate, correct identification was impossible without smell.

There is something paradoxical about odor's contribution to taste: when odor is added to a substance that is being tasted, people do not report that its smell has increased in strength. They say instead that its *taste* is enhanced (Murphy, Cain and Bartoshuk, 1977). Demonstrate this for yourself. Begin eating with your nostrils held closed, then release them. Opening your nostrils

means that odor will be added. But instead of experiencing this addition as *smell,* you will find that *taste* has become stronger. In other words, taste and smell blend into a single experience, and this combined experience is typically referred to as *taste.* Dalton and colleagues (2000) demonstrated how potent taste smell combinations can be. Using a forced choice staircase procedure (see Appendix), these researchers found that for certain combinations of odorant and tastant, the presence of one component, even at extremely low concentrations, facilitates detection of the other component. To take one example, the presence of a low concentration of saccharin (a tastant that evokes sweetness) lowers the threshold for detecting benzaldehyde (an odorant that evokes a cherry smell). The researchers speculated that such interactions may require that the tastant and odorant be congruent. Thus, sweetness and a cherry odor are congruent in the sense that benzaldehyde odor and sweet taste can coexist naturally. As preliminary evidence for their hypothesis, Dalton and colleagues showed that putting a solution of monosodium glutamate into the mouth leaves the threshold for detecting benzaldehyde unchanged. Monosodium glutamate and benzaldehyde represent a taste and a smell that do not naturally coexist. A comparable lack of interaction was found when deionized water was substituted for the monosodium glutamate solution. Again, incongruent substances failed to produce an interaction between taste and smell.

Taste-smell interactions are crucial to our enjoyment of food or drink. The importance of such interactions can be seen in "taste" experts, who develop the knack of attending to the *odors* of the food or drink they are sampling. If you've ever watched a serious wine taster at work, you know what we mean. First of all, wine tasters prefer to evaluate wine when it is close to room temperature, so that the odorous vapors are more abundant. To further promote the release of vapors, a taster will swirl the liquid around in the glass and will then deeply inhale the vapors with the nose placed right at the mouth of the glass. This odor information alone is often sufficient to identify the particular wine being sampled. Because wines vary along several dimensions, wine discrimination has become a popular vehicle for studying perceptual learning, the enhancement of perception brought about by practice (see, for example, Owen and Machamer, 1979). In fact, entire books have been written on the sensory evaluation of wine (Kramer, 1989).

SUMMARY AND PREVIEW

This examination of the "minor senses," olfaction and gustation, brings us to the end of our survey of seeing, hearing, touch, taste and smell. You should now have a more complete appreciation of how marvelously sensitive we human beings are to the noisy, odorous, light-reflecting, tasty objects that make up our world. And you should likewise appreciate that this world is defined by the human sensory nervous system. Other species with different nervous systems live in a world different from ours. The environment offers an abundance of opportunities for perception; whether one capitalizes on those opportunities depends on having receptors and brain mechanisms to register and process the various forms of sensory information available. Understanding perception requires that we examine *what* there is to be perceived (the environment as a source of stimulation), *how* the process is implemented (the mechanisms of perception) and, of course, how that information is ultimately used to influence behavior.

KEY TERMS

adaptation
anosmia
cilia
common chemical sense
conditioned taste aversion
cross-adaptation
cross-fiber theory
flavor
free nerve ending
mixture suppression
modification
multidimensional scaling (MDS)
nasal cycle
odor adaptation

odor hallucinations
olfactory brain
olfactory bulb
olfactory epithelium
olfactory nerve
olfactory sensory neuron (OSN)
papillae
pheromones
sensory-specific satiety
specific anosmia
taste buds
taste hedonics
taste suppression
tip of the nose phenomenon

BEHAVIORAL METHODS FOR STUDYING PERCEPTION

Members of our species have long been curious about perception. Our ancestors probably asked, "Why do colors disappear at night?" or "Why, as I've gotten older, is it harder for me to hear the sweet sound of birds at dawn?" For answers to these and similar questions, people relied on the only tool they had: introspective reflections. They tried to analyze the character of their own perceptual experiences and then fabricate explanations for those experiences. Today, too, introspection guides our intuitions about perception, but the field of perception would not have advanced to its current level of sophistication if introspection were the only available tool for investigation. This Appendix outlines some other, more sophisticated techniques that have evolved for quantifying sensory judgments. As we work through these techniques, keep in mind that their results are not obligated to conform to your introspective experience—for example, you will learn that we're able to react to sensory information far too weak to evoke a clear, conscious experience.

THE BIRTH OF PSYCHOPHYSICS

As science and commerce flourished, people demanded greater reliability and accuracy in sensory judgments. This fostered development of formal methods for assessing perception. In 1860, Gustav Theodor Fechner, a German physicist and philosopher, published a book in which he formalized behavioral methods that others had developed to study perception (Fechner, 1860/1966). Formalizing the methods' "rules" allowed people to compare different sets of observations. Fechner's methods continue to be important today, and many of the results described in this book came from application of those methods. We will go over those methods and some of their modern variants.

Though Fechner had great foresight, he could not anticipate all the many methods that are currently used. Some of these newer methods are described at various places in the text. These include preferential looking (chapters 5, 7 and 8), multidimensional scaling (chapters 12 and 13), magnitude estimation (chapters 10 and 12), reaction time (chapters 5 and 13), and various methods used to study animal perception (chapters 4, 5, 8, 11, 12 and 13). In addition, today we conduct research with powerful methods that were technically impossible until very recently, for example concurrent behavioral and physiological measurements and brain imaging (chapters 1, 4, 6, 8, 9, 11 and 13).

We will not present any method in elaborate detail; instead, we will summarize key features. To develop full detail would require a volume of its own. Incidentally, we have an unimpeachable precedent for keeping details to a minimum while emphasizing the major concepts. Fechner himself wrote:

> Had I wished . . . to set forth here all the special methods of experimentation and calculation that have to be taken into account in more detailed investigations, or had I wanted to provide a theoretical basis and experimental proof for all the rules that are applicable, I would have disturbed the flow of the argument, interfering with the interests of those who are more concerned with the general understanding of the methods than with their use by themselves. (1860/1966, p. 60)

Where should we start? When archaeologists unearth an ancient tool, their understanding of the tool depends on understanding what the tool was used for. Similarly, to understand the methods Fechner presented in his book, one must inquire first about the purposes Fechner had in mind for those methods. In other words, *why* did he want to measure perception?

An amateur philosopher with considerable training in physics, Fechner was interested in establishing a new science, which he termed **psychophysics.** Psychophysics, as envisioned by Fechner, was to be "an exact theory of the . . . relations of body and soul or, more generally, of the material and the mental, of the physical and psychological worlds" (1860/1966, p. 7). Appropriately enough, Fechner called his book *Elemente der Psychophysik* (German for Elements of Psychophysics). Fechner's program required some way to measure the sensations that physical stimuli evoke in human observers. Since these sensations arise from an interaction between the physical and psychological worlds, Fechner believed that if he could quantify the sensations evoked by various stimuli, he would be able to develop equations that would tie the two worlds together.

Suppose that like Fechner, you wanted to write a simple psychophysical equation that would relate the quantity of sensation to the intensity of a stimulus evoking that sensation. To portray such an equation, you might produce a graph relating sensation and intensity, with stimulus intensity on the horizontal axis and sensation magnitude on the vertical. For a psychophysical equation that is described by a straight line, you'd need to find out only two things before you could draw such a graph. First, you'd need to determine the minimum stimulus value that evoked any sensation whatever. This value, the psychophysical equation's x-intercept, defines the point at which the straight line intersects the horizontal axis. Second, you'd need to determine the rate at which the sensation grew as you increased stimulus intensity. Graphically, this rate of growth corresponds to the slope of the psychophysical equation. The first of these values (the x-intercept) is known as the **absolute threshold**: the stimulus intensity defining the transition between undetectable and detectable; the absolute threshold, in other words, is the intensity that an observer can just barely detect. The second of these values is known as the **difference threshold**: the minimum amount by which stimulus intensity must be changed in order to produce a noticeable change in the sensation. With certain assumptions (described below), knowledge of these two values—the absolute threshold and the difference threshold—would enable you to write the desired psychophysical equation. And this is what Fechner tried to do.

Crucial to Fechner's enterprise was the assumption that the difference threshold would be constant. If the difference threshold changed in value—say, from when you were working with weak stimuli to when you were working with strong stimuli—there would be no single value that could be used to estimate the slope of the psychophysical equation; instead, the slope itself would change from one part of the line to another, implying that the corresponding equation is more complex than that for a straight line. And in fact the difference threshold is most certainly *not* constant. Suppose, for example, you initially present to an observer a spot of light whose intensity is 100 units, a value that is easily visible. Now suppose you increase the light's intensity until the observer first notices a change from the initial level. Imagine that this new level had to be 110 units. The difference threshold here would be 110 − 100, or 10 units. If you repeated the process, beginning now with a light of 1000 units, you would find that the observer did not notice a change of just 10 units, as before. Instead, a much larger change would be required to produce a just noticeable change—say, a change from 1000 to 1100 units. So in this second case, the difference threshold would be 1100 − 1000, or 100 units.

From the work of his contemporary Ernst Weber, Fechner knew that although the difference threshold itself was not constant, it tended to be a constant *proportion* of the initial stimulus value. In the hypothetical examples just described, both difference thresholds were 10 percent of the initial stimulus. Using various stimuli, Weber had shown that a fixed-proportion increase in stimulus intensity was sufficient to produce a just noticeable change in sensation. To honor him, Fechner called this constancy **Weber's Law.** As we've just seen, Weber's Law states that

$$\Delta I / I = k$$

where ΔI ("delta *I*") signifies the difference threshold (the amount by which stimulus intensity must be increased in order to produce a just noticeable change), I signifies the initial stimulus intensity, and k signifies that the proportion on the left side of the equation is a constant despite changes in I.

Some methods developed by Fechner, which are the focus of this Appendix, were designed to measure **just noticeable differences** (or **JND**s, as they're sometimes called). Using these methods, others have ascertained that Weber's Law holds only approximately, thereby undermining Fechner's aim. However, the methods Fechner systematized continue to be used today. Since they play such a key role in the study of perception, it's worth spending some time summarizing them here. But Fechner's methods aren't the only important behavioral methods in use today. So after we've summarized Fechner's major methods, we'll turn to some modern variants of those methods. Finally, we'll consider methods that represent important new advances.

In most of the examples given below, we'll assume that the thresholds of interest are visual thresholds; however, as various chapters show, any of these methods could be adapted for studying hearing, smell, touch or taste as well. For vision, the absolute threshold is the minimum intensity of a stimulus light that an observer can see; lesser intensities produce no sensation. The difference threshold is the smallest perceivable difference in intensity between two flashes of light; smaller differences cannot be discerned.

Before we turn to the various ways for measuring absolute and difference thresholds, you should know that Fechner himself doubted how well one could measure a threshold that truly merited the description "absolute." He observed (1860/1966, p. 108) that even when no light whatever was present, observers in complete darkness tended to experience a dim, vague light that arose from what he termed an "inner source of light sensation." Today, we call this source of light **intrinsic light** or, more poetically, **dark light.** Fechner realized that intrinsic light would cause problems for an observer who tried to determine whether a stimulus did produce *some* sensation or whether the stimulus produced *no* sensation whatever. The problem, he realized, is that observers are liable to confuse this inner source of light with the real thing. This confusion would prevent the observer from making absolute judgments about the dim light alone; instead, the observer would have to discriminate the effects of a real, dim light from the effects of intrinsic light. In this sense, even the absolute threshold involves judging differences: the effect of real light adds to the effect associated with dark light. And if the effect of dark light varies from moment to moment (which it probably does), the judgment becomes even more complicated. Various studies have borne out Fechner's belief about intrinsic light, showing that this intrinsic light affects vision and psychophysical judgments in important ways (Barlow and Sparrock, 1964; Rushton, 1965).

FECHNER'S THREE METHODS

To measure thresholds, Fechner proposed three different behavioral methods, known today as the **method of limits,** the **method of constant stimuli** and the **method of adjustment.** Since Fechner wanted to measure both absolute thresholds and difference thresholds, he had to formulate two slightly different versions of each method—one version for each type of threshold that he needed to measure. Here, we'll present both versions for the method of limits and for the method of constant stimuli. Since the method of adjustment is used primarily to measure absolute thresholds, we'll describe only that version of the method.

Although the three methods differ in their details, they share some features. For example, all the methods restrict observers to one of two responses on each trial ("yes" or "no" for absolute thresholds; "stronger" or "weaker" for difference thresholds). Also, to measure an absolute threshold, all the methods specify presenting just *one* stimulus at a time. The observer's task is to report whether that stimulus elicits any sensation at all. To measure a difference threshold, all the methods require that *two* stimuli be presented. Here, the observer's task is to compare the sensations elicited by the two and report which is greater. So to measure the

absolute threshold, stimuli are weak, and the responses are either "Yes, I see it" or "No, I don't see it."
To measure difference thresholds, the intensity of one
stimulus, the *standard stimulus,* is greater than zero,
and the intensity of the other stimulus, the *comparison
stimulus,* may be either more intense or less intense
than the standard; the response categories are brighter
or dimmer. There are many variations on these methods but these three basic formats are recognizable in a
great many studies (Woodworth and Schlosberg,
1954; Ehrenstein and Ehrenstein, 1999).

The Method of Constant Stimuli

With this method, each of a fixed set of stimuli is presented multiple times in a quasi random order. The
frequency with which each stimulus elicits one of the
two responses is tallied and used to plot what is known
as a **psychometric function.** The threshold is the stimulus intensity that evokes a particular proportion of the
two responses.*

Absolute Threshold   The experimenter begins by
selecting a set of light intensities varying from very
weak (or zero intensity) to highly visible (typically,
somewhere between four and seven intensities are
tested). Stimuli are presented one at a time in a quasi
random order that ensures each will occur equally often. After every presentation, the observer reports
whether or not the light was seen. Once each light intensity has been presented many times (at least 20 to
25 times) the proportion of "Yes, seen" and "No, not
seen" responses is calculated for each light level and
plotted in a graphic format with intensity along the ab-
scissa and percentage seen along the ordinate; this format constitutes a psychometric function. Now, if there
were a fixed absolute threshold for detection, the psychometric function should look like the solid line in
the left-hand graph in Appendix Figure 1—the abrupt
transition from "not seen" to "seen" would occur at
this threshold intensity. In fact, however, psychometric functions never conform to this idealized represen-

tation. Instead, the curve increases gradually in a manner depicted by the curved line in the right-hand graph
in Appendix Figure 1. More intense lights evoke a
greater number of "seen" responses. This pattern of results means, therefore, that light intensities in the intermediate region (between "never seen" and "always
seen") are visible on some trials but not on others. The
threshold intensity, in other words, seems to vary from
trial to trial, within limits; there is no one intensity
value that consistently separates perfectly "visible"
from "invisible." Consequently, the definition of
"threshold intensity" must be a statistical one. By convention, the absolute threshold measured with the
Method of Constant Stimuli is defined as the intensity
value eliciting "seen" responses on 50 percent of the
trials. This 50 percent value can be estimated graphically, as shown in Appendix Figure 1. There are various reasons why the psychometric function has this
characteristic *S* shape and not an idealized step function whose values change abruptly from 0 to 100 percent. Among them are the constant fluctuations in sensitivity of any biological sensory system (including the
dark light mentioned earlier). Those inherent fluctuations mean that the background level of activity within
the nervous system is changing, and it is against that
background that an observer must detect activity associated with actual stimulation. Other contributing factors will be discussed later in this Appendix.

Difference Threshold   Two stimuli are presented
on each trial. One of these, the standard stimulus, has
a fixed intensity; the other, the comparison stimulus, is
selected randomly from a set of stimuli whose different intensities bracket the standard. On each trial the
observer judges whether the intensity of the comparison stimulus was stronger or weaker than that of the
standard. Many such judgments are obtained for all
pairs of comparison and standard stimuli.

Results are summarized by plotting the proportion
of trials on which each comparison stimulus is judged
to be stronger than the standard, yielding another type
of psychometric function. These proportions are then
used to identify comparison stimulus intensities that
are just noticeably different from the standard. Two
just noticeably different comparison stimuli are identified: one of these is the comparison stimulus that is
just noticeably *weaker* than the standard; the other is
the comparison stimulus that is just noticeably

---

*Although Fechner popularized it, the method of constant
stimuli had been devised several years earlier, by Friedrich
Hegelmaier, in one of the most important student projects
ever (Laming and Laming, 1992).

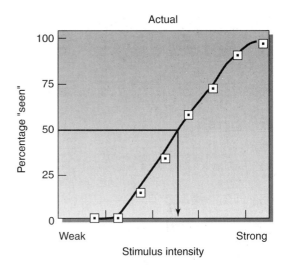

APPENDIX FIGURE 1
Ideal (left) and actual (right) results of an absolute threshold experiment using the method of constant stimuli.

stronger than the standard. Here, too, we find that performance is more variable than the ideal: a given stimulus difference may be discriminable on one trial but not on the next. So, again, we must define the difference threshold statistically. By convention, a comparison stimulus that 75 percent of the time is judged weaker than the standard is considered to be just noticeably *weaker* than that standard; also, a comparison stimulus that 75 percent of the time is judged stronger than the standard is considered to be just noticeably *stronger* than that standard. Once these two just noticeably different stimuli are identified, the threshold is calculated by averaging the absolute difference in intensity between the standard and each of the stimuli that are just noticeably different from the standard.

The Method of Limits

One drawback to the Method of Constant Stimuli is the need to collect lots of observations for each stimulus (absolute threshold) or for each set of stimulus pairings (difference threshold). The Method of Limits offers a shortcut, where on each trial the stimulus is changed gradually until the observer's response changes. The threshold is defined as that intensity of light at which the response changes.

Absolute Threshold   A single flash of light is changed in successive, discrete steps, and the observer's response to each is recorded. Suppose the light is initially so weak that the observer responds "No, I don't see it." In this case, the light is increased in steps until the observer *can* see it. The light intensity at which the observer's response changes is taken as an estimate of the threshold. Or the light may initially be intense enough that the observer responds "Yes, I see it." In this case, the light is decreased in steps until the observer can*not* see it. Again, the intensity of light at which the response changes provides an estimate of the threshold. A series of light flashes that approaches the threshold from below (starting with very weak stimuli) is called an *ascending series;* a series that approaches the threshold from above is called a *descending series.* Often, ascending and descending series yield systematically different estimates of the threshold, so most experimenters use both types of series in alternation and then average the results. Moreover, the threshold estimates from several series of, say, ascending trials may differ. This variability stems from the same sources that produce the variability in the Method of Constant Stimuli discussed above. In principle, the stimulus threshold estimated with the Method of Limits should correspond to the intensity value associated with the 50 percent point on a psychometric function obtained with the Method of Constant Stimuli.

Difference Threshold   On each trial, two flashes of light are presented—one called the *standard,* the other called the *comparison*; the pair may be presented either simultaneously, one next to the other, or successively, one after the other. The intensity of the standard light remains constant, and the intensity of the comparison light is changed in a series of steps. After each change, the observer judges the comparison stimulus as brighter or dimmer than the standard. In an ascending series, the comparison stimulus is initially weaker than the standard and it increases from trial to trial; in a descending series, the comparison stimulus is initially stronger than the standard and it decreases. A series terminates when the observer's response changes from "dimmer" to "brighter" (in an ascending series), or from "brighter" to "dimmer" (in a descending series). The threshold, then, is the absolute value of the difference between the lights at the time the response changed. As before, ascending and descending series may be alternated and the threshold estimates averaged.

The Method of Adjustment

In an even more efficient variant of the Method of Limits, the observer is given control over the intensity of the stimulus and instructed to adjust it so that it is just visible (absolute threshold) or appears to match some other, standard light (difference threshold).

Absolute Threshold   The experimenter provides the observer with the means to vary the intensity of a light. The observer then adjusts the intensity so that the light changes from invisible to just barely visible, providing one estimate of the absolute threshold. The observer also adjusts the light from visible to just barely invisible, providing another estimate of threshold. Typically, the two kinds of estimates are repeated several times and the results averaged. Observers report that they find this method easier to use than the method of limits, even though the two clearly resemble each other. Probably observers find it easier to judge the stimulus on the basis of continuous trial and error (method of adjustment) than when they see just one stimulus at a fixed value (method of limits).

MODIFICATIONS OF FECHNER'S METHODS

Over the years, researchers have modified each of Fechner's methods as the need arose. Sometimes these modifications were shaped by the apparatus and stimuli that were available to a particular researcher. Other times, the modifications were designed to minimize some deficiency of the method, or to promote efficiency. We'll consider two modifications that are particularly important.

The Staircase Method: A Modification of the Method of Limits

The deficiencies of the method of limits were apparent almost from its inception. As you'll recall, this method requires that a series of stimuli be presented, all of which elicit the same response—such as, "Yes, I see it." As a result, such a series teaches little about the location of the threshold, the stimulus at which responses change. Moreover, the method often involves presenting many stimuli that are far from the observer's actual threshold. The inclusion of these stimuli reduces the efficiency of the basic method of limits, since such stimuli contribute little to the estimate of threshold. A variant of the method of limits, the so-called **staircase method,** offers enhanced efficiency (Cornsweet, 1962). In a typical staircase, the experimenter may begin with an intensity well above the expected threshold region, and decreases the stimulus until the observer declares it invisible. When the response changes, the direction of stimulus change is reversed. Now intensity increases until the response changes again, following which the intensity decreases once more. In a typical staircase, alternations in the direction of stimulus change continue until six or seven reversals have occurred (see Appendix Figure 2). The threshold is then estimated by the average of all the stimulus intensities at which the observer's responses changed. With this staircase procedure, most stimulus values are concentrated in the threshold region, making it a more efficient procedure.

There's a problem, though, with this simple staircase procedure. As with the basic method of limits, a simple staircase allows the observer to become aware of the scheme that governs stimulus presentation. The observer's responses are then liable to be influenced

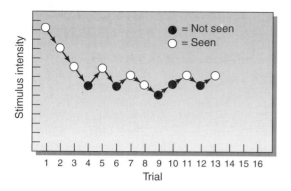

APPENDIX FIGURE 2
The results of a staircase experiment.

APPENDIX FIGURE 3
The results of an experiment using two interleaved staircases.

by that knowledge. For example, an observer may anticipate that the threshold is being approached and change the response prematurely. To overcome this problem, Cornsweet (1962) introduced a procedure that retains the efficiency of a staircase but minimizes the observer's knowledge of the direction from which the threshold is being approached. Cornsweet's idea was to interleave two or more concurrent staircases.

Appendix Figure 3 illustrates a simple case of two interleaved staircases and *strict alternation* between them. On trial *1,* staircase *A* begins with a stimulus that is expected to be above threshold, and the observer reports seeing it. On trial *2,* staircase *B* starts with a stimulus that is expected to be below threshold, and the observer reports not seeing it. On trial *3,* the next stimulus from staircase *A* is presented—at a lower intensity than before, since the observer saw it the first time. On trial *4,* the next stimulus from staircase *B* is presented, and so on. As Appendix Figure 3 shows, over the course of trials both staircases converge and the stimulus intensities tend to be concentrated around a single value, the threshold. A further improvement developed by Cornsweet involves *randomly* interleaving the two staircases so that the observer cannot figure out which staircase to expect from trial to trial.

Modifications of the Method of Constant Stimuli

Although constant stimuli's random presentation of stimuli precludes the problems associated with lim-

its's serial ordering of stimuli, constant stimuli, like limits, is inefficient. In particular, many of the stimuli presented are far enough away from the threshold to be of relatively little use. For instance, little information is gained from presenting light intensities that are always detectable or light intensities that can never be detected. This inefficiency can be avoided by pretesting, which allows the stimuli to be carefully tailored to the capacities of the observer. Alternatively, various methods have been developed to adapt or modify the stimulus set while the experiment itself is in progress (Andrews and Miller, 1978; Watt and Andrews, 1981; Watson and Pelli, 1983). This latter approach is a useful adjunct to pretesting because, as we've pointed out, the observer's sensitivity fluctuates somewhat during an experiment. As a result, a stimulus set optimized during pre-testing might not be optimal for the entire experiment. The most sophisticated and efficient versions of these adaptive strategies make use of a computer to constantly update and adapt the stimulus set.

There is another reason why many researchers consider the method of constant stimuli to be inefficient, at least for measuring difference thresholds: the method requires two stimuli per trial—a standard and a comparison—rather than just one. Naturally, it takes longer to present two stimuli than it does to present just one. Fortunately, the standard is probably superfluous in many circumstances (Morgan, Watamaniuk and McKee, 2000). Usually, an observer's judgments are just as precise in the absence of a standard as they are in the presence of one (Woodworth and Schlosberg, 1954, pp. 217–218).

To appreciate what omitting the standard entails, consider an experiment by Suzanne McKee (1981). To measure the difference threshold for visual velocity—the smallest difference in speed that an observer can discriminate—McKee used the method of constant stimuli but with the standard omitted. On each trial, a computer caused a single vertical line to move across a television display; only one line was presented per trial. The line's velocity on each trial was chosen randomly from a set of seven highly similar velocities. The observer watched a line pass by and judged whether its velocity was faster or slower than the mean of all seven velocities.

Note that McKee never actually had to show the observer which velocity was the mean. Instead, by watching a few presentations of all the velocities, the observers built up a highly accurate mental representation of the mean velocity. It should not surprise you that observers can make accurate perceptual comparisons even when there is no explicit standard present. After all, the method merely requires an observer to do what he or she does many times every day: combine separate samples of perceptual information into an accurate overall perceptual impression.

FORCED-CHOICE, OBJECTIVE METHODS

The methods discussed so far rely on the observer's own, subjective report of what is or is not seen. These reports are termed *subjective* because an experimenter cannot judge whether the observer was correct or incorrect. For instance, when an observer reports "I see it," we must take that report at face value; it cannot be disputed or verified. In a moment we'll mention why this may be a problem. But first let's consider an effective solution.

In recent decades, an alternative, objective approach, the **forced-choice method,** has gained considerable popularity. In an experiment using a forced-choice method, the observer must *prove* that he or she can see the stimulus, and the observer's claims can be checked.* The observer gives proof by identifying some characteristic of the light other than its intensity. For example, the experimenter might arrange to present a dim light either to the right or to the left of a fix-

ation point. The observer does not have to say whether the light was visible but instead merely identifies the light's position, responding either "left" or "right." Or the experimenter might present the light in just one of two successive test intervals and require the observer to indicate in which interval—first or second—the light was presented. In modern times, the forced-choice method was popularized by Blackwell (1946). However, the method had been devised nearly one hundred years earlier, by Bergmann (Fechner, 1860/1966, p. 242).** In order to measure visual acuity, Bergmann used a forced-choice method with grating patterns. He devised a way to vary the orientation of a test grating (recall Chapter 5), and then, instead of asking the observer whether a particular grating was visible or not, Bergmann forced the observer to identify the grating's orientation. (Incidentally, Bergmann not only devised the forced-choice method, he also discovered that stimulus uncertainty reduces detectability [see Chapter 5] and that some orientations are easier to see than others, such as the oblique effect [see Chapter 4].)

But what has been learned from the use of forced-choice methods that wasn't known before? For one thing, these methods show that the nervous system registers more sensory information than one is ordinarily aware of. Putting this another way, forced-choice research shows that people can discern lights so dim or sounds so weak that people claim they cannot see or hear them. Here's a typical demonstration of this remarkable fact.

Suppose that you begin by using one of Fechner's methods, say the method of adjustment, to measure an absolute threshold. After running many trials, you determine a light intensity that the observer says is "just

---

*The term *forced-choice* does not mean simply that the observer is forced to say something besides "I don't know." Rather, this procedure involves structuring stimulus presentations so that accuracy can be objectively verified. If the experimenter can unequivocally provide error feedback, the procedure is properly called *forced-choice.* Note, responses based on subjective impression—for instance, "this is louder than that"—even if responses are required after each stimulus presentation, are not genuinely forced-choice. When a listener reports that one tone is louder than another, how can you argue?

**A translation of Bergmann's paper is available in D'Zmura (1996).

barely visible". You then take that same "threshold" light intensity and present it to the same observer in a forced-choice experiment. The dim light is flashed either to the left or to the right of a fixation point while the observer tries to identify its location. Although such comments are not part of the actual data-collection procedure, the observer may frequently volunteer that her responses are mere guesses and that nothing was actually visible. After many trials, you tally up the number of times the observer was correct. Despite the observer's claims, you find that she was correct 100 percent of the time. Next you decrease the light's intensity to a level *below* the threshold value previously determined by the method of adjustment. When you repeat the forced-choice testing with this new, even dimmer light, the observer protests even more strongly, insisting after every trial that she hadn't seen the light and that she was only guessing about its location. Surprisingly, though, the observer continues to do well—perhaps getting 70 to 75 percent of the choices right. Note that this is well above chance level; if the observer were really just guessing, on average only 50 percent of the responses would be correct.

Similar results have been obtained in studies of the other senses. Typically, forced-choice testing confirms that stimuli can be discerned whose intensities are well below the absolute thresholds defined by Fechner's subjective methods. Don't misconstrue the import of this observation. People aren't lying when they make subjective threshold settings; they are relying on information necessary to generate a conscious experience of the stimulus, and the amount of information needed to support that decision appears to be greater than that required for forced-choice performance (where consciousness experience is not a necessary component of the judgment).

Forced-choice testing is also useful for eliminating extraneous (nonsensory) differences among observers. In subjective (nonforced-choice) tests, results can be strongly influenced by the criterion that the observer uses for saying whether or not a light was visible. The **criterion** is the implicit rule that the observer uses to translate sensory information into overt responses. For example, one observer may have a strict criterion; she will not report "seeing" a stimulus unless the sensory evidence is quite strong. Another observer may have a more lax criterion; she is satisfied with weaker sensory evidence. The first observer's responses might lead you to conclude that the observer's threshold was con-

siderably higher than the second observer's when in fact their apparent differences could have been caused by criterion differences alone.

Forced-choice methods, then, should be employed whenever you want to factor out possible criterion differences among observers. The same holds true if you are dealing with groups of observers whose criteria are likely to differ. Since many elderly people tend to be more reluctant about saying "Yes, I detect it," forced-choice methods are useful in comparing the sensory capacities of older and younger observers. To take another example, hospitalized schizophrenics may be reluctant to admit that they see anything that they are not absolutely sure about. So forced-choice methods are important in comparing the vision of schizophrenic and normal observers. In these comparisons and others, if *criterion* differences cannot be ruled out, it is impossible to be conclusive with respect to the source of the differences in *sensory* capacities. More commonly, researchers have to worry about the constancy of a single observer's criterion from one test to another. This would be important if one is interested in whether some treatment—such as perceptual training—changes an observer's ability to see, or whether the training had affected only the observer's willingness to *say* he sees something.

Before concluding this outline of forced-choice methods, we should note that some of Fechner's original methods can be converted into forced-choice versions. You can devise a forced-choice method of limits or a forced-choice method of constant stimuli. In fact, forced-choice staircases have become particularly popular, with the correctness or incorrectness of a person's responses determining whether the stimulus is increased or decreased from trial to trial.

SENSORY DECISION THEORY

There's another important topic that must be included in any survey of psychophysical methods. That topic is **sensory decision theory (SDT),** a term that covers a set of procedures and a sophisticated psychophysical theory (Green and Swets, 1966). SDT, sometimes also called **signal detection theory** in recognition of its origins in electrical engineering, offers psychophysics two distinct but complementary benefits. One benefit comes from SDT's procedures for expressing precisely and quantitatively what information is contained in some stimulus. In a visual stimulus, for example, the information includes the spatial distribution of light from different parts of the stimulus and a description of how that distribution changes with time. Characterizing the stimulus in this way allows you to determine the efficiency with which a human observer uses the potential information. Defining the potential information contained in a stimulus specifies an upper theoretical limit to observer performance. Knowing that theoretical limit makes it possible to compare the performance of a human observer against the performance of an ideal or perfect observer, that is, one who uses all the stimulus's information. If, as usually happens, information were lost by the eye or by other parts of the visual system, performance would be less than ideal. Take one example. Some light incident on the eye's cornea is either absorbed or reflected rather than transmitted into the eye itself. This loss of light, which is governed by the cornea's structure, reduces the amount of information potentially available in the stimulus. The eye's detection performance is limited, then, because the visual system never gets access to the information lost to absorption or reflection. With appropriate calculations, one can define precisely how much reduction in performance is mandated by this or any other information loss. Geisler (1989) puts this aspect of SDT to excellent use in a psychophysical analysis of the stages in visual processing.

SDT's other main strength lies in its explicit recognition that perceptual measurements are influenced not only by an observer's sensory capacities, but also by various *non*sensory factors. Such nonsensory influences on performance include the observer's criterion, which in turn is determined by motivational variables (Green, 1964). SDT offers a way to distinguish sensory from nonsensory factors, providing separate measures of both sorts of influences (MacMillan and Creelman, 1991). At the completion of a typical SDT experiment, one has two measures of an observer's

performance. One measure, d', reflects the observer's sensory capacity; the other measure, β, (beta), reflects the observer's criterion for acting on the information provided by the senses.*

As we've said, SDT recognizes that in a vision experiment the response "Yes, I see it" depends on two factors—sensory capacity and criterion. To distinguish the two, SDT compares the frequency with which the observer says "Yes" when some dim light *has* been presented and the frequency with which the observer says "Yes" when *no* light has been presented. Take an example. Suppose some observer says "Yes" every single time a very dim light is presented. You might think his eyes are very sensitive. However, you discover that the same observer also says "Yes" when no light whatever is presented. Clearly, you should not take every *yes* at face value.

To achieve its goals, SDT must always compare the observer's responses in two different circumstances. When vision is being assessed, SDT determines the observer's responses to a weak light (called *signal*) as well as to no light (called *noise*). Typically, these signal and noise trials are randomly intermixed. After each trial, the observer responds "Yes" or "No." A "Yes" response to a signal (such as during a trial involving presentation of light) is termed a "hit" (because the observer was correct, or made a hit); a "Yes" response to a noise trial (i.e., one *without* a light) is termed a "false alarm" (because the observer erred, saying he saw something when nothing had been presented). After presenting many signal trials randomly interspersed among noise trials, the experimenter tallies the proportion of signal trials on which the observer responded "Yes" and the proportion of noise trials on which the observer responded "Yes."

The two proportions, the hit rate and false alarm rate, can be plugged into equations to get the sought-after values of d' and β. It's not necessary to work

---

*One sensory area to which SDT has been applied is the question of whether acupuncture truly reduces the sensation of pain or merely makes a patient less willing to report the presence of pain. Experimental results with SDT are mixed; some data suggest a change only in the patient's criterion for reporting pain (Clark and Yang, 1974), other data suggest a genuine sensory change (Chapman, Chen and Bonica, 1977).

SDT has also been applied to problems in a wide variety of nonsensory areas. These include the study of memory

(Bujey et al., 2000; Dobbins et al., 2000; Slotnick et al., 2000), anxiety (Grossberg and Grant, 1978), medical diagnosis (Emmerich and Levine, 1970; Swets, 1979), identification in police lineups (Wells, Lindsay and Ferguson, 1979), perception of hazards in mine shafts (Blignaut, 1979), and decision making in many other areas (Swets, Dawes and Monahan, 2000). In each, SDT has been useful because of its ability to separate informational and motivational influences on judgments.

through the details of these calculations here; in fact, researchers generally rely on published tables to convert their hit and false alarm rates into d'.

To make sure that you've got the idea of SDT, consider a hypothetical experiment. Suppose that two observers are tested with the same dim light and that both achieve the same hit rate. However, one observer produces a higher false alarm rate than the other. Which observer has the higher sensitivity to the dim light? The answer is, the observer whose false alarm rate is lower—her responses indicate that she was superior in discriminating the presence of light from the absence of light. Sensory decision theory treats all tests of detection as tests of an observer's ability to discriminate the presence of a stimulus from its absence (recall Fechner's "inner source of light sensation"). Good discrimination is shown by the combination of a high hit rate and a low false alarm rate. A large difference between an observer's responses when there is a light and when there isn't a light signifies that she can distinguish between the two. Poor discrimination is evidenced when the hit and false alarm rates are equal or nearly equal. In the extreme, when the two rates are equal, you know that the observer has completely failed to distinguish between the absence and presence of a light—performance is at chance level, no matter how high the hit rate might be.

Our discussion of the observer's criterion for reporting sensory information has emphasized differences among observers. But you should recognize that any single observer's criterion varies, depending on a number of factors. SDT specifies how an observer's criterion is likely to change along with changes in the relative importance, to the observer, of hits and false alarms. If an observer is in a situation where it is vital to detect *all* the stimuli and the cost of making a few false alarms is trivial, then SDT predicts the observer will adopt a liberal criterion. This is exemplified in the situation of a radar operator who must monitor the radar for any sign of approach by an enemy. The operator must not miss any possible enemy intrusions whatever. However, if false alarms are costly—in monetary terms or in psychological ones—the observer should adopt a stricter criterion. This is exemplified in the situation of a person who on several successive nights has imagined the sound of a burglar and therefore called the police. He must be very cautious about sounding yet another false alarm.

SDT also specifies how the criterion might change along with changes in the probability that a stimulus

will occur. If the observer knows ahead of time that a stimulus is very likely to occur, then optimally one should adopt a liberal criterion for reporting the presence of the stimulus. However, if the observer knows that a stimulus is very unlikely, the optimal strategy is to adopt a strict criterion (that is, to require more powerful evidence before reporting that the very unlikely event has actually occurred).

PSYCHOPHYSICAL FUNCTIONS FROM PSYCHOMETRIC DATA

Each technique described in the previous sections produces a measure of the threshold, either an absolute threshold or a difference threshold. Any of these technique generates data that specify how performance changes with some stimulus variable that is scaled along an intensive dimension. For instance, Appendix Figure 1 plots the percentage of "seen" responses against light intensity. Curves of this form, as mentioned earlier, are called psychometric functions, and from such a curve we may derive a single intensity value as an estimate of the threshold.

In studying perception we are often interested in how the threshold changes with some stimulus variable. This requires that we measure the threshold repeatedly, over a range of values along some stimulus dimension. For instance, the visual threshold for detecting a spot of light varies depending on the wavelength of that light (recall Figure 3.30); the contrast threshold for detecting a grating pattern varies with the spatial frequency of the pattern (recall Figure 5.13). Likewise, in hearing the threshold intensity for detecting a tone varies with the tone's frequency (recall Figure 11.2). These represent measurements of absolute thresholds as the function of different values along a stimulus dimension of interest (for instance, spatial frequency). These kinds of curves—plots of threshold as the function of some stimulus variable—are called **psychophysical functions.** A psychophysical function represents a family of thresholds, not just a single threshold value. Thus, a psychophysical function more completely summarizes the operation of a sensory system than does a single threshold point from that function.

The examples given above are psychophysical functions for detection thresholds. It is also possible to generate a psychophysical function showing how a difference threshold varies with some stimulus variable.

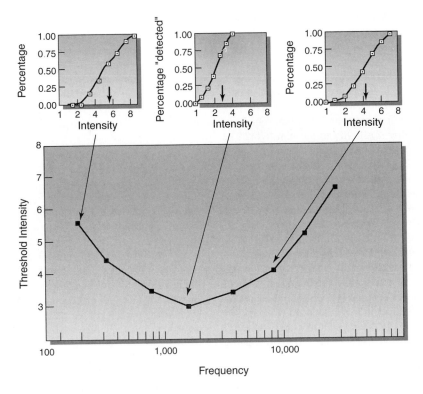

APPENDIX FIGURE 4
Construction of a psychophysical function from psychometric functions. Shown at the
top are three different psychometric functions that yield data points for the
psychophysical function.

Imagine, for example, measuring the smallest difference in wavelength that can just be discriminated from some standard wavelength value. This would constitute a wavelength discrimination threshold. This procedure could be repeated for a number of different standard wavelengths, thus generating a family of wavelength discrimination thresholds. Individual difference thresholds would then be plotted on a graph showing the magnitude of the difference threshold along the vertical axis and wavelength along the horizontal axis. Such a curve would constitute a psychophysical function.

You can think of a psychophysical function as a curve summarizing the data from a family of psychometric functions. Each data point on the psychophysical function is a threshold derived from a psychometric function. This relation is illustrated in Appendix

Figure 4, a schematic audibility function (see Chapter 11) and a sample of the associated psychometric functions. Each data point in the lower part of the figure is an intensity threshold just sufficient to detect a tone of given frequency. Also shown in schematic form are three psychometric functions associated with three of the thresholds; not shown are the psychometric functions for the other threshold values. All the psychometric functions would, incidentally, represent thresholds measured using a method of constant stimuli (recall Appendix Figure 1). One could, of course, measure the family of thresholds using, say, a method of adjustment, in which case there would be no associated psychometric function. Still, the psychophysical function would be the family of thresholds obtained by repeating the method of adjustment for a number of different stimulus values.

MAGNITUDE ESTIMATION AND THE POWER LAW

You've probably seen judges award points to athletes, such as divers or figure skaters, as a rating of their performance. Or maybe you've watched talent shows on television where audience members register their votes for contestants on an applause meter, the winner being the individual who gets the loudest applause. Perhaps you've been asked to rate how well you like different songs by assigning numbers to them, higher numbers indicating greater liking. In each of these instances, the individual doing the rating behaves like a measuring gauge—that person estimates the magnitude of some quality present in a given object, person or event, where *quality* refers to some psychological factor such as gracefulness, appeal and so forth.

This same strategy can be applied to the measurement of subjective sensory experiences such as the loudness of a sound or the brightness of a light. Used in this manner, such strategies fall under the rubric of **direct scaling techniques.** These techniques are called *direct* because the judgments people make presumably directly reflect the magnitude of some sensation they are experiencing. Those judgments, according to the advocates of direct scaling techniques, are just as valid as the reading of sound levels taken with a meter. In a way, direct scaling resembles introspection (recall Chapter 1), in that a person's subjective report is taken as reflecting the contents of conscious experiences such as loudness. However, in the case of direct scaling, the person's ratings are constrained in ways that make it possible to quantify the rating, thereby revealing regularities between the judgments of different people.

The person most responsible for the development of direct scaling techniques was S. S. Stevens. The various techniques he devised for studying the intensity of sensations associated with seeing, hearing, taste, smell, and touch are summarized in Stevens (1960). His most popular technique was magnitude estimation, the technique described in chapters 11 and 13 as it is applied to loudness and odor intensity. According to Stevens, the idea of assigning numbers to gauge the strength of a sensation came from a friendly challenge:

> It all started from a friendly argument with a colleague who said, "You seem to maintain that each loudness has a number and that if someone sounded a tone I should be able to tell him the number." I replied, "That's an interesting idea. Let's try it." (1956, p. 2)

Stevens responded by setting up an experiment and instructing participants as follows:

> You will be presented with a series of stimuli in irregular order. Your task is to tell how intense they seem by assigning numbers to them. Call the first stimulus any number that seems appropriate to you. Then assign successive numbers in such a way that they reflect your subjective impression. There is no limit to the range of numbers that you may use. You may use whole numbers, decimals or fractions. Try to make each number match the intensity as you perceive it. (1975, p. 30)

As a rule, the stimuli to be rated are presented several times each, in an irregular order. No training is necessary, so it is possible to test a person in a relatively short time, which is one reason for the method's popularity. Stevens used magnitude estimation to study all the senses. He discovered that for each sense modality, the *perceived* strength of a stimulus increased in proportion to the stimulus's *physical* intensity raised to some power or exponent. (This is the power law mentioned in Chapter 11.) Each sense modality has its own characteristic power or exponent, and some of these values are summarized in Appendix Figure 5. Note that the exponent for brightness is 0.3. This rather small value indicates that large increases in light intensity produce relatively small increases in brightness. In contrast, look at the exponent and graph line for electric shock. Here's a sensation that grows much faster than the intensity of the stimulus. In the case of electric shock, doubling the intensity causes about a tenfold change in the perceived strength of that shock. Interestingly, perceived length has an exponent of 1.0, indicating that perceived length corresponds almost perfectly with actual length.

Estimating the Magnitude of Loudness

Magnitude estimation seems deceptively simple: a person is instructed merely to assign numbers to sounds in proportion to their subjective intensity. Taking loudness as an example, if one sound seems three times louder than another, the louder sound should be assigned a number three times larger than the number assigned to the softer sound. The person is free to

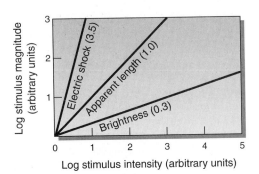

Log stimulus magnitude (arbitrary units)

Electric shock (3.5)

Apparent length (1.0)

Brightness (0.3)

Log stimulus intensity (arbitrary units)

APPENDIX FIGURE 5
Power functions for three different sensory judgments.

select any particular numbers, just so long as those numbers faithfully reflect what the person construes as loudness. No upper or lower limits are placed on the range of acceptable numbers, although sometimes the experimenter may arbitrarily assign a given number to one particular sound intensity. For instance, you might be told to let a rating of 100 correspond to the loudness of a 60-dB$_{SPL}$ sound, but from there on your ratings would be entirely up to you.

Given this latitude in assigning numbers to loudness, you might expect the outcome to be a jumble of idiosyncratic, meaningless numbers, but in fact, this does not happen. While the particular numbers assigned to various sound levels can vary from person to person, the relationships among those numbers show a remarkable degree of regularity among individuals. Of course, as sound intensity increases so does loudness. However, loudness grows more slowly than does intensity.

So loudness does not grow in a simple, additive fashion—with one unit increase in stimulus intensity producing one unit increase in subjective magnitude. Instead, loudness grows exponentially—with each single unit change in the stimulus producing some fraction of unit change in subjective magnitude. This seems to be true over the entire range of audible sound levels, and it holds for magnitude estimates of loudness obtained from just about everyone. S. S. Stevens (1960), who was among the first to think about loudness in this way, expressed this general finding in mathematical terms: loudness grows in proportion to intensity raised to the power, or exponent, 0.67. In mathematical notation,

$$L = k \cdot I^{0.67}$$

where L stands for loudness, I stands for intensity (expressed as sound pressure level) and k is a constant. This general formula is known as the **power law** of loudness growth. Figure 11.11 shows what this relation between intensity and loudness looks like graphically; plotted on the horizontal axis is the sound level, or intensity, of a pure tone, while plotted on the vertical axis are the numbers (the magnitude estimates of loudness) assigned to those various intensities. Note that in this graph, intensity and loudness are scaled in linear coordinates. Plotted in this way, the resulting loudness function appears curved; it is described as negatively accelerating, meaning that loudness grows more slowly than intensity.

Because the relation between intensity and loudness is exponential, replotting the points on logarithmic coordinates should yield a straight line. Taking the logarithm of both sides of the above equation yields

$$\log L = \log k + 0.67(\log I)$$

which is the general form of the equation for a straight line. So if both intensity and loudness ratings were expressed in logarithmic units, the curve summarizing the growth of loudness would be a straight line. The equation's constant, k, specifies where that straight line intersects the vertical axis; the point of intersection depends on the particular set of numbers used by the person to estimate loudness. The equation's exponent, 0.67, specifies the line's slope. A slope less than 1.0 means that subjective magnitude grows more slowly than intensity, while a slope greater than 1.0 indicates subjective magnitude grows more rapidly.

Stevens and other proponents of direct scaling developed methods besides magnitude estimation to measure sensation (see Gescheider, 1976). One of the more clever methods, called **cross-modality matching,** requires a person to equate the strengths of sensations arising from the stimulation of different sense modalities. To illustrate, a person might be asked to adjust the loudness of a sound until its strength matched the brightness of a light. At first glance, this kind of judgment sounds strange, but people actually have no trouble doing it. Probably, cross-modality matching is not so different from deciding how well you enjoyed a performance and clapping your hands with a vigor that reflects this enjoyment.

The matches between modalities conform to predictions derived from the power law. For example, to match a small increase in the intensity of an electric shock, a person requires a large increase in the intensity of a sound; this merely reflects the fact that perceived shock intensity grows much more rapidly than loudness.

These direct scaling techniques, particularly magnitude estimation, have recently been applied to psychological attributes other than sensory judgments. The seriousness of various crimes, the beauty of art works, and the perceived status of various occupations—these are some of the psychological attributes that have been quantified by means of direct scaling.

MULTIDIMENSIONAL SCALING

The procedures described so far have focused on the detection or discrimination of small differences in sensory stimulation or on the growth in sensation with intensity. Now we turn to a rather different procedure—**multidimensional scaling** (MDS)—designed to quantify the degree to which arrays of stimuli are comparable along some set dimension(s). Unlike the methods described above, MDS is typically applied to complex stimuli that are easily discriminable from one another. The goal with MDS is to construct a pictorial representation of the similarities among stimuli (Schiffman, Reynolds and Young, 1981). Technically speaking, MDS mathematically generates an *n*-dimensional space, or map, into which all stimuli being studied will fit. The number of dimensions required to construct that space provides revealing information about the similarities among the stimuli.

The stimuli in an MDS study can be almost anything—perfumes, cola drinks, beers, taste chemicals, colors, legislators, food flavors and so on. Regardless of what the stimuli are, though, an MDS study begins by asking people to judge how similar the stimuli are to one another.

Sometimes, a researcher does not know what basis people will use to make their similarity judgments. For example, if they're judging the similarity of a Chevrolet Corvette and a Mazda Miata, they might respond to the fact that both are sports cars (and judge them similar) or to the fact that they come from different countries (and judge them dissimilar). This can be a problem if the researcher wants to avoid biasing people's judgments. With taste and smell it's particularly hard to know the basis for perceptions of similarity and dissimilarity. Here MDS comes in extra handy, helping to define the perceptual basis for the judgments (even though the researcher doesn't know that basis ahead of time).

Let's start with a simple experiment. Suppose we concoct four different concentrations of sodium chloride (salt) in water. We give them two at a time to people who sip them and then make a numerical judgment of how similar the two are. Suppose they rate similarity on a scale from 100 meaning *perfect identity between the two,* all the way to 0 for *absolutely no similarity whatever* (other judgment schemes can also be used; see Schiffman, Reynolds and Young, 1981).

In our hypothetical study, salt solutions *A* and *C* are judged most similar, solutions *A* and *B* least similar, and the other pairs are judged as somewhere in between. How does one make a spatial map that corresponds to these judgments? The goal is to make a map with four points, *A, B, C* and *D;* the distances between the points should correspond to the judgments of similarity—similar salt solutions should be close together and dissimilar ones far apart. For convenience, we start with the pair *A* and *B*. Since these two solutions are judged least alike, their corresponding spots on the map should be far apart. Arbitrarily, we can position *A* at the left and *B* way to the right. Since *D* is judged equally similar to *C* and *B*, *D* should go about halfway between *C* and *B*. Finally, because *A* and *C* are judged quite similar, we know that *C* goes somewhere close to *A;* but we don't know whether to position it to the left or right. We get the answer by comparing judgments of *A* and *B*, on the one hand, with judgments of *B* and *C*, on the other. Since *C* and *B* are judged more similar than *A* and *B*, we know that *C* must lie somewhere between *A* and *B*. The complete arrangement is shown in panel A (top) of the diagram Appendix Figure 6. To validate our map, we can look at similarity judgments and corresponding points that we haven't used thus far. On the map, *C* is closer to *A* than to *D;* this is consistent with the fact that *C* is judged more similar to *A* than it is to *D*.

When the stimuli can be represented along a single straight line, it indicates judgments were made on the basis of a single aspect or dimension of the stimuli—in this case probably the intensity of the salt taste. Thus, the study with salt solutions led to a map that was a one-dimensional representation. In this hypothetical example involving salt solutions, a one-dimensional map makes sense because the solutions differed in only one way. With more complex stimuli, however, a one-dimensional map may be inadequate

A

B

APPENDIX FIGURE 6
Maps depicting dimensions derived from multidimensional scaling.

because people rely on more than one dimension to derive their similarity judgments. In such cases, a map of two or three dimensions might be needed. Let's take a simple example, based on an actual experiment (Schiffman, Reynolds and Young, 1981).

Suppose we take six brands of carbonated soft drinks (with brand identifications hidden): Coca-Cola, Pepsi-Cola, Dr Pepper, Diet Coke, Diet Pepsi-Cola and Diet Dr Pepper. As before, we allow people to sip pairs of the drinks and then ask for numerical judgments of how similar the two are. These similarity judgments are the data from which we will try to produce our perceptual map. Here are the hypothetical results. Coke and Pepsi are judged highly similar in taste, but each one is judged quite dissimilar from Dr Pepper. In addition, Coke, Pepsi, and Dr Pepper are each judged dissimilar to their respective diet versions. Finally, some pairs are judged to be particularly *dissimilar*: Coke (or Pepsi) versus Diet Dr Pepper, and Dr Pepper versus Diet Pepsi or Diet Coke.

With these results in hand, we proceed to produce an appropriate one-dimensional map. Again, we start by putting the most dissimilar stimuli at opposite ends of the line. For example, we place Coke and Pepsi at one end (close to each other) and Diet Dr Pepper at the other because these were judged extremely dissimilar. Now we've got a problem; other soft drinks were also judged extremely dissimilar—Dr Pepper versus the diet versions of Coke and Pepsi. If we try to place these on the same line we used for Diet Dr Pepper, Coke, and Pepsi, the map will necessarily contradict some of the similarity judgment data we collected. Try it for yourself. The solution is to make a two-dimensional map such as the one shown in panel B of Appendix Figure 6. The arrangement of the stimuli on this map is consistent with the idea that people were judging sodas on the basis of two criteria—whether they had a *cherry* taste (like Dr Pepper) and whether they had a *diet* taste. Note that the data themselves forced us to describe the perceptions in two dimensions.

Incidentally, it was fairly easy to create the maps in our two examples because both examples involved a small number of stimuli. Most MDS experiments, though, use a dozen or more stimuli, making it difficult to produce the right map "by hand." In those cases, researchers use a computer program containing sophisticated trial-and-error schemes for making the map. Programs available for this task are described in the excellent introduction to MDS by Schiffman and her colleagues (Schiffman, Reynolds and Young, 1981). MDS programs can also be found in many standard statistical software packages. These researchers also describe a whole series of uses of MDS, including the development of new consumer products.

This concludes our discussion of psychophysical methods used in perception research. Though Fechner's goals for psychophysics—an exact science of the relation between mind and body—have not been completely realized, there can be little doubt about the value of his contributions. As a result, today many people all over the world celebrate October 22, called by some "Fechner Day" (Boring, 1961). For on that date, in 1850, Fechner first got the idea for his psychophysics.

KEY TERMS

absolute threshold
β (beta)
criterion
cross-modality matching
d′
dark light
difference threshold
just noticeable difference (JND)
direct scaling techniques
forced-choice method
intrinsic light
method of adjustment

method of constant stimuli
method of limits
multidimensional scaling
power law
psychophysics
psychometric functions
psychophysical functions
sensory decision theory (SDT)
signal detection theory (SDT)
staircase method
Weber's law

GLOSSARY

Abney's Law The principle that the visual effectiveness of a light composed of different wavelengths can be predicted from the sum of the responses to the wavelengths considered separately.

absolute distance The distance from an observer to an object. See *relative distance.*

absolute threshold The minimum stimulus intensity that a person can detect. See *difference threshold.*

accommodation The variation in the eye's optical power brought about by temporary changes in the shape of the lens.

achromatic system In the opponent-process view of color vision, the pathway that generates and transmits information about an object's lightness. See *chromatic system.*

achromatopsia Inability to perceive the colors of objects, including familiar ones, as the result of damage to restricted regions of the brain.

acoustic energy The variations in air pressure produced by the vibration of an object.

acoustic reflex Muscular contractions within the middle ear that damp sound vibrations by stiffening the eardrum and restricting the movements of the ossicles.

acoustics The branch of physics concerned with sound.

action potentials Brief electrical discharges that are generated by a neuron and that represent the "vocabulary" of communication within the nervous system. See *axon.*

acupuncture Centuries-old technique for eliminating pain by insertion of fine needles into the body at specific sites

adaptation A reduction in the responsiveness of neurons, produced by prolonged stimulation.

additive color mixture A color that results when several component colors are combined in such a way that each component contributes a portion to the spectral composition of the combination. See *subtractive color mixture.*

aerial perspective The tendency for objects at a distance to appear less distinct, since light reflected from those objects must travel through atmosphere containing particles of dirt and water.

affordances   Uses of an object, governed by the object's structural characteristics.

afterimage   A visual sensation that persists after exposure to some intense stimulus; also, an illusory color produced by exposure to an intense stimulus.

agnosias   Neurological conditions in which people cannot recognize objects; depending on the sense involved, an agnosia is said to be visual, auditory, or tactile. See *prosopagnosia*.

akinetopsia   Inability to perceive visual motion as the result of damage to restricted regions of the brain.

aliasing   Creation of spurious low-frequency information when high-frequency information is undersampled, as by photoreceptor mosaic.

ambient system   The aspect of vision responsible for spatial orientation; uses information from peripheral as well as central vision. See *focal system*.

ambiguity problem   Because several stimulus variables jointly determine the response of any sensory neuron, a single neuron's response is ambiguous with respect to stimulus conditions.

Ames room   A specially constructed room in which the floor-to-ceiling heights as well as the sizes and shapes of the doors and windows have been distorted to make the room appear rectangular when viewed from one specific vantage point. To an observer looking into the room through a peephole, people of identical heights standing in different parts of the room look dramatically different in height. The Ames room illustrates how perceived distance influences perceived size.

amodal completion   Perception of an object's occluded region(s).

amplitude   The property of sound waves that is related to the magnitude of the change in air pressure produced by a sound source. This property, sometimes referred to as *intensity,* is related to loudness. See *intensity*.

analgesia   The elimination of pain. See *endorphins*.

analytic introspection   A method for studying perception in which trained people attend to and describe the experiences evoked by some stimulus.

anomalous myopia   A temporary myopia induced by lack of adequate stimuli for accommodation.

anosmia   An inability to smell odors. See specific anosmias.

Anton's syndrome   A neurological condition in which a cortically blind person denies his or her blindness.

anvil (incus)   The middle member of the three ossicles within the middle ear; it relays sound vibrations from the hammer to the stirrup.

apparent motion   The illusory impression, created by the rapid alternation of objects presented at different spatial locations, that the objects have moved smoothly from one location to the other. See *element movement, group movement*.

aqueous humor   A watery fluid, produced by the ciliary body, that nourishes structures within the eye's anterior chamber and helps maintain the eye's shape.

astigmatism   An error in refraction caused by variation in optical power along various meridians of the cornea.

audibility function (AF)   In hearing, a graph portraying threshold intensity as a function of the frequency of the test tone.

auditory canal   The hollow cavity leading from the pinna to the eardrum, which in humans is about 2.5 cm long and 7 mm in diameter.

auditory cortex   A region of the cortex devoted to analysis of complex sound information, including biologically relevant sounds involved in communication.

auditory image   With a complex sound field arising from several different auditory events, the information associated with just one of those events.

auditory nerve   The bundle of nerve fibers innervating the cochlea and carrying information from the ear to higher stages of the auditory system. Also known as the *eighth cranial nerve*.

autokinetic effect   The illusory impression of motion created when a small stationary target is seen in a homogeneous dim field.

axon   The portion of a neuron over which action potentials are conducted. A group of axons constitute a *nerve* or a *tract*. See *action potential*.

bandpass noise   Noise containing a restricted, contiguous band of frequencies.

basilar membrane   The thin sheet of tissue separating the tympanic canal and the cochlear duct.

beta (β)   In sensory decision theory, a measure of the observer's bias.

binaural   Listening with two ears. See *monaural.*

binaural cues   Sources of sound information for localizing a sound source by comparing the sounds received by the two ears.

binaural unmasking   A reduction in the ability of masking noise heard with both ears to mask another sound heard by one ear only. See *masking.*

binocular   Seeing with two eyes. See *monocular.*

binocular cell   A visual cortical cell receiving excitatory input from both eyes.

binocular rivalry   The alternation of a percept over time between one eye's view and the other eye's view when the two eyes view very different stimuli.

blindsight   The ability of some cortically blind people to point to the location of a light that they cannot see.

blobs   Clusters of color-opponent cells in the upper layers of the visual cortex. Cells within these clusters, often referred to as blob cells, receive input from color-selective cells of the parvocellular pathway.

Bloch's Law   The principle that all stimuli in which the product of time and intensity is constant will be equally detectable.

blue-yellow cells   Neurons showing a polarized response to spectral lights, which increases over one portion of the spectrum and decreases over another portion; the transition between the two types of responses occurs between the regions of the spectrum called blue and yellow. See *red-green cells.*

bone conduction   The transmission of sound wave vibrations through the bones of the skull to the cochlea. A procedure for testing the integrity of the cochlea in the presence of middle-ear damage.

Braille   System of writing in which letters or characters are represented by patterns of tangible dots.

brightness   The dimension of color experience related to the amount of light emitted by an object. See *hue, saturation.*

broadband noise   Noise whose energy covers a wide range of frequencies.

cataract   Clouding that reduces the lens's transparency and, hence, degrades the quality of the retinal image.

center frequency   The frequency lying at the center of the range of frequencies contained in bandpass noise.

change blindness   Failure to notice an otherwise conspicuous change because of the diversion of attention. See *inattentional blindness.*

choroid   A dark, spongy structure containing blood vessels that supply nourishment to the retina; because of its heavy pigmentation, the choroid absorbs scattered light.

chromatic system   In the opponent-process view of color vision, the pathway that generates and transmits information about an object's color. See *achromatic system.*

cilia   A tiny tuft of thin hairs projecting out of each olfactory receptor cell and extending through the mucous layer into the nasal cavity; thought to be the site where odorous molecules trigger electrical changes in the olfactory receptor cell.

ciliary body   Located in the eye, a spongy network of tissue that manufactures aqueous humor.

closure   The Gestalt principle of organization referring to the tendency of the visual system to obscure small breaks or gaps in objects. See *proximity, similarity.*

cochlea   A coiled, fluid-filled chamber in the inner ear containing the specialized organ for hearing, the basilar membrane.

cochlear emissions   Sounds that are generated entirely from within the cochlea.

cochlear nucleus   A structure receiving input from the auditory nerve; its cells exhibit a high degree of frequency tuning.

cocktail party effect   The ability to attend selectively to the speech of one person in the midst of many other speakers.

color constancy   The tendency of an object's color to remain unchanged despite changes in the spectrum of light falling on—and reflected by—that object.

color contrast A change in color appearance brought about by juxtaposing particular color pairs.

color deficiency In humans, a departure from normal trichromatic color vision; takes various forms, including anomalous trichromacy, dichromacy, and monochromacy.

common chemical sense An aspect of olfaction responsible for the detection of strong concentrations of potentially dangerous substances; responsible for the "feeling" in the nose produced by certain substances.

complementary Describing two colors that can be mixed to form white.

complex cells Visual cortical cells that do not exhibit clearly defined ON and OFF regions within their receptive fields, making it difficult to predict what stimulus will produce the largest response. See *simple cells.*

composite light According to Newton, any light that is made up of several different color components. See *pure light.*

computer vision The ability of machines, notably computers, to perceive and interpret a visual scene.

conditioned taste aversion Learned avoidance of certain taste substances, usually following nausea from ingesting the substance.

conduction loss A form of hearing loss attributable to a disorder in the outer or middle ear; it typically involves an overall loss in sensitivity at all sound frequencies. See *sensory/neural loss.*

cone of confusion The set of points in space that potentially could have given rise to any one interaural time difference or interaural intensity difference.

cones Photoreceptors that are specialized for daylight and color vision. See *rods.*

configural processing Integration of various object features into a comprehensive, global configuration. See *featural processing.*

configural superiority effect The finding that, under some circumstances, a complex figure, or part of a complex figure, may be seen more readily than one of its parts presented in isolation.

conjunctive Referring to those movements of the eye in which both eyes move in the same direction. See *vergence.*

contralateral fibers In the case of vision, those optic nerve fibers that project from one eye to the opposite side of the brain. See *ipsilateral fibers.*

contrast The difference in light intensity between an object and its immediate surroundings; also, the intensity difference between adjacent bars in a grating.

contrast sensitivity function (CSF) A graph depicting a person's ability to see targets of various spatial frequency; on the x-axis is the spatial frequency of the test target; on the y-axis is sensitivity, the reciprocal of the minimum contrast needed to see the test target.

contrast threshold The minimum contrast needed to see some target.

convergence The ability of the eyes to turn inward, toward each other, in order to fixate a nearby object.

convergence insufficiency Difficulty with turning the eyes inward to fixate a nearby object.

cornea The transparent portion of the eye's front surface, which refracts light and allows it to pass into the eyeball.

cortical deafness Impaired hearing that results from damage to the auditory cortex.

cortical magnification The mapping of the retina onto the visual cortex so that the representation of the fovea is exaggerated or magnified.

criterion The implicit rule used by an observer in order to convert sensory information into overt responses.

critical band The restricted range of frequencies that mask a given test frequency. The critical band reflects the frequency tuning of the neurons that detect the test frequency.

critical flicker frequency (CFF) The highest perceptible rate of temporal variation in light intensity.

cross-adaptation A temporary loss in sensitivity to one odor following exposure to a different odor.

cross-fiber theory The idea that taste qualities are represented by the pattern of neural activity among an ensemble of neurons; also has application in vision, hearing, and smell.

cross-modality matching   A psychophysical procedure in which one sort of stimulus (for instance, a light) is adjusted so that the sensation the stimulus produces matches the sensation produced by a different sort of stimulus (for instance, a sound).

crowding effect   The tendency for small letters to be difficult to read when they are in close proximity to one another.

crystalline lens   The elliptical optical element located immediately behind the iris of the eye. Temporary variations in thickness alter the eye's accommodation, or optical power.

cutoff frequency   The spatial frequency at which a lens's transfer function falls to zero; the highest frequency that a lens can image; the highest frequency to which a visual system can respond.

d'   In sensory decision theory, a measure of sensitivity.

dark adaptation   The increase in visual sensitivity that accompanies time in darkness following exposure to light.

dark light   See *intrinsic light.*

decibel (dB)   A unit for expressing sound amplitude.

delay line   Key element in a theory designed to explain binaural cells' sensitivity to interaural time differences. The delay line retards the arrival of signals from one ear relative to those from the other ear.

depth of field   The range of distances over which the image of a scene remains sharply focused; varies with pupil size.

depth perception   The ability to perceive the three-dimensional locations of objects in relation to the perceiver's position in space. Besides specifying distance, depth perception allows a perceiver to segregate objects from their backgrounds and to discern the three-dimensional shapes of objects.

detection   The process by which an object is picked out from its surroundings; also, the process by which the presence of some object is perceived.

dichromatic   Referring to a person whose eye contains two types of cone photopigments.

difference threshold   The minimum amount by which stimulus intensity must be changed in order to produce a just noticeable change in sensation. See *absolute threshold.*

diffuse fibers   In touch system, first-order afferent neurons having large receptive fields with poorly defined borders.

diplesthesia   In touch, the illusory experience of two objects when only one is actually present.

diplopia   Double vision, a condition that results when images from the two eyes are seen separately and simultaneously.

direct scaling techniques   A set of psychophysical procedures for measuring subjective sensory experiences such as loudness or brightness; these procedures are based on the assumption that people can rate sensory magnitude.

direction-selective cell   A neuron in the visual cortex that responds most vigorously to a particular direction of target movement.

direction selectivity   A tendency of some neurons in the visual system to respond most strongly to objects that move in a particular direction.

discrimination   The process by which one object is distinguished from another.

discrimination threshold   The minimum physical difference, usually an intensity difference, that allows two objects to be distinguished from each other.

disparity-selective cells   Cells in the visual cortex that receive input from both eyes and that respond only when an object is situated at a particular distance from the two eyes. See *stereoblindness.*

distance senses   See *far senses.*

divergent   Referring to light whose wavefronts spread outward, usually as the light proceeds away from its source.

DoG   Difference of gaussian, a category of visual patterns whose limited spatial frequency content make them useful in the study of spatial vision.

dorsal stream   Hierarchically arranged brain areas within the occipital and parietal lobes, thought to register information about visual motion and spatial location. See *parietal pathway;* contrast with *ventral stream.*

dualism The philosophical view that mental events need not be associated with neural events. See *materialism*.

duplex Referring to the co-existence within the eye of two different systems, scotopic and photopic. The scotopic system provides high sensitivity in dim light; the photopic system provides high resolution under daylight conditions.

duplex theory In hearing, the idea that the interaural time difference (ITD) is used to localize low-frequency sounds and the interaural intensity difference (IID) is used to localize high-frequency sounds.

dynamic visual acuity The finest spatial detail that can be resolved; measured while a target is moving.

eardrum (tympanic membrane) The thin, oval membrane that covers the end of the auditory canal and separates the outer ear and the middle ear; it vibrates when sound waves strike it.

eccentricity The distance between the center of the retina and the location of the retinal image cast by an object.

echoes Reflected sound waves.

efferent fibers In the auditory system, neural projections from the brain back to the cochlea.

egocentric direction The direction in which an object is located relative to an observer.

electromagnetic radiation Energy that is produced by oscillation of electrically charged material; light encompasses a small portion of the electromagnetic spectrum.

element movement In an ambiguous type of apparent movement, the percept that some of the stimulus's components are stationary while one component moves back and forth. See *apparent motion, group movement*.

Emmert's law The perceived size of an image of fixed retinal size varies directly with perceived viewing distance.

emmetropic Referring to an eye whose focal point, in the absence of accommodation, coincides exactly with the retina.

endorphins Naturally occurring morphine-like chemicals that can ease pain. See *analgesia*.

equal loudness contours A set of curves describing the sound intensities at which different frequencies all sound equal in loudness. See *loudness matching*.

Eustachian tube The opening connecting the middle ear and the throat, which maintains air pressure within the middle ear at nearly the same value as the air pressure in the outside environment.

evoked potential (EP) The electrical response in a collection of neurons that is provoked by a stimulus.

extraocular muscles In humans, six large muscles attached to the globe of the eye; by rotating the eyeball within the orbit, the coordinated contractions of these muscles control the direction of gaze. See *rectus muscles*.

face-inversion effect Difficulty recognizing distortions in features of a face, distortions readily perceived when the face is viewed upright.

far senses (distance senses) Senses, such as vision, that enable an organism to perceive objects or events some distance away. See *near senses*.

featural processing Ability to perceive individual components, or features, of an object without being able to integrate those components into a global form. See *configural processing*.

fibrous tunic The strong, leathery outermost layer of the eyeball.

figure/ground organization The tendency to see part of a scene (the figure) as a solid, well-defined object standing out against a less distinct background (the ground).

flavor A complex sensation associated with food, based on the food's taste, temperature, texture, and smell.

flicker Temporal variation in light intensity; also, the percept of such temporal variation.

floaters Debris that drifts about within the eye's vitreous casting shadows on the retina and producing dark spots that appear to move along with the eye.

fMRI Functional magnetic resonance imaging, a for localizing regions of neural activity within the brain. See *PET*.

focal system The aspect of vision that is responsible for object identification and discrimination; predominantly uses central, rather than peripheral, vision. See *ambient system*.

forced-choice Said of a response used in the forced-choice method. See *forced-choice method*.

forced-choice method A psychophysical procedure in which a person must identify the interval during which a stimulus occurred; in an alternative version, the person must identify the spatial location at which a stimulus was presented.

Fourier analysis A method for calculating the frequency content of any temporal or spatial signal; can be used to determine the spatial frequency content of a visual scene or other target.

fovea Pit or depression in the retina; the region of sharpest vision.

free nerve endings Nerve cells in the olfactory epithelium that mediate the common chemical sense.

frequency theory The idea that the basilar membrane vibrates as a unit in response to sound, in synchrony with sound pressure changes. See *place theory*.

frequency tuning curve A graph describing the sensitivity of an auditory neuron to tones of various frequencies.

fundamental frequency The lowest frequency among the set of frequencies associated with a complex sound.

gate theory of pain The view that perception of pain involves the interplay between two fiber groups, one which can modulate the strength of signals in the other.

geons In one theory of visual recognition, the geometric elements into which seen objects are decomposed. The term is short for *geo*metrical ic*ons*.

Gestalt principles of organization Certain stimulus properties that control the perceptual grouping of objects. See *closure, good continuation, proximity, similarity*.

glaucoma A relatively common ocular disorder in which fluid pressure builds up within the eyeball, eventually causing blindness if not corrected.

global motion The experience of motion in a single direction that arises from a stimulus whose elements move in a variety of different directions.

good continuation The tendency to see neighboring elements as grouped together when they are potentially connected by straight or smoothly curving lines.

grating A target consisting of alternating darker and lighter bars, used to study spatial vision. See *sinusoidal grating*.

group movement In an ambiguous type of apparent movement, the percept that all stimulus components move back and forth *en masse* (as a group). See *apparent motion, element movement*.

grouping The aggregation of several related elements into a larger coherent unit. A key part of the recognition process.

habituation The process by which an organism ceases to respond to some stimulus.

hair cells The ears' receptors. See *inner hair cells, outer hair cells*.

hammer (malleus) The outermost of the three ossicles within the middle ear; one end of the hammer is attached to the eardrum, and the other end relays sound vibrations to the anvil.

haptics Sensory information that depends upon both touch and kinesthesis.

harmonics Acoustic frequencies that are multiples of one another, often occurring in speech and music. Harmonic tones tend to be perceptually grouped in hearing.

Hermann grid A regular, geometric pattern within which illusory spots are seen; the presence and strength of the illusory spots depend on the spacing of the grid's elements.

hertz (Hz) A unit for expressing the frequency with which the intensity of a sound or a light varies over time.

horopter An imaginary plane in visual space that contains objects whose images fall on corresponding points of the retina of the left and right eyes; any object situated on the horopter will be seen as single.

hue   The dimension of color experience that distinguishes among red, orange, yellow, green, blue, and so on; the dimension of color most strongly determined by light's wavelength; commonly used as synonym for *color.* See *brightness, saturation.*

hypercolumn   An aggregation of columns of cortical cells whose receptive fields overlap on the same restricted region of the retina.

hyperopic   Referring to an abnormally short eyeball, in which the image is blurred because the eye's focal point lies behind the retina.

identification   The process of distinguishing a particular object.

illusions   Perceptual errors.

illusory conjunction   Condition in which features that actually belong to separate objects appear to be combined.

image   The spatial distribution of light energy produced by the action of some optical system.

inattentional blindness   Impairment in perceiving the appearance of or changes to unattended objects. See *change blindness.*

incus   See *anvil.*

induced motion   The illusory impression, created when moving contours are nearby a stationary object, that the stationary object is moving.

inner hair cells (IHCs)   The approximately 3.5 flask-shaped structures situated along the length of the basilar membrane of the human ear. See *outer hair cells.*

intensity   The physical variable expressing the strength or amplitude of a stimulus, such as light or sound. Intensity can be measured by physical devices such as photometers and sound-level meters. See *amplitude.*

interaural intensity difference (IID)   The difference in the intensity of sound arriving at the two ears; one of the sources of information for sound localization. See *interaural time difference.*

interaural time difference (ITD)   The difference in the time of arrival of a sound wave at the two ears; one of the sources of information for sound localization. See *interaural intensity difference.*

interposition   A monocular depth cue based on occlusion of a distant object by a closer one.

intrinsic light (dark light)   The impression, in complete darkness, of a dim cloud of light.

inverse optics   The problem of determining what objects in the world generated a given image on the retina.

ipsilateral fibers   In the case of vision, those optic nerve fibers that project from one eye to the same side of the brain. See *contralateral fibers.*

iris   The two-layered ring of tissue that gives the eye its characteristic color.

isoluminant   Property of multiple surfaces that differ only in hue, not brightness or saturaction.

K cells   Class of visual cells characterized by small cell bodies; little is currently known about their visual function. See *M cells* and *P cells.*

kinesthesis   Information about the movement and position of a limb that derives from receptors that are in the muscles, tendons, and joints of that limb.

lateral geniculate nucleus   A group of nerve cell bodies arranged in layers in the thalamus, each layer receiving input from either the left eye or the right eye; the major relay station between the eye and the visual cortex.

lateral inhibition   Antagonistic neural interaction between adjacent regions of a sensory surface, such as the retina.

lesion   Damage to a restricted region of the body, particularly some portion of the nervous system.

lightness   A perceptual variable that is correlated with light intensity.

lightness constancy   The tendency for the perceived lightness of an object to remain constant despite variation in the level of its illumination.

lightness contrast   An effect in which a fixed physical intensity of light produces different perceived lightnesses depending upon the intensity of the light's background.

linear perspective   The convergence of lines that makes a two-dimensional representation of a scene appear to be three-dimensional.

LLI Language based learning impairment.

localization ability An observer's capacity to identify the position of some stimulus.

loudness The subjective experience associated with sound intensity.

loudness matching A psychophysical procedure in which a listener adjusts the intensity of one tone until it sounds as loud as another tone. See *equal loudness contours*.

M cells Retinal ganglion cells characterized by relatively large cell bodies and axons, large receptive fields, strong response to small differences in light levels in receptive field center and surround, and lack of sensitivity to stimulus wavelength. See *P cells*.

Mach bands Illusory spatial gradations in perceived lightness that occur in the absence of corresponding gradations in the actual spatial distribution of light.

macula The small, circular central region of the retina where vision is most acute.

magnitude estimation A psychophysical procedure in which people assign numbers to stimuli in proportion to the perceived intensity of those stimuli.

magnocellular layers In the lateral geniculate nucleus, layers containing large cells; layers 1 and 2.

malleus See *hammer*.

masking A reduction in one stimulus's visibility or loudness as a result of the juxtaposition of another, stronger stimulus. See *binaural unmasking*.

materialism The philosophical view that ascribes all mental experiences to neural events. See *dualism*.

McGurk effect Auditory misperception of a spoken phoneme that occurs when the speaker's mouth appears to be uttering a different phoneme.

mechanoreceptors Receptors that respond to deformation of the skin.

medial geniculate nucleus A structure in the thalamus that is part of the auditory system.

Meissner corpuscles An encapsulated touch receptor located in the skin's upper layer.

melody contour The rise and fall of successive notes in a musical passage.

meridional amblyopia A loss in visual acuity for lines of a particular orientation.

Merkel disk An unencapsulated touch receptor located at an intermediate depth within the skin.

metamers Two or more objects that appear identical despite acute physical differences.

method of adjustment A psychophysical procedure in which a person adjusts a stimulus so that it is just detectable (absolute threshold) or until a just noticeable change is produced (difference threshold).

method of constant stimuli A psychophysical procedure in which each of a fixed set of stimuli is presented in random order.

method of limits A psychophysical procedure in which the stimulus intensity changes progressively in small steps until the person's response changes, for example, from "No, I don't see it" to "Yes, I do see it."

microelectrode A thin wire that can be inserted into brain tissue in order to record action potentials.

microspectrophotometry A technique for measuring, at various wavelengths, the quantity of light reflected or absorbed by a small object; used to measure cone photopigments.

missing fundamental With a complex series of harmonic tones, the fundamental tone of the series may continue to be heard despite the fact that it has been physically removed.

mixture suppression The strength of odor produced by some substance presented alone may be reduced when that same substance is presented in combination with another.

monaural Listening with one ear. See *binaural*.

monochromat A person whose eye contains just one type of cone photopigment.

monocular Seeing with one eye. See *binocular*.

motion aftereffect (waterfall illusion) The illusory impression, after prolonged viewing of movement in one direction, that a stationary object is moving in the opposite direction.

motion capture An object that moves in one direction over a field of randomly moving elements causes those elements to appear to move in the same direction as the object itself.

motion parallax A source of potent monocular depth information based on differences in relative motion between images of objects located at different distances from an observer.

multichannel model The hypothesis that spatial vision is the product, in part, of sets of neurons responsive to different spatial frequencies.

multidimensional scaling (MDS) A quantitative technique for geometrically representing similarity among stimuli.

multiple object tracking Ability to keep track, over time, of multiple, spatially dispersed, independently-moving objects.

myelin A membrane that insulates a neuron's axon and speeds conduction of nerve impulses along that axon.

myopic Referring to an abnormally long eye, in which the retinal image is blurred because the eye's focal point lies in front of the retina.

naive realism The philosophical view that perception accurately portrays all objects and events in the world.

nanometer A unit of length in the metric system corresponding to one-billionth of a meter, used for specifying wavelength of light.

nasal cycle Periodic alternation in which first one then the other nostril is obstructed.

near senses Senses, such as touch, that require close proximity between the perceiver and the object or event to be perceived. See *far senses.*

neon spreading The illusory migration of color from one region into neighboring regions.

neurogram A graph depicting variations over time in the neural activity within a large number of frequency-selective neurons in response to a complex sound.

neutral point In a dichromatic eye, the wavelength of light that appears white (neutral in color).

Newton's color circle A geometric arrangement of colors summarizing the results of mixing varying amounts of different colors.

nociceptors Special class of skin receptors responsive to noxious stimulation. See *free nerve-endings.*

noise A complex sound whose many constituent frequencies combine to produce a random waveform.

nonspectral colors Colors, such as purple, that are not found in the spectrum.

object-based attention The view that attention is always directed at objects, not spatial locations.

oblique effect The tendency for lines oriented vertically or horizontally to be more visible than lines oriented along a diagonal.

occipital lobe A region of the brain involved in vision; located at the brain's posterior.

ocular dominance The variation in strength of excitatory input from the two eyes to a binocular cell of the visual cortex.

oculomotor cues Kinesthetic cues to depth derived from muscular contractions of the extraocular muscles.

odor adaptation A reduction in odor sensitivity following prolonged exposure to an odorous substance.

odor constancy The tendency of an odor's perceived intensity to remain constant despite variations in the flow rate of air drawn into the nose.

odor hallucinations Odors experienced without any physical stimulus; a phenomenon sometimes associated with brain damage.

olfactory brain A cluster of neural structures that receives projections from the olfactory bulb via the olfactory tract.

olfactory bulb The brain structure that receives input from the olfactory nerve.

olfactory epithelium A patch of tissue situated near the top of the nasal cavity and containing the olfactory receptor cells.

olfactory nerve The bundle of axons from olfactory receptor cells that project to the olfactory bulb, carrying information about odorous substances from the nose to the brain. Also called the *first cranial nerve.*

olfactory sensory neuron A bipolar (double-ended) nerve cell that captures odorant molecules and initiates the neural signals for smell.

ophthalmoscope An optical device used to visualize the inside of the eye.

optic ataxia A neurological disorder characterized by difficulties in the visual guidance of limb movement.

optic chiasm The point at which nerve fibers from the two eyes are rerouted to higher visual centers, with some fibers from each eye projecting to the same side of the brain (ipsilateral fibers) and the remainder projecting to the opposite side of the brain (contralateral fibers).

optic disk The region of the eye where the optic nerve penetrates the retina; also, the region where major blood vessels enter and exit the eye's interior.

optic nerve The bundle of axons of retinal ganglion cells that carries visual information from the eye to the brain. Also known as the *second cranial nerve.*

optic tracts The two bundles of axons of retinal ganglion cells formed after the nerve fibers exit the optic chiasm.

orbit Cavity in the skull that houses the eyeball and its supporting structures.

organ of Corti The receptor organ for hearing, situated within the cochlear duct.

orientation The degree of inclination of a contour within a two-dimensional plane.

orientation constancy Tendency to judge visual orientation based on gravity, regardless of head position.

orientation selectivity A unique property of visual cortical cells, whereby they respond best to contours of a particular orientation, with the response decreasing as the orientation deviates increasingly from the preferred value.

ossicles A series of three tiny bones that transmit sound vibrations from the eardrum to the oval window. See *anvil, hammer, stirrup.*

otosclerosis A disorder of the middle ear involving immobilization of the stirrup.

outer hair cells (OHCs) The approximately 12,000 cylindrical structures situated along the length of the basilar membrane of the human ear. See *inner hair cells.*

oval window The small opening into the inner ear, which is covered by a thin membrane and which receives vibrations from the eardrum via the ossicles.

P cells Retinal ganglion cells characterized by relatively small cell bodies and axons, small receptive fields, weak response to small differences in light levels in receptive field center and surround, and good sensitivity to stimulus wavelength. See *M cells.*

Pacinian corpuscle An encapsulated touch receptor located in the skin's lower layer.

papillae Protuberances distributed over the tongue's surface, the walls of which are lined with taste buds.

parietal cortex A major division of the cerebral cortex; the parietal cortex covers the upper, rear portion of the side of the brain; receives information from touch system.

parietal pathway Hierarchically arranged brain areas within the occipital and parietal lobes, thought to register information about visual motion and spatial locations. See *dorsal stream.*

parvocellular layers In the lateral geniculate nucleus, layers containing small cells; layers 3 through 6.

perceived distance The apparent visual separation between two objects or between an object and the viewer.

perception The acquisition and processing of sensory information in order to see, hear, taste, smell, or feel objects in the world; also guides an organism's actions with respect to those objects. Perception may involve conscious awareness of objects and events; this awareness is termed a *percept.*

perfect pitch The comparatively rare ability to identify any musical note played or to reproduce vocally any named note. See *relative pitch.*

perimetry A procedure for measuring a visual field, which involves determining the positions in visual space where a person can and cannot see a small spot of light.

PET scan An image of the brain, or other structure, that is created by means of positron emission tomography.

phantom limb Perception that an amputated limb is still attached to the body.

pheromones Odors that serve as sexual signals.

phonagnosia Inability to identify speakers by means of their voices.

phoneme A sound difference that affects the meaning of an utterance; widely regarded as the fundamental unit of speech.

phosphenes Visual sensations arising entirely from neural events within the visual pathways, in the absence of light stimulation.

photon The smallest unit of light energy.

photopic Referring to vision under daylight levels of illumination. See *scotopic*.

photopigment Light-sensitive molecules within a photoreceptor; light causes the photopigment to isomerize, releasing energy that alters the photoreceptor's electrical potential.

photoreceptors Specialized nerve cells (rods and cones) in the eye that contain photopigment; absorption of light by these cells triggers changes in the cells' electrical potential.

pigment epithelium A layer of the retina that helps to dispose of cellular debris.

pinna The part of the ear projecting from the side of the head; by influencing the frequency composition of sound waves entering the ear, this prominent structure plays a role in sound localization.

pitch The subjective counterpart to sound frequency.

place theory The idea that different portions of the basilar membrane vibrate in response to different sound frequencies. See *frequency theory*.

power law The psychophysical principle that sensation magnitude tends to grow as a power function of stimulus intensity.

presbycusis In hearing, an age-related gradual loss of sensitivity to high-frequency tones.

presbyopia A significant decline in accommodative ability beginning in middle age.

primitives In theories of vision, simple elements that are thought to be building blocks for perception.

profile analysis The process by which the relative activity of various neurons registers some property of a stimulus.

proprioception The sense that enables one to feel where one's limbs are.

prosopagnosia An inability to recognize faces. See *agnosias*.

proximity The Gestalt principle of organization referring to the perceptual tendency to group together objects that are near one another. See *closure, similarity*.

psychometric function A graph showing the frequency with which each stimulus elicits each of two possible responses.

psychophysical function A graph showing the threshold as a function of some stimulus variable.

psychophysics The branch of perception that is concerned with establishing quantitative relations between physical stimulation and perceptual events.

punctate fibers In touch system, first-order afferent neurons have small receptive fields with sharply defined borders.

pupil The aperture in the eye formed by two sets of concentric bands of muscle; the constriction and dilation of these muscles vary the diameter of the pupil.

pure light According to Newton, any light that cannot be broken down into constituent colors. See *composite light*.

pure tones Sinusoidal variations in sound pressure, such as those produced by striking a tuning fork.

Purkinje shift Perceptual variation in the relative lightness of different colors as illumination changes from daylight to twilight.

pursuit eye movements Smooth movements of the eyes that allow them to follow a moving target.

random-dot stereogram A pair of pictures composed of black and white dots randomly positioned within the pictures; when such pictures are viewed stereoscopically (one picture seen by each eye), a vivid sensation of depth results, making an object appear to stand out from its surroundings.

rapidly adapting (RA) fibers First-order afferent neurons that respond in a relatively transient manner to sustained deformation of the skin.

receptive field The area of the retina within which the activity of a neuron can be influenced; sometimes defined in terms of the region of visual space from which a neuron can be influenced.

recognition by components Theory that any view of an object can be represented as an arrangement of just a few, simple three-dimensional forms. See *geons.*

rectus muscles Four of the extraocular muscles; largely responsible for moving the eyeball back and forth horizontally (medial rectus and lateral rectus) and up and down vertically (superior rectus and inferior rectus). See *extraocular muscles.*

red-green cells Neurons showing a polarized response to spectral lights, which increases over one portion of the spectrum and decreases over another portion; the transition between the two types of responses occurs between the regions of the spectrum called green and red. See *blue-yellow cells.*

refraction The bending of light by an optical element such as a lens.

relative distance The distance between two objects. See *absolute distance.*

relative pitch The comparatively common ability to identify a tonal interval without necessarily knowing the particular tones that make up that interval. See *perfect pitch.*

resolution The ability to distinguish spatial details of an object.

resonant frequency The frequency at which a given object vibrates when set into motion.

reticular activating system A brain stem structure that governs an organism's general level of arousal.

retina The innermost layer of the eyeball, where light is detected by photoreceptors and transduced into neural signals that are processed by collector cells.

retinal disparity A slight difference in lateral separation between objects seen by the left eye and by the right eye; makes stereopsis possible. See *stereopsis.*

retinal ganglion cells The collector cells that are responsible for the last stage of visual processing within the retina; axons of the retinal ganglion cells constitute the optic nerve.

retinal image The distribution of light falling on the retina; the quality and overall intensity of this image influence visual perception.

retinotopic map A neural representation within the visual system that preserves the spatial layout of the retina.

Ricco's Law The principle that stimuli will be equally detectable if the product of their intensity and area is constant.

rods Photoreceptors that are specialized for vision under dim light. See *cones.*

Rorschach test A projective psychological test in which people are shown inkblots and asked to describe what they see.

round window The thin membrane that covers a small opening into the middle ear; displacement of this membrane compensates for pressure variations within the cochlea.

Ruffini endings An unencapsulated touch receptor located at an intermediate depth within the skin.

saccades Rapid, jerky movements of the eyes, which function to change fixation from one location to another.

saturation The dimension of color experience that distinguishes pale or washed-out colors from vivid colors. See *brightness, hue.*

scale Relative size or extent.

sclera The tough, dense material that forms the eye's outermost coat; seen from the front, the sclera is the white of the eye.

sclerosis The hardening of any living tissue; hardening of the eye's crystalline lens may play a role in presbyopia. See *presbyopia.*

scotoma A region of blindness within the visual field.

scotopic Referring to vision under dim levels of illumination. See *photopic.*

selective adaptation A method of studying mechanisms of perception, in which a person's sensitivity to particular targets is depressed by prolonged exposure to one particular target.

sensory decision theory (SDT) A quantitative treatment of detection and discrimination performance, in which the observer is characterized as a maker of statistical decisions; the system also prescribes techniques that allow the observer's sensitivity to the stimulus to be estimated independently of the observer's criterion, or

preference for particular responses. Also called *signal detection theory.*

sensory/neural loss   A form of hearing loss originating within the inner ear or the auditory pathways; may involve selective loss of sensitivity to a limited range of frequencies. See *conduction loss.*

sensory-specific satiety   Eating one particular food may diminish hunger for that food without affecting hunger for other foods.

sensory transduction   The process occurring within sensory receptors by which physical energy (stimulus) is converted into neural signals.

shading   A gradient in the level of reflected light across the surface of a three-dimensional object. This gradient provides a cue to depth, since flat, two-dimensional surfaces don't cast shadows.

signal detection theory   See *sensory decision theory.*

similarity   The Gestalt principle of organization referring to the perceptual tendency to group together objects that are similar to one another in texture, shape, and so on. See *closure, proximity.*

simple cells   Visual cortical cells that exhibit clearly defined ON and OFF regions within their receptive fields. See *complex cells.*

single cell recording   The use of a microelectrode to record the neural activity of individual nerve cells as they respond to stimulation.

sinusoidal grating   A target in which the intensity of darker and lighter bars varies sinusoidally over space. See *grating.*

size aftereffect   A change in the apparent size of an object following inspection of an object of a different size.

size constancy   The tendency for an object's perceived size to remain constant despite changes in the size of the retinal image of that object as viewing distance varies.

slowly adapting (SA) fibers   First-order afferent neurons that respond in a relatively sustained manner to sustained deformation of the skin.

smooth eye movements   Smooth movements of the eyes, which can function in the pursuit of a moving target.

solipsism   The belief that no one exists other than oneself.

sound localization   Ability to identify the position of some sound stimulus.

sound pressure level (SPL)   A reference level for sound intensity.

spatial frequency   For a grating target, the number of pairs of bars imaged within a given distance on the retina; units of spatial frequency are cycles/mm or, equivalently, cycles/degree of visual angle.

spatial phase   The position of a grating relative to some visual landmark.

spatial summation   The process by which neural signals from neighboring retinal areas are combined, thereby increasing sensitivity. See *temporal summation.*

specific anosmias   Conditions in which people have normal odor sensitivity for some substances but reduced sensitivity for other substances. See *anosmia.*

specific nerve energies   The doctrine that the qualitative nature of a sensation depends on which particular nerve fibers are stimulated.

spectral colors   Hues that are present in a spectrum created by diffracting white light as, for example, in a rainbow.

spectrogram   A graph depicting the frequency composition of a sound as a function of time.

squint   See *strabismus.*

stabilized retinal images   Images whose location on the retina remains fixed despite movements of the eye.

staircase method   A psychophysical procedure in which the stimulus presentations, governed by a person's responses, are made to bracket the threshold; an interactive variant of the method of limits.

stapes   See *stirrup.*

stereoblindness   The inability to see depth using retinal disparity information, a condition thought to result from a reduction in the number of binocular visual cells in the visual cortex. See *disparity-selective cells.*

stereopsis   Binocular depth perception based on retinal disparity. See *retinal disparity.*

stereoscope   An optical device for presenting pictures separately to the two eyes.

stimulus The pattern of physical energy set up by an object or event in the environment.

stimulus uncertainty Lack of knowledge about some property or properties of a stimulus; such uncertainty reduces the stimulus's detectability.

stirrup (stapes) The innermost of the ossicles within the middle ear; attached to the oval window, it receives sound vibrations from the anvil and sets the oval window into vibration.

strabismus Squint; a condition in which the two eyes are misaligned, making normal binocular fixation impossible.

structure from motion (SFM) The impression of an object's shape that derives from the object's motion.

subjective contours Illusory contours or surfaces, especially like those devised by Kanizsa.

subjective idealism The view that the physical world is entirely the product of the mind.

subtractive color mixture A color produced when each of a number of components absorbs a portion of the light's spectrum, thereby subtracting that portion from the reflected spectrum. See *additive color mixture.*

superior colliculus A subcortical brain structure located in the midbrain; this structure plays a role in the initiation and guidance of eye movements.

symmetry Tendency for parts of an object centered about a given axis of orientation to be highly similar in shape, texture and/or color.

synapse A tiny gap between adjacent nerve cells. See *transmitter substance.*

tactile agnosia Inability to recognize objects by touch, resulting from damage to the somatosensory cortex.

taste buds Garlic-shaped structures lining the walls of the papillae on the tongue and containing chemical-sensitive cells that register the presence of taste solutions.

taste hedonics Judgments of the pleasantness of taste substances.

taste modification Alteration in the taste of one substance when it is sampled together with another substance.

taste suppression The reduction in the strength of one taste sensation by another; for example, sugar suppresses the bitter taste of coffee.

tectorial membrane An awninglike layer of tissue arching over the hair cells within the inner ear.

temporal pathway Hierarchically arranged brain areas within the occipital and temporal lobes, thought to be involved in visual object perception. See *ventral steam.*

temporal summation The process by which signals from a neuron or neurons are cumulated over time, thereby increasing sensitivity. See *spatial summation.*

temporary threshold shift A short-lived decrease in hearing sensitivity caused by exposure to noise.

texture contrast Adjacent regions of a visual scene distinguished by differences in texture.

texture gradient A form of perspective in which the density of a surface's texture increases with distance, providing information about the slant of the surface.

threshold intensity The minimum sound intensity necessary to elicit a neural response from an auditory neuron.

tilt aftereffect A temporary change in the perceived orientation of lines following adaptation to lines of a similar, but not identical, orientation.

timbre The quality of sound that distinguishes different musical instruments. See *harmonics.*

tinnitus An annoying, persistent ringing in the ears.

tip of the nose effect The phenomenon in which an odor seems familiar though one cannot name it.

tonotopic organization The orderly layout of preferred frequencies over the length of the basilar membrane.

touch acuity Ability to distinguish a small separation between two closely adjacent stimuli applied to the skin.

transcranial magnetic stimulation Called TMS, a technique whereby a brief, intense pulse of magnetic energy is applied to the scalp to disrupt temporarily normal neural processing.

transfer function   A graph showing, for various target spatial frequencies, the contrast contained in an image.

transmitter substance   One of several different neurochemicals that diffuse across synaptic gaps between adjacent nerve cells, allowing cells to communicate with one another. See *synapse.*

transparency   The property of a nonopaque object that makes it possible to see other objects located behind the nonopaque one. Transparency implies depth without occlusion.

traveling wave   The movement of the basilar membrane in response to fluctuations in fluid pressure with the cochlea.

trichromatic   Referring to a person whose eye contains three types of cone photopigments.

unilateral neglect   Neurological disorder in which a patient ignores events on one side of the body.

univariance principle   The hypothesis that any photoreceptor's response corresponds to just a single variable, the amount of light absorbed; because photoreceptors obey the univariance principle, the wavelength characteristics of light that stimulate a photoreceptor are not directly represented in the receptor's response.

vascular tunic   The middle layer of the eyeball; responsible for much of the eye's nourishment.

ventral stream   Hierarchically arranged brain areas within the occipital and temporal lobes, thought to be involved in visual object perception. See *temporal pathway;* contrast with *dorsal stream.*

vergence   Referring to eye movements in which the two eyes move in opposite directions. See *conjunctive.*

vernier acuity   Visual ability to perceive slight spatial offsets between neighboring lines, even when those offsets are smaller in angular subtense than the diameter of a single photoreceptor in the eye.

vestibular   The system responsible for the body's sense of balance.

vestibular eye movements   Eye movements that promote the steadiness of gaze by compensating for movements of the head and body.

vestibule   A chamber in the inner ear involved in vestibular eye movements.

view-based recognition   The theory that recognition of object depends upon multiple, stored views of that object.

visual acuity   A measure of the smallest detail that a person can resolve.

visual cues   Sources of depth information based on monocular and binocular image properties.

visual field   The extent of visual space over which vision is possible with the eyes held in a fixed position.

visual masking   The reduction of one target's visibility by the presentation of another target nearby in time and space.

vitreous   The thick transparent fluid that fills the eye's largest chamber.

waterfall illusion   See *motion aftereffect.*

wavelength   The distance from the peak of one wave to the peak of the next. For electromagnetic radiation, such as light, wavelength is determined by the rate at which the emitting substance oscillates. This physical property of light, specified in nanometers, is related to the perceptual experience of hue.

Weber's Law   The principle that for various stimulus intensities the difference threshold tends to be a constant fraction of the stimulus.

window of visibility   The range of spatial frequencies that, with sufficient contrast, an observer can see.

word superiority effect   The finding that, under some conditions, an entire word may be read more rapidly (or be seen more easily) than just one of the word's letters.

Young-Helmholtz theory   The theory that human color vision is trichromatic—that is, it depends on the responses of three types of cones.

REFERENCES

Abadi, R., and **Pascal, E.** (1989) The recognition and management of albinism. Ophthalmic and Physiological Optics, 9, 3–15.

Ackerman, D. (1990) A natural history of the senses. New York: Random House.

Adams, A. J., Wang, L. S., Wong, L., and **Gould, B.** (1988) Visual acuity changes with age: Some new perspectives. American Journal of Optometry and Physiological Optics, 65, 403–406.

Adams, A. J., Zisman, F., Rodic, R., and **Cavender, J.** (1982) Chromaticity and luminosity changes in glaucoma and diabetes. In G. Verriest (ed.), Colour vision deficiencies, VI. Proceedings of the Sixth Symposium of the International Research Group on Colour Vision Deficiencies. The Hague: W. Junk, 413–416.

Addams, R. (1834/1964) An account of a peculiar optical phaenomenon. In W. Dember (ed.), Visual perception: The nineteenth century. New York: John Wiley & Sons, 81–83.

Adelson, E. (1993) Perceptual organization and the judgment of brightness. Science, 262, 2042–2044.

Adelson, E. H., and **Movshon, A. J.** (1982) Phenomenal coherence of moving visual patterns. Nature, 300, 523–525.

Adrian, E. D., and **Zotterman, Y.** (1926) The impulses produced by sensory nerve endings: III. Impulses set up by touch and pressure. Journal of Physiology, 61, 465–483.

Ahissar, E., Bergman, H., and **Vaadia, E.** (1992). Encoding of sound-source location and movement: Activity of single neurons and interactions between adjacent neurons in the monkey auditory cortex. Journal of Neurophysiology, 67, 203–215.

Ahlstrom, R., Berglund, R., Berglund, U., Engen, T., and **Lindvall, T.** (1987) A comparison of odor perception in smokers, nonsmokers, and passive smokers. American Journal of Otolaryngology, 8, 1–6.

Ahlstrom, R., Berglund, R., Berglund, U., Lindvall, T., and **Wennberg, A.** (1986) Impaired odor perception in tank cleaners. Scandinavian Journal of Work and Environmental Health, 12, 574–581.

Ahlstrom, V., Blake, R., and **Ahlstrom, U** (1997) Perception of biological motion. Perception, 26, 1539–48.

Alais, D. and **Blake, R.** (1999) Neural strength of visual attention gauged by motion adaptation. Nature Neuroscience, 2, 1015–1018.

Albano, J. E., Mishkin, M., Westbrook, L. E., and **Wurtz, R. H.** (1982) Visuomotor deficits following ablation of monkey colliclus. Journal of Neurophysiology, 48, 338–351.

Albrecht, D. G., Farrar, S. B., and **Hamilton, D. B.** (1984) Spatial contrast adaptation characteristics of neurones recorded in the cat's visual cortex. Journal of Physiology, 347, 713–739.

Alho, K., Kujala, T., Paavilainen, P., Summala, H., and **Naatanen, R.** (1993) Auditory processing in visual brain areas of the early blind: evidence from event-related potentials. Electroencephalography and Clinical Neurophysiology, 86, 418–427.

Alpern, M. (1981) Color blind color vision. Trends in Neurosciences, 4, 131–135.

Amoore, J. E. (1970) Molecular basis of odor. Springfield, Ill.: Thomas.

Amoore, J. E. (1991) Specific anosmias. In T. V. Getchell, R. L. Doty, L. M. Bartoshuk and J. B. Snow (eds.), Smell and taste in health and disease. New York: Raven Press, 655–664.

Andersen, R. A., and **Bradley, D. C.** (1998) Perception of three-dimensional structure from motion. Trends in Cognitive Science, 2, 222–228.

Anderson, B. L. (1994) The role of partial occlusion in stereopsis. Nature, 367, 365–368.

Andrew, T. J., Halpern, A. D., and **Purves, D.** (1997) Correlated size variations in human visual cortex, lateral geniculate nucleus, and optic tract. Journal of Neuroscience, 17, 2859–2868.

Andrews, D. P., and **Miller, D. T.** (1978) Acuity for spatial separation as a function of stimulus size. Vision Research, 18, 615–620.

Anholt, R. R. H. (1991) Odor recognition and olfactory transduction: The new frontier. Chemical Senses, 16, 421–427.

Anliker, J. A., Bartoshuk, L., Ferris, A. N., and **Hooks, L. D.** (1991) Children's food preferences and genetic sensitivity to the bitter taste of 6-n-propythiouracil (PROP). American Journal of Clinical Nutrition, 54, 316–320.

Annis, R. C., and **Frost, B.** (1973) Human visual ecology and orientation anisotropies in acuity. Science, 182, 729–731.

Anstis, S. (1998) Picturing peripheral acuity. Perception, 27, 817–825.

Anstis, S. M. (1974) A chart demonstrating variations in acuity with retinal position. Vision Research, 14, 589–592.

Anstis, S. M. (1978) Apparent movement. In R. Held, H. W. Leibowitz, and H.-L. Teuber (eds.), Handbook of sensory physiology, vol. 8. Berlin: Springer-Verlag, 655–673.

Anyanwu, E. (1997) Mental imagery of photic stimulation provokes paroxysmal EEG activity in a photosensitive patient who self-induces seizures. Italian Journal of Neurological Science, 18, 93–100.

Appelle, S. (1972) Perception and discrimination as a function of stimulus orientation: The oblique effect in man and animals. Psychological Bulletin, 78, 266–278.

Applegate, W. B., Miller, S. T., Elam, J. T., Freeman, J. M., Wood, T. O., and **Gettlefinger, T. C.** (1987) Impact of cataract surgery with lens implantation on vision and physical function in elderly patients. Journal of the American Medical Association, 257, 1064–1066.

Arezzo, J. C., Schaumburg, H. H., and **Petersen, C. A.** (1983) Rapid screening for peripheral neuropathy: A field study with the Optacon. Neurology, 33, 626–629.

Argentieri, Domenico (n.d.) Essay on Leonardo's Optics. New York: Regnaland Co. P. 436.

Ashmead, D. H., LeRoy, D. and **Odom, R.** (1990) Perception of the relative distances of nearby sound sources. Perception & Psychophysics, 47, 326–331.

Ashmead, D. H., Wall, R. S., Abinger, K. A., Eaton, S. B., Snook-Hill, M., and **Yang, X.** (1998) Spatial hearing in children with visual disabilities. Perception, 27, 105–122.

Aslin, R. N. (1981) Development of smooth pursuit in human infants. In D. F. Fisher, R. A. Monty, and J. W. Senders (eds.), Eye movements: Cognition and visual perception. Hillsdale, N.J.: Erlbaum, 31–51.

Atkinson, J., and **Braddick, O. J.** (1998) Research methods in infant vision. In R. H. S. Carpenter and J. G. Robson (eds.) Vision Research: A practical approach, 161–186.

Axelsson, A., and **Lindgren, F.** (1978) Hearing in pop musicians. Acta Otolaryngology, 85, 225–231.

Axelsson, A., Eliasson, A., and **Israelsson, B.** (1995) Hearing in pop/rock musicians: a follow-up study. Ear and Hearing, 16, 245–53.

Azzopardi, P., and **Cowey, A.** (1993) Preferential representation of the fovea in the primary visual cortex. Nature, 361, 719–721.

Badinand-Hubert, N., Bureau, M., Hirsch, E., Masnou, P., Nahum, L., Parain, D., and **Naquet, R.** (1998) Epilepsies and video games: results of a multicentric study. Electroencephaloghy & Clinical Neurophysiology, 107, 422–427.

Bahill, A. T., and **LaRitz, T.** (1984) Why can't batters keep their eyes on the ball? American Scientist, 72, 249–253.

Baird, J. C. (1982) The moon illusion: II. A reference theory. Journal of Experimental Psychology: General, 111, 304–315.

Baker, C. L., and Braddick, O. J. (1982) Does segregation of differently moving areas depend on relative or absolute displacement? Vision Research, 22, 851–856.

Baker, C. L., Jr., Hess, R. F., and Zihl, J. (1991) Residual motion perception in a "motion-blind" patient, assessed with limited-lifetime random dot stimuli. Journal of Neuroscience, 11, 454–61.

Baldwin, W. R. (1981) A review of statistical studies of relations between myopia and ethnic, behavioral, and physiological characteristics. American Journal of Optometry and Physiological Optics, 58, 516–527.

Ball, K., and Sekuler, R. (1981) Cues reduce direction uncertainty and enhance motion detection. Perception & Psychophysics, 30, 119–128.

Banks, M. S. (1982) The development of spatial and temporal contrast sensitivity. Current Eye Research, 2, 191–198.

Banks, M. S., Aslin, R. N., and Letson, R. D. (1975) Sensitive period for the development of human binocular vision. Science, 190, 675–677.

Banks, M. S., and Bennett, P. J. (1988) Optical and photoreceptor immaturities limit the spatial and chromatic vision of human neonates. Journal of Optical Society of America A, 5, 2059–2079.

Banks, W. P. (1970) Signal detection theory and human memory. Psychological Bulletin, 74, 81–99.

Barac-Cikoja, D., and Turvey, M. T. (1991). Perceiving aperture size by striking. Journal of Experimental Psychology: Human Perception and Performance, 17, 330–346.

Bariniga, M. (1999) The clock plot thickens. Science, 284, 421–422.

Bariniga, M. (1999) Salmon follow watery odors home. Science, 286, 705–706.

Barlow, H. B. (1972) Single units and sensation: A neuron doctrine for perceptual psychology? Perception, 1, 371–395.

Barlow, H. B., Blakemore, C., and Pettigrew, J. D. (1967) The neural mechanism of binocular depth discrimination. Journal of Physiology, 193, 327–342.

Barlow, H. B. (1998) Cerebral predictions. Perception, 27, 885–888.

Barlow, H. B., Fitzhugh, R., and Kuffler, S. W. (1957) Change of organization in the receptive fields of the cat's retina during dark adaptation. Journal of Physiology, 137, 327–337.

Barlow, H. B., and Hill, R. M. (1963) Evidence for a physiological explanation of the waterfall illusion. Nature, 200, 1345–1347.

Barlow, H. B., and Sparrock, J. M. B. (1964) The role of afterimages in dark adaptation. Science, 144, 1309–1314.

Barnes, C. S., Wei J. P., and Shevell S. K. (1999) chromatic induction with remote chromatic contrast varied in magnitude, spatial frequency, and chromaticity. Vision Research, 39, 3561–3574.

Barrett, B. T., Whitaker, D., McGraw, P. V., and Herbert, A. M. (1999) Discriminating mirror symmetry in foveal and extra-foveal vision. Vision Research, 39, 3737–3744.

Barsky, A. J., Goodson, J. D., Lane, R. S., and Cleary, P. D. (1988) The amplification of somatic symptoms. Psychosomatic Medicine, 50, 510–519.

Bartoshuk, L. M. (1974) Taste illusions: Some demonstrations. Annals of the New York Academy of Sciences, 237, 279–285.

Bartoshuk, L. M. (1975) Taste mixtures: Is mixture suppression related to compression? Physiology & Behavior, 14, 643–649.

Bartoshuk, L. M. (1978) History of taste research. In E. C. Carterette and M. P. Friedman (eds.), Handbook of perception, vol. 6A. New York: Academic Press, 3–18.

Bartoshuk, L. M. (1980) Separate worlds of taste. Psychology Today, 14, 48–63.

Bartoshuk, L. M., Dateo, G.tnP., Vandenbelt, D. J., Buttrick, R. L., and Long, L. (1969) Effects of Gymnema sylvestra and Synsepalum dulcificum on taste in man. In C. Pfaffmann (ed.), Olfaction and taste, vol. 3. New York: Rockefeller University Press, 436–444.

Batteau, D. W. (1967) The role of the pinna in human localization. Proceedings of the Royal Society of London (Series B), 168, 158–180.

Bauer, R. M. (1984) Autonomic recognition of names and faces in prosopagnosia: a neuropsychological application of the Guilty Knowledge Test. Neuropsychologia, 22, 457–469.

Beattie, G. W., Cutler, A., and Pearson, M. (1982) Why is Mrs. Thatcher interrupted so often? Nature, 300, 744–747.

Bechtel, W., and Abrahamsen, A. (1991) Connectionism and the mind, an introduction to parallel processing in networks. Cambridge: Basil Blackwell.

Beck, J., Prazdny, K., and Rosenfeld, A. (1983) A theory of textural segmentation. In J. Beck, B. Hope, and A. Rosenfeld (eds.), Human and machine vision. New York: Academic Press, 1–38.

Beckers, G., and Zeki, S. (1995) The consequences of inactivating areas V1 and V5 on visual motion perception. Brain, 118, 49–60.

Bedichek, R. (1960) The sense of smell. Garden City, N.Y.: Doubleday.

Behrmann, M., Nelson, J., and Sekuler, E. B. (1999) Visual complexity in letter-by-letter reading: "pure" alexia is not pure. Neuropsychologia, 36, 1115–1132.

Beidler, L. M. (1978). Biophysics and chemistry of taste. In E. C. Carterette and M. P. Friedman (eds.), Handbook of perception, vol. 6A. New York: Academic Press, 21–49.

Beidler, L. M., and Smallman, R. L. (1965) Renewal of cells within taste buds. Journal of Cell Biology, 27, 263–272.

Bekesy, G. von (1960) Experiments in hearing. New York: McGraw-Hill.

Bekesy, G. von, and Rosenblith, W. A. (1951) The mechanical properties of the ear. In S. S. Stevens (ed.), Handbook of experimental psychology. New York: John Wiley & Sons, 1075–1115.

Belendiuk, K., and Butler, R. A. (1978) Directional hearing under progressive impoverishment of binaural cues. Sensory Processes, 2, 58–70.

Benedetti, F. (1985) Processing of tactile spatial information with crossed fingers. Journal of Experimental Psychology: Human Perception and Performance, 11, 517–525.

Benedetti, F. (1986) Tactile diplopia (diplesthesia) on the human fingers. Perception, 15, 83–91.

Benedetti, F. (1991) Reorganization of tactile perception following the simulated amputation of one finger. Perception, 20, 687–692.

Bennett, P. J., Sekuler, A. B., and Ozin, L. (1999) Effects of aging on calculation efficiency and equivalent noise. Journal of the Optical Society of America A, 16, 654–668.

Benton, A. L. (1980) The neuropsychology of facial recognition. American Psychologist, 35, 176–186.

Berger, A., Henderson, M., and Nadoolman, W. (1995) Oral capsaicin provides temporary relief from oral mucositis pain secondary to chemotherapy/radiation therapy. Journal of Pain and Pain Management, 10, 243–248.

Berglund, B., Berglund, U., Engen, T., and Lindvall, T. (1971) The effect of adaptation on odor detection. Perception & Psychophysics, 9, 435–438.

Bergman, M. (1966) Hearing in the Mabaans. Archives of Otolaryngology, 81, 75–79.

Berkeley, G. (1709/1950) A new theory of vision. London: Dent.

Berkley, M. A., and Watkins, D. W. (1971) Visual acuity of the cat estimated from evoked cerebral potentials. Nature, 234, 91–92.

Berlin, B., and Kay P. (1969) Basic color terms: Their universality and evolution. Berkeley: University of California Press.

Bertenthal, B. I. (1996) Origins and early development of perception, action, and representation. Annual Review of Psychology, 47, 431–59.

Bertino, M., and Chan, M. M. (1986) Taste perception and diet in individuals with Chinese and European ethnic backgrounds. Chemical Senses, 11, 229–241.

Bexton, W. H., Heron, W., and Scott, T. H. (1954) Effects of decreased variation in the sensory environment. Canadian Journal of Psychology, 8, 70–76.

Biederman, I. (1987) Recognition-by-components: A theory of human image understanding. Psychological Review, 94, 115–147.

Biederman, I. (1990) Higher-level vision. In D. N. Osherson, S. Kosslyn, and J. Hollerbach (eds.), An invitation to cognitive science: Visual cognition and action. Cambridge: M. I. T. Press, 41–72.

Birren, F. (1941) The story of color: From ancient mysticism to modern science. Westport, Conn.: Crimson Press.

Blackwell, H. R. (1946) Contrast thresholds of the human eye. Journal of the Optical Society of America, 36, 624–643.

Blake, R. (1988a) Cat spatial vision. Trends in Neurosciences, 11, 78–83.

Blake, R. (1988b) Dichoptic reading: the role of meaning in binocular rivalry. Perception & Psychophysics, 44, 133–141.

Blake, R. (1993) Cats perceive biological motion. Psychological Science, 4 54–57.

Blake, R. (1997) What can be perceived in the absence of visual awareness? Current Directions in Psychological Science, 6, 157–162.

Blake, R. (1998) The behavioural analysis of animal vision. In J. G. Robson, and R. H. S. Carpenter (eds.) Vision Research: A practical approach. Oxford: Oxford University Press, 137–160.

Blake, R., and Fox, R. (1972) Interocular transfer of adaptation to spatial frequency during retinal ischaemia. Nature, 240, 76–77.

Blake, R., and Hirsch, H. V. B. (1975) Deficits in binocular depth perception in cats after alternating monocular deprivation. Science, 190, 1114–1116.

Blake, R., Westendorf, D. H., and Overton, R. (1980) What is suppressed during binocular rivalry? Perception, 9, 223–232.

Blake, R., and Wilson, H. R. (1991) Neural models of stereoscopic vision. Trends in Neurosciences, 14, 445–452.

Blakemore, C. (1976) The conditions required for the maintenance of binocularity in the kitten's visual cortex. Journal of Physiology, 261, 423–444.

Blakemore, C., and Campbell, F. W. (1969) On the existence of neurones in the human visual system selectively senstive to the orientation and size of retinal images. Journal of Physiology, 203, 237–260.

Blakemore, C., Muncey, J. P. J., and Ridley, R. M. (1973) Stimulus specificity in the human visual system. Vision Research, 13, 1915–1931.

Blakemore, C., Nachmias, J., and Sutton, P. (1970) The perceived spatial frequency shift: Evidence for frequency selective neurones in the human brain. Journal of Physiology, 210, 727–750.

Blanz, V., Tarr, M. J., Bülthoff, H. H. (1999) What object attributes determine canonical views? Perception, 28, 575–600.

Blignaut, C. J. H. (1979) The perception of hazard: II. The contribution of signal detection to hazard perception. Ergonomics, 22, 1177–1183.

Bliven, B., Jr. (1976) Annals of architecture: A better sound. New Yorker, 52, 51–135.

Bloom, H. S., Criswell, E. L., Pennypacker, H. S., Catania, A. C., and Adams, C. K. (1982) Major stimulus dimensions determining detection of simulated breast lesions. Perception & Psychophysics, 32, 251–260.

Bobrow, N. A., Money, J., and Lewis, V. G. (1971) Delayed puberty, eroticism, and sense of smell: A psychological study of hypogonadotropism, osmatic and anosmatic (Kallmann's syndrome). Archives of Sexual Behavior, 1, 329–344.

Bock, O. (1993) Localization of objects in the peripheral visual field. Behavioural Brain Research, 56, 77–84.

Bodis-Wollner, I. (1972) Visual acuity and contrast sensitivity in patients with cerebral lesions. Science, 178, 769–771.

Boll, F. (1877/1977) On the anatomy and physiology of the retina. Vision Research, 17, 1253–1267.

Bonnano, G. A., and Stilling, N. A. (1986) Preference, familiarity, and recognition after repeated brief exposures to random geometric shapes. American Journal of Psychology, 99, 403–415.

Boorstin, D. J. (1985) The discoverers. New York: Vintage Books.

Booth J. R., Epelboim J., and Steinman, R. M. (1996) The relative importance of spaces and meaning in reading. Presented at the meeting of the Cognitive Science Society.

Borg, E., and Counter, S. A. (1989) The middle-ear muscles. Scientific American, 261, 74–80.

Boring, E. G. (1930) A new ambiguous figure. American Journal of Psychology, 42, 444.

Boring, E. G. (1942) Sensation and perception in the history of experimental psychology. New York: Appleton-Century-Crofts.

Boring, E. G. (1961) Fechner: Inadvertent founder of psychophysics. Psychometrika, 26, 3–8.

Bornstein, M. H., Kessen, W., and Weiskopf, S. (1976) The categories of hue in infancy. Science, 191, 201–202.

Bough, E. W. (1970) Stereoscopic vision in macaque monkey: A behavioural demonstration. Nature, 225, 42–44.

Boycott, B. B., and Wässle, H. (1999) Parallel processing in the mammalian retina. Investigative Ophthalmology & Visual Science, 40, 1313–1327.

Boynton, R. M. (1982) Spatial and temporal approaches for studying color vision: A review. In G. Verriest (ed.), Colour vision deficiencies, VI. Proceedings of the Sixth Symposium of the International Research Group on Colour Vision Deficiencies. The Hague: W. Junk, 1–14.

Boynton, R. M., and Gordon, J. (1965) Bezold-Brücke hue shift measured by color naming technique. Journal of the Optical Society of America, 55, 78–86.

Boynton, R. M., and Olson, C. X. (1987) Locating basic colors in the OSA space. Color Research and Applications, 12, 94–105.

Bracewell, R. N. (1989) The Fourier transform. Scientific American, 260, 86–95.

Braddick, O. (1993) Segmentation versus integration in visual motion processing. Trends in Neuroscience, 16, 263–268.

Bradley, R. M. (1979) Effects of aging on the sense of taste: Anatomical considerations. In S. S. Han and D. H. Coons (eds.), Special senses in aging: A current biological assessment. Ann Arbor, Mich.: Institute of Gerontology, University of Michigan, 3–8.

Bradley, R. M. (1991) Salivary secretion. In T V. Getchell, R. L. Doty, L. M. Bartoshuk and J. B.

Snow (eds.), Smell and taste in health and disease. New York: Raven Press, 127–144.

Brammer, A. J., and **Verillo, R. T.** (1988) Tactile changes in hands occupationally exposed to vibration. Journal of the Acoustical Society of America, 84, 1940–1941.

Braunstein, M. L., and **Payne, J. W.** (1969) Perspective and form ratio as determinants of relative slant judgments. Journal of Experimental Psychology, 81, 584–590.

Braunstein, M. L. and **Stern, K. R.** (1980) Static and dynamic factors in the perception of rotary motion. Perception & Psychophysics, 27, 313–320.

Bravo, M., and **Blake R.** (1990) Preattentive vision and perceptual groups. Perception, 19, 515–522.

Bravo, M., Blake, R., and **Morrison, S.** (1988) Cats see subjective contours. Vision Research, 28, 861–865.

Brawn, P., and **Snowden, R. J.** (1999) Can one pay attention to a particular color? Perception & Psychophysics, 61, 860–873.

Bregman, A. S. (1990) Auditory scene analysis. Cambridge: M.I.T. Press.

Bregman, A. S., and **Mills, M. I.** (1982) Perceived movement: The Flintstone constraint. Perception, 11, 201–206.

Bregman, A. S., and **Pinker, S.** (1978) Auditory streaming and the building of timbre. Canadian Journal of Psychology, 31, 151–159.

Breitmeyer, B. G. (1975) Simple reaction time as a measure of the temporal response properties of transient and sustained channels. Vision Research, 15, 1411–1412.

Breitmeyer, B. G. (1984). Visual Masking. Oxford, England: Oxford University Press.

Brindley, G. S. (1970) Physiology of the retina and visual pathway. Baltimore: Williams & Wilkins.

Brindley, G. S., and **Lewin, W. S.** (1968) The sensations produced by electrical stimulation of the visual cortex. Journal of Physiology, 196, 479–493.

Broadbent, D. E. (1977) The hidden preattentive process. American Psychologist, 32, 109–118.

Bronkhorst, A. W., and **Houtgast, T.** (1999) Auditory distance perception in rooms. Nature, 397, 517–520.

Brouwer, J. N., Glaser, D., Segerstad, C. H. A., Hellekant, G., Ninomiya, Y., and **van der Wel, H.** (1983) The sweetness-inducing effect of miraculin: Behavioral and neurophysiological experiments in the rhesus monkey, Macaca mulatta. Journal of Physiology, 337, 221–240.

Brown, J. F. (1931) The visual perception of velocity. Psychologische Forschung, 14, 199–232.

Brown, J. L., and **Mueller, C. G.** (1965) Brightness discrimination and brightness contrast. In C. H. Graham (ed.), Vision and visual perception. New York: John Wiley & Sons, 208–250.

Brown, J. M., and **Weisstein, N.** (1988) A spatial frequency effect on perceived depth. Perception & Psychophysics, 44, 157–166.

Bruce, V. (1994) Stability from variation: the case of face recognition. Quarterly Journal of Experimental Psychology, 47A, 5–28.

Bruce, V., Burton, A. M., Hanna, E., Healey, P., Mason, O., Coombes, A., Fright, R., and **Linney, A.** (1993) Sex discrimination: how do we tell the difference between male and female faces? Perception, 22, 131–152.

Bruner, J. S., and **Potter, M. C.** (1964) Interference in visual recognition. Science, 144, 424–425.

Bruno, N. and **Cutting, J. E.** (1988) Minimodularity and the perception of layout. Journal of Experimental Psychology: General, 117, 161–170.

Buchsbaum, G., and **Gottschalk, A.** (1983) Trichromacy, opponent colours coding, and the optimum colour information in the retina. Proceedings of the Royal Society of London, Series B, 220, 89–113.

Buck, L. B. (1992) The olfactory multigene family. Current Opinion in Neurobiology, 2, 282–288.

Buck, L. B. (1996) Information coding in the vertebrate olfactory system. Annual Review of Neuroscience, 19, 517–544.

Buonomano, D. V., and **Merzenich, M. M.** (1998) Cortical plasticity: from synapses to maps. Annual Review of Neuroscience, 21, 149–186.

Burger, J. F. (1958) Front-back discrimination of the hearing system. Acustica, 8, 302–310.

Burke, W., and **Cole, A. M.** (1978) Extra-retinal influences on the lateral geniculate nucleus. Review of Physiology, Biochemistry, and Pharmacology, 80, 105-166.

Burr, D. C., and **Ross, J.** (1982) Contrast sensitivity at high velocities. Vision Research, 22, 479–484.

Bushnell, M. C., Goldberg, M. E. and **Robinson, D. L.** (1981) Behavioral enhancement of visual responses in monkey cerebral cortex. I. Modulation in posterior parietal cortex related to selective visual attention. Journal of Neurophysiology, 46, 755–772.

Butler, R. A. (1986) The bandwidth effect on monaural and binaural localization. Hearing Research, 21, 67–73.

Butler, R. A., Humanski, R. A. and **Musicant, A. D.** (1990) Binaural and monaural localization of sound in two-dimensional space. Perception, 19, 241–256.

Butterworth, G., and **Castillo, M.** (1976) Coordination of auditory and visual space in newborn infants. Perception, 5, 155–160.

Cabe, P. A., and **Pittenger, J. B.** (2000) Human sensitivity to acoustic information from vessel filling. Journal of Experimental Psychology: Human Perception & Performance, 26, 313–324.

Cain, W. S. (1973) Spatial discrimination of cutaneous warmth. American Journal of Psychology, 86, 169–181.

Cain, W. S. (1977) Differential sensitivity for smell: Noise at the nose. Science, 195, 796–798.

Cain, W. S. (1978) The odoriferous environment and the appliaiton of olfactory research. In E. C. Carterette and M. P. Friedman (eds.). Handbook of perception, vol. 7. New York: Academic Press, 277–304.

Cain, W. S. (1982) Odor identification by males and females: Predictions versus performance. Chemical Senses, 7, 129–142.

Cain, W. S., Cometto-Muñiz, J. E., and **de Wijk, R. A.** (1992) Techniques in the quantitative study of human olfaction. In **M. J. Serby** and **K. L. Chobor** (eds..) Science of Olfaction. New York: Springer-Verlag, 279–308.

Cain, W. S., and **Engen, T.** (1969) Olfactory adaptation and the scaling of odor intensity. In C. Pfaffmann (ed.), Olfaction and taste, vol. 3. New York: Rockefeller University Press, 127–157.

Cain, W. S. and **Gent, J. F.** (1991) Olfactory sensitivity: Reliability, generality, and association with aging. Journal of Experimental Psychology: Human Perception and Performance, 17, 382–391.

Cain, W. S., and **Murphy, C. L.** (1980) Interaction between chemoreceptive modalities of odour irritation. Nature, 284, 255–257.

Cain, W. S., and **Turk, A.** (1985) Smell of danger: An analysis of LP-gas odorization. American Industrial Hygiene Association Journal, 46, 115–126.

Calis, G., and **Leeuwenberg, E.** (1981) Grounding the figure. Journal of Experimental Psychology: Human Perception and Performance, 7, 1386–1397.

Calvert, G. A., Bullmore, E. T., Branner, M. J., Campbell, R., Williams, S. C. R., McGuire, P. K., Woodruff, P. W. R., Iversen, S. D., and

David, A. S. (1997) Activation of auditory cortex during silent lipreading. Science, 276, 593–596.

Campbell, D. T. (1974) Evolutionary epistemology. In P. A. Schlipp (ed.), The philosophy of Karl Popper. LaSalle, Ill.: Open Court, 413–463.

Campbell, F. W. and **Kulikowski, J. J.** (1972) The visual evoked potential as a function of contrast of a grating pattern. Journal of Physiology, 222, 345–356.

Campbell, F. W., and **Robson, J. G.** (1968) Application of Fourier analysis to the visibility of gratings. Journal of Physiology, 197, 551–566.

Campbell, R., Zihl, J., Massaro, D., Munhall, K., and **Cohen, M. M.** (1997) Speech reading in the akinetopsic patient, L. M. Brain, 120, 1793–1803.

Carey, S., and **Diamond, R.** (1977) From piecemeal to configurational representation of faces. Science, 195, 312–314.

Carlson, M., and **Burton, H.** (1988) Recovery of tactile function after damage to primary or secondary somatic sensory cortex in infant Macaca mulatta. Journal of Neuroscience, 8, 833–859.

Carlsson, K., Petrovic P., Skare, S., Petersson, K. M., and **Ingvar, M.** (2000) Tickling expectations: neural processing in anticipation of a sensory stimulus. Journal of Cognitive Neuroscience 12, 691–703.

Carlsson, L., Knave, B., Lennerstrand, G., and **Wibom, R.** (1984) Glare from outdoor high mast lighting: Effects on visual acuity and contrast sensitivity in comparative studies of different floodlighting systems. Acta Ophthalmologica, 62, 84–93.

Carmody, D. P., Kundel, H. L., and **Toto, L. C.** (1984) Comparison scans while reading chest images: Taught, but not practiced. Investigative Radiology, 19, 462–466.

Carmody, D. P., Nodine, C. F., and **Kundel, H. L.** (1980) An analysis of perceptual and cognitive factors in radiographic interpretation. Perception, 9, 339–344.

Carpenter, P. A., and **Daneman, M.** (1981) Lexical access and error recovery in reading: A model based on eye fixations. Journal of Verbal Learning and Verbal Behavior, 20, 137–160.

Carpenter, R. H. S. (1992). Turning vision into action. Current Biology, 2, 288–290.

Carr, C. E., and **Konishi, M.** (1988) Axonal delay lines for time measurement in the owl's brainstem. Proceedings of the National Academy of Sciences, 85, 8311–8315.

Carrasco, M., Penpeci-Talgar, C., and **Eckstein, M.** (2000). Spatial attention increases contrast sensitivity across the CSF: Support for signal enhancement. Vision Research, 40, 1203–1216.

Carter, J. H. (1982) The effects of aging upon selected visual functions: Color vision, field of vision, and accommodation. In R. Sekuler, D. Kline, and K. Dismukes (eds.), Aging and human visual function. New York: Liss, 120–130.

Casagrande, V. A. (1994) A third parallel visual pathway to primate area V1. Trends in Neurosciences, 17, 305–310.

Catania, K. (2000) A star is born. Natural History, 109, 66–69.

Caterina, M. J., Leffler, A., Malmberg, A. B., Martin, W. J., Trafton, J., Petersen-Zeitz, K. R., Koltzenburg, M., Basbaum, A. I., and **Julius, D.** (2000) Impaired nociception and pain sensation in mice lacking the capsaicin receptor. Science, 220, 306–313.

Cattell, J. M. (1886) The inertia of the eye and brain. Brain, 8, 295–312.

Cave, C. (1997) Very long-lasting priming in picture naming. Psychological Science, 8, 322–325.

Chambers, D., and **Reisberg, D.** (1992) What an image depicts depends on what an image means. Cognitive Psychology, 24, 145–174.

Chance, F. S., Nelson, S. B., and **Abbott, L. F.** (1999) Complex cells as cortically amplified simple cells. Nature Neuroscience, 2, 277–282.

Chapman, C. R., Chen, A. C., and **Bonica, J. J.** (1977) Effects of intrasegmental electrical acupuncture on dental pain: Evaluation by threshold estimation and sensory decision theory. Pain, 3, 213–227.

Chaudhari, N., Landin, A. M., and **Roper, S. D.** (2000) A metabotropic glutamate receptor variant functions as a taste receptor. Nature Neuroscience, 3, 113–119.

Chevreul, M. (1839/1967) The principles of harmony and contrast of colors. F. Birren (ed.). New York: Reinhold.

Christensen, D. (1999) What's that smell? Science News, 155, 316.

Chu, S., and **Downes, J. J.** (2000) Odour-evoked autobiographical memories: psychological investigations of Proustian phenomena. Chemical Senses, 25, 111–6.

Chubb, C., and **Sperling, G.** (1988) Drift-balanced random stimuli: A general basis for studying non-Fourier motion perception. Journal of the Optical Society of America A 5, 1986–2007.

Chun, M. (2000) Contextual cueing of visual attention. Trends in Cognitive Sciences, 4, 170–178.

Chun, M. and **Nakayama, K.** (2000) On the functional role of implicit visual memory for the adaptive deployment of attention across scenes. Visual Cognition, 7, 65–81.

Churchland, P. M. (1988) Matter and consciousness: A contemporary introduction to the philosophy of mind (revised edition). Cambridge: M.I.T. Press.

Clark, W. C., and **Yang, J. C.** (1974) Acupunctural analgesia? Evaluation by signal detection theory. Science, 184, 1096–1098.

Claus, R., Hoppen, H. O., and **Karg, H.** (1981) The secret of truffles: A steroidal pheromone? Experientia, 37, 1178–1179.

Cohen, J. (1969) Sensation and perception: II. Audition and the minor senses. Chicago: Rand McNally.

Cohen, L. (1959) Perception of reversible figures after brain injury. Archives of Neurology and Psychiatry, 81, 765–775.

Cohen, L. G., Celnik, P., Pascual-Leone, A, Corwell, B., Faiz, L., Dambrosla, J., Honda, M., Sadato, N., Gerloff, C., Catala, M. D. and **Hallett, M.** (1997) Functional relevance of cross-modal plasticity in blind humans. Nature, 389, 180–183.

Colby, C. L. and **Goldberg, M. E.** (1999) Space and attention in parietal cortex. Annual Review of Neuroscience, 22, 319–349.

Cole, J. D. (1995) Pride and a Daily Marathon. Cambridge MA: MIT Press.

Coles, R. R. A., and **Hallam, R. S.** (1987) Tinnitus and its management. British Medical Bulletin, 43, 983–998.

Collett, T. S., Schwarz, U. and **Sobel, E. C.** (1992) The interaction of oculomotor cues and stimulus size in stereoscopic depth constancy. Perception, 20, 733–754.

Collewijn, H., Martins, A. J., and **Steinman, R. M.** (1983) Compensatory eye movements during active and passive head movements: Fast adaptation to changes in visual magnification. Journal of Physiology, 340, 259–286.

Collings, V. B. (1974) Human taste response as a function of locus on the tongue and soft palate. Perception & Psychophysics, 16, 169–174.

Collins, B. L., and **Worthey, J. A.** (1984) The role of color in lighting for meat and poultry inspection.

U.S. Department of Commerce, National Bureau of Standards Report No. 84-2829. Washington, D.C.

Cometto-Muñiz, J. E., and **Cain, W. S.** (1982) Perception of nasal pungency in smokers and nonsmokers. Physiology & Behavior, 29, 727–731.

Cometto-Muñiz, J. E., and **Cain, W. S.** (1984) Temporal integration of pungency. Chemical Senses, 8, 315–327.

Cometto-Muñiz, J. E., and **Cain, W. S.** (1996) Physicochemical determinants and functional properties of the senses of irritation and smell. In R. B. Gammage and B. A. Berven (eds.) Indoor Air and Human Health (second edition). Boca Raton, FL: CRC Press, 53–65.

Cometto-Muñiz, J. E., Cain, W. S., and **Hudnell, H. K.** (1997) Agonistic sensory effects of airborne chemicals in mixtures: Odor, nasal pungency, and eye irritation. Perception & Psychophysics, 59, 665–674.

Corbetta, M., Miezin, R. M., Dobmeyer, S., Shulman, G. L. and **Petersen, S. E.** (1991) Selective and divided attention during visual discriminations of shape, color, and speed: Functional anatomy by positron emission tomography. Journal of Neuroscience, 11, 2382–2402.

Corbin, A. (1986) The foul and the fragrant: Odor and the French social imagination. Cambridge: Harvard University Press.

Corcoran, D. W. J., and **Rouse, R. O.** (1970) An aspect of perceptual organization involved in reading typed and handwritten words. Quarterly Journal of Experimental Psychology, 22, 526–530.

Corina, D. P., Vaid, J., and **Bellugi, U.** (1992) The linguistic basis of left hemisphere specialization. Science, 255, 1258–1260.

Cornsweet, T. N. (1962) The staircase-method in psychophysics. American Journal of Psychology, 75, 485–491.

Cornsweet, T. N. (1970) Visual perception. New York: Academic Press.

Corso, J. F. (1981) Aging sensory systems and perception. New York: Praeger.

Cowart, B. J. (1981) Development of taste perception in humans: Sensitivity and preference throughout the life span. Psychological Bulletin, 90, 43–73.

Cowey, A., and **Heywood, C. A.** (1995) There's more to colour than meets the eye. Behavioural Brain Research, 71, 89–100.

Cowey, A., and **Heywood, C. A.** (1997) Cerebral achromatopsia: colour blindness despite wavelength processing. Trends in Cognitive Science, 1, 133–139.

Craig, J. C. (1985) Attending to two fingers: Two hands are better than one. Perception & Psychophysics, 38, 496–511.

Craig, J. C., and **Johnson, K. O.** (2000) The two-point threshold: Not a measure of tactile spatial resolution. Current Directions in Psychological Science, 9, 29–32.

Craig, A. D., Bushnell, M. C., Zhang E. T., and **Blomqvist, A.** (1994) A thalamic nucleus specific for pain and temperature sensation. Nature, 372, 770–773.

Craig, J. C., Reiman, E. M., Evans, A., and **Bushnell, M. C.** (1996) Functional imaging of an illusion of pain. Nature, 384, 258–260.

Craig, J. C., and **Rollman, G. B.** (1999) Somesthesis. Annual Review of Psychology, 50, 305–331.

Craver-Lemley, C., and **Reeves, A.** (1992) How visual imagery interferes with vision. Psychological Review, 99, 633–649.

Crawford, M. L. J., and **Marc, R. E.** (1976) Light transmission of cat and monkey eyelids. Vision Research, 16, 323–324.

Critchley, M. (1979) The divine banquet of the brain. New York: Raven Press.

Crocker, E. C., and **Henderson, L. F.** (1927) Analysis and classification of odors. American Perfumer and Essential Oil Review, 22, 325–327.

Croner, L. J., and **Albright T. D.** (1997) Image segmentation enhances discrimination of motion in visual noise. Vision Research, 37, 1415–1427.

Crowe, S. J., Guild, S. R., and **Polvost, L. M.** (1934) Observations on the pathology of high-tone deafness. Bulletin of the Johns Hopkins Hospital, 54, 315–379.

Culham, J. C., Brandt, S. A., Cavanagh, P., Kanwisher, N. G., Dale, A. M., and **Tootell, R. B.** (1998) Cortical fMRI activation produced by attentive tracking of moving targets. Journal of Neurophysiology, 80, 2657–2670.

Culham, J. C., Dukelow, S. P., Vilis, T., Hassard, F. A., Gati, J. S., Menon, R. S., Goodale, M. A. (1999) Recovery of fMRI activation in motion area MT following storage of the motion aftereffect. Journal of Neurophysiology, 81, 388–93.

Curcio, C. A., and **Hendrickson, A. E.** (1991) Organization and development of the primate photoreceptor mosaic. In: N. Osborne and J. Chadere (eds.). Progress in Retinal Research. Oxford: Pergamon, 89–120.

Currier, R. D. (1994) A two-and-a-half color rainbow. Archives of Neurology, 51, 1090–1092.

Cutting, J. E. (1997) How the eye measures reality and virtual reality. Behavior Research Methods, Instruments, & Computers, 29, 27–36.

Cutting, J. E., and **Proffitt, D. R.** (1981) Gait perception as an example of how we may perceive events. In R. Walk and H. L. Pick (eds.), Intersensory perception and sensory integration. New York: Plenum Press, 249–273.

D'Zmura, M. (1996). Bergmann on visual resolution. Perception, 25, 1223–1234.

Dabak, A. G. and **Johnson, D. H.** (1992) Function-based modeling of binaural processing: Interaural phase. Hearing Research, 58, 200–212.

Dakin, S. C., and **Herbert, A. M.** (1998) The spatial region of integration for visual symmetry detection, Proceedings of the Royal society of London-Biological Sciences, 265, 659–664.

Dallos, P. (1981) Cochlear physiology. Annual Review of Psychology, 32, 153–190.

Dallos, P. (1992) The active cochlea. Journal of Neuroscience, 12, 4575–4585.

Dallos, P., and **Cheatham, M. A.** (1976) Production of cochlear potentials by inner and outer hair cells. Journal of the Acoustical Society of America, 60, 510–512.

Dalton, P., Doolittle, N., Nagata, H., and **Breslin, P. A. S.** (2000) The merging of the senses: Integration of subthreshold taste and smell. Nature Neuroscience, 3, 431–432.

Dalton, J. (1798/1948) Extraordinary facts relating to the vision of colour: With observations. In W. Dennis (ed.), Readings in the history of psychology. New York: Appleton-Century-Crofts, 102–111.

Damasio, A. R. (1985) Prosopagnosia. Trends in Neurosciences, 8, 132–135.

Damasio, A. R. (1989) Time-locked multiregional retroactivation: A systems-level proposal for the neural substrates of recall and recognition. Cognition, 33, 25–62.

Damasio, A. R., and **Benton, A. L.** (1979) Impairment of hand movements under visual guidance. Neurology, 29, 170–178.

Damasio, A. R., Damasio, H., and **van Hoesen, G. W.** (1982) Prosopagnosia: Anatomic basis and behavioral mechanisms. Neurology, 32, 331–341.

Damasio, A. R., Tranel, D., and **Damasio, H.** (1990) Face agnosia and the neural substrates of memory. Annual Review of Neuroscience, 13, 89–109.

Dannenbaum, R. M., and **Dykes, R. W.** (1988) Sensory loss in the hand after sensory stroke: Therapeutic rationale. Archives of Physical Medicine and Rehabilitation, 69, 833–839.

Dannenbring, G. L. (1976) Perceived auditory continuity with alternately rising and falling frequency transitions. Canadian Journal of Psychology, 30, 99–114.

Darian-Smith, I. (1984) The sense of touch: Performance and peripheral neural processes. In I. Darian-Smith (ed.) Handbook of physiology: vol. 3, part 2. Bethesda, MD: American Physiological Society, 739–788.

Darian-Smith, I., Goodwin, A., Sugitani, M., and **Heywood, J.** (1984) The tangible features of textured surfaces: Their representation in the monkey's somatosensory cortex. In G. Edelman, W. E. Gall, and M. W. Cowan (eds.), Dynamic aspects of neocortical function. New York: John Wiley & Sons, 475–500.

Dartnall, H. J. A., Bowmaker, J. K., and **Mollon, J. D.** (1983) Human visual pigments: Microspectrophotometric results from the eyes of seven persons. Proceedings of the Royal Society of London, Series B, 220, 115–130.

Das, A., and Gilbert, C. D. (1999) Topography of contextual modulations mediated by short-range interactions in primary visual cortex. Nature, 399, 655–661.

Daum, K. M. (1983) Accommodative dysfunction. Documenta Ophthalmologica, 55, 177–198.

Davidoff, J. B. (1975) Differences in visual perception: The individual eye. New York: Academic Press.

Davidoff, J., Davies, I., and **Roberson, D.** (1999) Colour categories in a stone-age tribe. Nature, 398, 203–204.

Davis, H., Deatherage, B. H., Rosenblut, B., Fernandez, C., Kimura, R., and **Smith, C. A.** (1958) Modification of cochlear potentials produced by streptomycin poisoning and by extensive venous obstructions. Laryngoscope, 68, 596–627.

Davis, H., and **Silverman, S. R.** (1960) Hearing and deafness. New York: Holt, Rinehart & Winston.

Davis, L. B., and **Porter, R. H.** (1991) Persistent effects of early odor exposure on human neonates. Chemical Senses, 16, 169–174.

Davis, R. G. (1977) Acquisition of verbal associations to olfactory and abstract visual stimuli of varying similarity. Journal of Experimental Psychology: Human Learning and Memory, 3, 37–51.

Davis, R. G. (1981) The role of nonolfactory context cues in odor identification. Perception & Psychophysics, 30, 83–89.

Dawkins, R. (1996) The blind watchmaker. New York: WW Norton.

de Boer, I. (1956) Pitch of inharmonic signals. Nature, 178, 535–536.

de Gelder, B., Teunisse, J. P., and Benson, P. J. (1997) Categorical perception of facial expressions: categories and their internal structure. Cognition and Emotion, 11, 1–23.

De Graaf, C., and Zandstra, E. H. (1999) Sweetness intensity and pleasantness in children, adolescents, and adults. Physiology & Behavior, 67, 513–520.

de Monasterio, F. M., and Gouras, P. (1975) Functional properties of ganglion cells of the rhesus monkey retina. Journal of Physiology, 251, 167–195.

De Wijk, R. A., and Cain, W. S. (1994) Odor identification by name by edibility: Life-span development and safety. Human Factors, 36, 182–187.

DeAngelis, G.C. (2000) Seeing in three dimensions: the neurophysiology of stereopsis. Trends in Cognitive Sciences, 4, 80–90.

DeCasper, A. J., and Fifer, W. P. (1980) Of human bonding: Newborns prefer their mothers' voices. Science, 208, 174–176.

Dennett, D. C. (1991) Consciousness explained. Boston: Little, Brown.

Denton, G. G. (1980) The influence of visual pattern on perceived speed. Perception, 9, 393–402.

Derby, C. D., Ache, B. W., and Kennel, E. W. (1985) Mixture suppression: Electrophysiological evaluation of the contribution of peripheral and central neural components. Chemical Senses, 10, 301–316.

Derrington, A. M., Krauskopf, J., and Lennie, P. (1984) Chromatic mechanisms in lateral geniculate nucleus of macaque. Journal of Physiology, 357, 241–265.

Desimone, R. (1991). Face-selective cells in the temporal cortex of monkeys. Journal of Cognitive Neuroscience, 3, 1–8.

Desor, J. A., and Beauchamp, G. K. (1974) The human capacity to transmit olfactory information. Perception & Psychophysics, 16, 551–556.

Detwiler, P. B., Hodgkin, A. L., and McNaughton, P. A. (1980) Temporal and spatial characteristics of the voltage response of rods in the retina of the turtle. Journal of Physiology, 300, 213–250.

DeValois, R. L., and DeValois, K. K. (1975) Neural coding of color. In E. C. Carterette and M. P. Friedman (eds.). Handbook of perception, vol. 5. New YorK: Academic Press, 117–166.

DeValois, R. L., and DeValois, K. K. (1988) Spatial vision. New York: Oxford University Press.

DeValois, R. L., Smith, C. J., Kitai, S. T., and Karoly, A. J. (1958) Responses of single cells in different layers of the primate lateral geniculate nucleus to monochromatic light. Science, 127, 238–239.

Dewson, J., Pribram, K., and Lynch, J. (1969) Effects of ablations of temporal cortex upon speech sound discrimination in the monkey. Experimental Neurology, 24, 579–591.

De Yoe, E. A., and van Essen, D. C. (1988) Concurrent processing streams in monkey visual cortex. Trends in Neurosciences, 11, 219–226.

Dichgans, J., and Brandt, T. (1978) Visual-vestibular interaction: Effects on self-motion perception and postural control. In R. M. Held, H. W. Leibowitz, and H.-L. Teuber (eds.), Handbook of sensory physiology, vol. 8. Berlin: Springer-Verlag, 756–804.

Dobelle, W. H., and Mladejovsky, M. G. (1974) Phosphenes produced by electrical stimulation of human occipital cortex, and their application to the development of a prosthesis for the blind. Journal of Physiology, 243, 553–576.

Dobelle, W. H., Mladejovsky, M. G., Evans, J. R., Roberts, T. S., and Girvin, J. P. (1976) "Braille" reading by a blind volunteer by visual cortex stimulation. Nature, 259, 111–112.

Dodd, B. (1977) The role of vision in the perception of speech. Perception, 6, 31–40.

Dobkins, K. R. (2000) Moving colors in the lime light. Neuron, 25, 15–18.

Dodge, R. (1900) The illusion of clear vision during eye movement. Psychological Bulletin, 2, 193–199.

Dolan, R. J., Fink, G. R., Rolls, E., Booth, M., Holmes, A., Frackowiak, R. S. J., and Friston, K. J. (1997) How the brain learns to see objects and faces in an impoverished context. Nature, 389, 596–599.

Dolnick, E. (1991) Deafness as culture. Atlantic Monthly, 272, 37–53.

Dosher, B. A., Sperling, G. and **Wurst, S. A.** (1986) Tradeoffs between stereopsis and proximity luminance covariance. Vision Research, 26, 973–990.

Doty, R. L. (1986) Odor-guided behavior in mammals. Experientia, 42, 257–271.

Doty, R. L., Green, P. A., Ram, C., and **Yankell, S. L.** (1982) Communication of gender from human breath odors: Relationship to perceived intensity and pleasantness. Hormones and Behavior, 16, 13–22.

Doty, R. L., Shaman, P., Applebaum, S. L., Giberson, R., Siksorski, L., and **Rosenberg, L.** (1984) Smell identification ability: Changes with age. Science, 226, 1441–1443.

Douek, E. (1974) The sense of smell and its abnormalities. Edinburgh: Churchill Livingstone.

Dowling, J. E. (1966) Night blindness. Scientific American, 215, 78–84.

Dowling, J. E. (1998) Creating mind: How the brain works. New York: Norton.

Dowling, W. J. (1978) Scale and contour: Two components of a theory of memory for melodies. Psychological Review, 85, 341–354.

Dowling, W. J., and **Fujitani, D. S.** (1971) Contour, interval, and pitch recognition in memory for melodies. Journal of the Acoustical Society of America, 49, 524–531.

Drasdo, N. (1977) The neural representation of visual space. Nature, 266, 554–556.

Drayna, D., Manichaikul, A., de Lange, M., Snieder, H., and **Spector, T.** (2001). Genetic correlates of musical pitch recognition in humans, Science, 291, 1969–1972.

Dreher, B., Fukada, Y., and **Rodieck, R. W.** (1976) Identification, classification, and anatomical segregation of cells with X-like and Y-like properties in the lateral geniculate nucleus of old-world primates. Journal of Physiology, 29, 433–452.

Drewnowski, A., Bellisle, F., Aimez, P., and **Remy, B.** (1987) Taste and bulimia. Physiology & Behavior, 41, 621–626.

Drewnowski, A., Grinker, J. A., and **Hirsch, J.** (1982) Obesity and flavor perception: Multidimensional scaling of soft drinks. Appetite: Journal of Intake Research, 3, 361–368.

Drewnowski, A., Henderson, S. A., and **Shore, A. B.** (1997) Taste responses to naringin, a flavonoid, and the acceptance of grapefruit juice are related to genetic sensitivity to 6-n-propylthiouracil. American Journal of Clinical Nutrition, 66, 391–397.

DuBose, C. N., Cardello, A., and **Maller, O.** (1980) Effects of colorants and flavorants on identification, perceived flavor intensity, and hedonic quality of fruit-flavored beverages and cake. Journal of Food Science, 45, 1393–1399, 1415.

Duchamp-Viret, P., Duchamp, A., and **Vigouroux, M.** (1989) Amplifying role of convergence in olfactory system. A comparative study of receptor cell and second-order neuron sensitivities. Journal of Neurophysiology, 61, 1085–1094.

Duhamel, J.-R., Colby, C. L., and **Goldberg, M. E.** (1992). The updating of the representation of visual space in parietal cortex by intended eye movements. Science, 255, 90–92.

Duncker, K. (1929/1938) Induced motion. In W. D. Ellis (ed.), A source book of Gestalt psychology. New York: Humanities Press, 161–172.

Duncker, K. (1939) The influence of past experience upon perceptual properties. American Journal of Psychology, 52, 255–267.

Eccles, J. (1979) The human mystery. Berlin: Springer-Verlag.

Eckstein, M. P., Whiting, J. S., and **Thomas, J. P.** (1996) Role of knowledge in human visual temporal integration in spatiotemporal noise. Journal of the Optical Society of America A, 13, 1960–1968.

Edelman, S., and **Bülthoff, H.** (1992) Orientation dependence in the recognition of familiar and novel views of three-dimensional objects. Vision Research, 32, 2385–2400.

Edwards, P. A., and **Jurs, P. C.** (1989) Correlation of odor intensities with structural properties of odorants. Chemical Senses, 14, 281–291.

Egeth, H. E., and **Yantis, S.** (1997) Visual attention: Control, representation, and time course. Annual Review of Psychology, 48, 269–297.

Egly, R., Driver, J., Rafal, R. D. (1994) Shifting visual attention between objects and locations: evidence from normal and parietal lesion subjects. Journal of Experimental Psychology: General, 123, 161–177.

Ehrenstein, W. H., Ehrenstein, A. (1999) Psychophysical methods. In U. Windhorst and H. Johansson (eds.) Modern Techniques in Neuroscience Research. Berlin: Springer-Verlag, 1211–1241.

Eimas, P. D., and **Corbit, J. D.** (1973) Selective adaptation of linguistic feature detectors. Cognitive Psychology, 4, 99–109.

Ekman, P. (1984) Expression and the nature of emotion. In K. R. Scherer and P. Ekman (eds.) Approaches to emotion. Hillsdale, N.: Erlbaum.

Elbert, T., Pantev, C., Wienbruch, C., Rockstroh, B., and Taub, E. (1995) Increased cortical representation of the fingers of the left hand in string players. Science, 27, 305–307.

Elkins, J. (1996) The object stares back: On the nature of seeing. New York: Harvest Books.

Emmerich, D. S., and Levine, F. M. (1970) Differences in auditory sensitivity of chronic schizophrenic patients and normal controls determined by use of a forced-choice procedure. Diseases of the Nervous System, 31, 552–557.

Engel, S. A., Glover, G. H., Wandell, B. A. (1997) Retinotopic organization in human visual cortex and the spatial precision of functional MRI. Cerebral Cortex, 7, 181–192.

Engel, S., Zhang, X., and Wandell, B. (1997) Colour tuning in the human visual cortex measured with functional magnetic resonance imaging. Nature, 388, 68–71.

Engen, T. (1960) Effects of practice and instruction on olfactory thresholds. Perceptual and Motor Skills, 10, 195–198.

Engen, T. (1982) The perception of odors. New York: Academic Press.

Engen, T. (1987) Remembering odors and their names. American Scientist, 75, 497–503.

Enright, J. T. (1989) Manipulating stereopsis and vergence in an outdoor setting: Moon, sky and horizon. Vision Research, 29, 1815–1824.

Enroth-Cugell, C., Hertz, B. G., and Lennie, P. (1977) Convergence of rod and cone signals in the cat's retina. Journal of Physiology, 269, 297–318.

Epelboim, J., Booth, J. R., and Steinman, R. M. (1994) Reading unspaced text: implications for theories of reading eye movements. Vision Research, 34, 1735–1766.

Epelboim, J., Booth, J. R., Ashkenazy, R., Taleghani, A., and Steinman, R. M. (1997) Fillers and spaces in text: the importance of word recognition during reading. Vision Research, 37, 2899–2914.

Epstein, R., and Kanwisher, N. (1998) A cortical representation of the local visual environment. Nature, 392, 598–601.

Epstein, W. (1963) The influences of assumed size on apparent distance. American Journal of Physiology, 76, 257–265.

Erickson, R. P. (1968) Stimulus coding in topographic and nontopographic afferent modalities: On the significance of the activity of individual sensory neurons. Psychological Review, 75, 447–465.

Erickson, R. P. (1982) Studies on the perception of taste: Do primaries exist? Physiology & Behavior, 28, 57–62.

Erickson, R. P. (1984) On the neural bases of behavior. American Scientist, 72, 233–241.

Eriksson-Mangold, M. M., and Erlandsson, S. I. (1984) The psychological importance of nonverbal sounds. Scandinavian Audiology, 13, 243–249.

Essock, E. A., Krebs, W. K., and Prather, J. R. (1992) An anisotropy of human tactile sensitivity and its relation to the visual oblique effect. Experimental Brain Research, 91, 520–524.

Evans, E. F. (1982a) Functional anatomy of the auditory system. In H. B. Barlow and J. D. Mollon (eds.), The senses. Cambridge, England: Cambridge University Press, 251–306.

Evans, E. F. (1982b) Functions of the auditory system. In H. B. Barlow and J. D. Mollon (eds.), The senses. Cambridge, England: Cambridge University Press, 307–331.

Exner, S. (1888) Über optische Bewegungsempfindungen. Biologisches Centralblatt, 8, 437–448.

Fahle, M., Edelman, S., and Poggio, T. (1995) Fast perceptual learning in hyperacuity. Vision Research, 35, 3003–3013.

Fantz, R. L. (1961) The origin of form perception. Scientific American, 204, 66–72.

Farah, M. J. (1992) Agnosia. Current Opinion in Neurobiology, 2, 162–164.

Farrell, M. J., and Robertson, I. H. (1998) Mental rotation and the automatic updating of body-centered spatial relationships. Journal of Experimental Psychology: Learning, Memory and Cognition, 24, 227–233.

Faurion, A., Cerf, B., van de Moortele, P. F., Lobel, E., Mac Leod, P., and Le Bihan, D. (2000) Human taste cortical areas studied with functional magnetic resonance imaging: evidence of functional lateralization related to handedness. Neuroscience Letters, 277, 189–192.

Fay, R. R. (1988) Comparative psychoacoustics. Hearing Research, 34, 295–306.

Fechner, G. T. (1860/1966) Elements of psychophysics. D. H. Howes and E. G. Boring (eds.), H. E. Adler (trans.). New York: Holt, Rinehart and Winston.

Federal Railroad Administration. (1992) Rail-highway crossing accident/incident inventory bulletin, calendar year 1991. Washington, D.C.: U.S. Department of Transportation.

Felleman, D. J., and **Van Essen, D. C.** (1991) Distributed hierarchical processing in the primate cerebral cortex. Cerebral Cortex, 1, 1–47.

Fendrich, R., Wessinger, C. M., and **Gazzaniga, M. S.** (1992) Residual vision in a scotoma: implications for blindsight. Science, 258, 1489–1491.

Ferrie, C. D., De Marco, P., Grunewald, R. A., Giannakodimos, S., and **Panayiotopoulos, C. P.** (1994) Video game induced seizures. Journal of Neurology, Neurosurgery & Psychiatry, 57, 925–931.

Ferster, D. (1981) A comparison of binocular depth mechanisms in areas 17 and 18 of the cat visual cortex. Journal of Physiology, 311, 623–655.

Field, D. J. (1987) Relations between the statistics of natural images and the response properties of cortical cells. Journal of the Optical Society of America A, 4, 2379–2394.

Field, D. J. (1987) Relations betwen the statistics of natural images and the response properties of cells in macaque visual cortex. Journal of the Optical Society of America A 4 2379–2394.

Field, D. J., Hayes, A., and **Hess, R.** (1993) Contour integration by the human visual system: evidence for a local "association field". Vision Research, 33, 173–193.

Fields, H. L. (1987) Pain. New York: McGraw-Hill.

Finke, R. (1985) Theories relating mental imagery to perception. Psychological Bulletin, 98, 236–259.

Fischer, R., Griffin, F., England, S., and **Carn, S. M.** (1961) Taste thresholds and food dislikes. Nature, 191, 1328.

Fitch, R. H., Miller, S., and **Tallal, P.** (1997) Neurobiology of speech perception. Annual Review of Neuroscience, 20, 331–353.

Fitzpatrick, D. C., Batra, R., Stanford, T. R., and **Kuwada, S.** (1997) A neuronal population code for sound localization. Nature, 388, 871–874.

Fletcher, H. (1940) Auditory patterns. Review of Modern Physics, 12, 47–65.

Fletcher, H. F., and **Munson, W. A.** (1933) Loudness, its definition, measurement, and calculation. Journal of the Acoustical Society of America, 5, 82–108.

Fletcher, S. W., O'Malley, M. S., and **Bunce, L. A.** (1985) Physicians' abilities to detect lumps in silicone breast models. Journal of the American Medical Association, 253, 2224–2228.

Foerstl, H., Owen, A. M., and **David, A. S.** (1993) Gabriel Anton and "Anton's symptom": On focal diseases of the brain which are not perceived by the patient (1898). Neuropsychiatry, Neuropsychology, and Behavioral Neurology, 6, 1–6.

Foley, J. M. (1980) Binocular distance perception. Psychological Review, 87, 411–434.

Fox, R. (1978) Visual masking. In R. Held, H. W. Leibowitz, and H.-L. Teuber (eds.), Handbook of sensory physiology, vol. 8. Berlin: Springer-Verlag, 629–653.

Fox, R., Aslin, R. N., Shea, S. L., and **Dumais, S. T.** (1980) Stereopsis in human infants. Science, 207, 323–324.

Fox, R., Lehmkuhle, S. W., and **Bush, R. C.** (1977) Stereopsis in the falcon. Science, 197, 79–81.

Fox, R., and **McDaniel, C.** (1982) The perception of biological motion by human infants. Science, 218, 486–487.

Francis, S., Rolls, E. T., Bowtell, R., McGlone, F., O'Doherty, J., Browning, A., Clare, S., and **Smith, E.** (1999) The representation of pleasant touch in the brain and its relationship with taste and olfactory areas. Neuroreport, 10, 453–459.

Frank, M. (1973) An analysis of hamster afferent taste nerve response functions. Journal of General Physiology, 61, 588–618.

Freedman, M. S., Lucas, R. J., Soni, B., von Schantz, M., Munoz, M., David-Gray, Z., and **Foster, R.** (1999) Regulation of mammalian circadian behavior by non-rod, non-cone, ocular photoreceptors. Science, 284, 502–504.

Freeman, R. D., and **Pettigrew, J. D.** (1973) Alteration of visual cortex from environmental asymmetries. Nature, 246, 359–360.

Freeman, W. J. (1991) The physiology of perception. Scientific American, 264, 78–85.

Freund, M. S., and **Lewis, N. S.** (1995) A chemically civerse conducting polymer-based electronic nose, Proceedings of the National Academy of Science, USA, 92, 2652.

Freud, S. (1910/1938) The psychopathology of everyday life. In A. A. Brill (ed. and trans.), The basic writings of Sigmund Freud. New York: Modern Library, 35–178.

Freud, S. (1930/1961) Civilization and its discontents. New York: W. W. Norton.

Freytag, E., and **Sachs, J. S.** (1968) Abnormalities of the central visual pathways contributing to traffic accidents. Journal of the American Medical Association, 204, 871–873.

Frisby, J. P., and **Clatworthy, J. L.** (1975) Learning to see complex random-dot stereograms. Perception, 4, 173–178.

Frisby, J. P., and Mayhew, J. E. W. (1976) Rivalrous texture stereograms. Nature, 264, 53–56.

Frisina, D. R., and Frisina, R. D. (1997) Speech recognition in noise and presbycusis: relations to possible neural mechanisms. Hearing Research, 106, 95–104.

Fry, G. A., Bridgman, C. S., and Ellerbrock, V. J. (1949) The effect of atmospheric scattering on binocular depth perception. American Journal of Optometry, 26, 9–15.

Frye, R. E., Doty, R. L., and Schwartz, B. (1989) Influence of cigarette smoking on olfaction: Evidence for a dose-response relationship. Journal of the American Medical Association, 263, 1233–1236.

Fuchs, A., and Binder, M. D. (1983) Fatigue resistance of human extraocular muscles. Journal of Neurophysiology, 49, 28–34.

Fullard, J. H., and Barclay, R. M. R. (1980) Audition in spring species of arctiid moths as a possible response to differential levels of insectivorous bat predation. Canadian Journal of Zoology, 58, 1745–1750.

Furchtgott, E., and Friedman, M. P. (1960) The effect of hunger and taste on odor RLs. Journal of Comparative and Physiological Psychology, 53, 576–581.

Gamble, E. A. M. C. (1921) Review of Der Geruch by Hans Henning. American Journal of Psychology, 32, 290–295.

Garb, J., and Stunkard, A. J. (1974) Taste aversions in man. American Journal of Psychiatry, 131, 1204–1207.

Garcia, J., and Koelling, R. A. (1966) Relation of cue to consequences in avoidance learning. Psychonomic Science, 4, 123–124.

Garcia-Medina, M. R., and Cain, W. S. (1982) Bilateral integration in the common chemical sense. Physiology & Behavior, 29, 349–353.

Gardner, R. J. M., and Sutherland, G. R. (1989) Chromosome abnormalities and genetic counseling. Oxford: Oxford University Press.

Garfield, E. (1983) The tyranny of the horn—Automobile, that is. Current Contents, 26, 5–11.

Garner, W. R. (1962) Uncertainty and structure as psychological concepts. New York: John Wiley & Sons.

Gauthier, I., Behrmann, M., and Tarr, M. J. (1999) Can face recognition really be dissociated from object recognition? Journal of Cognitive Neuroscience, 11, 349–70.

Gauthier, I., and Tarr, M. J. (1997) Becoming a 'Greeble' expert: Exploring the face recognition mechanism. Vision Research, 37, 1673–1682.

Gauthier, I., Tarr, M. J., Anderson, A. W., Skudlarski, P., and Gore, J. C. (1999) Activation of the middle fusiform 'face area' increases with expertise in recognizing novel objects. Nature Neuroscience, 2, 568–73.

Gauthier, I., Williams, P., Tarr, M. J., and Tanaka, J. (1998) Training 'greeble' experts: a framework for studying expert object recognition processes. Vision Research, 38, 2401–2428.

Gegenfurtner, K. R., Kiper, D. C., and Fenstemaker, S. B. (1996) Processing of color, form, and motion in macaque area V2. Visual Neuroscience, 13, 161–172.

Geisler, W. S. (1989) Sequential ideal-observer analysis of visual discriminations. Psychological Review, 96, 267–314.

Geisler, W. S., Perry, J. S., Super, B. J., and Gallogly, D. P. (2001) Edge co-occurrence in natural images predicts contour grouping performance. Vision Research, 41, 711–724.

Gelb, A. (1929) Die Farbenkonstanz der Sehdinge. In A. Bethe et al. (eds) Handbuch der normalen und pathologischen physiologie, vol. 12, Berlin: Springer-Verlag, 594–678.

Geldard, F. A., and Sherrick, C. E. (1986) Space, time and touch. Scientific American, 255, 90–95.

George, P. A. and Hole, G. J. (1995) Factors influencing the accuracy of age estimates of unfamiliar faces. Perception, 24, 1059–1073.

Gescheider, G. A. (1976) Psychophysics: Method and theory. Hillsdale, N.J.: Erlbaum.

Gescheider, G. A., Sklar, B. F., van Doren, C. L., and Verillo, R. T. (1985) Vibrotactile forward masking: Psychophysical evidence for a triplex theory of cutaneous mechanoreception. Journal of Acoustical Society of America, 78, 534–543.

Gesteland, R. C. (1986) Speculations on receptor cells as analyzers and filters. Experientia, 42, 287–291.

Getchell, T. V., Doty, R. L., Bartoshuk, L. M., and Snow, J. B. (eds.). (1991) Smell and taste in health and disease. New York: Raven Press.

Geyer, L. H., and DeWald, C. G. (1973) Feature lists and confusion matrices. Perception & Psychophysics, 14, 471–482.

Gibson, E. J. (1965) Learning to read. Science, 148, 1066–1072.

Gibson, E. J. (1969) Principles of perceptual learning. New York: Appleton-Century-Crofts.

Gibson, J. J. (1947) Motion picture testing and research. AAF Aviation Psychology Report No. 7. Washington, D.C.: U. S. Army Air Force.

Gibson, J. J. (1950) The perception of the visual world. Boston: Houghton-Mifflin.

Gibson, J. J. (1966) The senses considered as perceptual systems. Boston: Houghton-Mifflin.

Gibson, J. J. (1979) The ecological approach to visual perception. Boston: Houghton-Mifflin.

Gilbert, C. D. (1992) Horizontal integration and cortical dynamics. Neuron, 9, 1–13.

Gilchrist, A. L. (1977) Perceived lightness depends on perceived spatial arrangement. Science, 195, 185–187.

Gilchrist, A. L. (1988) Lightness contrast and failures of constancy: A common explanation. Perception & Psychophysics, 43, 415–424.

Gilden, D. L., Blake, R., and **Hurst, J.** (1992) Imagined motion is influenced by adaptation. Thirty-third annual meetings of the Psychonomic Society, St. Louis.

Gilinsky, A. S. (1955) The effect of attitude upon the perception of size. American Journal of Psychology, 68, 173–192.

Gillan, D. J. (1982) Mixture suppression: The effect of spatial separation between sucrose and NaCl. Perception & Psychophysics, 32, 504–510.

Gillan, D. J. (1984) Evidence for peripheral and central processes in taste adaptation. Perception & Psychophysics, 35, 1–4.

Ginsberg, M. D., Yoshii, F., Vibulsresth, S., Chang, J. Y., Durara, R., Barker, W. W., and **Boothe, T. E.** (1987) Human task-specific somatosensory activation. Neurology, 37, 1301–1308.

Ginsburg, A. P., Evans, D. W., Sekuler, R., and Harp, S. A. (1982) Contrast sensitivity predicts pilots' performance in aircraft simulators. American Journal of Optometry and Physiological Optics, 59, 105–108.

Gittleman, J. L., and **Harvey, P. H.** (1980) Why are distasteful prey not cryptic? Nature, 286, 149–150.

Glanville, E. V., and **Kaplan, A. R.** (1965) Food preference and sensitivity of taste for bitter compounds. Nature, 205, 851–853.

Glickstein, M. (1988) The discovery of the visual cortex. Scientific American, 259, 118–127.

Goethe, J. W. von. (1840/1970) Theory of colours. C. L. Eastlake (trans.). Cambridge: M.I.T. Press.

Gold, J., Bennett, P. J., and **Sekuler, A. B.** (1999) Signal but not noise changes with perceptual learning. Nature, 402, 176–178.

Goldberg, M. E., and **Wurtz, R. H.** (1972) Activity of superior colliculus in behaving monkey: I. Visual receptive fields of single neurons. Journal of Neurophysiology, 35, 542–559.

Goldenberg, G., Muellbacher, W., Nowak, A. (1995) Imagery without perception: A case study of anosognosia for cortical blindness. Neuropsychologia, 33, 1373–1382.

Goldman, A. I. (1976) Discrimination and perceptual knowledge. Journal of Philosophy, 73, 771–791.

Gonzalez, F. and **Perez, R.** (1998) Neural mechanisms underlying stereoscopic vision. Progress in Neurobiology, 55, 191–224.

Goodale, M. A. (1998) Visuomotor control: where does vision end and action begin? Current Biology, 8, R489–R491.

Goodale, M. A. and **Humphrey, G. K.** (1998) The objects of action and perception. Cognition, 67, 181–207.

Goodale, M. A., and **Milner, A. D.** (1992) Separate visual pathways for perception and action. Trends in Neurosciences, 15, 20–25.

Goodale, M. A., Pelisson, D., and **Prablanc, C.** (1986) Large adjustments in visually guided reaching do not depend on vision of the hand or perception of target displacement. Nature, 320, 748–750.

Gootjes, L., Raij, Salmelin, R., and **Hari, R.** (1999) Left-hemisphere dominance for processing of vowels: a whole-scalp neuromagnetic study. NeuroReport, 10, 2987–2991.

Gordon, B. (1972) The superior colliculus of the brain. Scientific American, 227, 72–82.

Gouk, P. (1988) The harmonic roots of Newtonian science. In J. Fauvel, R. Flood, M. Shortland, and R. Wilson (eds.), Let Newton be! A new perspective on his life and works. Oxford, England: Oxford University Press, 100–125.

Gouras, P., and **Zrenner, E.** (1981) Color coding in the primate retina. Vision Research, 21, 1591–1598.

Graham, C. A., and **McGrew, W. C.** (1980) Menstrual synchrony in female undergraduates living on a coeducational campus. Psychoneuroendocrinology, 5, 253–259.

Graham, C. H. (1965) Visual space perception. In C. H. Graham (ed.), Vision and visual perception. New York: John Wiley & Sons, 504–547.

Grant, A. C., Thiagarajah, M. C., Sathian, K. (2000) Tactile perception in blind Braille readers: A psychophysical study of acuity and hyperacuity using gratings and dot patterns. Perception & Psychophysics, 62, 301–312.

Grant, V. W. (1942) Accommodation and convergence in visual space perception. Journal of Experimental Psychology, 31, 89–104.

Graziadei, P. P. C. (1973) Cell dynamics in the olfactory mucosa. Tissue and Cell, 5, 113–131.

Green, D. M. (1964) Consistency of auditory detection judgments. Psychological Review, 71, 392–407.

Green, D. M. (1982) Profile analysis: A different view of auditory intensity discrimination. American Psychologist, 38, 133–142.

Green, D. M., Kidd, G., Jr., and **Picardi, M. C.** (1983) Successive versus simultaneous comparison in auditory discrimination. Journal of the Acoustical Society of America, 73, 639–643.

Green, D. M., and **Nguyen, Q. T.** (1988) Profile analysis: Detecting dynamic spectral changes. Hearing Research, 32, 147–164.

Green, D. M., and **Swets, J. A.** (1966) Signal detection theory and psychophysics. New York: John Wiley & Sons.

Green, J. A., Jones, L. E., and **Gustafson, E. E.** (1987) Perception of cries by parents and nonparents: Relation to cry acoustics. Developmental Psychology, 23, 370–382.

Green, M. (1980) Orientation-specific adaptation: Effects of checkerboards on the detectability of gratings. Perception, 9, 369–377.

Greenberg, D. P. (1989) Light reflection models for computer graphics. Science, 244, 166–173.

Greenwald, A. G., Spangenberg, E. R., Pratkanis, A. R., and **Eskenazi, J.** (1991) Double-blind tests of subliminal self-help audiotapes. Psychological Science, 2, 119–122.

Greer, C. A. (1991) Structural organization of the olfactory system. In T. V. Getchell, R. L. Doty, L. M. Bartoshuk and J. B. Snow (eds.), Smell and taste in health and disease. New York: Raven Press, 65–81.

Gregory, R. L. (1970) The intelligent eye. New York: McGraw-Hill.

Gregory, R. L. (1978) Eye and brain: The psychology of seeing (3rd ed.). New York: McGraw-Hill.

Gregory, R. L. (1979) The aesthetics of anaesthetics. Perception, 8, 123–124.

Gregory, R. L. (1992) How can perceptual science help the handicapped? Perception, 21, 1–6.

Gregory, R. L., and **Drysdale, A. E.** (1976) Squeezing speech into the deaf ear. Nature, 264, 748–751.

Greve, K. W., and **Bauer, R. M.** (1990) Implicit learning of new faces in prosopagnosia: An application of the mere-exposure paradigm. Neuropsychologia, 28, 1035–1042.

Griffin, D. (1959) Echoes of bats and men. New York: Doubleday/Anchor.

Griffiths, T. D., Büchel, C., Frackowiak, S. J. and **Patterson, R. D.** (1998) Analysis of temporal structure in sound by the human brain. Nature Neuroscience, 1, 422–427.

Griffiths, T. D., Rees, A., Witton, C., Shakir, T. A., Henning, G. B., Green, G. G. R. (1996) Evidence for a sound movement area in the human cerebral cortex. Nature, 383, 425–427.

Grinker, J., and **Hirsch, J.** (1972) Metabolic and behavioral correlates of obesity. In K. Porter and J. Knight (eds.), Physiology, emotion, and psychosomatic illness. Amsterdam: Elsevier, 349–374.

Grosof, D. H., Shapley, R. M., and **Hawken, M. J.** (1996) Macaque V1 neurons can signal "illusory" contours. Nature, 365, 550–552.

Gross, C. G. (1998) Brain, Vision, and Memory: Tales in the History of Neurosience. Cambridge: The MIT Press, 181–210.

Grossberg, J. M., and **Grant, B. F.** (1978) Clinical psychophysics; Applications of ratio scaling and signal detection methods to research on pain, fear, drugs, and medical decision making. Psychological Bulletin, 85, 1154–1176.

Gross-Isseroff, R., and **Lancet, D.** (1988) Concentration-dependent changes of perceived odor quality. Chemical Senses, 13, 191–204.

Grosslight, J. H., Fletcher, H. J., Masterton, R. B., and **Hagen, R.** (1978) Monocular vision and landing performance in general aviation pilots: Cyclops revisited. Human Factors, 20, 27–33.

Grossman, E., Donnelly, M., Price, R., Morgan, V., Pickens, D., Neighbor, G. and **Blake, R.** (2000) Brain areas involved in perception of biological motion. Journal of Cognitive Neuroscience, 12, 711–720.

Gruber, H. E., and **Dinnerstein, A. J.** (1965) The role of knowledge in distance perception. American Journal of Psychology, 78, 575–581.

Gulyas, B., Roland, P. I. (1994) Processing and analysis of form, colour and binocular disparity in the human brain: Functional anatomy by positron emission tomography. European Journal of Neuroscience, 6, 1811–1822.

Gur, M. and **Akri, V.** (1992) Isoluminant stimuli may not expose the full contribution of color to visual functioning: Spatial contrast sensitivity measurements indicate interaction of color and luminance signals. Vision Research, 32, 1253–1262.

Gurnsey, R., Herbert, A. M., Kenemy, J. (1998). Bilateral symmetry embedded in noise is detected accurately only at fixation. Vision Research, 38, 3795–803.

Guski, R. (1990) Auditory localization: Effects of reflecting surfaces. Perception, 19, 819–830.

Guth, S. K. (1981) The science of seeing—A search for criteria. American Journal of Optometry and Physiological Optics, 58, 870–885.

Gwosdow, A. R., Steven, J. C., Berglund, L. G., and **Stolwijk, J. A. J.** (1986) Skin friction and fabric sensations in neutral and warm environments. Textile Research Journal, 56, 574–580.

Hackney, C. M. (1987) Anatomical features of the auditory pathway from cochlea to cortex. British Medical Bulletin, 43, 780–801.

Hadjikhani N, Liu, A. K., Dale, A. M,, Cavanagh, P., and **Tootell, R. B. H.** (1998) Retintopy and color sensitivity in human visual cortical area V8. Nature Neuroscience, 1, 235–241.

Haegerstrom-Portnoy, G., Schneck, M. E., and **Brabyn, J. A.** (1999) Seeing into old age: vision function beyond acuity. Optometry & Vision Science, 76, 141–58.

Haenny, P. E., Maunsell, J. H. R., and **Schiller, P. H.** (1988) State dependent activity in monkey visual cortex: II. Retinal and extraretinal factors in V4. Experimental Brain Research, 69, 245–259.

Hall, M. J., Bartoshuk, L. M., Cain, W. S., and **Stevens, J. C.** (1975) PTC taste blindness and taste of caffeine. Nature, 253, 442–443.

Haller, R., Rummel, C., Henneberg, S., Pollmer, U., and **Koster, E. P.** (1999) The influence of early experience with vanillin on food preference later in life. Chemical Senses, 24, 465–7.

Halpern, B. P. (1983) Tasting and smelling as active, exploratory sensory processes. American Journal of Otolaryngology, 4, 246–249.

Halpern, D. L., Blake, R., and **Hillenbrand, J.** (1986) Psychoacoustics of a chilling sound. Perception & Psychophysics, 39, 77–80.

Halsey, R. M., and **Chapanis, A.** (1951) On the number of absolutely identifiable spectral hues.

Journal of the Optical Society of America, 41, 1057–1058.

Hamilton, R. H., and **Pascual-Leone, A.** (1998) Cortical plasticity associated with Braille learning. Trends in Cognitive Sciences, 2, 168–174.

Handel, S. (1989) Listening: An introduction to the perception of auditory events. Cambridge: M.I.T. Press.

Hanson, C. H., and **Hansen, R. D.** (1988) Finding the face in the crowd: an anger superiority effect. Journal of Personality and Social Psychology, 54, 917–924.

Hanson, D. R., and **Fearn, R. W.** (1975) Hearing acuity in young people exposed to pop music and other noise. Lancet, 2, 203–205.

Hari, R., Hämäläinen, M., Kaukoranta, E., Mäkelä, J., Joutsiniemi, S.-L. and **Tiihonen, J.** (1989) Selective listening modifies activity of the human auditory cortex. Experimental Brain Research, 74, 463–470.

Harlow, H. F., and **Harlow, M. K.** (1966) Learning to love. Scientific American, 54, 244–272.

Harmon, L. D. (1973) The recognition of faces. Scientific American, 229, 70–82.

Harris, J. (1998). "How was it for me?" Uses of introspection in the study of perception. Perception, 27, 1137–1140.

Harris, C. R. and **Christenfeld, N.** (1999) Can a machine tickle? Psychonomic Bulletin & Review, 6, 504–510.

Hart, W. M., Jr (1992) The eyelids. In Adler's physiology of the eye. (9th ed., Ch. 1) St. Louis, MO: Mosby.

Hartline, H. K. (1938) The response of single optic nerve fibers of the vertebrate eye to illumination of the retina. American Journal of Physiology, 121, 400–415.

Harvey, L. O., Jr. (1986). Visual memory: What is remembered? In F. Klix and H. Hagendorf (eds.), Human memory and cognitive capabilities. The Hague: Elsevier, 173–187.

Harvey, L. O., Jr., and **Doan, V. V.** (1990). Visual masking at different polar angles in the two-dimensional Fourier plane. Journal of the Optical Society of America A, 7, 116–127.

Harvey, L. O., Jr., Roberts, J. O., and **Gervais, M. J.** (1983) The spatial frequency basis of internal representations. In H.-G. Geissler, H. F. J. M. Buffart, E. L. J. Leeuwenberg, and V. Sarris (eds.), Modern issues in perception. Rotterdam: North-Holland, 217–226.

Harwerth, R. S., Smith, E. L., Crawford, M. L. J. and **von Noorden, G. K.** (1997) Stereopsis and disparity vergence in monkeys with subnormal binocular vision. Vision Research, 37, 483–493.

Hatsopoulos, N. G., and **Warren, W. H., Jr.** (1991). Visual navigation with a neural network. Neural Networks, 4, 303–317.

Hawkins, J. E., Jr. (1988) Auditory physiological history: A surface view. In A. F. Jahn and J. Santos-Sacci (eds.), Physiology of the ear. New York: Raven Press, 1–28.

Haxby, J. V., Grady, C. L., Horowitz, B., Ungergleider, L. G., Mishkin, M., Carson, R. E., Herscovitch, P., Schapiro, M. B., and **Rapoport, S. C.** (1991) Dissociation of object and spatial visual processing pathways in human extrastriate cortex. Proceedings of National Academy of Sciences: USA. 88, 1621–1625.

Hayhoe, M. M., Bensinger, D. G., Ballard, D. H. (1998) Task constraints in visual working memory. Vision Research, 38, 125-137

Hazel, C. A., Petre, K. L., Armstrong, R. A., Benson, M. T. and **Frost, N. A.** (2000) Visual function and subjective quality of life compared in subjects with acquired macular degeneration. Investigative Ophthalmology & Visual Science, 41, 1309–1315.

He, S., Cohen, E. R., and **Hu, X.** (1998) Close correlation between activity in brain area MT/V5 and the perception of a visual motion aftereffect. Current Biology, 8, 1215–1218.

Hebb, D. O. (1949) The organization of behavior. New York: John Wiley & Sons.

Hecht, S., Shlaer, S., and **Pirenne, M. H.** (1942) Energy, quanta, and vision. Journal of General Physiology, 25, 819–840.

Heeger, D. J. (1999) Linking visual perception with human brain activity. Current Opinion in Neurobiology, 9, 474–479.

Heffner, R. S., and **Heffner, H. E.** (1985) Hearing in mammals: The least weasel. Journal of Mammalogy, 66, 745–755.

Heffner, R. S., and **Heffner, H. E.** (1992) Visual factors in sound localization in mammals. Journal of Comparative Neurology, 317, 219–232.

Heinemann, E. G., Tulving, E., and **Nachmias, J.** (1959) The effect of oculomotor adjustments on apparent size. American Journal of Psychology, 72, 32–45.

Heller, M. A. (1986) Central and peripheral influences on tactual reading. Perception & Psychophysics, 39, 197–204.

Helmholtz, H. L. F. von (1909/1962) Treatise on physiological optics (3rd ed.). J. P. C. Southall (ed.). New York: Dover.

Helmholtz, H. L. F. von (1877/1954) On the sensation of tone as a psychological basis for the theory of music (2nd ed.). A. J. Ellis (trans. and ed.). New York: Dover.

Hemilä, S., Nummela, S., and **Reuter, T.** (1995) What middle ear parameters tell about impedance matching and high frequency hearing. Hearing Research, 85, 31–44.

Henderson, J. M., and **Hollingworth, A.** (1999) High-Level Scene Perception. Annual Review of Psychology, 50, 243–271.

Henderson, J. M., and **Hollingworth, A.** (1998) Eye Movements during Scene Viewing: An Overview. In G Underwood (ed.). Eye Guidance while Reading and While Watching Dynamic Scenes. Oxford: Elsevier, 269–293.

Hendry, S. H., and **Reid, R. C.** (2000) The koniocellular pathway in primate vision. Annual Review of Neuroscience, 23, 127–153.

Hendry, S. H. C., and **Calkins, D. J.** (1998) Neuronal chemistry and functional organization in the primate visual system. Trends in Neuroscience, 21, 344–349.

Henkin, R. I. (1982) Olfaction in human disease. In G. B. English, (ed.), Looseleaf series in otolaryngology. New York: Harper & Row, 1–39.

Henning, H. (1916) Der Geruch. Leipzig: Barth.

Hershenson, M. (1989) The moon illusion. Hillsdale, N.J.: Erlbaum.

Hess, R. and **Field, D.** (1999) Integration of contours: new insights. Trends in Cognitive Sciences, 1999, 3, 480–486.

Heywood, S., and **Ratcliff, G.** (1975) Long-term oculomotor consequences of unilateral colliculectomy in man. In G. Lennerstrand and P. Bach-y-Rita (eds.), Basic mechanisms of ocular motility and their clinical implications. Elmsford, N.Y.: Pergamon Press, 561–564.

Hikosaka, O., Tanaka, M., Sakamoto, M., and **Iwamura, Y.** (1985) Deficits in manipulative behaviors induced by local injections of muscimol in the first somatosensory cortex of the conscious monkey. Behavior Research, 325, 375–380.

Hildreth, E. (1986) Edge detection. In Encyclopedia of artificial intelligence, vol. 1. New York: John Wiley & Sons, 257–267.

Hillman, H. (1993) The possible pain experienced during execution by different methods. Perception, 22, 745–753.

Hindley, P. (1997) Psychiatric aspects of hearing impairments. Journal of Child Psychology and Psychiatry, 38, 101–117.

Hiris, E., and **Blake, R.** (1992) Another perspective on the visual motion aftereffect. Proceedings of the National Academy of Sciences, 89, 9025–9028.

Hirsch, J., DeLaPaz, R. L., Relkin, N. R., Victor, J., Kim, K., Li, T., Borden, P., Rubin, N., and **Shapley, R.** (1995) Illusory contours activate specific regions in human visual cortex: evidence from functional magnetic resonance imaging. Proceedings of the National Academy of Sciences: USA, 92, 6469–6473.

Hirsch, J., and **Miller, W. H.** (1987) Does cone positional disorder limit resolution? Journal of the Optical Society of America A, 4, 1481–1492.

Hoffman, D. D. (1998) Visual intelligence. New York: Norton.

Hofman, P. M., van Riswick, J. G. A., and **van Opstal, A. J.** (1998) Relearning sound localization with new ears. Nature Neuroscience, 1, 417–421.

Hole, G. J. (1994) Configurational factors in the perception of unfamiliar faces. Perception, 23, 65–74.

Holland, H. H. (1967) Attenuation provided by fingers, palms, tragi and V51R ear plugs. Journal of the Acoustical Society of America, 41, 1545.

Hollins, M., Delemos, K. A. and **Goble, A. K.** (1996) Vibrotactile adaptation of the RA system: a psychophysical analysis. In O. Franzen, R. Johansson, and L. Terenius (eds.) Somesthesis and the Neurobiology of the Somatosensory Cortex. Basel: Birkhauser Verlag.

Hollins, M. and **Risner, S. R.** (2000) Evidence for the duplex theory of tactile texture perception. Perception & Psychophysics, 62, 695–705.

Hollins, M., Sigurdsson, A., Fillingim, L. and **Goble, A. K.** (1996) Vibrotactile threshold is elevated in temporomandibular disorders. Pain, 67, 889–96.

Hollo, A. (1977) Age four. In Sojourner microcosms: New and selected poems. Berkeley, Calif.: Blue Wind Press, 30.

Holmes, G. (1918) Disturbances of vision by cerebral lesions. British Journal of Ophthalmology, 2, 353–384.

Holway, A. F., and **Boring, E. G.** (1941) Determinants of apparent visual size with distance variant. American Journal of Psychology, 54, 21–37.

Hood, D. C., and **Finkelstein, M. A.** (1986) Sensitivity to light. In K. Boff, L. Kaufman, and J. Thomas (eds.), Handbook of perception and human performance, vol. 1. New York: Wiley-Interscience, 5.1–5.66.

Hopfield, J. J. (1991) Olfactory computations and object perception. Proceedings of the National Academy of Sciences, 88, 6462–6466.

Horner, D. G. (1982) Can vision predict baseball players' hitting ability? American Journal of Optometry and Physiological Optics, 59, 69.

Horton, J. C., and **Hocking, D. R.** (1996) Intrinsic variability of ocular dominance column periodicity in normal macaque monkeys. Journal of Neuroscience, 16, 7228–7239.

Horwitz, G. D., and **Newsome, W. T.** (1999) Separate signals for target selection and movement specification in the superior colliculus. Science, 284, 1158–1161.

Hotson, J., Braun, D., Herzberg, W., and **Boman, D.** (1994) Transcranial magnetic stimulation of extrastriate cortex degrades human motion direction discrimination. Vision Research, 34, 2115–2123.

Houde, J. F., and **Jordan, M. I.** (1998) Sensorimotor adaptation in speech production. Science, 279, 1213–1216.

Houston, R. A. (1917) Newton and the colours of the spectrum. Science Progress, 12, 250–264.

Howard, I. P., Bergström, S. S., and **Masao, O.** (1990) Shape from shading in different frames of reference. Perception, 19, 523–530.

Howard, I. P. (1982) Human visual orientation. J. Wiley and Sons: New York.

Howard, I. P., and **Rogers, B. J.** (1995) Binocular Vision. New York: Oxford University.

Hubel, D. H. (1988) Eye, brain, and vision. WH Freeman, New York.

Hubel, D. H., and **Wiesel, T. N.** (1962) Receptive fields, binocular interaction, and functional architecture in the cat's visual cortex. Journal of Physiology, 160, 106–154.

Hubel, D. H., and **Wiesel, T. N.** (1974a) Uniformity of monkey striate cortex: A parallel relationship between field size, scatter, and magnification factor. Journal of Comparative Neurology, 158, 295–306.

Hubel, D. H., and **Wiesel, T. N.** (1974b) Sequence regularity and geometry of orientation columns in the monkey striate cortex. Journal of Comparative Neurology, 158, 267–294.

Hubel, D. H., and **Wiesel, T. N.** (1977) Functional architecture of macaque monkey visual cortex. Proceedings of the Royal Society of London, 198, 1–59.

Hubel, D. H., Wiesel, T. N., and **LeVay, S.** (1977) Plasticity of ocular dominance columns in monkey striate cortex Philosphical Transactions of the Royal Society of London Series B, 278, 377–409.

Hubel, D. H., Wiesel, T. N., and **Stryker, M. P.** (1978) Anatomical demonstration of orientation columns in macaque monkey. Journal of Comparative Neurology, 177, 361–380.

Hughes, A. (1977) The topography of vision in mammals of contrasting life style: Comparative optics and retinal organization. In F. Crescitelli (ed.). Handbook of sensory physiology, vol. VII/5. Berlin: Springer-Verlag, 613–756.

Hughes, H. (1999) Sensory exotica: a world beyond human experience. Cambridge: MIT Press.

Hulbert, A. (1999) Colour vision: Is colour constancy real? Current Biology, 9, R558–R561.

Humayun, M., de Juan, E. and **Dagnelie, G.** (1996) Visual perception elicited by electrical stimulation of retina in blind humans, Archives of Ophthalmology, 114, 40–46.

Hume, D. (1739/1963) A treatise of human nature. In V. C. Chappel (ed.), The philosophy of David Hume. New York: Modern Library, 11–311.

Humphrey, N. K. (1974) Species and individuals in the perceptual world of monkeys. Perception, 3, 105–114.

Hunt, D. M., Dulai, K., Bowmaker, J. K., and **Mollon, J. D.** (1995) The chemistry of John Dalton's color blindness. Science, 257, 984–988.

Hunt, S. P., and **Mantyth, P. W.** (2001) The molecular dynamics of pain control. Nature Reviews Neuroscience, 2, 83–91.

Hurd, P. D., and **Blevins, J.** (1984) Aging and the color of pills. New England Journal of Medicine, 310, 202.

Hurvich, L. M. (1969) Hering and the scientific establishment. American Psychologist, 24, 497–514.

Hurvich, L. M. (1981) Color vision. Sunderland, Mass.: Sinauer Associates.

Iavecchia, J. H., Iavecchia, H. P., and **Roscoe, S. N.** (1983) The moon illusion revisited. Aviation, Space, and Environmental Medicine, 54, 39–46.

Ito, M., and **Gilbert, C. D.** (1999) Attention modulates contextual influences in the primary visual cortex of alert monkeys. Neuron, 22, 593–604.

Ittelson, W. H. (1951) Size as a cue to distance: Static localization. American Journal of Psychology, 64, 54–67.

Ittelson, W. H. (1952/1968) The Ames demonstrations in perception. New York: Hafner.

Jacobs, G. H. (1993) The distribution and nature of colour vision among the mammals. Biological Review, 68, 413–471.

Jacobs, G. H. (1996) Primate photopigments and primate color vision. Proceedings of the National Academy of Sciences: USA. 93, 577–581.

Jacobs, G. H. (1998) Photopigments and seeing—lessons from natural experiments: the Proctor lecture. Investigative Ophthalmology & Visual Science, 39, 2204–2216.

Jacobsen, A., and **Gilchrist, A.** (1988) The ratio principle holds over a million-to-one range of illumination. Perception & Psychophysics, 43, 1–6.

James, W. (1890) The principles of psychology. 2 vols. New York: Holt.

James, W. (1892) Psychology: A briefer course. New York: Holt.

Jameson, D., and **Hurvich, L. M.** (1978) Dichromatic color language: "Reds" and "greens" don't look alike but their colors do. Sensory Processes, 2, 146–155.

Jameson, D., and **Hurvich, L. M.** (1989) Essay concerning color constancy. Annual Review of Psychology, 40, 1–22.

Jamison, R. N. (1996) Influence of weather on report of pain. International Association for the Study of Pain Newsletter, July/August.

Jeffress, L. A. (1948) A place theory of sound localization. Journal of Comparative and Physiological Psychology, 41, 35–39.

Jeffress, L. A., and **Taylor, R. W.** (1961) Lateralization vs. localization. Journal of the Acoustical Society of America, 33, 482–483.

Jeghers, H. (1937) The degree and prevalence of vitamin A deficiency in adults. Journal of the American Medical Association, 109, 756–762.

Jenmalm, P. and **Johansson, R. S.** (1997) Visual and somatosensory information about object shape control manipulative fingertip forces. Journal of Neuroscience, 17, 4486–4499.

Jessell, T. M., and **Kelly, D.** (1991). Pain and analgesia. In E. R. Kandel, J. H. Schwartz, and T. M. Jessell (eds.), Principles of neural science. New York: Elsevier, 385–399.

Johansson, G. (1975) Visual motion perception. Scientific American, 232, 76–88.

Johansson, G., von Hofsten, C., and **Jansson, G.** (1980) Event perception. Annual Review of Psychology, 31, 27–64.

Johansson, R. S., and **Vallbo, A. B.** (1979) Tactile sensibility in the human hand: Relative and absolute densities of four types of mechanoreceptive units in the glabrous skin. Journal of Physiology, 286, 283–300.

Johansson, R. S. and **Vallbo, A. B.** (1983) Tactile sensory coding in the glabrous skin of the human hand. Trends in Neurosciences, 6, 27–32.

Johns, T., and **Keen, S. L.** (1985) Determinants of taste perception and classification among the Aymara of Bolivia. Ecology of Food and Nutrition, 16, 253–271.

Johnson, D. M., and **Hafter, E. R.** (1980) Uncertain-frequency detection: Cuing and condition of observation. Perception & Psychophysics, 28, 143–149.

Johnson, K. O., and **Hsiao, S. S.** (1992) Neural mechanisms of tactual form and texture perception. Annual Review of Neuroscience, 15, 227–250.

Johnson, K. O., and **Lamb, G. H.** (1981) Neural mechanisms of spatial tactile discrimination: Neural patterns evoked by Braille-like dot patterns in the monkey. Journal of Physiology, 310, 117–144.

Johnson-Laird, P. N. (1988) The computer and the mind: An introduction to cognitive science. Cambridge: Harvard University Press.

Johnsrude, I. S., Zatorre, R. J., Milner, B. A., and **Evans, A. C.** (1997) Left-hemisphere specialization for the processing of acoustic transients. NeuroReport, 8, 1761–1765.

Johnston, J. C., and **McClelland, J. L.** (1973) Visual factors in word perception. Perception & Psychophysics, 14, 365–370.

Johnston, J. C., and **McClelland, J. L.** (1974) Perception of letters in words: Seek not and ye shall find. Science, 184, 1192–1194.

Jolicoeur, P., Ullman, S., and **Mackay, M.** (1986). Curve tracing: a possible basic operation in the perception of spatial relations. Memory & Cognition, 14, 129–40.

Joyce, J. (1922/1934) Ulysses. New York: Random House.

Joyce, J. (1939/1967) Finnegans wake. New York: Viking Press.

Judd, D. B. (1960) Appraisal of Land's work on two-primary color projections. Journal of the Optical Society of America, 50, 254–268.

Julesz, B. (1971) Foundations of cyclopean perception. Chicago: University of Chicago Press.

Julesz, B. (1984) A brief outline of the texton theory of human vision. Trends in Neurosciences, 7, 41–45.

Julesz, B. (1991) Early vision and focal attention. Reviews of Modern Physics, 63, 735–772.

Just, M. A., and **Carpenter, P. A.** (1980) A theory of reading: From eye fixations to comprehension. Psychological Review, 87, 329–354.

Kaas, J. H. (1987) Somatosensory cortex. In G. Adelman (ed.), Encyclopedia of neuroscience, vol. 2. Boston: Birkhauser. Pp. 1113–1117.

Kaas, J. H. (1991) Plasticity of sensory and motor maps in adult mammals. Annual Review of Neuroscience, 14, 137–167.

Kaas, J. H., and **Florence, S. L.** (1996) Brain reorganization and experience. Peabody Journal of Education, 71, 152–167.

Kaas, J. H., Florence, S. L., and **Jain, N.** (1999) Subcortical contributions to massive cortical reorganization. Neuron, 22, 657–660.

Kaiser, P. K. and **Boynton, R. M.** (1996) Human Color Vision. The Optical Society of America: Washington, D. C.

Kaitz, M., Good, A., Rokem, A. M., and **Eidelman, A.** (1987) Mothers' recognition of their newborns by olfactory cues. Developmental Psychobiology, 20, 587–591.

Kaitz, M., Lapidot, P., Bronner, R. and **Eidelman, A. I.** (1992) Parturient women can recognize their infants by touch. Developmental Psychology, 28, 35–39.

Kalmus, H. (1955) The discrimination by the nose of the dog of individual human odours and in particular the odour of twins. British Journal of Animal Behaviour, 3, 25–31.

Kanizsa, G. (1976) Subjective contours. Scientific American, 234, 48–52.

Kant, I. (1798/1978) Anthropology from a Pragmatic Point of View (editor H. H. Rudnick; translator by V. L. Dodwell), Carbondale, Ill.: Southern Illinois University Press.

Kanwisher, N., McDermott, J. and **Chun, M. M.** (1997) The fusiform face area: a module in human extrastriate cortex specialized for face perception. Journal of Neuroscience, 17, 4302–4311.

Kapadia, M. K., Westheimer, G., and **Gilbert, C. D.** (1999) Dynamics of spatial summation in primary visual cortex of alert monkeys. Preceedings of the National Academy of Science, USA, 96, 12073–12078.

Kaplan, E., Shapley, R. M., and **Purpura, K.** (1988) Color and luminance contrast as tools for probling the primate retina. Neuroscience Research Supplement 8, S151–S165.

Karni, A., and **Sagi, D.** (1993) The time course of learning a visual skill. Nature, 365, 250–252.

Katz, D. (1925) Der Aufbau der Tastwelt. Zeitschrift fur Psychologie, 11 [see also L. E. Krueger (1970) "David Katz" Der Aufbau der Tastwelt (the world of touch): A synopsis. Perception & Psychophysics, 7, 337–341].

Kauer, J. S. (1991) Contributions of topography and parallel processing to odor coding in the vertebrate olfactory pathway. Trends in Neurosciences, 14, 79–85.

Kaufman, L. (1974) Sight and mind: An introduction to visual perception. New York: Oxford University Press.

Kaufman, L., and **Rock, I.** (1962) The moon illusion. Scientific American, 207, 120–132.

Kaukoranta, E., Hari, R., and **Lounasmaa, O. V.** (1987) Responses of the human auditory cortex to vowel onset after fricative consonants. Experimental Brain Research, 69, 19–23.

Keller, H. (1904/08) The world I live in. New York: Century.

Keller, H. (1908) Sense and sensibility. Century Magazine, 75, 566–577, 773–783.

Kelling, S. T., and **Halpern, B. P.** (1987) Taste judgments and gustatory stimulus duration: Simple taste reaction times. Chemical Senses, 12, 543–562.

Kellman, P. J., and **Shipley, T. F.** (1991) A theory of visual interpolation in object perception. Cognitive Psychology, 23, 141–221.

Kelly, D. H. (1976) Pattern detection and the two-dimensional Fourier transform: Flickering checkerboards and chromatic mechanisms. Vision Research, 16, 277–289.

Kemp, D. T. (1979) Evidence of mechanical nonlinearity and frequency-selective wave amplification in the cochlea. Archives of Otorhinolaryngology, 224, 37–45.

Kendrick, K. M., Levy, F., and **Keverne, E. B.** (1992) Changes in the sensory processing of olfactory signals induced by birth in sheep. Science, 256, 833–836.

Kenshalo, D. (1972) The cutaneous senses. In J. W. Kling and L. A. Riggs (eds.), Woodworth and Schlosberg's experimental psychology (3rd ed.), vol. 1. New York: Holt, Rinehart & Winston.

Kersten, D. (1987) Predictability and redundancy of natural images. Journal of the Optical Society of America A, 4, 2395–2401.

Kersten, D., Mamassian, P. and **Knill, D. C.** (1997) Moving cast shadows induce apparent motion in depth. Perception, 26, 171–192.

Kertsa, L. G. (1962) Voice identifications. Nature, 196, 1253–1257.

Keuning, J. (1968) On the nasal cycle. International Rhinology, 6, 99–136.

Keverne, E. B. (1982) Chemical senses. In H. B. Barlow and J. D. Mollon (eds.), The senses. Cambridge: Cambridge University Press, 428–447.

Kiang, N. Y. S. (1968) A survey of recent developments in the study of auditory physiology. Annals of Otology, Rhinology, and Laryngology, 77, 656–675.

Kiang, N. Y. S. (1975) Stimulus representation in the discharge pattern of auditory neurons. In E. L. Eagles (ed.), The nervous system, vol. 3. New York: Raven Press, 81–96.

Kinchla, R. A. (1974) Detecting target elements in multielement arrays: A confusability model. Perception & Psychophysics, 15, 149–158.

Kinchla, R. A., and **Wolfe, J. M.** (1979) The order of visual processing: "Top-down," "bottom-up," or "middle-out." Perception & Psychophysics, 25, 225–231.

King, A. J., and **Moore, D. R.** (1991) Plasticity of auditory maps in the brain. Trends in Neurosciences, 14, 31–37.

Kinney, J. A., Luria, S. M., Ryan, A. P., Schlicting, C. L., and **Paulson, H. M.** (1980) The vision of submariners and national guardsmen: A longitudinal study. American Journal of Optometry and Physiological Optics, 57, 469–478.

Kirkpatrick, P. (1963) Batting the ball. American Journal of Physics, 31, 606–613.

Klatzky, R. L., Lederman, S. J., and **Metzger, V.** (1985). Identifying objects by touch: An "expert" system. Perception & Psychophysics, 37, 299–302.

Klinke, R., Kral, A., Heid, S., Tillein, J., and **Hartmann, R.** (1999) Recruitment of the auditory cortex in congenitally deaf cats by long-term cochlear electrostimulation. Science, 285, 1729–1733.

Knierim, J. J., and **van Essen, D. C.** (1992) Visual cortex: Cartography, connectivity and concurrent processing. Current Opinion in Neurobiology, 2, 150–155.

Knudsen, E. I., and **Brainard, M. S.** (1995) Creating a unified representation of visual and auditory space in the brain. Annual Review of Neuroscience, 18, 19–43.

Knudsen, E. I. (1998) Capacity for plasticity in the adult owl auditory system expanded by juvenile experience. Science, 279, 1531–1533.

Knudsen, E. I., du Lac, S., and **Easterly, S. D.** (1987) Computational maps in the brain. Annual Review of Neuroscience, 10, 41–65.

Knudsen, E. I., and **Konishi, M.** (1978) A neural map of auditory space in the owl. Science, 200, 795–797.

Knudsen, E. I., and **Konishi, M.** (1980) Monaural occlusion shifts receptive-field locations of auditory midbrain units in the owl. Journal of Neurophysiology, 44, 687–695.

Kobatake, E., Wang, G., and **Tanaka, K.** (1998) Effects of Shape-Discrimination Training on the Selectivity of Inferotemporal Cells in Adult Monkeys. Journal of Neurophysiology, 80, 324–330.

Kobayakawa, T., Ogaw, A. H., Kaneda, H., Ayabe-Kanamura, S., Endo, H., and **Saito, S.** (1999) Spatio-temporal analysis of cortical activity evoked by gustatory stimulation in humans. Chemical Senses, 24, 201–9.

Koelega, H. S., and **Koster, E. P.** (1974) Some experiments on sex differences in odor perception. Annals of the New York Academy of Sciences, 237, 234–246.

Koenig, W. (1950) Subjective effects in binaural hearing. Journal of the Acoustical Society of America, 22, 61–62.

Koffka, K. (1935) Principles of gestalt psychology. New York: Harcourt, Brace & World.

Köhler, W. (1920/1938) Physical gestalten. In W. D. Ellis (ed.), A source book of gestalt psychology. New York: Humanities Press, 17–54.

Köhler, W. (1969) The task of gestalt psychology. Princeton: Princeton University Press.

Kolb, B., and **Whishaw, I. Q.** (1996) Fundamentals of Human Neuropsychology (4th ed.). New York: W. H. Freeman.

Koretz, J. F., and **Handelman, G. H.** (1988) How the human eye focuses. Scientific American, 259, 92–99.

Korte, M., Rauschecker, J. P. (1993) Auditory spatial tuning of cortical neurons is sharpened in cats with early blindness. Journal of Neurophysiology, 70, 1717–1721.

Kosslyn, S. M. (1994) Image and brain: The resolution of the imagery debate. Cambridge: MIT Press.

Kosslyn, S. M., and **Koenig, O.** (1992). Wet mind, the new cognitive neuroscience. New York: The Free Press.

Kosslyn, S. M., Pascual-Leone, A., Felician, O., Camposano, S., Keenan, J. P., Thompson, W. L., Ganis, G., Sukel, K. E., and **Alpert, N. M.** (1999). The role of area 17 in visual imagery: Convergent evidence from PET and rTMS. Science, 284, 167–170.

Kosslyn, S. M., Sukel, K. E., and **Bly, B. M.** (1999) Squinting with the mind's eye: effects of stimulus resolution on imaginal and perceptual comparisons. Memory & Cognition 27, 276–287.

Kovács, G., Vogels, R., and **Orban, G.** (1995) Selectivity of macaque inferior temporal neurons for partially occluded shapes. Journal of Neuroscience, 15, 1984–1997.

Kovács, I., Kozma, P., Fehér, A., and **Benedek, G.** (1999) Late maturation of visual spatial integration in humans. Proceedings of the National Academy of Sciences: USA, 96, 12204–12209.

Kovács, I., Polat, U., Pennefather, P. M., Chandna, A., and **Norcia, A. M.** (2000) A new test of contour integration deficits in patients with a history of disrupted binocular experience during visual development. Vision Research, 40, 1775–1783.

Kowler, E. (1989) Cognitive expectations, not habits, control anticipatory smooth oculomotor pursuit. Vision Research, 29, 1049–1058.

Kowler, E., and **Martins, A. J.** (1982) Eye movements of preschool children. Science, 215, 997–999.

Kraft, J. M., and **Brainard, D. H.** (1999) Mechanisms of color constancy under nearly natural viewing. Proceedings of the National Academy of Sciences: USA, 96, 307–312.

Kramer, M. (1989) Making sense of wine. New York: W. W. Morrow & Co.

Kraus, N., McGee, T. J., Carrell, T. D., Zecker, S. G., Nicol, T. G., and **Koch, D. B.** (1996) Auditory neurophysiologic responses and discrimination deficits in children with learning problems. Science, 273, 971–973.

Krauzlis, R. J., and **Stone, L. S.** (1999) Tracking with the mind's eye. Trends in Neurosciences, 22, 544–550

Kristensen, S., and **Gimsing, S.** (1988) Occupational hearing impairment in pig-breeders. Scandinavian Audiology, 17, 191–192.

Krueger, L. E. (1975) Familiarity effects in visual information processing. Psychological Bulletin, 82, 949–974.

Kuhl, P. K., Andruski, J. E., Chistovich, I. A., Chistovich, L. A., Kozhevnikova, E. V., Ryskina, V. L., Stolyarova, E. I., Sundberg, U., and **Lacerda, F.** (1997) Cross-language analysis of phonetic units in language addressed to infants. Science, 277, 684–686.

Kuhl, P. K., and **Meltzoff, A. N.** (1982) The bimodal perception of speech in infancy. Science, 218, 1138–1141.

Kühne, W. (1879/1977) Chemical processes in the retina. Vision Research, 17, 1273–1316.

Kujala, T., Alho, K., Huotilainen, M., Ilmoniemi, R. J., Lehtokoski, A., Leinonen, A., Rinne, T., Salonen, O., Sinkkonen, J., Standertskjold-Nordenstam, C. G., and **Naatanen, R.** (1997) Electrophysiological evidence for cross-modal plasticity in humans with early- and late-onset blindness. Psychophysiology, 34, 213–216.

Kulkarni, A., and **Colburn, H. S.** (1998) Role of spectral detail in sound-source localization. Nature, 396, 747–749.

Kuller, R., and **Mikellides, B.** (1993) Simulated studies of color, arousal and comfort. In R.W. Marans and D. Stokols (eds.), Environmental Simulation: Research and Policy Issues. New York: Plenum Press, 163–190.

Kundel, H. L., and **Nodine, C. F.** (1983) A visual concept shapes image perception. Radiology, 146, 363–368.

Kunkler-Peck, A. J., and **Turvey, M.T.** (2000) Hearing shape. Journal of Experimental Psychology: Human Perception & Performance, 26, 279–294.

Künnapas, T. M. (1968) Distance perception as a function of available visual cues. Journal of Experimental Psychology, 77, 523–529.

Kunst-Wilson, W. R., and **Zajonc, R. B.** (1980) Affective discrimination of stimuli that cannot be recognized. Science, 207, 557–558.

Kurtenbach, W., Sternheim, C. E., and **Spillmann, L.** (1984) Change in hue of spectral colors by dilution with white light (Abney effect). Journal of the Optical Society of America A, 1, 365–372.

Kurtz, D., and **Butter, C. M.** (1980) Impairments in visual discrimination performance and gaze shifts in monkeys with superior colliculus lesions. Brain Research, 196, 109–124.

Kuthan, V. (1987) Some contributions of J. E. Purkyne to the visual physiology. Physiologia Bohemoslovaca, 36, 255–267.

LaBerge, D., and **Buchsbaum, M. S.** (1990) Positron emission tomographic measurements of pulvinar activity during an attention task. Journal of Neuroscience, 10, 613–619.

LaBerge, D., Carter, M., and **Brown, V.** (1992) A network simulation of thalamic circuit operations in selective attention. Neural Computation, 4, 318–331.

Ladefoged, P., and **Broadbent, D. E.** (1957) Information conveyed by vowels. Journal of the Acoustical Society of America, 29, 98–104.

Laing, D. G. (1988) Relationship between the differential adsorption of odorants by the olfactory mucus and their perception in mixtures. Chemical Senses, 13, 463–471.

Laming, D., and **Laming, J.** (1992) F. Hegelmaier: on memory for the length of a line Psychological Research, 54, 233–239.

Lamme, V. A. F. (1995) The neurophysiology of figure/ground segregation in primary visual cortex. Journal of Neuroscience, 15, 1605–1615.

Lancet, D. (1986) Vertebrate olfactory reception. Annual Review of Neuroscience, 9, 329–355.

Lancker, D. R. V., Kreiman, J. and **Cummings, J.** (1989) Voice perception deficits: Neuroanatomical correlates of phonagnosia. Journal of Clinical and Experimental Neuropsychology, 11, 665–674.

Land, E. H. (1959) Experiments in color vision. Scientific American, 200, 84–94, 96, 99.

Land, M. F., and **Furneaux, S.** (1997) The knowledge base of the oculomotor system. Philosophical Transactions of the Royal Society, London (Series B), 352, 1231–1239.

Landau, B. (1991) Spatial representation of objects in the young blind child. Cognition, 38, 145–178.

Lappin, J. S., Doner, J. F., and **Kottas, B. L.** (1979) Minimal conditions for the visual detection of structure and motion in three dimensions. Science, 209, 717–719.

Lawless, H. T., and **Engen, T.** (1977) Association to odors: Interference, memories, and verbal labeling. Journal of Experimental Psychology, 3, 52–59.

Lawless, H. T., Glatter, S., and **Hohn, C.** (1991) Context-dependent changes in the perception of odor quality. Chemical Senses, 16, 349–360.

Leclerc, C., Saint-Amour, D., Lavoie, M. E., Lassonde, M., and **Lepore, F.** (2000) Brain functional reorganization in early blind humans revealed by auditory event-related potentials. Neuroreport, 11, 545–550.

Lederman, S. J. (1976) The "callus-thenics" of touching. Canadian Journal of Psychology, 30, 82–89.

Lederman, S. J., and **Klatzky, R. L.** (1987). Hand movements: A window into haptic object recognition. Cognitive Psychology, 19, 342–348.

Lederman, S. J., and **Klatzky, R. L.** (1990) Haptic classification of common objects: Knowledge-driven exploration. Cognitive Psychology, 22, 421–459.

Lederman, S. J., Klatzky, R. L., and **Pawluk, D. T.** (1993) Lessons from the study of biological touch for robot haptic sensing. In H. Nicholls (ed.), Advanced tactile sensing for robotics In World scientific series in robotics and automated systems, vol. 5, Singapore: World Scientific Publishing, 193–220.

Lederman, S. J., and **Taylor, M. M.** (1972) Fingertip force, surface geometry, and the perception of roughness by active touch. Perception & Psychophysics, 12, 401–408.

Lee, D. N. (1976) A theory of visual control of braking based on information about time-to-collision. Perception, 5, 437–459.

Lee, D. N. (1980) The optic flow field: The foundation of vision. Philosophical Transactions of the Royal Society of London, Series B, 290, 169–179.

Lee, D. N., and **Reddish, P. E.** (1981) Plummeting gannets: A paradigm of ecological optics. Nature, 293, 293–294.

Lee, H. W., Hong, S. B., Seo, D. W., Tae, W. S., and **Hong S. C.** (2000) Mapping of functional organization in human visual cortex: electrical cortical stimulation. Neurology, 54, 849–854.

Leehey, S. C., Moskowitz-Cook, A., Brill, S., and **Held, R.** (1975) Orientational anisotropy in infant vision. Science, 190, 900–902.

Lefebvre, P. P., Malgrange, B., Staecker, H., Moonen, G., and **van de Water, T. R.** (1993) Retinoic acid stimulates regeneration of mammalian auditory hair cells. Science, 260, 692–695.

Legge, G. E., Klitz, T. S., and **Tjan, B. S.** (1997) Mr. Chips: An ideal-observer model of reading. Psychological Review, 104, 524–553.

LeGrand, Y. (1968) Light, colour, and vision (2nd ed.). R. W. G. Hunt and F. R. W. Hunt (trans.). London: Chapman & Hall.

Lehky, S. R., Sejnowski, T. J. and **Desimone, R.** (1992) Predicting responses of nonlinear neurons in monkey striate cortex to complex patterns. Journal of Neuroscience, 12, 3568–3581.

Lehmkuhle, S. W., and **Fox, R.** (1977) Global stereopsis in the cat. Paper presented at the Association for Research in Vision and Ophthalmology, Sarasota, Fla.

Leibowitz, H. W. (1983) A behavioral and perceptual analysis of grade crossing accidents. Operation Lifesaver National Symposium 1982. Chicago: National Safety Council.

Leibowitz, H. W., and **Moore, D.** (1966) Role of changes in accommodation and convergence in the perception of size. Journal of the Optical Society of America, 56, 1120–1122.

Leibowitz, H. W., and **Owens, D. A.** (1975) Anomalous myopias and the intermediate dark focus of accomodation. Science, 189, 646–648.

Leibowitz, H. W., and **Owens, D. A.** (1976). Night myopia: Cause and a possible basis for amelioration. American Journal of Optometry and Physiological Optics, 53, 709–717.

Lennie, P., and **D'Zmura, M.** (1988) Mechanisms of color vision. CRC Critical Reviews in Neurobiology, 3, 333–400.

Lennie, P., Krauskopf, J., and **Sclar, G.** (1990) Chromatic mechanisms in striate cortex of macaque. Journal of Neuroscience, 10, 649–669.

Leopold, D. A., and **Logothetis, N. K.** (1996) Activity changes in early visual cortex reflect monkeys' percepts during binocular rivalry. Nature, 379, 549–553.

Leopold, D. A., and **Logothetis, N. K.** (1999) Multistable phenomena: changing views in perception, Trends in Cognitive Sciences, 3, 254–264.

Lerner, M. R., Gyorgyi, T. K., Reagan, J., Roby-Shemkovitz, A., Rybczynski, R., and **Vogt, R.** (1990) Peripheral events in moth olfaction. Chemical Senses, 15, 191–198.

Lessard, N., Paré, M., Lepore, F., and **Lassonde, M.** (1998) Early-blind human subjects localize sound sources better than sighted subjects. Nature, 395, 278–280.

Leventhal, A. G., Thompson, K. G., Liu, D., Zhou, Y., and **Ault, S. J.** (1995) Concomitant sensitivity to orientation, direction, and color of cells in layers 2, 3, and 4 of monkey striate cortex. Journal of Neuroscience, 1995, 15, 1808–1818.

Levi, D. M., and **Sharma, V.** (1998) Integration of local orientation in strabismic amblyopia. Vision Research, 38, 775–781.

Levinson, E., and **Sekuler, R.** (1976) Adaptation alters perceived direction of motion. Vision Research, 16, 779–781.

Lewis, A., and **Del Priore, L. V.** (1988) The biophysics of visual photoreception. Physics Today, 41, 38–46.

Li, X., Logan, R. J., and **Pastore, R. E.** (1991) Perception of acoustic source characteristics: Walking sounds. Journal of the Acoustical Society of America, 90, 3036–3049.

Liberman, M. C. (1982) The cochlear frequency map for the cat: Labelling auditory nerve fibers of known characteristics. Journal of the Acoustical Society of America, 72, 1441–1449.

Lindemann, B. (2000) A taste for umami. Nature Neuroscience, 3, 99–100.

Linden, D. E. J., Kallenbach, U., Heinecke, A, Singer, W., and **Goebel, R.** (1999) The myth of upright vision: a psychophysical and functional imaging study of adaptation to inverting spectacles. Perception, 28, 469–481.

Linder, M. E., and **Gilman, A. G.** (1992) G proteins. Scientific American, 267, 56–65.

Lindsay, P. H., and **Norman, D. A.** (1977) Human information processing (2nd ed.). New York: Academic Press.

Liss, J. M., Weismer, G., and **Rosenbek, J. C.** (1990) Selected acoustic characteristics of speech production in very old males. Journal of Gerontology: Psychological Sciences, 45, 35–45.

Livingstone, M. S., and **Hubel, D. H.** (1981) Effects of sleep and arousal on the processing of visual information in the cat. Nature, 291, 554–561.

Livingstone, M. S., and **Hubel, D. H.** (1984) Anatomy and physiology of a color system in primate primary visual cortex. Journal of Neuroscience, 4, 309–356.

Livingstone, M., and **Hubel, D. H.** (1988) Segregation of form, color, movement, and depth: Anatomy, physiology, and perception. Science, 240, 740–749.

Locke, J. (1690/1924) An essay concerning human understanding (abridged and edited by A. S. Pringle-Pattison). Oxford, England: Clarendon Press.

Loftus, E. F., and **Kliner, M. R.** (1992) Is the unconscious smart or dumb? The American Psychologist, 47, 761–765.

Logothetis, N. (1998) Single units and conscious vision. Philosophical Transactions of the Royal Society of London (Series B), 353, 1801–1818.

Logothetis, N. K., and **Schall, J. D.** (1989) Neuronal correlates of subjective visual perception. Science, 245, 761–763.

Loomis, J. M. (1981) Tactile pattern perception. Perception, 10, 5–27.

Loomis, J. M. (1990) A model of character recognition and legibility. Journal of Experimental Psychology: Human Perception and Performance, 16, 106–120.

Loomis, J. M., Klatzky, R. L., and **Lederman, S. J.** (1991). Similarity of tactual and visual picture recognition with limited field of view. Perception, 20, 167–178.

Lotto, R. B., Williams, S. M., and **Purves, D.** (1999) An empirical basis for Mach bands. Proceedings of the National Academy of Sciences: USA, 96, 5239–5244.

Luck, S. J., Chelazzi, L., Hillyard, S. A., and **Desimone, R.** (1997) Neural mechanisms of spatial selective attention to areas V1, V2 and V4 of macaque visual cortex. Journal of Neurophysiology, 77, 24–42.

Luck, S. J., Vogel, E. K., and **Shapiro, K. L.** (1996) Word meanings can be accessed but not reported during the attentional blink. Nature, 383, 616–618.

Ludel, J. (1978) Introduction to sensory processes. New York: Freeman.

Lythgoe, J. N. (1979) The ecology of vision. Oxford, England: Clarendon Press.

Macdonald, D., and **Brown, R.** (1985) The smell of success. New Scientist, 106, 10–14.

Mack, A., and **Rock, I.** (1998) Inattentional blindness. Cambridge MA: MIT Press.

MacMillan, N. A., and **Creelman, C.** (1991) Detection theory: A user's guide. Cambridge, England: Cambridge University Press.

MacNichol, E. (1964) Three-pigment color vision. Scientific American, 211, 48–56.

Maffei, L., and **Fiorentini, A.** (1973) The visual cortex as a spatial frequency analyzer. Vision Research, 13, 1255–1267.

Makous, J. C., and **Middlebrooks, J. C.** (1990) Two-dimensional sound localization by human listeners. Journal of the Acoustical Society of America, 87, 2188–2200.

Malakoff, D. (1999) Following the scent of avian olfaction. Science, 286, 704–705.

Malcolm, R. (1984) Pilot disorientation and the use of a peripheral vision display. Aviation, Space, and Environmental Medicine, 55, 231–238.

Malpelli, J. G., and **Baker, F. H.** (1975) The representation of the visual field in the lateral geniculate nucleus of Macaca mulatta. Journal of Comparative Neurology, 161, 569–594.

Mandler, G., Nakamura, Y., and **Shebo van Zandt, B. J.** (1987) Nonspecific effects of exposure on stimuli that cannot be recognized. Journal of Experimental Psychology: Learning, Memory, and Cognition, 13(4), 646–648.

Manley, G. A., Koppl, C., and **Konishi, M.** (1988) A neural map of interaural intensity differences in the brain stem of the barn owl. Journal of Neuroscience, 8, 2665–2676.

Mansfield, R. (1974) Neural basis of orientation perception in primate vision. Science, 186, 1133–1135.

Marcar, V. L., Zihl, J., and **Cowey, A.** (1997) Comparing the visual deficits of a motion blind patient with the visual deficits of monkeys with area MT removed. Neuropsychologia, 35, 1459–1465.

Marendaz, C., Stivalet, P., Barraclough, L., and **Walkowiac, P.** (1993) Effect of gravitational cues on the visual search for orientation. Journal of Experimental Psychology: Human Perception & Performance, 19, 1266–1277.

Marin, O. S. M. (1976) Neurobiology of language: An overview. Annals of the New York Academy of Sciences, 280, 900–912.

Mariotte, E. (1668/1948) The discovery of the blindspot. In W. Dennis (ed.), Readings in the history of psychology. New York: Appleton-Century-Crofts, 42–43.

Marks, L. E., and **Wheeler, M. E.** (1998) Attention and the detectability of weak taste stimuli. Chemical Senses, 23, 19–29.

Mark, L. S., and **Todd, J. T.** (1983) The perception of growth in three dimensions. Perception & Psychophysics, 33, 193–196.

Marotta, J. J., Perrot, T. S., Nicolle, D., Servos, P., and **Goodale, M. A.** (1995) Adapting to monocular vision: grasping with one eye Experimental Brain Research, 104, 107–114.

Marr, D. (1976) Early processing of visual information. Philosophical Transactions of the Royal Society, Series B, 275, 483–524.

Marr, D. (1982) Vision. New York: W. H. Freeman.

Marron, J. A., and **Bailey, I. L.** (1982) Visual factors and orientation-mobility performance. American Journal of Optometry and Physiological Optics, 59, 413–426.

Martin, G. (1987) The world through a starling's eye. New Scientist, 114, 49–51.

Martin, K. A. C. (1988) The lateral geniculate nucleus strikes back. Trends in Neurosciences, 11, 192–194.

Massaro, D. W., and **Cohen, M. M.** (1996) Perceiving speech from inverted faces. Perception & Psychophysics, 58, 1047–1065.

Massaro, D. W., and **Egan, P. B.** (1996) Perceiving affect from the voice and the face. Psychonomic Bulletin & Review, 3, 215–221.

Massaro, D. W., and **Stork, D. G.** (1998) speech recognition and sensory integration. American Scientist, 86, 236–244.

Masterton, R. B., and **Imig, T. J.** (1984) Neural mechanisms of sound localization. Annual Review of Physiology, 46, 275–280.

Masterton, R. B., Thompson, G. C., Bechtold, J. K., and **Robards, M. J.** (1975) Neuroanatomical basis of binaural phase-difference analysis for sound localization: A comparative study. Journal of Comparative and Physiological Psychology, 89, 379–386.

Mather, G., and **Harris, J.** (1998) Theoretical models of the motion aftereffect. In G. Mather, F. Verstraten, and S. Anstis (eds.) The Motion Aftereffect: A Modern Perspective. Cambridge: MIT Press, 157–185.

Mather, G., and **Moulden, B.** (1980) A simultaneous shift in apparent direction: Further evidence for a "distribution-shift" model of direction coding. Quarterly Journal of Experimental Psychology, 32, 325–333.

Matin, L. (1986) Visual localization and eye movements. In K. Boff, L. Kaufman, and J. Thomas (eds.), Handbook of perception and human performance. New York: Wiley, 20–1 - 20–45.

Matin, L., and **MacKinnon, G. E.** (1964) Autokinetic movement: Selective manipulation of directional components by image stabilization. Science, 143, 147–148.

Mattingly, I. G., and **Liberman, A. M.** (1988) Specialized perceiving systems for speech and other biologically significant sounds. In G. M. Edelman, W. E. Gall, and W. M. Cowan (eds.), Auditory function: Neurobiological bases of hearing. New York: John Wiley & Sons, 775–793.

Maunsell, J. (1995) The brain's visual world: representation of visual targets in cerebral cortex. Science, 270, 764–769.

Maunsell, J. H. R., and **Newsome, W. T.** (1987) Visual processing in monkey extrastriate cortex. Annual Review of Neuroscience, 10, 363–401.

Maurer, D., Lewis, T. L., Brent, H. P., and **Levin, A. V.** (1999) Rapid improvement in the acuity of infants after visual input. Science, 286, 108-110.

May, M. (1994) Three-dimensional mammography. American Scientist, 82, 421–422.

Mayr, E. (1982) The growth of biological thought: Diversity, evolution, and inheritance. Cambridge MA: Belknap Press/Harvard University Press.

McAdams, S. (1984) Spectral fusion, spectral parsing, and the formation of auditory images. Paris: IRCAM.

McBurney, D. H. (1974) Are there primary tastes for man? Chemical Senses and Flavor, 1, 17–28.

McBurney, D. H. (1978) Psychological dimensions and perceptual analyses of taste. In E. C. Carterette and M. P. Friedman (eds.), Handbook of perception, vol. 6A. New York: Academic Press, 125–155.

McBurney, D. H., and **Gent, J. F.** (1979) On the nature of taste qualities. Psychological Bulletin, 86, 151–167.

McBurney, D. H., and **Moskat, L. J.** (1975) Taste thresholds in college-age smokers and nonsmokers. Perception & Psychophysics, 18, 71–73.

McBurney, D. H., Smith, D. V., and **Shick, T. R.** (1972) Gustatory cross adaptation: Sourness and bitterness. Perception & Psychophysics, 11, 228–232.

McCabe, P. A., and **Dey, F. L.** (1965) The effect of aspirin upon auditory sensitivity. Annals of Otology, Rhinology, and Laryngology, 74, 312–325.

McClelland, J. L., and **Rumelhart, D. E.** (1981) An interactive activation model of context effects in letter perception: Part 1. An account of basic findings. Psychological Review, 88, 375–407.

McConkie, G. W., and **Rayner, K.** (1975) The span of the effective stimulus during a fixation in reading. Perception & Psychophysics, 17, 578–586.

McCutcheon, N. B., and **Saunders, J.** (1972) Human taste papilla stimulation: Stability of quality judgments over time. Science, 175, 214–216.

McDermott, H. J., and **McKay, C. M.** (1997) Musical pitch perception iwth electrical stimulation of the cochlea. Journal of the Ascoustical Society of America, 101, 1622–1631.

McElheny, V. K. (1999) Insisting on the impossible: The life of Edwin Land, inventor of instant photography. Reading, MA: Perseus Books.

McFadden, D. (1982) Tinnitus: Facts, theories and treatments. Washington, D.C.: National Academy of Sciences Press.

McFadden, D. (1998) Sex differences in the auditory system. Developmental Neuropsychology, 14, 261–298.

McFadden, D., and **Callaway, N. L.** (1999) Better discrimination of small changes in commonly encountered than in less commonly encountered auditory stimuli. Journal of Experimental Psychology: Human Perception and Performance, 25, 543–560.

McFadden, D., and **Plattsmier, H. S.** (1983) Aspirin can potentiate the temporary hearing loss induced by intense sounds. Hearing Research, 9, 295–316.

McFadden, D., Plattsmier, H. S., and **Pasanen, E. G.** (1984) Aspirin-induced hearing loss as a model of sensorineural hearing loss. Hearing Research, 16, 251–260.

McGurk, H., and **MacDonald, J.** (1976) Hearing lips and seeing voices. Nature, 264, 746–748.

McIntosh, A. R., Sekuler, A. B., Penpeci, C., Rajah, M. N., Grady, C. L. , Sekuler, R., and **Bennett, P. J.** (1999) Recruitment of unique neural systems supporting visual memory in normal aging. Current Biology, 9, 1275–1278.

McKee, S. P. (1981) A local mechanism for differential velocity detection. Vision Research, 21, 491–500.

Mealey, L., Bridgstock, R., and **Townsend, G. C.** (1999) Symmetry and perceived facial attractiveness: a monozygotic co-twin comparison. Journal of Personality & Social Psychology, 76, 151–158.

Meenan, J. P., and **Miller, L. A.** (1994) Perceptual flexibility after frontal or temporal lobectomy. Neuropsychologia, 32, 1145–1149.

Meiselman, H. L., and **Dzendolet, E.** (1967) Variability in gustatory quality identification. Perception & Psychophysics, 2, 496–498.

Melzack, R. (1992) Phantom limbs. Scientific American, 266, 120–126.

Mendelson, J. R. (1992) Neural selectivity for interaural frequency disparity in cat primary auditory cortex. Hearing Research, 58, 47–56.

Mennella, J. A., and **Beauchamp, G. K.** (1999) Experience with a flavor in mother's milk modifies the infant's acceptance of flavored cereal. Developmental Psychobiology, 35, 197–203.

Menon, R. S., Ogawa, S., Strupp, J. P., and **Ugurbil, K.** (1997) Ocular dominance in human V1 demonstrated by functional magnetic resonance imaging. Journal of Neurophysiology, 77, 2780–2787.

Merbs, S. L., and Nathans, J. (1992) Absorption spectra of human cone pigments. Nature, 356, 433–435.

Merigan, W. H., and Maunsell, J. H. R. (1993) How parallel are the primate visual pathways? Annual Review of Neuroscience, 16, 369–402.

Merker, H. (1992) Listening: Ways of hearing in a silent world. New York: HarperCollins.

Merzenich, M. M. (1987) Dynamic neocortical processes and the origins of higher brain functions. In J. P. Changeux and M. Konishi (eds.), Neural and molecular bases of learning. Chichester, England: John Wiley & Sons, 337–358.

Merzenich, M. M., Jenkins, W. M., Johnston, P., Schreiner, C., Miller, S. L., and Tallal, P. (1996) Temporal processing deficits of language-learning impaired children ameliorated by training. Science, 271, 77–81.

Merzenich, M. M., Nelson, R. J., Kaas, J. H., Stryker, M. P., Jenkins, W. M., Zook, J. M., Cynader, M. S., and Schoppmann, A. (1987) Variability in hand surface representations in Area-3B and Area-1 in adult owl and squirrel monkeys. Journal of Comparative Neurology, 258, 281–296.

Metelli, F. (1974) The perception of transparency. Scientific American, 230, 90–98.

Michaels, C. F., and Carello, C. (1981) Direct perception. Englewood Cliffs, N.J.: Prentice-Hall.

Middlebrooks, J. C., and Green, D. M. (1991) Sound localization by human listeners. Annual Review of Psychology, 42, 135–159.

Miller, G. (1962) Decision units in the perception of speech. IRE Transactions on Information Theory, 8, 81–83.

Miller, I. J., Jr., and Bartoshuk, L. M. (1991) Taste perception, taste bud distribution, and spatial relationships. In T. V. Getchell, R. L. Doty, L. M. Bartoshuk, and J. B. Snow, Jr. (eds.), Smell and taste in health and disease. New York: Raven Press, 175–204.

Miller, I. J., Jr., and Reedy, F. E. (1990) Variations in human taste bud density and taste intensity perception. Physiology, and Behavior, 47, 1213–1219.

Mills, A. W. (1960) Lateralization of high-frequency tones. Journal of the Acoustical Society of America, 32, 132–134.

Milner, B. (1968) Visual recognition and recall after right temporal-lobe excision in man. Neuropsychologia, 6, 191–209.

Mishkin, M. (1987) The role of striate cortex in the guidance of eye movements in the monkey. Journal of Neuroscience, 7, 776–794.

Mistlin, A. J., and Perrett, D. I. (1990). Visual and somatosensory processing in the macaque temporal cortex: The role of "expectation". Experimental Brain Research, 82, 437–450.

Mitchell, S. C. (1996) The fish-odor syndrome. Perspectives in Biology and Medicine, 39, 514–526.

Mitchell, D. E., Freeman, R. D., Millidot, M., and Haegerstrom, G. (1973) Meridional amblyopia: Evidence for modification of the human visual system by early visual experience. Vision Research, 13, 535–558.

Mitchell, D. E., and Ware, C. (1974) Interocular transfer of a visual aftereffect in normal and stereoblind humans. Journal of Physiology, 236, 707–721.

Miyamoto, R. T., Kirk, K. I., Robbins, A. M., Todd, S., Riley, A. and Pisoni, D. B. (1997) Speech perception and speech intelligibility in children with multichannel cochlear implants. In W. Arnold (ed.) Advances in Oto-Rhino-Laryngology. Basel: S. Karger, 198–203.

Miyashita, Y. (1993) Inferior temporal cortex: Where visual perception meets memory. Annual Review of Neuroscience, 16, 245–263.

Mody, M., Schwartz, R. G., Gravel, J. S., and Ruben, R. J. (1999) Speech perception and verbal memory in children with and without histories of otitis media. Journal of Speech, Language and Hearing Research, 42, 1069–1079.

Moller, A. R. (1974) Responses of units in cochlear nucleus to sinusoidally amplitude-modulated tones. Experimental Neurology, 45, 104–117.

Mollon, J. (1992) Worlds of difference. Nature, 356, 378–379.

Mollon, J. D. (1989) "Tho' she kneel'd in that place where they grew . . . " The uses and origins of primate colour vision. Journal of Experimental Biology, 146, 21–38.

Mombaerts, P. (1999) Seven-transmembrane proteins as odorant and chemosensory receptors. Science, 286, 707–711.

Moncrieff, R. W. (1956) Olfactory adaptation and odor likeness. Journal of Physiology, 133, 301–316.

Moore, B. (1986) Frquency selectivity. London: Academic Press.

Moore, C. M., Yantis, S., and Vaughan, B. (1998) Object-based visual selection: Evidence from perceptual completion. Psychological Science, 9, 104–110.

Moore, M. E., Linker, E., and **Purcell, M.** (1965) Taste sensitivity after eating: A signal detection approach. American Journal of Psychology, 78, 107–111.

Morales, D., and **Pashler, H.** (1999) No role for colour in symmetry perception. Nature, 399, 115–116.

Moran, J., and **Desimone, R.** (1985) Selective attention gates visual processing in the extrastriate cortex. Science, 229, 782–784.

Moray, N. (1959) Attention in dichotic listening: Affective cues and the influence of instructions. Quarterly Journal of Experimental Psychology, 11, 56–60.

Morgan, M. J., Watamaniuk, S. N., and **McKee, S. P.** (2000) The use of an implicit standard for fdmeasuring discrimination thresholds. Vision Research, 40, 2341–2349.

Moscovitch. M., Winocur, G., and **Behrmann, M.** (1997) What is special about face recognition? Nineteen experiments on a person with visual object agnosia and dyslexia but normal face recognition. Journal of Cognitive Neuroscience, 9, 554–604.

Moses, Y., Ullman, S., and **Edelman, S.** (1996) Generalization to novel images in upright and inverted faces. Perception, 25, 443–461.

Moskowitz, H. R. (1978) Taste and food technology: Acceptability, aesthetics, and preference. In E. C. Carterette and M. P. Friedman (eds.), Handbook of perception, vol. 6A. New York: Academic Press, 157–194.

Moulton, D. G. (1974) Dynamics of cell populations in the olfactory epithelium. Annals of the New York Academy of Sciences, 237, 52–61.

Mountcastle, V. B. (1975) The view from within: Pathways to the study of perception. Johns Hopkins Medical Journal, 136, 109–131.

Mountcastle, V. B. (1984) Central nervous mechanisms in mechanoreceptive sensibility. In I. Darian-Smith (ed.), Handbook of physiology: The nervous system III. Bethesda, Md.: American Physiological Society, 789–878.

Mountcastle, V. B., Talbot, W. H., and **Kornhuber, H. H.** (1966) The neural transformation of mechanical stimuli delivered to the monkey's hand. In A.V.S. de Reuck and J. Knight (eds.). Touch, Heat and Pain (A CIBA Foundation Symposium), London: Churchill.

Movshon, J. A. (1975) The velocity tuning of single units in cat striate cortex. Journal of Physiology, 249, 445–468.

Movshon, J. A., and **Lennie, P.** (1979) Pattern-selective adaptation in visual cortical neurones. Nature, 278, 850–852.

Movshon, J. A., Adelson, E. H., Gizzi, M. S., and **Newsome, W. T.** (1986) The analysis of moving visual patterns. In C. Chagas, R. Gattas and C. G. Gross. (eds.) Pattern Recognition Mechanisms. Springer-Verlag, 177–151.

Mozel, M. M., Smith, B., Smith, P., Sullivan, R., and **Swender, P.** (1969) Nasal chemoreception in flavor identification. Archives of Otolaryngology, 90, 367–373.

Mühlnickel, W., Elbert, T., Taub, E., and **Flor, H.** (1998) Reorganization of auditory cortex in tinnitus. Proceedings of the National Academy of Sciences: USA, 95, 10340–10343.

Münte, T. F., Kohlmetz, C., Nagel, W., and **Altenmüller, E.** (2001) Superior auditory spatial tuning in conductors. Nature 409, 580.

Murphy, B. J. (1978) Pattern thresholds for moving and stationary gratings during smooth eye movement. Vision Research, 18, 521–530.

Murphy, C., and **Cain, W. S.** (1986) Odor identification: The blind are better. Physiology & Behavior, 37, 177–180.

Murphy, C., Cain, W. S., and **Bartoshuk, L. M.** (1977) Mutual action of taste and olfaction. Sensory Processes, 1, 204–211.

Nadel, L., Culicover, P., Cooper, L. A., and **Harnish, R. M.** (eds.), (1989) Neural connections, mental computations. Cambridge: M. I. T. Press.

Nadol, J. B. (1993) Hearing loss. New England Journal of Medicine, 329, 1092–1102.

Nagel, T. (1991) What is it like to be a bat? In T. Nagel, Mortal questions. Cambridge, England: Cambridge University Press, 165–180.

Naka, K. I., and **Rushton, W. A. H.** (1966) S-potentials from colour units in the retina of fish Cyprinidae. Journal of Physiology, 185, 536–555.

Nakayama, K., and **Shimojo, S.** (1990) Da Vinci stereopsis: depth and subjective occluding contours from unpaired image points. Vision Research, 30, 1811–1825.

Nakayama, K., Shimojo, S., and **Ramachandran, V. S.** (1990) Transparency: Relation to depth, subjective contours, luminance, and neon color spreading. Perception, 19, 497–513.

Nakayama, K., Shimojo, S., and **Silverman, G. H.** (1989) Stereoscopic depth: Its relation to image segmentation, grouping and the recognition of occluded objects. Perception, 18, 55–68.

Nathans, J. (1989) The genes for color vision. Scientific American, 260, 42–49.

Navon, D. (1977) Forest before trees: The precedence of global features in visual perception. Cognitive Psychology, 9, 353–383.

Navon, D., and **Norman, J.** (1983) Does global precedence really depend on visual angle? Journal of Experimental Psychology: Human Perception and Performance, 9, 955–965.

Nawrot, M., and **Blake, R.** (1991) The interplay between stereopsis and structure from motion. Perception & Psychophysics, 49, 230–244.

Nawrot, M. and **Blake, R.** (1993) On the perceptual identity of dynamic stereopsis and kinetic depth. Vision Research, 33, 1561–1571.

Neider, A., and **Wagner, H.** (1999) Perception and neuronal coding of subjective contours in the owl. Nature Neuroscience, 2, 660–663.

Neitz, M., and **Neitz, J.** (1995) Numbers and ratios of visual pigment genes for normal red-green color vision. Science, 267, 1013–1016.

Neitz, J. M., Neitz, and **Jacobs, G. H.** (1993). More than three different cone pigments among people with normal color vision. Vision Research, 33, 117–122.

Neri, P., Morrone, M. C., and **Burr, D. C.** (1998) Seeing biological motion. Nature, 395, 894–896.

Neumayer, C. (1992) Tetrachromatic color vision in goldfish: evidence from color mixture experiments. Journal of Comparative Physiology A, 171, 639–649.

Newsome, W. T., Britten, K. H., and **Movshon, J. A.** (1989) Neuronal correlates of a perceptual decision. Nature, 341, 52–54.

Newsome, W. T., and **Paré, E. B.** (1988) A selective impairment of motion perception following lesions of the middle temporal visual area (MT). Journal of Neuroscience, 8, 2201–2211.

Newton, I. (1704/1952) Opticks, or a treatise of the reflections, refractions, inflections & colours of light (4th ed.). New York: Dover.

Nicolelis, M. A. (2001) Actions from thoughts. Nature 409 suppl: 403–7.

Niemeyer, W., and **Starlinger, I.** (1981) Do the blind hear better? Investigations on auditory processing in congenital or early acquired blindness: II. Central functions. Audiology, 20, 510–515.

Nisbett, R., and **Wilson, T. D.** (1977) Telling more than we can know: Verbal reports on mental processes. Psychological Review, 84, 231–259.

Nissen, M. J., Corkin, S., Buonanno, F. S., Growdon, J. H., Wray, S. H., and **Bauer, J. A., Jr.** (1985) Spatial vision in Alzheimer's disease. general findings and a case report. Archives of Neurology, 42, 667–671.

Nixon, J. C., and **Glorig, A.** (1961) Noise-induced permanent threshold shift at 2000 cps and 4000 cps. Journal of the Acoustical Society of America, 33, 904–908.

Nobili, R., Mammoano, F., and **Ashmore, J.** (1998) How well do we understand the cochlea? Trends in Neuroscience, 21, 159–167.

Noble, W. (1983) Hearing, hearing impairment, and the audible world: A theoretical essay. Audiology, 22, 325–338.

Norcia, A. M., and **Tyler, C. W.** (1985) Spatial frequency sweep VEP: Visual acuity development during the first year of life. Vision Research, 25, 1399–1403.

Nordby, K. (1990). Vision in a complete achromat: a personal account. In R. Hess, L. Sharpe, and K. Nordby (eds.), Night vision: Basic, clinical and applied aspects. Cambridge: Cambridge University Press. Pp. 290–315.

Norman, J. F., and **Lappin, J. S.** (1992) The detection of surface curvature defined by optical motion. Perception & Psychophysics, 51, 386–396.

Nothdurft, H. C. (1985) Discrimination of higher-order textures. Perception, 14, 551–560.

NRC (1989) Myopia: Prevalence and progression. Washington, D. C.: National Academy Press.

Nummela, S. (1995) Scaling of the mammalian middle ear. Hearing Research, 85, 18–30.

O'Doherty, J., Rolls, E. T., Francis, S., Bowtell, R., McGlone, F., Kobal, G., Renner, B., and **Ahne G.** (2000) Sensory-specific satiety-related olfactory activation of the human orbitofrontal cortex. Neuroreport, 11, 399–403.

Oldfield, S. R., and **Parker, S. P. A.** (1984a) Acuity of sound localization: A topography of auditory space. I. Normal hearing conditions. Perception, 13, 581–600.

Oldfield, S. R., and **Parker, S. P. A.** (1984b) Acuity of sound localization: A topography of auditory space. II. Pinna cues absent. Perception, 13, 601–617.

Oldfield, S. R., and **Parker, S. P. A.** (1986) Acuity of sound localization: A topography of auditory space. III. Monaural hearing conditions. Perception, 15, 67–81.

Olshausen, B. A., and **Field, D. J.** (2000) Vision and the coding of natural images. American Scientist, 88, 238–245.

Olson, H. F. (1967) Music, physics, and engineering (2nd ed.). New York: Dover.

Orbach, H. S., and **Wilson, H. R.** (1999) Factors limiting peripheral pattern discrimination. Spatial Vision, 12, 83–106.

Orban, G. A., Vandenbussche, E., and **Vogels, R.** (1984) Human orientation discrimination tested with long stimuli. Vision Research, 24, 121–128.

O'Regan, J. K., Rensink, R. A., and **Clark, J. J.** (1999) Change-blindness as a result of "mudsplashes". Nature, 398, 34.

O'Shea, R. P. (1991) Thumb's rule tested: visual angle of thumb's width is about 2 deg. Perception, 20, 415–418.

O'Shea, R. P., Blackburn, S. G., and **Ono, H.** (1993) Aerial perspective, contrast, and depth perception. Paper presented at the Association for Research in Vision and Opthalmology, Sarasota, Fla.

O'Shea, R. P., Blackburn, S. G., and **Ono, H.** (1994) Contrast as a depth cue. Vision Research, 34, 1595–1604.

O'Shea, R. P., Sekuler, R., and **Govan, D. G.** (1997) Blur and contrast as pictorial depth cues. Perception, 26, 599–612.

Owen, D. (1980) Camouflage and mimicry. Chicago: University of Chicago Press.

Owen, D. H., and **Machamer, P. K.** (1979) Bias-free improvement in wine discrimination. Perception, 8, 199–209.

Owens, D. A. (1984) The resting state of the eyes. American Scientist, 72, 378–387.

Owsley, C. J., Sekuler, R., and **Siemsen, D.** (1983) Contrast sensitivity throughout adulthood. Vision Research, 23, 689–699.

Packwood, J., and **Gordon, B.** (1975) Stereopsis in normal domestic cat, Siamese cat, and cat raised with alternating monocular occlusion. Journal of Neurophysiology, 38, 1485–1499.

Palmer, S. E., Rosch, E., and **Chase, P.** (1981) Canonical perspective and the perception of objects. In J. Long and A. Baddeley (eds.), Attention and performance, vol. 9. Hillsdale, N.J.: Erlbaum, 135–151.

Palmer, S. E. (1999) Vision science: From photons to phenomenology. Cambridge: MIT Press.

Pangborn, R. M. (1960) Influence of color on the discrimination of sweetness. American Journal of Psychology, 73, 229–238.

Pantev, C., Oostenveld, R., Engelien, A., Ross, B., Roberts, L. E., and **Hoke, M.** (1998) Increased auditory representation in musicians. Nature, 392, 811–814.

Pantle, A. (1998) How do measues of the motion aftereffect measure up? In G. Mather, F. Verstraten and S. Anstis (eds.) The Motion Aftereffect: A Modern Perspective. MIT Press: Cambridge, 25–39.

Pantle, A., and **Petersik, J. T.** (1979) Factors controlling the competing sensations produced by a bistable stroboscopic motion display. Vision Research, 19, 143–154.

Pantle, A., and **Picciano, L.** (1976) A multistable movement display: Evidence for two separate motion systems in human vision. Science, 193, 500–502.

Park, D. (1999) The fire within the eye. A historical essay on the nature and meaning of light. Princeton, N.J.: Princeton University Press.

Parker, D. E. (1980) The vestibular apparatus. Scientific American, 243, 118–135.

Pascual-Leone, A., and **Torres, F.** (1993) Plasticity of the sensorimotor representation of the reading finger in Braille. Brain, 116, 39–52.

Paterson, C. A. (1979) Crystalline lens. In R. E. Records (ed.), Physiology of the human eye and visual system. New York: Harper & Row, 232–260.

Patterson, K., and **Ralph, M.** (1999) Selective disorders of reading? Current Opinion in Neurobiology, 9, 235–239.

Pearlman, A. L., Birch, J., and **Meadows, J. C.** (1979) Cerebral color blindness: An acquired defect in hue discrimination. Annals of Neurology, 5, 253–261.

Peli, E., Goldstein, R. B., Young, G. M., Trempe, C. L., and **Buzney, S. M.** (1991) Image enhancement for the visually impaired. Investigative Ophthalmology & Visual Science, 32, 2337–2350.

Pelli, D. (1999) Close encounters —An artist shows that size affects shape. Science, 285, 844–846.

Pelli, D. G., Robson, J. G., and **Wilkins, A. J.** (1988) The design of a new letter chart for measuring contrast sensitivity. Clinical Vision Science, 2, 187–199.

Penfield, W., and **Faulk, M. E.** (1955) The insula. Further observation on its function. Brain, 78, 445–470.

Penfield, W., and **Perrot, P.** (1963) The brain's record of auditory and visual experience. Brain, 86, 595–696.

Perkins, S. (2000) Eau, brother! Science News, 157, 125–127.

Perky, C. W. (1910) An experimental study of imagination. American Journal of Psychology, 21, 422–452.

Perrett, D. I., Lee, K. J., Penton-Voak, I., Rowland, D., Yoshikawa, S., Burt, D. M., Henzi, S. P., Castles, D. L., and **Akamatsu, S.** (1998) Effects of sexual dimorphism on facial attractiveness. Nature, 394, 884–887.

Perrett, D. I., Oram, M. W., Harries, M. H., Bevan, R., Hietanen, J. K., Benson, P. J., and **Thomas, S.** (1991) Viewer-centered and object-centered coding of heads in the macaque temporal cortex. Experimental Brain Research, 86, 159–173.

Perrott, D. R., Ambarsoom, H., and **Tucker, J.** (1987) Changes in head position as a measure of auditory localization performance: Auditory psychomotor coordination under monaural and binaural listening conditions. Journal of the Acoustical Society of America, 82, 1637–1645.

Peterhans, E., and **von der Heydt, R.** (1991) Subjective contours—Bridging the gap between psychophysics and physiology. Trends in Neurosciences, 14, 112–119.

Petersen, S. E., Robinson, D. L., and **Morris, J. D.** (1987). Contributions of the pulvinar to visual spatial attention. Neuropsychology, 25, 97–105.

Petersik, J. T. (1978) Possible role of transient and sustained visual mechanisms in the determination of similarity judgments. Perceptual and Motor Skills, 47, 683–698.

Peterson, S. E., Fox, P. T., Posner, M. I., Mintun, M., and **Raichle, M. E.** (1988). Positron emission tomographic studies of the cortical anatomy of single word processing. Nature, 331, 585–589.

Pettet, M. W., McKee, S. P., and **Grzywacz, N. M.** (1999) Constraints on long range interactions mediating contour detection. Vision Research, 38, 865–879.

Pfaffmann, C. (1955) Gustatory nerve impulses in rat, cat, and rabbit. Journal of Neurophysiology, 18, 429–440.

Pfaffmann, C., and **Bartoshuk, L. M.** (1989) Psychophysical mapping of a human case of left unilateral ageusia. Chemical Senses, 14, 738.

Pfaffmann, C., and **Bartoshuk, L. M.** (1990) Taste loss due to herpes zoster oticus: an update after 19 months. Chemical Senses, 15, 657–658.

Phillips, D. P. and **Farmer, M. E.** (1990) Acquired word deafness, and the temporal grain of sound representation in the primary auditory cortex. Behavioural Brain Research, 40, 85–94.

Phillips, J. R., Johansson, R. S., and **Johnson, K. O.** (1992) Responses of human mechanoreceptive afferents to embossed dot arrays scanned across fingerpad skin. Journal of Neuroscience, 12, 827–839.

Pierce, J., and **Halpern, B. P.** (1996) Orthonasal and retronasal odorant identification based on vapor phase input from common substances. Chemical Senses 21, 529–543.

Pirenne, M. H. (1967) Vision and the eye (2nd ed.). London: Chapman and Hall.

Pirenne, M. H. (1970) Optics, painting, and photography. Cambridge, England: Cambridge University Press.

Pittenger, J. B., and **Shaw, R. E.** (1975) Aging faces as viscal-elastic events: Implications for a theory of nonrigid shape perception. Journal of Experimental Psychology: Human Perception and Performance, 1, 374–382.

Pittenger, J. B., Shaw, R. E., and **Mark, L. S.** (1979) Perceptual information for the age level of faces as a higher-order invariant of growth. Journal of Experimental Psychology: Human Perception and Performance, 5, 478–493.

Platt, J. R., and **Racine, R. J.** (1985) Effect of frequency, timbre, experience, and feedback on musical tuning skills. Perception & Psychophysics, 38, 543–553.

Poggio, T. (1984) Vision by man and machine. Scientific American, 250, 106–116.

Poggio, T., Verri, A., and **Torre, V.** (1991) Green theorems and qualitative properties of the optical flow (Memo No. 1289). M. I. T., Artificial Intelligence Laboratory: Cambridge.

Pointer, M. R., and **Atridge, G. G.** (1998) The number of discernible colours. Color Research And Application, 1998, 23, 52–54.

Pokorny, J., Graham, C. H., and **Lanson, R. N.** (1968) Effect of wavelength on foveal grating acuity. Journal of the Optical Society of America, 58, 1410–1414.

Polat, U. (1999) Functional architecture of long-range perceptual interactions. Spatial Vision, 12, 143–162.

Pollack, I., and **Rose, M.** (1967) Effect of head movement on the localization of sounds in the equatorial plane. Perception & Psychophysics, 2, 591–596.

Polyak, S. (1957) The vertebrate visual system. Chicago: University of Chicago Press.

Polyak, S. L. (1941) The retina. Chicago: University of Chicago Press.

Pomerantz, J. R. (1981) Perceptual organization in information processing. In M. Kubovy and J. R. Pomerantz (eds.), Perceptual organization. Hillsdale, N.J.: Erlbaum, 141–180.

Pons, T. P., Garraghty, P. E., Friedman, D. P., and **Mishkin, M.** (1987) Physiological evidence for serial processing in somatosensory cortex. Science, 237, 417–420.

Porter, R. H. (1991) Human reproduction and the mother-infant relationship. In T. V. Getchell, R. L. Doty, L. M. Bartoshuk and J. B. Snow (eds.), Smell and taste in health and disease. New York: Raven Press, 429–444.

Posner, M. I. (1980) Orienting of attention. Quarterly Journal of experimental Psychology, 32, 3–25.

Posner, M. I. (1992) Attention as a cognitive and neural system. Current Directions in Psychological Science, 1, 11–14.

Posner, M. I., Snyder, C. R., and **Davidson, B. J.** (1980) Attention and the detection of signals. Journal of experimental Psychology: General, 109, 160–174.

Potter, M. C. (1966) On perceptual recognition. In J. S. Bruner (ed.), Studies in cognitive growth. New York: John Wiley & Sons, 103–134.

Price, D. D. (2000) Psychological and neural mechanisms of the affective dimension of pain. Science, 288, 1769–1772.

Preuss, T., Qi, H., and **Kaas, J. H.** (1999) Distinctive compartmental organization of human primary visual cortex. Proceedings of the National Academy of Sciences USA, 96, 11601–11606.

Pringle, R., and **Egeth, H. E.** (1988) Mental curve tracing with elementary stimuli. Journal of experimental Psychology: Human Perception and Performance, 14, 716–728.

Prinz, W. (1992) Why don't we perceive our brain states? European Journal of Cognitive Psychology, 4, 1–20.

Prinzmetal, W. (1992) The word-superiority effect does not require a t-scope. Perception & Psychophysics, 51, 473–484.

Prinzmetal, W., Amiri, H., Allen. K., and **Edwards, T.** (1998) Phenomenology of attention: 1. Color, location, orientation, and spatial frequency. Journal of Experimental Psychology: Human Perception & Performance, 24, 261–282.

Pritchard, R. M. (1961) Stabilized images on the retina. Scientific American, 204, 72–78.

Pritchard, R. M., Heron, W., and **Hebb, D. O.** (1960) Visual perception approached by the method of stabilized images. Canadian Journal of Psychology, 14, 67–77.

Pritchard, T. C. (1991) The primate gustatory system. In T. V. Getchell, R. L. Doty, L. M. Bartoshuk and J. B. Snow, Jr. (eds.), Smell and taste in health and disease. New York: Raven Press, 109–126.

Proust, M. (1928) Swann's way. New York: Random House.

Puccetti, R., and **Dykes, R. W.** (1978) Sensory cortex and the mind-brain problem. Behaviour and Brain, 1, 337–344.

Pylyshyn, Z. W., and **Storm, R. W.** (1988) Tracking multiple independent targets: Evidence for a parallel tracking mechanism. Spatial Vision, 3, 179–197.

Quinlan, P. T., and **Wilton R. N.** (1998). Grouping by proximity or similarity? Competition between the Gestalt principles in vision. Perception, 27, 417–430.

Rafal, R., Smith J., Krantz J., Cohen A., and **Brennan C.** (1990) Extrageniculate vision in hemianopic humans: saccade inhibition by signals in the blind field. Science, 250, 118–121.

Raghubir, P., and **Krishna A.** (1999) Vital dimensions in volume perception: Can the eye fool the stomach? Journal of Marketing Research, 36, 313–326.

Rainville, P., Duncan, G. H., Price, D. D., Carrier, B., and **Bushnell, M. C.** (1997) Pain affect encoded in human anterior cingulate but not somatosensory cortex. Science, 277, 968–971.

Ramachandran, V. S. (1988) Perceiving shape from shading. Scientific American, 259, 76–83.

Ramachandran, V. S. (1992) Blind spots. Scientific American, 266, 86–91.

Ramachandran, V. S., Rao, M. V., and **Vidyasagar, T. R.** (1973) Apparent movement with subjective contours. Vision Research, 13, 1399–1401.

Ramachandran, V. S., and **Anstis, S. M.** (1986) The perception of apparent motion. Scientific American, 254, 102–109.

Ramachandran, V. S., and **Blakeslee, S.** (1998) Phantoms in the brain. New York: Wm. Morrow & Co.

Ramachandran, V. S., and **Cavanagh, P.** (1987) Motion capture anisotropy. Vision Research, 27, 97–106.

Ramachandran, V. S. and Hirstein, W. (1999) The science of art: a neurological theory of aesthetic experience. Journal of Consciousness Studies, 6, 15–51.

Ramirez, I. (1990) Why do sugars taste good? Neuroscience & Biobehavioral Reviews, 14, 125–134.

Randolph, M., and Semmes, J. (1974) Behavioral consequences of selective subtotal ablations in the postcentral gyrus of the Macaca mulatta. Brain Research, 70, 55–70.

Rao, A. R., and Lohse, G. L. (1996). Toward a texture naming system: Identifying relevant dimensions of texture. Vision Research, 36, 1649–1670.

Ratliff, F. (1972) Contour and contrast. Scientific American, 226, 90–101.

Ratliff, F. (1976) On the psychophysical basis of universal color names. Proceedings of American Philosophical Society, 120, 311–330.

Ratliff, F. (1984) Why Mach bands are not seen at the edges of a step. Vision Research, 24, 163–165.

Rauschecker, J. P. (1999) Making brain circuits listen. Science, 285, 1686–1687.

Rauschecker, J. P, Tian B., and Hauser, M. (1995) Processing of complex sounds in the macaque nonprimary auditory cortex. Science, 268, 111–114.

Rauschecker, J. P. (1998) Cortical processing of complex sounds. Current Opinion in Neurobiology, 8, 516–521.

Rauschecker, J. P. (1999) Auditory cortical plasticity: a comparison with other sensory systems. Trends in Neurosciences, 22, 74–80.

Rauschecker, J. P., and Knieperet, U. (1994) Auditory localization behavior in visually deprived cats. European Journal of Neuroscience, 6, 149–160.

Rayner, K. (1978) Eye movements in reading and information processing. Psychological Bulletin, 85, 618–660.

Rayner, K. (1998) Eye movements in reading and information processing: 20 years of research. Psychological Bulletin, 124, 372–422.

Rayner, K., and Bertera, J. H. (1979) Reading without a fovea. Science, 206, 468–469.

Rayner, K., Inhoff, A. W., Morrison, R. E., Slowiaczek, M. L., and Bertera, J. H. (1981) Masking of foveal and parafoveal vision during eye fixations in reading. Journal of Experimental Psychology: Human Perception and Performance, 7, 167–179.

Rayner, K., and Pollatsek, A. (1987) Eye movements in reading: A tutorial review. In M. Coltheart (ed.), Attention and performance, vol. 12: The psychology of reading. Hove, England: Erlbaum, 327–362.

Reagan, R. (1990) An American life. New York: Simon & Schuster.

Reber, A. S. (1992) The cognitive unconscious: An evolutionary perspective. Consciousness and Cognition, 1, 93–133.

Recanzone, G. H., Jenkins, W. M., Hradek, G. T., and Merzenich, M. M. (1992) Progressive improvement in discriminative abilities in adult owl monkeys performing a tactile frequency discrimination task. Journal of Neurophysiology, 67, 1015–1030.

Recanzone, G. H., Merzenich, M. M., Jenkins, W. M., Grajski, K. A., and Dinse, H. R. (1992) Topographic reorganization of the hand representation in cortical area 3b of owl monkeys trained in a frequency discrimination task. Journal of Neurophysiology, 67, 1031–1056.

Recanzone, G. H., Schreiner, C. E., and Merzenich, M. M. (1993) Plasticity in the frequency representation in the primary auditory cortex following discrimination training in adult owl monkeys. Journal of Neuroscience.

Rechtschaffen, A., and Mednick, S. (1955) The autokinetic word technique. Journal of Abnormal and Social Psychology, 51, 346.

Records, R. E. (1979) Retina: Metabolism and photochemistry. In R. E. Records (ed.), Physiology of the human eye and visual system. New York: Harper & Row, 296–318.

Reeves, A. (1982) Letter to the editors. Vision Research, 22, 711.

Regan, B. C., Julliot, C., Simmen, B., Viénot, F., Charles-Dominique, P., and Mollon, J. D. (1998) Frugivory and colour vision in Alouatta seniculus, a trichromatic platyrrhine monkey. Vision Research, 38, 3321–3327.

Regan, D. (1988) Low contrast letter charts and sinewave grating tests in ophthalmological and neurological disorders. Clinical Vision Science, 2, 235–250.

Regan, D. (1992). Visual judgements and misjudgements in cricket, and the art of flight. Perception, 21, 91–116.

Rehn, T. (1978) Perceived odor intensity as a function of airflow through the nose. Sensory Processes, 2, 198–205.

Reichardt, W. (1961) Autocorrelation, a principle for the evaluation of sensory information by the central nervous system. In W. A. Rosenblith (ed.), Sensory communication. New York: John Wiley & Sons. Pp. 303–318.

Reicher, G. M. (1969) Perceptual recognition as a function of meaningfulness of stimulus material. Journal of Experimental Psychology, 81, 275–280.

Reid, T. (1813/1970) An inquiry into the human mind. Chicago: University of Chicago Press.

Relkin, E. M., and **Doucet, J. R.** (1997) Is loudness simply proportional to the auditory nerve spike count? Journal of the Acoustical Society of America, 101, 2735–2740.

Rentschler, I., Jüttner, M., Unzicker, A., and **Landis, T.** (1999) Innate and learned components of human visual preference. Current Biology, 9, 665–671.

Repp, B. (1996) The art of inaccuracy: why pianists' errors are difficult to hear. Music Perception, 14, 161–184.

Rezek, D. L. (1987) Olfactory deficits as a neurologic sign in dementia of the Alzheimer type. Archives of Neurology, 44, 1030–1032.

Ricci, C., and **Blundo, C.** (1990) Perception of ambiguous figures after focal brain lesions. Neuropsychologia, 28, 1163–1173.

Richards, W. (1971) The fortification illusions of migraines. Scientific American, 224, 88–98.

Richardson, J. T. E., and **Zucco, G. M.** (1989) Cognition and olfaction: A review. Psychological Bulletin, 105, 352–360.

Rieser, J. J., Ashmead, D. H., Talor, C. R., and **Youngquist, G. A.** (1990) Visual perception and the guidance of locomotion without vision of previously seen targets. Perception, 19, 675–689.

Riggs, L. A., Ratliff, F., Cornsweet, J. C., and **Cornsweet, T. N.** (1953) The disappearance of steadily fixated visual test objects. Journal of the Optical Society of America, 43, 495–501.

Riggs, L. A., Volkmann, F. C., and **Moore, R. K.** (1981) Suppression of the blackout due to blinks. Vision Research, 21, 1075–1079.

Ripoll, H., and **Fleurance, P.** (1988) What does keeping one's eye on the ball mean? Ergonomics, 31, 1647–1654.

Rivest, J., and **Cavanagh, P.** (1996) Localizing contours defined by more than one attribute. Vision Research, 36, 53–66.

Rizzo, J. F., and **Wyatt, J. L.** (1997) Prospects for a visual prosthesis. Neuroscientist, 3, 251–262.

Rizzo, M., Nawrot, M., Blake, R., and **Damasio, A.** (1992) A human visual disorder resembling Area V4 dysfunction in the monkey. Neurology, 42, 1175–1180.

Rizzo, M., and **Nawrot, M.** (1998) Perception of movement and shape in Alzheimer's disease. Brain, 121, 2259–2270.

Rizzo, M., Reinach, S., McGehee., D., and **Dawson, J.** (1997) Simulated car crashes and crash predictors in drivers with Alzheimer Disease. Archives of Neurology, 54, 545–551.

Robinson, D. L., Bowman, E. M., and **Kertzman C.** (1995) Covert orienting of attention in macaques. II. Contributions of parietal cortex. Journal of Neurophysiology, 74, 698–712.

Robson, J. G. (1966) Spatial and temporal contrast-sensitivity functions of the visual system. Journal of the Optical Society of America, 56, 1141–1142.

Rock, I., Gopnik, A., and **Hall, S** (1994) Do young children reverse ambiguous figures? Perception, 23, 635–644.

Rock, I., Hall, S., and **Davis, J.** (1994) Why do ambiguous figures reverse? Acta Psychologia, 87, 33–59.

Rock, I., and **Mitchener, K.** (1992) Further evidence of failure of reversal of ambiguous figures by uninformed subjects. Perception, 21, 39–45.

Rock, I., and **Palmer, S.** (1990) The legacy of Gestalt psychology. Scientific American, 263, 84–90.

Röder, B., Teder-Sälajärvi, W., Sterr, A., Rösler, F., Hillyard, S. A., and **Neville, H.J.** (1999) Improved auditory spatial tuning in blind humans. Nature, 400, 162–166.

Rodin, J., Bartoshuk, L., Peterson, C., and **Schank, D.** (1990) Bulimia and taste: Possible interactions. Journal of Abnormal Psychology, 99, 32–39.

Roelfsema, P. R., Scholte, H. S., and **Spekreijse H.** (1999) Temporal constraints on the grouping of contour segments into spatially extended objects. Vision Research, 1939, 1509–29.

Roelfsema, P. R., Lamme, V. A., and **Spekreijse, H.** (1998) Object-based attention in the primary visual cortex of the macaque monkey. Nature, 395, 376–81.

Rogers, B. J., and **Collett, T. S.** (1989) The appearance of surfaces specified by motion parallax and binocular disparity. Quarterly Journal of Experimental Psychology, 41A, 697–717.

Rogers, B. J., and **Graham, M. E.** (1979) Motion parallax as an independent cue for depth perception. Perception, 8, 125–134.

Rogers, B. J., and **Graham, M. E.** (1984) Aftereffects from motion parallax and stereoscopic depth: Similarities and interactions. In L. Spillmann and B. R. Wooten (eds.), Sensory experience, adaptation, and perception. Hillsdale, N.J.: Erlbaum. Pp. 603–619.

Roland, P. E. (1976) Focal increase of cerebral blood flow during stereognostic testing in man. Archives of Neurology, 33, 551–558.

Rolls, B. (1986) Sensory-specific satiety. Nutrition Reviews, 44, 93–101.

Rolls, B., Van Duijvenvoorde, P. M., and **Rolls, E. T.** (1984) Pleasantness changes and food intake in a varied four-course meal. Appetite, 5, 337–348.

Rolls, E. T., Critchley, H. D., Browning, A., and **Hernadi, I.** (1998) The neurophysiology of taste and olfaction in primates, and umami flavor. Annals of the New York Academy of Science, 855, 426–37.

Rolls, E. T. (2000) The representation of umami taste in the taste cortex. Journal of Nutrition, 130, 960S–965S.

Ronchi, V. (1970) The nature of light: An historical survey. Cambridge: Harvard University Press.

Roorda, A. and **Williams, D. R.** (1999). The arrangement of the three cone classes in the living human eye. Nature. Vol. 397, 11, 520–522.

Roper, S. D. (1992) The microphysiology of peripheral taste organs. Journal of Neuroscience, 12, 1127–1134.

Rose, J. E., Brugge, J. F., Anderson, D. J., and **Hind, J. E.** (1967) Phase-locked response to low-frequency tones in single auditory nerve fibers of the squirrel monkey. Journal of Neurophysiology, 30, 769–793.

Rosenfeld, A. (1988) Computer vision. Advances in Computers, 27, 265–308.

Rossi, A. F., Rittenhouse, C. D., and **Paradiso, M. A.** (1996) The representation of brightness in primary visual cortex. Science, 273, 1104–107.

Rouquier, S., Blancher, A., and **Giorgi, D.** (2000) The olfactory receptor gene repertoire in primates and mouse: Evidence for reduction of the functional fraction in primates. Proceedings of the National Academy of Sciences: USA, 97, 2870–2874.

Royster, J. D., Royster, L. H., and **Killion, M. C.** (1991) Sound exposures and hearing thresholds of symphony orchestra musicians. Journal of the Acoustical Society of America, 89, 2793–2803.

Rozin, P. (1978) The use of characteristic flavorings in human culinary practice. In C. M. Apt (ed.), Flavor: Its chemical, behavioral, and commercial aspects. Proceedings of the Arthur D. Little Symposium. Boulder, Colo.: Westview Press, 101–128.

Rozin, P. (1979) Preference and affect in food selection. In J. H. A. Kroeze (ed.), Preference behavior and chemoreception. London: Information Retrieval. Pp. 289–302.

Rozin, P. (1982) "Taste-smell confusions" and the duality of the olfactory sense. Perception & Psychophysics, 31, 397–401.

Rozin, P. (1990) Social and moral aspects of food and eating. In I. Rock (ed.), The legacy of Solomon Asch: Essays in cognition and social psychology. Hillsdale, N.J.: Erlbaum, 97–110.

Ruben, R. J. (1992) The ontogeny of human hearing. Acta Oto-laryngolica, 112, 192–196.

Rubert, S. L., Hollender, M. H., and **Mehrhof, E. G.** (1961) Olfactory hallucinations. Archives of General Psychiatry, 5, 121–126.

Rubin, G. S., and **Turano, K** (1992) Reading without saccadic eye movements.Vision Research 32, 895–902.

Rubin, M. L., and **Walls, G. L.** (1969) Fundamentals of visual science. Springfield, Ill.: Thomas.

Rucker, C. W. (1971) A history of the ophthalmoscope. Rochester, Minn.: Whiting.

Rushton, W. A. H. (1965) Visual adaptation. The Ferrier Lecture. Proceedings of the Royal Society of London, Series B, 162, 20–46.

Rushton, W. A. H. (1979) King Charles II and the blind spot. Vision Research, 19, 225.

Russel, M. J. (1976) Human olfactory communication. Nature, 260, 520–522.

Russell, I. J. (1987) The physiology of the organ of Corti. British Medical Bulletin, 43, 802–820.

Saarinen, J., Levi D. M., and **Shen, B.** (1997) Integration of local pattern elements into a global shape in human vision. Proceedings of the National Academy of Sciences: USA, 94, 8267–8271.

Sacks, O. (1985) The man who mistook his wife for a hat, and other clinical tales. New York: Summit Books.

Sacks, O. (1995) An anthropologist on Mars. New York: Knopf.

Sadato, N, Pascual-Leone A., Grafman, J., Ibanez, V., Deiber, M.-P., Dold, G., and Hallett, M. (1996) Activation of the primary visual cortex by Braille reading in blind subjects. Nature, 380, 526–528.

Safire, W. (1979) Mondegreens: I led the pigeons to the flag. New York Times Magazine, May 27, 9–10.

Salzman, C. D., Murasugi, C. M., Britten, K. H., and Newsome, W. T. (1992) Microstimulation in visual Area MT: Effects on direction discrimination performance. Journal of Neuroscience, 12, 2331–2355.

Sample, P. A., Boynton, R. M., and Weinreb, R. N. (1988) Isolating the color vision loss in primary open-angle glaucoma. American Journal of Ophthalmology, 106, 686–691.

Samuel, A. G. (1983) We really is worse than you or them, and so are ma and pa: Reply. Journal of Experimental Psychology: Human Perception and Performance, 9, 321–322.

Samuel, A. G. (1989) Insights from a failure of selective adaptation: Syllable-initial and syllable-final consonants are different. Perception & Psychophysics, 45, 485–493.

Sary, G., Vogels, R., and Orban G. (1993) Cue-invariant shape selectivity of macaque inferior temporal neurons. Science, 260, 995–997.

Sauvan, X. M., and Peterhans E. (1999) Orientation constancy in neurons of monkey visual cortex. Visual Cognition, 6, 43–54.

Savelsbergh, G. J. P., Whiting, H. T. A., and Bootsma, R. J. (1991) Grasping tau. Journal of Experimental Psychology: Human Perception and Performance, 17, 315–322.

Sawatari, A., and Callaway, E. M. (1996) Convergence of magno- and parvocellular pathways in layer 4B of macaque primary visual cortex. Nature, 380, 442–446.

Schaal, B. (1988) Olfaction in infants and children: Developmental and functional perspectives. Chemical Senses, 13, 145–190.

Schab, F. R. (1991) Odor memory: Taking stock. Psychological Bulletin, 109, 242–251.

Schacter, D. L. (1989) On the relation between memory and consciousness: Dissociable interactions and conscious experience. In H. L. Roediger, III and F. I. M. Craik (eds.), Varieties of memory and consciousness: Essays in honor of Endel Tulving. Hillsdale, N.J.: Erlbaum. Pp. 355–389.

Schall, J. D. (1991) Neural basis of saccadic eye movements in primates. In A. G. Leventhal (ed.), The neural basis of visual function. London: Macmillan. Pp. 388–442.

Scharf, B., Quigley, S., Aoki, C., Peachey, N., and Reeves, A. (1987) Focused auditory attention and frequency selectivity. Perception & Psychophysics, 42, 215–223.

Schechter, P. J., and Henkin, R. I. (1974) Abnormalities of taste and smell after head trauma. Journal of Neurology, Neurosurgery, and Psychiatry, 37, 802–810.

Schein, O. D., West, S., Munoz, B., Vitale, S., Maguire, M., Taylor, H. R., and Bressler, N. M. (1994) Cortical lenticular opacification: distribution and location in a longitudinal study. Investigative Ophthalmology & Visual Science, 35, 363–366.

Schiff, W. (1965) Perception of impending collision. Psychological Monographs, 79, 1–26.

Schiffman, H. R. (1967) Size estimation of familiar objects under informative and reduced conditions of viewing. American Journal of Psychology, 80, 229–235.

Schiffman, S. S. (1974) Physiochemical correlates of olfactory quality. Science, 185, 112–117.

Schiffman, S. S. (1997) Taste and smell losses in normal aging and disease. Journal of the American Medical Association, 278, 1357–1362.

Schiffman, S. S., and Dackis, C. (1975) Taste of nutrients: Amino acids, vitamins, and fatty acids. Perception & Psychophysics, 17, 140–146.

Schiffman, S. S., and Erickson, R. P. (1980) The issue of primary tastes versus a taste continuum. Neuroscience & Biobehavioral Reviews, 4, 109–117.

Schiffman, S. S., Reynolds, M. L., and Young, F. L. (1981) Introduction to multidimensional scaling. New York: Academic Press.

Schiller, P. H., and Logothetis, N. K. (1990) The color-opponent and broad-band channels in the primate visual system. Trends in Neurosciences, 13, 392–398.

Schiller, P. H., Sandell, J. H., and Maunsell, J. H. R. (1986) Functions of the ON and OFF channels of the visual system. Nature, 322, 824–825.

Schlagel, R. H. (1984) A reasonable reply to Hume's scepticism. British Journal of the Philosophy of Science, 35, 359–374.

Schmidt, E. M., Bak, M. J., Hambrecht, F. T., Kufta, C. V., O'Rourke, D. K., and

Vallabhanath, P. (1996) Feasibility of a visual Prosthesis for the blind based on intracortical microstimulation of the visual cortex. Brain, 119, 507–522.

Schneider, R. A., and **Wolf, S.** (1955) Olfactory perception thresholds for citral utilizing a new type of olfactorium. Journal of Applied Physiology, 8, 337–342.

Scholl, B. J. (in press) Objects and attention: The state of the art. Cognition (Special issue on "Objects and attention").

Schoups, A. A., Vogels, R., and **Orban, G. A.** (1995) Human perceptual learning in identifying the oblique orientation: retinotopy, orientation specificity and monocularity. Journal of Physiology: London, 483, 797–810.

Schultz, G., and **Melzack, R.** (1991) The Charles Bonnet syndrome: "Phantom visual images." Perception, 20, 809–826.

Schwartz, B. S., Doty, R. L., Monroe, C., Frye, R., and **Barker, S.** (1989) Olfactory function in chemical workers exposed to acrylate and methacrylate vapors. American Journal of Public Health, 79, 613–618.

Schyns, P. G., and **Oliva, O.** (1997) Flexible diagnosticity-driven, rather than fixed, perceptually determined scale selection and face recognition. Perception, 26, 1027–1038.

Scott, T. R., and **Plata-Salaman, C. R.** (1991) Coding of taste quality. In T. V. Getchell, R. L. Doty, L. M. Bartoshuk, and J. B. Snow, Jr. (eds.) Smell and taste in health and disease. New York: Raven Press, 345–368.

Seagraves, M. A., Goldberg, M. E., Deng, S. Y., Bruce, C. J., Ungerleider, L. G., and **Mishkin, M.** (1987) The role of striate cortex in the guidance of eye movements in the monkey. Journal of Neuroscience, 7, 776–794.

Segal, S. J., and **Fusella, V.** (1970) Influence of imaged pictures and sounds on detection of visual and auditory signals. Journal of Experimental Psychology, 83, 458–464.

Sekuler, A. B., and **Palmer, S. E.** (1992) Perception of partly occluded objects: A microgenetic analysis. Journal of Experimental Psychology: General, 121, 95–111.

Sekuler, R. W. (1965) Spatial and temporal determinants of visual backward masking. Journal of Experimental Psychology, 70, 401–406.

Sekuler, R., Owsley, C. J., and **Berenberg, R.** (1986) Contrast sensitivity during provoked visual impairment in multiple sclerosis. Ophthalmic and Physiological Optics, 6, 229–232.

Sekuler, R. W. (1965) Spatial and temporal determinants of visual backward masking. Journal of Experimental Psychology, 70, 401–406.

Sekuler, R., and **Blake, R.** (1999) Star Trek on the brain: Alien minds, human minds. New York: W. H. Freeman.

Sekuler, R., and **Sekuler, A. B.** (2000) Visual perception and cognition. In J. G. Evans, T. F. Williams, G. K. Wilcock, J.-P. Michel, B. L. Beattie, and G. K. Wilcock (eds.) Oxford Textbook of Geriatric Medicine, 2nd Edition, Oxford: Oxford University Press, 874–880.

Sergent, J., and **Poncet, M.** (1990) From covert to overt recognition of faces in a prosopagnostic patient. Brain, 113, 989–1004.

Sergent, J. A., and **Villemure, J.-G.** (1989) Prosopagnosia in a right hemispherectomized patient. Brain, 112, 975–995.

Seyfarth, R. M., and **Cheney, D. L.** (1984) The natural vocalizations of non-human primates. Trends in Neurosciences, 7, 66–73.

Shannon, R. V., Zeng, F.-G., Kamath, V., Wygonski, J., and **Ekelid, M.** (1995) Speech recognition with primarily temporal cues. Science, 270, 303–304.

Shapley, R. (1996) Art and perception of nature: Illusory contours in the paintings of Ellsworth Kelly. Perception, 25, 1259–1261.

Sharma, S., and **Moskowitz, H.** (1972) Effect of marijuana on the visual autokinetic phenomenon. Perceptual and Motor Skills, 35, 891–894.

Sharon, D., Glusman, G., Pilpel, Y., Khen, M., Gruetzner, F., Haaf, T., and **Lancet, D.** (1999) Primate evolution of an olfactory receptor cluster: diversification by gene conversion and recent emergence of pseudogenes. Genomics, 61, 24–36.

Sharpe, L. T., and **Nordby, K.** (1990) Total colour-blindness: An introduction. In R. F. Hess, L. T. Sharpe, and K. Nordby (eds.), Night vision: Basic, clinical and applied aspects. Cambridge, England: Cambridge University Press, 253–289.

Shaw, E. A. G. (1974) Transformation of sound pressure level from the free field to the eardrum in the horizontal plane. Journal of the Acoustical Society of America, 56, 1848–1861.

Shaw, R., and **Bransford, J.** (1977) Introduction: Psychological approaches to the problem of knowledge. In R. Shaw and J. Bransford (eds.),

Perceiving, acting, and knowing. Hillsdale, N.J.: Erlbaum, 1–39.

Sheehan, W. (1988) Planets and perception: Telescopic views and interpretations, 1609–1909. Tempe, Ariz.: University of Arizona Press.

Shepard, R. N. (1981) Psychophysical complementarity. In M. Kubovy and J. R. Pomerantz (eds.), Perceptual organization. Hillsdale, N.J.: Erlbaum. Pp. 279–341.

Shepard, R. N., and **Cooper, L. A.** (1982) Mental images and their transformations. Cambridge: M.I.T. Press.

Shepard, R. N. (1990) Mind sights. New York: Freeman.

Shepherd, G. M., and **Firestein, S.** (1991) Making scents of olfactory transduction. Current Biology, 1, 204–206.

Sherrick, C. E., and **Cholewiak, R. W.** (1986) Cutaneous sensitivity. In K. Boff, L. Kaufman, and J. Thomas (eds.), Handbook of perception and human performance, vol. 1. New York: Wiley-Interscience, 12.1–12.58.

Shevell, S. K., and **Wei, J.** (1998) chromatic induction: border contrast or adaptation to surrounding light. Vision Research, 38, 1561–1566.

Shiffrar, M., and **Freyd, J. J.** (1990) Apparent motion of the human body. Psychological Science, 1, 257–264.

Shulman, G. L., Ollinger, J. M., Akbudak, E., Conturo, T. E., Snyder, A. Z., Petersen, S. E., and **Corbetta, M.** (1999) Areas involved in encoding and applying directional expectations to moving objects. Journal of Neuroscience, 19, 9480–9496.

Shutty, M. S., Cunduff, G., and **DeGood, D. E.** (1992) Pain complaint and the weather: weather sensitivity and symptom complaints in chronic pain patients. Pain, 49, 199–204.

Siegel, J. A., and **Siegel, W.** (1977) Absolute identification of notes and intervals by musicians. Perception & Psychophysics, 21, 143–152.

Siegel, R. K. (1984) Hostage hallucinations: Visual imagery induced by isolation and life-threatening stress. Journal of Nervous and Mental Disease, 172, 264–272.

Siegel, R. M., and **Andersen, R. A.** (1990) The perception of structure from visual motion in monkey and man. Journal of Cognitive Neuroscience, 2, 306–319.

Sillar, K. T., and **Roberts, A.** (1988) A neuronal mechanism for sensory gating during locomotion in a vertebrate. Nature, 331, 262–265.

Simons, D. J. (2000) Attentional capture and inattentional blindness. Trends in Cognitive Sciences, 4, 147–155.

Simons, D. J., and **Levin, D. T.** (1998) Failure to detect changes in people in real-world interactions. Psychonomic Bulletin & Review, 5, 644–649.

Sinai, M. J., Ooi, T. L., and **He, Z. H.** (1998) Terrain influences the accurate judgment of distance. Nature, 395, 497–500.

Singer, W., Tretter, F., and **Yinon, U.** (1979) Inverted vision causes selective loss of striate cortex neurons with binocular, vertically oriented receptive fields. Brain Research, 170, 177–181.

Singh, M., and **Hoffman, D. D.** (1998) Part boundaries alter the perception of transparency. Psychological Science, 9, 370–378.

Sjoberg, S. A., Neitz, M., and **Balding, S. D., Neitz J** (1998) L-cone pigment genes expressed in normal colour vision. Vision Research, 38, 3213–3219.

Sinnott, J., Beecher, M., Moody, D., and **Stebbins, W.** (1976) Speech and sound discrimination by monkeys and humans. Journal of the Acoustical Society of America, 60, 687–695.

Skinner, B. F. (1957) Verbal behavior. New York: Appleton-Century-Crofts.

Smith, A. T. (1994) Correspondence-based on energy-based detection of second-order motion in human vision. Journal of the Optical Society of America A, 11, 1940–1948.

Smith, M., Smith, L. G., and **Levinson, B.** (1982) The use of smell in differential diagnosis. Lancet, 2, 1452.

Smith, V. C., and **Pokorny, J.** (1975) Spectral sensitivity of the foveal cone photopigments between 400 and 500 nm. Vision Research, 15, 161–71.

Smith-Swintosky, V. L., Plata-Salaman, C. R., and **Scott, T. R.** (1991) Gustatory neural coding in the monkey cortex: Stimulus quality. Journal of Neurophysiology, 66, 1156–1165.

Snowden, R. J. (1999) Visual perception: here's mud in your eye. Current Biology, 9, R336–R337.

Snowden, R. J., and **Verstraten, F. A. J.** (1999) Motion transparency: Making models of motion perception transparent. Trends in Cognitive Sciences, 3, 369–377.

Snyder, A. W., and **Barlow, H. B.** (1988) Revealing the artist's touch. Nature, 331, 117–118.

Snyder, S. H., Sklar, P. B., Hwang, P. M., and **Pevsner, J.** (1989) Molecular mechanisms of olfaction. Trends in Neurosciences, 12, 35–38.

Sobel, N., Prabhakaran, V., Zhao, Z., Desmond, J. E., Glover, G. H., Sullivan, E. V., and Gabrieli, J. D. (2000) Time course of odorant-induced activation in the human primary olfactory cortex. Journal of Neurophysiology, 83, 537–551.

Sobel, N, Prabhakaran V, Desmond J. E., Glover G. H., Goode R L, Sullivan E. V., Gabrieli J. D. (1998) Sniffing and smelling: separate subsystems in the human olfactory cortex. Nature, 392, 282–286.

Sobel, N., Khan, R. M., Hartley, C. A., Sullivan E. V., and Gabrieli, J. D. (2000) Sniffing longer rather than stronger to maintain olfactory detection threshold. Chemical Senses, 25, 1–8.

Sompolinsky, H., and Shapley, R. (1997) New perspectives on the mechanisms for orientation selectivity. Current Opinion in Neurobiology, 7, 514–522.

Sorensen, P. (1992) Morphing magic. Computer Graphics World, 15, 36–43.

Southall, J. P. C. (1937/1961) Introduction to physiological optics. New York: Dover.

Sparks, D. L. (1988) Neural cartography: Sensory and motor maps in the superior colliculus. Brain, Behavior and Evolution, 31, 49–56.

Spelke, E. S., Breinlinger, K., Jacobson, K., and Phillips, A. (1993). Gestalt relations and object perception: A developmental study. Perception, 22, 1483–1502.

Sperling, G., Budiansky, J., Spivak, J. G., and Johnson, M. C. (1971) Extremely rapid visual search: The maximum rate of scanning letters for the presence of a numeral. Science, 174, 307–311.

Sperling, G., and Lu, Z. L. (1998) A system analysis of visual motion perception. In T. Watanabe (ed.) High-level motion processing: Computational, neurobiological, and psychophysical perspectives. Cambridge: MIT Press, 154–183.

Sperry, R. W. (1980) Mind-brain interaction: Mentalism, yes; dualism, no. Neurosciences, 5, 195–206.

Spitzer, H., Desimone, R., and Moran, J. (1988) Increased attention enhances both behavioral and neuronal performance. Science, 240, 338–340.

Stabell, U., Stabell, B., and Fugelli, A. (1992) Mechanisms of long-term dark adaptation. Scandinavian Journal of Psychology, 33, 12–19.

Starlinger, I., and Niemeyer, W. (1981) Do the blind hear better? Investigations on auditory processing in congenital or early acquired blindness: I. Peripheral functions. Audiology, 20, 503–509.

Steel, K. P. (1998) Progress in progressive hearing loss. Science, 279, 1870–1871.

Steel, K. P., and Brown, S. D. M. (1998) More deafness genes. Science, 280, 1403.

Stein, B. E., Wallace, M. T., and Meredith, M. A. (1995) Neural mechanisms mediating attention and orientation to multisensory cues. In M. S. Gazzaniga (ed.) The Cognitive Neurosciences. Cambridge: MIT Press, 683–702.

Steinbach, M. J., and Money, K. E. (1973) Eye movements of the owl. Vision Research, 13, 889–891.

Steinman, R. M. (1976) Role of eye movements in maintaining a phenomenally clear and stable world. In R. A. Monty and J. W. Senders (eds.), Eye movements and psychological processes. Hillsdale, N.J.: Erlbaum, 121–154.

Steinman, R. M., Cushman, W. B., and Martins, A. J. (1982) The precision of gaze. Human Neurobiology, 1, 97–109.

Steinman, R. M., Kowler, E., and Collewijn, H. (1990) New directions for oculomotor research. Vision Research, 30, 1845–1864.

Steinschneider, M., Arezzo, J., and Vaughn, H. G. (1982) Speech-evoked activity in the auditory radiations and cortex of the awake monkey. Brain Research, 252, 353–365.

Sterr, A., Muller, M. M., Elbert, T., Rockstroh, B., Pantev, C., and Taub, E. (1998) Perceptual correlates of changes in cortical representation of fingers in blind multifinger Braille readers. Journal of Neuroscience, 18, 4417–4423.

Stevens, J. C. (1979) Thermo-tactile interactions: Some influences of temperature on touch. In D. R. Kenshalo (ed.), Sensory function of the skin of humans. New York: Plenum Press.

Stevens, J. C., and Cain, W. S. (1986) Aging and the perception of nasal irritation. Physiology & Behavior, 37, 323–328.

Stevens, J. C. and Choo, K. K. (1998) Temperature sensitivity of the body surface over the life span. Somatosensory and Motor Research, 15, 13–28.

Stevens, J. C., and Patterson, M. Q. (1995) Dimensions of spatial acuity in the touch sense: changes over the life span. Somatosensory and Motor Research, 12, 29–47.

Stevens, J. K., Emerson, R. C., Gerstein, G. L., Kallos, T., Neufield, G. R., Nichols, C. W., and Rosenquist, A. C. (1976) Paralysis of the awake human: Visual perception. Vision Research, 16, 93–98.

Stevens, K. A. (1981) The information content of texture gradients. Biological Cybernetics, 42, 95–105.

Stevens, K. A. (1983) Evidence relating subjective contours and interpretations involving interposition. Perception, 12, 491–500.

Stevens, K. A., and Brookes, A. (1988) Integrating stereopsis with monocular interpretations of planar surfaces. Vision Research, 28, 371–386.

Stevens, S. S. (1956) The direct estimation of sensory magnitude—Loudness. American Journal of Psychology, 69, 1–25.

Stevens, S. S. (1960) Psychophysics of sensory function. American Scientist, 48, 226–252.

Stevens, S. S. (1975) Psychophysics: An introduction to its perceptual, neural, and social prospects. New York: John Wiley & Sons.

Stevens, S. S., and Guirao, M. (1967) Loudness functions under inhibition. Perception & Psychophysics, 2, 459–465.

Stevens, S. S., and Newman, E. B. (1934) The localization of pure tones. Proceedings of the National Academy of Sciences, 20, 593–596.

Stoffregen, T. A., and Pittenger, J. B. (1995) Human echolocation as a basic form of perception and action. Ecological Psychology, 7, 181–216.

Stone, H., and Pryor, G. (1967) Some properties of the olfactory system of man. Perception & Psychophysics, 2, 516–518.

Stone, J. V. (1998) Object recognition using spatiotemporal signatures. Vision Research, 38, 947–951.

Stratton, G. M. (1897) Vision without inversion of the retinal image. Psychological Review, 4, 341–360.

Stypulkowski, P. H. (1990) Mechanisms of salicylate ototoxicity. Hearing Research, 46, 113–146.

Suga, N. (1990) Biosonar and neural computation in bats. Scientific American, 262, 60–68.

Sugase, Y., Yamane, S., Ueno, S., and Kawano, K. (1999) Global and fine information coded by single neurons in the temporal visual cortex. Nature, 400, 869–872.

Summerfield, Q. (1975) How a full account of segmental perception depends on prosody and vice versa. In A. Cohen and S. G. Nooteboom (eds.), Structure and process in speech perception. New York: Springer-Verlag, 51–68.

Summerfield, Q. (1992) Lipreading and audio-visual speech perception. Philosophical

Transactions of the Royal Society of London, B, 335, 71–78.

Sur, M., Garraghty, P. E., and Roe, A. W. (1988) Experimentally induced visual projections into auditory thalamus and cortex. Science, 242, 1437–1441.

Süskind, P. (1986) Perfume: The story of a murderer. Translated by J. E. Woods. New York: A. A. Knopf.

Svirsky, M. A., Robbins, A. M., Kirk, K. I., Pisoni, D., and Miyamoto, R. T. (2000) Language development in profoundly deaf children with cochlear implants. Psychological Science, 11, 153–159.

Swets, J. A. (1973) The relative operating characteristic in psychology. Science, 182, 990–1000.

Swets, J. A. (1979) ROC analysis applied to the evaluation of medical imaging techniques. Investigative Radiology, 14, 109–121.

Swets, J. A., Dawes, R. M., and Monahan, J. (2000) Psychological science can improve diagnostic decisions. Psychological Science in the Public Interest, 1–26.

Swets, J. A., Tanner, W. P., Jr., and Birdsall, T. G. (1961) Decision processes in perception. Psychological Review, 68, 301–340.

Swift, J. (1726/1890). Gulliver's travels. London: George Routledge and Sons.

Syrkin., G., and Gur, M. (1997) Colour and luminance interact to improve pattern recognition. Perception, 26, 127–140.

Talamo, B. R., Rudel, R., Kosik, K. S., Lee V. M.-Y., Adelman, L., and Kauer, J. S. (1989) Pathological changes in olfactory neurons in patients with Alzheimer's disease. Nature, 337, 736–739.

Tallal, P., and Pierce, M. (1973) Defects of non-verbal auditory perception in chilrden with developmental aphasia. Nature, 2412, 468–469.

Tallal, P., Miller, S. L., Bedi, G., Byma, G., Wang, X., Nagarajan, S. S., Schreiner, C., Jenkins, W. M., and Merzenich, M. M. (1996) Language comprehension in language-learning impaired children improved with acoustically modified speech. Science, 271, 81–84.

Tanaka, T. W., and Farah, M. J. (1993) Parts and wholes in face recognition. Quarterly Journal of Experimental Psychology, 46A, 225–245.

Tanaka, K., Fukada, Y., and Saito, H. (1989). Underlying mechanisms of the response specificity of expansion/contraction and rotation cells in the dorsal part of the medial superior temporal area of the macaque monkey. Journal of Neurophysiology, 62, 642–656.

Tanaka, K., and Saito, H. (1989) Analysis of motion of the visual field by direction, expansion/contraction, and rotation cells clustered in the dorsal part of the medial superior temporal area of the macaque monkey. Journal of Neurophysiology, 62, 626–641.

Tanaka, K. (1997) Mechanisms of visual object recognition: Monkey and human studies. Current Opinion in Neurobiology, 7, 523–529.

Tanaka, Y., Kamo, T., Yoshida, M., and Yamadori, A. (1991) So-called cortical deafness. Brain, 114, 2385–2401.

Tarr, M. J. (1995) Rotating objects to recognize them: A case study on the role of viewpoint dependency in the recognition of three-dimensional objects. Psychonomic Bulletin and Review, 2, 55–82.

Tartter, V. C. (1991) Identifiability of vowels and speakers from whispered syllables. Perception & Psychophysics, 49, 365–372.

Taylor, C. A. (1965) The physics of musical sounds. New York: Elsevier.

Taylor, M. M., and Williams, E. (1966) Acoustic trauma in the sports hunter. Laryngoscope, 76, 969–979.

Taylor, R. (1994) Brave new nose: sniffing out human sexual chemistry. Journal of NIH Research, 6, 47–51.

Taylor, W. (1988) Biological effects of the hand-arm vibration syndrome: Historical perspective and current research. Journal of the Acoustical Society of America, 83, 415–422.

Teghtsoonian, R., Teghtsoonian, M., Berglund, B., and Berglund, U. (1978) Invariance of odor strength with sniff vigor: An olfactory analogue to size constancy. Journal of Experimental Psychology: Human Perception and Performance, 4, 144–152.

Teller, D. Y. (1989) The domain of visual science. In L. Spillmann and J. S. Werner (eds.), Visual perception: The Neurophysiological Foundations. New York: Academic Press, 11–21.

Teller, D. Y. (1997) First glances: the vision of infants. The Friedenwald lecture. Investigative Ophthalmology & Visual Science, 38, 2183–203.

Teller, D. Y., and Movshon, J. A. (1986) Visual development. Vision Research, 26, 1438–1506.

Terhardt, E., and Ward, W. D. (1982) Recognition of musical key: Exploratory study. Journal of the Acoustical Society of America, 72, 26–33.

Tesch-Römer, C. (1997) Psychological effects of hearing aid use in older adults. Journal of Gerontology: Psychological Sciences, 52B, P127–P138.

Tetewsky, S. J., and Duffy C. J. (1999) Visual loss and getting lost in Alzheimer's disease. Neurology 52, 958–965

Teuber, H.-L, Battersby, W. S., and Bender, M. B. (1960) Visual field defects after penetrating missle wounds of the brain. Cambridge: Harvard University Press.

Thimbleby, H. W., and Neesham, C. (1993) How to play tricks with dots. New Scientist, 140, 26–29.

Thompson, E., Palacios, A., and Varcla, F. J. (1992). Ways of coloring: Comparative color vision as a case study for cognitive science. Behavioral and Brain Sciences, 15, 1–74.

Thompson, P. (1980) Margaret Thatcher: a new illusion. Perception, 9, 483–484.

Thompson, P. (1984) The coding of velocity of motion in the human visual system. Vision Research, 24, 41–45.

Thompson, P. (1998) Tuning of the motion aftereffect, In G. Mather, F. Verstraten, and S. Anstis (eds.) The Motion Aftereffect: A Modern Perspective. MIT Press: Cambridge, 41–55.

Thorn, F., Gwiazda, J., Cruz, A. A. V., Bauer, J. A., and Held, R. (1994) The development of eye alignment, convergence, and sensory binocularity in young infants. Investigative Opthalmology & Visual Science, 35, 544–553.

Thornbury, J. M., and Mistretta, C. M. (1981) Tactile sensitivity as a function of age. Journal of Gerontology, 36, 34–39.

Thurlow, W. R., and Runge, P. S. (1967) Effect of induced head movements on localization of direction of sounds. Journal of the Acoustical Society of America, 42, 480–488.

Till, R. E. (1978) Age-related differences in binocular backward-masking with visual noise. Journal of Gerontology, 33, 702–710.

Timney, B., and Muir, D. W. (1976) Orientation anisotropy: Incidence and magnitude in Caucasian and Chinese subjects. Science, 193, 699–700.

Titchener, E. B. (1915) A beginner's psychology. New York: Macmillan.

Todd, J. T., and Akerstrom, R. A. (1987) Perception of three-dimensional form from patterns of optical texture. Journal of Experimental Psychology: Human Perception and Performance, 13, 242–255.

Todd, J. T., and Mingolla, E. (1984) Simulations of curved surfaces from patterns of optical texture. Journal of Experimental Psychology: Human Perception and Performance, 10, 734–739.

Todd, J. T., and Norman, J. F. (1991) The visual perception of smoothly curved surfaces from minimal apparent motion sequences. Perception & Psychophysics, 50, 509–523.

Todrank, J., and Bartoshuk, L. M. (1991) A taste illusion: Taste sensation localized by touch. Physiology & Behavior, 50, 1027–1031.

Tolhurst, D. J., and Tadmor, Y. (1997) Contrast discrimination in complex images. Perception, 26, 1011–1025.

Tong, F., and Nakayama, K. (1999) Robust representations for faces: evidence from visual search. Journal of Experimental Psychology: Human Perception & Performance, 25, 1016–1035.

Toller, S. V. (1999). Assessing the impact of anosmia: review of a questionnaire's findings. Chemical Senses, 24, 705–712.

Tonndorf, J. (1987) The analogy between tinnitus and pain: A suggestion for a physiological basis of chronic tinnitus. Hearing Research, 28, 271–275.

Tonndorf, J. (1988) The external ear. In A. F. Jahn and J. Santos-Sacchi (eds.), Physiology of the ear. New York: Raven Press, 29–39.

Tootell, R. B. H., Reppas, J. B., Dale, A. M., Look, R. B., Sereno, M. I., Malach, R., Brady, T. J., and Rosen, B. R. (1995) Visual motion aftereffect in human cortical area MT revealed by magnetic resonance imagery. Nature, 375, 139–141.

Tootell, R. B. H., Reppas, J. B., Kwong, K. K., Malach, R., Born, R. T., Brady, T. J., Rosen, B. R., and Belliveau, J. W. (1995) Functional analysis of human MT and related visual cortical areas using magnetic resonance imaging. Journal of Neuroscience, 15, 3215–3230.

Tootell, R. B. H., Hadjikhani, N. K., Mendola, J. D., Marrett, S. and Dale, A. (1998). From retinotopy to recognition: fMRI in human visual cortex. Trends in Cognitive Science, 2, 174–183.

Torebjork, H. E., Vallbo, A. B., and Ochoa, J. L. (1987) Intraneural microstimulation in man: Its relation to specificity of tactile sensations. Brain, 110, 1509–1530.

Torrealba, F., Guillery, R. W., Eysel, U., Polley, E. H., and Mason, C. A. (1982) Studies of retinal representations within the cat's optic tract. Journal of Comparative Neurology, 211, 377–396.

Tovee, M. J. (1994) The molecular genetics and evoluton of primate colour vision. Trends in Neuroscience, 17, 30–37.

Tovee, M. J. (1998) Face processing: Getting by with a little help from its friends. Current Biology, 8, R317–R320.

Tranel, D., and Damasio, A. R. (1985). Knowledge without awareness: An autonomic index of facial recognition by prosopagnosics. Science, 228, 1453–1454.

Tranel, D., Damasio, A. R., and Damasio, H. (1988) Intact recognition of facial expression, gender, and age in patients with impaired recognition of face identity. Neurology, 38, 690–696.

Treede, R. D., Kenshalo, D. R., Gacely, R. H., and Jones, A. K. (1999) The cortical representation of pain, Pain, 79, 105–111.

Treisman, A. (1986) Features and objects in visual processing. Scientific American, 255, 114–125.

Tresilian, J. R. (1999) Visually timed action: time-out for 'tau'? Trends in Cognitive Sciences, 3, 301–310.

Treue, S., and Maunsell, J. H. (1999) Effects of attention on the processing of motion in macaque middle temporal and medial superior temporal visual cortical areas. Journal of Neuroscience, 19, 7591–602.

Treue, S, and Trujillo, J. C. (1999) Feature-based attention influences motion processing gain in macaque visual cortex. Nature, 399, 575–579.

Tsotsos, J. K. (1995) Towards a Computational Model of Visual Attention. In T. Papathomas, C. Chubb, A. Gorea, and E. Kowler (eds.) Early Vision and Beyond. Cambridge: MIT Press/Bradford Books, 207–218.

Tsotsos, J. K. (1997) Limited capacity of any realizable perceptual system is a sufficient reason for attentive behavior. Consciousness and Cognition, 6, 429–436.

Turner, J., Braunstein, J. L., and Andesen G. J. (1995) Detection of surfaces in structure from motion. Journal of Experimental Psychology: Human Perception & Performance, 21, 809–821.

Tyler, C. W. (1981) Specific deficits of flicker sensitivity in glaucoma and ocular hypertension. Investigative Ophthalmology & Visual Science, 20, 204–212.

Uhlrich, D. J., Essock, E. A., and Lehmkuhle, S. (1981) Cross-species correspondence of spatial contrast sensitivity functions. Behavioral Brain Research, 2, 291–299.

Ullman, S. (1979) The interpretation of visual motion. Cambridge: M.I.T. Press.

Vaina, L. M. (1998) Complex motion perception and its deficits. Current Opinion in Neurobiology, 8, 494–502.

Valentine, T. (1988) Upside-down faces; a review of the effect of inversion on face recognition. British Journal of Psychology, 79, 471–491.

Vallbo, A. B., and **Hagbarth, K. E.** (1968) Activity from skin mechanoreceptors recorded percutaneously in awake human subject. Experimental Neurology, 21, 270–289.

Vallbo, A. B., and **Johansson, R. S.** (1984) Properties of cutaneous mechanoreceptors in the human hand related to touch sensation. Human Neurobiology, 3, 3–14.

Van Boven R. W., and **Johnson, K. O.** (1994) The limit of tactile spatial resolution in humans: grating orientation discrimination at the lip, tongue and finger. Neurology, 44, 2361–2364.

Van Doren, C. L., Pelli, D. G., Verrillo, R. T. (1987) A device for measuring tactile spatiotemporal sensitivity. Journal of the Acoustical Society of America, 81, 1906–1916.

Van Tonder, G. J., and **Ejima., Y** (2000) Bottom-up clues in target finding: Why a Dalmatian my be mistaken for an elephant. Perception, 29, 149–157.

Varney, N. R. (1988) The prognostic significance of anosmia in patients with closed-head trauma. Journal of Clinical and Experimental Neuropsychology, 10, 250–254.

Verheijen, F. J. (1963) Apparent relative movement of "unsharp" and "sharp" visual patterns. Nature, 199, 160–161.

Vernon, P. E. (1977) Absolute pitch: A case study. British Journal of Psychology, 68, 485–489.

Verrillo, R. T. (1962) Investigation of some parameters of the cutaneous threshold for vibration. Journal of the Acoustical Society of America, 34, 1768–1773.

Vienot, F., Brettel, H., M'Barek, A. B., Mollon, J. D. (1995) What do colour-blind people see? Nature, 376, 127–128.

Volkmann, F. C., Riggs, L. A., and **Moore, R. K.** (1980) Eyeblinks and visual suppression. Science, 207, 900–902.

von der Heydt, R., Peterhans, E., and **Baumgartner, G.** (1984) Illusory contours and cortical neuron responses. Science, 234, 1260–1262.

von Melchner, L., Pallas S. L., and **Sur, M.** (2000) Visual behaviour mediated by retinal projections directed to the auditory pathway. Nature, 404, 871–876.

von Noorden, G. K. (1981) New clinical aspects of stimulus deprivation amblyopia. American Journal of Ophthalmology, 92, 416–421.

Wade, N. J. (1988) On the late invention of the stereoscope. Perception, 16, 785–818.

Wade, N. J., and **Verstraten, F. A. J.** (1998) Introduction and historical overview. In G. Mather, F. Verstraten, and S. Anstis (eds.) The Motion Aftereffect: A Modern Perspective. Cambridge: MIT Press, 1–23.

Wald, G. (1950) Eye and camera. Scientific American, 183, 32–41.

Walker, J. (1984) How to stop a spinning object by humming and perceive curious blue arcs around a light. Scientific American, 250, 136–144.

Wall, J. T. (1988) Variable organization in cortical maps of the skin as an indication of the lifelong adaptive capacities of circuits in the mammalian brain. Trends in Neurosciences, 12, 549–557.

Wall, P. D., and **Melzack, R.** (1994) Textbook of Pain, 3rd Edition. Edinburgh: Churchill Livingstone.

Wallace, P. (1977) Individual discrimination of humans by odor. Physiology & Behavior, 19, 577–579.

Wallach, H. (1963) The perception of neutral colors. Scientific American, 208, 107–116.

Wallach, H., and **Floor, L.** (1971) The use of size matching to demonstrate the effectiveness of accommodation and convergence as cues for distance. Perception & Psychophysics, 10, 423–428.

Wallach, H., and **O'Connell, D. N.** (1953) The kinetic depth effect. Journal of Experimental Psychology, 45, 205–217.

Wallis, G. (1998) Temporal order in human object recognition learning. Journal of Biological Systems 6, 299–313.

Wallis G., and **Bülthoff, H.** (1999) Learning to recognize objects. Trends in Cognitive Science, 3, 22–31.

Walls, G. L. (1942) The vertebrate eye and its adaptive radiation. New York: Hafner.

Walls, G. L. (1960) Land! Land! Psychological Bulletin, 57, 29–48.

Walsh, V. and Cowey, A. (1998) Magnetic stimulation studies of visual cognition. Trends in Cognitive Sciences, 2, 103–110.

Walsh, V., Ellison, A., Battelli, L., and Cowey, A. (1998) Task-specific impairments and enhancements induced by magnetic stimulation of human visual area V5. Proceedings of the Royal Society London (Series B), 265, 537–543.

Wandell, B. A. (1995) Foundations of vision. Sunderland MA; Sinauer Associates.

Wandell, B. A. (1999) Computational neuroimaging of human visual cortex. Annual Review of Neuroscience, 22, 145–173.

Ward, W. D. (1966) Temporary threshold shift in males and females. Journal of the Acoustical Society of America, 40, 478–485.

Wang, Y., Smallwood, P. M., Cowan, M., Blesh, D., Lawler, A., and Nathans, J. (1999) Mutually exclusive expression of human red and green visual pigment-reporter transgenes occurs at high frequency in murine cone photoreceptors. Proceedings of the National Academy of Sciences: USA, 96, 5251–5256.

Ward, W. D. (1968) Susceptibility to auditory fatigue. In W. D. Neff (ed.), Contributions to sensory physiology, vol. 3. New York: Academic Press, 195–225.

Ward, W. D. (1970) Musical perception. In J. V. Tobias (ed.), Foundations of modern auditory theory, vol. 1. New York: Academic Press, 407–447.

Ward, W. D., and Glorig, A. (1961) A case of firecracker-induced hearing loss. Laryngoscope, 71, 1590–1596.

Warren, R. M. (1970) Perceptual restoration of missing speech sounds. Science, 167, 392–393.

Warren, S., Hämäläinen, H. A., and Gardner, E. P. (1986) Objective classification of motion- and direction-sensitive neurons in primary somatosensory cortex of awake monkeys. Journal of Neurophysiology, 56, 598–632.

Warren, W. H., Jr., Blackwell, A. W., and Morris, M. W. (1989). Age differences in perceiving the direction of self-motion from optical flow. Journal of Gerontology: Psychological Sciences, 44, 147–153.

Warren, W. H., Jr., Morris, M. W., and Kalish, M. L. (1988) Perception of translational heading from optical flow. Journal of Experimental Psychology: Human Perception and Performance, 14, 646–660.

Warren, W. H., Jr., Young, D. S., and Lee, D. N. (1986) Visual control of step length during running over irregular terrain. Journal of Experimental Psychology: Human Performance and Perception, 12, 259–266.

Warren, W. H., Jr. (1984) Perceiving affordances: visual guidance of stair climbing. Journal of Experimental Psychology: Human Perception & Performance, 10, 683–703.

Warren, W. H., Jr. (1998) The state of flow. In T. Watanbe (ed.) High-level motion perception. Cambridge: MIT Press, 316–358.

Wasserman, G. S. (1978) Color vision: An historical perspective. New York: John Wiley & Sons.

Wässle, H., Peichl, L., and Boycott, B. B. (1981) Dendritic territories of cat retinal ganglion cells. Nature, 292, 344–345.

Wässle, H. (1999) A patchwork of cones. Nature, 397, 474–475.

Watamaniuk, S. N. J., and Heinen, S. J. (1999) Human smooth pursuit direction discrimination. Vision Research, 39, 59–70

Watson, A. B., and Pelli, D. G. (1983) QUEST: A Bayesian adaptive psychometric method. Perception & Psychophysics, 33, 113–120.

Watt, R. J., and Andrews, D. P. (1981) APE: Adaptive probit estimation of psychometric functions. Current Psychological Reviews, 1, 205–214.

Watts, R. G., and Bahill, A. T. (1990). Keep your eye on the ball: The science and folklore of baseball. New York: W. H. Freeman.

Weale, R. A. (1982) A biography of the eye. London: Lewis.

Weale, R. A. (1986) Retinal senescence. In N. Osborne and J. Chader (eds.), Progress in retinal research, vol. 5. Oxford: Pergamon Press, 53–73.

Webster, M., and Mollon, J. D. (1995) Colour constancy influenced by contrast adaptation. Nature, 373, 694–698.

Weinstein, S. (1968) Intensive and extensive aspects of tactile sensitivity as a function of body part, sex and laterality. In D. R. Kenshalo (ed.), The skin senses. Springfield, Ill.: Thomas.

Weisenberger, J. M., and Miller, J. D. (1987) The role of tactile aids in providing information about acoustic stimuli. Journal of the Acoustical Society of America, 82, 906–916.

Weiskrantz, L. (1995) Blindsight — Not an island unto itself. Current Directions in Psychological Science, 4, 146–151.

Weisskopf, V. F. (1976) Is physics human? Physics Today, 29, 23–29.

Weisstein, N., and **Harris, C. S.** (1974) Visual detection of line segments: An object-superiority effect. Science, 186, 752–755.

Welch, R. B., and **Warren, D. H.** (1980) Immediate perceptual response to intersensory discrepancy. Psychological Bulletin, 88, 638–667.

Weliky, M., Bosking, W. H., and **Fitzpatrick, D.** (1996) A systematic map of direction preference in primary visual cortex. Nature, 379, 725–728.

Wells, D. L., and **Hepper, P. G.** (2000) The discrimination of dog odours by humans, Perception, 29, 111–115.

Wells, G. L., Lindsay, R. C. L., and **Ferguson, T. J.** (1979) Accuracy, confidence, and juror perceptions in eyewitness identification. Journal of Applied Psychology, 64, 440–448.

Wenger, M. A., Jones, F. N., and **Jones, M. H.** (1956) Physiological psychology. New York: Holt, Rinehart & Winston.

Werker, J. F., and **Tees, R. C.** (1992) The organization and reorganization of human speech perception. Annual Review of Neuroscience, 15, 377–402.

Werner, G., and **Whitsel, B. L.** (1973) Functional organization of the somatosensory cortex. In A. Iggo (ed.), Handbook of sensory physiology, vol. 2: Somatosensory system. New York: Springer-Verlag.

Werner, J. S., Cicerone, C. M., Kliegl, R., and **DellaRosa, D.** (1984) Spectral efficiency of blackness induction. Journal of the Optical Society of America A, 1, 981–986.

Wertheimer, M. (1912/1961) Experimental studies on the seeing of motion. T. Shipley (trans. and ed.), Classics in psychology, New York: Philosophical Library, 1032–1088.

Wertheimer, M. (1923/1958) Principles of perceptual organization. In D. C. Beardslee and M. Wertheimer (eds.), Readings in perception. Princeton, N.J.: Van Nostrand, 115–135.

Wertheimer, M. (1957) Perception and the Rorschach. Journal of Projective Techniques, 21, 209–216.

Wertheimer, M. (1961) Psychomotor coordination of auditory and visual space at birth. Science, 134, 1692–1693.

Wessinger, C. M., Buonocore, M., Kussmaul, C. L., and **Mangun, G. R.** (1997) Tonotopy in human auditory cortex examined with funtional magnetic resonance imaging. Human Brain Mapping, 5, 18–25.

Westfall, R. S. (1980) Never at rest: A biography of Isaac Newton. Cambridge, England: Cambridge University Press.

Westheimer, G. (1999) Gestalt theory reconfigured: Max Wertheimer's anticipation of recent developments in visual neuroscience. Perception, 28, 5–16.

Wever, E. G. (1978) The reptile ear. Princeton, N.J.: Princeton University Press.

Wever, E. G., and **Bray, C. W.** (1937) The perception of low tones and the resonance-volley theory. Journal of Psychology, 3, 101–114.

Wheatstone, C. (1838/1964) Some remarkable phenomena of binocular vision. In W. N. Dember (ed.), Visual perception: The nineteenth century. New York: John Wiley & Sons, 114–129.

Wheeler, D. D. (1970) Processes in word recognition. Cognitive Psychology, 1, 59–85.

White, H. E., and **Levatin, P.** (1962) "Floaters" in the eye. Scientific American, 206, 119–127.

Wiesel, T. N., and **Hubel, D. H.** (1960) Receptive fields of ganglion cells in the cat's retina. Journal of Physiology, 153, 583–594.

Wiesel, T. N., and **Hubel, D. H.** (1966) Spatial and chromatic interactions in the lateral geniculate body of the rhesus monkey. Journal of Neurophysiology, 29, 1115–1156.

Wightman, F., and **Kistler, D.** (1998) Of Vulcan ears, human ears and "earprints." Nature Neuroscience, 1, 337–339.

Wightman, F., and **Kistler, D. J.** (1980) A new "look" at auditory space perception. In G. van den Brink and F. A. Bilsen (eds.), Psychophysical, physiological and behavioral studies in hearing. Delft: Delft University Press, 441–448.

Wightman, F. L., and **Kistler, D. J.** (1989a) Headphones simulation of free-field listening. I. Stimulus synthesis. Journal of the Acoustical Society of America, 85, 858–867.

Wightman, F. L., and **Kistler, D. J.** (1989b) Headphones simulation of free-field listening: II. Psychophysical validation. Journal of the Acoustical Society of America, 85, 868–878.

Wightman, F. L., Kistler, D., and **Arruda, M.** (1989) The hierarchy of sound localization cues revealed by experiments in a simulated free-field. Association for Research in Otolaryngology, 12, 65.

Wilkins, P. A., and **Acton, W. I.** (1982) Noise and accidents: A review. Annals of Occupational Hygiene, 25, 249–260.

Williams, D. R., MacLeod, D. I. A., and **Hayhoe, M. M.** (1981) Punctate sensitivity of the blue-sensitive mechanism. Vision Research, 21, 1357–1375.

Williams, D., Phillips, G., and Sekuler, R. (1986) Hysteresis in the perception of motion direction as evidence for neural cooperativity. Nature, 324, 253–255.

Williams, S. M., McCoy, A. N., and Purves, D. (1998) Proceedings of the National Academy of Sciences: USA, 95, 13296–13300.

Wilmington, D., Gray, L., and Jahrsdoerfer, R. (1994) Binaural processing after corrected congenital unilateral conductive hearing loss. Hearing Research, 74, 99–114.

Wilson, B. S., Finley, C. C., Lawson, D. T., Wolford, R. D., Eddington, D. K., and Rabinowitz, W. M. (1991) Better speech recognition with cochlear implants. Nature, 352, 236–238.

Wilson, H. R., Ferrara, V. P., and Yo, C. (1992) A psychophysically motivated model of two-dimensional motion perception. Visual Neuroscience, 9, 79–98.

Wilson, H. R., Mets, M. B., Nagy, S. E., and Kressel, A. B. (1988) Albino spatial vision as an instance of arrested visual development. Vision Research, 28, 979–990.

Winderickz, J., Lindsey, D. T., Sanocki, E., Teller, D. Y., Motulsky, A. G., and Deeb, S. S. (1992) Polymorphism in red photopigment underlies variation in colour matching. Nature, 356, 431–433.

Winn, B., Whitaker, D., Elliott, D. B. and Phillips, N. J. (1994) Factors affecting light-adapted pupil size in normal human subjects. Investigative Ophthalmology & Visual Science, 35, 1132–1137.

Winter, R. (1976) The smell book: Scents, sex, and society. Philadelphia: Lippincott.

Wise, L. Z., and Irvine, D. R. F. (1988) Topographic organization of interaural intensity difference sensitivity in deep layers of cat superior colliculus: Implications for auditory spacial representation. Journal of Neurophysiology, 54, 185–211.

Wise, P. M., Olsson, M. J., and Cain, W. S. (2000) Quantification of odor quality. Chemical Senses, 25, 429–443.

Wist, E. R. (1976) Dark adaptation and the Hermann grid illusion. Perception & Psychophysics, 20, 10–12.

Wolfe, J. M. (1984) Global factors in the Hermann grid illusion. Perception, 13, 33–40.

Wolfson, S. S., and Landy, M. S. (1998) Examining edge- and region-based texture analysis mechanisms. Vision Research, 38, 439–446.

Wood, J. B., and Harkins, S. W. (1987) Effects of age, stimulus selection, and retrieval environment on odor identification. Journal of Gerontology, 42, 584–588.

Woodworth, R. S. (1938) Experimental psychology. New York: Holt.

Woodworth, R. S., and Schlosberg, H. (1954) Experimental psychology (2nd ed.). New York: Holt.

Wright, B. A., Lombardino, L. J., King, W. M., Puranik, C. S., Leonard, C. M., and Merzenich, M. M. (1997) Deficits in auditory temporal and spectral resolution in language-impaired children. Nature, 387, 176–178.

Wright, E. (1992) The original of E. G. Boring's "young girl/mother-in-law" drawing and its relation to the pattern of a joke. Perception, 21, 273–275.

Wright, R. H. (1966) Why is an odour? Nature, 209, 551–554.

Wrzesniewski, A., McCauley, C., and Rozin, P. (1999) Odor and affect: individual differences in the impact of odor on liking for places, things and people. Chemical Senses, 24, 713–21.

Wuerger, S., Shapley, R., and Rubin N. (1996) "On the visually perceived direction of motion" by Hans Wallach: 60 years later. Perception, 25, 1317–1367.

Wysocki, C. J., and Beauchamp, G. (1984) Ability to smell androstenone is genetically determined. Proceedings of the National Academy of Sciences, 81, 4899–4902.

Wysocki, C. J., Pierce, J. D., and Gilbert, A. N. (1991) Geographic, cross-cultural, and individual variation in human olfaction. In T. V. Getchell, R. L. Doty, L. M. Bartoshuk, and J. B. Snow, Jr. (eds.), Smell and taste in health and disease. New York: Raven Press, 287–314.

Yang, Y., and Blake, R. (1991) Spatial frequency tuning of human stereopsis. Vision Research, 31, 1177–1189.

Yantis, S. (1992) Multielement visual tracking: Attention and perceptual organization. Cognitive Psychology, 24, 295–340.

Yantis, S. (1993) Stimulus-driven attentional capture. Current Directions in Psychological Science, 2, 156–161.

Yellott, J. I., Jr. (1982) Spectral analysis of spatial sampling by photoreceptors: Topological disorder prevents aliasing. Vision Research, 22, 1205–1210.

Yeshurun, Y., and Carrasco M. (1998). Attention improves or impairs visual performance by enhancing spatial resolution. Nature, 396, 72–75.

Yonas, A. (1984) Reaching as a measure of infant spatial perception. In G. Gottlieb and N. A. Krasnegor (eds.), Measurement of audition and vision in the first year of postnatal life: A methodological review. Norwood, N.J.: Ablex.

Yost, W. A. (1991) Auditory image perception and analysis: The basis for hearing. Hearing Research, 56, 8–18.

Yost, W. A. (2000) Fundamentals of hearing: An introduction (4th ed.). New York: Academic Press.

Yost, W. A., Patterson, R., and **Sheft, S. A.** (1996) A time domain description for the pitch strength of iteratetd rippled noise. Journal of the Acoustical Society of America, 99, 1066–1078.

Young, F. A. (1981) Primate myopia. American Journal of Optometry and Physiological Optics, 58, 560–566.

Young, P. T. (1928) Auditory localization with acoustical transposition of the ears. Journal of Experimental Psychology, 11, 399–429.

Young, T. (1801/1948) Observations on vision. In W. Dennis (ed.), Readings in the history of psychology. New York: Appleton-Century-Crofts, 96–101.

Yuille, A. L. and **Grzywacz, N. M.** (1988) A computational theory for the perception of coherent visual motion. Nature, 333, 71–74.

Yuodelis, C., and **Hendrickson, A.** (1986) A qualitative analysis of the human fovea during development. Vision Research, 26, 847–855.

Zacks, J. (1970) Temporal summation phenomena at threshold: Their relation to visual mechanisms. Science, 170, 197–199.

Zadnik, K., Satariano, W. A., Mutti, D. O., and **Sholtz, R. I.,** and **Adams, A. J.** (1994) The effect of parental history of myopia on children's eye size. Journal of the American Medical Association, 271, 1323–1327.

Zatorre, R. J., Evans, A. C., and **Meyer, E.** (1994) Nerual mechanisms underlying meoldic perception and memory for pitch. Journal of Neuroscience, 14, 1908–1919.

Zeki, S. (1980) The representation of colours in the cerebral cortex. Nature, 284, 412–418.

Zellner, D. A., Bartoli, A. M., and **Eckard, R.** (1991) Influence of color on odor identification and likeing ratings. American Journal of Psychology, 104, 547–561.

Zellner, D. A., and **Kautz, M. A.** (1990) Color affects perceived odor intensity. Journal of Experimental Psychology: Human Perception & Performance, 16, 391–397.

Zelman, S. (1973) Correlation of smoking history with hearing loss. Journal of the American Medical Association, 223, 920.

Zeng, F. G., and **Shannon, R. V.** (1994) Loudness-coding mechanisms inferred from electrical stimulation of the human auditory system. Science, 264, 564–566.

Zhou, Y.-D., and **Fuster, J. M.** (1996) Mnemonic neuronal activity in somatosensory cortex. Proceedings of the National Academy of Sciences: USA, 93, 10533–10537.

Zimbardo, P. G., Andersen, S. M., and **Kabat, L. G.** (1981) Induced hearing deficit generates experimental paranoia. Science, 212, 1529–1531.

Zisman, F., and **Adams, A. J.** (1982) Spectral sensitivity of cone mechanisms in juvenile diabetes. In G. Verriest (ed.), Colour vision deficiencies, VI. Proceedings of the Sixth Symposium of the International Research Group on Colour Vision Deficiencies. The Hague: W. Junk, 127–131.

Zrenner, E. (1983) Neurophysiological apsects of color vision in primates. Berlin: Springer-Verlag.

Zurek, P. M. (1981) Spontaneous narrowband acoustic signals emitted by human ears. Journal of the Acoustical Society of America, 69, 514–523.

Zwicker, E., and **Scharf, B.** (1965) A model of loudness summation. Psychological Review, 72, 3–26.

CREDITS

FIGURE 2.31 Photograph courtesy of John Dowling, Harvard University.

BOX 3.1 quote From the poem "Age Four" from *Sojourner Microcosms: New and Selected Poems, 1959-1977* by Anselm Hollo copyright 1977. Published by Blue Wind Press.

FIGURE 3.18 Lotto, Williams and Purves, from "Mach bands as empirically derived associations" in PNAS, National Academy of Sciences, U.S.A., ©1999, volume 96, figure 3, page 5247.

FIGURE 3.22 Photograph courtesy of Edward Adelson, M.I.T.

FIGURE 3.27 Photographs courtesy of Wilson Geisler, University of Texas, Austin.

Figure 3.28 Anstis, S.M., from "A chart demonstrating variations in acuity with retinal position." Vision Research, 1974, 14, 589-592. Used with permission.

FIGURE 4.5 Photograph courtesy of David Calkins, University of Rochester.

FIGURE 4.8 Photograph courtesy of Todd Preuss, University of Louisiana-Lafayette, and Jon Kaas, Vanderbilt University.

FIGURE 4.14 Photograph courtesy of Jonathan Horton, University of California, San Francisco.

FIGURE 4.18 Photograph courtesy of Vivien Casagrande, Vanderbilt University.

Figure 4.19 Felleman, D.J. and Van Essen, D.C., from "Distributed hierarchical processing in the primate cerebral cortex." Cerebral Cortex, 1991, 1, 1-17.

QUOTE Marr, D., from "Early processing of visual information." Philosophical Transactions of the Royal Society, Series B, 1976, 275, 483-524.

FIGURE 5.1 Photograph courtesy of Jet Propulsion Laboratory, NASA; contour analyses courtesy of Sang-Hun Lee, Vanderbilt University.

FIGURE 5.2 Photograph courtesy of Susan Adcock.

FIGURE 5.3 Photograph courtesy of Philippe Schyns and Aude Oliva.

FIGURE 5.18 Photograph courtesy of Terry Lewis and Daphne Maurer, McMaster University.

FIGURE 5.32 (Images from Brodartz [1966]) A photographic album for artists and designers. New York: Dover. Courtesy of the publisher).

FIGURE 5.33 Julesz, B., from "A brief outline of the texton theory of human vision." *Trends in Neurosciences,* 1984, 7, 41-45.

FIGURE 5.35 Reprinted from the book by Bois, Cowart and Pacquement (1992), with permission of the publisher and the artist.

FIGURE 5.44 Adapted from Kova'cs, Polat, Pennefather, Chandna, and Norcia, 2000; images courtesy of Ilona Kova'cs.

FIGURE 5.45 Adapted from Jolicouer, Ullman, and Mackay, 1986.

FIGURE 5.47 Based on images provided by Ingo Rentschler.

FIGURE 6.1 Photograph courtesy of Jet Propulsion Laboratory and NASA.

FIGURE 6.2 Photograph courtesy of John Henderson and Andrew Hollingworth, Michigan State University.

FIGURE 6.3 Photograph courtesy of Isabelle Bülthoff, Max Planck Institute, Tuebingen.

FIGURE 6.6 Photograph courtesy of Volker Blanz.

FIGURE 6.9 From Dolan, Fink, Rolls, Booth, Homes, Frackowiak, and Friston, 1997; images courtesy of Ray Dolan.

FIGURE 6.13 Reproduced with permission from *Star Trek on the Brain: Alien Minds, Human Minds*, 1999, by Robert Sekuler and Randolph Blake, Freeman Press.

FIGURE 6.16 Photographs courtesy of Ron Rensink, University of British Columbia.

COLOR PLATE 1 Reprinted from "Rends in Cognitive Science" in *From Retinotopy to Recognition: fMRI in Human Visual Cortex*", 1998, Volume 2, page 2, 174.

COLOR PLATE 8 Collection of Randolph & Elaine Blake.

COLOR PLATE 13 – Otto, R.B., and Purves, D. "An Empirical Explanation of Color Contrast" in PNAS, ©2000, Volume 97, figure 6a, pages 12834-12839.

FIGURE 8.31 Kersten, D., Mamassian, P., and Knill, D. "Moving Cast Shadows Induce Apparent Motion in Depth" in *Perception,* 1997, Volume 26, figures 1 & 2, pp. 181-192.

FIGURE 8.32 Kersten, D., Mamassian, P., and Knill, D. "Moving Cast Shadows Induce Apparent Motion in Depth" in *Perception,* 1997, Volume 26, figures 1 & 2, pp. 181-192.

FIGURE 8.36 Illustration courtesy of Ken Nakayama.

FIGURE 11.3 Reprinted with permission from "Progress in Progressive Hearing Loss" by K. P. Steel, *Science,* 279: 1870-1871, Copyright 1998, American Association for the Advancement of Science.

FIGURE 11.20 Figure courtesy of Fred Wightman, University of Wisconsin.

FIGURE 12.5 Photograph courtesy of National Braille Press.

FIGURE 12.14 Lederman, S.J., from "Skin and touch." *The Encyclopedia of Human Biology,* copyright 1991, Academic Press.

NAME INDEX

SUBJECT INDEX